S0-ARN-329

Fundamentals of Biochemistry:

Life at the Molecular Level

Voet • Voet • Pratt

Third Edition

Selected Chapters

Copyright © 2010 by John Wiley & Sons, Inc.

All rights reserved.

No part of this publication may be reproduced, stored in a retrieval system or transmitted in any form or by any means, electronic, mechanical, photocopying, recording, scanning or other-wise, except as permitted under Sections 107 or 108 of the 1976 United States Copyright Act, without either the prior written permission of the Publisher, or authorization through payment of the appropriate per-copy fee to the Copyright Clearance Center, Inc., 222 Rosewood Drive, Danvers, MA 01923, website www.copyright.com. Requests to the Publisher for permission should be addressed to the Permissions Department, John Wiley & Sons, Inc., 111 River Street, Hoboken, NJ 07030-5774, (201)748-6011, fax (201)748-6008, website http://www.wiley.com/go/permissions.

To order books or for customer service, please call 1(800)-CALL-WILEY (225-5945).

Printed in the United States of America.

ISBN   978-0-470-56242-0

Printed and bound by IPAK.

10 9 8 7 6 5 4 3 2 1

Brief Contents

PART I **INTRODUCTION**
1 Introduction to the Chemistry of Life 1
2 Water 22

PART II **BIOMOLECULES**
3 Nucleotides, Nucleic Acids, and Genetic Information 39
4 Amino Acids 74
5 Proteins: Primary Structure 91
6 Proteins: Three-Dimensional Structure 125
7 Protein Function: Myoglobin and Hemoglobin, Muscle Contraction, and Antibodies 176
8 Carbohydrates 219
9 Lipids and Biological Membranes 245
10 Membrane Transport 295

PART III **ENZYMES**
11 Enzymatic Catalysis 322
12 Enzyme Kinetics, Inhibition, and Control 363
13 Biochemical Signaling 405

PART IV **METABOLISM**
14 Introduction to Metabolism 448
15 Glucose Catabolism 485
16 Glycogen Metabolism and Gluconeogenesis 530
17 Citric Acid Cycle 566
18 Electron Transport and Oxidative Phosphorylation 596

Solutions to Problems SP-1
Glossary G-1
Index I-1

Media Resources

To accompany
FUNDAMENTALS OF BIOCHEMISTRY 3/e

WILEY PLUS WileyPLUS, along with the companion website for the book (www.wiley.com/college/voet), contain an extensive set of resources for enhancing student understanding of biochemistry. These are keyed to the text and in most cases are specifically called out with a red mouse icon.

A complete listing is available in the Guide to Media Resources starting on p. xxv at the front of the text.

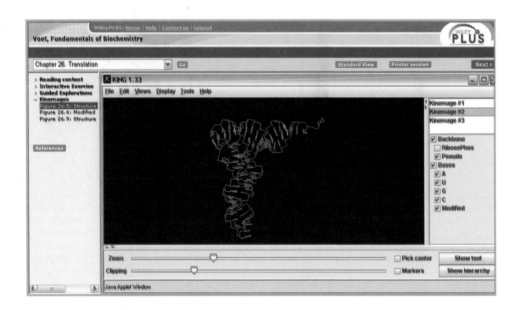

■ KINEMAGES

A set of 22 exercises comprising 55 individual 3-dimensional images of selected proteins and nucleic acids can be manipulated by users as suggested by an accompanying script.

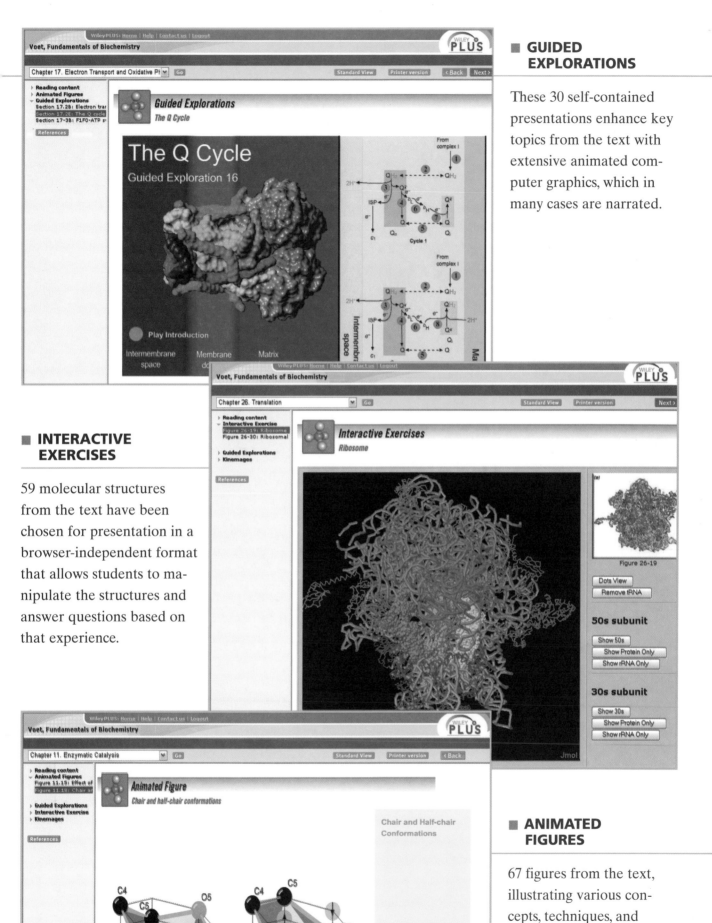

GUIDED EXPLORATIONS

These 30 self-contained presentations enhance key topics from the text with extensive animated computer graphics, which in many cases are narrated.

INTERACTIVE EXERCISES

59 molecular structures from the text have been chosen for presentation in a browser-independent format that allows students to manipulate the structures and answer questions based on that experience.

ANIMATED FIGURES

67 figures from the text, illustrating various concepts, techniques, and processes, are presented as brief animations.

Success in Biochemistry is just a click away...

Every one of your students has the potential to make a difference. And realizing that potential starts right here, in your course.

When students succeed in your course—when they stay on-task and make the breakthrough that turns confusion into confidence—they are empowered to realize the possibilities for greatness that lie within each of them. We know your goal is to create an environment where students reach their full potential and experience the exhilaration of academic success that will last them a lifetime. *WileyPLUS* can help you reach that goal.

WILEY PLUS

Wiley**PLUS** is an online suite of resources—including the complete text—that will help your students:

* come to class better prepared for your lectures
* get immediate feedback and context-sensitive help on assignments and quizzes
* track their progress throughout the course

"I just wanted to say how much this program helped me in studying... I was able to actually see my mistakes and correct them. ... I really think that other students should have the chance to use *WileyPLUS*."

Ashlee Krisko, *Oakland University*

www.wileyplus.com

88% of students surveyed said it improved their understanding of the material.*

FOR INSTRUCTORS

WileyPLUS is built around the activities you perform in your class each day. With WileyPLUS you can:

Prepare & Present

Create outstanding class presentations using a wealth of resources such as enhanced art, PowerPoint slides containing text art optimized for presentation, animated figures, Guided Explorations, Interactive Exercises (featuring Jmol rendered 3D molecules), and kinemages. You can even add materials you have created yourself.

Create Assignments

Automate the assigning and grading of homework or quizzes by using the provided question banks, featuring over 700 conceptual questions, with detailed answer feedback.

Track Student Progress

Keep track of your students' progress and analyze individual and overall class results.

Now Available with WebCT, eCollege, and ANGEL Learning!

> "It has been a great help, and I believe it has helped me to achieve a better grade."
>
> Michael Morris,
> *Columbia Basin College*

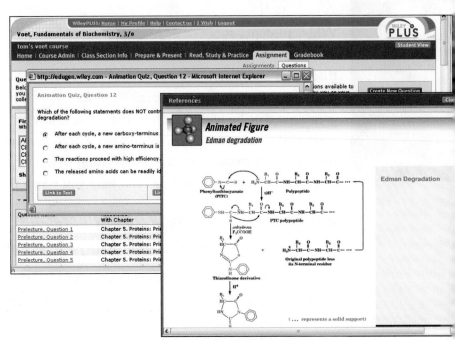

FOR STUDENTS

You have the potential to make a difference!

WileyPLUS is a powerful online system packed with features to help you make the most of your potential and get the best grade you can!

With WileyPLUS you get:

- A complete online version of your text and other study resources.

- Problem-solving help, instant grading, and feedback on your homework and quizzes.

- The ability to track your progress and grades throughout the term.

For more information on what *WileyPLUS* can do to help you and your students reach their potential, please visit www.wileyplus.com/experience.

82% of students surveyed said it made them better prepared for tests. *

*Based upon 7,000 responses to student surveys in academic year 2006-2007.

THIRD EDITION

FUNDAMENTALS OF
Biochemistry
LIFE AT THE MOLECULAR LEVEL

Donald Voet
University of Pennsylvania

Judith G. Voet
Swarthmore College, Emeritus

Charlotte W. Pratt
Seattle Pacific University

WILEY

John Wiley & Sons, Inc.

IN MEMORY OF WILLIAM P. JENCKS

scholar, teacher, friend

Vice-President & Executive Publisher	Kaye Pace
Associate Publisher	Petra Recter
Marketing Manager	Amanda Wainer
Assistant Editor	Alyson Rentrop
Senior Production Editor	Sandra Dumas
Production Manager	Dorothy Sinclair
Director of Creative Services	Harry Nolan
Cover Design	Madelyn Lesure
Text Design	Laura C. Ierardi
Photo Department Manager	Hilary Newman
Photo Editors	Hilary Newman, Sheena Goldstein
Illustration Editor	Sigmund Malinowski
Pathways of Discovery Portraits	Wendy Wray
Senior Media Editor	Thomas Kulesa
Production Management Services	Suzanne Ingrao/Ingrao Associates

Background Photo Cover Credit: Lester Lefkowitz/Getty Images

Inset Photo Credits: Based on X-ray structures by (left to right) Thomas Steitz, Yale University; Daniel Koshland, Jr., University of California at Berkeley; Emmanual Skordalakis and James Berger, University of California at Berkeley; Nikolaus Grigorieff and Richard Henderson, MRC Laboratory of Molecular Biology, U.K.; Thomas Steitz, Yale University.

This book was set in 10/12 Times Ten by Aptara and printed and bound by Courier/Kendallville. The cover was printed by Phoenix Color Corporation.

This book is printed on acid free paper. ∞

Copyright © 2008 by Donald Voet, Judith G. Voet, and Charlotte W. Pratt. All rights reserved.

No part of this publication may be reproduced, stored in a retrieval system or transmitted in any form or by any means, electronic, mechanical, photocopying, recording, scanning or otherwise, except as permitted under Sections 107 or 108 of the 1976 United States Copyright Act, without either the prior written permission of the Publisher, or authorization through payment of the appropriate per-copy fee to the Copyright Clearance Center, Inc., 222 Rosewood Drive, Danvers, MA 01923, website www.copyright.com. Requests to the Publisher for permission should be addressed to the Permissions Department, John Wiley & Sons, Inc., 111 River Street, Hoboken, NJ 07030-5774, (201)748-6011, fax (201)748-6008, website http://www.wiley.com/go/permissions.

To order books or for customer service, please call 1-800-CALL WILEY (225-5945).

ISBN-13   978-0470-12930-2

Printed in the United States of America

10 9 8 7 6 5 4 3 2

About the Authors

Donald Voet received a B.S. in Chemistry from the California Institute of Technology, a Ph.D. in Chemistry from Harvard University with William Lipscomb, and did postdoctoral research in the Biology Department at MIT with Alexander Rich. Upon completion of his postdoctoral research, Don took up a faculty position in the Chemistry Department at the University of Pennsylvania where, for the past 38 years, he has taught a variety of biochemistry courses as well as general chemistry. His major area of research is the X-ray crystallography of molecules of biological interest. He has been a visiting scholar at Oxford University, the University of California at San Diego, and the Weizmann Institute of Science in Israel. Together with Judith G. Voet, he is Co-Editor-in-Chief of the journal *Biochemistry and Molecular Biology Education*. He is a member of the Education Committee of the International Union of Biochemistry and Molecular Biology. His hobbies include backpacking, scuba diving, skiing, travel, photography, and writing biochemistry textbooks.

Judith ("Judy") Voet received her B.S. in Chemistry from Antioch College and her Ph.D. in Biochemistry from Brandeis University with Robert H. Abeles. She has done postdoctoral research at the University of Pennsylvania, Haverford College, and the Fox Chase Cancer Center. Her main area of research involves enzyme reaction mechanisms and inhibition. She taught Biochemistry at the University of Delaware before moving to Swarthmore College. She taught there for 26 years, reaching the position of James H. Hammons Professor of Chemistry and Biochemistry before going on "permanent sabbatical leave." She has been a visiting scholar at Oxford University, University of California, San Diego, University of Pennsylvania, and the Weizmann Institute of Science, Israel. She is Co-Editor-in-Chief of the journal *Biochemistry and Molecular Biology Education*. She has been a member of the Education and Professional Development Committee of the American Society for Biochemistry and Molecular Biology as well as the Education Committee of the International Union of Biochemistry and Molecular Biology. Her hobbies include hiking, backpacking, scuba diving, and tap dancing.

Charlotte Pratt received her B.S. in Biology from the University of Notre Dame and her Ph.D. in Biochemistry from Duke University under the direction of Salvatore Pizzo. Although she originally intended to be a marine biologist, she discovered that Biochemistry offered the most compelling answers to many questions about biological structure–function relationships and the molecular basis for human health and disease. She conducted postdoctoral research in the Center for Thrombosis and Hemostasis at the University of North Carolina at Chapel Hill. She has taught at the University of Washington and currently teaches at Seattle Pacific University. In addition to working as an editor of several biochemistry textbooks, she has co-authored *Essential Biochemistry* and previous editions of *Fundamentals of Biochemistry*.

Brief Contents

PART I **INTRODUCTION**
1 | Introduction to the Chemistry of Life   1
2 | Water   22

PART II **BIOMOLECULES**
3 | Nucleotides, Nucleic Acids, and Genetic Information   39
4 | Amino Acids   74
5 | Proteins: Primary Structure   91
6 | Proteins: Three-Dimensional Structure   125
7 | Protein Function: Myoglobin and Hemoglobin, Muscle Contraction, and Antibodies   176
8 | Carbohydrates   219
9 | Lipids and Biological Membranes   245
10 | Membrane Transport   295

PART III **ENZYMES**
11 | Enzymatic Catalysis   322
12 | Enzyme Kinetics, Inhibition, and Control   363
13 | Biochemical Signaling   405

PART IV **METABOLISM**
14 | Introduction to Metabolism   448
15 | Glucose Catabolism   485
16 | Glycogen Metabolism and Gluconeogenesis   530
17 | Citric Acid Cycle   566
18 | Electron Transport and Oxidative Phosphorylation   596
19 | Photosynthesis   640
20 | Lipid Metabolism   677
21 | Amino Acid Metabolism   732
22 | Mammalian Fuel Metabolism: Integration and Regulation   791

PART V **GENE EXPRESSION AND REPLICATION**
23 | Nucleotide Metabolism   817
24 | Nucleic Acid Structure   848
25 | DNA Replication, Repair, and Recombination   893
26 | Transcription and RNA Processing   942
27 | Protein Synthesis   985
28 | Regulation of Gene Expression   1037

Solutions to Problems   SP-1
Glossary   G-1
Index   I-1

Contents

Preface   xviii

Acknowledgments   xxi

Instructor and Student Resources   xxiii

Guide to Media Resources   xxv

PART I INTRODUCTION

1 Introduction to the Chemistry of Life   1

1 The Origin of Life   2
A. Biological Molecules Arose from Inorganic Materials   2
B. Complex Self-replicating Systems Evolved from Simple Molecules   3

2 Cellular Architecture   5
A. Cells Carry Out Metabolic Reactions   5
B. There Are Two Types of Cells: Prokaryotes and Eukaryotes   7
C. Molecular Data Reveal Three Evolutionary Domains of Organisms   9
D. Organisms Continue to Evolve   11

3 Thermodynamics   11
A. The First Law of Thermodynamics States That Energy Is Conserved   12
B. The Second Law of Thermodynamics States That Entropy Tends to Increase   13
C. The Free Energy Change Determines the Spontaneity of a Process   14
D. Free Energy Changes Can Be Calculated from Equilibrium Concentrations   15
E. Life Obeys the Laws of Thermodynamics   17

BOX 1-1 **PATHWAYS OF DISCOVERY**
Lynn Margulis and the Theory of Endosymbiosis   10

BOX 1-2 **PERSPECTIVES IN BIOCHEMISTRY**
Biochemical Conventions   13

2 Water   22

1 Physical Properties of Water   23
A. Water Is a Polar Molecule   23
B. Hydrophilic Substances Dissolve in Water   25
C. The Hydrophobic Effect Causes Nonpolar Substances to Aggregate in Water   26

D. Water Moves by Osmosis and Solutes Move by Diffusion   29

2 Chemical Properties of Water   30
A. Water Ionizes to Form H^+ and OH^- 30
B. Acids and Bases Alter the pH   32
C. Buffers Resist Changes in pH   34

BOX 2-1 **BIOCHEMISTRY IN HEALTH AND DISEASE**
The Blood Buffering System   36

PART II BIOMOLECULES

3 Nucleotides, Nucleic Acids, and Genetic Information   39

1 Nucleotides   40
2 Introduction to Nucleic Acid Structure   43
A. Nucleic Acids Are Polymers of Nucleotides   43
B. The DNA Forms a Double Helix   44
C. RNA Is a Single-Stranded Nucleic Acid   47

3 Overview of Nucleic Acid Function   47
A. DNA Carries Genetic Information   48
B. Genes Direct Protein Synthesis   49

4 Nucleic Acid Sequencing   50
A. Restriction Endonucleases Cleave DNA at Specific Sequences   51
B. Electrophoresis Separates Nucleic Acid According to Size   52
C. DNA Is Sequenced by the Chain-Terminator Method   53
D. Entire Genomes Have Been Sequenced   57
E. Evolution Results from Sequence Mutations   58

5 Manipulating DNA   59
A. Cloned DNA Is an Amplified Copy   60
B. DNA Libraries Are Collections of Cloned DNA   62
C. DNA Is Amplified by the Polymerase Chain Reaction   65
D. Recombinant DNA Technology Has Numerous Practical Applications   67

BOX 3-1 **PATHWAYS OF DISCOVERY**
Francis Collins and the Gene for Cystic Fibrosis   56

BOX 3-2 **PERSPECTIVES IN BIOCHEMISTRY**
DNA Fingerprinting   66

BOX 3-3 **PERSPECTIVES IN BIOCHEMISTRY**
Ethical Aspects of Recombinant DNA Technology   70

4 Amino Acids   74

1 Amino Acid Structure   74
A. Amino Acids Are Dipolar Ions   75

B. Peptide Bonds Link Amino Acids   78

C. Amino Acid Side Chains Are Nonpolar, Polar, or Charged   78

D. The pK Values of Ionizable Groups Depend on Nearby Groups   81

E. Amino Acid Names Are Abbreviated   81

2 Stereochemistry   82

3 Amino Acid Derivatives   86

A. Protein Side Chains May Be Modified   86

B. Some Amino Acids Are Biologically Active   86

BOX 4-1 **PATHWAYS OF DISCOVERY**
William C. Rose and the Discovery of Threonine   75

BOX 4-2 **PERSPECTIVES IN BIOCHEMISTRY**
The *RS* System   85

BOX 4-3 **PERSPECTIVES IN BIOCHEMISTRY**
Green Fluorescent Protein   87

5 Proteins: Primary Structure   91

1 Polypeptide Diversity   91

2 Protein Purification and Analysis   94

A. Purifying a Protein Requires a Strategy   94

B. Salting Out Separates Proteins by Their Solubility   97

C. Chromatography Involves Interaction with Mobile and Stationary Phases   98

D. Electrophoresis Separates Molecules According to Charge and Size   101

3 Protein Sequencing   104

A. The First Step Is to Separate Subunits   104

B. The Polypeptide Chains Are Cleaved   107

C. Edman Degradation Removes a Peptide's First Amino Acid Residue   109

D. Mass Spectrometry Determines the Molecular Masses of Peptides   110

E. Reconstructed Protein Sequences Are Stored in Databases   112

4 Protein Evolution   114

A. Protein Sequences Reveal Evolutionary Relationships   114

B. Proteins Evolve by the Duplication of Genes or Gene Segments   117

BOX 5-1 **PATHWAYS OF DISCOVERY**
Frederick Sanger and Protein Sequencing   105

6 Proteins: Three-Dimensional Structure   125

1 Secondary Structure   127

A. The Planar Peptide Group Limits Polypeptide Conformations   127

B. The Most Common Regular Secondary Structures Are the α Helix and the β Sheet   129

C. Fibrous Proteins Have Repeating Secondary Structures   134

D. Most Proteins Include Nonrepetitive Structure   139

2 Tertiary Structure   140

A. Most Protein Structures Have Been Determined by X-Ray Crystallography or Nuclear Magnetic Resonance   141

B. Side Chain Location Varies with Polarity   145

C. Tertiary Structures Contain Combinations of Secondary Structure   146

D. Structure Is Conserved More than Sequence   150

E. Structural Bioinformatics Provides Tools for Storing, Visualizing, and Comparing Protein Structural Information   151

3 Quaternary Structure and Symmetry   154

4 Protein Stability   156

A. Proteins Are Stabilized by Several Forces   156

B. Proteins Can Undergo Denaturation and Renaturation   158

5 Protein Folding   161

A. Proteins Follow Folding Pathways   161

B. Molecular Chaperones Assist Protein Folding   165

C. Some Diseases Are Caused by Protein Misfolding   168

BOX 6-1 **PATHWAYS OF DISCOVERY**
Linus Pauling and Structural Biochemistry   130

BOX 6-2 **BIOCHEMISTRY IN HEALTH AND DISEASE**
Collagen Diseases   137

BOX 6-3 **PERSPECTIVES IN BIOCHEMISTRY**
Thermostable Proteins   159

BOX 6-4 **PERSPECTIVES IN BIOCHEMISTRY**
Protein Structure Prediction and Protein Design   163

7 Protein Function: Myoglobin and Hemoglobin, Muscle Contraction, and Antibodies 176

1 Oxygen Binding to Myoglobin and Hemoglobin 177
A. Myoglobin Is a Monomeric Oxygen-Binding Protein 177
B. Hemoglobin Is a Tetramer with Two Conformations 181
C. Oxygen Binds Cooperatively to Hemoglobin 184
D. Hemoglobin's Two Conformations Exhibit Different Affinities for Oxygen 186
E. Mutations May Alter Hemoglobin's Structure and Function 194

2 Muscle Contraction 197
A. Muscle Consists of Interdigitated Thick and Thin Filaments 198
B. Muscle Contraction Occurs When Myosin Heads Walk Up Thin Filaments 205
C. Actin Forms Microfilaments in Nonmuscle Cells 207

3 Antibodies 209
A. Antibodies Have Constant and Variable Regions 210
B. Antibodies Recognize a Huge Variety of Antigens 212

BOX 7-1 **PERSPECTIVES IN BIOCHEMISTRY**
Other Oxygen-Transport Proteins 181

BOX 7-2 **PATHWAYS OF DISCOVERY** Max Perutz and the Structure and Function of Hemoglobin 182

BOX 7-3 **BIOCHEMISTRY IN HEALTH AND DISEASE**
High-Altitude Adaptation 192

BOX 7-4 **PATHWAYS OF DISCOVERY**
Hugh Huxley and the Sliding Filament Model 200

BOX 7-5 **PERSPECTIVES IN BIOCHEMISTRY**
Monoclonal Antibodies 213

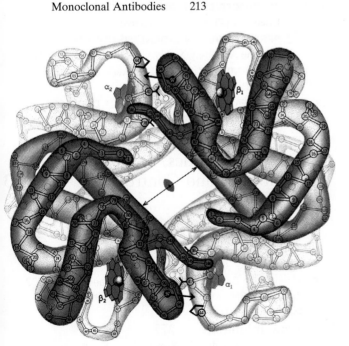

8 Carbohydrates 219

1 Monosaccharides 220
A. Monosaccharides Are Aldoses or Ketoses 220
B. Monosaccharides Vary in Configuration and Conformation 221
C. Sugars Can Be Modified and Covalently Linked 224

2 Polysaccharides 226
A. Lactose and Sucrose Are Disaccharides 227
B. Cellulose and Chitin Are Structural Polysaccharides 228
C. Starch and Glycogen Are Storage Polysaccharides 230
D. Glycosaminoglycans Form Highly Hydrated Gels 232

3 Glycoproteins 234
A. Proteoglycans Contain Glycosaminoglycans 234
B. Bacterial Cell Walls Are Made of Peptidoglycan 235
C. Many Eukaryotic Proteins Are Glycosylated 238
D. Oligosaccharides May Determine Glycoprotein Structure, Function, and Recognition 240

BOX 8-1 **BIOCHEMISTRY IN HEALTH AND DISEASE**
Lactose Intolerance 227

BOX 8-2 **PERSPECTIVES IN BIOCHEMISTRY**
Artificial Sweeteners 228

BOX 8-3 **BIOCHEMISTRY IN HEALTH AND DISEASE**
Peptidoglycan-Specific Antibiotics 238

9 Lipids and Biological Membranes 245

1 Lipid Classification 246
A. The Properties of Fatty Acids Depend on Their Hydrocarbon Chains 246
B. Triacylglycerols Contain Three Esterified Fatty Acids 248
C. Glycerophospholipids Are Amphiphilic 249
D. Sphingolipids Are Amino Alcohol Derivatives 252
E. Steroids Contain Four Fused Rings 254
F. Other Lipids Perform a Variety of Metabolic Roles 257

2 Lipid Bilayers 260
A. Bilayer Formation Is Driven by the Hydrophobic Effect 260
B. Lipid Bilayers Have Fluidlike Properties 261

3 Membrane Proteins 263
A. Integral Membrane Proteins Interact with Hydrophobic Lipids 263
B. Lipid-Linked Proteins Are Anchored to the Bilayer 267
C. Peripheral Proteins Associate Loosely with Membranes 269

4 Membrane Structure and Assembly 269
A. The Fluid Mosaic Model Accounts for Lateral Diffusion 270
B. The Membrane Skeleton Helps Define Cell Shape 272
C. Membrane Lipids Are Distributed Asymmetrically 274
D. The Secretory Pathway Generates Secreted and Transmembrane Proteins 278

   E. Intracellular Vesicles Transport Proteins   282
   F. Proteins Mediate Vesicle Fusion   287
BOX 9-1 **BIOCHEMISTRY IN HEALTH AND DISEASE**
   Lung Surfactant   250
BOX 9-2 **PATHWAYS OF DISCOVERY** Richard Henderson and
   the Structure of Bacteriorhodopsin   266
BOX 9-3 **BIOCHEMISTRY IN HEALTH AND DISEASE** Tetanus
   and Botulinum Toxins Specifically Cleave SNAREs   288

10 Membrane Transport   295

1 Thermodynamics of Transport   296
2 Passive-Mediated Transport   297
   A. Ionophores Carry Ions across Membranes   297
   B. Porins Contain β Barrels   298
   C. Ion Channels Are Highly Selective   299
   D. Aquaporins Mediate the Transmembrane Movement of
   Water   306
   E. Transport Proteins Alternate between Two
   Conformations   307
3 Active Transport   311
   A. The $(Na^+–K^+)$–ATPase Transports Ions in Opposite
   Directions   311
   B. The Ca^{2+}–ATPase Pumps Ca^{2+} Out of the Cytosol   313
   C. ABC Transporters Are Responsible for Drug
   Resistance   314
   D. Active Transport May Be Driven by Ion Gradients   316
BOX 10-1 **PERSPECTIVES IN BIOCHEMISTRY**
   Gap Junctions   308
BOX 10-2 **PERSPECTIVES IN BIOCHEMISTRY** Differentiating
   Mediated and Nonmediated Transport   309
BOX 10-3 **BIOCHEMISTRY IN HEALTH AND DISEASE**
   The Action of Cardiac Glycosides   313

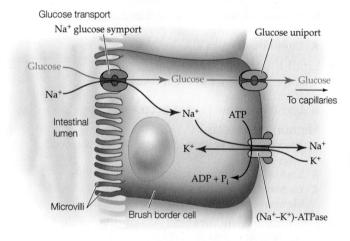

PART III **ENZYMES**

11 Enzymatic Catalysis   322

1 General Properties of Enzymes   323
   A. Enzymes Are Classified by the Type of Reaction They
   Catalyze   324
   B. Enzymes Act on Specific Substrates   325
   C. Some Enzymes Require Cofactors   326
2 Activation Energy and the Reaction
   Coordinate   328
3 Catalytic Mechanisms   330
   A. Acid–Base Catalysis Occurs by Proton Transfer   331
   B. Covalent Catalysis Usually Requires a Nucleophile   333
   C. Metal Ion Cofactors Act as Catalysts   335
   D. Catalysis Can Occur through Proximity and Orientation
   Effects   336
   E. Enzymes Catalyze Reactions by Preferentially Binding the
   Transition State   338
4 Lysozyme   339
   A. Lysozyme's Catalytic Site Was Identified through Model
   Building   340
   B. The Lysozyme Reaction Proceeds via a Covalent
   Intermediate   343
5 Serine Proteases   347
   A. Active Site Residues Were Identified by Chemical
   Labeling   348
   B. X-Ray Structures Provided Information about Catalysis,
   Substrate Specificity, and Evolution   348
   C. Serine Proteases Use Several Catalytic Mechanisms   352
   D. Zymogens Are Inactive Enzyme Precursors   357
BOX 11-1 **PERSPECTIVES IN BIOCHEMISTRY**
   Effects of pH on Enzyme Activity   332
BOX 11-2 **PERSPECTIVES IN BIOCHEMISTRY** Observing
   Enzyme Action by X-Ray Crystallography   342
BOX 11-3 **BIOCHEMISTRY IN HEALTH AND DISEASE**
   Nerve Poisons   349
BOX 11-4 **BIOCHEMISTRY IN HEALTH AND DISEASE**
   The Blood Coagulation Cascade   358

12 Enzyme Kinetics, Inhibition, and Control   363

1 Reaction Kinetics   364
   A. Chemical Kinetics Is Described by Rate Equations   364
   B. Enzyme Kinetics Often Follows the Michaelis–Menten
   Equation   366
   C. Kinetic Data Can Provide Values of V_{max} and K_M 372
   D. Bisubstrate Reactions Follow One of Several Rate
   Equations   375
2 Enzyme Inhibition   377
   A. Competitive Inhibition Involves Inhibitor Binding at an
   Enzyme's Substrate Binding Site   377

B. Uncompetitive Inhibition Involves Inhibitor Binding to the Enzyme–Substrate Complex   381

C. Mixed Inhibition Involves Inhibitor Binding to Both the Free Enzyme and the Enzyme–Substrate Complex   382

3 Control of Enzyme Activity   386

    A. Allosteric Control Involves Binding at a Site Other Than the Active Site   386

    B. Control by Covalent Modification Often Involves Protein Phosphorylation   390

4 Drug Design   394

    A. Drug Discovery Employs a Variety of Techniques   394

    B. A Drug's Bioavailability Depends on How It Is Absorbed and Transported in the Body   396

    C. Clinical Trials Test for Efficacy and Safety   396

    D. Cytochromes P450 Are Often Implicated in Adverse Drug Reactions   398

BOX 12-1   **PERSPECTIVES IN BIOCHEMISTRY**
Isotopic Labeling   367

BOX 12-2   **PATHWAYS OF DISCOVERY**
J.B.S. Haldane and Enzyme Action   369

BOX 12-3   **PERSPECTIVES IN BIOCHEMISTRY**
Kinetics and Transition State Theory   372

BOX 12-4   **BIOCHEMISTRY IN HEALTH AND DISEASE**
HIV Enzyme Inhibitors   384

13   Biochemical Signaling   405

1 Hormones   406

    A. Pancreatic Islet Hormones Control Fuel Metabolism   407

    B. Epinephrine and Norepinephrine Prepare the Body for Action   409

    C. Steroid Hormones Regulate a Wide Variety of Metabolic and Sexual Processes   410

    D. Growth Hormone Binds to Receptors in Muscle, Bone, and Cartilage   411

2 Receptor Tyrosine Kinases   412

    A. Receptor Tyrosine Kinases Transmit Signals across the Cell Membrane   413

    B. Kinase Cascades Relay Signals to the Nucleus   416

    C. Some Receptors Are Associated with Nonreceptor Tyrosine Kinases   422

    D. Protein Phosphatases Are Signaling Proteins in Their Own Right   425

3 Heterotrimeric G Proteins   428

    A. G Protein–Coupled Receptors Contain Seven Transmembrane Helices   429

    B. Heterotrimeric G Proteins Dissociate on Activation   430

    C. Adenylate Cyclase Synthesizes cAMP to Activate Protein Kinase A   432

    D. Phosphodiesterases Limit Second Messenger Activity   435

4 The Phosphoinositide Pathway   436

    A. Ligand Binding Results in the Cytoplasmic Release of the Second Messengers IP_3 and Ca^{2+} 437

    B. Calmodulin Is a Ca^{2+}-Activated Switch   438

    C. DAG Is a Lipid-Soluble Second Messenger That Activates Protein Kinase C   440

D. Epilog: Complex Systems Have Emergent Properties   442

BOX 13-1   **PATHWAYS OF DISCOVERY**
Rosalyn Yalow and the Radioimmunoassay (RIA)   408

BOX 13-2   **PERSPECTIVES IN BIOCHEMISTRY**
Receptor–Ligand Binding Can Be Quantitated   414

BOX 13-3   **BIOCHEMISTRY IN HEALTH AND DISEASE**
Oncogenes and Cancer   421

BOX 13-4   **BIOCHEMISTRY IN HEALTH AND DISEASE**
Drugs and Toxins That Affect Cell Signaling   435

BOX 13-5   **BIOCHEMISTRY IN HEALTH AND DISEASE**
Anthrax   444

PART IV METABOLISM

14   Introduction to Metabolism   448

1 Overview of Metabolism   449

    A. Nutrition Involves Food Intake and Use   449

    B. Vitamins and Minerals Assist Metabolic Reactions   450

    C. Metabolic Pathways Consist of Series of Enzymatic Reactions   451

    D. Thermodynamics Dictates the Direction and Regulatory Capacity of Metabolic Pathways   455

    E. Metabolic Flux Must Be Controlled   457

2 "High-Energy" Compounds   459

    A. ATP Has a High Phosphoryl Group-Transfer Potential   460

    B. Coupled Reactions Drive Endergonic Processes   462

    C. Some Other Phosphorylated Compounds Have High Phosphoryl Group-Transfer Potentials   464

    D. Thioesters Are Energy-Rich Compounds   468

3 Oxidation–Reduction Reactions   469

    A. NAD^+ and FAD Are Electron Carriers   469

    B. The Nernst Equation Describes Oxidation–Reduction Reactions   470

    C. Spontaneity Can Be Determined by Measuring Reduction Potential Differences   472

4 Experimental Approaches to the Study of Metabolism   475

    A. Labeled Metabolites Can Be Traced   475

    B. Studying Metabolic Pathways Often Involves Perturbing the System   477

    C. Systems Biology Has Entered the Study of Metabolism   477

BOX 14-1   **PERSPECTIVES IN BIOCHEMISTRY**
Oxidation States of Carbon   453

BOX 14-2   **PERSPECTIVES IN BIOCHEMISTRY**
Mapping Metabolic Pathways   454

BOX 14-3   **PATHWAYS OF DISCOVERY**
Fritz Lipmann and "High-Energy" Compounds   460

BOX 14-4   **PERSPECTIVES IN BIOCHEMISTRY**
ATP and ΔG 462

15 Glucose Catabolism 485

1 Overview of Glycolysis 486

2 The Reactions of Glycolysis 489
A. Hexokinase Uses the First ATP 489
B. Phosphoglucose Isomerase Converts Glucose-6-Phosphate to Fructose-6-Phosphate 490
C. Phosphofructokinase Uses the Second ATP 491
D. Aldolase Converts a 6-Carbon Compound to Two 3-Carbon Compounds 492
E. Triose Phosphate Isomerase Interconverts Dihydroxyacetone Phosphate and Glyceraldehyde-3-Phosphate 494
F. Glyceraldehyde-3-Phosphate Dehydrogenase Forms the First "High-Energy" Intermediate 497
G. Phosphoglycerate Kinase Generates the First ATP 499
H. Phosphoglycerate Mutase Interconverts 3-Phosphoglycerate and 2-Phosphoglycerate 499
I. Enolase Forms the Second "High-Energy" Intermediate 500
J. Pyruvate Kinase Generates the Second ATP 501

3 Fermentation: The Anaerobic Fate of Pyruvate 504
A. Homolactic Fermentation Converts Pyruvate to Lactate 505
B. Alcoholic Fermentation Converts Pyruvate to Ethanol and CO_2 506
C. Fermentation Is Energetically Favorable 509

4 Regulation of Glycolysis 510
A. Phosphofructokinase Is the Major Flux-Controlling Enzyme of Glycolysis in Muscle 511
B. Substrate Cycling Fine-Tunes Flux Control 514

5 Metabolism of Hexoses Other than Glucose 516
A. Fructose Is Converted to Fructose-6-Phosphate or Glyceraldehyde-3-Phosphate 516
B. Galactose Is Converted to Glucose-6-Phosphate 518
C. Mannose Is Converted to Fructose-6-Phosphate 520

6 The Pentose Phosphate Pathway 520
A. Oxidative Reactions Produce NADPH in Stage 1 522
B. Isomerization and Epimerization of Ribulose-5-Phosphate Occur in Stage 2 523
C. Stage 3 Involves Carbon–Carbon Bond Cleavage and Formation 523
D. The Pentose Phosphate Pathway Must Be Regulated 524

BOX 15-1 **PATHWAYS OF DISCOVERY**
Otto Warburg and Studies of Metabolism 488
BOX 15-2 **PERSPECTIVES IN BIOCHEMISTRY** Synthesis of 2,3-Bisphosphoglycerate in Erythrocytes and Its Effect on the Oxygen Carrying Capacity of the Blood 502
BOX 15-3 **PERSPECTIVES IN BIOCHEMISTRY**
Glycolytic ATP Production in Muscle 510
BOX 15-4 **BIOCHEMISTRY IN HEALTH AND DISEASE**
Glucose-6-Phosphate Dehydrogenase Deficiency 526

16 Glycogen Metabolism and Gluconeogenesis 530

1 Glycogen Breakdown 532
A. Glycogen Phosphorylase Degrades Glycogen to Glucose-1-Phosphate 534
B. Glycogen Debranching Enzyme Acts as a Glucosyltransferase 536
C. Phosphoglucomutase Interconverts Glucose-1-Phosphate and Glucose-6-Phosphate 537

2 Glycogen Synthesis 540
A. UDP–Glucose Pyrophosphorylase Activates Glucosyl Units 540
B. Glycogen Synthase Extends Glycogen Chains 541
C. Glycogen Branching Enzyme Transfers Seven-Residue Glycogen Segments 543

3 Control of Glycogen Metabolism 545
A. Glycogen Phosphorylase and Glycogen Synthase Are Under Allosteric Control 545
B. Glycogen Phosphorylase and Glycogen Synthase Undergo Control by Covalent Modification 545
C. Glycogen Metabolism Is Subject to Hormonal Control 550

4 Gluconeogenesis 552
A. Pyruvate Is Converted to Phosphoenolpyruvate in Two Steps 554
B. Hydrolytic Reactions Bypass Irreversible Glycolytic Reactions 557
C. Gluconeogenesis and Glycolysis Are Independently Regulated 558

5 Other Carbohydrate Biosynthetic Pathways 560

BOX 16-1 **PATHWAYS OF DISCOVERY**
Carl and Gerty Cori and Glucose Metabolism 533
BOX 16-2 **BIOCHEMISTRY IN HEALTH AND DISEASE**
Glycogen Storage Diseases 538
BOX 16-3 **PERSPECTIVES IN BIOCHEMISTRY**
Optimizing Glycogen Structure 544
BOX 16-4 **PERSPECTIVES IN BIOCHEMISTRY**
Lactose Synthesis 560

17 Citric Acid Cycle 566

1 Overview of the Citric Acid Cycle 567

2 Synthesis of Acetyl-Coenzyme A 570
A. Pyruvate Dehydrogenase Is a Multienzyme Complex 570
B. The Pyruvate Dehydrogenase Complex Catalyzes Five Reactions 572

3 Enzymes of the Citric Acid Cycle 576
A. Citrate Synthase Joins an Acetyl Group to Oxaloacetate 577
B. Aconitase Interconverts Citrate and Isocitrate 578
C. NAD^+-Dependent Isocitrate Dehydrogenase Releases CO_2 579

D. α-Ketoglutarate Dehydrogenase Resembles Pyruvate Dehydrogenase   580
E. Succinyl-CoA Synthetase Produces GTP   580
F. Succinate Dehydrogenase Generates $FADH_2$ 582
G. Fumarase Produces Malate   583
H. Malate Dehydrogenase Regenerates Oxaloacetate   583

4 Regulation of the Citric Acid Cycle   583
A. Pyruvate Dehydrogenase Is Regulated by Product Inhibition and Covalent Modification   585
B. Three Enzymes Control the Rate of the Citric Acid Cycle   585

5 Reactions Related to the Citric Acid Cycle   588
A. Other Pathways Use Citric Acid Cycle Intermediates   588
B. Some Reactions Replenish Citric Acid Cycle Intermediates   589
C. The Glyoxylate Cycle Shares Some Steps with the Citric Acid Cycle   590

BOX 17-1 **PATHWAYS OF DISCOVERY**
Hans Krebs and the Citric Acid Cycle   569

BOX 17-2 **BIOCHEMISTRY IN HEALTH AND DISEASE**
Arsenic Poisoning   576

BOX 17-3 **PERSPECTIVES IN BIOCHEMISTRY**
Evolution of the Citric Acid Cycle   592

18 Electron Transport and Oxidative Phosphorylation   596

1 The Mitochondrion   597
A. Mitochondria Contain a Highly Folded Inner Membrane   597
B. Ions and Metabolites Enter Mitochondria via Transporters   599

2 Electron Transport   600
A. Electron Transport Is an Exergonic Process   601
B. Electron Carriers Operate in Sequence   602
C. Complex I Accepts Electrons from NADH   604
D. Complex II Contributes Electrons to Coenzyme Q   609
E. Complex III Translocates Protons via the Q Cycle   611
F. Complex IV Reduces Oxygen to Water   615

3 Oxidative Phosphorylation   618
A. The Chemiosmotic Theory Links Electron Transport to ATP Synthesis   618
B. ATP Synthase Is Driven by the Flow of Protons   622
C. The P/O Ratio Relates the Amount of ATP Synthesized to the Amount of Oxygen Reduced   629
D. Oxidative Phosphorylation Can Be Uncoupled from Electron Transport   630

4 Control of Oxidative Metabolism   631
A. The Rate of Oxidative Phosphorylation Depends on the ATP and NADH Concentrations   631
B. Aerobic Metabolism Has Some Disadvantages   634

BOX 18-1 **PERSPECTIVES IN BIOCHEMISTRY** Cytochromes Are Electron-Transport Heme Proteins   610

BOX 18-2 **PATHWAYS OF DISCOVERY**
Peter Mitchell and the Chemiosmotic Theory   619

BOX 18-3 **PERSPECTIVES IN BIOCHEMISTRY** Bacterial Electron Transport and Oxidative Phosphorylation   621

BOX 18-4 **PERSPECTIVES IN BIOCHEMISTRY** Uncoupling in Brown Adipose Tissue Generates Heat   632

BOX 18-5 **BIOCHEMISTRY IN HEALTH AND DISEASE**
Oxygen Deprivation in Heart Attack and Stroke   635

19 Photosynthesis   640

1 Chloroplasts   641
A. The Light Reactions Take Place in the Thylakoid Membrane   641
B. Pigment Molecules Absorb Light   643

2 The Light Reactions   645
A. Light Energy Is Transformed to Chemical Energy   645
B. Electron Transport in Photosynthetic Bacteria Follows a Circular Path   647
C. Two-Center Electron Transport Is a Linear Pathway That Produces O_2 and NADPH   650
D. The Proton Gradient Drives ATP Synthesis by Photophosphorylation   661

3 The Dark Reactions   663
   A. The Calvin Cycle Fixes CO_2 663
   B. Calvin Cycle Products Are Converted to Starch, Sucrose, and Cellulose   668
   C. The Calvin Cycle Is Controlled Indirectly by Light   670
   D. Photorespiration Competes with Photosynthesis   671
BOX 19-1 **PERSPECTIVES IN BIOCHEMISTRY**
   Segregation of PSI and PSII   662

20 Lipid Metabolism   677

1 Lipid Digestion, Absorption, and Transport   678
   A. Triacylglycerols Are Digested before They Are Absorbed   678
   B. Lipids Are Transported as Lipoproteins   680
2 Fatty Acid Oxidation   685
   A. Fatty Acids Are Activated by Their Attachment to Coenzyme A   686
   B. Carnitine Carries Acyl Groups across the Mitochondrial Membrane   686
   C. β Oxidation Degrades Fatty Acids to Acetyl-CoA   688
   D. Oxidation of Unsaturated Fatty Acids Requires Additional Enzymes   690
   E. Oxidation of Odd-Chain Fatty Acids Yields Propionyl-CoA   692
   F. Peroxisomal β Oxidation Differs from Mitochondrial β Oxidation   698
3 Ketone Bodies   698
4 Fatty Acid Biosynthesis   701
   A. Mitochondrial Acetyl-CoA Must Be Transported into the Cytosol   701
   B. Acetyl-CoA Carboxylase Produces Malonyl-CoA   702
   C. Fatty Acid Synthase Catalyzes Seven Reactions   703
   D. Fatty Acids May Be Elongated and Desaturated   707
   E. Fatty Acids Are Esterified to Form Triacylglycerols   711
5 Regulation of Fatty Acid Metabolism   711
6 Synthesis of Other Lipids   714
   A. Glycerophospholipids Are Built from Intermediates of Triacylglycerol Synthesis   714
   B. Sphingolipids Are Built from Palmitoyl-CoA and Serine   717
   C. C_{20} Fatty Acids Are the Precursors of Prostaglandins   718
7 Cholesterol Metabolism   721
   A. Cholesterol Is Synthesized from Acetyl-CoA   721
   B. HMG-CoA Reductase Controls the Rate of Cholesterol Synthesis   725
   C. Abnormal Cholesterol Transport Leads to Atherosclerosis   727
BOX 20-1 **BIOCHEMISTRY IN HEALTH AND DISEASE**
   Vitamin B_{12} Deficiency   696
BOX 20-2 **PATHWAYS OF DISCOVERY** Dorothy Crowfoot Hodgkin and the Structure of Vitamin B_{12} 697
BOX 20-3 **PERSPECTIVES IN BIOCHEMISTRY**
   Triclosan: An Inhibitor of Fatty Acid Synthesis   708

BOX 20-4 **BIOCHEMISTRY IN HEALTH AND DISEASE**
   Sphingolipid Degradation and Lipid Storage Diseases   720

21 Amino Acid Metabolism   732

1 Protein Degradation   732
   A. Lysosomes Degrade Many Proteins   732
   B. Ubiquitin Marks Proteins for Degradation   733
   C. The Proteasome Unfolds and Hydrolyzes Ubiquitinated Polypeptides   734
2 Amino Acid Deamination   738
   A. Transaminases Use PLP to Transfer Amino Groups   738
   B. Glutamate Can Be Oxidatively Deaminated   742
3 The Urea Cycle   743
   A. Five Enzymes Carry out the Urea Cycle   743
   B. The Urea Cycle Is Regulated by Substrate Availability   747
4 Breakdown of Amino Acids   747
   A. Alanine, Cysteine, Glycine, Serine, and Threonine Are Degraded to Pyruvate   748
   B. Asparagine and Aspartate Are Degraded to Oxaloacetate   751
   C. Arginine, Glutamate, Glutamine, Histidine, and Proline Are Degraded to α-Ketoglutarate   751
   D. Isoleucine, Methionine, and Valine Are Degraded to Succinyl-CoA   753
   E. Leucine and Lysine Are Degraded Only to Acetyl-CoA and/or Acetoacetate   758
   F. Tryptophan Is Degraded to Alanine and Acetoacetate   758
   G. Phenylalanine and Tyrosine Are Degraded to Fumarate and Acetoacetate   760
5 Amino Acid Biosynthesis   763
   A. Nonessential Amino Acids Are Synthesized from Common Metabolites   764
   B. Plants and Microorganisms Synthesize the Essential Amino Acids   769
6 Other Products of Amino Acid Metabolism   774
   A. Heme Is Synthesized from Glycine and Succinyl-CoA   775
   B. Amino Acids Are Precursors of Physiologically Active Amines   780
   C. Nitric Oxide Is Derived from Arginine   781
7 Nitrogen Fixation   782
   A. Nitrogenase Reduces N_2 to NH_3 783
   B. Fixed Nitrogen Is Assimilated into Biological Molecules   786
BOX 21-1 **BIOCHEMISTRY IN HEALTH AND DISEASE**
   Homocysteine, a Marker of Disease   755
BOX 21-2 **BIOCHEMISTRY IN HEALTH AND DISEASE**
   Phenylketonuria and Alcaptonuria Result from Defects in Phenylalanine Degradation   762
BOX 21-3 **BIOCHEMISTRY IN HEALTH AND DISEASE**
   The Porphyrias   778

22 Mammalian Fuel Metabolism: Integration and Regulation 791

1 Organ Specialization 792
  A. The Brain Requires a Steady Supply of Glucose 793
  B. Muscle Utilizes Glucose, Fatty Acids, and Ketone Bodies 794
  C. Adipose Tissue Stores and Releases Fatty Acids and Hormones 795
  D. Liver Is the Body's Central Metabolic Clearinghouse 796
  E. Kidney Filters Wastes and Maintains Blood pH 798
  F. Blood Transports Metabolites in Interorgan Metabolic Pathways 798

2 Hormonal Control of Fuel Metabolism 799

3 Metabolic Homeostasis: The Regulation of Energy Metabolism, Appetite, and Body Weight 804
  A. AMP-Dependent Protein Kinase Is the Cell's Fuel Gauge 804
  B. Adiponectin Regulates AMPK Activity 806
  C. Leptin Is a Satiety Hormone 806
  D. Ghrelin and PYY_{3-36} Act as Short-Term Regulators of Appetite 807
  E. Energy Expenditure Can Be Controlled by Adaptive Thermogenesis 808

4 Disturbances in Fuel Metabolism 809
  A. Starvation Leads to Metabolic Adjustments 809
  B. Diabetes Mellitus Is Characterized by High Blood Glucose Levels 811
  C. Obesity Is Usually Caused by Excessive Food Intake 814
BOX 22-1 **PATHWAYS OF DISCOVERY** Frederick Banting and Charles Best and the Discovery of Insulin 812

PART V GENE EXPRESSION AND REPLICATION

23 Nucleotide Metabolism 817

1 Synthesis of Purine Ribonucleotides 818
  A. Purine Synthesis Yields Inosine Monophosphate 818
  B. IMP Is Converted to Adenine and Guanine Ribonucleotides 821
  C. Purine Nucleotide Biosynthesis Is Regulated at Several Steps 822
  D. Purines Can Be Salvaged 823

2 Synthesis of Pyrimidine Ribonucleotides 824
  A. UMP Is Synthesized in Six Steps 824
  B. UMP Is Converted to UTP and CTP 826
  C. Pyrimidine Nucleotide Biosynthesis Is Regulated at ATCase or Carbamoyl Phosphate Synthetase II 827

3 Formation of Deoxyribonucleotides 828
  A. Ribonucleotide Reductase Converts Ribonucleotides to Deoxyribonucleotides 828
  B. dUMP Is Methylated to Form Thymine 834

4 Nucleotide Degradation 839
  A. Purine Catabolism Yields Uric Acid 839
  B. Some Animals Degrade Uric Acid 842
  C. Pyrimidines Are Broken Down to Malonyl-CoA and Methylmalonyl-CoA 845
BOX 23-1 **BIOCHEMISTRY IN HEALTH AND DISEASE** Inhibition of Thymidylate Synthesis in Cancer Therapy 838
BOX 23-2 **PATHWAYS OF DISCOVERY** Gertrude Elion and Purine Derivatives 844

24 Nucleic Acid Structure 848

1 The DNA Helix 849
  A. DNA Can Adopt Different Conformations 849
  B. DNA Has Limited Flexibility 855
  C. DNA Can Be Supercoiled 857
  D. Topoisomerases Alter DNA Supercoiling 859

2 Forces Stabilizing Nucleic Acid Structures 864
  A. DNA Can Undergo Denaturation and Renaturation 864
  B. Nucleic Acids Are Stabilized by Base Pairing, Stacking, and Ionic Interactions 866
  C. RNA Structures Are Highly Variable 868

3 Fractionation of Nucleic Acids 872
  A. Nucleic Acids Can Be Purified by Chromatography 872
  B. Electrophoresis Separates Nucleic Acids by Size 872

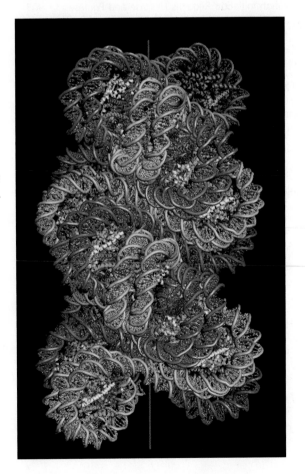

4 DNA–Protein Interactions 874
   A. Restriction Endonucleases Distort DNA on Binding 875
   B. Prokaryotic Repressors Often Include a DNA-Binding Helix 876
   C. Eukaryotic Transcription Factors May Include Zinc Fingers or Leucine Zippers 879

5 Eukaryotic Chromosome Structure 883
   A. Histones Are Positively Charged 884
   B. DNA Coils around Histones to Form Nucleosomes 884
   C. Chromatin Forms Higher-Order Structures 887

BOX 24-1 **PATHWAYS OF DISCOVERY**
   Rosalind Franklin and the Structure of DNA 850

BOX 24-2 **BIOCHEMISTRY IN HEALTH AND DISEASE**
   Inhibitors of Topoisomerases as Antibiotics and Anticancer Chemotherapeutic Agents 865

BOX 24-3 **PERSPECTIVES IN BIOCHEMISTRY**
   The RNA World 871

25 DNA Replication, Repair, and Recombination 893

1 Overview of DNA Replication 894

2 Prokaryotic DNA Replication 896
   A. DNA Polymerases Add the Correctly Paired Nucleotide 896
   B. Replication Initiation Requires Helicase and Primase 903
   C. The Leading and Lagging Strands Are Synthesized Simultaneously 904
   D. Replication Terminates at Specific Sites 908
   E. DNA Is Replicated with High Fidelity 909

3 Eukaryotic DNA Replication 910
   A. Eukaryotes Use Several DNA Polymerases 910
   B. Eukaryotic DNA Is Replicated from Multiple Origins 911
   C. Telomerase Extends Chromosome Ends 914

4 DNA Damage 916
   A. Environmental and Chemical Agents Generate Mutations 916
   B. Many Mutagens Are Carcinogens 919

5 DNA Repair 920
   A. Some Damage Can Be Directly Reversed 920
   B. Base Excision Repair Requires a Glycosylase 921
   C. Nucleotide Excision Repair Removes a Segment of a DNA Strand 923
   D. Mismatch Repair Corrects Replication Errors 924
   E. Some DNA Repair Mechanisms Introduce Errors 925

6 Recombination 926
   A. Homologous Recombination Involves Several Protein Complexes 926
   B. DNA Can Be Repaired by Recombination 932
   C. Transposition Rearranges Segments of DNA 934

BOX 25-1 **PATHWAYS OF DISCOVERY**
   Arthur Kornberg and DNA Polymerase I 898

BOX 25-2 **PERSPECTIVES IN BIOCHEMISTRY**
   Reverse Transcriptase 912

BOX 25-3 **BIOCHEMISTRY IN HEALTH AND DISEASE**
   Telomerase, Aging, and Cancer 915

BOX 25-4 **PERSPECTIVES IN BIOCHEMISTRY**
   DNA Methylation 918

BOX 25-5 **PERSPECTIVES IN BIOCHEMISTRY**
   Why Doesn't DNA Contain Uracil? 921

26 Transcription and RNA Processing 942

1 Prokaryotic RNA Transcription 943
   A. RNA Polymerase Resembles Other Polymerases 943
   B. Transcription Is Initiated at a Promoter 943
   C. The RNA Chain Grows from the 5' to 3' End 947
   D. Transcription Terminates at Specific Sites 950

2 Transcription in Eukaryotes 952
   A. Eukaryotes Have Several RNA Polymerases 953
   B. Each Polymerase Recognizes a Different Type of Promoter 958
   C. Transcription Factors Are Required to Initiate Transcription 960

3 Posttranscriptional Processing 965
   A. Messenger RNAs Undergo 5' Capping, Addition of a 3' Tail, and Splicing 965
   B. Ribosomal RNA Precursors May Be Cleaved, Modified, and Spliced 976
   C. Transfer RNAs Are Processed by Nucleotide Removal, Addition, and Modification 980

BOX 26-1 **PERSPECTIVES IN BIOCHEMISTRY** Collisions between DNA Polymerase and RNA Polymerase 949

BOX 26-2 **BIOCHEMISTRY IN HEALTH AND DISEASE**
   Inhibitors of Transcription 954

BOX 26-3 **PATHWAYS OF DISCOVERY** Richard Roberts and Phillip Sharp and the Discovery of Introns 968

27 Protein Synthesis   985

1 The Genetic Code   986
   A. Codons Are Triplets That Are Read Sequentially   986
   B. The Genetic Code Was Systematically Deciphered   987
   C. The Genetic Code Is Degenerate and Nonrandom   988

2 Transfer RNA and Its Aminoacylation   991
   A. All tRNAs Have a Similar Structure   991
   B. Aminoacyl–tRNA Synthetases Attach Amino Acids to tRNAs   994
   C. A tRNA May Recognize More than One Codon   998

3 Ribosomes   1000
   A. The Prokaryotic Ribosome Consists of Two Subunits   1001
   B. The Eukaryotic Ribosome Is Larger and More Complex   1007

4 Translation   1008
   A. Chain Initiation Requires an Initiator tRNA and Initiation Factors   1010
   B. The Ribosome Decodes the mRNA, Catalyzes Peptide Bond Formation, Then Moves to the Next Codon   1014
   C. Release Factors Terminate Translation   1026

5 Posttranslational Processing   1028
   A. Ribosome-Associated Chaperones Help Proteins Fold   1028
   B. Newly Synthesized Proteins May Be Covalently Modified   1029

BOX 27-1 **PERSPECTIVES IN BIOCHEMISTRY**
   Evolution of the Genetic Code   990

BOX 27-2 **PERSPECTIVES IN BIOCHEMISTRY**
   Expanding the Genetic Code   1000

BOX 27-3 **BIOCHEMISTRY IN HEALTH AND DISEASE**
   The Effects of Antibiotics on Protein Synthesis   1024

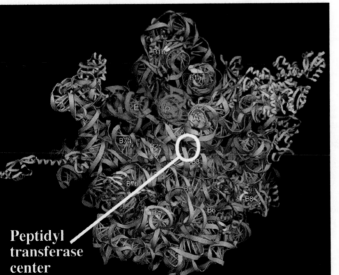

Peptidyl transferase center

28 Regulation of Gene Expression   1037

1 Genome Organization   1038
   A. Gene Number Varies among Organisms   1038
   B. Some Genes Occur in Clusters   1042
   C. Eukaryotic Genomes Contain Repetitive DNA Sequences   1043

2 Regulation of Prokaryotic Gene Expression   1046
   A. The *lac* Operon Is Controlled by a Repressor   1046
   B. Catabolite-Repressed Operons Can Be Activated   1050
   C. Attenuation Regulates Transcription Termination   1051
   D. Riboswitches Are Metabolite-Sensing RNAs   1054

3 Regulation of Eukaryotic Gene Expression   1055
   A. Chromatin Structure Influences Gene Expression   1055
   B. Eukaryotes Contain Multiple Transcriptional Activators   1067
   C. Posttranscriptional Control Mechanisms Include RNA Degradation   1073
   D. Antibody Diversity Results from Somatic Recombination and Hypermutation   1077

4 The Cell Cycle, Cancer, and Apoptosis   1081
   A. Progress through the Cell Cycle Is Tightly Regulated   1081
   B. Tumor Suppressors Prevent Cancer   1084
   C. Apoptosis Is an Orderly Process   1086
   D. Development Has a Molecular Basis   1090

BOX 28-1 **BIOCHEMISTRY IN HEALTH AND DISEASE**
   Trinucleotide Repeat Diseases   1044

BOX 28-2 **PERSPECTIVES IN BIOCHEMISTRY**
   X Chromosome Inactivation   1057

BOX 28-3 **PERSPECTIVES IN BIOCHEMISTRY**
   Nonsense-Mediated Decay   1074

APPENDICES

Solutions to Problems   SP-1

Glossary   G-1

Index   I-1

Preface

The last several years have seen enormous advances in biochemistry, particularly in the areas of structural biology and bioinformatics. Against this backdrop, we asked *What do students of modern biochemistry really need to know and how can we, as authors, help them in their pursuit of this knowledge?* We concluded that it is more important than ever to provide a solid biochemical foundation, rooted in chemistry, to prepare students for the scientific challenges of the future. With that in mind, we re-examined the contents of *Fundamentals of Biochemistry,* focusing on basic principles and striving to polish the text and improve the pedagogy throughout the book so that it is even more accessible to students. At the same time, we added new material in a way that links it to the existing content, mindful that students assimilate new information only in the proper context. We believe that students are best served by a textbook that is complete, clearly written, and relevant to human health and disease.

New For The Third Edition

The newest edition of *Fundamentals of Biochemistry* includes significant changes and updates to the contents. These changes include:

■ A new chapter, Chapter 13, on Biochemical Signaling covers the role of hormones, receptors, G proteins, second messengers, and other aspects of inter- and intracellular communication. Placing these topics in a single chapter allows more comprehensive coverage of this rapidly changing field, which is critical for understanding such processes as fuel metabolism and cancer growth.

■ Chapter 14 (Introduction to Metabolism) includes a new discussion of vitamins, minerals, and macronutrients, as part of a more wholistic approach to human metabolism. Expanded coverage of DNA chip technology and applications reflects growth in this area. In addition, a section on Systems Biology describes the cutting-edge fields of genomics, transcriptomics, proteomics, and metabolomics, along with some relevant laboratory techniques.

■ P/O ratios have been updated throughout the metabolism chapters (so that each electron pair from NADH corresponds to 2.5 rather than 3 ATP) to match the most recent research findings.

■ Chapter 22 (Mammalian Fuel Metabolism: Integration and Regulation) has been extensively revised to incorporate recent advances in human metabolic studies, with a new section on metabolic homeostasis that includes a discussion of appetite and body weight regulation. New material on AMP-dependent protein kinase and the hormone adiponectin describes some of the newly discovered biochemistry behind metabolic regulation.

■ Other additions to the third edition were prompted by advances in many different fields, for example, new information on the analysis of short tandem repeats for DNA fingerprinting, bacterial biofilms, viral membrane fusion events, structures and functions of ABC transporters such as P-glycoprotein responsible for drug resistance, chromatin structure, elements involved in initiating RNA transcription, and posttranscriptional protein processing.

We have given significant thought to the pedagogy within the text and have concentrated on fine-tuning and adding

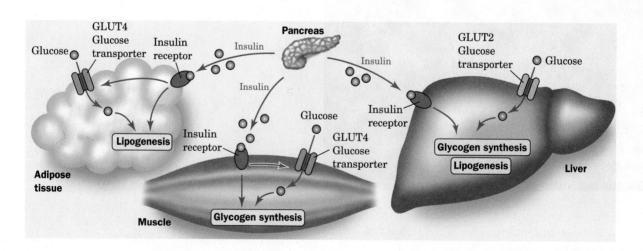

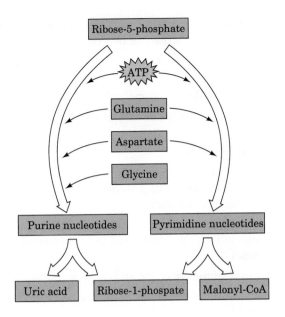

some new elements to promote student learning. These enhancements include the following:

- Numerous macromolecular structures are displayed with newly revealed details, and well over 100 figures have been replaced with state-of-the-art molecular graphics.

- Seven metabolic overview figures have been reworked to better emphasize their physiological relevance.

- Three new Pathways of Discovery Boxes have been added to focus on the scientific contributions of Lynn Margulis (Chapter 1), Rosalyn Yalow (Chapter 13), and Gertrude Elion (Chapter 23). These provide a better sense of history and emphasize that the study of biochemistry is a human endeavor.

- **Learning Objectives** placed at the beginning of each section of a chapter guide students as they read.

- Each section concludes with a set of study questions, entitled **Check Your Understanding,** to provide a quick review of the preceding material.

- Thirty new end-of-chapter problems with complete solutions have been added to provide students with more opportunities to apply their knowledge.

- New **overview figures** summarize multistep metabolic pathways and the interrelationships among them.

 ## Organization

As in the second edition, the text begins with two introductory chapters that discuss the origin of life, evolution, thermodynamics, the properties of water, and acid–base chemistry. Nucleotides and nucleic acids are covered in Chapter 3, since an understanding of the structures and functions of these molecules supports the subsequent study of protein evolution and metabolism.

Four chapters (4 through 7) explore amino acid chemistry, methods for analyzing protein structure and sequence, secondary through quaternary protein structure, protein folding and stability, and structure–function relationships in hemoglobin, muscle proteins, and antibodies. Chapter 8 (Carbohydrates), Chapter 9 (Lipids and Biological Membranes), and Chapter 10 (Membrane Transport) round out the coverage of the basic molecules of life.

The next three chapters examine proteins in action, introducing students first to enzyme mechanisms (Chapter 11), then shepherding them through discussions of enzyme kinetics, the effects of inhibitors, and enzyme regulation (Chapter 12). These themes are continued in Chapter 13, which describes the components of signal transduction pathways.

Metabolism is covered in a set of chapters, beginning with an introductory chapter (Chapter 14) that provides an overview of metabolic pathways, the thermodynamics of "high-energy" compounds, and redox chemistry. Central metabolic pathways are presented in detail (e.g., glycolysis, glycogen metabolism, and the citric acid cycle in Chapters 15–17) so that students can appreciate how individual enzymes catalyze reactions and work in concert to perform complicated biochemical tasks. Chapters 18 (Electron Transport and Oxidative Phosphorylation) and 19 (Photosynthesis) complete a sequence that emphasizes energy-producing pathways. Not all pathways are covered in full detail, particularly those related to lipids (Chapter 20), amino acids (Chapter 21), and nucleotides (Chapter 23). Instead, key enzymatic reactions are highlighted for their interesting chemistry or regulatory importance. Chapter 22, on the integration of metabolism, discusses organ specialization and metabolic regulation in mammals.

Five chapters describe the biochemistry of nucleic acids, beginning with Chapter 24, which discusses the structure of

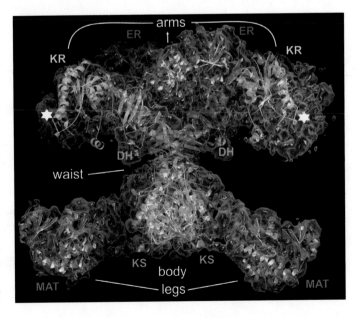

DNA and its interactions with proteins. Chapters 25–27 cover the processes of replication, transcription, and translation, highlighting the functions of the RNA and protein molecules that carry out these processes. Chapter 28 deals with a variety of mechanisms for regulating gene expression, including the histone code and the roles of transcription factors and their relevance to cancer and development.

Traditional Pedagogical Strengths

Successful pedagogical elements from the first and second editions of *Fundamentals of Biochemistry* have been retained. Among these are:

- the division of chapters into **numbered sections** for easy navigation
- **key sentences** printed in italic to assist with quick visual identification
- boldfaced **key terms**

- a **list of terms** at the end of each chapter, with the **page numbers** where the terms are first defined
- a comprehensive **glossary containing over 1200 terms** in an appendix
- **overview figures** for many metabolic processes
- figures illustrating **detailed enzyme mechanisms** throughout the text
- **sample calculations**
- **PDB identification codes** in the figure legend for each molecular structure so that students can download and explore structures on their own.
- Enrichment material, including clinical correlations, technical descriptions, and historical perspectives placed in **text boxes.**
- a **numbered summary** at the end of each chapter
- an expanded set of **problems** (with **complete solutions** in an appendix)
- a list of references for each chapter, selected for their relevance and user-friendliness.

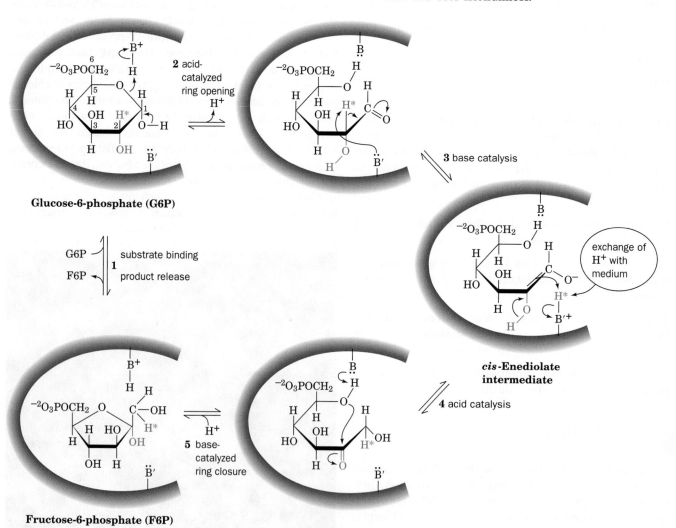

Glucose-6-phosphate (G6P)

2 acid-catalyzed ring opening

3 base catalysis

exchange of H$^+$ with medium

cis-Enediolate intermediate

1 substrate binding / product release

4 acid catalysis

5 base-catalyzed ring closure

Fructose-6-phosphate (F6P)

Acknowledgments

This textbook is the result of the dedicated effort of many individuals, several of whom deserve special mention: Laura Ierardi cleverly combined text figures and tables in designing each of the textbook's pages. Suzanne Ingrao, our Production Coordinator, skillfully managed the production of the textbook. Madelyn Lesure designed the book's typography and cover. Kevin Molloy, our Acquisitions Editor, skillfully organized and managed the project until his departure, and Petra Recter, Associate Publisher, saw us through to publication. Hilary Newman and Elyse Rieder acquired many of the photographs in the textbook and kept track of all of them. Connie Parks, our copy editor, put the final polish on the manuscript and eliminated large numbers of grammatical and typographical errors. Sandra Dumas was our in-house Production Editor at Wiley. Sigmund Malinowski coordinated the illustration program, with contributions from Joan Kalkut and artist Elizabeth Morales. Amanda Wainer spearheaded the marketing campaign. Special thanks to Geraldine Osnato and Aly Rentrop, Project Editors, who coordinated and managed an exceptional supplements package, and to Tom Kulesa, Media Editor, who substantially improved and developed the media resources, website, and WileyPLUS program. Thanks go also to Ann Shinnar for her careful review of the Test Bank.

The atomic coordinates of many of the proteins and nucleic acids that we have drawn for use in this textbook were obtained from the Research Collaboratory for Structural Bioinformatics Protein Data Bank. We created these drawings using the molecular graphics programs RIBBONS by Mike Carson; GRASP by Anthony Nicholls, Kim Sharp, and Barry Honig; and PyMOL by Warren DeLano.

The interactive computer graphics diagrams that are presented on the website that accompanies this textbook are either Jmol images or Kinemages. Jmol is a free, open source, interactive, web browser applet for manipulating molecules in three dimensions. It is based on the program RasMol by Roger Sayle, which was generously made publicly available. The Jmol images in the Interactive Exercises were generated by Stephen Rouse. Kinemages are displayed by the program KiNG, which was written and generously provided by David C. Richardson who also wrote and provided the program PREKIN, which DV and JGV used to help generate the Kinemages. KiNG (Kinemage, Next Generation) is an interactive system for three-dimensional vector graphics that runs on Windows, Mac OS X, and Linux/Unix systems.

The Internet Resources and Student Printed Resources were prepared by the following individuals. Bioinformatics Exercises: Paul Craig, Rochester Institute of Technology, Rochester, New York; Online Homework Exercises and Classroom Response Questions: Rachel Milner and Adrienne Wright, University of Alberta, Edmonton, Alberta, Canada; Online Self-Study Quizzes: Steven Vik, Southern Methodist University, Dallas, Texas; Case Studies: Kathleen Cornely, Providence College, Providence, Rhode Island; Student Companion: Akif Uzman, University of Houston-Downtown, Houston, Texas; Test Bank: Marilee Benore-Parsons, University of Michigan-Dearborn, Dearborn, Michigan and Robert Kane, Baylor University, Waco, Texas.

We wish to thank those colleagues who have graciously devoted their time to offer us valuable comments and feedback as it relates to our textbook. Our reviewers include:

ALABAMA
Michael E. Friedman, *Auburn University*
CALIFORNIA
Marjorie A. Bates, *University of California Los Angeles*
Lukas Buehler, *University of California San Diego*
Charles E. Bowen, *California Polytechnic University*
Richard Calendar, *University of California Berkeley*
Gopal Iyer, *University of California Los Angeles*
Carla Koehler, *University of California Los Angeles*
Michael A. Marletta, *University of California Berkeley*
Douglas McAbee, *California State University Long Beach*
Angelika Niema, *Keck Graduate Institute*

Tim Osborne, *University of California Irvine*
Stanley M. Parsons, *University of California Santa Barbara*
Leigh Plesniak, *University of San Diego*
Christian K. Roberts, *University of California Los Angeles*
Pam Stacks, *San Jose State University*
Koni Stone, *California State University Stanislaus*
Leon Yengoyan, *San Jose State University*
FLORIDA
Fazal Ahmad, *University of Miami School of Medicine*
Peggy R. Borum, *University of Florida Gainesville*
Glenn Cunningham, *University of Central Florida*
Frans Huijing, *University of Miami School of Medicine*
Robley J. Light, *Florida State University*

David J. Merkler, *University of South Florida Tampa*
Thomas L. Selby, *University of Central Florida*
GEORGIA
Giovanni Gadda, *Georgia State University*
Stephan Quirk, *Georgia Institute of Technology*
ILLINOIS
Jeffrey A. Frick, *Illinois Wesleyan University*
Lowell P. Hager, *University of Illinois Urbana-Champaign*
Robert MacDonald, *Northwestern University*
Stephen Meredith, *University of Chicago*
Ken Olsen, *Loyola University*
Phoebe A. Rice, *University of Chicago*
Gary Spedding, *Butler University*
INDIANA
Thomas Goyne, *Valparaiso University*
Ann L. Kirchmaier, *Purdue University West Lafayette*

IOWA
Donald Beitz, *Iowa State University*
LaRhee Henderson, *Drake University*
KANSAS
Lawrence C. Davis, *Kansas State University*
Michael Keck, *Emporia State University*
KENTUCKY
Steven R. Ellis, *University of Louisville*
Stefan Paula, *Northern Kentucky University*
LOUISIANA
Marion L. Carroll, *Xavier University of Louisiana*
Jim D. Karam, *Tulane University Health Sciences Center*
Eric R. Taylor, *University of Louisiana at Lafayette*
Candace Timpte, *University of New Orleans*
William C. Wimley, *Tulane University Health Sciences Center*
MAINE
Gale Rhodes, *University of Southern Maine*
MARYLAND
Bonnie Diehl, *Johns Hopkins University*
J. Norman Hansen, *University of Maryland*
Jason D. Kahn, *University of Maryland College Park*
Tom Stanton, *University of Maryland Shady Grove*
MASSACHUSETTS
Robert D. Lynch, *University of Massachusetts Lowell*
Lynmarie K. Thompson, *University of Massachusetts*
Adele Wolfson, *Wellesley College*
Michael B. Yaffe, *Massachusetts Institute of Technology*
MICHIGAN
Kenneth Balazovich, *University of Michigan Ann Arbor*
Deborah Heyl-Clegg, *Eastern Michigan University*
Michael LaFontaine, *Ferris State University*
Kathleen V. Nolta, *University of Michigan*
Robert Stach, *University of Michigan Flint*
Marty Thompson, *Michigan Technical University*
MISSISSIPPI
Jeffrey Evans, *University of Southern Mississippi*
Kenneth O. Willeford, *Mississippi State University*
Robert P. Wilson, *Mississippi State University*
MISSOURI
Mark E. Martin, *University of Missouri Columbia*
William T. Morgan, *University of Missouri Kansas City*
Michael R. Nichols, *University of Missouri St Louis*
Peter Tipton, *University of Missouri Columbia*
MONTANA
Larry L. Jackson, *Montana State University*
Martin Teintze, *Montana State University*

NEBRASKA
Ruma Banerjee, *University of Nebraska*
Frank A. Kovack, *University of Nebraska*
NEVADA
Bryan Spangelo, *University of Nevada Las Vegas*
NEW HAMPSHIRE
Anita S. Kline, *University of New Hampshire*
NEW JERSEY
Cathy Yang, *Rowan University*
NEW MEXICO
James Hageman, *New Mexico State University*
NEW YORK
Jacquelyn Fetrow, *University of Albany*
Burt Goldberg, *New York University*
Martin Horowitz, *New York Medical College*
Terry Platt, *University of Rochester*
Raghu Sarma, *State University of New York at Stony Brook*
Scott Severance, *Canisius College*
Ann E. Shinnar, *Touro College*
Burton Tropp, *Queens College CUNY*
Joseph T. Warden, *Rensselaer Polytechnic Institute*
NORTH CAROLINA
Arno L. Greenleaf, *Duke University*
OHIO
Caroline Breitenberger, *The Ohio State University*
Susan C. Evans, *Ohio University*
Dave Mascotti, *John Carroll University*
Gary E. Means, *Ohio State University*
Daniel Smith, *University of Akron*
John Turchi, *Wright State University*
OKLAHOMA
Paul F. Cook, *University of Oklahoma*
Kenneth Weed, *Oral Roberts University*
PENNSYLVANIA
Michael Borenstein, *Temple University*
David J. Edwards, *University of Pittsburgh*
Jan Feng, *Temple University*
Diane W. Husic, *East Stroudsburg University*
Teh-hui Kao, *Pennsylvania State University*
Laura Mitchell, *St. Joseph's University*
Allen T. Phillips, *Pennsylvania State University*
Philip A. Rea, *University of Pennsylvania*
Michael Sypes, *Pennsylvania State University*
George Tuszynski, *Temple University*
Joan Wasilewski, *The University of Scranton*
Michelle W. Wien, *Saint Joseph's University*
Bruce Wightman, *Muhlenberg College*
Michael Wilson, *Temple University*
RHODE ISLAND
Kathleen Cornely, *Providence College*
Mary Louise Greeley, *Salve Regina University*
Kimberly Mowry, *Brown University*
SOUTH CAROLINA
Jessup M. Shivley, *Clemson University*
Kerry Smith, *Clemson University*
Takita Felder Sumter, *Winthrop University*

SOUTH DAKOTA
Joel E. Houglum, *South Dakota State University*
Daniel Cervantes Laurean, *South Dakota State University*
TENNESSEE
Scott Champney, *East Tennessee State University*
Paul C. Kline, *Middle Tennessee State University*
Gerald Stuffs, *Vanderbilt University*
Jubran M. Wakim, *Middle Tennessee State University*
TEXAS
Helen Cronenberger, *University of Texas San Antonio*
Joseph Eichberg, *University of Houston*
George E. Fox, *University of Houston*
Edward D. Harris, *Texas A&M University*
David W. Hoffman, *University of Texas at Austin*
Bob Kane, *Baylor University*
Barrie Kitto, *University of Texas at Austin*
W. E. Kurtin, *Trinity University*
Glen B. Legge, *University of Houston*
Robert Renthal, *University of Texas San Antonio*
Linda J. Roman, *University of Texas San Antonio*
Rick Russell, *University of Texas Austin*
Jane Torrie, *Tarrant County College Northwest*
Akif Uzman, *University of Houston-Downtown*
Steven B. Vik, *Southern Methodist University*
Linette M. Watkins, *Southwest Texas State University*
William Widger, *University of Houston*
Ryland E. Young, *Texas A&M University*
UTAH
Scott A. Ensign, *Utah State University*
Steven W. Graves, *Brigham Young University*
VIRGINIA
Robert F. Diegelmann, *Virginia Commonwealth University*
William M. Grogan, *Virginia Commonwealth University*
Jeff Kushner, *James Madison University*
WASHINGTON
Ronald Brosemer, *Washington State University*
Michael D. Griswold, *Washington State University*
Christine M. Smith, *University of Puget Sound*
Steve Sylvester, *Washington State University Vancouver*
David C. Teller, *University of Washington*
WEST VIRGINIA
Giri R. Sura, *West Virginia State University*
WISCONSIN
Lisa C. Kroutil, *University of Wisconsin River Falls*

AUSTRALIA
Graham Parslow, *University of Melbourne*

Instructor and Student Resources

WileyPLUS

Provided at **no charge** when packaged with a new textbook or available for purchase stand alone.

Text and *WileyPLUS* bundle: 978-0-470-28104-8

***WileyPLUS* stand alone: 978-0-470-10207-7**

WileyPLUS combines the complete, dynamic online text with all the teaching and learning resources you need, in an easy-to-use system. *WileyPLUS* allows you to deliver all or a portion of your course online. With *WileyPLUS* you can:

■ Create and assign online homework that is automatically graded and closely correlated to the text. Over 750 conceptually-based questions, organized by chapter and topic, offer students practice with instant feedback that explains why an answer choice is right or wrong.

■ Manage your students' results in the online gradebook.

■ Build media-rich class presentations.

■ Customize your course to meet your course objectives.

■ Additional valuable resources in electronic format. These include:

    New! ■ ***Bioinformatics Exercises:*** A set of newly updated exercises covering the contents and uses of databases related to nucleic acids, protein sequences, protein structures, enzyme inhibition, and other topics. These exercises use real data sets, pose specific questions, and prompt students to obtain information from online databases and to access the software tools for analyzing such data.

    ■ ***Guided Explorations:*** 30 self-contained presentations, many with narration, employ extensive animated computer graphics to enhance student understanding of key topics.

    ■ ***Interactive Exercises:*** 59 molecular structures from the text have been rendered in Jmol, a browser-independent interface for manipulating structures in three dimensions, and paired with questions designed to facilitate comprehension of concepts. A tutorial for using Jmol is also provided.

    ■ ***Kinemages:*** A set of 22 exercises comprising 55 three-dimensional images of selected proteins and nucleic acids that can be manipulated by users as suggested by accompanying text.

    ■ ***Animated Figures:*** 67 figures from the text, illustrating various concepts, techniques, and processes, are presented as brief animations to facilitate learning.

    New! ■ ***Online Homework Exercises:*** Over 750 conceptually-based questions, which you can sort by chapter and/or topic, may be assigned as graded homework or additional practice. Each question features immediate, descriptive feedback for students that explains why an answer is right or wrong.

    New! ■ ***Online Self-Study Quizzes:*** Quizzes to accompany each chapter consisting of multiple choice, true/false and fill in the blank questions, with instant feedback to help students master concepts.

    New! ■ ***Online Prelecture Questions:*** Each chapter includes multiple choice questions that address common student misconceptions.

    ■ ***Case Studies:*** A set of 33 case studies use problem-based learning to promote understanding of biochemical concepts. Each case presents data from the literature and asks questions that require students to apply principles to novel situations, often involving topics from multiple chapters in the textbook.

    New! ■ ***"Take Note!" Workbook:*** Available for download in PDF format, this contains the most important figures, diagrams, and art from the text that illustrate key concepts. Each page contains ample space for note taking and writing.

    New! ■ ***Wiley Encyclopedia of Chemical Biology:*** Most chapters include a link to a carefully selected article from the ***Wiley Encyclopedia of Chemical Biology.*** This is the first reference work in the widely expanding field of chemical biology. Links to relevant articles will facilitate deeper research and encourage additional reading.

INTERNET RESOURCES

Most of the *"additional resources"* listed above (i.e., Bioinformatics Exercises, etc.) can also be accessed at the following URL: http://www.wiley.com/college/voet.

■ PRINTED STUDENT RESOURCE

Student Companion to *Fundamentals of Biochemistry 3E*

Offered at no **additional charge** when purchased with a new textbook or can be purchased separately:

Text and *Student Companion* bundle: 978-0-470-28439-1
Student Companion separately: 978-0-470-22842-5

This newly updated study resource is designed to help students master basic concepts and to enhance their analytic skills. Each chapter contains a summary, a review of essential concepts, and additional problems.

■ INSTRUCTOR RESOURCES

These can be accessed through **WileyPLUS.**

- **PowerPoint Slides** of all the figures and tables in the text. The figures are optimized for classroom projection, with bold leader lines and large labels, and are also available for importing individually as jpeg files from the *Wiley Image Gallery*.

- **Test Bank** with almost 1,200 questions, containing a variety of question types (multiple choice, matching, fill in the blank, and short answer). Each question is keyed to the relevant section in the text as well as to the key topic and is rated by difficulty level. (Tests can be created and administered online or with test-generator software.)

- **New!** ■ **Classroom Response Questions ("clicker questions") for each chapter.** These interactive questions, for classroom response systems, facilitate classroom participation and discussion. These questions can also be used by instructors as prelecture questions that help gauge students' knowledge of overall concepts, while addressing common misconceptions.

- **New!** ■ Access to the **Molecular and Life Sciences Visual Library** which provides a large collection of figures from a variety of Wiley Life Science texts, including *Cell and Molecular Biology 5E* by Gerald Karp and *Principles of Genetics 4E* by D. Peter Snustad and Michael J. Simmons. These can be used in lecture presentations.

If you wish to gain access to *Instructor Resources* (PowerPoint, Test Bank, etc.) but do not wish to access them through *WileyPLUS,* please contact your local Wiley sales representative. You can locate your Wiley sales representative by clicking *"Who's My Rep?"* after typing in your school affiliation at the following URL: www.wiley.com/college.

Guide to Media Resources

The book website (www.wiley.com/college/voet) offers the following resources to enhance student understanding of biochemistry. These are all keyed to figures or sections in the text. They are called out in the text with a red mouse icon or margin note.

Chapter		Media Type	Title	Text Reference
2	Water	Animated Figure	Titration curves for acetic acid, phosphate, and ammonia	Fig. 2-17
		Animated Figure	Titration of polyprotic acid	Fig. 2-18
		Case Study	1. Acute Aspirin Overdose: Relationship to the Blood Buffering	Pg. 38
3	Nucleotides, Nucleic Acids, and Genetic Information	Guided Exploration	1. Overview of transcription and translation	Section 3-3B
		Guided Exploration	2. DNA sequence determination by the chain-terminator method	Section 3-4C
		Guided Exploration	3. PCR and site-directed mutagenesis	Section 3-5C
		Interactive Exercise	1. Three-dimensional structure of DNA	Fig. 3-6
		Animated Figure	Construction of a recombinant DNA molecule	Fig. 3-26
		Animated Figure	Cloning with bacteriophage λ	Fig. 3-27
		Animated Figure	Site-directed mutagenesis	Fig. 3-30
		Kinemage	2-1. Structure of DNA	Fig. 3-6
		Kinemage	2-2. Watson-Crick base pairs	Fig. 3-8
		Bioinformatics Exercise	Chapter 3. Databases for the Storage and "Mining" of Genome Sequences	Pg. 72
5	Proteins: Primary Structure	Guided Exploration	4. Protein sequence determination	Section 5-3
		Guided Exploration	5. Protein evolution	Section 5-4A
		Animated Figure	Enzyme-linked immunosorbent assay	Fig. 5-3
		Animated Figure	Ion exchange chromatography	Fig. 5-6
		Animated Figure	Gel filtration chromatography	Fig. 5-7
		Animated Figure	Edman degradation	Fig. 5-15
		Animated Figure	Generating overlapping fragments to determine the amino acid sequence of a polypeptide	Fig. 5-18
		Case Study	2. Histidine-Proline-rich Glycoprotein as a Plasma pH Sensor	Pg. 123
		Bioinformatics Exercise	Chapter 5. Using Databases to Compare and Identify Related Protein Sequences	Pg. 124
6	Proteins: Three-Dimensional Structure	Guided Exploration	6. Stable helices in proteins: the α helix	Section 6-1B
		Guided Exploration	7. Hydrogen bonding in β sheets	Section 6-1B
		Guided Exploration	8. Secondary structures in proteins	Section 6-2C
		Interactive Exercise	2. Glyceraldehyde-3-phosphate dehydrogenase	Fig. 6-31
		Animated Figure	The α helix	Fig. 6-7
		Animated Figure	β sheets	Fig. 6-9
		Animated Figure	Symmetry in oligomeric proteins	Fig. 6-34
		Animated Figure	Mechanism of protein disulfide isomerase	Fig. 6-42
		Kinemage	3-1. The peptide group	Fig. 6-2, 6-4, 6-5
		Kinemage	3-2. The α helix	Fig. 6-7
		Kinemage	3-3. β sheets	Fig. 6-9, 6-10, 6-11
		Kinemage	3-4. Reverse turns	Fig. 6-14
		Kinemage	4-1, 4-2. Coiled coils	Fig. 6-15
		Kinemage	4-3, 4-4. Collagen	Fig. 6-18
		Kinemage	5. Cytochrome c	Fig. 6-27, 6-32
		Case Study	4. The Structure of Insulin	Pg. 174
		Case Study	5. Characterization of Subtilisin from the Antarctic Psychrophile Bacillus TA41	Pg. 174
		Case Study	6. A Collection of Collagen Cases	Pg. 174
		Bioinformatics Exercise	Chapter 6. Visualizing Three-Dimensional Protein Structures	Pg. 174

Chapter	Media Type	Title	Text Reference
7 Protein Function: Myoglobin and Hemoglobin, Muscle Contraction, and Antibodies	Interactive Exercise	3. Structure of a mouse antibody	Fig. 7-38
	Animated Figure	Oxygen-binding curve of hemoglobin	Fig. 7-6
	Animated Figure	Movements of heme and F helix in hemoglobin	Fig. 7-8
	Animated Figure	The Bohr effect	Fig. 7-11
	Animated Figure	Effect of BPG and CO_2 on hemoglobin	Fig. 7-13
	Animated Figure	Mechanism of force generation in muscle	Fig. 7-32
	Kinemage	6-1. Myoglobin structure	Fig. 7-1, 7-3
	Kinemage	6-2, 6-3. Hemoglobin structure	Fig. 7-5
	Kinemage	6-3. BPG binding to hemoglobin	Fig. 7-14
	Kinemage	6-4. Conformational changes in hemoglobin	Fig. 7-8
	Kinemage	6-5. Changes at $\alpha_1-\beta_2/\alpha_2-\beta_1$ interfaces in hemoglobin	Fig. 7-9
	Case Study	8. Hemoglobin, the Oxygen Carrier	Pg. 217
	Case Study	9. Allosteric Interactions in Crocodile Hemoglobin	Pg. 217
	Case Study	10. The Biological Roles of Nitric Oxide	Pg. 217
8 Carbohydrates	Kinemage	7-1. D-Glucopyranose, α and β anomers	Fig. 8-4, 8-5
	Kinemage	7-2. Sucrose	Section 8-2A
	Kinemage	7-3. Hyaluronate	Fig. 8-12
	Kinemage	7-4. Structure of a complex carbohydrate	Fig. 8-19
9 Lipids and Biological Membranes	Guided Exploration	9. Membrane structure and the fluid mosaic model	Section 9-4A
	Interactive Exercise	4. Model of phospholipase A_2 and glycerophospholipid	Fig. 9-6
	Animated Figure	Secretory pathway	Fig. 9-35
	Kinemage	8-1. Bacteriorhodopsin	Fig. 9-22
	Kinemage	8-3. OmpF porin	Fig. 9-23
10 Membrane Transport	Interactive Exercise	5. The K^+ channel selectivity filter	Fig. 10-5
	Animated Figure	Model for glucose transport	Fig. 10-13
	Case Study	3. Carbonic Anhydrase II Deficiency	Pg. 320
	Case Study	14. Shavings from the Carpenter's Bench: The Biological Role of the Insulin C-peptide	Pg. 320
	Case Study	17. A Possible Mechanism for Blindness Associated with Diabetes: Na^+-Dependent Glucose Uptake by Retinal Cells	Pg. 320
11 Enzymatic Catalysis	Guided Exploration	10. The catalytic mechanism of serine proteases	Section 11-5C
	Interactive Exercise	6. Pancreatic RNase S	Fig. 11-9
	Interactive Exercise	7. Carbonic anhydrase	Fig. 11-13
	Interactive Exercise	8. Hen egg white lysozyme	Fig. 11-17
	Animated Figure	Effect of preferential transition state binding	Fig. 11-15
	Animated Figure	Chair and half-chair conformations	Fig. 11-18
	Kinemage	9. Hen egg white lysozyme-catalytic mechanism	Fig. 11-17, 11-19, 11-21
	Kinemage	10-1. Structural overview of a trypsin/inhibitor complex	Fig. 11-25, 11-31
	Kinemage	10-2. Evolutionary comparisons of proteases	Fig. 11-28
	Kinemage	10-3. A transition state analog bound to chymotrypsin	Fig. 11-30
	Case Study	11. Nonenzymatic Deamidization of Asparagine and Glutamine Residues in Proteins	Pg. 362
12 Enzyme Kinetics, Inhibition, and Control	Guided Exploration	11. Michaelis-Menten kinetics, Lineweaver-Burk plots, and enzyme inhibition	Section 12-1
	Interactive Exercise	9. HIV protease	Box 12-4
	Animated Figure	Progress curve for an enzyme-catalyzed reaction	Fig. 12-2
	Animated Figure	Plot of initial velocity versus substrate concentration	Fig. 12-3
	Animated Figure	Double-reciprocal (Lineweaver-Burk) plot	Fig. 12-4
	Animated Figure	Lineweaver-Burk plot of competitive inhibition	Fig. 12-7
	Animated Figure	Lineweaver-Burk plot of uncompetitive inhibition	Fig. 12-8
	Animated Figure	Lineweaver-Burk plot of mixed inhibition	Fig. 12-9
	Animated Figure	Plot of v_o versus [aspartate] for ATCase	Fig. 12-10
	Kinemage	11-1. Structure of ATCase	Fig. 12-12, 12-13
	Kinemage	11-2. Conformational changes in ATCase	Fig. 12-13
	Kinemage	14-1. Glycogen phosphorylase	Fig. 12-14

Chapter	Media Type	Title	Text Reference
	Kinemage	14-2 and 14-3. Conformational changes in glycogen phosphorylase	Fig. 12-15
	Case Study	7. A Storage Protein from Seeds of *Brassica nigra* Is a Serine Protease Inhibitor	Pg. 403
	Case Study	12. Production of Methanol in Ripening Fruit	Pg. 403
	Case Study	13. Inhibition of Alcohol Dehydrogenase	Pg. 403
	Case Study	15. Site-Directed Mutagenesis of Creatine Kinease	Pg. 403
	Case Study	19. Purification of Rat Kidney Sphingosine Kinease	Pg. 403
	Bioinformatics Exercise	Chapter 12. Enzyme Inhibitors and Rational Drug Design	Pg. 404
13 Biochemical Signaling	Guided Exploration	12. Hormone signaling by the receptor tyrosine kinase system	Section 13-2A
	Guided Exploration	13. Hormone signaling by the adenylate cyclase system	Section 13-3C
	Interactive Exercise	10. X-ray structure of human growth hormone (hGH)	Fig. 13-3
	Interactive Exercise	11. Tyrosine kinase domain of insulin receptor	Fig. 13-5
	Interactive Exercise	12. A heterotrimeric G protein	Fig. 13-19
	Interactive Exercise	13. C subunit of protein kinase A	Fig. 13-21
	Animated Figure	The Ras signaling cascade	Fig. 13-7
	Animated Figure	The phosphoinositide signaling system	Fig. 13-24
	Kinemage	15. cAMP-dependent protein kinase (PKA)	Fig. 13-21
	Kinemage	16-1 The structure of calmodulin	Fig. 13-27
	Kinemage	16-2 Calmodulin complex with target polypeptide	Fig. 13-28
14 Introduction to Metabolism	Interactive Exercise	14. Conformational changes in *E. coli* adenylate kinase	Fig. 14-9
	Case Study	16. Allosteric Regulation of ATCase	Pg. 484
	Bioinformatics Exercises	Chapter 14. Metabolic Enzymes, Microarrays, and Proteomics	Pg. 484
15 Glucose Catabolism	Guided Exploration	14. Glycolysis overview	Section 15-1
	Interactive Exercise	15. Conformational changes in yeast hexokinase	Fig. 15-2
	Interactive Exercise	16. Yeast TIM in complex with 2-phosphoglycolate	Fig. 15-6
	Interactive Exercise	17. TPP binding to pyruvate decarboxylase	Fig. 15-19
	Animated Figure	Overview of glycolysis	Fig. 15-1
	Animated Figure	Mechanism of aldolase	Fig. 15-5
	Animated Figure	Mechanism of GAPDH	Fig. 15-9
	Animated Figure	PFK activity versus F6P concentration	Fig. 15-23
	Kinemage	12-1, 12-2 Triose phosphate isomerase	Fig. 15-6
	Kinemage	13-1 Phosphofructokinase	Fig. 15-22
	Kinemage	13-2 Allosteric changes in phosphofructokinase	Fig. 15-24
	Case Study	18. Purification of Phosphofructokinase 1-C	Pg. 529
	Case Study	20. NAD$^+$-dependent Glyceraldehyde-3-Phosphate Dehydrogenase from *Thermoproteus tenax*	Pg. 529
16 Glycogen Metabolism and Gluconeogenesis	Guided Exploration	15. Control of glycogen metabolism	Section 16-3B
	Animated Figure	Overview of glucose metabolism	Fig. 16-1
	Animated Figure	Major phosphorylation and dephosphorylation systems in glycogen metabolism	Fig. 16-13
	Animated Figure	Comparison of gluconeogenesis and glycolysis	Fig. 16-15
	Animated Figure	Transport of PEP and oxaloacetate from mitochondrion to cytosol	Fig. 16-20
	Animated Figure	Pathway for dolichol-PP-oligosaccharide synthesis	Fig. 16-27
	Case Study	22. Carrier-Mediated Uptake of Lactate in Rat Hepatocytes	Pg. 564
	Case Study	26. The Role of Specific Amino Acids in the Peptide Hormone Glucagon in Receptor Binding and Signal Transduction	Pg. 564
17 Citric Acid Cycle	Guided Exploration	16. Citric acid cycle overview	Section 17-1
	Interactive Exercise	18. Conformational changes in citrate synthase	Fig. 17-9
	Animated Figure	Overview of oxidative fuel metabolism	Fig. 17-1
	Animated Figure	Reactions of the citric acid cycle	Fig. 17-2
	Animated Figure	Regulation of the citric acid cycle	Fig. 17-16
	Animated Figure	Amphibolic functions of the citric acid cycle	Fig. 17-17
	Case Study	21. Characterization of Pyruvate Carboxylase from *Methanobacterium thermoautotrophicum*	Pg. 595

Chapter	Media Type	Title	Text Reference
18 Electron Transport and Oxidative Phosphorylation	Guided Exploration	17. Electron transport and oxidative phosphorylation overview	Section 18-2B
	Guided Exploration	18. The Q cycle	Section 18-2E
	Guided Exploration	19. F_1F_0-ATP synthase and the binding change mechanism	Section 18-3B
	Interactive Exercise	19. Complex III	Fig. 18-14
	Interactive Exercise	20. Cytochrome *c* residues involved in intermolecular complex formation	Fig. 18-16
	Interactive Exercise	21. Bovine heart cyctochrome c oxidase	Fig. 18-17
	Interactive Exercise	22. F_1-ATP synthase	Fig. 18-22
	Animated Figure	The mitochondrial electron transport chain	Fig. 18-8
	Animated Figure	Coupling of electron transport and ATP synthesis	Fig. 18-20
	Animated Figure	The binding change mechanism of ATP synthesis	Fig. 18-24
	Animated Figure	Coordinated control of glycolysis and the citric acid cycle	Fig. 18-29
	Kinemage	5. Cytochrome *c*	Fig. 18-16
	Case Study	24. Uncoupling Proteins in Plants	Pg. 639
	Case Study	27. Regulation of Sugar and Alcohol Metabolism in *Saccharomyces cerevisiae*	Pg. 639
	Case Study	33. Modification of Subunit *c* from Bovine Mitochondrial ATPase	Pg. 639
19 Photosynthesis	Guided Exploration	20. Two-center photosynthesis (Z-scheme) overview	Section 19-2C
	Interactive Exercise	23. Light-harvesting complex LH-2	Fig. 19-5
	Interactive Exercise	24. *Rb. sphaeroides* reaction center	Fig. 19-8
	Interactive Exercise	25. Ferredoxin	Fig. 19-22
	Interactive Exercise	26. Ferredoxin–$NADP^+$ reductase	Fig. 19-23
	Animated Figure	Electronic states of chlorophyll	Fig. 19-6
	Animated Figure	The Calvin cycle	Fig. 19-26
	Animated Figure	Mechanism of RuBP carboxylase	Fig. 19-28
	Kinemage	8-2 Photosynthetic reaction center	Fig. 19-8, 19-9
20 Lipid Metabolism	Interactive Exercise	27. Active site of medium-chain acyl-CoA dehydrogenase	Fig. 20-13
	Interactive Exercise	28. X-Ray structure of methylmalonyl-CoA mutase	Fig. 20-18
	Animated Figure	Receptor-mediated endocytosis	Fig. 20-8
	Animated Figure	β-oxidation pathway of fatty acyl-CoA	Fig. 20-12
	Animated Figure	Comparison of fatty acid β oxidation and fatty acid biosynthesis	Fig. 20-23
	Animated Figure	Reaction sequence for biosynthesis of fatty acids	Fig. 20-26
	Case Study	23. The Role of Uncoupling Proteins in Obesity	Pg. 731
21 Amino Acid Metabolism	Interactive Exercise	29. Ubiquitin	Fig. 21-1
	Interactive Exercise	30. The bifunctional enzyme tryptophan synthase	Fig. 21-35
	Interactive Exercise	31. *A vinelandii* nitrogenase	Fig. 21-41
	Animated Figure	Mechanism of PLP-dependent transamination	Fig. 21-8
	Animated Figure	The urea cycle	Fig. 21-9
22 Mammalian Fuel Metabolism: Integration and Regulation	Interactive Exercise	32. Human leptin	Fig. 22-13
	Animated Figure	The Cori cycle	Fig. 22-6
	Animated Figure	The glucose-alanine cycle	Fig. 22-7
	Animated Figure	GLUT4 activity	Fig. 22-8
	Case Study	25. Glycogen Storage Diseases	Pg. 816
	Case Study	28. The Bacterium *Helicobacter pylori* and Peptic Ulcers	Pg. 816
	Case Study	30. Phenylketonuria	Pg. 816
23 Nucleotide Metabolism	Interactive Exercise	33. *E coli* ribonucleotide reductase	Fig. 23-9
	Interactive Exercise	34. Human dihydrofolate reductase	Fig. 23-17
	Interactive Exercise	35. Murine adenosine deaminase	Fig. 23-20
	Animated Figure	Metabolic pathway for *de novo* biosynthesis of IMP	Fig. 23-1
	Animated Figure	Control of purine biosynthesis pathway	Fig. 23-4
	Animated Figure	The *de novo* synthesis of UMP	Fig. 23-5
	Animated Figure	Regulation of pyrimidine biosynthesis	Fig. 23-8
24 Nucleic Acid Structure	Guided Exploration	21. DNA structures	Section 24-1A
	Guided Exploration	22. DNA supercoiling	Section 24-1C

Chapter	Media Type	Title	Text Reference
	Guided Exploration	23. Transcription factor–DNA interactions	Section 24-4B
	Guided Exploration	24. Nucleosome structure	Section 24-5B
	Interactive Exercise	36. An RNA-DNA helix	Fig. 24-4
	Interactive Exercise	37. Yeast topoisomerase II	Fig. 24-16
	Interactive Exercise	38. A hammerhead ribozyme	Fig. 24-26
	Interactive Exercise	39. A portion of phage 434 repressor in complex with target DNA	Fig. 24-32
	Interactive Exercise	40. *E. coli trp* repressor–operator complex	Fig. 24-33
	Interactive Exercise	41. *E. coli met* repressor–operator complex	Fig. 24-34
	Interactive Exercise	42. A three-zinc finger segment of Zif268 in complex with DNA	Fig. 24-35
	Interactive Exercise	43. GAL4 DNA-binding domain in complex with DNA	Fig. 24-36
	Interactive Exercise	44. GCN4 bZIP region in complex with DNA	Fig. 24-38
	Interactive Exercise	45. Max binding to DNA	Fig. 24-39
	Animated Figure	UV absorbance spectra of native and heat-denatured DNA	Fig. 24-19
	Animated Figure	Example of DNA melting curve	Fig. 24-20
	Kinemage	17-1, 17-4, 17-5, 17-6. Structures of A, B, and Z DNAs	Fig. 24-2
	Kinemage	17-2. Watson-Crick base pairs	Fig. 24-1
	Kinemage	17-3. Nucleotide sugar conformations	Fig. 24-7
	Kinemage	18-1. *Eco*RI endonuclease in complex with DNA	Fig. 24-30
	Kinemage	18-2. *Eco*RV endonuclease in complex with DNA	Fig. 24-31
	Kinemage	19. 434 phage repressor in complex with DNA	Fig. 24-32
	Kinemage	20. GCN4 leucine zipper motif	Fig. 24-37
	Case Study	31. Hyperactive Dnase I Variants: A Treatment for Cystic Fibrosis	Pg. 892
25 DNA Replication, Repair, and Recombination	Guided Exploration	25. The replication of DNA in *E. coli*	Section 25-2B
	Interactive Exercise	46. *E. coli* DNA Pol I Klenow fragment with double-helical DNA	Fig. 25-10
	Interactive Exercise	47. *E. coli* Tus in complex with Ter-containing DNA	Fig. 25-19
	Interactive Exercise	48. Structure of PCNA	Fig. 25-20
	Interactive Exercise	49. HIV reverse transcriptase	Box 25-2
	Animated Figure	Meselson and Stahl experiment	Fig. 25-1
	Animated Figure	Holliday model of general recombination	Fig. 25-36
	Case Study	32. Glucose-6-Phosphate Dehydrogenase Activity and Cell Growth	Pg. 941
26 Transcription and RNA Processing	Interactive Exercise	50. RNA polymerase II	Fig. 26-12
	Interactive Exercise	51. TATA-binding protein in complex with TATA box	Fig. 26-16
	Interactive Exercise	52. Self-splicing group I intron from *Tetrahymena*	Fig. 26-30
27 Protein Synthesis	Guided Exploration	26. The structure of tRNA	Section 27-2
	Guided Exploration	27. The structures of aminoacyl–tRNA synthetases and their interactions with tRNAs	Section 27-2B
	Guided Exploration	28. Translational initiation	Section 27-4A
	Guided Exploration	29. Translational elongation	Section 27-4B
	Interactive Exercise	53. Ribosomal subunits in complex with three tRNAs and an mRNA	Fig. 27-17
	Interactive Exercise	54. Elongation factor EF-Tu in its complexes with GDP and GMPPNP	Fig. 27-29
	Kinemage	21-1. Structure of yeast tRNA^{Phe}	Fig. 27-5
	Kinemage	21-2. Modified bases in tRNAs	Fig. 27-4
	Kinemage	22. Structure of GlnRS–tRNA^{Gln}–ATP	Fig. 27-8
	Case Study	29. Pseudovitamin D Deficiency	Pg. 1035
28 Regulation of Gene Expression	Guided Exploration	30. The regulation of gene expression by the *lac* repressor system	Section 28-2A
	Interactive Exercise	55. CAP–cAMP dimer in complex with DNA	Fig. 28-13
	Interactive Exercise	56. Glucocorticoid receptor DNA-binding domain in complex with DNA	Fig. 28-33
	Interactive Exercise	57. Cdk2 phosphorylated at Thr 160	Fig. 28-41
	Interactive Exercise	58. DNA-binding domain of human p53 in complex with its target DNA	Fig. 28-42
	Interactive Exercise	59. Engrailed protein homeodomain in complex with its target DNA	Fig. 28-53

Clinical Applications

Acidosis and alkalosis (p. 36)
Gene therapy (p. 69)
Scurvy and collagen diseases (p. 137)
Amyloidoses and Alzheimer's disease (p. 168)
Transmissible spongiform encephalopathies (TSEs) (p. 170)
High-altitude adaptation (p. 192)
Hemolytic anemia and polycythemia (p. 194)
Sickle-cell anemia and malaria (p. 195)
Muscular dystrophy (p. 205)
Autoimmune diseases (p. 214)
Lactose intolerance (p. 227)
Penicillin and vancomycin (p. 238)
ABO blood groups (p. 242)
Lung surfactant (p. 250)
Sphingolipid storage diseases (p. 253)
Steroid hormones (p. 255)
Addison's and Cushing's diseases (p. 255)
I-cell disease (p. 286)
Tetanus and botulinum toxins (p. 288)
Cardiac glycosides and heart failure (p. 313)
Drug resistance (p. 314)
Cystic fibrosis (p. 315)
Nerve poisons (p. 349)
Acute pancreatitis (p. 357)
Blood coagulation (p. 358)
Methanol poisoning (p. 379)
HIV enzyme inhibitors (p. 384)
Drug design (p. 394)
Clinical trials (p. 397)
Drug–drug interactions (p. 398)
Insulin and glucagon (p. 407)
Epinephrine and norepinephrine (p. 409)
Growth disorders (p. 411)
Klinefelter's and Turner's syndromes (p. 411)
Oncogenes and cancer (p. 421)
Leukemia (p. 424)
Bubonic plague (p. 426)
Cholera and pertussis (p. 435)
Viagra action (p. 436)
Anthrax (p. 444)
Vitamin deficiency diseases (p. 450)

Erythrocyte enzyme deficiencies (p. 502)
Beriberi (p. 508)
Fructose intolerance and galactosemia (p. 518)
Glucose-6-phosphate dehydrogenase deficiency (p. 526)
Glycogen storage diseases (p. 538)
Bacitracin (p. 563)
Arsenic poisoning (p. 576)
Myocardial infarction and stroke (p. 635)
Low- and high-density lipoproteins (LDL & HDL) (p. 681)
Sudden infant death syndrome (SIDS) (p. 688)
Pernicious anemia (p. 696)
Aspirin and nonsteroidal anti-inflammatory drugs (NSAIDs) (p. 719)
COX-2 inhibitors (p. 719)
Statins and atherosclerosis (p. 727)
Hypercholesterolemia (p. 728)
Hyperammonemia (p. 742)
Folic acid and spina bifida and anencephaly (p. 755)
Phenylketonuria and alcaptonuria (p. 762)
Porphyria (p. 778)
Diabetes (p. 811)
Obesity (p. 814)
Starvation (p. 809)
Metabolic syndrome (p. 815)
Lesch-Nyhan syndrome (p. 824)
Toxoplasmosis (p. 826)
Antifolates (p. 838)
Severe combined immunodeficiency disease (SCID) (p. 840)
Gout (p. 843)
Topoisomerase inhibitors (p. 865)
Telomerase, aging, and cancer (p. 915)
Mutagenesis and carcinogenesis (p. 919)
Xeroderma pigmentosum and Cockayne's syndrome (p. 924)
Antibiotics that inhibit transcription (p. 954)
Antibiotics that inhibit translation (p. 1024)
Trinucleotide repeat diseases (p. 1094)
Genomic imprinting and Prader-Willi and Angelman syndromes (p. 1067)
Generation of antibody diversity (p. 1077)
Tumor suppressors: p53 and pRb (p. 1084)

Introduction to the Chemistry of Life

Early earth, a tiny speck in the galaxy, contained simple inorganic molecules that gave rise to the first biological macromolecules. These, in turn, gained the ability to self-organize and self-replicate, eventually forming cellular life-forms. [Lynette Cook/Photo Researchers.]

■ CHAPTER CONTENTS

1 The Origin of Life
- **A.** Biological Molecules Arose from Inorganic Materials
- **B.** Complex Self-replicating Systems Evolved from Simple Molecules

2 Cellular Architecture
- **A.** Cells Carry Out Metabolic Reactions
- **B.** There Are Two Types of Cells: Prokaryotes and Eukaryotes
- **C.** Molecular Data Reveal Three Evolutionary Domains of Organisms
- **D.** Organisms Continue to Evolve

3 Thermodynamics
- **A.** The First Law of Thermodynamics States That Energy Is Conserved
- **B.** The Second Law of Thermodynamics States That Entropy Tends to Increase
- **C.** The Free Energy Change Determines the Spontaneity of a Process
- **D.** Free Energy Changes Can Be Calculated from Equilibrium Concentrations
- **E.** Life Obeys the Laws of Thermodynamics

Biochemistry is, literally, the study of the chemistry of life. Although it overlaps other disciplines, including cell biology, genetics, immunology, microbiology, pharmacology, and physiology, biochemistry is largely concerned with a limited number of issues:

1. What are the chemical and three-dimensional structures of biological molecules?
2. How do biological molecules interact with each other?
3. How does the cell synthesize and degrade biological molecules?
4. How is energy conserved and used by the cell?
5. What are the mechanisms for organizing biological molecules and coordinating their activities?
6. How is genetic information stored, transmitted, and expressed?

Biochemistry, like other modern sciences, relies on sophisticated instruments to dissect the architecture and operation of systems that are inaccessible to the human senses. In addition to the chemist's tools for separating, quantifying, and otherwise analyzing biological materials, biochemists take advantage of the uniquely biological aspects of their subject by examining the evolutionary histories of organisms, metabolic systems, and individual molecules. In addition to its obvious implications for human health, biochemistry reveals the workings of the natural world, allowing us to understand and appreciate the unique and mysterious condition that we call life. In this introductory chapter, we will review some aspects of chemistry and biology—including chemical evolution, the different types of cells, and basic principles of thermodynamics—in order to help put biochemistry in context and to introduce some of the themes that recur throughout this book.

LEARNING OBJECTIVES

■ Understand that simple inorganic compounds combined to form more complex molecules through a process of chemical evolution.
■ Become familiar with the common functional groups and linkages in biological molecules.

Table 1-1	Most Abundant Elements in the Human Body[a]	
Element	**Dry Weight (%)**	
C	61.7	
N	11.0	
O	9.3	
H	5.7	
Ca	5.0	
P	3.3	
K	1.3	
S	1.0	
Cl	0.7	
Na	0.7	
Mg	0.3	

[a]Calculated from Frieden, E., *Sci. Am.* **227**(1), 54–55 (1972).

1 The Origin of Life

Certain biochemical features are common to all organisms: the way hereditary information is encoded and expressed, for example, and the way biological molecules are built and broken down for energy. The underlying genetic and biochemical unity of modern organisms suggests they are descended from a single ancestor. Although it is impossible to describe exactly how life first arose, paleontological and laboratory studies have provided some insights about the origin of life.

A | Biological Molecules Arose from Inorganic Materials

Living matter consists of a relatively small number of elements (Table 1-1). For example, C, H, O, N, P, Ca, and S account for ~97% of the dry weight of the human body (humans and most other organisms are ~70% water). Living organisms may also contain trace amounts of many other elements, including B, F, Al, Si, V, Cr, Mn, Fe, Co, Ni, Cu, Zn, As, Se, Br, Mo, Cd, I, and W, although not every organism makes use of each of these substances.

The earliest known fossil evidence of life is ~3.5 billion years old (Fig. 1-1). The preceding **prebiotic era,** which began with the formation of the earth ~4.6 billion years ago, left no direct record, but scientists can experimentally duplicate the sorts of chemical reactions that might have given rise to living organisms during that billion-year period.

The atmosphere of the early earth probably consisted of small, simple compounds such as H_2O, N_2, CO_2, and smaller amounts of CH_4 and NH_3. In the 1930s, Alexander Oparin and J. B. S. Haldane independently suggested that ultraviolet radiation from the sun or lightning discharges caused the molecules of the primordial atmosphere to react to form simple **organic** (carbon-containing) **compounds.** This process was replicated in 1953 by Stanley Miller and Harold Urey, who subjected a mixture of H_2O, CH_4, NH_3, and H_2 to an electric discharge for about a week. The resulting solution contained water-soluble organic compounds, including several amino acids (which are components of proteins) and other biochemically significant compounds.

The assumptions behind the Miller–Urey experiment, principally the composition of the gas used as a starting material, have been challenged by some scientists who have suggested that the first biological molecules were generated in a quite different way: in the dark and under water. Hydrothermal vents in the ocean floor, which emit solutions of metal

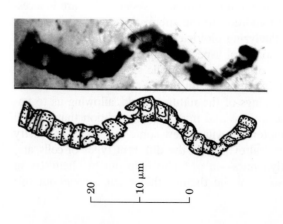

■ **Figure 1-1 | Microfossil of filamentous bacterial cells.** This fossil (shown with an interpretive drawing) is from ~3.4-billion-year-old rock from Western Australia. [Courtesy of J. William Schopf, UCLA.]

sulfides at temperatures as high as 400°C (Fig. 1-2), may have provided conditions suitable for the formation of amino acids and other small organic molecules from simple compounds present in seawater.

Whatever their actual origin, the early organic molecules became the precursors of an enormous variety of biological molecules. These can be classified in various ways, depending on their composition and chemical reactivity. A familiarity with organic chemistry is useful for recognizing the **functional groups** (reactive portions) of molecules as well as the **linkages** (bonding arrangements) among them, since these features ultimately determine the biological activity of the molecules. Some of the common functional groups and linkages in biological molecules are shown in Table 1-2.

B | Complex Self-replicating Systems Evolved from Simple Molecules

During a period of chemical evolution, simple organic molecules condensed to form more complex molecules or combined end-to-end as **polymers** of repeating units. In a **condensation reaction,** the elements of water are lost. The rate of condensation of simple compounds to form a stable polymer must therefore be greater than the rate of **hydrolysis** (splitting by adding the elements of water; Fig. 1-3). In the prebiotic environment, minerals such as clays may have catalyzed polymerization reactions and sequestered the reaction products from water. The size and composition of prebiotic macromolecules would have been limited by the availability of small molecular starting materials, the efficiency with which they could be joined, and their resistance to degradation.

Obviously, *combining different functional groups into a single large molecule increases the chemical versatility of that molecule,* allowing it to perform chemical feats beyond the reach of simpler molecules. (This principle of emergent properties can be expressed as "the whole is greater than the sum of its parts.") Separate macromolecules with complementary arrangements of functional groups can associate with each other (Fig. 1-4), giving rise to more complex molecular assemblies with an even greater range of functional possibilities.

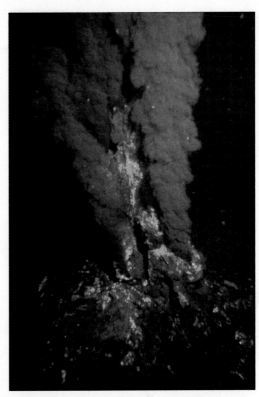

■ Figure 1-2 | A hydrothermal vent. Such ocean-floor formations are known as "black smokers" because the metal sulfides dissolved in the superheated water they emit precipitate on encountering the much cooler ocean water. [© J. Edmond. Courtesy of Woods Hole Oceanographic Institution.]

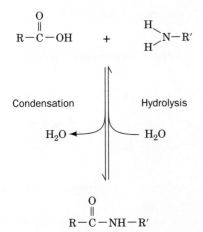

■ Figure 1-3 | Reaction of a carboxylic acid with an amine. The elements of water are released during condensation. In the reverse process—hydrolysis—water is added to cleave the amide bond. In living systems, condensation reactions are not freely reversible.

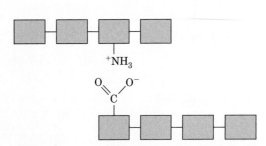

■ Figure 1-4 | Association of complementary molecules. The positively charged amino group interacts electrostatically with the negatively charged carboxylate group.

Table 1-2 Common Functional Groups and Linkages in Biochemistry

Compound Name	Structure[a]	Functional Group or Linkage
Amine[b]	RNH_2 or $\overset{+}{R}NH_3$ R_2NH or $R_2\overset{+}{N}H_2$ R_3N or $R_3\overset{+}{N}H$	$-N\big\langle$ or $-\overset{+}{\underset{\vert}{\overset{\vert}{N}}}-$ (amino group)
Alcohol	ROH	—OH (hydroxyl group)
Thiol	RSH	—SH (sulfhydryl group)
Ether	ROR	—O— (ether linkage)
Aldehyde	$R-\overset{O}{\overset{\Vert}{C}}-H$	$-\overset{O}{\overset{\Vert}{C}}-$ (carbonyl group)
Ketone	$R-\overset{O}{\overset{\Vert}{C}}-R$	$-\overset{O}{\overset{\Vert}{C}}-$ (carbonyl group)
Carboxylic acid[b]	$R-\overset{O}{\overset{\Vert}{C}}-OH$ or $R-\overset{O}{\overset{\Vert}{C}}-O^-$	$-\overset{O}{\overset{\Vert}{C}}-OH$ (carboxyl group) or $-\overset{O}{\overset{\Vert}{C}}-O^-$ (carboxylate group)
Ester	$R-\overset{O}{\overset{\Vert}{C}}-OR$	$-\overset{O}{\overset{\Vert}{C}}-O-$ (ester linkage) $R-\overset{O}{\overset{\Vert}{C}}-$ (acyl group)[c]
Thioester	$R-\overset{O}{\overset{\Vert}{C}}-SR$	$-\overset{O}{\overset{\Vert}{C}}-S-$ (thioester linkage) $R-\overset{O}{\overset{\Vert}{C}}-$ (acyl group)[c]
Amide	$R-\overset{O}{\overset{\Vert}{C}}-NH_2$ $R-\overset{O}{\overset{\Vert}{C}}-NHR$ $R-\overset{O}{\overset{\Vert}{C}}-NR_2$	$-\overset{O}{\overset{\Vert}{C}}-N\big\langle$ (amido group) $R-\overset{O}{\overset{\Vert}{C}}-$ (acyl group)[c]
Imine (Schiff base)[b]	$R{=}NH$ or $R{=}\overset{+}{N}H_2$ $R{=}NR$ or $R{=}\overset{+}{N}HR$	$\big\rangle C{=}N-$ or $\big\rangle C{=}\overset{+}{N}\big\langle$ (imino group)
Disulfide	R—S—S—R	—S—S— (disulfide linkage)
Phosphate ester[b]	$R-O-\overset{O}{\underset{OH}{\overset{\Vert}{P}}}-O^-$	$-\overset{O}{\underset{OH}{\overset{\Vert}{P}}}-O^-$ (phosphoryl group)
Diphosphate ester[b]	$R-O-\overset{O}{\underset{O^-}{\overset{\Vert}{P}}}-O-\overset{O}{\underset{OH}{\overset{\Vert}{P}}}-O^-$	$-\overset{O}{\underset{O^-}{\overset{\Vert}{P}}}-O-\overset{O}{\underset{OH}{\overset{\Vert}{P}}}-O^-$ (phosphoanhydride group)
Phosphate diester[b]	$R-O-\overset{O}{\underset{O^-}{\overset{\Vert}{P}}}-O-R$	$-O-\overset{O}{\underset{O^-}{\overset{\Vert}{P}}}-O-$ (phosphodiester linkage)

[a]R represents any carbon-containing group. In a molecule with more than one R group, the groups may be the same or different.

[b]Under physiological conditions, these groups are ionized and hence bear a positive or negative charge.

[c]If attached to an atom other than carbon.

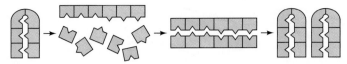

■ **Figure 1-5** | **Replication through complementarity.** In this simple case, a polymer serves as a template for the assembly of a complementary molecule, which, because of intramolecular complementarity, is an exact copy of the original.

Specific pairing between complementary functional groups permits one member of a pair to determine the identity and orientation of the other member. *Such complementarity makes it possible for a macromolecule to replicate, or copy itself, by directing the assembly of a new molecule from smaller complementary units.* Replication of a simple polymer with intramolecular complementarity is illustrated in Fig. 1-5. A similar phenomenon is central to the function of DNA, where the sequence of bases on one strand (e.g., A-C-G-T) absolutely specifies the sequence of bases on the strand to which it is paired (T-G-C-A). When DNA replicates, the two strands separate and direct the synthesis of complementary daughter strands. Complementarity is also the basis for transcribing DNA into RNA and for translating RNA into protein.

A critical moment in chemical evolution was the transition from systems of randomly generated molecules to systems in which molecules were organized and specifically replicated. Once macromolecules gained the ability to self-perpetuate, the primordial environment would have become enriched in molecules that were best able to survive and multiply. The first replicating systems were no doubt somewhat sloppy, with progeny molecules imperfectly complementary to their parents. Over time, **natural selection** would have favored molecules that made more accurate copies of themselves.

■ **CHECK YOUR UNDERSTANDING**

Summarize the major stages of chemical evolution.
Be able to identify the functional groups and linkages in Table 1-2.
Describe what occurs during a condensation reaction and a hydrolysis reaction.

2 | Cellular Architecture

The types of systems described so far would have had to compete with all the other components of the primordial earth for the available resources. A selective advantage would have accrued to a system that was sequestered and protected by boundaries of some sort. How these boundaries first arose, or even what they were made from, is obscure. One theory is that membranous **vesicles** (fluid-filled sacs) first attached to and then enclosed self-replicating systems. These vesicles would have become the first cells.

A | Cells Carry Out Metabolic Reactions

The advantages of **compartmentation** are several. In addition to receiving some protection from adverse environmental forces, an enclosed system can maintain high local concentrations of components that would otherwise diffuse away. More concentrated substances can react more readily, leading to increased efficiency in polymerization and other types of chemical reactions.

A membrane-bounded compartment that protected its contents would gradually become quite different in composition from its surroundings. Modern cells contain high concentrations of ions, small molecules, and large molecular aggregates that are found in only traces—if at all—outside the

LEARNING OBJECTIVES

■ Understand the advantages of compartmentation and enzymes in cellular chemistry.
■ Know the differences between prokaryotes and eukaryotes.
■ Become familiar with the major eukaryotic organelles.
■ Understand the relationship between archaebacteria, eubacteria, and eukaryotes.
■ Understand the central principles of evolution by natural selection.

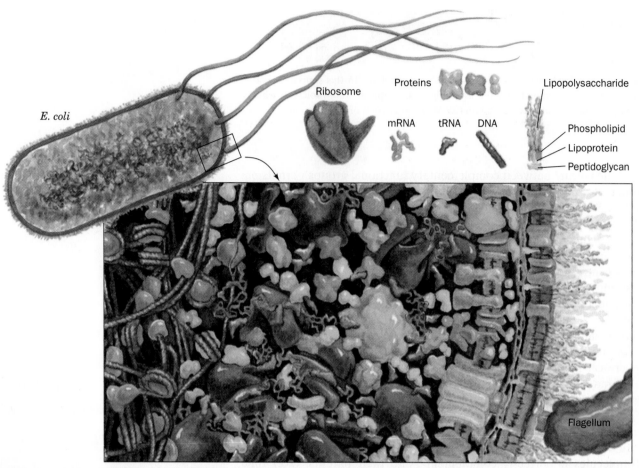

Ribosome

Proteins

Lipopolysaccharide

E. coli

mRNA   tRNA   DNA

Phospholipid

Lipoprotein

Peptidoglycan

Flagellum

■ **Figure 1-6** | **Cross section of an *E. coli* cell.** The right side of the drawing shows the multilayered cell wall and membrane. The cytoplasm in the middle region of the drawing is filled with ribosomes engaged in protein synthesis. The left side of the drawing contains a dense tangle of DNA. This drawing corresponds to a millionfold magnification. Only the largest macromolecules and molecular assemblies are shown. In a living cell, the remaining space in the cytoplasm would be crowded with smaller molecules and water (the water molecules would be about the size of the period at the end of this sentence). [After a drawing by David Goodsell, UCLA.]

cell. For example, the **Escherichia coli (E. coli)** cell contains millions of molecules representing some 3000 to 6000 different compounds (Fig. 1-6). A typical animal cell may contain 100,000 different types of molecules.

Early cells depended on the environment to supply building materials. As some of the essential components in the prebiotic soup became scarce, natural selection favored organisms that developed mechanisms for synthesizing the required compounds from simpler but more abundant **precursors.** The first metabolic reactions may have used metal or clay **catalysts** (a catalyst is a substance that promotes a chemical reaction without itself being changed). In fact, metal ions are still at the heart of many chemical reactions in modern cells. Some catalysts may also have arisen from polymeric molecules that had the appropriate functional groups.

In general, biosynthetic reactions require energy; hence the first cellular reactions also needed an energy source. The eventual depletion of preexisting energy-rich substances in the prebiotic environment would have stimulated the development of energy-producing metabolic pathways. For example, photosynthesis evolved relatively early to take advantage of a practically inexhaustible energy supply, the sun. However, the accumulation of O_2 generated from H_2O by photosynthesis (the modern atmosphere is 21% O_2) presented an additional challenge to organisms adapted to life in an oxygen-poor atmosphere. Metabolic refinements eventually permitted organisms not only to avoid oxidative damage but to use O_2 for oxidative metabolism, a much more efficient form of energy metabolism than anaerobic metabolism. Vestiges of ancient life can be seen in the anaerobic metabolism of certain modern organisms.

Early organisms that developed metabolic strategies to synthesize biological molecules, conserve and utilize energy in a controlled fashion, and replicate within a protective compartment were able to propagate in an ever-widening range of habitats. Adaptation of cells to different external conditions ultimately led to the present diversity of species. Specialization of individual cells also made it possible for groups of differentiated cells to work together in multicellular organisms.

B | There Are Two Types of Cells: Prokaryotes and Eukaryotes

All modern organisms are based on the same morphological unit, the cell. There are two major classifications of cells: the **eukaryotes** (Greek: *eu,* good or true + *karyon,* kernel or nut), which have a membrane-enclosed **nucleus** encapsulating their DNA; and the **prokaryotes** (Greek: *pro,* before), which lack a nucleus. *Prokaryotes, comprising the various types of bacteria, have relatively simple structures and are almost all unicellular* (although they may form filaments or colonies of independent cells). *Eukaryotes, which are multicellular as well as unicellular, are vastly more complex than prokaryotes.* (**Viruses** are much simpler entities than cells and are not classified as living because they lack the metabolic apparatus to reproduce outside their host cells.)

Prokaryotes are the most numerous and widespread organisms on the earth. This is because their varied and often highly adaptable metabolisms suit them to an enormous variety of habitats. Prokaryotes range in size from 1 to 10 μm and have one of three basic shapes (Fig. 1-7): spheroidal (cocci), rodlike (bacilli), and helically coiled (spirilla). Except for an outer

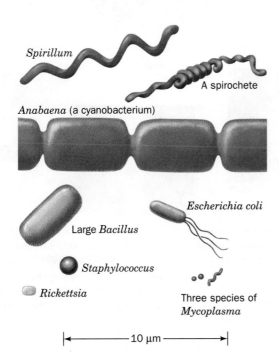

Spirillum

A spirochete

Anabaena (a cyanobacterium)

Escherichia coli

Large *Bacillus*

Staphylococcus

Rickettsia

Three species of *Mycoplasma*

|← —————— 10 μm —————— →|

■ **Figure 1-7** | **Scale drawings of some prokaryotic cells.**

cell membrane, which in most cases is surrounded by a protective cell wall; nearly all prokaryotes lack cellular membranes. However, the prokaryotic **cytoplasm** (cell contents) is by no means a homogeneous soup. Different metabolic functions are believed to be carried out in different regions of the cytoplasm (Fig. 1-6). The best characterized prokaryote is *Escherichia coli,* a 2 μm by 1 μm rodlike bacterium that inhabits the mammalian colon.

Eukaryotic cells are generally 10 to 100 μm in diameter and thus have a thousand to a million times the volume of typical prokaryotes. It is not size, however, but a profusion of membrane-enclosed **organelles** that best characterizes eukaryotic cells (Fig. 1-8). In addition to a nucleus, eukaryotes have an **endoplasmic reticulum,** the site of synthesis of many cellular components, some of which are subsequently modified in the **Golgi apparatus.** The bulk of aerobic metabolism takes place in **mitochondria** in almost all eukaryotes, and photosynthetic cells contain **chloroplasts.** Other organelles, such as **lysosomes** and **peroxisomes,** perform specialized functions. **Vacuoles,** which are more prominent in plant cells, usually function as storage depots. The **cytosol** (the cytoplasm minus its membrane-bounded organelles) is organized by the **cytoskeleton,** an extensive array of filaments that also gives the cell its shape and the ability to move.

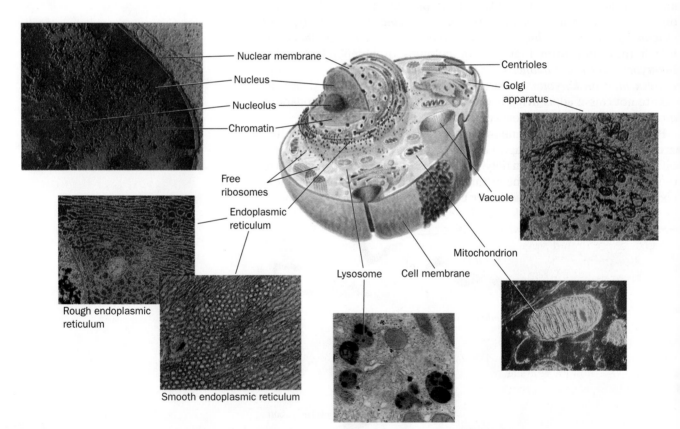

■ **Figure 1-8** │ **Diagram of a typical animal cell accompanied by electron micrographs of its organelles.** Membrane-bounded organelles include the nucleus, endoplasmic reticulum, lysosome, peroxisome (not pictured), mitochondrion, vacuole, and Golgi apparatus. The nucleus contains chromatin (a complex of DNA and protein) and the nucleolus (the site of ribosome synthesis). The rough endoplasmic reticulum is studded with ribosomes; the smooth endoplasmic reticulum is not. A pair of centrioles help organize cytoskeletal elements. A typical plant cell differs mainly by the presence of an outer cell wall and chloroplasts in the cytosol. [Nucleus: Tektoff-RM, CNRI/Photo Researchers; rough endoplasmic reticulum and Golgi apparatus: Secchi-Lecaque/Roussel-UCLAF/CNRI/Photo Researchers; smooth endoplasmic reticulum: David M. Phillips/Visuals Unlimited; mitochondrion: CNRI/Photo Researchers; lysosome: Biophoto Associates/Photo Researchers.]

The various organelles that compartmentalize eukaryotic cells represent a level of complexity that is largely lacking in prokaryotic cells. Nevertheless, prokaryotes are more efficient than eukaryotes in many respects. Prokaryotes have exploited the advantages of simplicity and miniaturization. Their rapid growth rates permit them to occupy ecological niches in which there may be drastic fluctuations of the available nutrients. In contrast, the complexity of eukaryotes, which renders them larger and more slowly growing than prokaryotes, gives them the competitive advantage in stable environments with limited resources. It is therefore erroneous to consider prokaryotes as evolutionarily primitive compared to eukaryotes. Both types of organisms are well adapted to their respective lifestyles.

C | Molecular Data Reveal Three Evolutionary Domains of Organisms

The practice of lumping all prokaryotes in a single category based on what they lack—a nucleus—obscures their metabolic diversity and evolutionary history. Conversely, the remarkable morphological diversity of eukaryotic organisms (consider the anatomical differences among, say, an amoeba, an oak tree, and a human being) masks their fundamental similarity at the cellular level. Traditional taxonomic schemes (**taxonomy** is the science of biological classification), which are based on gross morphology, have proved inadequate to describe the actual relationships between organisms as revealed by their evolutionary history (**phylogeny**).

Biological classification schemes based on reproductive or developmental strategies more accurately reflect evolutionary history than those based solely on adult morphology. But *phylogenetic relationships are best deduced by comparing polymeric molecules—RNA, DNA, or protein—from different organisms.* For example, analysis of RNA led Carl Woese to group all organisms into three domains (Fig. 1-9). The **archaea** (also known as **archaebacteria**) are a group of prokaryotes that are as distantly related to other prokaryotes (the **bacteria,** sometimes called **eubacteria**) as both groups are to eukaryotes **(eukarya).** The archaea include some unusual organisms: the **methanogens** (which produce CH_4), the **halobacteria** (which thrive in concentrated brine solutions), and certain **thermophiles** (which inhabit hot springs). The pattern of branches in Woese's diagram indicates the divergence of different types of organisms (each branch point represents a common ancestor). The three-domain scheme also shows that animals, plants, and fungi constitute only a small portion of all life-forms. Such phylogenetic trees supplement the fossil record, which provides a patchy record of life prior to about 600 million years before the present (multicellular organisms arose about 700–900 million years ago).

It is unlikely that eukaryotes are descended from a single prokaryote, because the differ-

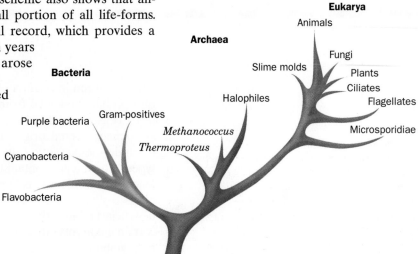

■ **Figure 1-9 | Phylogenetic tree showing three domains of organisms.** The branches indicate the pattern of divergence from a common ancestor. The archaea are prokaryotes, like bacteria, but share some features with eukaryotes. [After Wheelis, M.L., Kandler, O., and Woese, C.R., *Proc. Natl. Acad. Sci.* **89,** 2931 (1992).]

BOX 1-1 PATHWAYS OF DISCOVERY

Lynn Margulis and the Theory of Endosymbiosis

Lynn Margulis (1938–)

After growing up in Chicago and enrolling in the University of Chicago at age 16, Lynn Margulis intended to be a writer. Her interest in biology was sparked by a required science course for which she read Gregor Mendel's accounts of his experiments with the genetics of pea plants. Margulis continued her studies at the University of Wisconsin Madison and at the University of California Berkeley, earning a doctorate in 1963. Her careful consideration of cellular structures led her to hypothesize that eukaryotic cells originated from a series of endosymbiotic events involving multiple prokaryotes. The term *endo* (Greek: within) refers to an arrangement in which one cell comes to reside inside another. This idea was considered outrageous at the time (1967), but many of Margulis's ideas have since become widely accepted.

Endosymbiosis as an explanation for the origin of mitochondria had been proposed by Ivan Wallin in 1927, who noted the similarity between mitochondria and bacteria in size, shape, and cytological staining. Wallin's hypothesis was rejected as being too fantastic and was ignored until it was taken up again by Margulis. By the 1960s, much more was known about mitochondria (and chloroplasts), including the fact that they contained DNA and reproduced by division. Margulis did not focus all her attention on the origin of individual organelles but instead sought to explain the origin of the entire eukaryotic cell, which also includes centrioles, another possible bacterial relic. Her paper, "On the Origin of Mitosing cells," was initially rejected by several journals before being accepted by the *Journal of Theoretical Biology*. The notion that a complex eukaryotic cell could arise from a consortium of mutually dependent prokaryotic cells was incompatible with the prevailing view that evolution occurred as a series of small steps. Evolutionary theory of the time had no room for the dramatic amalgamation of cells—and their genetic material—that Margulis

had proposed. Nevertheless, the outspoken Margulis persisted, and by the time she published *Symbiosis in Cell Evolution* in 1981, much of the biological community had come on board.

Two main tenets of Margulis's theory, that mitochondria are the descendants of oxygen-respiring bacteria and chloroplasts were originally photosynthetic bacteria, are almost universally accepted. The idea that the eukaryotic cytoplasm is the remnant of an archaebacterial cell is still questioned by some biologists. Margulis is in the process of collecting evidence to support a fourth idea, that cilia and flagella and some sensory structures such as the light-sensing cells of the eye are descendants of free-living spirochete bacteria. Margulis's original prediction that organelles such as mitochondria could be isolated and cultured has not been fulfilled. However, there is ample evidence for the transfer of genetic material between organelles and the nucleus, consistent with Margulis's theory of endosymbiosis. In fact, current theories of evolution include the movement of genetic material among organisms, as predicted by Margulis, in addition to small random mutations as agents of change.

Perhaps as an extension of her work on bacterial endosymbiosis, Margulis came to recognize that the interactions among many different types of organisms as well as their interactions with their physical environment constitute a single self-regulating system. This notion is part of the Gaia hypothesis proposed by James Lovelock, which views the entire earth as one living entity (Gaia was a Greek earth goddess). However, Margulis has no patience with those who seek to build a modern mythology based on Gaia. She is adamant about the importance of using scientific tools and reasoning to discover the truth and is irritated by the popular belief that humans are the center of life on earth. Margulis understands that human survival depends on our relationships with waste-recycling, water-purifying, and oxygen-producing bacteria, with whom we have been evolving, sometimes endosymbiotically, for billions of years.

Sagan, L., On the origin of mitosing cells, *J. Theor. Biol.* **14**, 255–274 (1967)

ences between bacteria and eukaryotes are so profound. Instead, eukaryotes probably evolved from the association of archaebacterial and eubacterial cells. The eukaryotic genetic material includes features that suggest an archaebacterial origin. In addition, the mitochondria and chloroplasts of modern eukaryotic cells resemble bacteria in size and shape, and both types of organelles contain their own genetic material and protein synthetic machinery. Evidently, as Lynn Margulis proposed, mitochondria and chloroplasts evolved from free-living bacteria that formed **symbiotic** (mutually beneficial) relationships with a primordial eukaryotic cell (Box 1-1). In fact, certain eukaryotes that lack mitochondria or chloroplasts permanently harbor symbiotic bacteria.

D | Organisms Continue to Evolve

The natural selection that guided prebiotic evolution continues to direct the evolution of organisms. Richard Dawkins has likened evolution to a blind watchmaker capable of producing intricacy by accident, although such an image fails to convey the vast expanse of time and the incremental, trial-and-error manner in which complex organisms emerge. Small **mutations** (changes in an individual's genetic material) arise at random as the result of chemical damage or inherent errors in the replication process. *A mutation that increases the chances of survival of the individual increases the likelihood that the mutation will be passed on to the next generation.* Beneficial mutations tend to spread rapidly through a population; deleterious changes tend to die along with the organisms that harbor them.

The theory of evolution by natural selection, which was first articulated by Charles Darwin in the 1860s, has been confirmed through observation and experimentation. It is therefore useful to highlight several important—and often misunderstood—principles of evolution:

1. *Evolution is not directed toward a particular goal.* It proceeds by random changes that may affect the ability of an organism to reproduce under the prevailing conditions. An organism that is well adapted to its environment may fare better or worse when conditions change.
2. *Variation among individuals* allows organisms to adapt to unexpected changes. This is one reason why genetically homogeneous populations (e.g., a corn crop) are so susceptible to a single challenge (e.g., a fungal blight). A more heterogeneous population is more likely to include individuals that can resist the adversity and recover.
3. *The past determines the future.* New structures and metabolic functions emerge from preexisting elements. For example, insect wings did not erupt spontaneously but appear to have developed gradually from small heat-exchange structures.
4. *Evolution is ongoing,* although it does not proceed exclusively toward complexity. An anthropocentric view places human beings at the pinnacle of an evolutionary scheme, but a quick survey of life's diversity reveals that simpler species have not died out or stopped evolving.

> ■ **CHECK YOUR UNDERSTANDING**
>
> What is the role of compartmentation in cellular chemistry?
> List the differences between prokaryotes and eukaryotes.
> How are the three evolutionary domains of organisms related to each other?
> Summarize the process of evolution by natural selection.

3 | Thermodynamics

The normal activities of living organisms—moving, growing, reproducing—demand an almost constant input of energy. Even at rest, organisms devote a considerable portion of their biochemical apparatus to the acquisition and utilization of energy. The study of energy and its effects on matter falls under the purview of **thermodynamics** (Greek: *therme,* heat + *dynamis,* power). Although living systems present some practical challenges to thermodynamic analysis, *life obeys the laws of thermodynamics.* Understanding thermodynamics is important not only for describing a particular process—such as a biochemical reaction—in terms that can be quantified, but also for predicting whether that process *can* actually occur, that is, whether the process is spontaneous. To begin, we will review the fundamental laws of thermodynamics. We will then turn our attention to free energy and how it relates to chemical reactions. Finally, we will look at how biological systems deal with the laws of thermodynamics.

> **LEARNING OBJECTIVES**
>
> ■ Understand the first and second laws of thermodynamics and how they apply to living systems.
> ■ Understand the relationship between free energy, enthalpy, and entropy.
> ■ Understand the meaning of spontaneity for a biological process.
> ■ Understand the relationship between equilibrium constants and free energy changes.

A | The First Law of Thermodynamics States That Energy Is Conserved

In thermodynamics, a **system** is defined as the part of the universe that is of interest, such as a reaction vessel or an organism; the rest of the universe is known as the **surroundings.** The system has a certain amount of **energy, U.** *The first law of thermodynamics states that energy is conserved;* it can be neither created nor destroyed. However, when the system undergoes a change, some of its energy can be used to perform work. The energy change of the system is defined as the difference between the **heat (q)** absorbed by the system from the surroundings and **work (w)** done by the system on the surroundings. The Greek letter Δ (Delta) indicates change.

$$\Delta U = U_{\text{final}} - U_{\text{initial}} = q - w \qquad [1\text{-}1]$$

Heat is a reflection of random molecular motion, whereas work, which is defined as force times the distance moved under its influence, is associated with organized motion. Force may assume many different forms, including the gravitational force exerted by one mass on another, the expansional force exerted by a gas, the tensional force exerted by a spring or muscle fiber, the electrical force of one charge on another, and the dissipative forces of friction and viscosity. Because energy can be used to perform different kinds of work, it is sometimes useful to speak of energy taking different forms, such as mechanical energy, electrical energy, or chemical energy—all of which are relevant to biological systems.

Most biological processes take place at constant pressure. Under such conditions, the work done by the expansion of a gas (pressure–volume work) is $P\Delta V$. Consequently, it is useful to define a new thermodynamic quantity, the **enthalpy** (Greek: *enthalpein,* to warm in), abbreviated **H:**

$$H = U + PV \qquad [1\text{-}2]$$

Then, when the system undergoes a change at constant pressure,

$$\Delta H = \Delta U + P\Delta V = q_P - w + P\Delta V \qquad [1\text{-}3]$$

where q_P is defined as the heat at constant pressure. Since we already know that in this system $w = P\Delta V$,

$$\Delta H = q_P - P\Delta V + P\Delta V = q_P \qquad [1\text{-}4]$$

In other words, the change in enthalpy is equivalent to heat. Moreover, the volume changes in most biochemical reactions are insignificant ($P\Delta V \approx 0$), so the differences between their ΔU and ΔH values are negligible, and hence the energy change for the reacting system is equivalent to its enthalpy change. Enthalpy, like energy, heat, and work, is given units of joules. (Some commonly used units and biochemical constants and other conventions are given in Box 1-2.)

Thermodynamics is useful for indicating the spontaneity of a process. A **spontaneous process** occurs without the input of additional energy from outside the system. (Thermodynamic spontaneity has nothing to do with how quickly a process occurs.) The first law of thermodynamics, however, cannot by itself determine whether a process is spontaneous. Consider two objects of different temperatures that are brought together. Heat spontaneously flows from the warmer object to the cooler one, never vice versa. Yet either process would be consistent with the first law of thermodynamics since the aggregate energy of the two objects does not change. Therefore, an additional criterion of spontaneity is needed.

BOX 1-2 PERSPECTIVES IN BIOCHEMISTRY

Biochemical Conventions

Modern biochemistry generally uses Système International (SI) units, including meters (m), kilograms (kg), and seconds (s) and their derived units, for various thermodynamic and other measurements. The following table lists the commonly used biochemical units, some useful biochemical constants, and a few conversion factors.

Units

Energy, heat, work	joule (J)	$kg \cdot m^2 \cdot s^{-2}$ or $C \cdot V$
Electric potential	volt (V)	$J \cdot C^{-1}$

Prefixes for units

mega (M)	10^6	nano (n)	10^{-9}
kilo (k)	10^3	pico (p)	10^{-12}
milli (m)	10^{-3}	femto (f)	10^{-15}
micro (μ)	10^{-6}	atto (a)	10^{-18}

Conversions

angstrom (Å)	10^{-10} m
calorie (cal)	4.184 J
kelvin (K)	degrees Celsius (°C) + 273.15

Constants

Avogadro's number (N)	6.0221×10^{23} molecules $\cdot mol^{-1}$
Coulomb (C)	6.241×10^{18} electron charges
Faraday ($\mathscr{F}$)	96,485 $C \cdot mol^{-1}$ or 96,485 $J \cdot V^{-1} \cdot mol^{-1}$
Gas constant (R)	8.3145 $J \cdot K^{-1} \cdot mol^{-1}$
Boltzmann constant (k_B)	1.3807×10^{-23} $J \cdot K^{-1}$ (R/N)
Planck's constant (h)	6.6261×10^{-34} $J \cdot s$

Throughout this text, molecular masses of particles are expressed in units of **daltons (D),** which are defined as l/12th the mass of a ^{12}C atom (1000 D = 1 **kilodalton, kD**). Biochemists also use **molecular weight,** a dimensionless quantity defined as the ratio of the particle mass to l/12th the mass of a ^{12}C atom, which is symbolized M_r (for relative molecular mass).

B | The Second Law of Thermodynamics States That Entropy Tends to Increase

According to the second law of thermodynamics, spontaneous processes are characterized by the conversion of order to disorder. In this context, disorder is defined as the number of energetically equivalent ways, W, of arranging the components of a system. To make this concept concrete, consider a system consisting of two bulbs of equal volume, one of which contains molecules of an ideal gas (Fig. 1-10). When the stopcock connecting the bulbs is open, the molecules become randomly but equally distributed between the two bulbs. The equal number of gas molecules in each bulb is not the result of any law of motion; it is because the probabilities of all other distributions of the molecules are so overwhelmingly small. Thus, the probability of all the molecules in the system spontaneously rushing into the left bulb (the initial condition) is nil, even though the energy and enthalpy of this arrangement are exactly the same as those of the evenly distributed molecules.

The degree of randomness of a system is indicated by its **entropy** (Greek: *en*, in + *trope*, turning), abbreviated S:

$$S = k_B \ln W \qquad [1\text{-}5]$$

where k_B is the **Boltzmann constant.** The units of S are $J \cdot K^{-1}$ (absolute temperature, in units of kelvins, is a factor because entropy varies with temperature; e.g., a system becomes more disordered as its temperature rises). The most probable arrangement of a system is the one that maximizes W and hence S. Thus, if a spontaneous process, such as the one shown in Fig. 1-10, has overall energy and enthalpy changes (ΔU and ΔH) of zero, its entropy change (ΔS) must be greater than zero; that is,

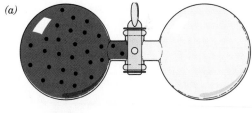
(a)

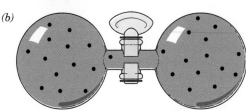
(b)

■ **Figure 1-10 | Illustration of entropy.** In (*a*), a gas occupies the leftmost of two equal-sized bulbs and hence the entropy is low. When the stopcock is opened (*b*), the entropy increases as the gas molecules diffuse back and forth between the bulbs and eventually become distributed evenly, half in each bulb.

the number of equivalent ways of arranging the final state must be greater than the number of ways of arranging the initial state. Furthermore because

$$\Delta S_{\text{system}} + \Delta S_{\text{surroundings}} = \Delta S_{\text{universe}} > 0 \qquad [1\text{-}6]$$

all processes increase the entropy—that is, the disorder—of the universe

In chemical and biological systems, it is impractical, if not impossible to determine the entropy of a system by counting all the equivalent arrangements of its components (W). However, there is an entirely equivalent expression for entropy that applies to the constant-temperature conditions typical of biological systems: for a spontaneous process,

$$\Delta S \geq \frac{q}{T} \qquad [1\text{-}7]$$

Thus, the entropy change in a process can be experimentally determined from measurements of heat.

C | The Free Energy Change Determines the Spontaneity of a Process

The spontaneity of a process cannot be predicted from a knowledge of the system's entropy change alone. For example, 2 mol of H_2 and 1 mol of O_2 when sparked, react to form 2 mol of H_2O. Yet two water molecules, each of whose three atoms are constrained to stay together, are more ordered than are the three diatomic molecules from which they formed. Thus, the reaction occurs with a decrease in the system's entropy.

What, then, is the thermodynamic criterion for a spontaneous process? Equations 1-4 and 1-7 indicate that at constant temperature and pressure

$$\Delta S \geq \frac{q_P}{T} = \frac{\Delta H}{T} \qquad [1\text{-}8]$$

Thus,

$$\Delta H - T\Delta S \leq 0 \qquad [1\text{-}9]$$

This is the true criterion for spontaneity as formulated, in 1878, by J. Willard Gibbs. He defined the **Gibbs free energy (G,** usually called just **free energy**) as

$$G = H - TS \qquad [1\text{-}10]$$

The change in free energy for a process is ΔG. Consequently, spontaneous processes at constant temperature and pressure have

$$\boxed{\Delta G = \Delta H - T\Delta S < 0} \qquad [1\text{-}11]$$

Such processes are said to be **exergonic** (Greek: *ergon,* work). Processes that are not spontaneous have positive ΔG values ($\Delta G > 0$) and are said to be **endergonic;** they must be driven by the input of free energy. If a process is exergonic, the reverse of that process is endergonic and vice versa. Thus, the ΔG value for a process indicates whether the process can occur spontaneously in the direction written. Processes at **equilibrium** those in which the forward and reverse reactions are exactly balanced, are characterized by $\Delta G = 0$. For the most part, only changes in free energy enthalpy, and entropy (ΔG, ΔH, and ΔS) can be measured, not their absolute values (G, H, and S).

A process that is accompanied by an increase in enthalpy ($\Delta H > 0$) which opposes the process, can nevertheless proceed spontaneously if the

Table 1-3	Variation of Reaction Spontaneity (Sign of ΔG) with the Signs of ΔH and ΔS	
ΔH	ΔS	$\Delta G = \Delta H - T\Delta S$
−	+	The reaction is both enthalpically favored (exothermic) and entropically favored. It is spontaneous (exergonic) at all temperatures.
−	−	The reaction is enthalpically favored but entropically opposed. It is spontaneous only at temperatures *below* $T = \Delta H/\Delta S$.
+	+	The reaction is enthalpically opposed (endothermic) but entropically favored. It is spontaneous only at temperatures *above* $T = \Delta H/\Delta S$.
+	−	The reaction is both enthalpically and entropically opposed. It is nonspontaneous (endergonic) at all temperatures.

entropy change is sufficiently positive ($\Delta S > 0$; Table 1-3). Conversely, a process that is accompanied by a decrease in entropy ($\Delta S < 0$) can proceed if its enthalpy change is sufficiently negative ($\Delta H < 0$). It is important to emphasize that *a large negative value of ΔG does not ensure that a process such as a chemical reaction will proceed at a measurable rate. The rate depends on the detailed mechanism of the reaction, which is independent of ΔG.*

Free energy as well as energy, enthalpy, and entropy are **state functions.** In other words, their values depend only on the current state or properties of the system, not on how the system reached that state. Therefore, *thermodynamic measurements can be made by considering only the initial and final states of the system and ignoring all the stepwise changes in enthalpy and entropy that occur in between.* For example, it is impossible to directly measure the energy change for the reaction of glucose with O_2 in a living organism because of the numerous other simultaneously occurring chemical reactions. But since ΔG depends on only the initial and final states, the combustion of glucose can be analyzed in any convenient apparatus, using the same starting materials (glucose and O_2) and end products (CO_2 and H_2O) that would be obtained *in vivo*.

D | Free Energy Changes Can Be Calculated from Equilibrium Concentrations

The entropy (disorder) of a substance increases with its volume. For example, a collection of gas molecules, in occupying all of the volume available to it, maximizes its entropy. Similarly, dissolved molecules become uniformly distributed throughout their solution volume. Entropy is therefore a function of concentration.

If entropy varies with concentration, so must free energy. Thus, *the free energy change of a chemical reaction depends on the concentrations of both its reacting substances (reactants) and its reaction products.* This phenomenon has great significance because many biochemical reactions operate spontaneously in either direction depending on the relative concentrations of their reactants and products.

Equilibrium Constants Are Related to ΔG. The relationship between the concentration and the free energy of a substance A is approximately

$$\overline{G}_A = \overline{G}_A^\circ + RT \ln [A] \qquad [1\text{-}12]$$

where $\overline{G}_A$ is known as the **partial molar free energy** or the **chemical potential** of A (the bar indicates the quantity per mole), $\overline{G}_A^\circ$ is the partial molar free energy of A in its **standard state,** R is the gas constant, and [A] is the molar concentration of A. Thus, for the general reaction

$$aA + bB \rightleftharpoons cC + dD$$

the free energy change is

$$\Delta G = c\overline{G}_C + d\overline{G}_D - a\overline{G}_A - b\overline{G}_B \qquad [1\text{-}13]$$

and

$$\Delta G^\circ = c\overline{G}_C^\circ + d\overline{G}_D^\circ - a\overline{G}_A^\circ - b\overline{G}_B^\circ \qquad [1\text{-}14]$$

because free energies are additive and the free energy change of a reaction is the sum of the free energies of the products less those of the reactants. Substituting these relationships into Eq. 1-12 yields

$$\Delta G = \Delta G^\circ + RT \ln\left(\frac{[C]^c[D]^d}{[A]^a[B]^b}\right) \qquad [1\text{-}15]$$

where ΔG° is the free energy change of the reaction when all of its reactants and products are in their standard states (see below). Thus, the expression for the free energy change of a reaction consists of two parts: (1) a constant term whose value depends only on the reaction taking place and (2) a variable term that depends on the concentrations of the reactants and the products, the stoichiometry of the reaction, and the temperature.

For a reaction at equilibrium, there is no *net* change because the free energy change of the forward reaction exactly balances that of the reverse reaction. Consequently, $\Delta G = 0$, so Eq. 1-15 becomes

$$\boxed{\Delta G^\circ = -RT \ln K_{eq}} \qquad [1\text{-}16]$$

where K_{eq} is the familiar **equilibrium constant** of the reaction:

$$K_{eq} = \frac{[C]_{eq}^c[D]_{eq}^d}{[A]_{eq}^a[B]_{eq}^b} = e^{-\Delta G^\circ/RT} \qquad [1\text{-}17]$$

The subscript "eq" denotes reactant and product concentrations at equilibrium. (The equilibrium condition is usually clear from the context of the situation, so equilibrium concentrations are usually expressed without this subscript.) *The equilibrium constant of a reaction can therefore be calculated from standard free energy data and vice versa* (see Sample Calculation 1-1).

K Depends on Temperature. The manner in which the equilibrium constant varies with temperature can be seen by substituting Eq. 1-11 into Eq. 1-16 and rearranging:

$$\ln K_{eq} = \frac{-\Delta H^\circ}{R}\left(\frac{1}{T}\right) + \frac{\Delta S^\circ}{R} \qquad [1\text{-}18]$$

where H° and S° represent enthalpy and entropy in the standard state. Equation 1-18 has the form $y = mx + b$, the equation for a straight line. A plot of $\ln K_{eq}$ versus $1/T$, known as a **van't Hoff plot,** permits the values of ΔH° and ΔS° (and hence ΔG°) to be determined from measurements of K_{eq} at two (or more) different temperatures. This method is

---

SAMPLE CALCULATION 1-1

The standard free energy change for a reaction is -15 kJ·mol^{-1}. What is the equilibrium constant for the reaction?

Since ΔG° is known, Eq. 1-17 can be used to calculate K_{eq}. Assume the temperature is 25°C (298 K):

$K_{eq} = e^{-\Delta G^\circ/RT}$

$K_{eq} = e^{-(-15,000\ \text{J·mol}^{-1})/(8.314\ \text{J·K}^{-1}\text{·mol}^{-1})(298\ \text{K})}$

$K_{eq} = e^{6.05}$

$K_{eq} = 426$

often more practical than directly measuring ΔH and ΔS by calorimetry (which measures the heat, q_P, of a process).

Biochemists Have Defined Standard-State Conventions. In order to compare free energy changes for different reactions, it is necessary to express ΔG values relative to some standard state (likewise, we refer the elevations of geographic locations to sea level, which is arbitrarily assigned the height of zero). According to the convention used in physical chemistry, a solute is in its standard state when the temperature is 25°C, the pressure is 1 atm, and the solute has an **activity** of 1 (activity of a substance is its concentration corrected for its nonideal behavior at concentrations higher than infinite dilution).

The concentrations of reactants and products in most biochemical reactions are usually so low (on the order of millimolar or less) that their activities are closely approximated by their molar concentrations. Furthermore, because biochemical reactions occur near neutral pH, biochemists have adopted a somewhat different standard-state convention:

1. The activity of pure water is assigned a value of 1, even though its concentration is 55.5 M. This practice simplifies the free energy expressions for reactions in dilute solutions involving water as a reactant, because the $[H_2O]$ term can then be ignored.

2. The hydrogen ion (H^+) activity is assigned a value of 1 at the physiologically relevant pH of 7. Thus, the biochemical standard state is pH 7.0 (neutral pH, where $[H^+] = 10^{-7}$ M) rather than pH 0 ($[H^+] = $ 1 M), the physical chemical standard state, where many biological substances are unstable.

3. The standard state of a substance that can undergo an acid–base reaction is defined in terms of the total concentration of its naturally occurring ion mixture at pH 7. In contrast, the physical chemistry convention refers to a pure species whether or not it actually exists at pH 0. The advantage of the biochemistry convention is that the total concentration of a substance with multiple ionization states, such as most biological molecules, is usually easier to measure than the concentration of one of its ionic species. Since the ionic composition of an acid or base varies with pH, however, the standard free energies calculated according to the biochemical convention are valid only at pH 7.

Under the biochemistry convention, the standard free energy changes of reactions are customarily symbolized by $\Delta G^{\circ\prime}$ to distinguish them from physical chemistry standard free energy changes, ΔG°. If a reaction includes neither H_2O, H^+, nor an ionizable species, then $\Delta G^{\circ\prime} = \Delta G^\circ$.

E | Life Obeys the Laws of Thermodynamics

At one time, many scientists believed that life, with its inherent complexity and order, somehow evaded the laws of thermodynamics. However, elaborate measurements on living animals are consistent with the conservation of energy predicted by the first law. Unfortunately, experimental verification of the second law is not practicable, since it requires dismantling an organism to its component molecules, which would result in its irreversible death. Consequently, it is possible to assert only that the entropy of living matter is less than that of the products to which it decays. *Life persists, however, because a system (a living organism) can be ordered at the expense of disordering its surroundings to an even greater extent.* In other words, the total entropy of the system plus its surroundings increases, as required by the second law. Living organisms achieve order by disordering (breaking down) the nutrients they consume. Thus, the entropy content of food is as important as its energy content.

Living Organisms Are Open Systems. Classical thermodynamics applies primarily to reversible processes in **isolated systems** (which cannot exchange matter or energy with their surroundings) or in **closed systems** (which can only exchange energy). An isolated system inevitably reaches equilibrium. For example, if its reactants are in excess, the forward reaction will proceed faster than the reverse reaction until equilibrium is attained ($\Delta G = 0$), at which point the forward and reverse reactions exactly balance each other. In contrast, **open systems,** which exchange both matter and energy with their surroundings, can reach equilibrium only after the flow of matter and energy has stopped.

Living organisms, which take up nutrients, release waste products, and generate work and heat, are open systems and therefore can never be at equilibrium. They continuously ingest high-enthalpy, low-entropy nutrients, which they convert to low-enthalpy, high-entropy waste products. The free energy released in this process powers the cellular activities that produce the high degree of organization characteristic of life. If this process is interrupted, the system ultimately reaches equilibrium, which for living things is synonymous with death. An example of energy flow in an open system is illustrated in Fig. 1-11. Through photosynthesis, plants convert radiant energy from the sun, the primary energy source for life on the earth, to the chemical energy of carbohydrates and other organic substances. The plants, or the animals that eat them then metabolize these substances to power such functions as the synthesis of biomolecules, the maintenance of intracellular ion concentrations, and cellular movements.

Living Things Maintain a Steady State. Even in a system that is not at equilibrium, matter and energy flow according to the laws of thermodynamics. For example, materials tend to move from areas of high concentration to areas of low concentration. This is why blood takes up O_2 in the lungs where O_2 is abundant, and releases it to the tissues, where O_2 is scarce.

Living systems are characterized by being in a **steady state.** This means that all flows in the system are constant so that the system does not change

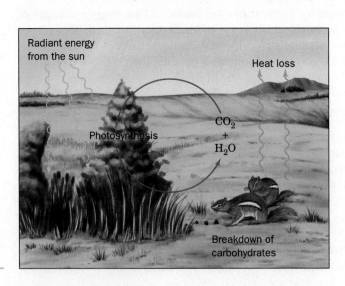

■ **Figure 1-11** | **Energy flow in the biosphere.** Plants use the sun's radiant energy to synthesize carbohydrates from CO_2 and H_2O. Plants or the animals that eat them eventually metabolize the carbohydrates to release their stored free energy and thereby return CO_2 and H_2O to the environment.

with time. Energy flow in the biosphere (Fig. 1-11) is an example of a system in a steady state. Slight perturbations from the steady state give rise to changes in flows that restore the system to the steady state. In all living systems, energy flow is exclusively "downhill" ($\Delta G < 0$). In addition, nature is inherently dissipative, so the recovery of free energy from a biochemical process is never total and some energy is always lost to the surroundings.

Enzymes Catalyze Biochemical Reactions. Nearly all the molecular components of an organism can potentially react with each other, and many of these reactions are thermodynamically favored (spontaneous). Yet only a subset of all possible reactions actually occur to a significant extent in a living organism. The rate of a particular reaction depends not on the free energy difference between the initial and final states but on the actual path through which the reactants are transformed to products. Living organisms take advantage of catalysts, substances that increase the rate at which the reaction approaches equilibrium without affecting the reaction's ΔG. Biological catalysts are referred to as **enzymes,** most of which are proteins.

Enzymes accelerate biochemical reactions by physically interacting with the reactants and products to provide a more favorable pathway for the transformation of one to the other. Enzymes increase the rates of reactions by increasing the likelihood that the reactants can interact productively. Enzymes cannot, however, promote reactions whose ΔG values are positive.

A multitude of enzymes mediate the flow of energy in every cell. As free energy is harvested, stored, or used to perform cellular work, it may be transferred to other molecules. And although it is tempting to think of free energy as something that is stored in chemical bonds, chemical energy can be transformed into heat, electrical work, or mechanical work, according to the needs of the organism and the biochemical machinery with which it has been equipped through evolution.

■ CHECK YOUR UNDERSTANDING

Explain the first and second laws of thermodynamics.

How does the free energy change for a process depend on its enthalpy and entropy changes? What makes a process spontaneous?

How is the free energy change for a chemical reaction related to the equilibrium constant?

How does life persist despite the laws of thermodynamics?

SUMMARY

1. A model for the origin of life proposes that organisms ultimately arose from simple organic molecules that polymerized to form more complex molecules capable of replicating themselves.

2. Compartmentation gave rise to cells that developed metabolic reactions for synthesizing biological molecules and generating energy.

3. All cells are either prokaryotic or eukaryotic. Eukaryotic cells contain a variety of membrane-bounded organelles.

4. Phylogenetic evidence groups organisms into three domains: archaea, bacteria, and eukarya.

5. Natural selection determines the evolution of species.

6. The first law of thermodynamics (energy is conserved) and the second law (spontaneous processes increase the disorder of the universe) apply to biochemical processes. The spontaneity of a process is determined by its free energy change ($\Delta G = \Delta H - T\Delta S$): spontaneous reactions have $\Delta G < 0$ and nonspontaneous reactions have $\Delta G > 0$.

7. The equilibrium constant for a process is related to the standard free energy change for that process.

8. Living organisms are open systems that maintain a steady state.

KEY TERMS

prebiotic era **2**
organic compound **2**
functional group **3**
linkage **3**
polymer **3**
condensation reaction **3**

hydrolysis **3**
replication **5**
natural selection **5**
vesicle **5**
compartmentation **5**
precursor **6**

catalyst **6**
eukaryote **7**
nucleus **7**
prokaryote **7**
virus **7**
cytoplasm **8**

organelle **8**
endoplasmic reticulum **8**
Golgi apparatus **8**
mitochondrion **8**
chloroplast **8**
lysosome **8**

peroxisome **8**
vacuole **8**
cytosol **8**
cytoskeleton **8**
taxonomy **9**
phylogeny **9**
archaea **9**
bacteria **9**
eukarya **9**
methanogens **9**
halobacteria **9**

thermophiles **9**
symbiosis **10**
mutation **11**
thermodynamics **11**
system **12**
surroundings **12**
U **12**
q **12**
w **12**
H **12**
q_P **12**

spontaneous process **12**
D **13**
kD **13**
W **13**
S **13**
k_B **13**
G **14**
exergonic **14**
endergonic **14**
equilibrium **14**
state function **15**

$\overline{G}_A$ **16**
$\overline{G}_A^\circ$ **16**
standard state **16**
equilibrium constant **16**
van't Hoff plot **16**
activity **17**
isolated system **18**
closed system **18**
open system **18**
steady state **18**
enzyme **19**

PROBLEMS

1. Identify the circled functional groups and linkages in the compound below.

2. Why is the cell membrane not an absolute barrier between the cytoplasm and the external environment?

3. A spheroidal bacterium with a diameter of 1 μm contains two molecules of a particular protein. What is the molar concentration of the protein?

4. How many glucose molecules does the cell in Problem 3 contain when its internal glucose concentration is 1.0 mM?

5. (a) Which has greater entropy, liquid water at 0°C or ice at 0°C? (b) How does the entropy of ice at −5°C differ, if at all, from its entropy at −50°C?

6. Does entropy increase or decrease in the following processes?

   (a) $N_2 + 3 H_2 \longrightarrow 2 NH_3$

   (b) $H_2N-\overset{\overset{O}{\|}}{C}-NH_2 + H_2O \longrightarrow CO_2 + 2 NH_3$

   Urea

   (c)
   1 M NaCl ⟶ 0.5 M NaCl

(d)

3-Phosphoglycerate   **2-Phosphoglycerate**

7. Consider a reaction with $\Delta H = 15$ kJ and $\Delta S = 50$ J·K^{-1}. Is the reaction spontaneous (a) at 10°C, (b) at 80°C?

8. Calculate the equilibrium constant for the reaction

   $$glucose\text{-}1\text{-}phosphate + H_2O \longrightarrow glucose + H_2PO_4^-$$

   at pH 7.0 and 25°C ($\Delta G^{\circ\prime} = -20.9$ kJ·mol^{-1}).

9. Calculate $\Delta G^{\circ\prime}$ for the reaction A + B $\rightleftharpoons$ C + D at 25°C when the equilibrium concentrations are [A] = 10 μM, [B] = 15 μM, [C] = 3 μM, and [D] = 5 μM. Is the reaction exergonic or endergonic under standard conditions?

10. $\Delta G^{\circ\prime}$ for the isomerization reaction

    $$glucose\text{-}1\text{-}phosphate\ (G1P) \rightleftharpoons glucose\text{-}6\text{-}phosphate\ (G6P)$$

    is −7.1 kJ·mol^{-1}. Calculate the equilibrium ratio of [G1P] to [G6P] at 25°C.

11. For the reaction A $\longrightarrow$ B at 298 K, the change in enthalpy is −7 kJ·mol^{-1} and the change in entropy is −25 J·K^{-1}·mol^{-1}. Is the reaction spontaneous? If not, should the temperature be increased or decreased to make the reaction spontaneous?

12. For the conversion of reactant A to product B, the change in enthalpy is 7 kJ·mol^{-1} and the change in entropy is 20 J·K^{-1}·mol^{-1}. Above what temperature does the reaction become spontaneous?

13. Label the following statements true or false:

    (a) A reaction is said to be spontaneous when it can proceed in either the forward or reverse direction.

    (b) A spontaneous process always happens very quickly.

    (c) A nonspontaneous reaction will proceed spontaneously in the reverse direction.

    (d) A spontaneous process can occur with a large decrease in entropy.

14. Two biochemical reactions have the same $K_{eq} = 5 \times 10^?$ at temperature $T_1 = 298$ K. However, Reaction 1 has $\Delta H^\circ =$

-28 kJ$\cdot$mol^{-1} and Reaction 2 has $\Delta H^\circ = +28$ kJ$\cdot$mol^{-1}. The two reactions utilize the same reactants. Your lab partner has proposed that you can get more of the reactants to proceed via Reaction 2 rather than Reaction 1 by lowering the temperature of the reaction. Will this strategy work? Why or why not? How much would the temperature have to be raised or lowered in order to change the value of K_2/K_1 from 1 to 10?

REFERENCES

Origin and Evolution of Life

Anet, F.A.L., The place of metabolism in the origin of life, *Curr. Opin. Chem. Biol.* **8,** 654–659 (2004). [Discusses various hypotheses proposing that life originated as a self-replicating system or as a set of catalytic polymers.]

Bada, J.L. and Lazcano, A., Prebiotic soup—revisiting the Miller experiment, *Science* **300,** 745–756 (2003).

Nisbet, E.G. and Sleep, N.H., The habitat and nature of early life, *Nature* **409,** 1083–1091 (2001). [Explains some of the hypotheses regarding the early earth and the origin of life, including the possibility that life originated at hydrothermal vents.]

Cells

Baldauf, S.L., The deep roots of eukaryotes, *Science* **300,** 1703–1706 (2003). [Describes some recent discoveries that raise questions about the taxonomy of eukaryotes.]

Campbell, N.A. and Reece, J.B., *Biology* (7th ed.), Benjamin/Cummings (2005). [This and other comprehensive general biology texts provide details about the structures of prokaryotes and eukaryotes.]

DeLong, E.F. and Pace, N.R., Environmental diversity of bacteria and archaea, *Syst. Biol.* **593,** 470–478 (2001). [Describes some of the challenges of classifying microbial organisms among the three domains.]

Goodsell, D.S., A look inside the living cell, *Am. Scientist* **80,** 457–465 (1992); *and* Inside a living cell, *Trends Biochem. Sci.* **16,** 203–206 (1991).

Lodish, H., Berk, A., Matsudaria, P., Kaiser, C. A., Krieger, M., Scott, M.P., Zipursky, S.L., and Darnell, J., *Molecular Cell Biology* (5th ed.), Chapter 5, W.H. Freeman (2004). [This and other cell biology textbooks offer thorough reviews of cellular structure.]

Thermodynamics

Tinoco, I., Jr., Sauer, K., Wang, J.C., and Puglisi, J.C., *Physical Chemistry. Principles and Applications in Biological Sciences* (4th ed.), Chapters 2–5, Prentice-Hall (2002). [Most physical chemistry texts treat thermodynamics in some detail.]

van Holde, K.E., Johnson, W.C., and Ho, P.S., *Principles of Physical Biochemistry* (2nd ed.), Chapters 2 and 3, Prentice-Hall (2006).

2

Water

Coral reefs support a variety of vertebrates and invertebrates. The water that surrounds them is critical for their existence, acting as a solvent for biochemical reactions and determining the structures of the macromolecules. [Georgette Douwma/Taxi/Getty Images.]

■ CHAPTER CONTENTS

1 Physical Properties of Water
- **A.** Water Is a Polar Molecule
- **B.** Hydrophilic Substances Dissolve in Water
- **C.** The Hydrophobic Effect Causes Nonpolar Substances to Aggregate in Water
- **D.** Water Moves by Osmosis and Solutes Move by Diffusion

2 Chemical Properties of Water
- **A.** Water Ionizes to Form H^+ and OH^-
- **B.** Acids and Bases Alter the pH
- **C.** Buffers Resist Changes in pH

■ MEDIA RESOURCES

(Available at www.wiley.com/college/voet)
Animated Figure 2-17. Titration curves for acetic acid, phosphate, and ammonia
Animated Figure 2-18. Titration of a polyprotic acid
Case Study 1. Acute Aspirin Overdose: Relationship to the Blood Buffering System

Any study of the chemistry of life must include a study of water. Biological molecules and the reactions they undergo can be best understood in the context of their aqueous environment. Not only are organisms made mostly of water (about 70% of the mass of the human body is water), they are surrounded by water on this, the "blue planet." Aside from its sheer abundance, water is central to biochemistry for the following reasons:

1. Nearly all biological molecules assume their shapes (and therefore their functions) in response to the physical and chemical properties of the surrounding water.

2. The medium for the majority of biochemical reactions is water. Reactants and products of metabolic reactions, nutrients as well as waste products, depend on water for transport within and between cells.

3. Water itself actively participates in many chemical reactions that support life. Frequently, the ionic components of water, the H^+ and OH^- ions, are the true reactants. In fact, the reactivity of many functional groups on biological molecules depends on the relative concentrations of H^+ and OH^- in the surrounding medium.

All organisms require water, from the marine creatures who spend their entire lives in an aqueous environment to terrestrial organisms who must guard their watery interiors with protective skins. Not surprisingly, living organisms can be found wherever there is liquid water—in hydrothermal vents as hot as 121°C and in the cracks and crevices between rocks hundreds of meters beneath the surface of the earth. Organisms that survive desiccation do so only by becoming dormant, as seeds or spores.

An examination of water from a biochemical point of view requires a look at the physical properties of water, its powers as a solvent, and its chemical behavior—that is, the nature of aqueous acids and bases.

1 Physical Properties of Water

The colorless, odorless, and tasteless nature of water belies its fundamental importance to living organisms. Despite its bland appearance to our senses, water is anything but inert. Its physical properties—unique among molecules of similar size—give it unparalleled strength as a solvent. And yet its limitations as a solvent also have important implications for the structures and functions of biological molecules.

A | Water Is a Polar Molecule

A water molecule consists of two hydrogen atoms bonded to an oxygen atom. The O—H bond distance is 0.958 Å (1 Å = 10^{-10} m), and the angle formed by the three atoms is 104.5° (Fig. 2-1). The hydrogen atoms are not arranged linearly, because the oxygen atom's four sp^3 hybrid orbitals extend roughly toward the corners of a tetrahedron. Hydrogen atoms occupy two corners of the tetrahedron, and the nonbonding electron pairs of the oxygen atom occupy the other two corners (in a perfectly tetrahedral molecule, such as methane, CH_4, the bond angles are 109.5°).

Water Molecules Form Hydrogen Bonds. The angular geometry of the water molecule has enormous implications for living systems. Water is a **polar** molecule: the oxygen atom with its unshared electrons carries a partial negative charge ($\delta-$) of $-0.66e$, and the hydrogen atoms each carry a partial positive charge ($\delta+$) of $+0.33e$, where e is the charge of the electron. Electrostatic attractions between the dipoles of water molecules are crucial to the properties of water itself and to its role as a biochemical solvent. Neighboring water molecules tend to orient themselves so that the O—H bond of one water molecule (the positive end) points toward one of the electron pairs of the other water molecule (the negative end). The resulting directional intermolecular association is known as a **hydrogen bond** (Fig. 2-2).

In general, a hydrogen bond can be represented as D—H···A, where D—H is a weakly acidic "donor" group such as O—H, N—H, or sometimes S—H, and A is a weakly basic "acceptor" atom such as O, N, or occasionally S. Hydrogen bonds are structurally characterized by an H···A distance that is at least 0.5 Å shorter than the calculated **van der Waals distance** (the distance of closest approach between two nonbonded atoms). In water, for example, the O···H hydrogen bond distance is ~1.8 Å versus 2.6 Å for the corresponding van der Waals distance.

A single water molecule contains two hydrogen atoms that can be "donated" and two unshared electron pairs that can act as "acceptors," so

LEARNING OBJECTIVES

- Understand that water molecules are polar and form irregular hydrogen-bonded networks in the liquid state.
- Know the noncovalent forces that act on biomolecules.
- Understand why polar and ionic substances dissolve in water.
- Understand that the hydrophobic effect is the tendency for water to exclude nonpolar groups in order to maximize the entropy of water molecules.
- Understand the processes of osmosis and diffusion.

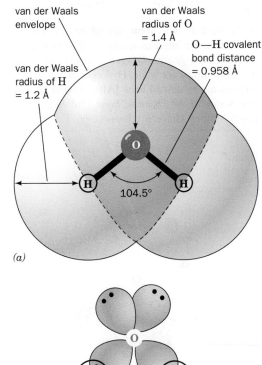

(a)

(b)

■ **Figure 2-1 | Structure of the water molecule.** (*a*) The shaded outline represents the van der Waals envelope, the effective "surface" of the molecule. (*b*) The oxygen atom's sp^3 orbitals are arranged tetrahedrally. Two orbitals contain nonbonding electron pairs (lone pairs).

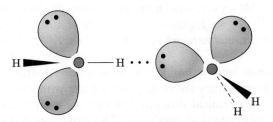

■ **Figure 2-2 | A hydrogen bond in water.** The strength of the interaction is maximal when the O—H covalent bond of one molecule points directly toward the lone-pair electron cloud of the other.

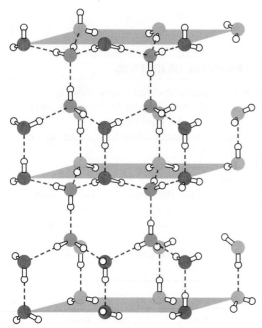

■ **Figure 2-3 | The structure of ice.** Each water molecule interacts tetrahedrally with four other water molecules. Oxygen atoms are red and hydrogen atoms are white. Hydrogen bonds are represented by dashed lines. [After Pauling, L., *The Nature of the Chemical Bond* (3rd ed.), p. 465, Cornell University Press (1960).]

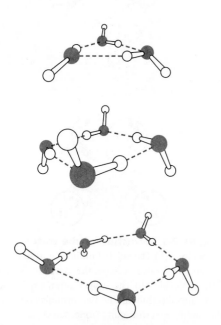

■ **Figure 2-4 | Rings of water molecules.** These models, containing three, four, or five molecules, are based on theoretical predictions and spectroscopic data. [After Liu, K., Cruzan, J.D., and Saykally, R.J., *Science* **271**, 929 (1996).]

each molecule can participate in a maximum of four hydrogen bonds with other water molecules. Although the energy of an individual hydrogen bond (~20 kJ·mol^{-1}) is relatively small (e.g., the energy of an O—H covalent bond is 460 kJ·mol^{-1}), the sheer number of hydrogen bonds in a sample of water is the key to its remarkable properties.

Ice Is a Crystal of Hydrogen-Bonded Water Molecules. The structure of ice provides a striking example of the cumulative strength of many hydrogen bonds. X-Ray and neutron diffraction studies have established that water molecules in ice are arranged in an unusually open structure. Each water molecule is tetrahedrally surrounded by four nearest neighbors to which it is hydrogen bonded (Fig. 2-3). As a consequence of its open structure, water is one of the very few substances that expands on freezing (at 0°C, liquid water has a density of 1.00 g·mL^{-1}, whereas ice has a density of 0.92 g·mL^{-1}).

The expansion of water on freezing has overwhelming consequences for life on the earth. Suppose that water contracted on freezing, that is, became more dense rather than less dense. Ice would then sink to the bottoms of lakes and oceans rather than float. This ice would be insulated from the sun so that oceans, with the exception of a thin surface layer of liquid in warm weather, would be permanently frozen solid (the water at great depths, even in tropical oceans, is close to 4°C, its temperature of maximum density). Thus, the earth would be locked in a permanent ice age and life might never have arisen.

The melting of ice represents the collapse of the strictly tetrahedral orientation of hydrogen-bonded water molecules, although hydrogen bonds between water molecules persist in the liquid state. In fact, liquid water is only ~15% less hydrogen bonded than ice at 0°C. Indeed, the boiling point of water is 264°C higher than that of methane, a substance with nearly the same molecular mass as H$_2$O but which is incapable of hydrogen bonding (substances with similar intermolecular associations and equal molecular masses should have similar boiling points). This difference reflects the extraordinary internal cohesiveness of liquid water resulting from its intermolecular hydrogen bonding.

The Structure of Liquid Water Is Irregular. Because each molecule of liquid water reorients about once every 10^{-12} s, very few experimental techniques can explore the instantaneous arrangement of these water molecules. Theoretical considerations and spectroscopic evidence suggest that molecules in liquid water are each hydrogen bonded to four nearest neighbors, as they are in ice. These hydrogen bonds are distorted, however, so the networks of linked molecules are irregular and varied. For example, three- to seven-membered rings of hydrogen-bonded molecules commonly occur in liquid water (Fig. 2-4), in contrast to the six-membered rings characteristic of ice (Fig. 2-3). Moreover, these networks continually break up and re-form every 2 × 10^{-11} s or so. *Liquid water therefore consists of a rapidly fluctuating, three-dimensional network of hydrogen-bonded H$_2$O molecules.*

Hydrogen Bonds and Other Weak Interactions Influence Biological Molecules. Biochemists are concerned not just with the strong covalent bonds that define chemical structure but with the weak forces that act under relatively mild physical conditions. The structures of most biological molecules are determined by the collective influence of many individually weak interactions. The weak electrostatic forces that interest biochemists include ionic interactions, hydrogen bonds, and van der Waals forces.

Table 2-1 Bond Energies in Biomolecules

Type of Bond	Example	Bond Strength $(kJ \cdot mol^{-1})$
Covalent	O—H	460
	C—H	414
	C—C	348
Noncovalent		
Ionic interaction	$-COO^- \cdots {}^+H_3N-$	86
van der Waals forces		
Hydrogen bond	$-O-H \cdots O\diagdown$	20
Dipole–dipole interaction	$\diagdown C=O \cdots \diagdown C=O$	9.3
London dispersion forces	$\underset{\overset{\|}{H}}{-}\overset{\overset{H}{\|}}{C}-H \cdots H-\overset{\overset{H}{\|}}{\underset{\underset{H}{\|}}{C}}-$	0.3

The strength of association of ionic groups of opposite charge depends on the chemical nature of the ions, the distance between them, and the polarity of the medium. In general, the strength of the interaction between two charged groups (i.e., the energy required to completely separate them in the medium of interest) is less than the energy of a covalent bond but greater than the energy of a hydrogen bond (Table 2-1).

The noncovalent associations between neutral molecules, collectively known as **van der Waals forces,** arise from electrostatic interactions among permanent or induced dipoles (the hydrogen bond is a special kind of dipolar interaction). Interactions among permanent dipoles such as carbonyl groups (Fig. 2-5a) are much weaker than ionic interactions. A permanent dipole also induces a dipole moment in a neighboring group by electrostatically distorting its electron distribution (Fig. 2-5b). Such dipole–induced dipole interactions are generally much weaker than dipole–dipole interactions.

At any instant, nonpolar molecules have a small, randomly oriented dipole moment resulting from the rapid fluctuating motion of their electrons. This transient dipole moment can polarize the electrons in a neighboring group (Fig. 2-5c), so that the groups are attracted to each other. These so-called **London dispersion forces** are extremely weak and fall off so rapidly with distance that they are significant only for groups in close contact. They are, nevertheless, extremely important in determining the structures of biological molecules, whose interiors contain many closely packed groups.

B | Hydrophilic Substances Dissolve in Water

Solubility depends on the ability of a solvent to interact with a solute more strongly than solute particles interact with each other. Water is said to be the "universal solvent." Although this statement cannot literally be true, water certainly dissolves more types of substances and in greater amounts than any other solvent. In particular, the polar character of water makes

(a) Interactions between permanent dipoles

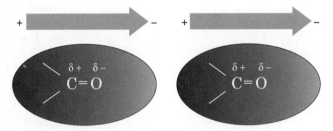

(b) Dipole–induced dipole interactions

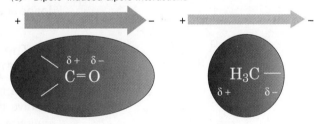

(c) London dispersion forces

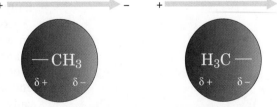

■ **Figure 2-5** | **Dipole–dipole interactions.**
The strength of each dipole is indicated by the thickness of the accompanying arrow.
(a) Interaction between permanent dipoles.
(b) Dipole–induced dipole interaction. (c) London dispersion forces.

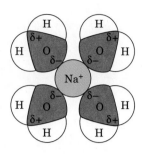

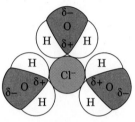

■ **Figure 2-6** | **Solvation of ions.** The dipoles of the surrounding water molecules are oriented according to the charge of the ion. Only one layer of solvent molecules is shown.

(a)

(b)

(c)

(d)

■ **Figure 2-7** | **Hydrogen bonding by functional groups.** Water forms hydrogen bonds with (*a*) hydroxyl groups, (*b*) keto groups, (*c*) carboxylate ions, and (*d*) ammonium ions.

it an excellent solvent for polar and ionic materials, which are said to be **hydrophilic** (Greek: *hydro,* water + *philos,* loving). On the other hand, nonpolar substances are virtually insoluble in water ("oil and water don't mix") and are consequently described as **hydrophobic** (Greek: *phobos,* fear). Nonpolar substances, however, are soluble in nonpolar solvents such as CCl_4 and hexane. This information is summarized by another maxim, "like dissolves like."

Why do salts such as NaCl dissolve in water? Polar solvents, such as water, weaken the attractive forces between oppositely charged ions (such as Na^+ and Cl^-) and can therefore hold the ions apart. (In nonpolar solvents, ions of opposite charge attract each other so strongly that they coalesce to form a solid salt.) An ion immersed in a polar solvent such as water attracts the oppositely charged ends of the solvent dipoles (Fig. 2-6). The ion is thereby surrounded by one or more concentric shells of oriented solvent molecules. Such ions are said to be **solvated** or, when water is the solvent, to be **hydrated.**

The water molecules in the hydration shell around an ion move more slowly than water molecules that are not involved in solvating the ion. In bulk water, the energetic cost of breaking a hydrogen bond is low because another hydrogen bond is likely to be forming at the same time. The cost is higher for the relatively ordered water molecules of the hydration shell. The energetics of solvation also play a role in chemical reactions, since a reacting group must shed its **waters of hydration** (the molecules in its hydration shell) in order to closely approach another group.

The bond dipoles of uncharged polar molecules make them soluble in aqueous solutions for the same reasons that ionic substances are water soluble. The solubilities of polar and ionic substances are enhanced when they carry functional groups, such as hydroxyl (OH), carbonyl (C=O), carboxylate (COO^-), or ammonium (NH_3^+) groups, that can form hydrogen bonds with water as illustrated in Fig. 2-7. Indeed, water-soluble biomolecules such as proteins, nucleic acids, and carbohydrates bristle with just such groups. Nonpolar substances, in contrast, lack hydrogen-bonding donor and acceptor groups.

C | The Hydrophobic Effect Causes Nonpolar Substances to Aggregate in Water

When a nonpolar substance is added to an aqueous solution, it does not dissolve but instead is excluded by the water. *The tendency of water to minimize its contacts with hydrophobic molecules is termed the* **hydrophobic effect.** Many large molecules and molecular aggregates, such as proteins, nucleic acids, and cellular membranes, assume their shapes at least partially in response to the hydrophobic effect.

Consider the thermodynamics of transferring a nonpolar molecule from an aqueous solution to a nonpolar solvent. In all cases, the free energy change is negative, which indicates that such transfers are spontaneous processes (Table 2-2). Interestingly, these transfer processes are either endothermic (positive ΔH) or isothermic ($\Delta H = 0$); that is, it is enthalpically more or less equally favorable for nonpolar molecules to dissolve in water as in nonpolar media. In contrast, the entropy change (expressed as $-T\Delta S$) is large and negative in all cases. Clearly, the transfer of a hydrocarbon from an aqueous medium to a nonpolar medium is entropically driven (i.e., the free energy change is mostly due to an entropy change).

Entropy, or "randomness," is a measure of the order of a system (Section 1-3B). If entropy increases when a nonpolar molecule leaves an aqueous solution, entropy must decrease when the molecule enters water,

Table 2-2	Thermodynamic Changes for Transferring Hydrocarbons from Water to Nonpolar Solvents at 25°C		
Process	ΔH (kJ·mol^{-1})	$-T\Delta S$ (kJ·mol^{-1})	ΔG (kJ·mol^{-1})
CH_4 in $H_2O \rightleftharpoons CH_4$ in C_6H_6	11.7	−22.6	−10.9
CH_4 in $H_2O \rightleftharpoons CH_4$ in CCl_4	10.5	−22.6	−12.1
C_2H_6 in $H_2O \rightleftharpoons C_2H_6$ in benzene	9.2	−25.1	−15.9
C_2H_4 in $H_2O \rightleftharpoons C_2H_4$ in benzene	6.7	−18.8	−12.1
C_2H_2 in $H_2O \rightleftharpoons C_2H_2$ in benzene	0.8	−8.8	−8.0
Benzene in $H_2O \rightleftharpoons$ liquid benzene[a]	0.0	−17.2	−17.2
Toluene in $H_2O \rightleftharpoons$ liquid toluene[a]	0.0	−20.0	−20.0

[a]Data measured at 18°C.
Source: Kauzmann, W., Adv. Protein Chem. **14**, 39 (1959).

This decrease in entropy when a nonpolar molecule is solvated by water is an experimental observation, not a theoretical conclusion. Yet the entropy changes are too large to reflect only the changes in the conformations of the hydrocarbons. Thus the entropy changes must arise mainly from some sort of ordering of the water itself. What is the nature of this ordering?

The extensive hydrogen-bonding network of liquid water molecules is disrupted when a nonpolar group intrudes. A nonpolar group can neither accept nor donate hydrogen bonds, so the water molecules at the surface of the cavity occupied by the nonpolar group cannot hydrogen bond to other molecules in their usual fashion. In order to maximize their hydrogen-bonding ability, these surface water molecules orient themselves to form a hydrogen-bonded network enclosing the cavity (Fig. 2-8). This orientation constitutes an ordering of the water structure since the number of ways that water molecules can form hydrogen bonds around the surface of a nonpolar group is fewer than the number of ways they can form hydrogen bonds in bulk water.

Unfortunately, the ever-fluctuating nature of liquid water's basic structure has not yet allowed a detailed description of this ordering process. One model proposes that water forms icelike hydrogen-bonded "cages" around the nonpolar groups. The water molecules of the cages are tetrahedrally hydrogen bonded to other water molecules, and the ordering of water molecules extends several layers beyond the first hydration shell of the nonpolar solute.

The unfavorable free energy of hydration of a nonpolar substance caused by its ordering of the surrounding water molecules has the net result that the nonpolar substance tends to be excluded from the aqueous phase. This is because the surface area of a cavity containing an aggregate of nonpolar molecules is less than the sum of the surface areas of the cavities that each of these molecules would individually occupy (Fig. 2-9). The

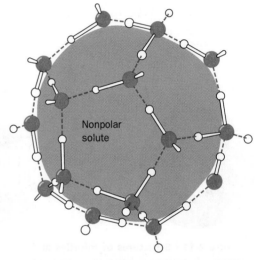

■ **Figure 2-8 | Orientation of water molecules around a nonpolar solute.** In order to maximize their number of hydrogen bonds, water molecules form a "cage" around the solute. Dashed lines represent hydrogen bonds.

■ **Figure 2-9 | Aggregation of nonpolar molecules in water.** (*a*) The individual hydration of dispersed nonpolar molecules (*brown*) decreases the entropy of the system because their hydrating water molecules (*dark blue*) are not as free to form hydrogen bonds. (*b*) Aggregation of the nonpolar molecules increases the entropy of the system, since the number of water molecules required to hydrate the aggregated solutes is less than the number of water molecules required to hydrate the dispersed solute molecules. This increase in entropy accounts for the spontaneous aggregation of nonpolar substances in water.

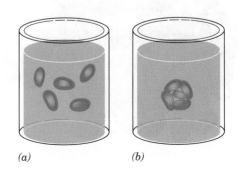

(a)   (b)

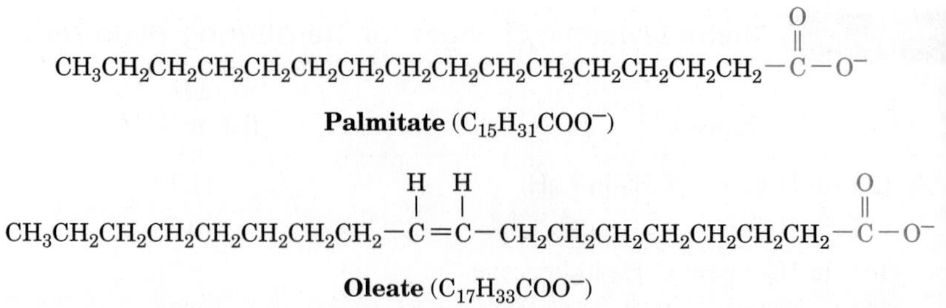

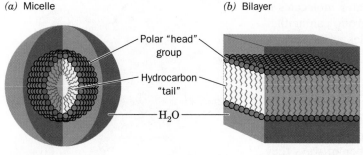

$$CH_3CH_2CH_2CH_2CH_2CH_2CH_2CH_2CH_2CH_2CH_2CH_2CH_2CH_2CH_2 \overset{\overset{\displaystyle O}{\|}}{-C} - O^-$$

Palmitate ($C_{15}H_{31}COO^-$)

$$CH_3CH_2CH_2CH_2CH_2CH_2CH_2CH_2 \overset{\overset{\displaystyle H}{|}}{-C} = \overset{\overset{\displaystyle H}{|}}{C} - CH_2CH_2CH_2CH_2CH_2CH_2CH_2 \overset{\overset{\displaystyle O}{\|}}{-C} - O^-$$

Oleate ($C_{17}H_{33}COO^-$)

■ **Figure 2-10** | **Fatty acid anions (soaps).** Palmitate and oleate are amphiphilic compounds; each has a polar carboxylate group and a long nonpolar hydrocarbon chain.

aggregation of the nonpolar groups thereby minimizes the surface area of the cavity and therefore maximizes the entropy of the entire system. In a sense, the nonpolar groups are squeezed out of the aqueous phase.

Amphiphiles Form Micelles and Bilayers. *Most biological molecules have both polar (or charged) and nonpolar segments and are therefore simultaneously hydrophilic and hydrophobic.* Such molecules, for example fatty acid ions (soaps; Fig. 2-10), are said to be **amphiphilic** or **amphipathic** (Greek: *amphi*, both; *pathos*, suffering). How do amphiphiles interact with an aqueous solvent? Water tends to hydrate the hydrophilic portion of an amphiphile, but it also tends to exclude the hydrophobic portion. Amphiphiles consequently tend to form structurally ordered aggregates. For example, **micelles** are globules of up to several thousand amphiphilic molecules arranged so that the hydrophilic groups at the globule surface can interact with the aqueous solvent while the hydrophobic groups associate at the center, away from the solvent (Fig. 2-11a). Of course, the model presented in Fig. 2-11a is an oversimplification, since it is geometrically impossible for all the hydrophobic groups to occupy the center of the micelle. Instead, the amphipathic molecules pack in a more disorganized fashion that buries most of the hydrophobic groups and leaves the polar groups exposed (Fig. 2-12).

Alternatively, amphiphilic molecules may arrange themselves to form **bilayered** sheets or vesicles in which the polar groups face the aqueous phase (Fig. 2-11b). In both micelles and bilayers, the aggregate is stabilized by the hydrophobic effect, the tendency of water to exclude hydrophobic groups.

The consequences of the hydrophobic effect are often called hydrophobic forces or hydrophobic "bonds." However, the term *bond* implies a dis-

(a) Micelle   *(b)* Bilayer

Polar "head" group

Hydrocarbon "tail"

H_2O

■ **Figure 2-11** | **Structures of micelles and bilayers.** In aqueous solution, the polar head groups of amphipathic molecules are hydrated while the nonpolar tails aggregate by exclusion from water. *(a)* A micelle is a spheroidal aggregate. *(b)* A bilayer is an extended planar aggregate.

■ **Figure 2-12** | **Model of a micelle.** Twenty molecules of octyl glucoside (an eight-carbon chain with a sugar head group) are shown in space-filling form in this computer-generated model. The polar O atoms of the glucoside groups are red and C atoms are gray. H atoms have been omitted for clarity. Computer simulations indicate that such micelles have an irregular, rapidly fluctuating structure (unlike the symmetric aggregate pictured in Fig. 2-11a) such that portions of the hydrophobic tails are exposed on the micelle surface at any given instant. [Courtesy of Michael Garavito and Shelagh Ferguson-Miller, Michigan State University.]

crete directional relationship between two entities. The hydrophobic effect acts indirectly on nonpolar groups and lacks directionality. Despite the temptation to attribute some mutual attraction to a collection of nonpolar groups excluded from water, their exclusion is largely a function of the entropy of the surrounding water molecules, not some "hydrophobic force" among them (the London dispersion forces between the nonpolar groups are relatively weak).

D | Water Moves by Osmosis and Solutes Move by Diffusion

The fluid inside cells and surrounding cells in multicellular organisms is full of dissolved substances ranging from small inorganic ions to huge molecular aggregates. The concentrations of these solutes affect water's **colligative properties,** the physical properties that depend on the concentration of dissolved substances rather than on their chemical features. For example, solutes depress the freezing point and elevate the boiling point of water by making it more difficult for water molecules to crystallize as ice or to escape from solution into the gas phase.

Osmotic pressure also depends on the solute concentration. When a solution is separated from pure water by a semipermeable membrane that permits the passage of water molecules but not solutes, water tends to move into the solution in order to equalize its concentration on both sides of the membrane. **Osmosis** is the movement of solvent from a region of high concentration (here, pure water) to a region of relatively low concentration (water containing dissolved solute). The **osmotic pressure** of a solution is the pressure that must be applied to the solution to prevent the inward flow of water; it is proportional to the concentration of the solute (Fig. 2-13). For a 1 M solution, the osmotic pressure is 22.4 atm. Consider the implications of osmotic pressure for living cells, which are essentially semipermeable sacs of aqueous solution. In order to minimize osmotic influx of water, which would burst the relatively weak cell membrane, many animal cells are surrounded by a solution of similar osmotic pressure (so there is no net flow of water). Another strategy, used by most plants and bacteria, is to enclose the cell with a rigid cell wall that can withstand the osmotic pressure generated within.

When an aqueous solution is separated from pure water by a membrane that is permeable to both water and solutes, solutes move out of the solution even as water moves in. The molecules move randomly, or **diffuse,** until the concentration of the solute is the same on both sides of the membrane. At this point, equilibrium is established; that is, there is no further *net* flow of water or solute (although molecules continue to move in and

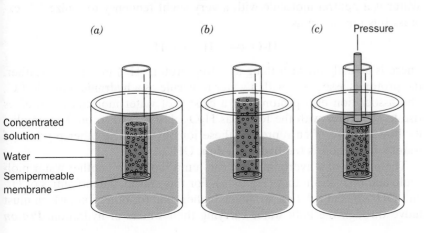

(a)   (b)   (c)   Pressure

Concentrated solution

Water

Semipermeable membrane

■ **Figure 2-13** | **Osmotic pressure.** (*a*) A water-permeable membrane separates a tube of concentrated solution from pure water. (*b*) As water moves into the solution by osmosis, the height of the solution in the tube increases. (*c*) The pressure that prevents the influx of water is the osmotic pressure (22.4 atm for a 1 M solution).

■ **Figure 2-14** | **Dialysis.** (*a*) A concentrated solution is separated from a large volume of solvent by a dialysis membrane (shown here as a tube knotted at both ends). Only small molecules can diffuse through the pores in the membrane. (*b*) At equilibrium, the concentrations of small molecules are nearly the same on either side of the membrane, whereas the macromolecules remain inside the dialysis bag.

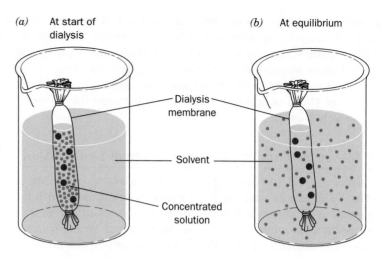

(*a*) At start of dialysis (*b*) At equilibrium

Dialysis membrane

Solvent

Concentrated solution

■ **CHECK YOUR UNDERSTANDING**

Compare hydrogen bonding in ice and in liquid water.

Describe the nature and relative strength of covalent bonds, ionic interactions, and van der Waals interactions (hydrogen bonds, dipole–dipole interactions, and London dispersion forces).

Explain why polar substances dissolve in water while nonpolar substances do not.

What is the role of entropy in the hydrophobic effect?

Explain why amphiphiles form micelles in water.

How does osmosis differ from diffusion? Which process occurs during dialysis?

LEARNING OBJECTIVES

■ Understand that water ionizes to form hydronium ions and hydroxide ions.
■ Understand that an acid can donate a proton and a base can accept a proton.
■ Understand how acids and bases affect the pH of a solution.
■ Understand the relationship between pH and pK for a solution of weak acid.
■ Understand how a buffer works.

out through the membrane). Note that the tendency for solutes to diffuse from an area of high concentration to an area of low concentration (i.e., down a concentration gradient) is thermodynamically favored because it is accompanied by an increase in entropy.

Diffusion of solutes is the basis for the laboratory technique of **dialysis.** In this process, solutes smaller than the pore size of the dialysis membrane freely exchange between the sample and the bulk solution until equilibrium is reached (Fig. 2-14). Larger substances cannot cross the membrane and remain where they are. Dialysis is particularly useful for separating large molecules, such as proteins or nucleic acids, from smaller molecules. Because small solutes (and water) move freely between the sample and the surrounding medium, dialysis can be repeated several times to replace the sample medium with another solution.

2 | Chemical Properties of Water

Water is not just a passive component of the cell or extracellular environment. By virtue of its physical properties, water defines the solubilities of other substances. Similarly, water's chemical properties determine the behavior of other molecules in solution.

A | Water Ionizes to Form H⁺ and OH⁻

Water is a neutral molecule with a very slight tendency to ionize. We express this ionization as

$$H_2O \rightleftharpoons H^+ + OH^-$$

There is actually no such thing as a free proton (H^+) in solution. Rather, the proton is associated with a water molecule as a **hydronium ion,** H_3O^+. The association of a proton with a cluster of water molecules also gives rise to structures with the formulas $H_5O_2^+$, $H_7O_3^+$, and so on. For simplicity, however, we often represent these ions by H^+. The other product of water's ionization is the **hydroxide ion,** OH^-.

The proton of a hydronium ion can jump rapidly to another water molecule and then to another (Fig. 2-15). For this reason, the mobilities of H^+ and OH^- ions in solution are much higher than for other ions, which must move through the bulk water carrying their waters of hydration. ***Proton*** *jumping* is also responsible for the observation that acid–base reactions are among the fastest reactions that take place in aqueous solution.

The ionization (dissociation) of water is described by an equilibrium expression in which the concentration of the parent substance is in the denominator and the concentrations of the dissociated products are in the numerator:

$$K = \frac{[H^+][OH^-]}{[H_2O]} \qquad [2\text{-}1]$$

K is the **dissociation constant** (here and throughout the text, quantities in square brackets symbolize the molar concentrations of the indicated substances, which in many cases are only negligibly different from their activities; Section 1-3D). Because the concentration of the undissociated H_2O ($[H_2O]$) is so much larger than the concentrations of its component ions, it can be considered constant and incorporated into K to yield an expression for the ionization of water,

$$K_w = [H^+][OH^-] \qquad [2\text{-}2]$$

The value of K_w, the ionization constant of water, is 10^{-14} at 25°C.

Pure water must contain equimolar amounts of H^+ and OH^-, so $[H^+] = [OH^-] = (K_w)^{1/2} = 10^{-7}$ M. Since $[H^+]$ and $[OH^-]$ are reciprocally related by Eq. 2-2, when $[H^+]$ is greater than 10^{-7} M, $[OH^-]$ must be correspondingly less and vice versa. Solutions with $[H^+] = 10^{-7}$ M are said to be **neutral**, those with $[H^+] > 10^{-7}$ M are said to be **acidic**, and those with $[H^+] < 10^{-7}$ M are said to be **basic**. Most physiological solutions have hydrogen ion concentrations near neutrality. For example, human blood is normally slightly basic with $[H^+] = 4.0 \times 10^{-8}$ M.

The values of $[H^+]$ for most solutions are inconveniently small and thus impractical to compare. A more practical quantity, which was devised in 1909 by Søren Sørenson, is known as the **pH:**

$$pH = -\log[H^+] = \log\frac{1}{[H^+]} \qquad [2\text{-}3]$$

The higher the pH, the lower is the H^+ concentration; the lower the pH, the higher is the H^+ concentration (Fig. 2-16). The pH of pure water is

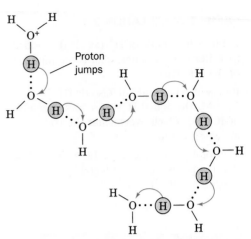

■ Figure 2-15 | Proton jumping. Proton jumps occur more rapidly than direct molecular migration, accounting for the observed high ionic mobilities of hydronium ions (and hydroxide ions) in aqueous solutions.

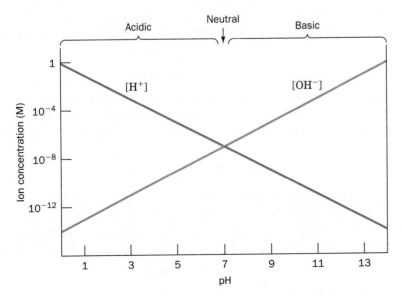

■ Figure 2-16 | Relationship of pH and the concentrations of H^+ and OH^- in water. Because the product of $[H^+]$ and $[OH^-]$ is a constant (10^{-14}), $[H^+]$ and $[OH^-]$ are reciprocally related. Solutions with relatively more H^+ are acidic (pH < 7), solutions with relatively more OH^- are basic (pH > 7), and solutions in which $[H^+] = [OH^-] = 10^{-7}$ M are neutral (pH = 7). Note the logarithmic scale for ion concentration.

SAMPLE CALCULATION 2-1

If 1.0×10^{-4} mole of H^+ (as HCl) is added to 1 liter of pure water, what is the final pH of the solution?

Pure water has a pH of 7, so its $[H^+] = 10^{-7}$ M. The added H^+ has a concentration of 10^{-4} M, which overwhelms the $[H^+]$ already present.

The total $[H^+]$ is therefore 1.0×10^{-4} M, so that the pH is equal to $-\log[H^+] = -\log(1.0 \times 10^{-4}) = 4$.

Table 2-3	pH Values of Some Common Substances	

Substance	pH
1 M NaOH	14
Household ammonia	12
Seawater	8
Blood	7.4
Milk	7
Saliva	6.6
Tomato juice	4.4
Vinegar	3
Gastric juice	1.5
1 M HCl	0

7.0, whereas acidic solutions have pH < 7.0 and basic solutions have pH > 7.0 (see Sample Calculation 2-1). Note that solutions that differ by one pH unit differ in $[H^+]$ by a factor of 10. The pH values of some common substances are given in Table 2-3.

B | Acids and Bases Alter the pH

H^+ and OH^- ions derived from water are fundamental to the biochemical reactions we shall encounter later in this book. Biological molecules, such as proteins and nucleic acids, have numerous functional groups that act as acids or bases, for example, carboxyl and amino groups. These molecules influence the pH of the surrounding aqueous medium, and their structures and reactivities are in turn influenced by the ambient pH. An appreciation of acid–base chemistry is therefore essential for understanding the biological roles of many molecules.

An Acid Can Donate a Proton. According to a definition formulated in 1923 by Johannes Brønsted and Thomas Lowry, *an **acid** is a substance that can donate a proton, and a **base** is a substance that can accept a proton.* Under the Brønsted–Lowry definition, an acid–base reaction can be written as

$$HA + H_2O \rightleftharpoons H_3O^+ + A^-$$

An acid (HA) reacts with a base (H_2O) to form the **conjugate base** of the acid (A^-) and the **conjugate acid** of the base (H_3O^+). Accordingly, the acetate ion (CH_3COO^-) is the conjugate base of acetic acid (CH_3COOH), and the ammonium ion (NH_4^+) is the conjugate acid of ammonia (NH_3). The acid–base reaction is frequently abbreviated

$$HA \rightleftharpoons H^+ + A^-$$

with the participation of H_2O implied. An alternative expression for a basic substance B is

$$HB^+ \rightleftharpoons H^+ + B$$

The Strength of an Acid Is Specified by Its Dissociation Constant. The equilibrium constant for an acid–base reaction is expressed as a dissociation constant with the concentrations of the "reactants" in the denominator and the concentrations of the "products" in the numerator:

$$K = \frac{[H_3O^+][A^-]}{[HA][H_2O]} \qquad [2\text{-}4]$$

In dilute solutions, the water concentration is essentially constant, 55.5 M ($1000 \text{ g} \cdot \text{L}^{-1}/18.015 \text{ g} \cdot \text{mol}^{-1} = 55.5$ M). Therefore, the term $[H_2O]$ is customarily combined with the dissociation constant, which then takes the form

$$K_a = K[H_2O] = \frac{[H^+][A^-]}{[HA]} \qquad [2\text{-}5]$$

For brevity, however, we shall henceforth omit the subscript "*a*."

The dissociation constants of some common acids are listed in Table 2-4. Because acid dissociation constants, like $[H^+]$ values, are sometimes cumbersome to work with, they are transformed to **pK** values by the formula

$$pK = -\log K \qquad [2\text{-}6]$$

which is analogous to Eq. 2-3.

Table 2-4	Dissociation Constants and pK Values at 25°C of Some Acids		

Acid	K	pK
Oxalic acid	5.37×10^{-2}	1.27 (pK_1)
H_3PO_4	7.08×10^{-3}	2.15 (pK_1)
Formic acid	1.78×10^{-4}	3.75
Succinic acid	6.17×10^{-5}	4.21 (pK_1)
Oxalate$^-$	5.37×10^{-5}	4.27 (pK_2)
Acetic acid	1.74×10^{-5}	4.76
Succinate$^-$	2.29×10^{-6}	5.64 (pK_2)
2-(N-Morpholino)ethanesulfonic acid (MES)	8.13×10^{-7}	6.09
H_2CO_3	4.47×10^{-7}	6.35 (pK_1)^a
Piperazine-N,N'-bis(2-ethanesulfonic acid) (PIPES)	1.74×10^{-7}	6.76
$H_2PO_4^-$	1.51×10^{-7}	6.82 (pK_2)
3-(N-Morpholino)propanesulfonic acid (MOPS)	7.08×10^{-8}	7.15
N-2-Hydroxyethylpiperazine-N'-2-ethanesulfonic acid (HEPES)	3.39×10^{-8}	7.47
Tris(hydroxymethyl)aminomethane (Tris)	8.32×10^{-9}	8.08
NH_4^+	5.62×10^{-10}	9.25
Glycine (amino group)	1.66×10^{-10}	9.78
HCO_3^-	4.68×10^{-11}	10.33 (pK_2)
Piperidine	7.58×10^{-12}	11.12
HPO_4^{2-}	4.17×10^{-13}	12.38 (pK_3)

The pK for the overall reaction $CO_2 + H_2O \rightleftharpoons H_2CO_3 \rightleftharpoons H^+ + HCO_3^-$; see Box 2-1.
Source: Dawson, R.M.C., Elliott, D.C., Elliott, W.H., and Jones, K.M., *Data for Biochemical Research* (3rd ed.), pp. 424–425, Oxford Science Publications (1986); *and* Good, N.E., Winget, G.D., Winter, W., Connolly, T.N., Izawa, S., and Singh, R.M.M., *Biochemistry* **5,** 467 (1966).

Acids can be classified according to their relative strengths, that is, their abilities to transfer a proton to water. The acids listed in Table 2-4 are known as **weak acids** because they are only partially ionized in aqueous solution ($K < 1$). Many of the so-called mineral acids, such as $HClO_4$, HNO_3, and HCl, are **strong acids** ($K \gg 1$). Since strong acids rapidly transfer all their protons to H_2O, *the strongest acid that can stably exist in aqueous solutions is H_3O^+.* Likewise, *there can be no stronger base in aqueous solutions than OH^-.* Virtually all the acid–base reactions that occur in biological systems involve H_3O^+ (and OH^-) and weak acids (and their conjugate bases).

The pH of a Solution Is Determined by the Relative Concentrations of Acids and Bases. The relationship between the pH of a solution and the concentrations of an acid and its conjugate base is easily derived. Equation 2-5 can be rearranged to

$$[H^+] = K\frac{[HA]}{[A^-]} \qquad [2\text{-}7]$$

Taking the negative log of each term (and letting pH $= -\log[H^+]$; Eq. 2-3) gives

$$pH = -\log K + \log\frac{[A^-]}{[HA]} \qquad [2\text{-}8]$$

SAMPLE CALCULATION 2-2

Calculate the pH of a 2 L solution containing 10 mL of 5 M acetic acid and 10 mL of 1 M sodium acetate.

First, calculate the concentrations of the acid and conjugate base, expressing all concentrations in units of moles per liter.

Acetic acid: (0.010 L)(5 M)/(2 L)
= 0.025 M

Sodium acetate: (0.010 L)(1 M)/(2 L)
= 0.005 M

Substitute the concentrations of the acid and conjugate base into the Henderson–Hasselbalch equation. Find the pK for acetic acid in Table 2-4.

pH = pK + log([acetate]/[acetic acid])

pH = 4.76 + log(0.005/0.025)

pH = 4.76 − 0.70

pH = 4.06

Substituting pK for −log K (Eq. 2-6) yields

$$pH = pK + \log\frac{[A^-]}{[HA]}$$ [2-9]

This relationship is known as the **Henderson–Hasselbalch equation.** *When the molar concentrations of an acid (HA) and its conjugate base (A⁻) are equal, log([A⁻]/[HA]) = log 1 = 0, and the pH of the solution is numerically equivalent to the pK of the acid.* The Henderson–Hasselbalch equation is invaluable for calculating, for example, the pH of a solution containing a known quantity of a weak acid and its conjugate base (see Sample Calculation 2-2). However, since the Henderson–Hasselbalch equation does not account for the ionization of water itself, it is not useful for calculating the pH of solutions of strong acids or bases. For example, in a 1 M solution of a strong acid, $[H^+]$ = 1 M and the pH is 0. In a 1 M solution of a strong base, $[OH^-]$ = 1 M, so $[H^+] = K_w/[OH^-] = 1 \times 10^{-14}$ M and the pH is 14.

C | Buffers Resist Changes in pH

Adding a 0.01-mL droplet of 1 M HCl to 1 L of pure water changes the pH of the water from 7 to 5, which represents a 100-fold increase in $[H^+]$. Such a huge change in pH would be intolerable to most biological systems, since even small changes in pH can dramatically affect the structures and functions of biological molecules. Maintaining a relatively constant pH is therefore of paramount importance for living systems. To understand how this is possible, consider the titration of a weak acid with a strong base.

Figure 2-17 shows how the pH values of solutions of acetic acid, $H_2PO_4^-$, and ammonium ion (NH_4^+) vary as OH^- is added. **Titration curves** such as these can be constructed from experimental observation or by using the Henderson–Hasselbalch equation to calculate points along the curve (see Sample Calculation 2-3). When OH^- reacts with HA, the products are A^- and water:

$$HA + OH^- \rightleftharpoons A^- + H_2O$$

Several details about the titration curves in Fig. 2-17 should be noted:

1. The curves have similar shapes but are shifted vertically along the pH axis.
2. The pH at the midpoint of each titration is numerically equivalent to the pK of its corresponding acid; at this point, [HA] = [A⁻].

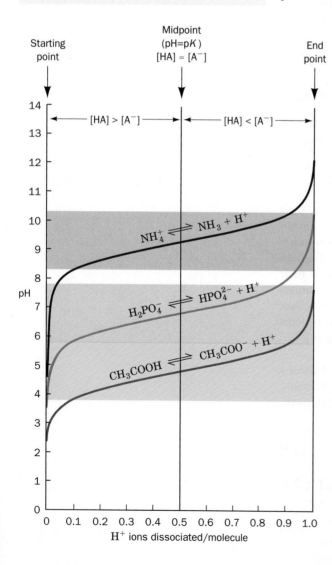

■ **Figure 2-17** | **Titration curves for acetic acid, phosphate, and ammonia.** At the starting point, the acid form predominates. As strong base (e.g., NaOH) is added, the acid is converted to its conjugate base. At the midpoint of the titration, where pH = pK, the concentrations of the acid and the conjugate base are equal. At the end point (equivalence point), the conjugate base predominates, and the total amount of OH^- that has been added is equivalent to the amount of acid that was present at the starting point. The shaded bands indicate the pH ranges over which the corresponding solution can function as a buffer. 🔁 **See the Animated Figures.**

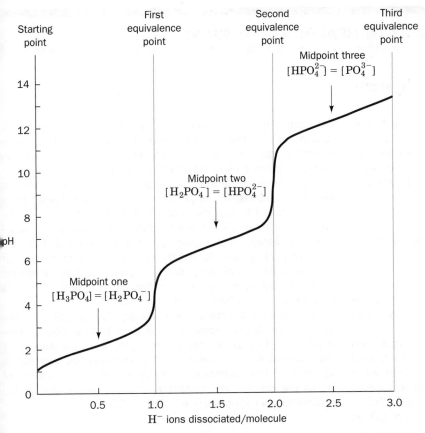

■ **Figure 2-18 | Titration of a polyprotic acid.** The first and second equivalence points for titration of H_3PO_4 occur at the steepest parts of the curve. The pH at the midpoint of each stage provides the pK value of the corresponding ionization.
🔁 **See the Animated Figures.**

3. The slope of each titration curve is much lower near its midpoint than near its wings. This indicates that *when [HA] ≈ [A⁻], the pH of the solution is relatively insensitive to the addition of strong base or strong acid.* Such a solution, which is known as an acid–base **buffer,** resists pH changes because small amounts of added H^+ or OH^- react with A^- or HA, respectively, without greatly changing the value of $\log([A^-]/[HA])$.

Substances that can lose more than one proton, or undergo more than one ionization, such as H_3PO_4 or H_2CO_3, are known as **polyprotic acids.** The titration curves of such molecules, as illustrated in Fig. 2-18 for H_3PO_4, are more complicated than the titration curves of monoprotic acids such as acetic acid. A polyprotic acid has multiple pK values, one for each ionization step. H_3PO_4, for example, has three dissociation constants because the ionic charge resulting from one proton dissociation electrostatically inhibits further proton dissociation, thereby increasing the values of the corresponding pK values. Similarly, a molecule with more than one ionizable group has a discrete pK value for each group. In a biomolecule that contains numerous ionizable groups with different pK values, the many dissociation events may yield a titration curve without any clear "plateaus."

Biological fluids, both intracellular and extracellular, are heavily buffered. For example, the pH of the blood in healthy individuals is closely

SAMPLE CALCULATION 2-3

Calculate the pH of a 1 L solution containing 0.1 M formic acid and 0.1 M sodium formate before and after the addition of 1 mL of 5 M NaOH. How much would the pH change if the NaOH were added to 1 L of pure water?

According to Table 2-4, the pK for formic acid is 3.75. Since [formate] = [formic acid], the $\log([A^-]/[HA])$ term of the Henderson–Hasselbalch equation is 0 and pH = pK = 3.75. The addition of 1 mL of NaOH does not significantly change the volume of the solution, so the [NaOH] is (0.001 L)(5 M)/(1 L) = 0.005 M.

Since NaOH is a strong base, it completely dissociates, and $[OH^-] = [NaOH] = 0.005$ M. This OH^- reacts with formic acid to produce formate and H_2O. Consequently, the concentration of formic acid decreases and the concentration of formate increases by 0.005 M.

The new formic acid concentration is 0.1 M − 0.005 M = 0.095 M, and the new formate concentration is 0.1 M + 0.005 M = 0.105 M. Substituting these values into the Henderson–Hasselbalch equation gives

$$pH = pK + \log([\text{formate}]/[\text{formic acid}])$$

$$pH = 3.75 + \log(0.105/0.095)$$

$$pH = 3.75 + 0.04$$

$$pH = 3.79$$

In the absence of the formic acid buffering system, the $[H^+]$ and therefore the pH can be calculated directly from K_w. Since $K_w = [H^+][OH^-] = 10^{-14}$,

$$[H^+] = \frac{10^{-14}}{[OH^-]} = \frac{10^{-14}}{(0.005)} = 2 \times 10^{-12} \text{ M}$$

$$pH = -\log[H^+] = -\log(2 \times 10^{-12}) = 11.7$$

BOX 2-1 BIOCHEMISTRY IN HEALTH AND DISEASE

The Blood Buffering System

Bicarbonate is the most significant buffer compound in human blood; other buffering agents, including proteins and organic acids, are present at much lower concentrations. The buffering capacity of blood depends primarily on two equilibria: (1) between gaseous CO_2 dissolved in the blood and carbonic acid formed by the reaction

$$CO_2 + H_2O \rightleftharpoons H_2CO_3$$

and (2) between carbonic acid and bicarbonate formed by the dissociation of H^+:

$$H_2CO_3 \rightleftharpoons H^+ + HCO_3^-$$

The overall pK for these two sequential reactions is 6.35. (The further dissociation of HCO_3^- to CO_3^{2-}, pK = 10.33, is not significant at physiological pH.)

When the pH of the blood falls due to metabolic production of H^+, the bicarbonate–carbonic acid equilibrium shifts toward more carbonic acid. At the same time, carbonic acid loses water to become CO_2, which is then expired in the lungs as gaseous CO_2. Conversely, when the blood pH rises, relatively more HCO_3^- forms. Breathing is adjusted so that increased amounts of CO_2 in

the lungs can be reintroduced into the blood for conversion to carbonic acid. In this manner, a near-constant hydrogen ion concentration can be maintained. The kidneys also play a role in acid–base balance by excreting HCO_3^- and NH_4^+.

Disturbances in the blood buffer system can lead to conditions known as **acidosis,** with a pH as low as 7.1, or **alkalosis,** with a pH as high as 7.6. (Deviations of less than 0.05 pH unit from the "normal" value of 7.4 are not significant.) For example, obstructive lung diseases that prevent efficient expiration of CO_2 can cause respiratory acidosis. Hyperventilatin accelerates the loss of CO_2 and causes respiratory alkalosis. Overproduction of organic acids from dietary precursors or sudden surges in lactic acid levels during exercise can lead to metabolic acidosis.

Acid–base imbalances are best alleviated by correcting the underlying physiological problem. In the short term, acidosis is commonly treated by administering $NaHCO_3$ intravenously. Alkalosis is more difficult to treat. Metabolic alkalosis sometimes responds to KCl or NaCl (the additional Cl^- helps minimize the secretion of H^+ by the kidneys), and respiratory alkalosis can be ameliorated by breathing an atmosphere enriched in CO_2.

controlled at pH 7.4 (see Box 2-1). The phosphate and bicarbonate ions in most biological fluids are important buffering agents because they have pKs in this range (Table 2-4). Moreover, many biological molecules, such as proteins and some lipids, as well as numerous small organic molecules, bear multiple acid–base groups that are effective buffer components in the physiological pH range.

The concept that the properties of biological molecules vary with the acidity of the solution in which they are dissolved was not fully appreciated before the twentieth century. Many early biochemical experiments were undertaken without controlling the acidity of the sample, so the results were often poorly reproducible. Nowadays, biochemical preparations are routinely buffered to simulate the properties of naturally occurring biological fluids. A number of synthetic compounds have been developed for use as buffers; some of these are included in Table 2-4. The **buffering capacity** of these weak acids (their ability to resist pH changes on addition of acid or base) is maximal when pH = pK. It is helpful to remember that a weak acid is in its useful buffer range within one pH unit of its pK (e.g., the shaded regions of Fig. 2-17). Above this range, where the ratio $[A^-]/[HA] > 10$, the pH of the solution changes rapidly with added strong base. A buffer is similarly impotent with the addition of strong acid when its pK exceeds the pH by more than one unit.

In the laboratory, the desired pH of the buffered solution determines which buffering compound is selected. Typically, the acid form of the compound and one of its soluble salts are dissolved in the (nearly equal) molar ratio necessary to provide the desired pH and, with the aid of a pH meter, the resulting solution is fine-tuned by titration with strong acid or base.

■ CHECK YOUR UNDERSTANDING

What are the products of water's ionization? How are these related by K_w?

Describe how to calculate pH from the concentration of H^+ or OH^-.

Define *acid* and *base*. What is the relationship between the strength of an acid and its pK value?

List some uses for the Henderson–Hasselbalch equation.

Be able to sketch a titration curve, and label its parts, for a monoprotic and a polyprotic acid.

What are the properties of useful buffer?

SUMMARY

1. Water is essential for all living organisms.

2. Water molecules can form hydrogen bonds with other molecules because they have two H atoms that can be donated and two unshared electron pairs that can act as acceptors.

3. Liquid water is an irregular network of water molecules that each form up to four hydrogen bonds with neighboring water molecules.

4. Hydrophilic substances such as ions and polar molecules dissolve readily in water.

5. The hydrophobic effect is the tendency of water to minimize its contacts with nonpolar substances.

6. Water molecules move from regions of high concentration to regions of low concentration by osmosis; solutes move from regions of high concentration to regions of low concentration by diffusion.

7. Water ionizes to H^+ (which represents the hydronium ion, H_3O^+) and OH^-.

8. The concentration of H^+ in solutions is expressed as a pH value; in acidic solutions pH < 7, in basic solutions pH > 7, and in neutral solutions pH = 7.

9. Acids can donate protons and bases can accept protons. The strength of an acid is expressed as its pK.

10. The Henderson–Hasselbalch equation relates the pH of a solution to the pK and concentrations of an acid and its conjugate base.

11. Buffered solutions resist changes in pH within about one pH unit of the pK of the buffering species.

KEY TERMS

polar **23**
hydrogen bond **23**
van der Waals distance **23**
van der Waals forces **25**
London dispersion forces **25**
hydrophilic **26**
hydrophobic **26**
solvation **26**
hydration **26**
waters of hydration **26**
hydrophobic effect **26**

amphiphilic **28**
amphipathic **28**
micelle **28**
bilayer **28**
colligative properties **29**
osmosis **29**
osmotic pressure **29**
diffusion **29**
dialysis **30**
hydronium ion **30**
hydroxide ion **30**

proton jumping **30**
dissociation constant **31**
K_w **31**
neutral solution **31**
acidic solution **31**
basic solution **31**
pH **31**
acid **32**
base **32**
conjugate base **32**
conjugate acid **32**

pK **32**
weak acid **33**
strong acid **33**
Henderson–Hasselbalch
  equation **34**
titration curve **34**
buffer **35**
polyprotic acid **35**
acidosis **36**
alkalosis **36**
buffering capacity **36**

PROBLEMS

1. Identify the potential hydrogen bond donors and acceptors in the following molecules:

   (a)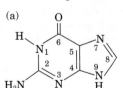

   (b)

   (c) COO^- $H-\overset{\displaystyle|}{\underset{\displaystyle NH_3^+}{C}}-CH_2-OH$

   (c) $H_2N-\overset{\displaystyle O}{\overset{\displaystyle \|}{C}}-NH_2$

   (d) $H_3C-CH_2-CH_3$

   (e) $H_3C-CH_2-\overset{\displaystyle O}{\overset{\displaystyle \|}{CH}}$

2. Occasionally, a C—H group can form a hydrogen bond. Why would such a group be more likely to be a hydrogen bond donor group when the C is next to N?

3. Rank the water solubility of the following compounds:

   (a) $H_3C-CH_2-O-CH_3$

   (b) $H_3C-\overset{\displaystyle O}{\overset{\displaystyle \|}{C}}-NH_2$

4. Where would the following substances partition in water containing palmitic acid micelles? (a) $^+H_3N-CH_2-COO^-$, (b) $^+H_3N-(CH_2)_{11}-COO^-$, (c) $H_3C-(CH_2)_{11}-COO^-$

5. Explain why water forms nearly spherical droplets on the surface of a freshly waxed car. Why doesn't water bead on a clean windshield?

6. Describe what happens when a dialysis bag containing pure water is suspended in a beaker of seawater. What would happen if the dialysis membrane were permeable to water but not solutes?

7. Draw the structures of the conjugate bases of the following acids:

(a)
$$
\begin{array}{c}
COO^- \\
| \\
CH \\
\| \\
HC \\
| \\
COOH
\end{array}
$$

(b)
$$
\begin{array}{c}
COOH \\
| \\
H-C-H \\
| \\
NH_3^+
\end{array}
$$

(c)
$$
\begin{array}{c}
COO^- \\
| \\
H-C-H \\
| \\
NH_3^+
\end{array}
$$

(d)
$$
\begin{array}{c}
COO^- \\
| \\
H-C-CH_2-COOH \\
| \\
NH_3^+
\end{array}
$$

8. Indicate the ionic species that predominates at pH 4, 8, and 11 for (a) ammonia and (b) phosphoric acid.

9. Calculate the pH of a 200 mL solution of pure water to which has been added 50 mL of 1 mM HCl.

10. Calculate the pH of a 1 L solution containing (a) 10 mL of 5 M NaOH, (b) 10 mL of 100 mM glycine and 20 mL of 5 M HCl, and (c) 10 mL of 2 M acetic acid and 5 g of sodium acetate (formula weight 82 g · mol^{-1}).

11. Calculate the standard free energy change for the dissociation of HEPES.

12. A solution is made by mixing 50 mL of 2.0 M K$_2$HPO$_4$ and 25 mL of 2.0 M KH$_2$PO$_4$. The solution is diluted to a final volume of 200 mL. What is the pH of the final solution?

13. What is the pK of the weak acid HA if a solution containing 0.1 M HA and 0.2 M A$^-$ has a pH of 6.5?

14. How many grams of sodium succinate (formula weight 140 g · mol^{-1}) and disodium succinate (formula weight 162 g · mol^{-1}) must be added to 1 L of water to produce a solution with pH 6.0 and a total solute concentration of 50 mM?

15. Estimate the volume of a solution of 5 M NaOH that must be added to adjust the pH from 4 to 9 in 100 mL of a 100 mM solution of phosphoric acid.

16. (a) Would phosphoric acid or succinic acid be a better buffer at pH 5? (b) Would ammonia or piperidine be a better buffer at pH 9? (c) Would HEPES or Tris be a better buffer a pH 7.5?

17. You need a buffer at pH 7.5 for use in purifying a protein a 4°C. You have chosen Tris, pK 8.08, $\Delta H° = 50$ kJ · mol^{-1}. You carefully make up 0.01 M Tris buffer, pH 7.5 at 25°C, and store it in the cold box to equilibrate it to the temperature of the purification. When you measure the pH of the temperature-equilibrated buffer it has increased to 8.1. What is the explanation for this increase? How can you avoid this problem?

18. Glycine hydrochloride (Cl$^-$H$_3$N$^+$CH$_2$COOH) is a diprotic acid that contains a carboxylic acid group and an ammonium group and is therefore called an amino acid. It is often used in biochemical buffers.

(a) Which proton would you expect to dissociate at a lower pH, the proton of the carboxylic acid group or the ammonium group?

(b) Write the chemical equations describing the dissociation of the first and second protons of Cl$^-$H$_3$N$^+$CH$_2$COOH.

(c) A solution containing 0.01 M Cl$^-$H$_3$N$^+$CH$_2$COOH and 0.02 M of the monodissociated species has pH = 2.65. What is the pK of this dissociation?

(d) In analogy with Figure 2-18, sketch the titration curve of this diprotic acid.

CASE STUDY

Case 1 (available at www.wiley.com/college/voet)
Acute Aspirin Overdose: Relationship to the Blood Buffering System

Focus concept: The carbonic acid–bicarbonate buffering system responds to an overdose of aspirin.

Prerequisite: Chapter 2

• Principles of acids and bases, including pK and the Henderson–Hasselbalch equation

• The carbonic acid–bicarbonate blood buffering system

REFERENCES

Finney, J.L., Water? What's so special about it? *Phil. Trans. R. Soc. Lond. B Biol. Sci.* **29,** 1145–1163 (2004). [Includes discussions of the structure of water molecules, hydrogen bonding, structures of ice and liquid water, and how these relate to biological function.]

Gerstein, M. and Levitt, M., Simulating water and the molecules of life, *Sci Am.* **279**(11), 101–105 (1998). [Describes the structure of water and how water interacts with other molecules.]

Good, N.E., Winget, G.D., Winter, W., Connolly, T.N., Izawa, S., and Singh, R.M.M., Hydrogen ion buffers for biological research, *Biochemistry* **5,** 467–477 (1966). [A classic paper on laboratory buffers.]

Halperin, M.L. and Goldstein, M.B., *Fluid, Electrolyte, and Acid–Base Physiology: A Problem-Based Approach* (3rd ed.), W.B. Saunders (1999). [Includes extensive problem sets with explanations of basic science as well as clinical effects of acid–base disorders.]

Jeffrey, G.A. and Saenger, W., *Hydrogen Bonding in Biological Structures,* Chapters 1, 2, and 21, Springer (1994). [Reviews hydrogen bond chemistry and its importance in small molecules and macromolecules.]

Segel, I.H., *Biochemical Calculations* (2nd ed.), Chapter 1, Wiley (1976). [An intermediate level discussion of acid–base equilibria with worked-out problems.]

Tanford, C., *The Hydrophobic Effect: Formation of Micelles and Biological Membranes* (2nd ed.), Chapters 5 and 6, Wiley–Interscience (1980). [Discusses the structures of water and micelles.]

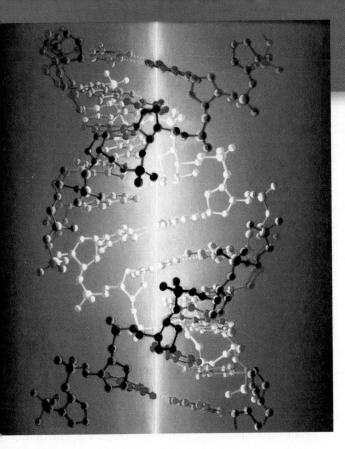

3

Nucleotides, Nucleic Acids, and Genetic Information

A DNA molecule consists of two strands that wind around a central axis, shown here as a glowing wire. [Illustration, Irving Geis. Image from the Irving Geis Collection/Howard Hughes Medical Institute. Rights owned by HHMI. Reproduction by permission only.]

■ MEDIA RESOURCES

(Available at www.wiley.com/college/voet)
Guided Exploration 1. Overview of transcription and translation
Guided Exploration 2. DNA sequence determination by the chain-terminator method
Guided Exploration 3. PCR and site-directed mutagenesis
Interactive Exercise 1. Three-dimensional structure of DNA
Animated Figure 3-26. Construction of a recombinant DNA molecule
Animated Figure 3-27. Cloning with bacteriophage λ
Animated Figure 3-30. Site-directed mutagenesis
Kinemage Exercise 2-1. Structure of DNA
Kinemage Exercise 2-2. Watson–Crick base pairs
Bioinformatics Exercises Chapter 3. Databases for the Storage and "Mining" of Genome Sequences

■ CHAPTER CONTENTS

1 Nucleotides

2 Introduction to Nucleic Acid Structure
  A. Nucleic Acids Are Polymers of Nucleotides
  B. DNA Forms a Double Helix
  C. RNA Is a Single-Stranded Nucleic Acid

3 Overview of Nucleic Acid Function
  A. DNA Carries Genetic Information
  B. Genes Direct Protein Synthesis

4 Nucleic Acid Sequencing
  A. Restriction Endonucleases Cleave DNA at Specific Sequences
  B. Electrophoresis Separates Nucleic Acids According to Size
  C. DNA Is Sequenced by the Chain-Terminator Method
  D. Entire Genomes Have Been Sequenced
  E. Evolution Results from Sequence Mutations

5 Manipulating DNA
  A. Cloned DNA Is an Amplified Copy
  B. DNA Libraries Are Collections of Cloned DNA
  C. DNA Is Amplified by the Polymerase Chain Reaction
  D. Recombinant DNA Technology Has Numerous Practical Applications

Despite obvious differences in lifestyle and macroscopic appearance, organisms exhibit striking similarity at the molecular level. The structures and metabolic activities of all cells rely on a common set of molecules that includes amino acids, carbohydrates, lipids, and nucleotides, as well as their polymeric forms. Each type of compound can be described in terms of its chemical makeup, its interactions with other molecules, and its physiological function. We begin our survey of biomolecules with a discussion of the **nucleotides** and their polymers, the **nucleic acids.**

Nucleotides are involved in nearly every facet of cellular life. Specifically, they participate in oxidation–reduction reactions, energy transfer, intracellular signaling, and biosynthetic reactions. Their polymers, the nucleic acids DNA and RNA, are the primary players in the storage and decoding of genetic information. Nucleotides and nucleic acids also perform structural and catalytic roles in cells. No other class of molecule participates in such varied functions or in so many functions that are essential for life.

Evolutionists postulate that the appearance of nucleotides permitted the evolution of organisms that could harvest and store energy from their surroundings and, most importantly, could make copies of themselves. Although the chemical and biological details of early life-forms are the subject of speculation, it is incontrovertible that life as we know it is inextricably linked to the chemistry of nucleotides and nucleic acids.

In this chapter, we briefly examine the structures of nucleotides and the nucleic acids DNA and RNA. We also consider how the chemistry of these molecules allows them to carry biological information in the form of a sequence of nucleotides. This information is expressed by the transcription of a segment of DNA to yield RNA, which is then translated to form protein. Because a cell's structure and function ultimately depend on its genetic makeup, we discuss how genomic sequences provide information about evolution, metabolism, and disease. Finally, we consider some of the techniques used in manipulating DNA in the laboratory. In later chapters, we will examine in greater detail the participation of nucleotides and nucleic acids in metabolic processes. Chapter 24 includes additional information about nucleic acid structures, DNA's interactions with proteins, and DNA packaging in cells, as a prelude to several chapters discussing the roles of nucleic acids in the storage and expression of genetic information.

1 Nucleotides

Nucleotides are ubiquitous molecules with considerable structural diversity. *There are eight common varieties of nucleotides, each composed of a nitrogenous base linked to a sugar to which at least one phosphate group is also attached.* The bases of nucleotides are planar, aromatic, heterocyclic molecules that are structural derivatives of either **purine** or **pyrimidine** (although they are not synthesized *in vivo* from either of these organic compounds).

Purine   **Pyrimidine**

The most common purines are **adenine (A)** and **guanine (G),** and the major pyrimidines are **cytosine (C), uracil (U),** and **thymine (T).** The purines form bonds to a five-carbon sugar (a pentose) via their N9 atoms, whereas pyrimidines do so through their N1 atoms (Table 3-1).

In **ribonucleotides,** the pentose is **ribose,** while in **deoxyribonucleotides** (or just **deoxynucleotides**), the sugar is **2′-deoxyribose** (i.e., the carbon at position 2′ lacks a hydroxyl group).

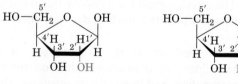

Ribose   **Deoxyribose**

LEARNING OBJECTIVE

■ Become familiar with the structures and nomenclature of the eight common nucleotides.

Table 3-1 Names and Abbreviations of Nucleic Acid Bases, Nucleosides, and Nucleotides

Base Formula	Base (X = H)	Nucleoside (X = ribose[a])	Nucleotide[b] (X = ribose phosphate[a])
	Adenine	Adenosine	Adenylic acid
	Ade	Ado	Adenosine monophosphate
	A	A	AMP
	Guanine	Guanosine	Guanylic acid
	Gua	Guo	Guanosine monophosphate
	G	G	GMP
	Cytosine	Cytidine	Cytidylic acid
	Cyt	Cyd	Cytidine monophosphate
	C	C	CMP
	Uracil	Uridine	Uridylic acid
	Ura	Urd	Uridine monophosphate
	U	U	UMP
	Thymine	Deoxythymidine	Deoxythymidylic acid
	Thy	dThd	Deoxythymidine monophosphate
	T	dT	dTMP

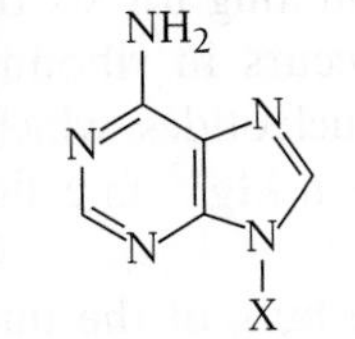

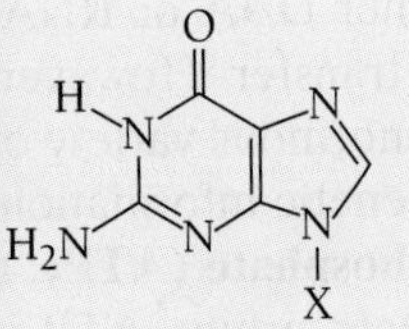

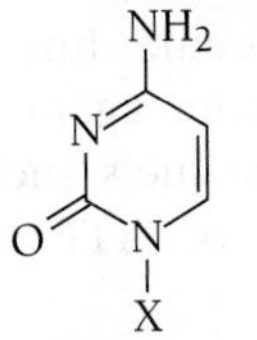

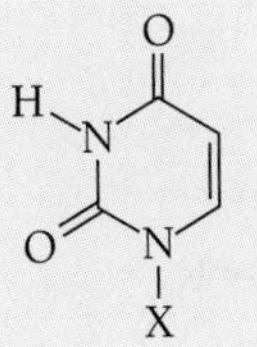

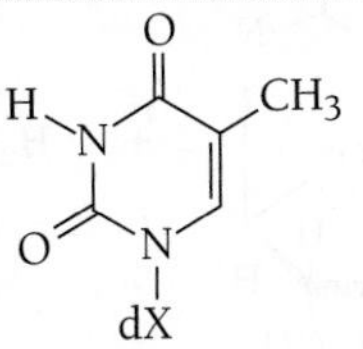

[a]The presence of a 2'-deoxyribose unit in place of ribose, as occurs in DNA, is implied by the prefixes "deoxy" or "d." For example, the deoxynucleoside of adenine is deoxyadenosine or dA. However, for thymine-containing residues, which rarely occur in RNA, the prefix is redundant and may be dropped. The presence of a ribose unit may be explicitly implied by the prefix "ribo."

[b]The position of the phosphate group in a nucleotide may be explicitly specified as in, for example, 3'-AMP and 5'-GMP.

Note that the "primed" numbers refer to the atoms of the pentose; "unprimed" numbers refer to the atoms of the nitrogenous base.

In a ribonucleotide or a deoxyribonucleotide, one or more phosphate groups are bonded to atom C3' or atom C5' of the pentose to form a 3'-nucleotide or a 5'-nucleotide, respectively (Fig. 3-1). When the phosphate group is absent, the compound is known as a **nucleoside.** A 5'-nucleotide can therefore be called a nucleoside-5'-phosphate. Nucleotides most commonly contain one to three phosphate groups at the C5' position and are called nucleoside monophosphates, diphosphates, and triphosphates.

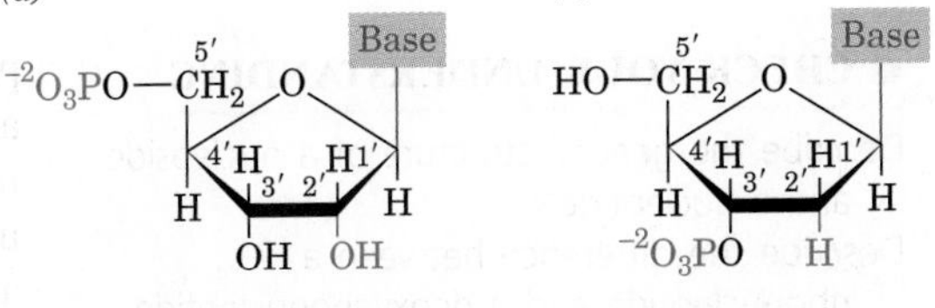

Figure 3-1 | Chemical structures of nucleotides. (a) A 5'-ribonucleotide and (b) a 3'-deoxynucleotide. The purine or pyrimidine base is linked to C1' of the pentose and at least one phosphate (red) is also attached. A nucleoside consists only of a base and a pentose.

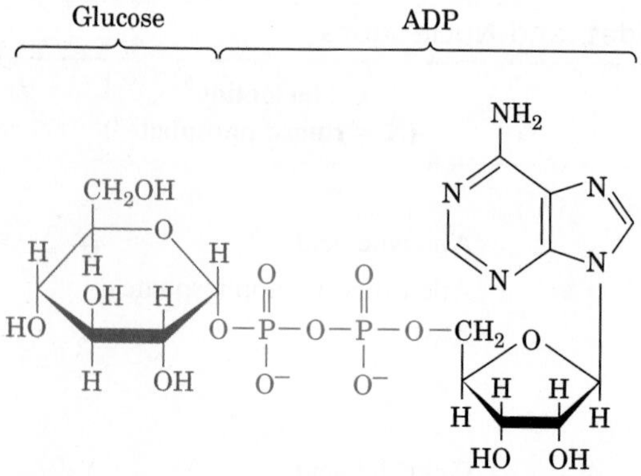

Glucose   ADP

■ **Figure 3-2** | **ADP–glucose.** In this nucleotide derivative, glucose (*blue*) is attached to adenosine (*black*) by a diphosphate group (*red*).

The structures, names, and abbreviations of the common bases, nucleosides, and nucleotides are given in Table 3-1. Ribonucleotides are components of **RNA (ribonucleic acid),** whereas deoxynucleotides are components of **DNA (deoxyribonucleic acid).** Adenine, guanine, and cytosine occur in both ribonucleotides and deoxynucleotides (accounting for six of the eight common nucleotides), but uracil primarily occurs in ribonucleotides and thymine occurs in deoxynucleotides. Free nucleotides, which are anionic, are almost always associated with the counterion Mg^{2+} in cells.

Nucleotides Participate in Metabolic Reactions. The bulk of the nucleotides in any cell are found in polymeric forms, as either DNA or RNA, whose primary functions are information storage and transfer. However, free nucleotides and nucleotide derivatives perform an enormous variety of metabolic functions not related to the management of genetic information.

Perhaps the best known nucleotide is **adenosine triphosphate (ATP),** a nucleotide containing adenine, ribose, and a triphosphate group. ATP is often mistakenly referred to as an energy-storage molecule, but it is more accurately termed an energy carrier or energy transfer agent. The process of photosynthesis or the breakdown of metabolic fuels such as carbohydrates and fatty acids leads to the formation of ATP from **adenosine diphosphate (ADP):**

Adenosine

Adenosine diphosphate (ADP)

Adenosine triphosphate (ATP)

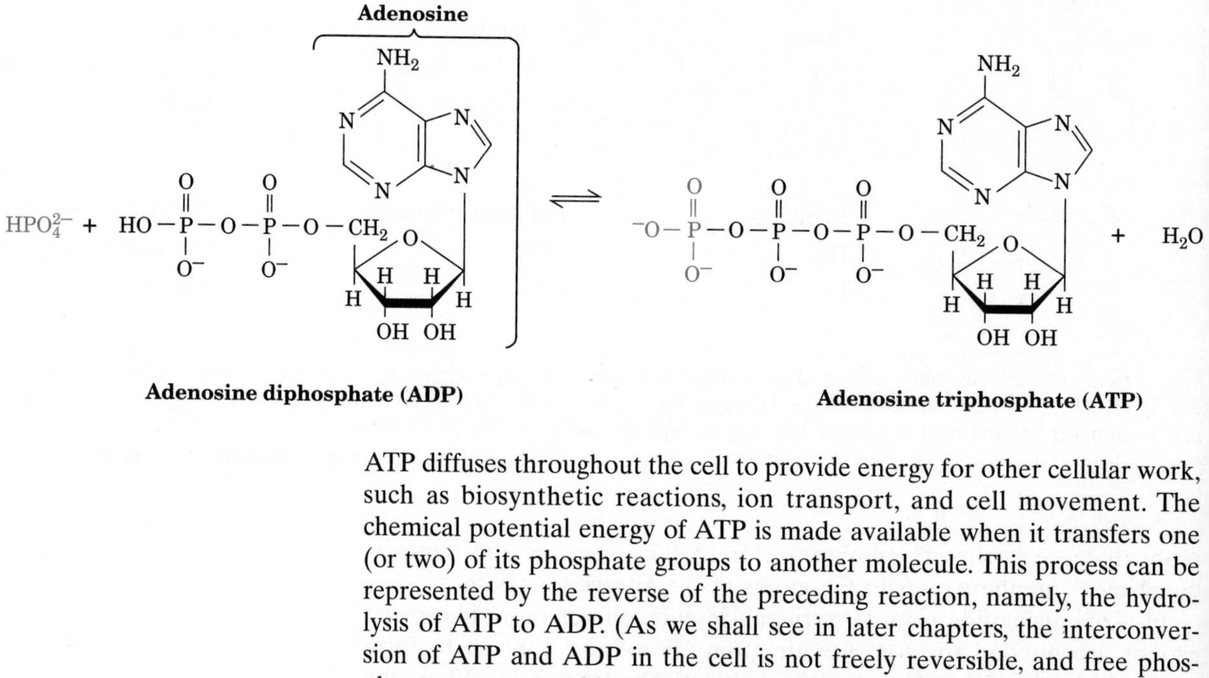

ATP diffuses throughout the cell to provide energy for other cellular work, such as biosynthetic reactions, ion transport, and cell movement. The chemical potential energy of ATP is made available when it transfers one (or two) of its phosphate groups to another molecule. This process can be represented by the reverse of the preceding reaction, namely, the hydrolysis of ATP to ADP. (As we shall see in later chapters, the interconversion of ATP and ADP in the cell is not freely reversible, and free phosphate groups are seldom released directly from ATP.) The degree to which ATP participates in routine cellular activities is illustrated by calculations indicating that while the concentration of cellular ATP is relatively moderate (~5 mM), humans typically recycle their own weight of ATP each day.

Nucleotide derivatives participate in a wide variety of metabolic processes. For example, starch synthesis in plants proceeds by repeated additions of glucose units donated by ADP–glucose (Fig. 3-2). Other nucleotide derivatives, as we shall see in later chapters, carry groups that undergo oxidation–reduction reactions. The attached group, which may be a small molecule such as glucose (Fig. 3-2) or even another nucleotide, is typically linked to the nucleotide through a mono- or diphosphate group.

■ **CHECK YOUR UNDERSTANDING**

Describe the general structure of a nucleoside and a nucleotide.
Describe the difference between a ribonucleotide and a deoxyribonucleotide.

2 Introduction to Nucleic Acid Structure

Nucleotides can be joined to each other to form the polymers that are familiar to us as RNA and DNA. In this section, we describe the general features of these nucleic acids. Nucleic acid structure is considered further in Chapter 24.

LEARNING OBJECTIVES

- Understand how nucleotides are linked together to form nucleic acids.
- Become familiar with the structural features of the DNA double helix.

A | Nucleic Acids Are Polymers of Nucleotides

The nucleic acids are chains of nucleotides whose phosphates bridge the 3' and 5' positions of neighboring ribose units (Fig. 3-3). The phosphates of these **polynucleotides** are acidic, so at physiological pH, nucleic acids are polyanions. The linkage between individual nucleotides is known as a **phosphodiester bond,** so named because the phosphate is esterified to two ribose units. Each nucleotide that has been incorporated into the polynucleotide is known as a **nucleotide residue.** The terminal residue whose C5'

(a)

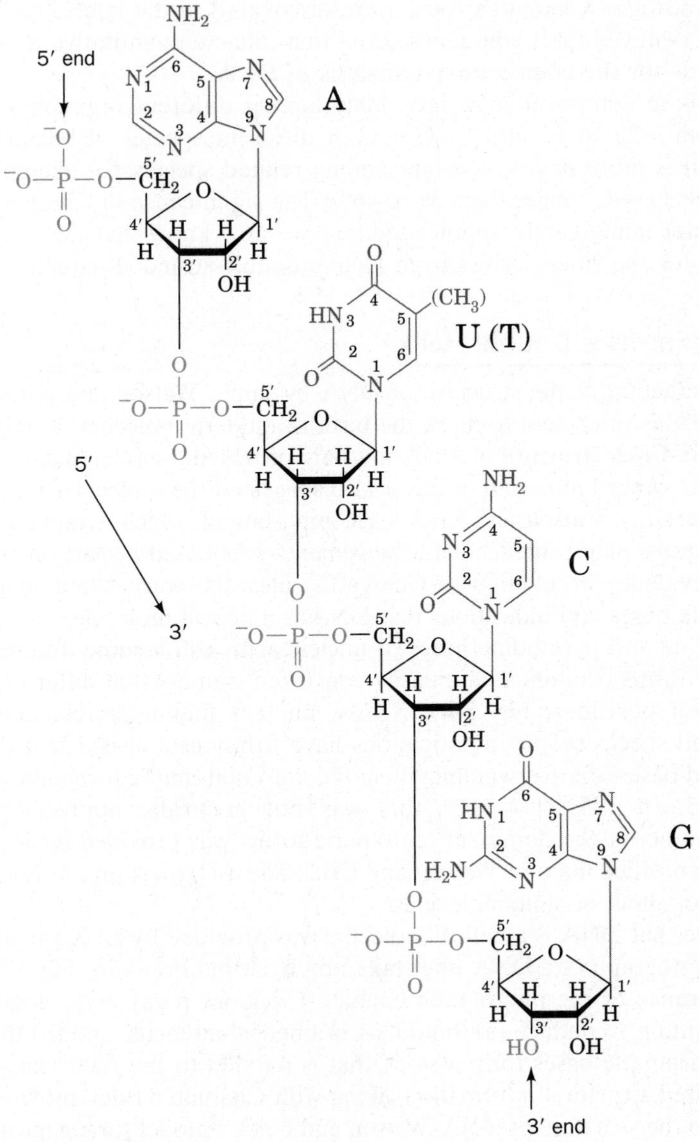

(b)

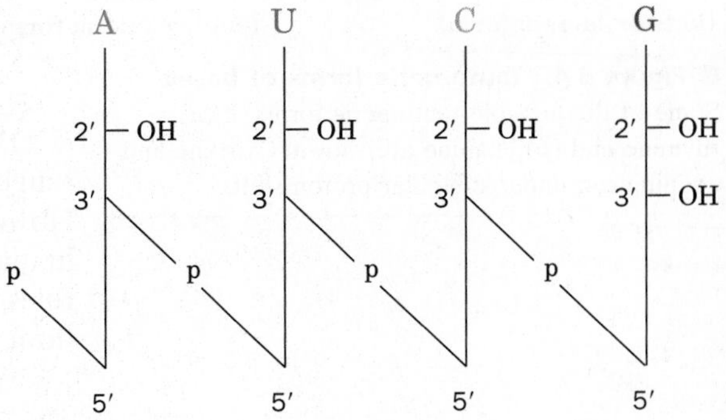

■ **Figure 3-3 | Chemical structure of a nucleic acid.** (a) The tetraribonucleotide adenylyl-3',5'-uridylyl-3',5'-cytidylyl-3',5'-guanylate is shown. The sugar atoms are primed to distinguish them from the atoms of the bases. By convention, a polynucleotide sequence is written with the 5' end at the left and the 3' end at the right. Thus, reading left to right, the phosphodiester bond links neighboring ribose residues in the 5' → 3' direction. The sequence shown here can be abbreviated pApUpCpG or just pAUCG (the "p" to the left of a nucleoside symbol indicates a 5' phosphoryl group). The corresponding deoxytetranucleotide, in which the 2'-OH groups are replaced by H and the uracil (U) is replaced by thymine (T), is abbreviated d(pApTpCpG) or d(pATCG). (b) Schematic representation of pAUCG. A vertical line denotes a ribose residue, the attached base is indicated by a single letter, and a diagonal line flanking an optional "p" represents a phosphodiester bond. The atom numbers for the ribose residue may be omitted. The equivalent representation of d(pATCG) differs only by the absence of the 2'-OH group and by the replacement of U by T.

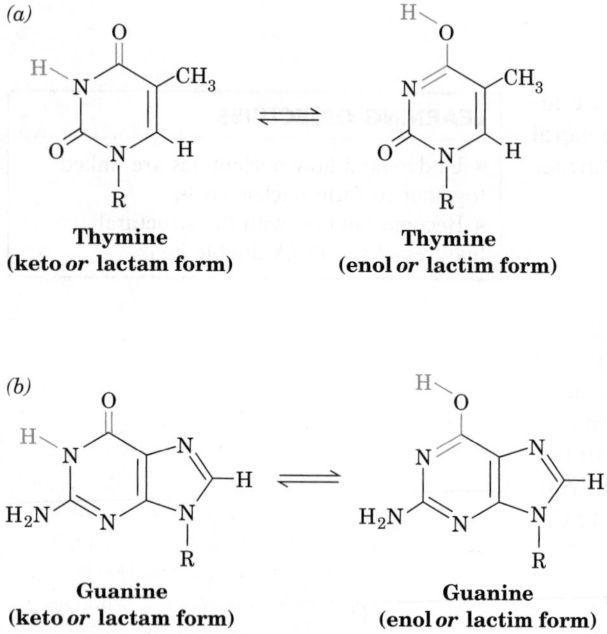

(a)

Thymine
(keto *or* lactam form)

Thymine
(enol *or* lactim form)

(b)

Guanine
(keto *or* lactam form)

Guanine
(enol *or* lactim form)

■ **Figure 3-4 | Tautomeric forms of bases.**
Some of the possible tautomeric forms of (*a*)
thymine and (*b*) guanine are shown. Cytosine and
adenine can undergo similar proton shifts.

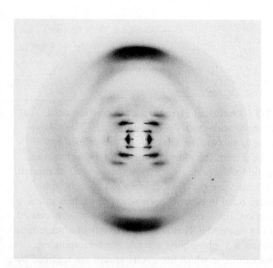

■ **Figure 3-5 | An X-ray diffraction photograph
of a vertically oriented DNA fiber.** This
photograph, taken by Rosalind Franklin,
provided key evidence for the elucidation of the
Watson–Crick structure. The central X-shaped
pattern indicates a helix, whereas the heavy black
arcs at the top and bottom of the diffraction
pattern reveal the spacing of the stacked bases
(3.4 Å). [Courtesy of Maurice Wilkins, King's
College, London.]

is not linked to another nucleotide is called the **5′ end,** and the
terminal residue whose C3′ is not linked to another nucleotide
is called the **3′ end.** By convention, the sequence of nucleotide
residues in a nucleic acid is written, left to right, from the 5′ end
to the 3′ end.

The properties of a polymer such as a nucleic acid may be very
different from the properties of the individual units, or
monomers, before polymerization. As the size of the polymer increases from **dimer, trimer, tetramer,** and so on through **oligomer**
(Greek: *oligo,* few), physical properties such as charge and solubility may change. In addition, *a polymer of nonidentical residues
has a property that its component monomers lack—namely, it contains information in the form of its sequence of residues.*

Chargaff's Rules Describe the Base Composition of DNA.
Although there appear to be no rules governing the nucleotide
composition of typical RNA molecules, DNA has equal numbers
of adenine and thymine residues (A = T) and equal numbers of
guanine and cytosine residues (G = C). These relationships,
known as **Chargaff's rules,** were discovered in the late 1940s by
Erwin Chargaff, who devised the first reliable quantitative methods for the compositional analysis of DNA.

DNA's base composition varies widely among different organisms. It
ranges from ~25 to 75 mol % G + C in different species of bacteria.
However, it is more or less constant among related species; for example,
in mammals G + C ranges from 39 to 46%. The significance of Chargaff's
rules was not immediately appreciated, but we now know that the structural basis for the rules derives from DNA's double-stranded nature.

B | DNA Forms a Double Helix

The determination of the structure of DNA by James Watson and Francis
Crick in 1953 is often said to mark the birth of modern molecular biology.
The **Watson–Crick structure** of DNA not only provided a model of what is
arguably the central molecule of life, it also suggested the molecular mechanism of heredity. Watson and Crick's accomplishment, which is ranked as
one of science's major intellectual achievements, was based in part on two
pieces of evidence in addition to Chargaff's rules: the correct tautomeric
forms of the bases and indications that DNA is a helical molecule.

The purine and pyrimidine bases of nucleic acids can assume different
tautomeric forms (**tautomers** are easily converted isomers that differ only
in hydrogen positions; Fig. 3-4). X-Ray, nuclear magnetic resonance
(NMR), and spectroscopic investigations have firmly established that the
nucleic acid bases are overwhelmingly in the keto tautomeric forms shown
in Fig. 3-3. In 1953, however, this was not generally appreciated.
Information about the dominant tautomeric forms was provided by Jerry
Donohue, an office mate of Watson and Crick and an expert on the X-ray
structures of small organic molecules.

Evidence that DNA is a helical molecule was provided by an X-ray diffraction photograph of a DNA fiber taken by Rosalind Franklin (Fig. 3-5).
The appearance of the photograph enabled Crick, an X-ray crystallogra-
pher by training, to deduce (a) that DNA is a helical molecule and (b) that
its planar aromatic bases form a stack that is parallel to the fiber axis.

The limited structural information, along with Chargaff's rules, provided
few clues to the structure of DNA; Watson and Crick's model sprang mostly
from their imaginations and model-building studies. Once the Watson–Crick

model had been published, however, its basic simplicity combined with its obvious biological relevance led to its rapid acceptance. Later investigations have confirmed the general accuracy of the Watson–Crick model, although its details have been modified.

The Watson–Crick model of DNA has the following major features:

1. Two polynucleotide chains wind around a common axis to form a **double helix** (Fig. 3-6).

2. The two strands of DNA are **antiparallel** (run in opposite directions), but each forms a right-handed helix. (The difference between a right-handed and a left-handed helix is shown in Fig. 3-7.)

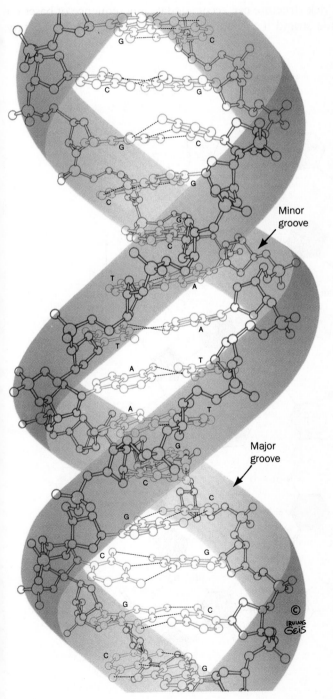

Minor groove

Major groove

■ **Figure 3-6** | **Three-dimensional structure of DNA.** The repeating helix is based on the structure of the self-complementary dodecamer d(CGCGAATTCGCG) determined by Richard Dickerson and Horace Drew. The view in this ball-and-stick model is perpendicular to the helix axis. The sugar–phosphate backbones (*blue, with green ribbon outlines*) wind around the periphery of the molecule. The bases (*red*) form hydrogen-bonded pairs that occupy the core. H atoms have been omitted for clarity. The two strands run in opposite directions. [Illustration, Irving Geis. Image from the Irving Geis Collection/Howard Hughes Medical Institute. Rights owned by HHMI. Reproduction by permission only.] *See Interactive Exercise 1 and Kinemage Exercise 2-1.*

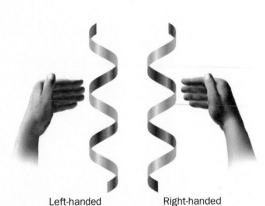

Left-handed   Right-handed

■ **Figure 3-7** | **Diagrams of left- and right-handed helices.** In each case, the fingers curl in the direction the helix turns when the thumb points in the direction the helix rises. Note that the handedness is retained when the helices are turned upside down.

3. The bases occupy the core of the helix and sugar–phosphate chains run along the periphery, thereby minimizing the repulsions between charged phosphate groups. The surface of the double helix contains two grooves of unequal width: the **major** and **minor grooves.**

4. Each base is hydrogen bonded to a base in the opposite strand to form a planar **base pair.** The Watson–Crick structure can accommodate only two types of base pairs. Each adenine residue must pair with a thymine residue and vice versa, and each guanine residue must pair with a cytosine residue and vice versa (Fig. 3-8). These hydrogen-bonding interactions, a phenomenon known as **complementary base pairing,** result in the specific association of the two chains of the double helix.

The Watson–Crick structure can accommodate any sequence of bases on one polynucleotide strand if the opposite strand has the complementary

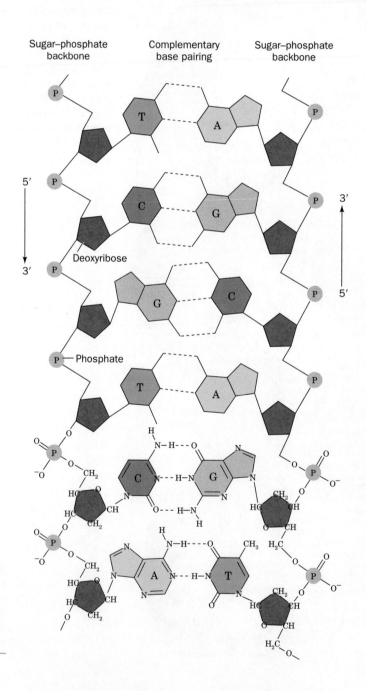

■ **Figure 3-8** | **Complementary strands of DNA.** Two polynucleotide chains associate by base pairing to form double-stranded DNA. A pairs with T, and G pairs with C by forming specific hydrogen bonds. *See* **Kinemage Exercise 2-2.**

base sequence. This immediately accounts for Chargaff's rules. More importantly, it suggests that *each DNA strand can act as a* **template** *for the synthesis of its complementary strand and hence that hereditary information is encoded in the sequence of bases on either strand.*

Most DNA Molecules Are Large. The extremely large size of DNA molecules is in keeping with their role as the repository of a cell's genetic information. Of course, an organism's **genome,** its unique DNA content, may be allocated among several **chromosomes** (Greek: *chromos,* color + *soma,* body), each of which contains a separate DNA molecule. Note that many organisms are **diploid;** that is, they contain two equivalent sets of chromosomes, one from each parent. Their content of unique **(haploid)** DNA is half their total DNA. For example, humans are diploid organisms that carry 46 chromosomes per cell; their haploid number is therefore 23.

Because of their great lengths, DNA molecules are described in terms of the number of base pairs **(bp)** or thousands of base pairs **(kilobase pairs, or kb).** Naturally occurring DNAs vary in length from ~5 kb in small DNA-containing viruses to well over 250,000 kb in the largest mammalian chromosomes. Although DNA molecules are long and relatively stiff, they are not completely rigid. We shall see in Chapter 24 that the DNA double helix forms coils and loops when it is packaged inside the cell. Furthermore, depending on the nucleotide sequence, DNA may adopt slightly different helical conformations. Finally, in the presence of other cellular components, the DNA may bend sharply or the two strands may partially unwind.

C | RNA Is a Single-Stranded Nucleic Acid

Single-stranded DNA is rare, occurring mainly as the hereditary material of certain viruses. In contrast, RNA occurs primarily as single strands, which usually form compact structures rather than loose extended chains (double-stranded RNA is the hereditary material of certain viruses). An RNA strand—which is identical to a DNA strand except for the presence of 2′-OH groups and the substitution of uracil for thymine—can base-pair with a complementary strand of RNA or DNA. As expected, A pairs with U (or T in DNA), and G with C. Base pairing often occurs intramolecularly, giving rise to **stem–loop** structures (Fig. 3-9) or, when loops interact with each other, to more complex structures.

The intricate structures that can potentially be adopted by single-stranded RNA molecules provide additional evidence that RNA can do more than just store and transmit genetic information. Numerous investigations have found that certain RNA molecules can specifically bind small organic molecules and can catalyze reactions involving those molecules. These findings provide substantial support for theories that *many of the processes essential for life began through the chemical versatility of small polynucleotides* (a situation known as the **RNA world**). We will further explore RNA structure and function in Section 24-2C.

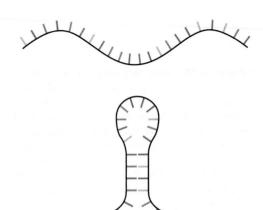

■ **Figure 3-9 | Formation of a stem–loop structure.** Base pairing between complementary sequences within an RNA strand allows the polynucleotide to fold back on itself.

■ **CHECK YOUR UNDERSTANDING**

Describe the double-helical structure of DNA. List the structural differences between DNA and RNA.

3 | Overview of Nucleic Acid Function

DNA is the carrier of genetic information in all cells and in many viruses. Yet a period of over 75 years passed from the time the laws of inheritance were discovered by Gregor Mendel until the biological role of DNA was elucidated. Even now, many details of how genetic information is expressed and transmitted to future generations are still unclear.

LEARNING OBJECTIVE

■ Understand that genetic information is contained in the sequence of nucleotides in DNA and can be expressed through its transcription into RNA, which is then translated into protein.

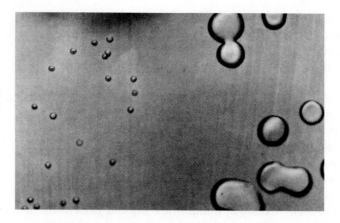

■ **Figure 3-10** | **Transformed pneumococci.** The large colonies are virulent pneumococci that resulted from the transformation of nonpathogenic pneumococci (smaller colonies) by DNA extracted from the virulent strain. We now know that this DNA contained a gene that was defective in the nonpathogenic strain. [From Avery, O.T., MacLeod, C.M., and McCarty, M., *J. Exp. Med.* **79,** 153 (1944). Copyright © 1944 by Rockefeller University Press.]

Mendel's work with garden peas led him to postulate that an individual plant contains a pair of factors (which we now call **genes**), one inherited from each parent. But Mendel's theory of inheritance, reported in 1866, was almost universally ignored by his contemporaries, whose knowledge of anatomy and physiology provided no basis for its understanding. Eventually, genes were hypothesized to be part of chromosomes, and the pace of genetic research greatly accelerated.

A | DNA Carries Genetic Information

Until the 1940s, it was generally assumed that genes were made of protein, since proteins were the only biochemical entities that, at the time, seemed complex enough to serve as agents of inheritance. Nucleic acids, which had first been isolated in 1869 by Friedrich Miescher, were believed to have monotonously repeating nucleotide sequences and were therefore unlikely candidates for transmitting genetic information.

It took the efforts of Oswald Avery, Colin MacLeod, and Maclyn McCarty to demonstrate that DNA carries genetic information. Their experiments, completed in 1944, showed that DNA—not protein—extracted from a virulent (pathogenic) strain of the bacterium *Diplococcus pneumoniae* was the substance that **transformed** (permanently changed) a nonpathogenic strain of the organism to the virulent strain (Fig. 3-10). Avery's discovery was initially greeted with skepticism, but it influenced Erwin Chargaff, whose rules (Section 3-2A) led to subsequent models of the structure and function of DNA.

The double-stranded, or duplex, nature of DNA facilitates its **replication.** When a cell divides, each DNA strand acts as a template for the assembly of its complementary strand (Fig. 3-11). Consequently, every progeny cell contains a complete DNA molecule (or a complete set of DNA molecules in organisms whose genomes contain more than one chromosome). Each DNA molecule consists of one parental strand and one daughter strand. Daughter strands are synthesized by the stepwise polymerization of nucleotides that specifically pair with bases on the parental strands. The mechanism of replication, while straightforward in principle, is exceedingly complex in the cell, requiring a multitude of cellular factors to proceed with fidelity and efficiency, as we shall see in Chapter 25.

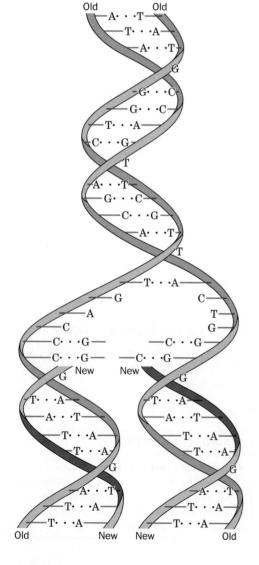

■ **Figure 3-11** | **DNA replication.** Each strand of parental DNA (*red*) acts as a template for the synthesis of a complementary daughter strand (*green*). Thus, the resulting double-stranded molecules are identical.

B | Genes Direct Protein Synthesis

The question of how sequences of nucleotides control the characteristics of organisms took some time to be answered. In experiments with the mold *Neurospora crassa* in the 1940s, George Beadle and Edward Tatum found that *there is a specific connection between genes and enzymes, the one gene–one enzyme theory.* Beadle and Tatum showed that mutant varieties of *Neurospora* that were generated by irradiation with X-rays required additional nutrients in order to grow. Presumably, the offspring of the radiation-damaged cells lacked the specific enzymes necessary to synthesize those nutrients.

The link between DNA and enzymes (nearly all of which are proteins) is RNA. *The DNA of a gene is **transcribed** to produce an RNA molecule that is complementary to the DNA. The RNA sequence is then **translated** into the corresponding sequence of amino acids to form a protein* (Fig. 3-12). These transfers of biological information are summarized in the so-called **central dogma of molecular biology** formulated by Crick in 1958 (Fig. 3-13).

Just as the daughter strands of DNA are synthesized from free deoxynucleoside triphosphates that pair with bases in the parent DNA strand, RNA strands are synthesized from free ribonucleoside triphosphates that pair with the complementary bases in one DNA strand of a gene (transcription is described in greater detail in Chapter 26). The RNA that corresponds to a protein-coding gene (called **messenger RNA,** or **mRNA**) makes its way to a **ribosome,** an organelle that is itself composed largely of RNA (**ribosomal RNA,** or **rRNA**). At the ribosome, each set of three nucleotides in the mRNA pairs with three complementary nucleotides in a small RNA molecule called a **transfer RNA,** or **tRNA** (Fig. 3-14). Attached to each tRNA molecule is its corresponding amino acid. The ribosome catalyzes the joining of amino acids, which are the monomeric units of proteins (protein synthesis is described in detail in Chapter 27). Amino acids are added to the growing protein chain according to the order in which the tRNA molecules bind to the mRNA. Since the nucleotide sequence of the mRNA in turn reflects the sequences of nucleotides in the gene, DNA directs the synthesis of proteins. It follows that alterations to the genetic material of an organism **(mutations)** may manifest themselves as proteins with altered structures and functions.

Using techniques that are described in the following sections and in other parts of this book, researchers can compile a catalog of all the

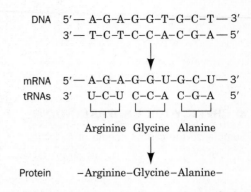

■ Figure 3-12 | Transcription and translation. One strand of DNA directs the synthesis of messenger RNA (mRNA). The base sequence of the transcribed RNA is complementary to that of the DNA strand. The message is translated when transfer RNA (tRNA) molecules align with the mRNA by complementary base pairing between three-nucleotide segments known as **codons.** Each tRNA carries a specific amino acid. These amino acids are covalently joined to form a protein. Thus, the sequence of bases in DNA specifies the sequence of amino acids in a protein.

See Guided Exploration 1
Overview of transcription and translation.

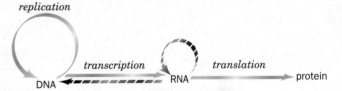

■ Figure 3-13 | The central dogma of molecular biology. Solid arrows indicate the types of information transfers that occur in all cells: DNA directs its own replication to produce new DNA molecules; DNA is transcribed into RNA; RNA is translated into protein. Dashed lines represent information transfers that occur only in certain organisms.

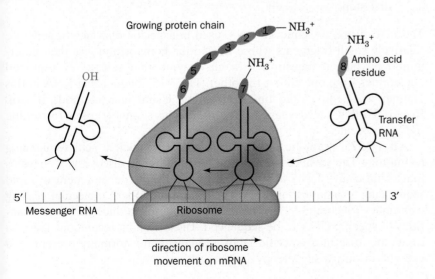

■ Figure 3-14 | Translation. tRNA molecules with their attached amino acids bind to complementary three-nucleotide sequences (codons) on mRNA. The ribosome facilitates the alignment of the tRNA and the mRNA, and it catalyzes the joining of amino acids to produce a protein chain. When a new amino acid is added, the preceding tRNA is ejected, and the ribosome proceeds along the mRNA.

information encoded in an organism's DNA. The study of the genome's size, organization, and gene content is known as **genomics.** By analogy, **transcriptomics** refers to the study of gene expression, which focuses on the set of mRNA molecules, or **transcriptome**, that is transcribed from DNA under any particular set of circumstances. Finally, **proteomics** is the study of the proteins (the **proteome**) produced as a result of transcription and translation. Although an organism's genome remains essentially unchanged throughout its lifetime, its transcriptome and proteome may vary significantly among different types of tissues, developmental stages, and environmental conditions.

■ **CHECK YOUR UNDERSTANDING**

Summarize the central dogma of molecular biology.

4 Nucleic Acid Sequencing

Much of our current understanding of protein structure and function rests squarely on information gleaned not from the proteins themselves, but indirectly from their genes. *The ability to determine the sequence of nucleotides in nucleic acids has made it possible to deduce the amino acid sequences of their encoded proteins and, to some extent, the structures and functions of those proteins. Nucleic acid sequencing has also revealed information about the regulation of genes.* Certain portions of genes that are not actually transcribed into RNA nevertheless influence how often a gene is transcribed and translated, that is, **expressed.** Moreover, efforts to elucidate the sequences in hitherto unmapped regions of DNA have led to the discovery of new genes and new regulatory elements. *Once in hand, a nucleic acid sequence can be duplicated, modified, and expressed, making it possible to study proteins that could not otherwise be obtained in useful quantities.* In this section, we describe how nucleic acids are sequenced and what information the sequences may reveal. In the following section, we discuss the manipulation of purified nucleic acid sequences for various purposes.

The overall strategy for sequencing any polymer of nonidentical units is

1. Cleave the polymer into specific fragments that are small enough to be fully sequenced.
2. Determine the sequence of residues in each fragment.
3. Determine the order of the fragments in the original polymer by repeating the preceding steps using a degradation procedure that yields a set of fragments that overlap the cleavage points in the first step.

The first efforts to sequence RNA used nonspecific enzymes to generate relatively small fragments whose nucleotide composition was then determined by partial digestion with an enzyme that selectively removed nucleotides from one end or the other (Fig. 3-15). Sequencing RNA in this manner was tedious and time-consuming. Using such methods, it took Robert Holley seven years to determine the sequence of a 76-residue tRNA molecule.

After 1975, dramatic progress was made in nucleic acid sequencing technology. The advances were made possible by the discovery of enzymes that could cleave DNA at specific sites and by the development of rapid sequencing techniques for DNA. The advent of modern molecular cloning techniques (Section 3-5) also made it possible to produce sufficient quantities of specific DNA to be sequenced. These cloning techniques are necessary because most specific DNA sequences are normally present in a genome in only a single copy.

LEARNING OBJECTIVES

■ Understand why restriction endonucleases are useful for generating DNA fragments.
■ Understand the steps required to sequence DNA by the chain-terminator method.
■ Understand what kinds of information have been provided by sequencing the human genome.
■ Understand that changes in DNA allow evolution to occur.

GCACUUGA
| snake venom
| phosphodiesterase

GCACUUGA
GCACUUG
GCACUU
GCACU
GCAC
GCA
GC   + Mononucleotides

■ **Figure 3-15 | Determining the sequence of an oligonucleotide using nonspecific enzymes.** The oligonucleotide is partially digested with snake venom phosphodiesterase, which breaks the phosphodiester bonds between nucleotide residues, starting at the 3′ end of the oligonucleotide. The result is a mixture of fragments of all lengths, which are then separated. Comparing the base composition of a pair of fragments that differ in length by one nucleotide establishes the identity of the 3′-terminal nucleotide in the larger fragment. Analysis of each pair of fragments reveals the sequence of the original oligonucleotide.

A | Restriction Endonucleases Cleave DNA at Specific Sequences

Many bacteria are able to resist infection by **bacteriophages** (viruses that are specific for bacteria) by virtue of a **restriction–modification system.** The bacterium modifies certain nucleotides in specific sequences of its own DNA by adding a methyl ($-CH_3$) group in a reaction catalyzed by a **modification methylase.** A **restriction endonuclease,** which recognizes the same nucleotide sequence as does the methylase, cleaves any DNA that has not been modified on at least one of its two strands. (An **endonuclease** cleaves a nucleic acid within the polynucleotide strand; an **exonuclease** cleaves a nucleic acid by removing one of its terminal residues.) This system destroys foreign (phage) DNA containing a recognition site that has not been modified by methylation. The host DNA is always at least half methylated, because although the daughter strand is not methylated until shortly after it is synthesized, the parental strand to which it is paired is already modified (and thus protects both strands of the DNA from cleavage by the restriction enzyme).

Type II restriction endonucleases are particularly useful in the laboratory. These enzymes cleave DNA within the four- to eight-base sequence that is recognized by their corresponding modification methylase. (Type I and Type III restriction endonucleases cleave DNA at sites other than their recognition sequences.) Over 3000 Type II restriction enzymes with over 200 different recognition sequences have been characterized. Some of the more widely used restriction enzymes are listed in Table 3-2. A

Table 3-2	Recognition and Cleavage Sites of Some Restriction Enzymes	
Enzyme	**Recognition Sequence**[a]	**Microorganism**
*Alu*I	AG↓CT	*Arthrobacter luteus*
*Bam*HI	G↓GATCC	*Bacillus amyloliquefaciens* H
*Bgl*I	GCCNNNNN↓NGGC	*Bacillus globigii*
*Bgl*II	A↓GATCT	*Bacillus globigii*
*Eco*RI	G↓AATTC	*Escherichia coli* RY13
*Eco*RII	↓CC(^A_T)GG	*Escherichia coli* R245
*Eco*RV	GAT↓ATC	*Escherichia coli* J62 pLG74
*Hae*II	RGCGC↓Y	*Haemophilus aegyptius*
*Hae*III	GG↓CC	*Haemophilus aegyptius*
*Hin*dIII	A↓AGCTT	*Haemophilus influenzae* R_d
*Hpa*II	C↓CGG	*Haemophilus parainfluenzae*
*Msp*I	C↓CGG	*Moraxella* species
*Pst*I	CTGCA↓G	*Providencia stuartii* 164
*Pvu*II	CAG↓CTG	*Proteus vulgaris*
*Sal*I	G↓TCGAC	*Streptomyces albus* G
*Taq*I	T↓CGA	*Thermus aquaticus*
*Xho*I	C↓TCGAG	*Xanthomonas holcicola*

[a]The recognition sequence is abbreviated so that only one strand, reading 5' to 3', is given. The cleavage site is represented by an arrow (↓). R, Y, and N represent a purine nucleotide, a pyrimidine nucleotide, and any nucleotide, respectively.

Source: Roberts, R.J. and Macelis, D., REBASE—the restriction enzyme database, http://rebase.neb.com.

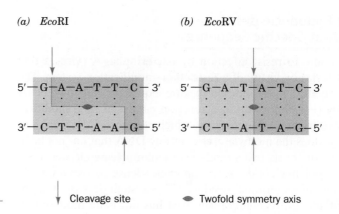

■ **Figure 3-16** | **Restriction sites.** The recognition sequences for Type II restriction endonucleases are palindromes, sequences with a twofold axis of symmetry. (*a*) Recognition site for *Eco*RI, which generates DNA fragments with sticky ends. (*b*) Recognition site for *Eco*RV, which generates blunt-ended fragments.

restriction enzyme is named by the first letter of the genus and the first two letters of the species of the bacterium that produced it, followed by its serotype or strain designation, if any, and a roman numeral if the bacterium contains more than one type of restriction enzyme. For example, *Eco*RI is produced by *E. coli* strain RY13.

Interestingly, most Type II restriction endonucleases recognize and cleave palindromic DNA sequences. A **palindrome** is a word or phrase that reads the same forward or backward. Two examples are "refer" and "Madam, I'm Adam." In a palindromic DNA segment, the sequence of nucleotides is the same in each strand, and the segment is said to have twofold symmetry (Fig. 3-16). Most restriction enzymes cleave the two strands of DNA at positions that are staggered, producing DNA fragments with complementary single-strand extensions. Restriction fragments with such **sticky ends** can associate by base pairing with other restriction fragments generated by the same restriction enzyme. Some restriction endonucleases cleave the two strands of DNA at the symmetry axis to yield restriction fragments with fully base-paired **blunt ends.**

B | Electrophoresis Separates Nucleic Acids According to Size

Treating a DNA molecule with a restriction endonuclease produces a series of precisely defined fragments that can be separated according to size. **Gel electrophoresis** is commonly used for the separation. In principle, a charged molecule moves in an electric field with a velocity proportional to its overall charge density, size, and shape. For molecules with a relatively homogeneous composition (such as nucleic acids), shape and charge density are constant, so the velocity depends primarily on size. Electrophoresis is carried out in a gel-like matrix, usually made from **agarose** (carbohydrate polymers that form a loose mesh) or **polyacrylamide** (a more rigid cross-linked synthetic polymer). The gel is typically held between two glass plates (Fig. 3-17). The molecules to be separated are applied to one end of the gel, and the molecules move through the pores in the matrix under the influence of an electric field. Smaller molecules move more rapidly through the gel and therefore migrate farther in a given time.

Following electrophoresis, the separated molecules may be visualized in the gel by an appropriate technique, such as addition of a stain that binds tightly to the DNA or by radioactive labeling. Depending on the dimensions of the gel and the visualization technique used, samples containing less than a nanogram of material can be separated and detected by gel electrophoresis. Several samples can be electrophoresed simultaneously. For example, the fragments obtained by digesting a DNA sample with

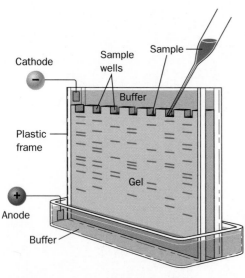

■ **Figure 3-17** | **Apparatus for gel electrophoresis.** Samples are applied in slots at the top of the gel and electrophoresed in parallel lanes. Negatively charged molecules such as DNA migrate through the gel matrix toward the anode in response to an applied electric field. Because smaller molecules move faster, the molecules in each lane are separated according to size. Following electrophoresis, the separated molecules may be visualized by staining, fluorescence, or a radiographic technique.

■ **Figure 3-18** | **Electrophoretogram of restriction digests.** The plasmid pAgK84 has been digested with (A) *Bam*HI, (B) *Pst*I, (C) *Bgl*II, (D) *Hae*III, (E) *Hinc*II, (F) *Sac*I, (G) *Xba*I, and (H) *Hpa*I. Lane I contains bacteriophage λ digested with *Hin*dIII as a standard since these fragments have known sizes. The restriction fragments in each lane are made visible by fluorescence against a black background. [From Slota, J.E. and Farrand, S.F., *Plasmid* **8**, 180 (1982). Copyright © 1982 by Academic Press.]

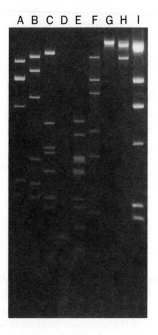

different restriction endonucleases can be visualized side by side (Fig. 3-18). The sizes of the various fragments can be determined by comparing their electrophoretic mobilities to the mobilities of fragments of known size.

C | DNA Is Sequenced by the Chain-Terminator Method

Here we discuss the most commonly used procedure for sequencing DNA, the **chain-terminator method,** which was devised by Frederick Sanger. The first step in this procedure is to obtain single polynucleotide strands. Complementary DNA strands can be separated by heating, which breaks the hydrogen bonds between bases. Next, polynucleotide fragments that terminate at positions corresponding to each of the four nucleotides are generated. Finally, the fragments are separated and detected.

The Chain-Terminator Method Uses DNA Polymerase. The chain-terminator method (also called the **dideoxy method**) uses an *E. coli* enzyme to make complementary copies of the single-stranded DNA being sequenced. The enzyme is a fragment of **DNA polymerase I,** one of the enzymes that participates in replication of bacterial DNA (Section 25-2A). Using the single DNA strand as a template, DNA polymerase I assembles the four deoxynucleoside triphosphates **(dNTPs),** dATP, dCTP, dGTP, and dTTP, into a complementary polynucleotide chain that it elongates in the 5′ → 3′ direction (Fig. 3-19).

DNA polymerase I can sequentially add deoxynucleotides only to the 3′ end of a polynucleotide. Hence, replication is initiated in the presence of a

> **See Guided Exploration 2**
> DNA sequence determination by the chain-terminator method.

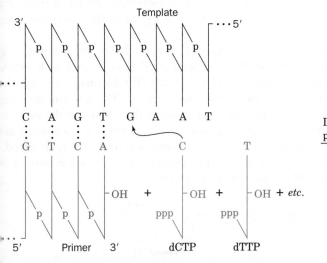
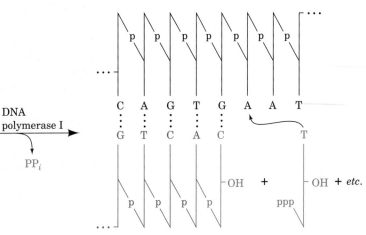

■ **Figure 3-19** | **Action of DNA polymerase I.** Using a single DNA strand as a template, the enzyme elongates the primer by stepwise addition of complementary nucleotides. Incoming nucleotides pair with bases on the template strand and are joined to the growing polynucleotide strand in the 5′ → 3′ direction. The polymerase-catalyzed reaction requires a free 3′-OH group on the growing strand. **Pyrophosphate** ($P_2O_7^{4-}$; PP_i) is released with each nucleotide addition.

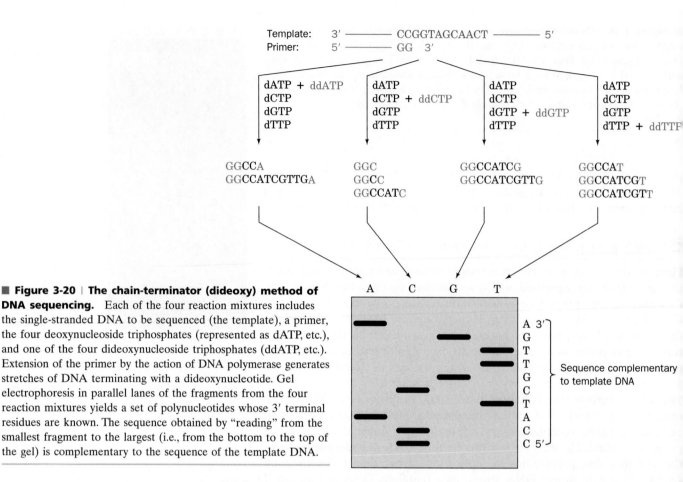

Template: 3' ———— CCGGTAGCAACT ———— 5'
Primer: 5' ———— GG 3'

dATP + ddATP	dATP	dATP	dATP
dCTP	dCTP + ddCTP	dCTP	dCTP
dGTP	dGTP	dGTP + ddGTP	dGTP
dTTP	dTTP	dTTP	dTTP + ddTTP

GGCCA	GGC	GGCCATCG	GGCCAT
GGCCATCGTTGA	GGCC	GGCCATCGTTG	GGCCATCGT
	GGCCATC		GGCCATCGTT

A   C   G   T

A 3'
G
T
T
G
C
T
A
C
C 5'

Sequence complementary to template DNA

■ **Figure 3-20** | **The chain-terminator (dideoxy) method of DNA sequencing.** Each of the four reaction mixtures includes the single-stranded DNA to be sequenced (the template), a primer, the four deoxynucleoside triphosphates (represented as dATP, etc.), and one of the four dideoxynucleoside triphosphates (ddATP, etc.). Extension of the primer by the action of DNA polymerase generates stretches of DNA terminating with a dideoxynucleotide. Gel electrophoresis in parallel lanes of the fragments from the four reaction mixtures yields a set of polynucleotides whose 3' terminal residues are known. The sequence obtained by "reading" from the smallest fragment to the largest (i.e., from the bottom to the top of the gel) is complementary to the sequence of the template DNA.

short polynucleotide (a **primer**) that is complementary to the 3' end of the template DNA and thus becomes the 5' end of the new strand. The primer base-pairs with the template strand, and nucleotides are sequentially added to the 3' end of the primer. If the DNA being sequenced is a restriction fragment, as it usually is, it begins and ends with a restriction site. The primer can therefore be a short DNA segment with the sequence of this restriction site.

DNA Synthesis Terminates after Specific Bases. In the chain-terminator technique (Fig. 3-20), the DNA to be sequenced is incubated with DNA polymerase I, a suitable primer, and the four dNTP **substrates** (reactants in enzymatic reactions) for the polymerization reaction. The reaction mixture also includes a "tagged" compound, either one of the dNTPs or the primer. The tag, which may be a radioactive isotope (e.g., ^{32}P) or a fluorescent label, permits the products of the polymerase reaction to be easily detected.

The key component of the reaction mixture is a small amount of a **2′,3′-dideoxynucleoside triphosphate (ddNTP),**

(P)—(P)—(P)—OCH₂ O   Base

2′,3′-Dideoxynucleoside triphosphate

which lacks the 3'-OH group of deoxynucleotides. *When the dideoxy analog is incorporated into the growing polynucleotide in place of the corresponding normal nucleotide, chain growth is terminated because addition of the next nucleotide requires a free 3'-OH.* By using only a small amount of the ddNTP, a series of truncated chains is generated, each of which ends with the dideoxy analog at one of the positions occupied by the corresponding base.

Relatively modest sequencing tasks use four reaction mixtures, each with a different ddNTP, and the reaction products are electrophoresed in parallel lanes. The lengths of the truncated chains indicate the positions where the dideoxynucleotide was incorporated. Thus, the sequence of the replicated strand can be directly read from the gel (Fig. 3-21). The gel must have sufficient resolving power to separate fragments that differ in length by only one nucleotide. Two sets of gels, one run for a longer time than the other, can be used to obtain the sequence of up to 800 bases of DNA. Note that the sequence obtained by the chain-terminator method is complementary to the DNA strand being sequenced.

Large Sequencing Projects Are Automated. Large-scale sequencing operations are accelerated by automation. In a variation of the chain-terminator method, the primers used in the four chain-extension reactions are each linked to a different fluorescent dye. The separately reacted mixtures are combined and subjected to gel electrophoresis in a single lane. As each fragment exits the bottom of the gel, its terminal base is identified by its characteristic fluorescence (Fig. 3-22) with an error rate of ~1%.

In the most advanced systems, the sequencing gel is contained in an array of up to 96 capillary tubes (rather than in a slab-shaped apparatus), sample preparation and sample loading are performed by robotic systems, and electrophoresis and data analysis are fully automated. These systems can simultaneously sequence 96 DNA samples averaging ~600 bases each with a turnaround time of ~2.5 hr and hence can identify up to 550,000 bases per day—all with only ~15 min of human attention (a skilled

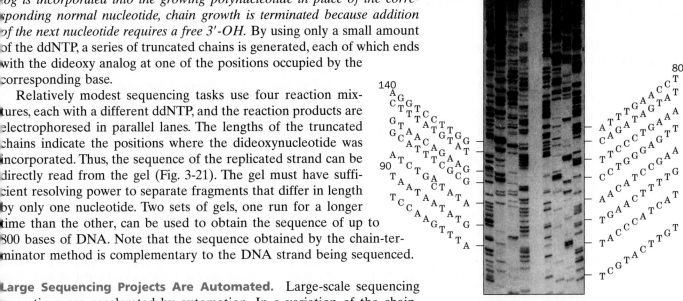

■ **Figure 3-21 | An autoradiogram of a sequencing gel.** The positions of radioactive DNA fragments produced by the chain-terminator method were visualized by laying X-ray film over the gel after electrophoresis. A second loading of the gel (the four lanes at right) was made 90 min after the initial loading in order to obtain the sequences of the smaller fragments. The deduced sequence of 140 nucleotides is written along the side. [From Hindley, J., DNA sequencing, *in* Work, T.S. and Burdon, R.H. (Eds.), *Laboratory Techniques in Biochemistry and Molecular Biology,* Vol. 10, p. 82, Elsevier (1983). Used by permission.]

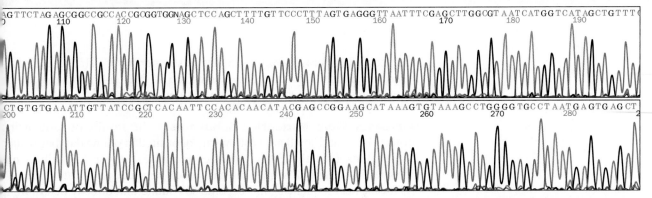

■ **Figure 3-22 | Automated DNA sequencing.** In this variant of the technique, a different fluorescent dye is attached to the primer in each of the four reaction mixtures in the chain-terminator procedure. The four reaction mixtures are combined for electrophoresis. Each of the four colored curves therefore represents the electrophoretic pattern of fragments containing one of the dideoxynucleotides: Green, red, black, and blue peaks correspond to fragments ending in ddATP, ddTTP, ddGTP, and ddCTP, respectively. The 3'-terminal base of each oligonucleotide, identified by the fluorescence of its gel band, is indicated by a single letter (A, T, G, or C). This portion of the readout corresponds to nucleotides 100–290 of the DNA segment being sequenced. [Courtesy of Mark Adams, The Institute for Genomic Research, Rockville, Maryland.]

BOX 3-1 **PATHWAYS OF DISCOVERY**

Francis Collins and the Gene for Cystic Fibrosis

Francis S. Collins (1950–)

By the mid-twentieth century, the molecular basis of several human diseases was appreciated. For example, sickle-cell anemia (Section 7-1E) was known to be caused by an abnormal hemoglobin protein. Studies of sickle-cell hemoglobin eventually revealed the underlying genetic defect, a mutation in a hemoglobin gene. It therefore seemed possible to trace other diseases to defective genes. But for many genetic diseases, even those with well-characterized symptoms, no defective protein had yet been identified. One such disease was cystic fibrosis, which is characterized mainly by the secretion of thick mucus that obstructs the airways and creates an ideal environment for bacterial growth. Cystic fibrosis is the most common inherited disease in individuals of northern European descent, striking about 1 in 2500 newborns and leading to death by early adulthood due to irreversible lung damage. It was believed that identifying the molecular defect in cystic fibrosis would lead to better understanding of the disease and to the ability to design more effective treatments.

Enter Francis Collins, who began his career by earning a doctorate in physical chemistry but then enrolled in medical school to take part in the molecular biology revolution. As a physician-scientist, Collins developed methods for analyzing large stretches of DNA in order to home in on specific genes, including the one that, when mutated, causes cystic fibrosis. By analyzing the DNA of individuals with the disease (who had two copies of the defective gene) and of family members who were asymptomatic carriers (with one normal and one defective copy of the gene), Collins

and his team localized the cystic fibrosis gene to the long arm of chromosome 7. They gradually closed in on a DNA segment that appears to be present in a number of mammalian species, which suggests that the segment contains an essential gene. The cystic fibrosis gene was finally identified in 1989. Collins had demonstrated the feasibility of identifying a genetic defect in the absence of other molecular information.

Once the cystic fibrosis gene was in hand, it was a relatively straightforward process to deduce the probable structure and function of the encoded protein, which turned out to be a membrane channel for chloride ions. When functioning normally, the protein helps regulate the ionic composition and viscosity of extracellular secretions. Discovery of the cystic fibrosis gene also made it possible to design tests to identify carriers so that they could take advantage of genetic counseling.

Throughout Collins' work on the cystic fibrosis gene and during subsequent hunts for the genes that cause neurofibromatosis and Huntington's disease, he was mindful of the ethical implications of the new science of molecular genetics. Collins has been a strong advocate for protecting the privacy of genetic information. At the same time, he recognizes the potential therapeutic use of such information. In his tenure as director of the human genome project, he was committed to making the results freely and immediately accessible, as a service to researchers and the individuals who might benefit from new therapies based on molecular genetics.

Riordan, J.R., Rommens, J.M., Kerem, B.-S., Alon, N., Rozmahel, R. Grzelczak, Z., Zielensky, J., Lok, S., Plavsic, N., Chou, J.-L., Drumm, M.L., Iannuzzi, M.C., Collins, F.S., and Tsui, L.-C., Identification of the cystic fibrosis gene: Cloning and characterization of complementary DNA, *Science* **245,** 1066–1073 (1989).

operator can identify only ~25,000 bases per year using the above-described manual methods). Sequencing the 3.2-billion-bp human genome required hundreds of such advanced sequencing systems.

Databases Store Nucleotide Sequences. The results of sequencing projects large and small are customarily deposited in online databases such as GenBank (see the Bioinformatics Exercises). Over 150 billion nucleotides in 80 million sequences have been recorded as of late 2006.

Nucleic acid sequencing has become so routine that directly determining a protein's amino acid sequence (Section 5-3) is generally far more time-consuming than determining the base sequence of its corresponding gene. In fact, nucleic acid sequencing is invaluable for studying genes whose products have not yet been identified. If the gene can be sequenced, the probable function of its protein product may be deduced by comparing the base sequence to those of genes whose products are already characterized (see Box 3-1).

D | Entire Genomes Have Been Sequenced

The advent of large-scale sequencing techniques brought to fruition the dream of sequencing entire genomes. However, the major technical hurdle in sequencing all the DNA in an organism's genome is not the DNA sequencing itself but, rather, assembling the tens of thousands to tens of millions of sequenced segments (depending on the size of the genome) into contiguous blocks and assigning them to their correct chromosomal positions. To do so required the development of automated sequencing protocols and mathematically sophisticated computer algorithms.

The first complete genome sequence to be determined, that of the bacterium *Haemophilus influenzae,* was reported in 1995 by Craig Venter. By mid-2007, the complete genome sequences of over 500 prokaryotes had been reported (with many more being determined) as well as those of dozens of eukaryotes, including humans, human pathogens, plants, and laboratory organisms (Table 3-3).

The determination of the ~3.2-billion-nucleotide human genome sequence was a gargantuan undertaking involving hundreds of scientists working in two groups, one led by Venter and the other by Francis Collins (Box 3-1), Eric Lander, and John Sulston. After over a decade of intense

Table 3-3 Some Sequenced Genomes

Organism	Genome Size (kb)	Number of Chromosomes
Mycoplasma genitalium (human parasite)	580	1
Rickettsia prowazekii (putative relative of mitochondria)	1,112	1
Haemophilus influenzae (human pathogen)	1,830	1
Escherichia coli (human symbiont)	4,639	1
Saccharomyces cerevisiae (baker's yeast)	11,700	16
Plasmodium falciparum (protozoan that causes malaria)	30,000	14
Caenorhabditis elegans (nematode)	97,000	6
Arabidopsis thaliana (dicotyledonous plant)	117,000	5
Drosophila melanogaster (fruit fly)	137,000	4
Oryza sativa (rice)	390,000	12
Danio rerio (zebra fish)	1,700,000	25
Gallus gallus (chicken)	1,200,000	40
Mus musculus (mouse)	2,500,000	20
Homo sapiens	3,200,000	23

effort, the "rough draft" of the human genome sequence was reported in early 2001 and the "finished" sequence was reported in mid-2003. This stunning achievement promises to revolutionize the way both biochemistry and medicine are viewed and practiced, although it is likely to require many years of further effort before its full significance is understood. Nevertheless, numerous important conclusions can already be drawn, including these:

1. About half the human genome consists of repeating sequences of various types.

2. Up to 60% of the genome is transcribed to RNA.

3. Only 1.1% to 1.4% of the genome (~2% of the transcribed RNA) encodes protein.

4. The human genome appears to contain only ~23,000 protein-encoding genes [also known as **open reading frames (ORFs)**] rather than the 50,000 to 140,000 ORFs that had previously been predicted. This compares with the ~6000 ORFs in yeast, ~13,000 in *Drosophila*, ~18,000 in *C. elegans,* and ~26,000 in *Arabidopsis* (although these numbers will almost certainly change as our ability to recognize ORFs improves).

5. Only a small fraction of human proteins are unique to vertebrates; most occur in other if not all life-forms.

6. Two randomly selected human genomes differ, on average, by only 1 nucleotide per 1250; that is, any two people are likely to be >99.9% genetically identical.

The obviously greater complexity of humans (vertebrates) relative to invertebrate forms of life is unlikely to be due to the not-much-larger numbers of ORFs that vertebrates encode. Rather, it appears that vertebrate proteins themselves are more complex than those of invertebrates; that is, vertebrate proteins tend to have more domains (modules) than invertebrate proteins, and these modules are more often selectively expressed through **alternative gene splicing** (a phenomenon in which a given gene transcript can be processed in multiple ways so as to yield different proteins when translated; Section 26-3A). Thus, many vertebrate genes encode several different although similar proteins.

E | Evolution Results from Sequence Mutations

One of the richest rewards of nucleic acid sequencing technology is the information it provides about the mechanisms of evolution. The chemical and physical properties of DNA, such as its regular three-dimensional shape and the elegant process of replication, may leave the impression that genetic information is relatively static. In fact, *DNA is a dynamic molecule, subject to changes that alter genetic information.* For example, the mispairing of bases during DNA replication can introduce errors known as **point mutations** in the daughter strand. Mutations also result from DNA damage by chemicals or radiation. More extensive alterations in genetic information are caused by faulty **recombination** (exchange of DNA between chromosomes) and the **transposition** of genes within or between chromosomes and, in some cases, from one organism to another. All these alterations to DNA provide the raw material for natural selection. When a mutated gene is transcribed and the messenger RNA is subsequently translated, the resulting protein may have properties that confer some advantage to the individual. As a beneficial change is passed from generation to

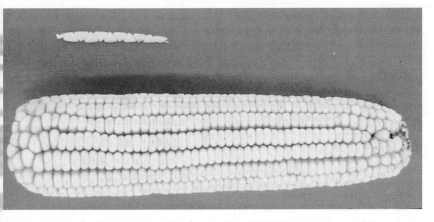

generation, it may become part of the standard genetic makeup of the species. Of course, many changes occur as a species evolves, not all of them simple and not all of them gradual.

Phylogenetic relationships can be revealed by comparing the sequences of similar genes in different organisms. The number of nucleotide differences between the corresponding genes in two species roughly indicates the degree to which the species have diverged through evolution. The regrouping of prokaryotes into archaea and bacteria (Section 1-2C) according to rRNA sequences present in all organisms illustrates the impact of sequence analysis.

Nucleic acid sequencing also reveals that species differing in **phenotype** (physical characteristics) are nonetheless remarkably similar at the molecular level. For example, humans and chimpanzees share 98–99% of their DNA. Studies of corn (maize) and its putative ancestor, teosinte, suggest that the plants differ in only a handful of genes governing kernel development (teosinte kernels are encased by an inedible shell; Fig. 3-23).

Small mutations in DNA are apparently responsible for relatively large evolutionary leaps. This is perhaps not so surprising when the nature of genetic information is considered. A mutation in a gene segment that does not encode protein might interfere with the binding of cellular factors that influence the timing of transcription. A mutation in a gene encoding an RNA might interfere with the binding of factors that affect the efficiency of translation. Even a minor rearrangement of genes could disrupt an entire developmental process, resulting in the appearance of a novel species. Notwithstanding the high probability that most sudden changes would lead to diminished individual fitness or the inability to reproduce, the capacity for sudden changes in genetic information is consistent with the fossil record. Ironically, the discontinuities in the fossil record that are probably caused in part by sudden genetic changes once fueled the adversaries of Charles Darwin's theory of evolution by natural selection.

5 | Manipulating DNA

Along with nucleic acid sequencing, techniques for manipulating DNA *in vitro* and *in vivo* (in the test tube and in living systems) have produced dramatic advances in biochemistry, cell biology, and genetics. In many cases, this **recombinant DNA technology** has made it possible to purify specific DNA sequences and to prepare them in quantities sufficient for study. Consider the problem of isolating a unique 1000-bp length of chromosomal DNA from *E. coli*. A 10-L culture of cells grown at a density of

■ **CHECK YOUR UNDERSTANDING**

Explain how the restriction–modification system operates.

Summarize the steps in the chain-terminator procedure for sequencing DNA.

What proportion of the human genome is transcribed? Translated?

Explain how evolution can result from a mutation in DNA.

LEARNING OBJECTIVES

■ Understand how recombinant DNA molecules are constructed and propagated.

■ Understand that a DNA library is a collection of cloned DNA segments that can be screened to find a particular gene.

■ Understand that the polymerase chain reaction copies and thereby amplifies a defined segment of DNA.

■ Understand that recombinant DNA technology can be used to manipulate genes for protein expression or for the production of transgenic organisms.

$\sim 10^{10}$ cells · mL^{-1} contains only ~ 0.1 mg of the desired DNA, which would be all but impossible to separate from the rest of the DNA using classical separation techniques (Sections 5-2 and 24-3). *Recombinant DNA technology, also called* **molecular cloning** *or* **genetic engineering,** *makes it possible to isolate, amplify, and modify specific DNA sequences.*

A | Cloned DNA Is an Amplified Copy

The following approach is used to obtain and amplify a segment of DNA:

1. A fragment of DNA of the appropriate size is generated by a restriction enzyme, by PCR (Section 3-5C), or by chemical synthesis.
2. The fragment is incorporated into another DNA molecule known as a **vector,** which contains the sequences necessary to direct DNA replication.
3. The vector—with the DNA of interest—is introduced into cells, where it is replicated.
4. Cells containing the desired DNA are identified, or selected.

Cloning refers to the production of multiple identical organisms derived from a single ancestor. The term **clone** refers to the collection of cells that contain the vector carrying the DNA of interest or to the DNA itself. In a suitable host organism, such as *E. coli* or yeast, large amounts of the inserted DNA can be produced.

Cloned DNA can be purified and sequenced (Section 3-4). Alternatively, if a cloned gene is flanked by the properly positioned regulatory sequences for RNA and protein synthesis, the host may also produce large quantities of the RNA and protein specified by that gene. Thus, cloning provides materials (nucleic acids and proteins) for other studies and also provides a means for studying gene expression under controlled conditions.

Cloning Vectors Carry Foreign DNA. A variety of small, autonomously replicating DNA molecules are used as cloning vectors. **Plasmids** are circular DNA molecules of 1 to 200 kb found in bacteria or yeast cells. Plasmids can be considered molecular parasites, but in many instances they benefit their host by providing functions, such as resistance to antibiotics, that the host lacks.

Some types of plasmids are present in one or a few copies per cell and replicate only when the bacterial chromosome replicates. However, the plasmids used for cloning are typically present in hundreds of copies per cell and can be induced to replicate until the cell contains two or three thousand copies (representing about half of the cell's total DNA). The plasmids that have been constructed for laboratory use are relatively small, replicate easily, carry genes specifying resistance to one or more antibiotics, and contain a number of conveniently located restriction endonuclease sites into which foreign DNA can be inserted. Plasmid vectors can be used to clone DNA segments of no more than ~ 10 kb. The *E. coli* plasmid designated **pUC18** (Fig. 3-24) is a representative cloning vector ("pUC" stands for plasmid-Universal Cloning).

Bacteriophage λ (Fig. 3-25) is an alternative cloning vector that can accommodate DNA inserts up to 16 kb. The central third of the 48.5-kb phage genome is not required for infection and can therefore be replaced

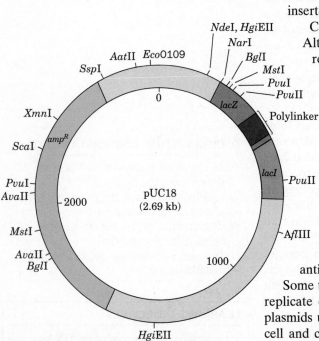

■ **Figure 3-24 | The plasmid pUC18.** As shown in this diagram, the circular plasmid contains multiple restriction sites, including a **polylinker** sequence that contains 13 restriction sites that are not present elsewhere on the plasmid. The three genes expressed by the plasmid are *amp*^{R}, which confers resistance to the antibiotic **ampicillin;** *lacZ,* which encodes the enzyme **β-galactosidase;** and *lacI,* which encodes a factor that controls transcription of *lacZ* (as described in Section 28-2A).

by foreign DNAs of similar size. The resulting **recombinant,** or **chimera** (named after the mythological monster with a lion's head, goat's body, and serpent's tail), is packaged into phage particles that can then be introduced into the host cells. One advantage of using phage vectors is that the recombinant DNA is produced in large amounts in easily purified form. **Baculoviruses,** which infect insect cells, are similarly used for cloning in cultures of insect cells.

Much larger DNA segments—up to several hundred kilobase pairs—can be cloned in large vectors known as **bacterial artificial chromosomes (BACs)** or **yeast artificial chromosomes (YACs).** YACs are linear DNA molecules that contain all the chromosomal structures required for normal replication and segregation during yeast cell division. BACs, which replicate in *E. coli,* are derived from circular plasmids that normally replicate long regions of DNA and are maintained at the level of approximately one copy per cell (properties similar to those of actual chromosomes).

Ligase Joins Two DNA Segments. A DNA segment to be cloned is often obtained through the action of restriction endonucleases. Most restriction enzymes cleave DNA to yield sticky ends (Section 3-4A). Therefore, as Janet Mertz and Ron Davis first demonstrated in 1972, *a restriction fragment can be inserted into a cut made in a cloning vector by the same restriction enzyme* (Fig. 3-26). The complementary ends of the two DNAs form base pairs **(anneal)** and the sugar–phosphate backbones are covalently **ligated,** or spliced together, through the action of an enzyme named **DNA ligase.** (A ligase produced by a bacteriophage can also join blunt-ended restriction fragments.) A great advantage of using a restriction enzyme to construct a recombinant DNA molecule is that the DNA insert can later be precisely excised from the cloned vector by cleaving it with the same restriction enzyme.

Selection Detects the Presence of a Cloned DNA. The expression of a chimeric plasmid in a bacterial host was first demonstrated in 1973 by Herbert Boyer and Stanley Cohen. A host bacterium can take up a plasmid when the two are mixed together, but the vector becomes permanently established in its bacterial host (transformation) with an efficiency of only ~0.1%. However, a single transformed cell can multiply without limit, producing large quantities of recombinant DNA. Bacterial cells are typically plated on a semisolid growth medium at a low enough density that discrete colonies, each arising from a single cell, are visible.

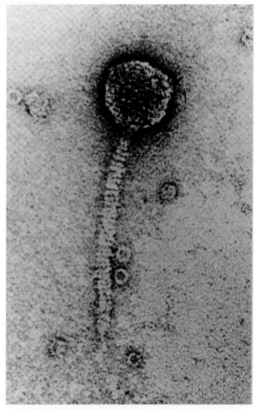

■ **Figure 3-25** | **Bacteriophage λ.** During phage infection, DNA contained in the "head" of the phage particle enters the bacterial cell, where it is replicated ~100 times and packaged to form progeny phage. [Electron micrograph courtesy of A.F. Howatson. From Lewin, B., *Gene Expression,* Vol. 3, Fig. 5.23, Wiley (1977).]

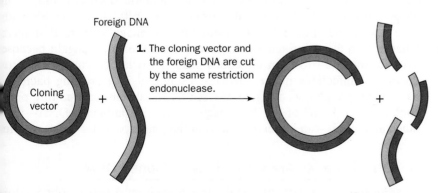

Foreign DNA

1. The cloning vector and the foreign DNA are cut by the same restriction endonuclease.

2. The sticky ends of the vector and the foreign DNA fragments anneal and are covalently joined by DNA ligase.

Cloning vector

Chimeric DNA

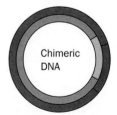

The result is a chimeric DNA containing a portion of the foreign DNA inserted into the vector.

■ **Figure 3-26** | **Construction of a recombinant DNA molecule.** ✎ **See the Animated Figures.**

It is essential to select only those host organisms that have been transformed and that contain a properly constructed vector. In the case of plasmid transformation, selection can be accomplished through the use of antibiotics and/or chromogenic (color-producing) substances. For example, the *lacZ* gene in the pUC18 plasmid (see Fig. 3-24) encodes the enzyme β-galactosidase, which cleaves the colorless compound **X-gal** to a blue product:

5-Bromo-4-chloro-3-indolyl-β-ᴅ-galactoside (X-gal)
(*colorless*)

β-ᴅ-Galactose   **5-Bromo-4-chloro-3-hydroxyindole**
(*blue*)

Cells of *E. coli* that have been transformed by an unmodified pUC18 plasmid form blue colonies. However, if the plasmid contains a foreign DNA insert in its polylinker region, the colonies are colorless because the insert interrupts the protein-coding sequence of the *lacZ* gene and no functional β-galactosidase is produced. Bacteria that have failed to take up any plasmid are also colorless due to the absence of β-galactosidase, but these cells can be excluded by adding the antibiotic ampicillin to the growth medium (the plasmid includes the gene *amp*^R, which confers ampicillin resistance). Thus, successfully transformed cells form colorless colonies in the presence of ampicillin. Genes such as amp^R are known as **selectable markers**.

Genetically engineered bacteriophage λ vectors contain restriction sites that flank the dispensable central third of the phage genome. This segment can be replaced by foreign DNA, but the chimeric DNA is packaged in phage particles only if its length is from 75 to 105% of the 48.5-kb wild-type λ genome (Fig. 3-27). Consequently, λ phage vectors that have failed to acquire a foreign DNA insert are unable to propagate because they are too short to form infectious phage particles. Of course, the production of infectious phage particles results not in a growing bacterial colony but in a **plaque,** a region of lysed bacterial cells, on a culture plate containing a "lawn" of the host bacteria. The recombinant DNA—now much amplified—can be recovered from the phage particles in the plaque.

B | DNA Libraries Are Collections of Cloned DNA

In order to clone a particular DNA fragment, it must first be obtained in relatively pure form. The magnitude of this task can be appreciated by considering that, for example, a 1-kb fragment of human DNA represents

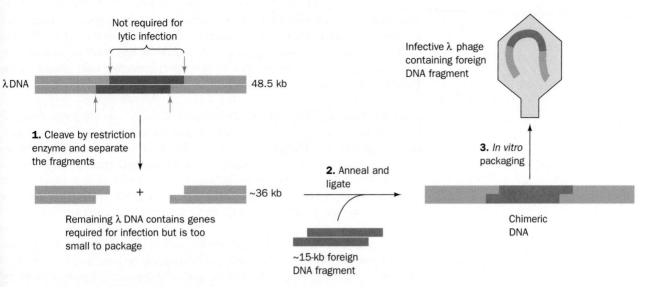

■ Figure 3-27 | Cloning with bacteriophage λ. Removal of a nonessential portion of the phage genome allows a segment of foreign DNA to be inserted. The DNA insert can be packaged into an infectious phage particle only if the insert DNA has the appropriate size. 🔊 **See the Animated Figures.**

only 0.000031% of the 3.2 billion-bp human genome. Of course, identifying a particular DNA fragment requires knowing something about its nucleotide sequence or its protein product. In practice, it is usually more difficult to identify a particular DNA fragment from an organism and then clone it than it is to clone all the organism's DNA that might contain the DNA of interest and then identify the clones containing the desired sequence.

A Genomic Library Includes All of an Organism's DNA. The cloned set of all DNA fragments from a particular organism is known as its **genomic library.** Genomic libraries are generated by a procedure known as **shotgun cloning.** The chromosomal DNA of the organism is isolated, cleaved to fragments of clonable size, and inserted into a cloning vector. The DNA is usually fragmented by partial rather than exhaustive restriction digestion so that the genomic library contains intact representatives of all the organism's genes, including those that contain restriction sites. DNA in solution can also be mechanically fragmented **(sheared)** by rapid stirring.

Given the large size of the genome relative to a gene, the shotgun cloning method is subject to the laws of probability. The number of randomly generated fragments that must be cloned to ensure a high probability that a desired sequence is represented at least once in the genomic library is calculated as follows: The probability P that a set of N clones contains a fragment that constitutes a fraction f, in bp, of the organism's genome is

$$P = 1 - (1 - f)^N \qquad [3\text{-}1]$$

Consequently,

$$N = \log(1 - P)/\log(1 - f) \qquad [3\text{-}2]$$

Thus, in order for P to equal 0.99 for fragments averaging 10 kb in length, $N = 2162$ for the 4600-kb *E. coli* chromosome and 63,000 for the 137,000-kb *Drosophila* genome. The use of BAC- or YAC-based genomic libraries with their large fragment lengths therefore greatly reduces the effort necessary to obtain a given gene segment from a large genome. After a BAC- or YAC-based clone containing the desired DNA has been identified (see below), its large DNA insert can be further fragmented and cloned again **(subcloned)** to isolate the target DNA.

A cDNA Library Represents Expressed Genes. A different type of DNA library contains only the expressed sequences from a particular cell type. Such a **cDNA library** is constructed by isolating all the cell's mRNAs and then copying them to DNA using a specialized type of DNA polymerase known as **reverse transcriptase** because it synthesizes DNA using RNA templates (Box 25-2). The **complementary DNA (cDNA)** molecules are then inserted into cloning vectors to form a cDNA library.

A Library Is Screened for the Gene of Interest. Once the requisite number of clones is obtained, the genomic library must be **screened** for the presence of the desired gene. This can be done by a process known as **colony** or *in situ* **hybridization** (Latin: *in situ,* in position; Fig. 3-28). The cloned yeast colonies, bacterial colonies, or phage plaques to be tested are transferred, by **replica plating,** from a master plate to a nitrocellulose filter (replica plating is also used to transfer colonies to plates containing different growth media). Next, the filter is treated with NaOH, which lyses the cells or phages and separates the DNA into single strands, which preferentially bind to the nitrocellulose. The filter is then dried to fix the DNA in place and incubated with a labeled **probe.** The probe is a short segment of DNA or RNA whose sequence is complementary to a portion of the DNA of interest. After washing away unbound probe, the presence of the probe on the nitrocellulose is detected by a technique appropriate for the label used (e.g., exposure to X-ray film for a radioactive probe, a process known as **autoradiography,** or illumination with an appropriate wavelength for a fluorescent probe). Only those colonies or plaques containing the desired gene bind the probe and are thereby detected. The corresponding clones can then be retrieved from the master plate. Using this technique, a

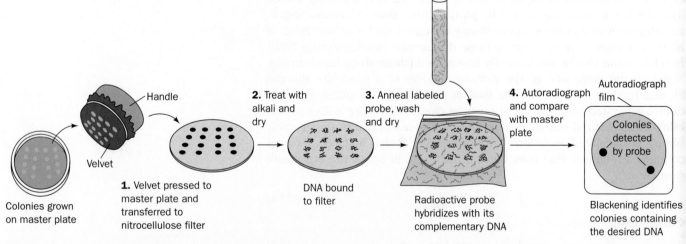

■ **Figure 3-28** | **Colony (*in situ*) hybridization.** Colonies are transferred from a "master" culture plate by replica plating. Clones containing the DNA of interest are identified by the ability to bind a specific probe. Here, binding is detected by laying X-ray film over the dried filter. Since the colonies on the master plate and on the filter have the same spatial distribution, positive colonies are easily retrieved.

human genomic library of ~1 million clones can be readily screened for the presence of one particular DNA segment.

Choosing a probe for a gene whose sequence is not known requires some artistry. The corresponding mRNA can be used as a probe if it is available in sufficient quantities to be isolated. Alternatively, if the amino acid sequence of the protein encoded by the gene is known, the probe may be a mixture of the various synthetic oligonucleotides that are complementary to a segment of the gene's inferred base sequence. Several disease-related genes have been isolated using probes specific for nearby markers, such as repeated DNA sequences, that were already known to be genetically linked to the disease genes.

C | DNA Is Amplified by the Polymerase Chain Reaction

Although molecular cloning techniques are indispensable to modern biochemical research, the **polymerase chain reaction (PCR)** is often a faster and more convenient method for amplifying a specific DNA. Segments of up to 6 kb can be amplified by this technique, which was devised by Kary Mullis in 1985. *In PCR, a DNA sample is separated into single strands and incubated with DNA polymerase, dNTPs, and two oligonucleotide primers whose sequences flank the DNA segment of interest. The primers direct the DNA polymerase to synthesize complementary strands of the target DNA* (Fig. 3-29). Multiple cycles of this process, each doubling the amount of the target DNA, geometrically amplify the DNA starting from as little as a single gene copy. In each cycle, the two strands of the duplex DNA are separated by heating, the primers are annealed to their complementary segments on the DNA, and the DNA polymerase directs the synthesis of the complementary strands. The use of a heat-stable DNA polymerase, such as *Taq polymerase* isolated from *Thermus aquaticus,* a bacterium that thrives at 75°C, eliminates the need to add fresh enzyme after each round of heating (heat inactivates most enzymes). Hence, in the presence of sufficient quantities of primers and dNTPs, PCR is carried out simply by cyclically varying the temperature.

Twenty cycles of PCR increase the amount of the target sequence around a millionfold ($\sim 2^{20}$) with high specificity. Indeed, PCR can amplify a target DNA present only once in a sample of 10^5 cells, so this method can be used without prior DNA purification. The amplified DNA can then be sequenced or cloned.

PCR amplification has become an indispensable tool. Clinically, it is used to diagnose infectious diseases and to detect rare pathological events such as mutations leading to cancer. Forensically, the DNA from a single hair or sperm can be am-

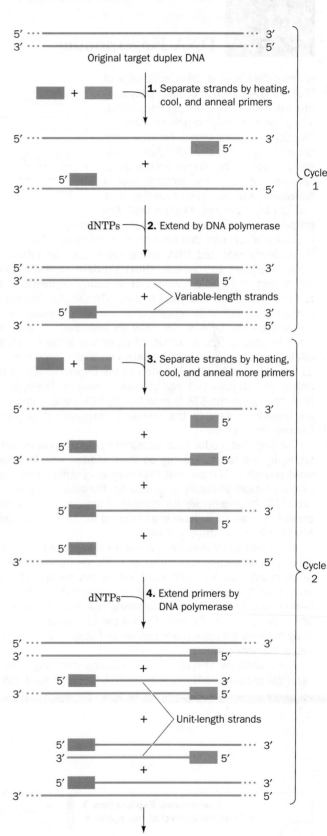

◀ **Figure 3-29 | The polymerase chain reaction (PCR).** In each cycle of the reaction, the strands of the duplex DNA are separated by heating, the reaction mixture is cooled to allow primers to anneal to complementary sequences on each strand, and DNA polymerase extends the primers. The number of "unit-length" strands doubles with every cycle after the second cycle. By choosing primers specific for each end of a gene, the gene can be amplified over a millionfold.

BOX 3-2 PERSPECTIVES IN BIOCHEMISTRY

DNA Fingerprinting

Forensic DNA testing takes advantage of DNA sequence variations or **polymorphisms** that occur among individuals. Many genetic polymorphisms have no functional consequences because they occur in regions of the DNA that contain many repetitions but do not encode genes (although if they are located near a "disease" gene, they can be used to track and identify the gene). Modern **DNA fingerprinting** methods examine these noncoding repetitive DNA sequences in samples that have been amplified by PCR.

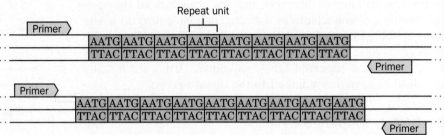

Tandemly repeated DNA sequences occur throughout the human genome and include **short tandem repeats (STRs),** which contain variable numbers of repeating segments of two to seven base pairs. The most popular STR sites for forensic use contain tetranucleotide repeats. The number of repeats at any one site on the DNA varies between individuals, even within a family. Each different number of repeats at a site is called an **allele,** and each individual can have two alleles, one from each parent. Since PCR is the first step of the fingerprinting process, only a tiny amount (~1 ng) of DNA is needed. The region of DNA containing the STR is amplified by PCR using primers that are complementary to the unique (nonrepeating) sequences flanking the repeats.

The amplified products are separated by electrophoresis and detected by the fluorescent tag on their primers. An STR allele is small enough (<500 bp) that DNA fragments differing by a four-base repeat can be readily differentiated. The allele designation for each STR site is generally the number of times a repeated unit is present. STR sites that have been selected for forensic use generally have 7 to 30 different alleles.

In the example shown here, the upper trace shows the fluorescence of the electrophoretogram of reference standards (the set of all possible alleles, each identified by the number of repeat units, from 13 to 23). The lower trace corresponds to the sample being tested, which contains two alleles, one with 16 repeats and one with 18 repeats. Several STR sites can be analyzed simultaneously by using the appropriate primers and tagging them with different fluorescence dyes.

The probability of two individuals having matching DNA fingerprints depends on the number of STR sites examined and the

number of alleles at each site. For example, if a pair of alleles at one site occurs in the population with a frequency of 10% (1/10), and a pair of alleles at a second site occurs with a frequency of 5% (1/20), then the probability that the DNA fingerprints from two individuals would match at both sites is 1 in 200 (1/10 × 1/20; the probabilities of independent events are multiplied). By examining multiple STR sites, the probability of obtaining matching fingerprints by chance becomes exceedingly small.

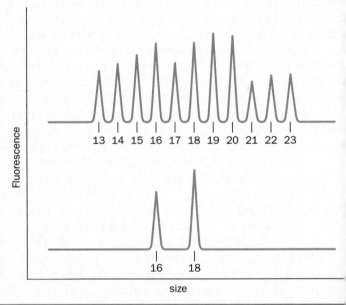

See Guided Exploration 3
PCR and site-directed mutagenesis.

plified by PCR so that it can be used to identify the donor (Box 3-2) Traditional ABO blood-type analysis requires a coin-sized drop of blood PCR is effective on pinhead-sized samples of biological fluids. Courts now consider DNA sequences as unambiguous identifiers of individuals, as are fingerprints, because the chance of two individuals sharing extended sequences of DNA is typically one in a million or more. In a few cases, PCR has dramatically restored justice to convicts who were released from prison on the basis of PCR results that proved their innocence—even many years after the crime-scene evidence had been collected.

D | Recombinant DNA Technology Has Numerous Practical Applications

The ability to manipulate DNA sequences allows genes to be altered and expressed in order to obtain proteins with improved functional properties or to correct genetic defects.

Cloned Genes Can Be Expressed. The production of large quantities of scarce or novel proteins is relatively straightforward only for bacterial proteins: A cloned gene must be inserted into an **expression vector,** a plasmid that contains properly positioned transcriptional and translational control sequences. The production of a protein of interest may reach 30% of the host's total cellular protein. Such genetically engineered organisms are called **overproducers.** Bacterial cells often sequester large amounts of useless and possibly toxic (to the bacterium) protein as insoluble inclusions, which sometimes simplifies the task of purifying the protein.

Bacteria can produce eukaryotic proteins only if the recombinant DNA that carries the protein-coding sequence also includes bacterial transcriptional and translational control sequences. Synthesis of eukaryotic proteins in bacteria also presents other problems. For example, many eukaryotic genes are large and contain stretches of nucleotides **(introns)** that are transcribed and excised before translation (Section 26-3A); bacteria lack the machinery to excise the introns. In addition, many eukaryotic proteins are posttranslationally modified by the addition of carbohydrates or by other reactions. These problems can be overcome by using expression vectors that propagate in eukaryotic hosts, such as yeast or cultured insect or animal cells.

Table 3-4 lists some recombinant proteins produced for medical and agricultural use. In many cases, purification of these proteins directly from human or animal tissues is unfeasible on ethical or practical grounds.

Table 3-4	Some Proteins Produced by Genetic Engineering
Protein	**Use**
Human insulin	Treatment of diabetes
Human growth hormone	Treatment of some endocrine disorders
Erythropoietin	Stimulation of red blood cell production
Colony-stimulating factors	Production and activation of white blood cells
Coagulation factors IX and X	Treatment of blood clotting disorders (hemophilia)
Tissue-type plasminogen activator	Lysis of blood clots after heart attack and stroke
Bovine growth hormone	Production of milk in cows
Hepatitis B surface antigen	Vaccination against hepatitis B

Expression systems permit large-scale, efficient preparation of the protein while minimizing the risk of contamination by viruses or other pathogens from tissue samples.

Site-Directed Mutagenesis Alters a Gene's Nucleotide Sequence

After isolating a gene, it is possible to modify the nucleotide sequence to alter the amino acid sequence of the encoded protein. **Site-directed mutagenesis,** a technique pioneered by Michael Smith, *mimics the natural process of evolution and allows predictions about the structural and functional roles of particular amino acids in a protein to be rigorously tested in the laboratory.*

Synthetic oligonucleotides are required to specifically alter genes through site-directed mutagenesis. An oligonucleotide whose sequence is identical to a portion of the gene of interest except for the desired base changes is used to direct replication of the gene. The oligonucleotide hybridizes to the corresponding **wild-type** (naturally occurring) sequence if there are no more than a few mismatched base pairs. Extension of the oligonucleotide, called a primer, by DNA polymerase yields the desired altered gene (Fig. 3-30). The altered gene can then be inserted into an appropriate vector. A mutagenized primer can also be used to generate altered genes by PCR.

Transgenic Organisms Contain Foreign Genes.

For many purposes it is preferable to tailor an intact organism rather than just a protein—true genetic engineering. Multicellular organisms expressing a gene from another organism are said to be **transgenic,** and the transplanted foreign gene is called a **transgene.**

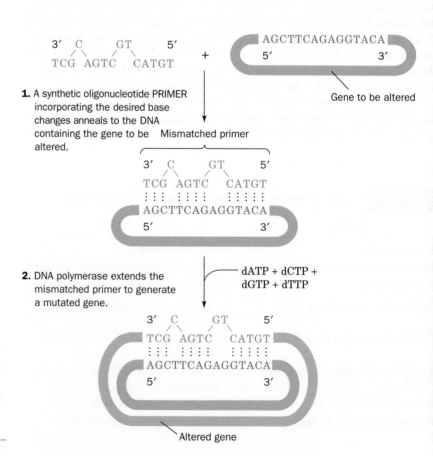

■ **Figure 3-30** | **Site-directed mutagenesis.** The altered gene can be inserted into a suitable cloning vector to be amplified, expressed, or used to generate a mutant organism. ✑ **See the Animated Figures.**

For the change to be permanent, that is, heritable, a transgene must be stably integrated into the organism's germ cells. For mice, this is accomplished by microinjecting cloned DNA encoding the desired altered characteristics into a fertilized egg and implanting it into the uterus of a foster mother. A well-known example of a transgenic mouse contains extra copies of a growth hormone gene (Fig. 3-31).

Transgenic farm animals have also been developed. Ideally, the genes of such animals could be tailored to allow the animals to grow faster on less food or to be resistant to particular diseases. Some transgenic farm animals have been engineered to secrete medically useful proteins into their milk. Harvesting such a substance from milk is much more cost-effective than producing the same substance in bacterial cultures.

One of the most successful transgenic organisms is corn (maize) that has been genetically modified to produce a protein that is toxic to plant-eating insects (but harmless to vertebrates). The toxin is synthesized by the soil microbe *Bacillus thuringiensis*. The toxin gene has been cloned into corn in order to confer protection against the European corn borer, a commercially significant pest that spends much of its life cycle inside the corn plant, where it is largely inaccessible to chemical insecticides. The use of "Bt corn," which is now widely planted in the United States, has greatly reduced the need for such toxic substances.

Transgenic plants have also been engineered for better nutrition. For example, researchers have developed a strain of rice with foreign genes that encode enzymes necessary to synthesize **β-carotene** (an orange pigment that is the precursor of **vitamin A**) and a gene for the iron-storage protein **ferritin**. The genetically modified rice, which is named "golden rice" (Fig. 3-32), should help alleviate vitamin A deficiencies (which afflict some 400 million people) and iron deficiencies (an estimated 30% of the world's population suffers from iron deficiency). Other transgenic plants include freeze-tolerant strawberries and slow-ripening tomatoes.

There is presently a widely held popular suspicion, particularly in Europe, that genetically modified or "GM" foods will somehow be harmful. However, extensive research, as well as considerable consumer experience, has failed to reveal any deleterious effects caused by GM foods (see Box 3-3).

Transgenic organisms have greatly enhanced our understanding of gene expression. Animals that have been engineered to contain a defective gene or that lack a gene entirely (a so-called **gene knockout**) also serve as experimental models for human diseases.

Genetic Defects Can Be Corrected. **Gene therapy** is the transfer of new genetic material to the cells of an individual in order to produce a therapeutic effect. Although the potential benefits of this as yet rudimentary technology are enormous, there are numerous practical obstacles to overcome. For example, the retroviral vectors (RNA-containing viruses) commonly used to directly introduce genes into humans can provoke a fatal immune response.

■ **Figure 3-31** | **Transgenic mouse.** The gigantic mouse on the left was grown from a fertilized ovum that had been microinjected with DNA containing the rat growth hormone gene. He is nearly twice the weight of his normal littermate on the right. [Courtesy of Ralph Brinster, University of Pennsylvania.]

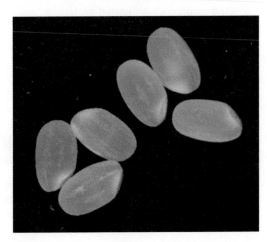

■ **Figure 3-32** | **Golden rice.** The white grains on the right are the wild type. The grains on the left have been engineered to store up to three times more iron and to synthesize β-carotene, which gives them their yellow color. [Courtesy of Ingo Potrykus.]

BOX 3-3 PERSPECTIVES IN BIOCHEMISTRY

Ethical Aspects of Recombinant DNA Technology

In the early 1970s, when genetic engineering was first discussed, little was known about the safety of the proposed experiments. After considerable debate, during which there was a moratorium on such experiments, regulations for recombinant DNA research were drawn up. The rules prohibit obviously dangerous experiments (e.g., introducing the gene for diphtheria toxin into *E. coli,* which would convert this human symbiont into a deadly pathogen). Other precautions limit the risk of accidentally releasing potentially harmful organisms into the environment. For example, many vectors must be cloned in host organisms with special nutrient requirements. These organisms are unlikely to survive outside the laboratory.

The proven value of recombinant DNA technology has silenced nearly all its early opponents. Certainly, it would not have been possible to study some pathogens, such as the virus that causes AIDS, without cloning. The lack of recombinant-induced genetic catastrophes so far does not guarantee that recombinant organisms won't ever adversely affect the environment. Nevertheless, the techniques used by genetic engineers mimic those used in nature—that is, mutation and selection—so natural and man-made organisms are fundamentally similar. In any case, people have been breeding plants and animals for several millennia already, and for many of the same purposes that guide experiments with recombinant DNA.

There are other ethical considerations to be faced as new genetic engineering techniques become available. Bacterial produced human growth hormone is now routinely prescribed to increase the stature of abnormally short children. However, should athletes be permitted to use this protein, as some reportedly have to increase their size and strength? Few would dispute the use of gene therapy, if it can be developed, to cure such genetic defects as sickle-cell anemia (Section 7-1E) and Lesch–Nyhan syndrome (Section 23-1D). If, however, it becomes possible to alter complex (i.e., multigene) traits such as athletic ability and intelligence, which changes would be considered desirable and who would decide whether to make them? Should gene therapy be used only to correct an individual's defects, or should it also be used to alter genes in the individual's germ cells so that succeeding generations would not inherit the defect? If it becomes easy to determine an individual's genetic makeup, should this information be used in evaluating applicants for educational and employment opportunities or for health insurance? These conundrums have led to the creation of a branch of philosophy, named **bioethics,** designed to deal with them.

■ CHECK YOUR UNDERSTANDING

What are the roles of the vector and DNA ligase in cloning DNA?

Explain how cells containing recombinant DNA are selected.

What is a DNA library and how can it be screened for a particular gene?

Describe the steps required to amplify a DNA segment by PCR.

Explain how site-directed mutagenesis can be used to produce an altered protein in bacterial cells.

What is the difference between manipulating a gene for gene therapy and for producing a transgenic organism?

The only documented success of gene therapy in humans has occurred in children with a form of **severe combined immunodeficiency disease (SCID)** known as **SCID-X1,** which without treatment would have required their isolation in a sterile environment to prevent fatal infection. SCID-X1 is caused by a defect in the gene encoding **γc cytokine receptor,** whose action is essential for proper immune system function. Bone marrow cells (the precursors of white blood cells) were removed from the bodies of SCID-X1 victims, incubated with a vector containing a normal γc cytokine receptor gene, and returned to their bodies. The transgenic bone marrow cells restored immune system function. However, because the viral vector integrates into the genome at random, the location of the transgene may affect the expression of other genes, triggering cancer. At least two children have developed leukemia (a white blood cell cancer) as a result of gene therapy for SCID-X1.

SUMMARY

1. Nucleotides consist of a purine or pyrimidine base linked to ribose to which at least one phosphate group is attached. RNA is made of ribonucleotides; DNA is made of deoxynucleotides (which contain 2′-deoxyribose).

2. In DNA, two antiparallel chains of nucleotides linked by phosphodiester bonds form a double helix. Bases in opposite strands pair: A with T, and G with C.

3. Single-stranded nucleic acids, such as RNA, can adopt stem–loop structures.

4. DNA carries genetic information in its sequence of nucleotides. When DNA is replicated, each strand acts as a template for the synthesis of a complementary strand.

5. According to the central dogma of molecular biology, one strand of the DNA of a gene is transcribed into mRNA. The RNA is then translated into protein by the ordered addition of amino acids that are bound to tRNA molecules that base-pair with the mRNA at the ribosome.

6. Restriction endonucleases that recognize certain sequences of DNA are used to specifically cleave DNA molecules.

7. Gel electrophoresis is used to separate and measure the sizes of DNA fragments.

8. In the chain-terminator method of DNA sequencing, the sequence of nucleotides in a DNA strand is determined by enzymatically synthesizing complementary polynucleotides that terminate with a dideoxy analog of each of the four nucleotides. Polynucleotide fragments of increasing size are separated by electrophoresis to reconstruct the original sequence.

9. Mutations and other changes to DNA are the basis for the evolution of organisms.

10. In molecular cloning, a fragment of foreign DNA is inserted into a vector for amplification in a host cell. Transformed cells can be identified by selectable markers.

11. Genomic libraries contain all the DNA of an organism. Clones harboring particular DNA sequences are identified by screening procedures.

12. The polymerase chain reaction amplifies selected sequences of DNA.

13. Recombinant DNA methods are used to produce wild-type or selectively mutagenized proteins in cells or entire organisms.

KEY TERMS

nucleotide 39
nucleic acid 39
nucleoside 41
RNA 42
DNA 42
polynucleotide 43
phosphodiester bond 43
nucleotide residue 43
5′ end 44
3′ end 44
monomer 44
dimer 44
trimer 44
tetramer 44
oligomer 44
Chargaff's rules 44
tautomer 44
double helix 45
antiparallel 45
major groove 46
minor groove 46
complementary base pairing 46
genome 47
chromosome 47
diploid 47

haploid 47
bp 47
kb 47
stem–loop 47
gene 48
transformation 48
replication 48
transcription 49
translation 49
central dogma of molecular biology 49
mRNA 49
ribosome 49
rRNA 49
tRNA 49
genomics 50
transcriptomics 50
proteomics 50
gene expression 50
bacteriophage 51
restriction–modification system 51
modification methylase 51
restriction endonuclease 51
endonuclease 51
exonuclease 51

palindrome 52
sticky ends 52
blunt ends 52
gel electrophoresis 52
chain-terminator procedure 53
dNTP 53
primer 54
ddNTP 54
ORF 58
alternative gene splicing 58
point mutation 58
recombination 58
transposition 58
phenotype 59
recombinant DNA technology 59
vector 60
cloning 60
clone 60
plasmid 60
recombinant DNA 61
BAC 61
YAC 61
anneal 61
ligation 61
selectable marker 62

plaque 62
DNA library 62
genomic library 63
shotgun cloning 63
reverse transcriptase 64
cDNA 64
screening 64
colony (in situ) hybridization 64
replica plating 64
probe 64
autoradiography 64
PCR 65
polymorphism 66
DNA fingerprinting 66
STR 66
allele 66
expression vector 67
overproducer 67
intron 67
site-directed mutagenesis 68
wild type 68
transgenic organism 68
transgene 68
gene knockout 69
gene therapy 69

PROBLEMS

1. Kinases are enzymes that transfer a phosphoryl group from a nucleoside triphosphate. Which of the following are valid kinase-catalyzed reactions?

(a) ATP + GDP → ADP + GTP

(b) ATP + GMP → AMP + GTP

(c) ADP + CMP → AMP + CDP

(d) AMP + ATP → 2 ADP

2. A diploid organism with a 45,000-kb haploid genome contains 21% G residues. Calculate the number of A, C, G, and T residues in the DNA of each cell in this organism.

3. A segment of DNA containing 20 base pairs includes 7 guanine residues. How many adenine residues are in the segment? How many uracil residues are in the segment?

4. Draw the tautomeric forms of (a) adenine and (b) cytosine.

5. The adenine derivative hypoxanthine can base-pair with both cytosine and adenine. Show the structures of these base pairs.

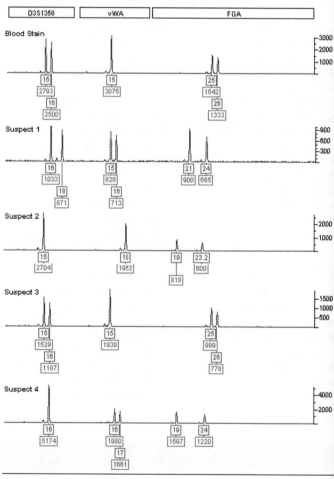

Hypoxanthine

6. Explain why the strands of a DNA molecule can be separated more easily at pH > 11.

7. How many different amino acids could theoretically be encoded by nucleic acids containing four different nucleotides if (a) each nucleotide coded for one amino acid; (b) consecutive sequences of two nucleotides coded for one amino acid; (c) consecutive sequences of three nucleotides coded for one amino acid; (d) consecutive sequences of four nucleotides coded for one amino acid?

8. The recognition sequence for the restriction enzyme *Taq*I is T↓CGA. Indicate the products of the reaction of *Taq*I with the DNA sequence shown.

      5′–ACGTCGAATC–3′
      3′–TGCAGCTTAG–5′

9. Using the data in Table 3-2, identify restriction enzymes that (a) produce blunt ends; (b) recognize and cleave the same sequence (called **isoschizomers**); (c) produce identical sticky ends.

10. Describe the outcome of a chain-terminator sequencing procedure in which (a) too little ddNTP is added; (b) too much ddNTP is added; (c) too few primers are present; (d) too many primers are present.

11. Calculate the number of clones required to obtain with a probability of 0.99 a specific 5-kb fragment from *C. elegans* (Table 3-3).

12. Describe how to select recombinant clones if a foreign DNA is inserted into the polylinker site of pUC18 and then introduced into *E. coli* cells.

13. Describe the possible outcome of a PCR experiment in which (a) one of the primers is inadvertently omitted from the reaction mixture; (b) one of the primers is complementary to several sites in the starting DNA sample; (c) there is a single-stranded break in the target DNA sequence, which is present in only one copy in the starting sample; (d) there is a double-stranded break in the target DNA sequence, which is present in only one copy in the starting sample.

14. Write the sequences of the two 12-residue primers that could be used to amplify the following DNA segment by PCR.

      ATAGGCATAGGCCCATATGGCATAAGG-
              CTTTATAATATGCGATAGGCGCTGGTCAG

15. (a) Why is a genomic library larger than a cDNA library for a given organism?

    (b) Why do cDNA libraries derived from different cell types within the same organism differ from each other?

16. A blood stain from a crime scene and blood samples from four suspects were analyzed by PCR using fluorescent primers associated with three STR loci: D3S1358, vWA, and FGA. The resulting electrophoretograms are shown below. The numbers beneath each peak identify the allele (upper box) and the height of the peak in relative fluorescence units (lower box).

    (a) Since everyone has two copies of each chromosome and therefore two alleles of each gene, what accounts for the appearance of only one allele at some loci?

    (b) Which suspect is a possible source of the blood?

    (c) Could the suspect be identified using just one of the three STR loci?

    (d) What can you conclude about the amount of DNA obtained from Suspect 1 compared to Suspect 4?

[From Thompson, W.C., Ford, S., Doom, T., Raymer, M., and Krane, D.E., Evaluating forensic DNA evidence: Essential elements of a competent defense review, *The Champion* **27,** 16–25 (2003).]

BIOINFORMATICS EXERCISES

Bioinformatics Exercises are available at www.wiley.com/college/voet.

Chapter 3
Databases for the Storage and "Mining" of Genome Sequences

1. **Finding Databases.** Locate databases for genome sequences and explore the meaning of terms related to them.
2. **The Institute for Genomic Research.** Explore a prokaryotic genome and find listings for eukaryotic genomes.
3. **Analyzing a DNA Sequence.** Given a DNA sequence, identify its open reading frame and translate it into a protein sequence.
4. **Sequence Homology.** Perform a BLAST search for homologs of a protein sequence.
5. **Plasmids and Cloning.** Predict the sizes of the fragments produced by the action of various restriction enzymes on plasmids.

REFERENCES

DNA Structure and Function

Bloomfield, V.A., Crothers, D.M., and Tinoco, I., Jr., *Nucleic Acids. Structures, Properties, and Functions,* University Science Books (2000).

Dickerson, R.E., DNA structure from A to Z, *Methods Enzymol.* **211,** 67–111 (1992). [Describes the various crystallographic forms of DNA.]

Thieffry, D., Forty years under the central dogma, *Trends Biochem. Sci.* **23,** 312–316 (1998). [Traces the origins, acceptance, and shortcomings of the idea that nucleic acids contain biological information.]

Watson, J.D. and Crick, F.H.C., Molecular structure of nucleic acids, *Nature* **171,** 737–738 (1953); *and* Genetical implications of the structure of deoxyribonucleic acid, *Nature* **171,** 964–967 (1953). [The seminal papers that are widely held to mark the origin of modern molecular biology.]

DNA Sequencing

Galperin, M.Y., The molecular biology database collection: 2007 update, *Nucleic Acids Res.* **35,** Database issue D3–D4 (2007). [This article cites 968 databases covering various aspects of molecular biology, biochemistry, and genetics. Additional articles in the same issue provide more information on individual databases. Freely available at http://nar.oxfordjournals.org.]

Graham, C.A. and Hill, A.J.M. (Eds.), *DNA Sequencing Protocols* (2nd ed.), Humana Press (2001).

Higgins, D. and Taylor, W. (Eds.), *Bioinformatics. Sequence, Structure and Databanks,* Oxford University Press (2000).

International Human Genome Sequencing Consortium, initial sequencing and analysis of the human genome, *Nature* **409,** 860–921 (2001); *and* Venter, J.C., *et al.,* the sequence of the human genome, *Science* **291,** 1304–1351 (2001). [These and other papers in the same issues of *Nature* and *Science* describe the data that constitute the draft sequence of the human genome and discuss how this information can be used in understanding biological function, evolution, and human health.]

International Human Genome Sequencing Consortium, finishing the euchromatic sequence of the human genome, *Nature* **431,** 931–945 (2004). [Describes the most up-to-date version of the human genome sequence.]

Recombinant DNA Technology

Ausubel, F.M., Brent, R., Kingston, R.E., Moore, D.D., Seidman, J.G., Smith, J.A., and Struhl, K., *Short Protocols in Molecular Biology* (5th ed.), Wiley (2002).

Nicholl, D.S.T., *An Introduction to Genetic Engineering* (2nd ed.), Cambridge University Press (2002).

Pingoud, A., Fuxreiter, M., Pingoud, V., and Wende, W., Type II restriction endonucleases: structure and mechanism, *Cell. Mol. Life Sci.* **62,** 685–707 (2005). [Includes an overview of different types of restriction enzymes.]

Sambrook, J., and Russell, D. *Molecular Cloning* (3rd ed.), Cold Spring Harbor Laboratory (2001). [A three-volume "bible" of laboratory protocols with accompanying background explanations.]

4

Amino Acids

In addition to the well-known taste sensations of sweet, sour, salty, and bitter is umami, the taste sensation elicited by monosodium glutamate (MSG), an amino acid commonly used as a flavor enhancer. [Jackson Vereen/Foodpix/PictureArts Corp.]

■ CHAPTER CONTENTS

1 Amino Acid Structure
- **A.** Amino Acids Are Dipolar Ions
- **B.** Peptide Bonds Link Amino Acids
- **C.** Amino Acid Side Chains Are Nonpolar, Polar, or Charged
- **D.** The p*K* Values of Ionizable Groups Depend on Nearby Groups
- **E.** Amino Acid Names Are Abbreviated

2 Stereochemistry

3 Amino Acid Derivatives
- **A.** Protein Side Chains May Be Modified
- **B.** Some Amino Acids Are Biologically Active

LEARNING OBJECTIVES

■ Know the overall structure of an amino acid and the structures of the 20 different R groups.

■ Understand how peptide bonds link amino acid residues in a polypeptide.

■ Understand that amino acids include ionizable groups whose p*K* values vary when the amino acid is part of a polypeptide.

When scientists first turned their attention to nutrition, early in the nineteenth century, they quickly discovered that natural products containing nitrogen were essential for the survival of animals. In 1839, the Dutch chemist G. J. Mulder coined the term **protein** (Greek: *proteios*, primary) for this class of compounds. The physiological chemists of that time did not realize that proteins were actually composed of smaller components, amino acids, although the first amino acids had been isolated in 1830. In fact, for many years, it was believed that substances from plants—including proteins—were incorporated whole into animal tissues. This misconception was laid to rest when the process of digestion came to light. After it became clear that ingested proteins were broken down to smaller compounds containing amino acids, scientists began to consider the nutritive qualities of those compounds (Box 4-1).

Modern studies of proteins and amino acids owe a great deal to nineteenth and early twentieth century experiments. We now understand that nitrogen-containing amino acids are essential for life and that they are the building blocks of proteins. The central role of amino acids in biochemistry is perhaps not surprising: Several amino acids are among the organic compounds believed to have appeared early in the earth's history (Section 1-1A). Amino acids, as ancient and ubiquitous molecules, have been co-opted by evolution for a variety of purposes in living systems. We begin this chapter by discussing the structures and chemical properties of the common amino acids, including their stereochemistry, and end with a brief summary of the structures and functions of some related compounds.

1 Amino Acid Structure

The analyses of a vast number of proteins from almost every conceivable source have shown that *all proteins are composed of 20 "standard" amino acids*. Not every protein contains all 20 types of amino acids, but most proteins contain most if not all of the 20 types.

The common amino acids are known as **α-amino acids** because they have a primary amino group (—NH$_2$) as a substituent of the **α carbon** atom, the carbon next to the carboxylic acid group (—COOH; Fig. 4-1)

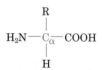

■ Figure 4-1 | General structure of an α-amino acid. The R groups differentiate the 20 standard amino acids.

BOX 4-1 PATHWAYS OF DISCOVERY

William C. Rose and the Discovery of Threonine

William C. Rose (1887–1985)

Identifying the amino acid constituents of proteins was a scientific challenge that grew out of studies of animal nutrition. At the start of the twentieth century, physiological chemists (the term *biochemist* was not yet used) recognized that not all foods provided adequate nutrition. For example, rats fed the corn protein zein as their only source of nitrogen failed to grow unless the amino acids tryptophan and lysine were added to their diet. Knowledge of metabolism at that time was mostly limited to information gleaned from studies in which intake of particular foods in experimental subjects (including humans) was linked to the urinary excretion of various compounds. Results of such studies were consistent with the idea that compounds could be transformed into other compounds, but clearly, nutrients were not wholly interchangeable.

At the University of Illinois, William C. Rose focused his research on nutritional studies to decipher the metabolic relationships of nitrogenous compounds. Among other things, his studies of rat growth and nutrition helped show that purines and pyrimidines were derived from amino acids but that those compounds could not replace dietary amino acids.

In order to examine the nutritional requirements for individual amino acids, Rose hydrolyzed proteins to obtain their component amino acids and then selectively removed certain amino acids. In one of his first experiments, he removed arginine and histidine from a hydrolysate of the milk protein casein. Rats fed on this preparation lost weight unless the amino acid histidine was added back to the food. However, adding back arginine did not compensate for the apparent requirement for histidine. These results prompted Rose to investigate the requirements for all the amino acids. Using similar experimental approaches, Rose demonstrated that cysteine, histidine, and tryptophan could not be replaced by other amino acids.

From preparations based on hydrolyzed proteins, Rose moved to mixtures of pure amino acids. Thirteen of the 19 known amino acids could be purified, and the other six synthesized. However, rats fed these 19 amino acids as their sole source of dietary nitrogen lost weight. Although one possible explanation was that the proportions of the pure amino acids were not optimal, Rose concluded that there must be an additional essential amino acid, present in naturally occurring proteins and their hydrolysates but not in his amino acid mixtures.

After several years of effort, Rose obtained and identified the missing amino acid. In work published in 1935, Rose showed that adding this amino acid to the other 19 could support rat growth. Thus, the twentieth and last amino acid, threonine, was discovered.

Experiments extending over the next 20 years revealed that 10 of the 20 amino acids found in proteins are nutritionally essential, so that removal of one of these causes growth failure and eventually death in experimental animals. The other 10 amino acids were considered "dispensable" since animals could synthesize adequate amounts of them.

Rose's subsequent work included verifying the amino acid requirements of humans, using graduate students as subjects. Knowing which amino acids were required for normal health—and in what amounts—made it possible to evaluate the potential nutritive value of different types of food proteins. Eventually, these findings helped guide the formulations used for intravenous feeding.

McCoy, R.H., Meyer, C.E., and Rose, W.C., Feeding experiments with mixtures of highly purified amino acids. VIII. Isolation and identification of a new essential amino acid, *J. Biol. Chem.* **112,** 283–302 (1935). [Freely available at http://www.jbc.org.]

The sole exception is proline, which has a secondary amino group (—NH—), although for uniformity we shall refer to proline as an α-amino acid. The 20 standard amino acids differ in the structures of their side chains **(R groups).** Table 4-1 displays the names and complete chemical structures of the 20 standard amino acids.

A | Amino Acids Are Dipolar Ions

The amino and carboxylic acid groups of amino acids readily ionize. The pK values of the carboxylic acid groups (represented by pK_1 in Table 4-1) lie in a small range around 2.2, while the pK values of the α-amino groups (pK_2) are near 9.4. *At physiological pH (~7.4), the amino groups are protonated and the carboxylic acid groups are in their conjugate base (carboxylate) form* (Fig. 4-2). An amino acid can therefore act as both an acid and a base.

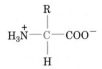

■ **Figure 4-2 | A dipolar amino acid.** At physiological pH, the amino group is protonated and the carboxylic acid group is unprotonated.

Table 4-1 Covalent Structures and Abbreviations of the "Standard" Amino Acids of Proteins, Their Occurrence, and the p*K* Values of Their Ionizable Groups

Name, Three-letter Symbol, and One-letter Symbol	Structural Formula[a]	Residue Mass (D)[b]	Average Occurrence in Proteins (%)[c]	pK_1 α-COOH[d]	pK_2 $\alpha\text{-}NH_3^+$[d]	pK_R Side Chain[d]
Amino acids with nonpolar side chains						
Glycine Gly G	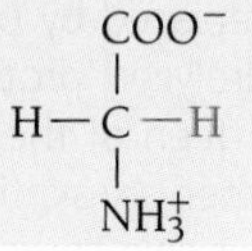	57.0	7.2	2.35	9.78	
Alanine Ala A	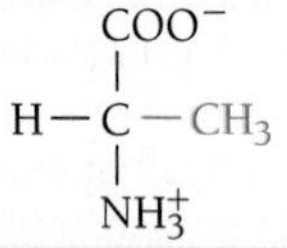	71.1	7.8	2.35	9.87	
Valine Val V	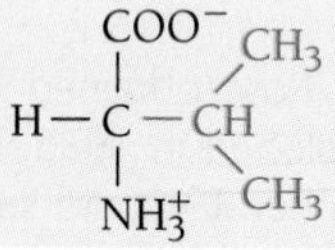	99.1	6.6	2.29	9.74	
Leucine Leu L	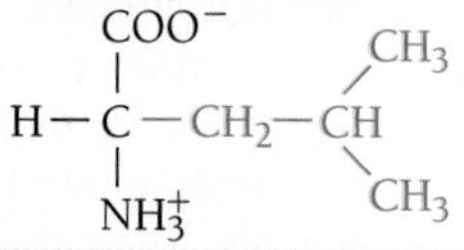	113.2	9.1	2.33	9.74	
Isoleucine Ile I	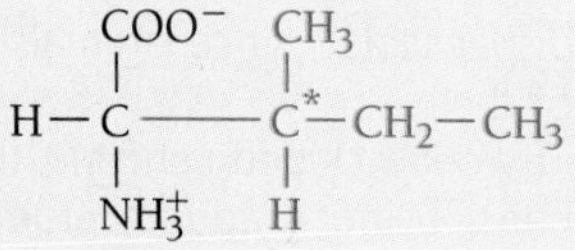	113.2	5.3	2.32	9.76	
Methionine Met M	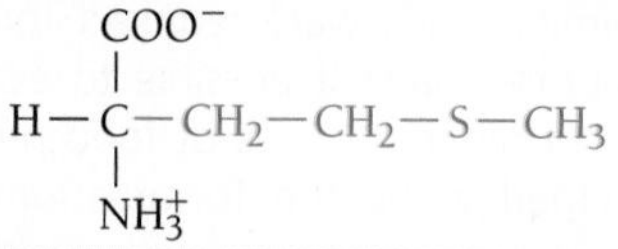	131.2	2.2	2.13	9.28	
Proline Pro P	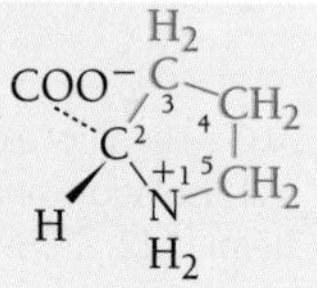	97.1	5.2	1.95	10.64	
Phenylalanine Phe F	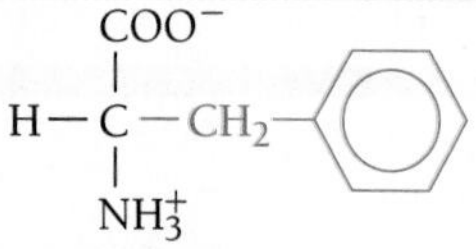	147.2	3.9	2.20	9.31	
Tryptophan Trp W	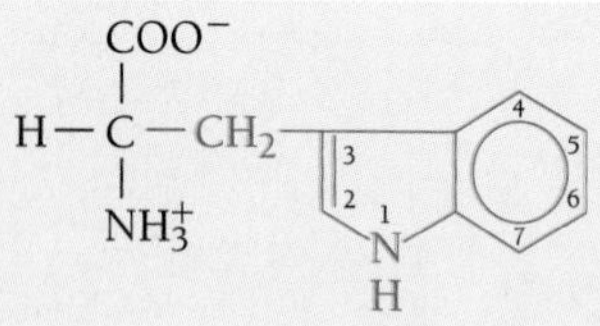	186.2	1.4	2.46	9.41	

[a]The ionic forms shown are those predominating at pH 7.0 (except for that of histidine[f]) although residue mass is given for the neutral compound. The C_α atoms, as well as those atoms marked with an asterisk, are chiral centers with configurations as indicated according to Fischer projection formulas (Section 4-2). The standard organic numbering system is provided for heterocycles.

[b]The residue masses are given for the neutral residues. For the molecular masses of the parent amino acids, add 18.0 D, the molecular mass of H_2O, to the residue masses. For side chain masses, subtract 56.0 D, the formula mass of a peptide group, from the residue masses.

[c]Calculated from a database of nonredundant proteins containing 300,688 residues as compiled by Doolittle, R.F., *in* Fasman, G.D. (Ed.), *Predictions of Protein Structure and the Principles of Protein Conformation,* Plenum Press (1989).

[d]Data from Dawson, R.M.C., Elliott, D.C., Elliott, W.H., and Jones, K.M., *Data for Biochemical Research* (3rd ed.), pp. 1–31, Oxford Science Publications (1986).

Table 4-1 (continued)

Name, Three-letter Symbol, and One-letter Symbol	Structural Formula[a]	Residue Mass (D)[b]	Average Occurrence in Proteins (%)[c]	pK₁ α-COOH[d]	pK₂ α-NH₃⁺[d]	pKᵣ Side Chain[d]
Amino acids with uncharged polar side chains						
Serine Ser S	$H-\underset{NH_3^+}{\overset{COO^-}{C}}-CH_2-OH$	87.1	6.8	2.19	9.21	
Threonine Thr T	$H-\underset{NH_3^+}{\overset{COO^-}{C}}-\underset{OH}{\overset{H}{C^*}}-CH_3$	101.1	5.9	2.09	9.10	
Asparagine[e] Asn N	$H-\underset{NH_3^+}{\overset{COO^-}{C}}-CH_2-\underset{NH_2}{\overset{O}{C}}$	114.1	4.3	2.14	8.72	
Glutamine[e] Gln Q	$H-\underset{NH_3^+}{\overset{COO^-}{C}}-CH_2-CH_2-\underset{NH_2}{\overset{O}{C}}$	128.1	4.3	2.17	9.13	
Tyrosine Tyr Y	$H-\underset{NH_3^+}{\overset{COO^-}{C}}-CH_2-$ (phenol ring)$-OH$	163.2	3.2	2.20	9.21	10.46 (phenol)
Cysteine Cys C	$H-\underset{NH_3^+}{\overset{COO^-}{C}}-CH_2-SH$	103.1	1.9	1.92	10.70	8.37 (sulfhydryl)
Amino acids with charged polar side chains						
Lysine Lys K	$H-\underset{NH_3^+}{\overset{COO^-}{C}}-CH_2-CH_2-CH_2-CH_2-NH_3^+$	128.2	5.9	2.16	9.06	10.54 (ε-NH₃⁺)
Arginine Arg R	$H-\underset{NH_3^+}{\overset{COO^-}{C}}-CH_2-CH_2-CH_2-NH-\underset{NH_2^+}{\overset{NH_2}{C}}$	156.2	5.1	1.82	8.99	12.48 (guanidino)
Histidine[f] His H	$H-\underset{NH_3^+}{\overset{COO^-}{C}}-CH_2-$ (imidazole ring)	137.1	2.3	1.80	9.33	6.04 (imidazole)
Aspartic acid[e] Asp D	$H-\underset{NH_3^+}{\overset{COO^-}{C}}-CH_2-\underset{O^-}{\overset{O}{C}}$	115.1	5.3	1.99	9.90	3.90 (β-COOH)
Glutamic acid[e] Glu E	$H-\underset{NH_3^+}{\overset{COO^-}{C}}-CH_2-CH_2-\underset{O^-}{\overset{O}{C}}$	129.1	6.3	2.10	9.47	4.07 (γ-COOH)

[a]The three- and one-letter symbols for asparagine *or* aspartic acid are Asx and B, whereas for glutamine *or* glutamic acid they are Glx and Z. The one-letter symbol for an undetermined or "nonstandard" amino acid is X.

[b]Both neutral and protonated forms of histidine are present at pH 7.0, since its pKᵣ is close to 7.0.

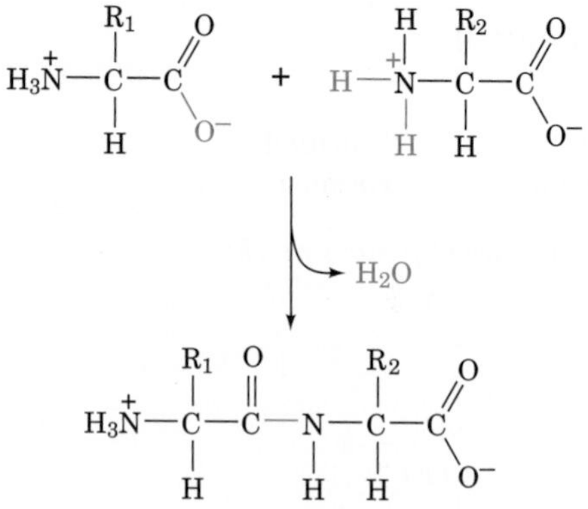

■ **Figure 4-3** | **Condensation of two amino acids.** Formation of a CO—NH bond with the elimination of a water molecule produces a dipeptide. The peptide bond is shown in red. The residue with a free amino group is the N-terminus of the peptide, and the residue with a free carboxylate group is the C-terminus.

Table 4-1 also lists the pK values for the seven side chains that contain ionizable groups (pK_R).

Molecules such as amino acids, which bear charged groups of opposite polarity, are known as **dipolar ions** or **zwitterions.** Amino acids, like other ionic compounds, are more soluble in polar solvents than in nonpolar solvents. As we shall see, the ionic properties of the side chains influence the physical and chemical properties of free amino acids and amino acids in proteins.

B | Peptide Bonds Link Amino Acids

Amino acids can be polymerized to form chains. This process can be represented as a **condensation reaction** (bond formation with the elimination of a water molecule), as shown in Fig. 4-3. The resulting CO—NH linkage, an amide linkage, is known as a **peptide bond.**

Polymers composed of two, three, a few (3–10), and many amino acid units are known, respectively, as **dipeptides**, **tripeptides**, **oligopeptides**, and **polypeptides.** These substances, however, are often referred to simply as "peptides." After they are incorporated into a peptide, the individual amino acids (the monomeric units) are referred to as amino acid **residues.**

Polypeptides are linear polymers rather than branched chains; that is, each amino acid residue participates in two peptide bonds and is linked to its neighbors in a head-to-tail fashion. The residues at the two ends of the polypeptide each participate in just one peptide bond. The residue with a free amino group (by convention, the leftmost residue, as shown in Fig. 4-3) is called the **amino terminus** or **N-terminus.** The residue with a free carboxylate group (at the right) is called the **carboxyl terminus** or **C-terminus.**

Proteins are molecules that contain one or more polypeptide chains. *Variations in the length and the amino acid sequence of polypeptides are major contributors to the diversity in the shapes and biological functions of proteins,* as we shall see in succeeding chapters.

C | Amino Acid Side Chains Are Nonpolar, Polar, or Charged

The most useful way to classify the 20 standard amino acids is by the polarities of their side chains. According to the most common classification scheme, there are three major types of amino acids: (1) those with

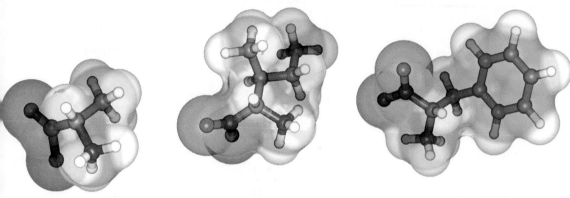

Alanine   Isoleucine   Phenylalanine

■ **Figure 4-4** | **Some amino acids with nonpolar side chains.** The amino acids are shown as ball-and-stick models embedded in transparent space-filling models. The atoms are colored according to type with C green, H white, N blue, and O red.

nonpolar R groups, (2) those with uncharged polar R groups, and (3) those with charged polar R groups.

The Nonpolar Amino Acid Side Chains Have a Variety of Shapes and Sizes. Nine amino acids are classified as having nonpolar side chains. The three-dimensional shapes of some of these amino acids are shown in Fig. 4-4. **Glycine** has the smallest possible side chain, an H atom. **Alanine, valine, leucine,** and **isoleucine** have aliphatic hydrocarbon side chains ranging in size from a methyl group for alanine to isomeric butyl groups for leucine and isoleucine. **Methionine** has a thioether side chain that resembles an *n*-butyl group in many of its physical properties (C and S have nearly equal electronegativities, and S is about the size of a methylene group). **Proline** has a cyclic pyrrolidine side group. **Phenylalanine** (with its phenyl moiety) and **tryptophan** (with its indole group) contain aromatic side groups, which are characterized by bulk as well as nonpolarity.

Uncharged Polar Side Chains Have Hydroxyl, Amide, or Thiol Groups. Six amino acids are commonly classified as having uncharged polar side chains (Table 4-1 and Fig. 4-5). **Serine** and **threonine** bear hydroxylic R groups of different sizes. **Asparagine** and **glutamine** have amide-bearing side chains of different sizes. **Tyrosine** has a phenolic group (and, like phenylalanine and tryptophan, is aromatic). **Cysteine** is unique among the

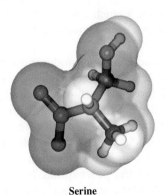

Serine   Glutamine

■ **Figure 4-5** | **Some amino acids with uncharged polar side chains.** Atoms are represented and colored as in Fig. 4-4. Note the presence of electronegative atoms on the side chains.

$$\underset{\text{Cysteine}}{\overset{\displaystyle\underset{|}{\text{C}=\text{O}}}{\underset{\displaystyle\underset{|}{\text{NH}}}{\text{H}-\text{C}-\text{CH}_2-\text{SH}}}} \quad + \quad \underset{\text{Cysteine}}{\overset{\displaystyle\underset{|}{\text{NH}}}{\underset{\displaystyle\underset{|}{\text{C}=\text{O}}}{\text{HS}-\text{CH}_2-\text{C}-\text{H}}}}$$

residue   residue

$$\frac{1}{2}\text{O}_2 \longrightarrow \text{H}_2\text{O}$$

$$\underset{\displaystyle\underset{|}{\text{NH}}}{\overset{\displaystyle\overset{|}{\text{C}=\text{O}}}{\text{H}-\text{C}-\text{CH}_2-\text{S}-\text{S}-\text{CH}_2-\text{C}-\text{H}}}\underset{\displaystyle\underset{|}{\text{C}=\text{O}}}{\overset{\displaystyle\overset{|}{\text{NH}}}{}}$$

■ **Figure 4-6** | **Disulfide-bonded cysteine residues.** The disulfide bond forms when the two thiol groups are oxidized.

20 amino acids in that it has a thiol group that can form a disulfide bond with another cysteine through the oxidation of the two thiol groups (Fig. 4-6).

Charged Polar Side Chains Are Positively or Negatively Charged.
Five amino acids have charged side chains (Table 4-1 and Fig. 4-7). The side chains of the basic amino acids are positively charged at physiological pH values. **Lysine** has a butylammonium side chain, and **arginine** bears a guanidino group. As shown in Table 4-1, **histidine** carries an imidazolium moiety. Note that only histidine, with a pK_R of 6.04, readily ionizes within the physiological pH range. Consequently, both the neutral and cationic forms occur in proteins. In fact, the protonation–deprotonation of histidine side chains is a feature of numerous enzymatic reaction mechanisms.

The side chains of the acidic amino acids, **aspartic acid** and **glutamic acid,** are negatively charged above pH 3; in their ionized state, they are often referred to as **aspartate** and **glutamate.** Asparagine and glutamine are, respectively, the amides of aspartic acid and glutamic acid.

The allocation of the 20 amino acids among the three different groups is somewhat arbitrary. For example, glycine and alanine, the smallest of the amino acids, and tryptophan, with its heterocyclic ring, might just as well be classified as uncharged polar amino acids. Similarly, tyrosine and cysteine, with their ionizable side chains, might also be thought of as charged polar amino acids, particularly at higher pH values. In fact, the deprotonated side chain of cysteine (which contains the thiolate anion, S$^-$) occurs in a variety of enzymes, where it actively participates in chemical reactions.

Inclusion of a particular amino acid in one group or another reflects not just the properties of the isolated amino acid, but its behavior when it is part of a polypeptide. The structures of most polypeptides depend on a tendency for polar and ionic side chains to be hydrated and for nonpolar side chains to associate with each other rather than with water. This property of polypeptides is the hydrophobic effect (Section 2-1C) in action. As we shall see, the chemical and physical properties of amino acid side chains also govern the chemical reactivity of the polypeptide. It is worthwhile studying the structures of the 20 standard amino acids in order to

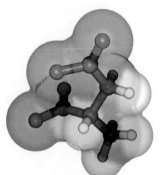

Aspartate

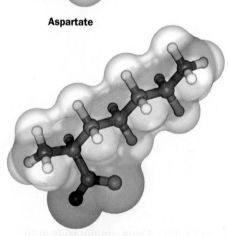

Lysine

■ **Figure 4-7** | **Some amino acids with charged polar side chains.** Atoms are represented and colored as in Fig. 4-4.

ppreciate how they vary in polarity, acidity, aromaticity, bulk, conforma-
onal flexibility, ability to cross-link, ability to hydrogen bond, and reac-
vity toward other groups.

) | The pK Values of Ionizable Groups Depend on Nearby Groups

he α-amino acids have two or, for those with ionizable side chains, three
cid–base groups. At very low pH values, these groups are fully proton-
ted, and at very high pH values, these groups are unprotonated. At
ntermediate pH values, the acidic groups tend to be unprotonated, and
he basic groups tend to be protonated. Thus, for the amino acid glycine,
·elow pH 2.35 (the pK value of its carboxylic acid group), the
$^+H_3NCH_2COOH$ form predominates. Above pH 2.35, the carboxylic acid
s mostly ionized but the amino group is still mostly protonated
($^+H_3NCH_2COO^-$). Above pH 9.78 (the pK value of the amino group),
he $H_2NCH_2COO^-$ form predominates. Note that *in aqueous solution, the
un-ionized form (H_2NCH_2COOH) is present only in vanishingly small
quantities.*

   The pH at which a molecule carries no net electric charge is known as
ts **isoelectric point, pI.** For the α-amino acids,

$$pI = \tfrac{1}{2}(pK_i + pK_j) \qquad [4\text{-}1]$$

where K_i and K_j are the dissociation constants of the two ionizations involving the neutral species. For monoamino, monocarboxylic acids such as
glycine, K_i and K_j represent K_1 and K_2. However, for aspartic and glutamic
acids, K_i and K_j are K_1 and K_R, whereas for arginine, histidine, and lysine,
hese quantities are K_R and K_2.

   Of course, amino acid residues in the interior of a polypeptide chain do
aot have free α-amino and α-carboxyl groups that can ionize (these groups
are joined in peptide bonds; Fig. 4-3). Furthermore, the pK values of all
onizable groups, including the N- and C-termini, usually differ from the
ɔK values listed in Table 4-1 for free amino acids. For example, the pK
values of α-carboxyl groups in unfolded proteins range from 3.5 to 4.0. In
the free amino acids, the pK values are much lower, because the positively
charged ammonium group electrostatically stabilizes the COO^- group, in
effect making it easier for the carboxylic acid group to ionize. Similarly,
the pK values for α-amino groups in proteins range from 7.5 to 8.5. In the
free amino acids, the pK values are higher, due to the electron-withdrawing
character of the nearby carboxylate group, which makes it more difficult
for the ammonium group to become deprotonated. In addition, the three-
dimensional structure of a folded polypeptide chain may bring polar side
chains and the N- and C-termini close together. The resulting electrostatic
interactions between these groups may shift their pK values up to several
pH units from the values for the corresponding free amino acids. For this
reason, the pI of a polypeptide, which is a function of the pK values of its
many ionizable groups, is not easily predicted and is usually determined
experimentally.

E | Amino Acid Names Are Abbreviated

The three-letter abbreviations for the 20 standard amino acids given in
Table 4-1 are widely used in the biochemical literature. Most of these
abbreviations are taken from the first three letters of the name of the
corresponding amino acid and are pronounced as written. The symbol **Glx**

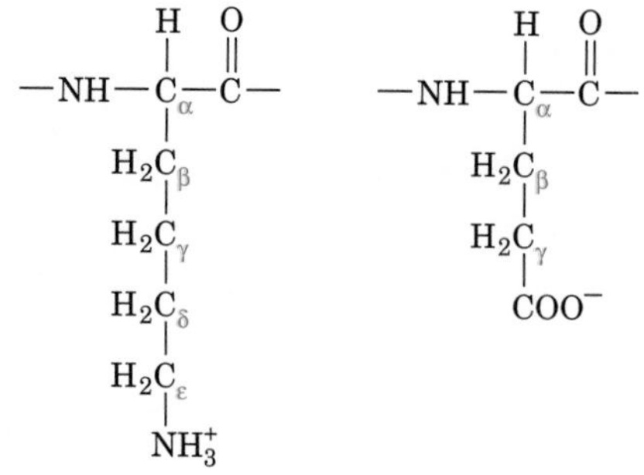

Lys   **Glu**

■ **Figure 4-8** | **Greek nomenclature for amino acids.** The carbon atoms are assigned sequential letters in the Greek alphabet, beginning with the carbon next to the carbonyl group.

indicates Glu or Gln, and similarly, **Asx** means Asp or Asn. This ambiguous notation stems from laboratory experience: Asn and Gln are easily hydrolyzed to Asp and Glu, respectively, under the acidic or basic conditions often used to recover them from proteins. Without special precautions, is impossible to tell whether a detected Glu was originally Glu or Gln, an likewise for Asp and Asn.

The one-letter symbols for the amino acids are also given in Table 4-1 This more compact code is often used when comparing the amino acid sequences of several similar proteins. Note that the one-letter symbol is usually the first letter of the amino acid's name. However, for sets of residue that have the same first letter, this is true only of the most abundan residue of the set.

Amino acid residues in polypeptides are named by dropping the suffix usually **-ine,** in the name of the amino acid and replacing it by **-y** Polypeptide chains are described by starting at the N-terminus and proceeding to the C-terminus. The amino acid at the C-terminus is given th name of its parent amino acid. Thus, the compound

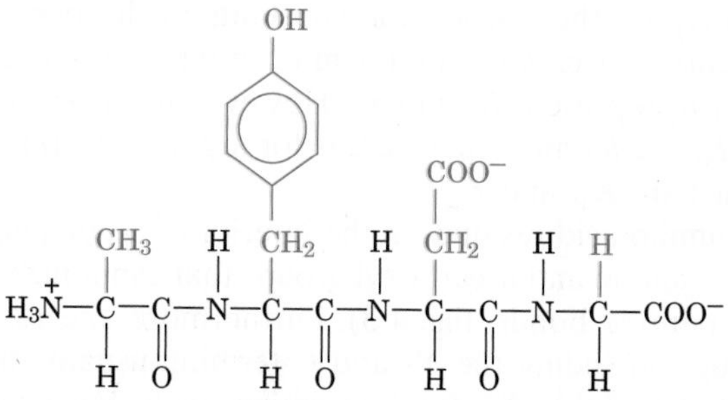

Ala — Tyr — Asp — Gly

is called alanyltyrosylaspartylglycine. Obviously, such names for polypeptide chains of more than a few residues are extremely cumbersome. The tetrapeptide above can also be written as Ala-Tyr-Asp-Gly using the three letter abbreviations, or AYDG using the one-letter symbols.

The various atoms of the amino acid side chains are often named in sequence with the Greek alphabet, starting at the carbon atom adjacent to the peptide carbonyl group. Therefore, as Fig. 4-8 indicates, the Lys residue is said to have an ε-amino group and Glu has a γ-carboxyl group Unfortunately, this labeling system is ambiguous for several amino acids Consequently, standard numbering schemes for organic molecules are also employed (and are indicated in Table 4-1 for the heterocyclic side chains)

2 Stereochemistry

With the exception of glycine, all the amino acids recovered from polypeptides are **optically active;** that is, they rotate the plane of polarized light The direction and angle of rotation can be measured using an instrument known as a **polarimeter** (Fig. 4-9).

Optically active molecules are asymmetric; that is, they are not superimposable on their mirror image in the same way that a left hand is no

■ **CHECK YOUR UNDERSTANDING**

Describe the overall structure of an amino acid.

Be able to identify the peptide bonds, amino acid residues, and the N- and C-termini of a polypeptide.

Draw the structures of the 20 standard amino acids and give their one- and three-letter abbreviations.

Classify the 20 standard amino acids by polarity, structure, type of functional group, and acid–base properties.

Why do the p*K* values of ionizable groups differ between free amino acids and amino acid residues in polypeptides?

LEARNING OBJECTIVES

■ Understand that amino acids and other biological compounds are chiral molecules whose configurations can be depicted by Fischer projections.

■ Understand that amino acids in proteins all have the L stereochemical configuration.

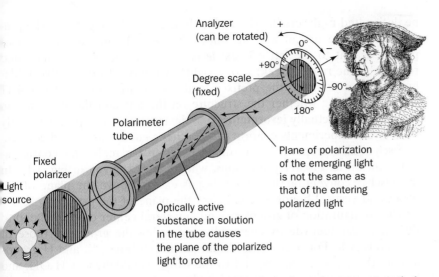

Figure 4-9 | **Diagram of a polarimeter.** This device is used to measure optical rotation.

superimposable on its mirror image, a right hand. This situation is characteristic of substances containing tetrahedral carbon atoms that have four different substituents. For example, the two molecules depicted in Fig. 4-10 are not superimposable; they are mirror images. The central atoms in such molecules are known as **asymmetric centers** or **chiral centers** and are said to have the property of **chirality** (Greek: *cheir*, hand). The C_α atoms of the amino acids (except glycine) are asymmetric centers. Glycine, which has two H atoms attached to its C_α atom, is superimposable on its mirror image and is therefore not optically active. Many biological molecules in addition to amino acids contain one or more chiral centers.

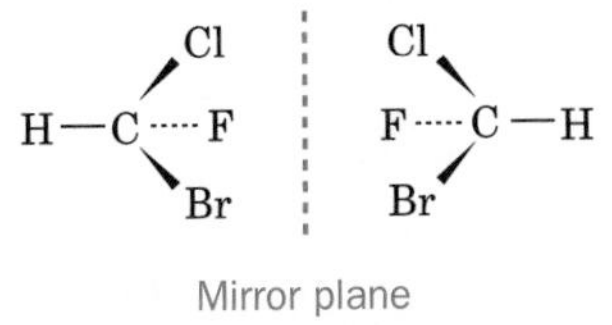

Chiral Centers Give Rise to Enantiomers. Molecules that are nonsuperimposable mirror images are known as **enantiomers** of one another. Enantiomeric molecules are physically and chemically indistinguishable by most techniques. *Only when probed asymmetrically, for example, by plane-polarized light or by reactants that also contain chiral centers, can they be distinguished or differentially manipulated.*

Unfortunately, there is no clear relationship between the structure of a molecule and the degree or direction to which it rotates the plane of polarized light. For example, leucine isolated from proteins rotates polarized light 10.4° to the left, whereas arginine rotates polarized light 12.5° to the right. (The enantiomers of these compounds rotate polarized light to the same degree but in the opposite direction.) It is not yet possible to predict optical rotation from the structure of a molecule or to derive the **absolute configuration** (spatial arrangement) of chemical groups around a chiral center from optical rotation measurements.

The Fischer Convention Describes the Configuration of Asymmetric Centers. Biochemists commonly use the **Fischer convention** to describe different forms of chiral molecules. In this system, the configuration of the groups around an asymmetric center is compared to that of **glyceraldehyde,** a molecule with one asymmetric center. In 1891, Emil Fischer proposed that the spatial isomers, or **stereoisomers,** of glyceraldehyde

Mirror plane

Figure 4-10 | **The two enantiomers of fluorochlorobromomethane.** The four substituents are tetrahedrally arranged around the central carbon atom. A dotted line indicates that a substituent lies behind the plane of the paper, a wedged line indicates that it lies above the plane of the paper, and a thin line indicates that it lies in the plane of the paper. The mirror plane relating the enantiomers is represented by a vertical dashed line.

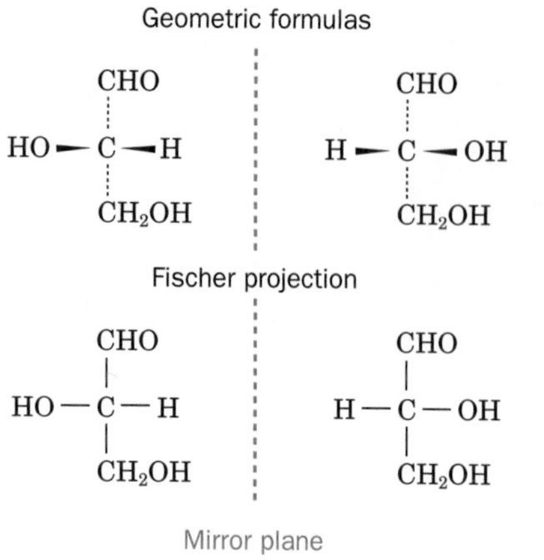

Geometric formulas

CHO

HO — C —H

CH$_2$OH

CHO

H — C — OH

CH$_2$OH

Fischer projection

CHO

HO — C—H

CH$_2$OH

CHO

H — C — OH

CH$_2$OH

Mirror plane

L-Glyceraldehyde   **D-Glyceraldehyde**

■ **Figure 4-11 | The Fischer convention.**
The enantiomers of glyceraldehyde are shown as geometric formulas (*top*) and as Fischer projections (*bottom*). In a Fischer projection, horizontal lines represent bonds that extend above the page and vertical lines represent bonds that extend below the page (in some Fischer projections, the central chiral carbon atom is not shown explicitly).

be designated D-glyceraldehyde and L-glyceraldehyde (Fig. 4-11). The prefix L (note the use of a small uppercase letter) signified rotation of polarized light to the left (Greek: *levo,* left), and the prefix D indicated rotation to the right (Greek: *dextro,* right) by the two forms of glyceraldehyde. Fischer assigned the prefixes to the structures shown in Fig. 4-11 without knowing whether the structure on the left and the structure on the right were actually **levorotatory** and **dextrorotatory,** respectively. Only in 1949 did experiments confirm that Fischer's guess was indeed correct.

Fischer also proposed a shorthand notation for molecular configurations, known as **Fischer projections,** which are also given in Fig. 4-11. In the Fischer convention, horizontal bonds extend above the plane of the paper and vertical bonds extend below the plane of the paper.

The configuration of groups around any chiral center can be related to that of glyceraldehyde by chemically converting the groups to those of glyceraldehyde. For α-amino acids, the amino, carboxyl, R, and H groups around the C$_\alpha$ atom correspond to the hydroxyl, aldehyde, CH$_2$OH, and H groups, respectively, of glyceraldehyde.

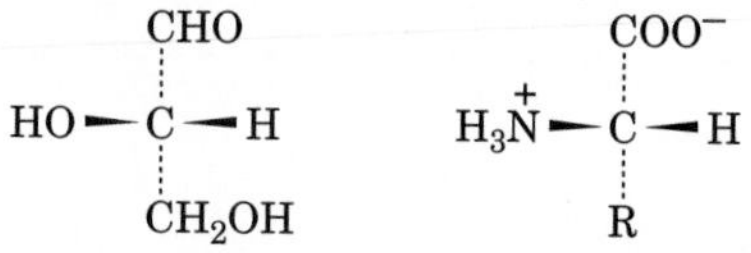

CHO

HO — C —H

CH$_2$OH

COO$^-$

H$_3\overset{+}{N}$ — C —H

R

L-Glyceraldehyde   **L-α-Amino acid**

Therefore, L-glyceraldehyde and L-α-amino acids are said to have the same **relative configuration.** *All amino acids derived from proteins have the L stereochemical configuration;* that is, they all have the same relative configuration around their C$_\alpha$ atoms. Of course, the L or D designation of an amino acid does not indicate its ability to rotate the plane of polarized light. Many L-amino acids are dextrorotatory.

The Fischer system has some shortcomings, particularly for molecules with multiple asymmetric centers. Each asymmetric center can have two possible configurations, so a molecule with n chiral centers has 2^n different possible stereoisomers. Threonine and isoleucine, for example, each have two chiral carbon atoms, and therefore each has four stereoisomers, or two pairs of enantiomers. [The enantiomers (mirror images) of the L forms are the D forms.] For most purposes, the Fischer system provides an adequate description of biological molecules. A more precise nomenclature system is also occasionally used by biochemists (see Box 4-2).

Life Is Based on Chiral Molecules. Consider the ordinary chemical synthesis of a chiral molecule, which produces a **racemic mixture** (containing equal amounts of each enantiomer). In order to obtain a product with net asymmetry, a chiral process must be employed. One of the most striking characteristics of life is its production of optically active molecules. *Biosynthetic processes almost invariably produce pure stereoisomers.* The fact that the amino acid residues of proteins all have the L configuration is just one example of this phenomenon. Furthermore, because most biological molecules are chiral, a given molecule—present in a single enantiomeric form—will bind to or react with only a single enantiomer of another compound. For example, a protein made of L-amino acid residues that reacts with a particular L-amino acid does not readily react with the D form of that amino acid. An otherwise identical synthetic protein made of D-amino acid residues, however, readily reacts only with the corresponding D-amino acid.

D-Amino acid residues are components of some relatively short (<20 residues) bacterial polypeptides. These polypeptides are perhaps most

BOX 4-2 PERSPECTIVES IN BIOCHEMISTRY

The *RS* System

A system to unambiguously describe the configurations of molecules with more than one asymmetric center was devised in 1956 by Robert Cahn, Christopher Ingold, and Vladimir Prelog. In the **Cahn–Ingold–Prelog** or ***RS* system,** the four groups surrounding a chiral center are ranked according to a specific although arbitrary priority scheme: Atoms of higher atomic number rank above those of lower atomic number (e.g., —OH ranks above —CH₃). If the first substituent atoms are identical, the priority is established by the next atom outward from the chiral center (e.g., —CH₂OH takes precedence over —CH₃). The order of priority of some common functional groups is

$$SH > OH > NH_2 > COOH > CHO > CH_2OH > C_6H_5 > CH_3 > H$$

The prioritized groups are assigned the letters W, X, Y, Z such that their order of priority ranking is W > X > Y > Z. To establish the configuration of the chiral center, it is viewed from the asymmetric center toward the Z group (lowest priority). If the order of the groups W → X → Y is clockwise, the configuration is designated R (Latin: *rectus,* right). If the order of W → X → Y is counterclockwise, the configuration is designated S (Latin: *sinistrus,* left).

L-Glyceraldehyde is (S)-glyceraldehyde because the three highest priority groups are arranged counterclockwise when the H atom (*dashed lines*) is positioned behind the chiral C atom (*large circle*).

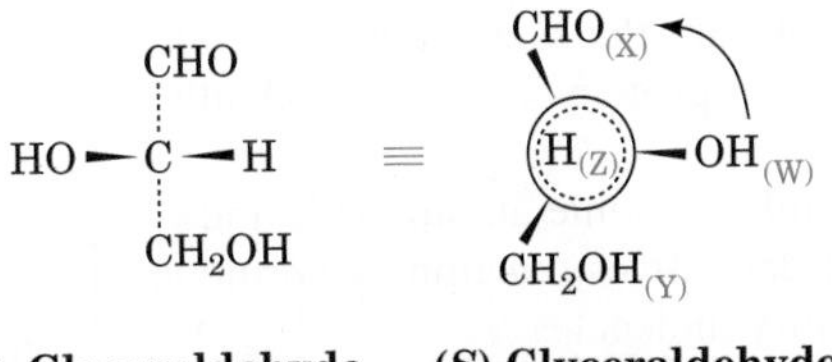

L-Glyceraldehyde   **(S)-Glyceraldehyde**

All the L-amino acids in proteins are (S)-amino acids except cysteine, which is (R)-cysteine because the S in its side chain increases its priority. Other closely related compounds with the same designation under the Fischer DL convention may have different representations under the RS system. The RS system is particularly useful for describing the chiralities of compounds with multiple asymmetric centers. Thus, L-threonine can also be called (2S,3R)-threonine.

---

widely distributed as constituents of bacterial cell walls (Section 8-3B). The presence of the D-amino acids renders bacterial cell walls less susceptible to attack by the **peptidases** (enzymes that hydrolyze peptide bonds) that are produced by other organisms to digest bacteria. Likewise, D-amino acids are components of many bacterially produced peptide antibiotics. Most peptides containing D-amino acids are not synthesized by the standard protein synthetic machinery, in which messenger RNA is translated at the ribosome by transfer RNA molecules with attached L-amino acids (Chapter 27). Instead, the D-amino acids are directly joined together by the action of specific bacterial enzymes.

The importance of stereochemistry in living systems is also a concern of the pharmaceutical industry. *Many drugs are chemically synthesized as racemic mixtures, although only one enantiomer has biological activity.* In most cases, the opposite enantiomer is biologically inert and is therefore packaged along with its active counterpart. This is true, for example, of the anti-inflammatory agent **ibuprofen,** only one enantiomer of which is physiologically active (Fig. 4-12). Occasionally, the inactive enantiomer of a useful drug produces harmful effects and must therefore be eliminated from the racemic mixture. The most striking example of this is the drug **thalidomide** (Fig. 4-13), a mild sedative whose inactive enantiomer causes

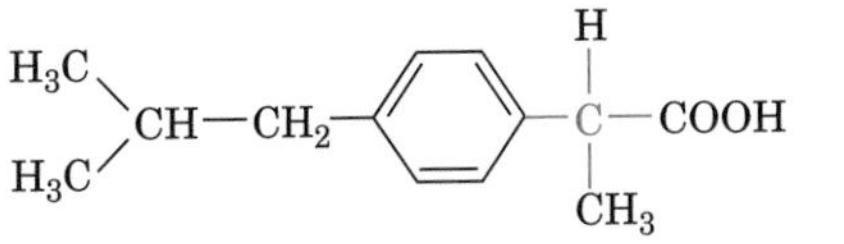

Ibuprofen

■ **Figure 4-12 | Ibuprofen.** Only the enantiomer shown has anti-inflammatory action. The chiral carbon is red.

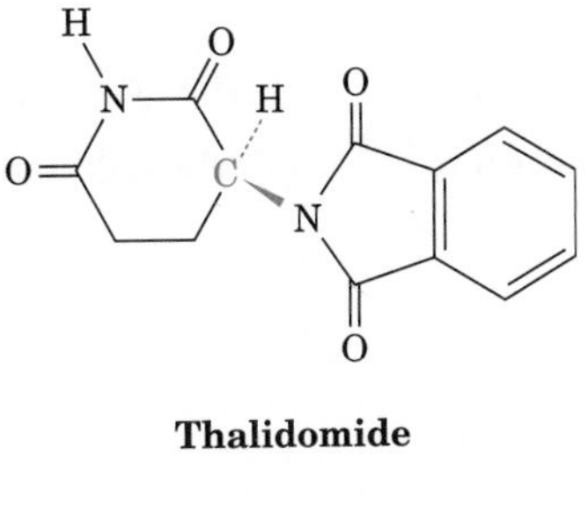

■ **Figure 4-13 | Thalidomide.** This drug was widely used in Europe as a mild sedative in the early 1960s. Its inactive enantiomer (not shown), which was present in equal amounts in the formulations used, causes severe birth defects in humans when taken during the first trimester of pregnancy. Thalidomide was often prescribed to alleviate the nausea (morning sickness) that is common during this period.

Thalidomide

■ **CHECK YOUR UNDERSTANDING**

Be able to identify the chiral carbons in the amino acids shown in Table 4-1.

Explain how the Fischer convention describes the absolute configuration of a chiral molecule.

LEARNING OBJECTIVES

■ Understand that the side chains of amino acid residues in proteins may be covalently modified.

■ Understand that some amino acids and amino acid derivatives function as hormones and regulatory molecules.

severe birth defects. Partly because of the unanticipated problems caused by inactive drug enantiomers, **chiral organic synthesis** has become an active area of medicinal chemistry.

3 Amino Acid Derivatives

The 20 common amino acids are by no means the only amino acids that occur in biological systems. "Nonstandard" amino acid residues are often important constituents of proteins and biologically active peptides. In addition, many amino acids are not constituents of polypeptides at all but independently play a variety of biological roles.

A | Protein Side Chains May Be Modified

The "universal" genetic code, which is nearly identical in all known life-forms (Section 27-1), specifies only the 20 standard amino acids of Table 4-1. Nevertheless, many other amino acids, some of which are shown in Fig. 4-14, are components of certain proteins. *In almost all cases, these unusual amino acids result from the specific modification of an amino acid residue after the polypeptide chain has been synthesized.*

Amino acid modifications include the simple addition of small chemical groups to certain amino acid side chains: hydroxylation, methylation, acetylation, carboxylation, and phosphorylation. Larger groups, including lipids and carbohydrate polymers, are attached to particular amino acid residues of certain proteins. The free amino and carboxyl groups at the N- and C-termini of a polypeptide can also be chemically modified. These modifications are often important, if not essential, for the function of the protein. In some cases, several amino acid side chains together form a novel structure (Box 4-3).

B | Some Amino Acids Are Biologically Active

The 20 standard amino acids undergo a bewildering number of chemical transformations to other amino acids and related compounds as part of their normal cellular synthesis and degradation. In a few cases, the intermediates of amino acid metabolism have functions beyond their immediate

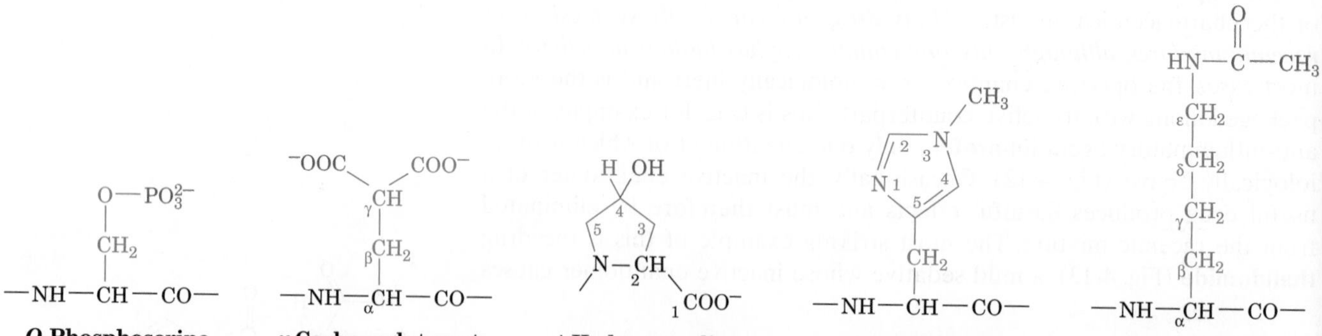

O-Phosphoserine   γ-Carboxyglutamate   4-Hydroxyproline   3-Methylhistidine   ε-*N*-Acetyllysine

■ **Figure 4-14 | Some modified amino acid residues in proteins.** The side chains of these residues are derived from one of the 20 standard amino acids after the polypeptide has been synthesized. The standard R groups are red, and the modifying groups are blue.

BOX 4-3 PERSPECTIVES IN BIOCHEMISTRY

Green Fluorescent Protein

Genetic engineers often link a protein-coding gene to a "reporter gene," for example, the gene for an enzyme that yields a colored reaction product. The intensity of the colored compound can be used to estimate the level of expression of the engineered gene. One of the most useful reporter genes is the one that codes for **green fluorescent protein (GFP).** This protein, from the bioluminescent jellyfish *Aequorea victoria,* fluoresces with a peak wavelength of 508 nm (green light) when irradiated by ultraviolet or blue light (optimally 400 nm).

Green fluorescent protein is nontoxic and intrinsically fluorescent; it requires no substrate or small molecule cofactor to fluoresce as do other highly fluorescent proteins. Consequently, when the gene for green fluorescent protein is linked to another gene, the level of expression of the fused genes can be measured noninvasively by fluorescence microscopy.

Green fluorescent protein consists of a chain of 238 amino acid residues. The light-emitting group is a derivative of three consecutive amino acids: Ser, Tyr, and Gly. After the protein has been synthesized, the three amino acids undergo spontaneous cyclization and oxidation. The carbonyl C atom of Ser forms a covalent bond to the amino N atom contributed by Gly, followed by the elimination of water and the oxidation of the C_α—C_β bond of Tyr to a double bond. The resulting structure contains a system of conjugated double bonds that gives the protein its fluorescent properties.

Fluorophore of green fluorescent protein

Cyclization between Ser and Gly is probably rapid, and the oxidation of the Tyr side chain (by O_2) is probably the rate-limiting step of fluorophore generation. Genetic engineering has introduced site-specific mutations that enhance fluorescence intensity and shift the wavelength of the emitted light to different colors, thereby making it possible to simultaneously monitor the expression of two or more different genes.

[© 1999 Steven Haddock and Trevor Rivers/Monterey Bay Aquarium Research Institute, Monterey, California.]

use as precursors or degradation products of the 20 standard amino acids. Moreover, many amino acids are synthesized not to be residues of polypeptides but to function independently. We shall see that many organisms use certain amino acids to transport nitrogen in the form of amino

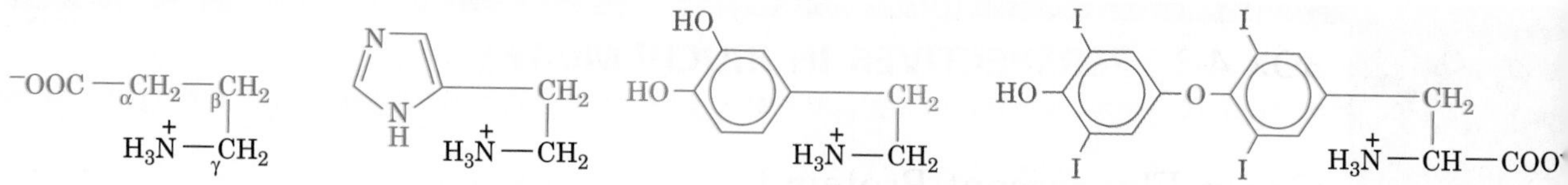

$^-OOC-\underset{\alpha}{CH_2}-\underset{\beta}{CH_2}$
$\underset{\gamma}{H_3\overset{+}{N}}-CH_2$

γ-Aminobutyric acid (GABA)

Histamine

Dopamine

Thyroxine

■ **Figure 4-15** | **Some biologically active amino acid derivatives.** The remaining portions of the parent amino acids are black and red, and additional groups are blue.

groups (Section 21-2A). Amino acids may also be oxidized as metabolic fuels to provide energy (Section 21-4). In addition, amino acids and their derivatives often function as chemical messengers for communication between cells (Fig. 4-15). For example, glycine, **γ-aminobutyric acid (GABA,** a glutamine decarboxylation product), and **dopamine** (a tyrosine derivative) are **neurotransmitters,** substances released by nerve cells to alter the behavior of their neighbors. **Histamine** (the decarboxylation product of histidine) is a potent local mediator of allergic reactions. **Thyroxine** (another tyrosine derivative) is an iodine-containing thyroid hormone that generally stimulates vertebrate metabolism.

Many peptides containing only a few amino acid residues have important physiological functions as hormones or other regulatory molecules. One nearly ubiquitous tripeptide called **glutathione** plays a role in cellular metabolism. Glutathione is a Glu–Cys–Gly peptide in which the γ-carboxylate group of the glutamate side chain forms an **isopeptide bond** with the amino group of the Cys residue (so called because a peptide bond is taken to be the amide bond formed between an α-carboxylate and an α-amino group of two amino acids). Two of these tripeptides (abbreviated **GSH**) undergo oxidation of their SH groups to form a dimeric disulfide-linked structure called **glutathione disulfide (GSSG):**

$$2 \ H_3\overset{+}{N}-\underset{\underset{COO^-}{|}}{CH}-CH_2-CH_2-\overset{\overset{O}{\|}}{C}-NH-\underset{\underset{\underset{SH}{|}}{\underset{CH_2}{|}}}{CH}-\overset{\overset{O}{\|}}{C}-NH-CH_2-COO^-$$

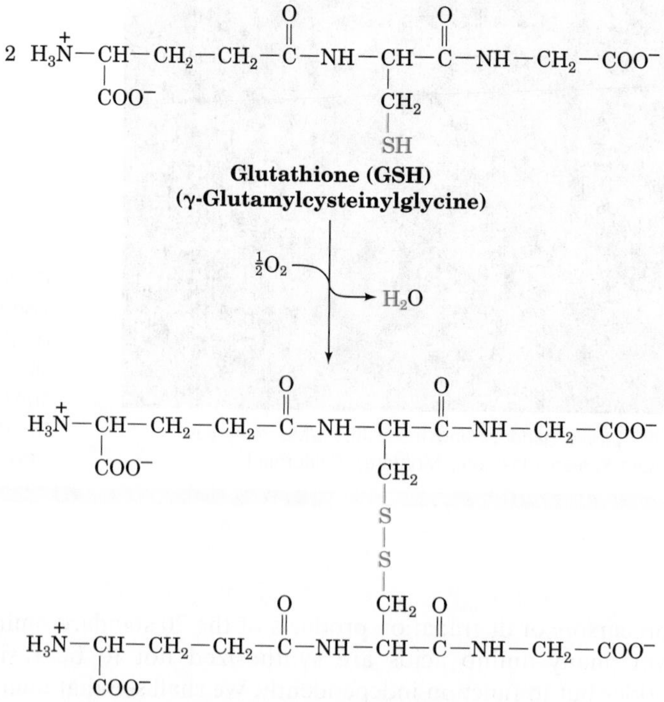

Glutathione (GSH)
(γ-Glutamylcysteinylglycine)

$$\tfrac{1}{2}O_2 \longrightarrow H_2O$$

$$H_3\overset{+}{N}-\underset{\underset{COO^-}{|}}{CH}-CH_2-CH_2-\overset{\overset{O}{\|}}{C}-NH-\underset{\underset{\underset{S}{|}}{\underset{CH_2}{|}}}{CH}-\overset{\overset{O}{\|}}{C}-NH-CH_2-COO^-$$

$$H_3\overset{+}{N}-\underset{\underset{COO^-}{|}}{CH}-CH_2-CH_2-\overset{\overset{O}{\|}}{C}-NH-\underset{\underset{CH_2}{|}}{CH}-\overset{\overset{O}{\|}}{C}-NH-CH_2-COO^-$$

Glutathione disulfide (GSSG)

Glutathione helps inactivate oxidative compounds that could potentially damage cellular structures, since the oxidation of GSH to GSSG is accompanied by the reduction of another compound (shown as O_2 above):

$$2\,GSH + X_{oxidized} \rightarrow GSSG + X_{reduced}$$

GSH must then be regenerated in a separate reduction reaction.

■ **CHECK YOUR UNDERSTANDING**

List some covalent modifications of amino acids in proteins.
List some functions of amino acid derivatives.

SUMMARY

1. At neutral pH, the amino group of an amino acid is protonated and its carboxylic acid group is ionized.

2. Proteins are polymers of amino acids joined by peptide bonds.

3. The 20 standard amino acids can be classified as nonpolar (Gly, Ala, Val, Leu, Ile, Met, Pro, Phe, Trp), uncharged polar (Ser, Thr, Asn, Gln, Tyr, Cys), and charged (Lys, Arg, His, Asp, Glu).

4. The pK values of the ionizable groups of amino acids may be altered when the amino acid is part of a polypeptide.

5. Amino acids are chiral molecules. Only L-amino acids are found in proteins (some bacterial peptides contain D-amino acids).

6. Amino acids may be covalently modified after they have been incorporated into a polypeptide.

7. Individual amino acids and their derivatives have diverse physiological functions.

KEY TERMS

protein 74
α-amino acid 74
α carbon 74
R group 75
zwitterion 78
condensation reaction 78
peptide bond 78
dipeptide 78

tripeptide 78
oligopeptide 78
polypeptide 78
residue 78
N-terminus 78
C-terminus 78
pI 81
optical activity 82

polarimeter 82
chiral center 83
chirality 83
enantiomers 83
absolute configuration 83
Fischer convention 83
stereoisomers 83
levorotatory 84

dextrorotatory 84
Fischer projection 84
racemic mixture 84
Cahn–Ingold–Prelog (RS) system 85
peptidase 85
neurotransmitter 88
isopeptide bond 88

PROBLEMS

1. Identify the amino acids that differ from each other by a single methyl or methylene group.

2. The 20 standard amino acids are called α-amino acids. Certain β-amino acids are found in nature. Draw the structure of β-alanine (3-amino-n-propionate).

3. Identify the hydrogen bond donor and acceptor groups in asparagine.

4. Draw the dipeptide Asp-His at pH 7.0.

5. Calculate the number of possible pentapeptides that contain one residue each of Ala, Gly, His, Lys, and Val.

6. Determine the net charge of the predominant form of Asp at (a) pH 1.0, (b) pH 3.0, (c) pH 6.0, and (d) pH 11.0.

7. Calculate the pI of (a) Ala, (b) His, and (c) Glu.

8. A sample of the amino acid tyrosine is barely soluble in water. Would a polypeptide containing only Tyr residues, poly(Tyr), be more or less soluble, assuming the total number of Tyr groups remains constant?

9. Circle the chiral carbons in the following compounds:

10. Draw the four stereoisomers of threonine.

11. The two $C_\alpha H$ atoms of Gly are said to be prochiral, because when one of them is replaced by another group, C_α becomes chiral. Draw a Fischer projection of Gly and indicate which H must be replaced with CH_3 to yield D-Ala.

12. The bacterially produced antibiotic gramicidin A forms channels in cell membranes that allow the free diffusion of Na^+

and K$^+$ ions, thereby killing the cell. This peptide consists of a sequence of D- and L-amino acids. The sequence of a segment of five amino acids in gramicidin A is R–Gly–L-Ala–D-Leu–L-Ala–D-Val–R'. Complete the Fischer projection below by adding the correct group to each vertical bond.

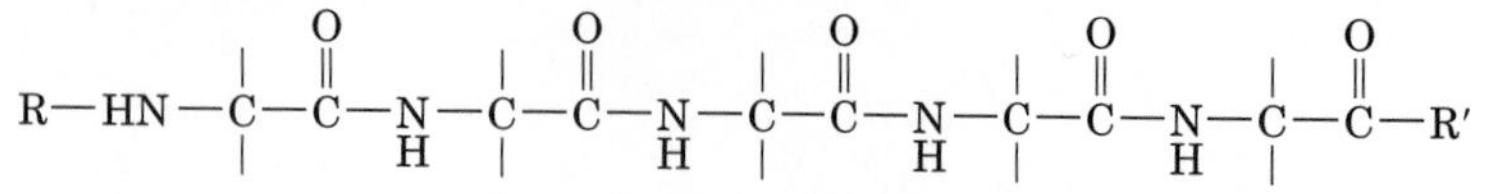

$$R-HN-\overset{\displaystyle O}{\underset{|}{\overset{|}{C}}}-\overset{\displaystyle O}{\underset{H}{\overset{||}{C}}}-\overset{}{\underset{|}{\overset{|}{N}}}-\overset{\displaystyle O}{\underset{|}{\overset{|}{C}}}-\overset{\displaystyle O}{\underset{H}{\overset{||}{C}}}-\overset{}{\underset{|}{\overset{|}{N}}}-\overset{\displaystyle O}{\underset{|}{\overset{|}{C}}}-\overset{\displaystyle O}{\underset{H}{\overset{||}{C}}}-\overset{}{\underset{|}{\overset{|}{N}}}-\overset{\displaystyle O}{\underset{|}{\overset{|}{C}}}-\overset{\displaystyle O}{\underset{H}{\overset{||}{C}}}-\overset{}{\underset{|}{\overset{|}{N}}}-\overset{\displaystyle O}{\underset{|}{\overset{|}{C}}}-\overset{\displaystyle O}{\overset{||}{C}}-R'$$

13. Describe isoleucine (as shown in Table 4-1) using the *RS* system.

14. Some amino acids are synthesized by replacing the keto group (C=O) of an organic acid known as an α-keto acid with an amino group (C—NH$_3^+$). Identify the amino acids that can be produced this way from the following α-keto acids:

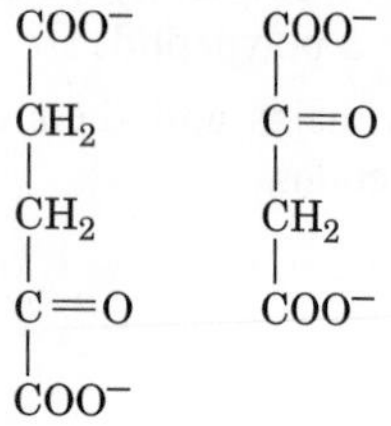

$$\begin{array}{ll} COO^- & COO^- \\ | & | \\ CH_2 & C=O \\ | & | \\ CH_2 & CH_2 \\ | & | \\ C=O & COO^- \\ | & \\ COO^- & \end{array}$$

15. Identify the amino acid residue from which the following groups are synthesized:

(a)
$$\begin{array}{cc} O & CH_2-OH \\ || & | \\ CH_3-C-NH-CH-CO- \end{array}$$

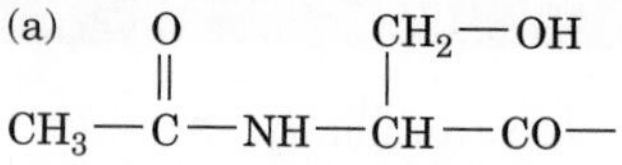

(b)
$$\begin{array}{ll} NH_3^+ & S-CH_3 \\ | & | \\ {}_6CH_2 & CH_2 \\ | & | \\ {}_5CH-OH & \quad\quad O \quad CH_2 \\ | & || \quad | \\ {}_4CH_2 & HC-NH-CH-CO- \\ | & \\ {}_3CH_2 & \\ | & \\ -NH-{}_2CH-{}_1CO- & \end{array}$$

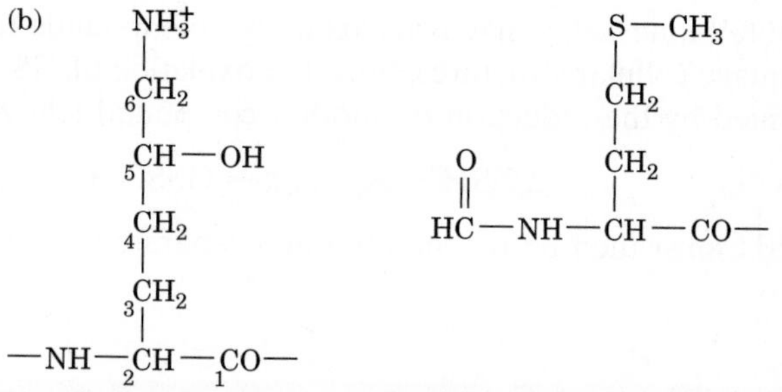

16. Draw the peptide ATLDAK. (a) Calculate its approximate p*I*. (b) What is its net charge at pH 7.0?

17. The protein insulin consists of two polypeptides termed the A and B chains. Insulins from different organisms have been isolated and sequenced. Human and duck insulins have the same amino acid sequence with the exception of six amino acid residues, as shown below. Is the p*I* of human insulin lower than or higher than that of duck insulin?

Amino acid residue	A8	A9	A10	B1	B2	B27
Human	Thr	Ser	Ile	Phe	Val	Thr
Duck	Glu	Asn	Pro	Ala	Ala	Ser

REFERENCES

Barrett, G.C. and Elmore, D.T., *Amino Acids and Peptides,* Cambridge University Press (2001). [Includes structures of the common amino acids along with a discussion of their chemical reactivities and information on analytical properties.]

Lamzin, V.S., Dauter, Z., and Wilson, K.S., How nature deals with stereoisomers, *Curr. Opin. Struct. Biol.* **5,** 830–836 (1995). [Discusses proteins synthesized from D-amino acids.]

Solomons, G. and Fryhle, C., *Organic Chemistry* (9th ed.), Chapter 5, Wiley (2008). [A discussion of chirality. Most other organic chemistry textbooks contain similar material.]

5

Proteins: Primary Structure

The great variation in structure and function among proteins reflects the astronomical variation in the sequences of their component amino acids: There are far more possible amino acid sequences than there are stars in the universe. [PhotoDisc, Inc./Getty Images.]

■ **MEDIA RESOURCES**

(Available at www.wiley.com/college/voet)
Guided Exploration 4. Protein sequence determination
Guided Exploration 5. Protein evolution
Animated Figure 5-3. Enzyme-linked immunosorbent assay
Animated Figure 5-6. Ion exchange chromatography
Animated Figure 5-7. Gel filtration chromatography
Animated Figure 5-15. Edman degradation
Animated Figure 5-18. Generating overlapping fragments to determine the amino acid sequence of a polypeptide
Case Study 2. Histidine–Proline-Rich Glycoprotein as a Plasma pH Sensor
Bioinformatics Exercises Chapter 5. Using Databases to Compare and Identify Related Protein Sequences

■ **CHAPTER CONTENTS**

1 Polypeptide Diversity

2 Protein Purification and Analysis
  A. Purifying a Protein Requires a Strategy
  B. Salting Out Separates Proteins by Their Solubility
  C. Chromatography Involves Interaction with Mobile and Stationary Phases
  D. Electrophoresis Separates Molecules According to Charge and Size

3 Protein Sequencing
  A. The First Step Is to Separate Subunits
  B. The Polypeptide Chains Are Cleaved
  C. Edman Degradation Removes a Peptide's First Amino Acid Residue
  D. Mass Spectrometry Determines the Molecular Masses of Peptides
  E. Reconstructed Protein Sequences Are Stored in Databases

4 Protein Evolution
  A. Protein Sequences Reveal Evolutionary Relationships
  B. Proteins Evolve by the Duplication of Genes or Gene Segments

Proteins are at the center of action in biological processes. Nearly all the molecular transformations that define cellular metabolism are mediated by protein catalysts. Proteins also perform regulatory roles, monitoring extracellular and intracellular conditions and relaying information to other cellular components. In addition, proteins are essential structural components of cells. A complete list of known protein functions would contain many thousands of entries, including proteins that transport other molecules and proteins that generate mechanical and electrochemical forces. And such a list would not account for the thousands of proteins whose functions are not yet fully characterized or, in many cases, are completely unknown.

One of the keys to deciphering the function of a given protein is to understand its structure. Like the other major biological macromolecules, the nucleic acids (Section 3-2) and the polysaccharides (Section 8-2), proteins are polymers of smaller units. But unlike many nucleic acids, proteins do not have uniform, regular structures. This is, in part, because the 20 kinds of amino acid residues from which proteins are made have widely differing chemical and physical properties (Section 4-1C). The sequence in which these amino acids are strung together can be analyzed directly, as we describe in this chapter, or indirectly, via DNA sequencing (Section 3-4). In either case, amino acid sequence information provides insights into the chemical and physical properties of proteins, their relationships to other proteins, and ultimately, their mechanisms of action in living organisms. After a brief introduction to the variety in protein structure we will examine some methods for purifying and analyzing proteins, procedures for determining the sequence of amino residues, and finally, some approaches to understanding protein evolution.

1 Polypeptide Diversity

LEARNING OBJECTIVE

■ Understand that the size and composition of polypeptides exhibit tremendous but not unlimited variety.

Like all polymeric molecules, proteins can be described in terms of levels of organization, in this case, their primary, secondary, tertiary, and quaternary structures. *A protein's **primary structure** is the amino acid sequence of its polypeptide chain,* or chains if the protein consists of more than one polypeptide. An example of an amino acid sequence is given in Fig. 5-1. Each residue is linked to the next via a peptide bond (Fig. 4-3). Higher levels of protein structure—secondary, tertiary, and quaternary—refer to the three-dimensional shapes of folded polypeptide chains and will be described in the next chapter.

Proteins are synthesized *in vivo* by the stepwise polymerization of amino acids in the order specified by the sequence of nucleotides in a gene. The direct correspondence between one linear polymer (DNA) and another (a polypeptide) illustrates the elegant simplicity of living systems and allows us to extract information from one polymer and apply it to the other.

The Theoretical Possibilities for Polypeptides Are Unlimited. With 20 different choices available for each amino acid residue in a polypeptide chain, it is easy to see that a huge number of different protein molecules are possible. For a protein of n residues, there are 20^n possible sequences. A relatively small protein molecule may consist of a single polypeptide chain of 100 residues. There are $20^{100} \approx 1.27 \times 10^{130}$ possible unique polypeptide chains of this length, a quantity vastly greater than the estimated number of atoms in the universe (9×10^{78}). Clearly, evolution has produced only a tiny fraction of the theoretical possibilities—a fraction that nevertheless represents an astronomical number of different polypeptides.

Actual Polypeptides Are Somewhat Limited in Size and Composition. In general, proteins contain at least 40 residues or so; polypeptides smaller than that are simply called **peptides.** The largest known polypeptide chain belongs to the 34,350-residue **titin,** a giant (3816 kD) protein that helps arrange the repeating structures of muscle fibers (Section 7-2A). However, *the vast majority of polypeptides contain between 100 and 1000 residues* (Table 5-1). **Multisubunit proteins** contain several identical and/or nonidentical chains called **subunits.** Some proteins are synthesized as single polypeptides that are later cleaved into two or more chains that remain associated; **insulin** is such a protein (Fig. 5-1).

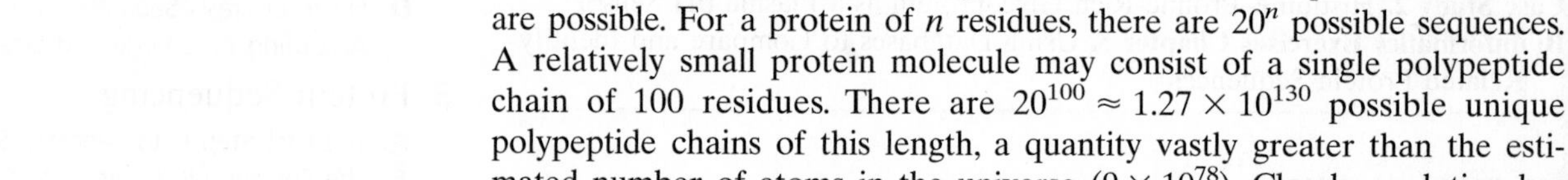

A chain

Gly−Ile−Val−Glu−Gln−Cys−Cys−Ala−Ser−Val−Cys−Ser−Leu−Tyr−Gln−Leu−Glu−Asn−Tyr−Cys−Asn
　　　　　　5　　　　　　　　　　10　　　　　　　　　　15　　　　　　　　　　21

B chain

Phe−Val−Asn−Gln−His−Leu−Cys−Gly−Ser−His−Leu−Val−Glu−Ala−Leu−Tyr−Leu−Val−Cys−Gly−Glu−Arg−Gly−Phe−Phe−Tyr−Thr−Pro−Lys−Ala
　　　　　　5　　　　　　　　　　10　　　　　　　　　　15　　　　　　　　　　20　　　　　　　　　　25　　　　　　　　　　30

■ **Figure 5-1** | **The primary structure of bovine insulin.** Note the intrachain and interchain disulfide bond linkages.

Table 5-1	Compositions of Some Proteins		
Protein	**Amino Acid Residues**	**Subunits**	**Protein Molecular Mass (D)**
Proteinase inhibitor III (bitter gourd)	30	1	3,427
Cytochrome *c* (human)	104	1	11,617
Myoglobin (horse)	153	1	16,951
Interferon-γ (rabbit)	288	2	33,842
Chorismate mutase (*Bacillus subtilis*)	381	3	43,551
Triose phosphate isomerase (*E. coli*)	510	2	53,944
Hemoglobin (human)	574	4	61,986
RNA polymerase (bacteriophage T7)	883	1	98,885
Nucleoside diphosphate kinase (*Dictyostelium discoideum*)	930	6	100,764
Pyruvate decarboxylase (yeast)	2,252	4	245,456
Glutamine synthetase (*E. coli*)	5,616	12	621,264
Titin (human)	34,350	1	3,816,188

The size range in which most polypeptides fall probably reflects the optimization of several biochemical processes:

1. Forty residues appears to be near the minimum for a polypeptide chain to fold into a discrete and stable shape that allows it to carry out a particular function.

2. Polypeptides with many hundreds of residues may approach the limits of efficiency of the protein synthetic machinery. The longer the polypeptide (and the longer its corresponding mRNA), the greater the likelihood of introducing errors during transcription and translation.

In addition to these mild constraints on size, polypeptides are subject to more severe limitations on amino acid composition. The 20 standard amino acids do not appear with equal frequencies in proteins. (Table 4-1 lists the average occurrence of each amino acid residue.) For example, the most abundant amino acids in proteins are Leu, Ala, Gly, Ser, Val, and Glu; the rarest are Trp, Cys, Met, and His.

Because each amino acid residue has characteristic chemical and physical properties, its presence at a particular position in a protein influences the properties of that protein. In particular, as we shall see, the three-dimensional shape of a folded polypeptide chain is a consequence of the intramolecular forces among its various residues. In general, a protein's hydrophobic residues cluster in its interior, out of contact with water, whereas its hydrophilic side chains tend to occupy the protein's surface.

The characteristics of an individual protein depend more on its amino acid sequence than on its amino acid composition per se, for the same reason that "kitchen" and its anagram "thicken" are quite different words. In addition, many proteins consist of more than just amino acid residues. They may form complexes with metal ions such as Zn^{2+} and Ca^{2+}, they may covalently or noncovalently bind certain small organic molecules, and they may be covalently modified by the posttranslational attachment of groups such as phosphates and carbohydrates.

■ CHECK YOUR UNDERSTANDING

Explain why polypeptides have such variable sequences.

What factors limit the size and composition of polypeptides?

LEARNING OBJECTIVES

■ Understand that environmental conditions affect a protein's stability during purification.

■ Understand that an assay is used to quantify a protein during purification.

■ Understand that increasing the salt concentration causes selective "salting out" (precipitation) of proteins with different solubilities.

■ Understand how a protein's ionic charge, polarity, size, and ligand-binding ability influence its chromatographic behavior.

■ Understand that gel electrophoresis and its variations can separate proteins according to charge, size, and isoelectric point.

2 Protein Purification and Analysis

Purification is an all but mandatory step in studying macromolecules, but it is not necessarily easy. Typically, a substance that makes up <0.1% of a tissue's dry weight must be brought to ~98% purity. Purification problems of this magnitude would be considered unreasonably difficult by most synthetic chemists! The following sections outline some of the most common techniques for purifying and, to some extent, characterizing proteins and other macromolecules. Most of these techniques can be used, sometimes in modified form, for nucleic acids and other types of biological molecules.

A | Purifying a Protein Requires a Strategy

The task of purifying a protein present in only trace amounts was once so arduous that many of the earliest proteins to be characterized were studied in part because they are abundant and easily isolated. For example, hemoglobin, which accounts for about one-third the weight of red blood cells, has historically been among the most extensively studied proteins. Most of the enzymes that mediate basic metabolic processes or that are involved in the expression and transmission of genetic information are common to all species. For this reason, a given protein is frequently obtained from a source chosen primarily for convenience, for example, tissues from domesticated animals or easily obtained microorganisms such as *E. coli* and *Saccharomyces cerevisiae* (Baker's yeast).

The development of molecular cloning techniques (Section 3-5) allows almost any protein-encoding gene to be isolated from its parent organism, specifically altered (genetically engineered) if desired, and expressed at high levels in a microorganism. Indeed, the cloned protein may constitute up to 40% of the microorganism's total cell protein (Fig. 5-2). This high level of protein production generally renders the cloned protein far easier to isolate than it would be from its parent organism (in which it may occur in vanishingly small amounts).

The first step in the isolation of a protein or other biological molecule is to get it out of the cell and into solution. Many cells require some sort of mechanical disruption to release their contents. Most of the procedures for lysing cells use some variation of crushing or grinding followed by filtration or centrifugation to remove large insoluble particles. If the target protein is tightly associated with a lipid membrane, a detergent or organic solvent may be used to solubilize the lipids and recover the protein.

pH, Temperature, and Other Conditions Must Be Controlled to Keep Proteins Stable. Once a protein has been removed from its natural environment, it becomes exposed to many agents that can irreversibly damage it. These influences must be carefully controlled at all stages of a purification process. The following factors should be considered:

1. **pH.** Biological materials are routinely dissolved in buffer solutions effective in the pH range over which the materials are stable (buffers are described in Section 2-2C). Failure to do so could cause their **denaturation** (structural disruption), if not their chemical degradation.

2. **Temperature.** The thermal stability of proteins varies. Although some proteins denature at low temperatures, most proteins denature at high temperatures, sometimes only a few degrees higher than their native environment. Protein purification is normally carried out at temperatures near 0°C.

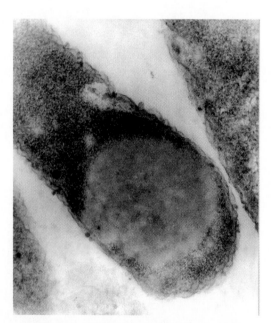

■ **Figure 5-2 | Inclusion body.** A genetically engineered organism that produces large amounts of a foreign protein often sequesters it in **inclusion bodies.** This electron micrograph shows an inclusion body of the protein prochymosin in an *E. coli* cell. [Courtesy of Teruhiko Beppu, Nikon University, Japan.]

3. *Presence of degradative enzymes.* Destroying tissues to liberate the molecule of interest also releases degradative enzymes, including **proteases** and **nucleases.** Degradative enzymes can be inhibited by adjusting the pH or temperature to values that inactivate them (provided this does not adversely affect the protein of interest) or by adding compounds that specifically block their action.

4. *Adsorption to surfaces.* Many proteins are denatured by contact with the air–water interface or with glass or plastic surfaces. Hence, protein solutions are handled so as to minimize foaming and are kept relatively concentrated.

5. *Long-term storage.* All the factors listed above must be considered when a purified protein sample is to be kept stable. In addition, processes such as slow oxidation and microbial contamination must be prevented. Protein solutions are sometimes stored under nitrogen or argon gas (rather than under air, which contains ~21% O_2) and/or are frozen at −80°C or −196°C (the temperature of liquid nitrogen).

Proteins Are Quantified by Assays. Purifying a substance requires some means for quantitatively detecting it. Accordingly, an **assay** must be devised that is specific for the target protein, highly sensitive, and convenient to use (especially if it must be repeated at every stage of the purification process).

Among the most straightforward protein assays are those for enzymes that catalyze reactions with readily detected products, because *the rate of product formation is proportional to the amount of enzyme present.* Substances with colored or fluorescent products have been developed for just this purpose. If no such substance is available for the enzyme being assayed, the product of the enzymatic reaction may be converted, by the action of another enzyme, to an easily quantified substance. This is known as a **coupled enzymatic reaction.** Proteins that are not enzymes can be detected by their ability to specifically bind certain substances or to produce observable biological effects.

Immunochemical procedures are among the most sensitive of assay techniques. **Immunoassays** use **antibodies,** proteins produced by an animal's immune system in response to the introduction of a foreign substance (an **antigen**). Antibodies recovered from the blood serum of an immunized animal or from cultures of immortalized antibody-producing cells bind specifically to the original protein antigen.

A protein in a complex mixture can be detected by its binding to its corresponding antibodies. In one technique, known as a **radioimmunoassay (RIA),** the protein is indirectly detected by determining the degree to which it competes with a radioactively labeled standard for binding to the antibody. Another technique, the **enzyme-linked immunosorbent assay (ELISA),** has many variations, one of which is diagrammed in Fig. 5-3.

Protein Concentrations Can Be Determined by Spectroscopy. The concentration of a substance in solution can be measured by **absorbance spectroscopy.** A solution containing a solute that absorbs light does so according to the **Beer–Lambert law,**

$$A = \log\frac{I_0}{I} = \varepsilon c l \qquad [5\text{-}1]$$

where A is the solute's **absorbance** (alternatively, its **optical density**), I_0 is the intensity of the incident light at a given wavelength λ, I is its transmitted intensity at λ, ε is the **absorptivity** (alternatively, the **extinction**

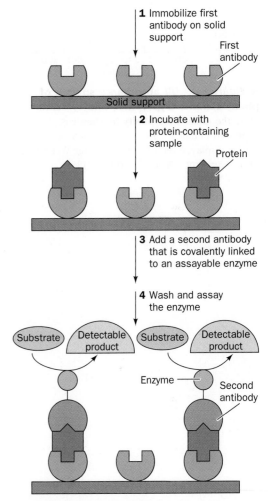

■ Figure 5-3 | Enzyme-linked immunosorbent assay. (**1**) An antibody against the protein of interest is immobilized on an inert solid such as polystyrene. (**2**) The solution to be assayed is applied to the antibody-coated surface. The antibody binds the protein of interest, and other proteins are washed away. (**3**) The protein–antibody complex is reacted with a second protein-specific antibody to which an enzyme is attached. (**4**) Binding of the second antibody–enzyme complex is measured by assaying the activity of the enzyme. The amount of substrate converted to product indicates the amount of protein present.
⌖ See the Animated Figures.

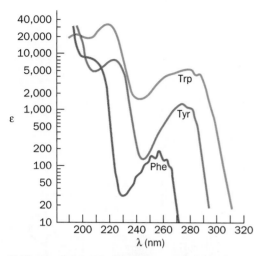

■ Figure 5-4 | UV absorbance spectra of phenylalanine, tryptophan, and tyrosine. Here the **molar absorptivity** (ε when c is expressed in mol·L^{-1}) for each aromatic amino acid is displayed on a log scale. [After Wetlaufer, D.B., *Adv. Prot. Chem.* **7,** 310 (1962).]

coefficient) of the solute at λ, c is its concentration, and l is the length of the light path in centimeters. The value of ε varies with λ; a plot of A or ε versus λ for the solute is called its **absorption spectrum.** If the value of ε for a substance is known, then its concentration can be spectroscopically determined.

Polypeptides absorb strongly in the ultraviolet (UV) region of the spectrum ($\lambda = 200$ to 400 nm) largely because their aromatic side chains (those of Phe, Trp, and Tyr) have particularly large extinction coefficients in this spectral region (ranging into the tens of thousands when c is expressed in mol·L^{-1}; Fig. 5-4). However, polypeptides do not absorb visible light ($\lambda = 400$ to 800 nm) so that they are colorless. Nevertheless, if a protein has a **chromophore** that absorbs in the visible region of the spectrum, this absorbance can be used to assay for the presence of the protein in a mixture of other proteins.

In order to follow the purification of a protein, it is important to measure the total amount of protein at every stage of the purification. Absorbance spectroscopy at 280 nm is a convenient way of doing so. However, since many substances that are likely to be present during a protein purification procedure (e.g., nucleic acids) also absorb UV light, and since proteins vary in their proportion of light-absorbing aromatic residues, spectroscopic measurements in the UV region can only provide estimates of the amount of protein present (although they can accurately determine the amount of a pure protein of known molar absorptivity). Moreover, spectroscopic methods are only moderately sensitive to proteins; they can minimally detect 50 to 100 μg of protein per milliliter.

Several techniques have been developed to circumvent these difficulties. For example, in the **Bradford assay,** the binding of the dye **Coomassie brilliant blue**

^-O_3S SO_3^-

CH$_2$ CH$_2$

N   N

H$_5$C$_2$ C$_2$H$_5$

R   R

R250: R = H
G250: R = CH$_3$

NH

OC$_2$H$_5$

Coomassie brilliant blue

to protein in acidic solution causes the dye's absorption maximum to shift from 465 nm to 595 nm. Hence the absorbance at 595 nm in a Bradford assay provides a direct measure of the amount of protein present. In addition, the Bradford assay is highly sensitive; it can detect as little as 1 μg of protein per milliliter.

Purification Is a Stepwise Process. Proteins are purified by **fractionation procedures.** In a series of independent steps, the various physicochemical properties of the protein of interest are used to separate it progressively from other substances. The idea is not necessarily to minimize the loss of the desired protein, but to *eliminate selectively the other components of the mixture so that only the required substance remains.*

Protein purification is considered as much an art as a science, with many options available at each step. While a trial-and-error approach can work, knowing something about the target protein (or the proteins it is to be separated from) simplifies the selection of fractionation procedures. Some of the procedures we discuss and the protein characteristics they depend on are as follows:

Protein Characteristic	Purification Procedure
Solubility	Salting out
Ionic Charge	Ion exchange chromatography
	Electrophoresis
	Isoelectric focusing
Polarity	Hydrophobic interaction chromatography
Size	Gel filtration chromatography
	SDS-PAGE
Binding Specificity	Affinity chromatography

B | Salting Out Separates Proteins by Their Solubility

Because a protein contains multiple charged groups, its solubility depends on the concentrations of dissolved salts, the polarity of the solvent, the pH, and the temperature. Some or all of these variables can be manipulated to selectively precipitate certain proteins while others remain soluble.

The solubility of a protein at low ion concentrations increases as salt is added, a phenomenon called **salting in.** The additional ions shield the protein's multiple ionic charges, thereby weakening the attractive forces between individual protein molecules (such forces can lead to aggregation and precipitation). However, as more salt is added, particularly with sulfate salts, the solubility of the protein again decreases. This **salting out** effect is primarily a result of the competition between the added salt ions and the other dissolved solutes for molecules of solvent. At very high salt concentrations, so many of the added ions are solvated that there is significantly less bulk solvent available to dissolve other substances, including proteins.

Since different proteins have different ionic and hydrophobic compositions and therefore precipitate at different salt concentrations, salting out is the basis of one of the most commonly used protein purification procedures. Adjusting the salt concentration in a solution containing a mixture of proteins to just below the precipitation point of the protein to be purified eliminates many unwanted proteins from the solution (Fig. 5-5). Then, after removing the precipitated proteins by filtration or centrifugation, the salt concentration of the remaining solution is increased to precipitate the desired protein. This procedure results in a significant purification and concentration of large quantities of protein. Ammonium

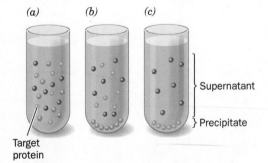

(a)   *(b)*   *(c)*

Supernatant

Precipitate

Target protein

■ **Figure 5-5** | **Fractionation by salting out.** (*a*) The salt of choice, usually ammonium sulfate, is added to a solution of macromolecules to a concentration just below the precipitation point of the protein of interest. (*b*) After centrifugation, the unwanted precipitated proteins (*red spheres*) are discarded and more salt is added to the supernatant to a concentration sufficient to salt out the desired protein (*green spheres*). (*c*) After a second centrifugation, the protein is recovered as a precipitate, and the supernatant is discarded.

Table 5-2	Isoelectric Points of Several Common Proteins

Protein	pI
Pepsin	<1.0
Ovalbumin (hen)	4.6
Serum albumin (human)	4.9
Tropomyosin	5.1
Insulin (bovine)	5.4
Fibrinogen (human)	5.8
γ-Globulin (human)	6.6
Collagen	6.6
Myoglobin (horse)	7.0
Hemoglobin (human)	7.1
Ribonuclease A (bovine)	9.4
Cytochrome c (horse)	10.6
Histone (bovine)	10.8
Lysozyme (hen)	11.0
Salmine (salmon)	12.1

sulfate, $(NH_4)_2SO_4$, is the most commonly used reagent for salting out proteins because its high solubility (3.9 M in water at 0°C) allows the preparation of solutions with high ionic strength. The pH may be adjusted to approximate the isoelectric point (pI) of the desired protein because a protein is least soluble when its net charge is zero. The pI's of some proteins are listed in Table 5-2.

C | Chromatography Involves Interaction with Mobile and Stationary Phases

The process of **chromatography** (Greek: *chroma*, color + *graphein*, to write) was discovered in 1903 by Mikhail Tswett, who separated solubilized plant pigments using solid adsorbents. In most modern chromatographic procedures, a mixture of substances to be fractionated is dissolved in a liquid (the "mobile" phase) and percolated through a column containing a porous solid matrix (the "stationary" phase). As solutes flow through the column, they interact with the stationary phase and are retarded. The retarding force depends on the properties of each solute. If the column is long enough, substances with different rates of migration will be separated. The chromatographic procedures that are most useful for purifying proteins are classified according to the nature of the interaction between the protein and the stationary phase.

Early chromatographic techniques used strips of filter paper as the stationary phase, whereas modern column chromatography uses granular derivatives of cellulose, agarose, or dextran (all carbohydrate polymers) or synthetic substances such as cross-linked polyacrylamide or silica. **High-performance liquid chromatography (HPLC)** employs automated systems with precisely applied samples, controlled flow rates at high pressures (up to 5000 psi), a chromatographic matrix of specially fabricated 3- to 300-μm-diameter glass or plastic beads coated with a uniform layer of chromatographic material, and on-line sample detection. This greatly improves the speed, resolution, and reproducibility of the separation—features that are particularly desirable when chromatographic separations are repeated many times or when they are used for analytical rather than preparative purposes.

Ion Exchange Chromatography Separates Anions and Cations. In **ion exchange chromatography,** charged molecules bind to oppositely charged groups that are chemically linked to a matrix such as cellulose or agarose. Anions bind to cationic groups on **anion exchangers,** and cations bind to anionic groups on **cation exchangers.** Perhaps the most frequently used anion exchanger is a matrix with attached **diethylaminoethyl (DEAE)** groups, and the most frequently used cation exchanger is a matrix bearing **carboxymethyl (CM)** groups.

DEAE: Matrix—CH_2—CH_2—$NH(CH_2CH_3)_2^+$
CM: Matrix—CH_2—COO^-

Proteins and other **polyelectrolytes** (polyionic polymers) that bear both positive and negative charges can bind to both cation and anion exchangers. *The binding affinity of a particular protein depends on the presence of other ions that compete with the protein for binding to the ion exchanger and on the pH of the solution, which influences the net charge of the protein.*

The proteins to be separated are dissolved in a buffer of an appropriate pH and salt concentration and are applied to a column containing the ion exchanger. The column is then washed with the buffer (Fig. 5-6). As

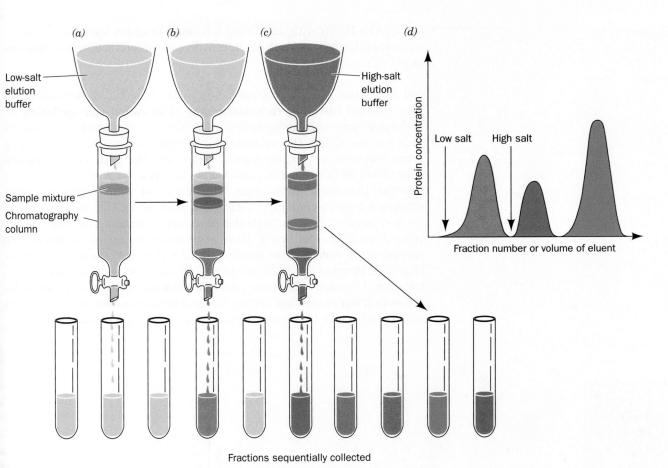

Figure 5-6 | Ion exchange chromatography. The tan region of the column represents the ion exchanger and the colored bands represent proteins. (*a*) A mixture of proteins dissolved in a small volume of buffer is applied to the top of the matrix in the column. (*b*) As elution progresses, the proteins separate into discrete bands as a result of their different affinities for the exchanger. In this diagram, the first protein (*red*) has passed through the column and has been isolated as a separate fraction. The other proteins remain near the top of the column. (*c*) The salt concentration in the eluant is increased to elute the remaining proteins. (*d*) The elution diagram of the protein mixture from the column. *See the Animated Figures.*

the column is washed, proteins with relatively low affinities for the ion exchanger move through the column faster than proteins that bind with higher affinities. The column effluent is collected in a series of fractions. Proteins that bind tightly to the ion exchanger can be **eluted** (washed through the column) by applying a buffer, called the **eluant,** that has a higher salt concentration or a pH that reduces the affinity with which the matrix binds the protein. The column effluent can be monitored for the presence of protein by measuring its absorbance at 280 nm. The eluted fractions can also be tested for the protein of interest using a more specific assay.

Hydrophobic Interaction Chromatography Purifies Nonpolar Molecules. Hydrophobic interactions between proteins and the chromatographic matrix can be exploited to purify the proteins. In **hydrophobic interaction chromatography,** the matrix material is lightly substituted with octyl or phenyl groups. At high salt concentrations, nonpolar groups on the surface of proteins "interact" with the hydrophobic groups; that is, both types of groups are excluded by the polar solvent (hydrophobic effects are augmented by increased ionic strength). The eluant is typically an aqueous buffer with decreasing salt concentrations, increasing concentrations of detergent (which disrupts hydrophobic interactions), or changes in pH.

Gel Filtration Chromatography Separates Molecules According to Size. In **gel filtration chromatography** (also called **size exclusion** or **molecular sieve chromatography**), molecules are separated according to their size and shape. The stationary phase consists of gel beads containing pores that span a relatively narrow size range. The pore size is typically determined by the extent of cross-linking between the polymers of the gel material. If an aqueous solution of molecules of various sizes is passed through a column containing such "molecular sieves," the molecules that are too large to pass through the pores are excluded from the solvent volume inside the gel beads. *These large molecules therefore traverse the column more rapidly than small molecules that pass through the pores* (Fig. 5-7). Because the pore size in any gel varies to some degree, gel filtration can be used to separate a range of molecules; larger molecules with access to fewer pores elute sooner (i.e., in a smaller volume of eluant) than smaller molecules that have access to more of the gel's interior volume.

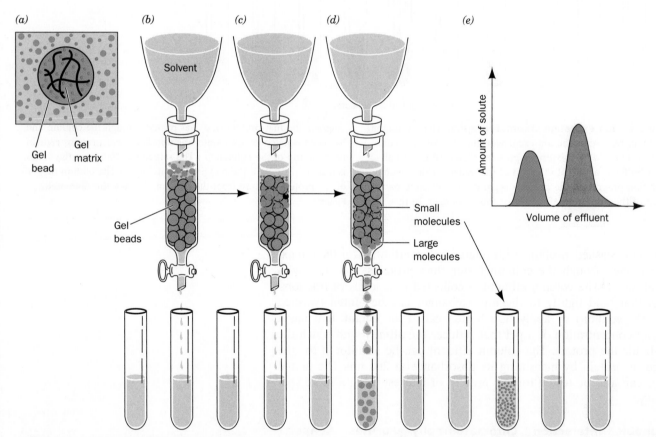

■ **Figure 5-7** | **Gel filtration chromatography.** (*a*) A gel bead consists of a gel matrix (*wavy solid lines*) that encloses an internal solvent space. Small molecules (*red dots*) can freely enter the internal space of the gel bead. Large molecules (*blue dots*) cannot penetrate the gel pores. (*b*) The sample solution is applied to the top of the column (the gel beads are represented as brown spheres). (*c*) The small molecules can penetrate the gel and consequently migrate through the column more slowly than the large molecules that are excluded from the gel. (*d*) The large molecules elute first and are collected as fractions. Small molecules require a larger volume of solvent to elute. (*e*) The elution diagram, or chromatogram, indicating the complete separation of the two components. ✑ **See the Animated Figures.**

Within the size range of molecules separated by a particular pore size, there is a linear relationship between the relative elution volume of a substance and the logarithm of its molecular mass (assuming the molecules have similar shapes). If a given gel filtration column is calibrated with several proteins of known molecular mass, the mass of an unknown protein can be conveniently estimated by its elution position.

Affinity Chromatography Exploits Specific Binding Behavior. A striking characteristic of many proteins is their ability to bind specific molecules tightly but noncovalently. This property can be used to purify such proteins by **affinity chromatography** (Fig. 5-8). In this technique, a molecule (a **ligand**) that specifically binds to the protein of interest (e.g., a nonreactive analog of an enzyme's substrate) is covalently attached to an inert matrix. *When an impure protein solution is passed through this chromatographic material, the desired protein binds to the immobilized ligand, whereas other substances are washed through the column with the buffer.* The desired protein can then be recovered in highly purified form by changing the elution conditions to release the protein from the matrix. The great advantage of affinity chromatography is its ability to exploit the desired protein's unique biochemical properties rather than the small differences in physicochemical properties between proteins exploited by other chromatographic methods. Accordingly, the separation power of affinity chromatography for a specific protein is often greater than that of other chromatographic techniques.

Affinity chromatography columns can be constructed by chemically attaching small molecules or proteins to a chromatographic matrix. In **immunoaffinity chromatography,** an antibody is attached to the matrix in order to purify the protein against which the antibody was raised. In all cases, the ligand must have an affinity high enough to capture the protein of interest but not so high as to prevent the protein's subsequent release without denaturing it. The bound protein can be eluted by washing the column with a solution containing a high concentration of free ligand or a solution of different pH or ionic strength.

In **metal chelate affinity chromatography,** a divalent metal ion such as Zn^{2+} or Ni^{2+} is attached to the chromatographic matrix so that proteins bearing metal-chelating groups (e.g., multiple His side chains) can be retained. Recombinant DNA techniques (Section 3-5) can be used to append a segment of six consecutive His residues, known as a **His-Tag,** to the N- or C-terminus of the polypeptide to be isolated. This creates a metal ion-binding site that allows the recombinant protein to be purified by metal chelate chromatography. After the protein has been eluted, usually by altering the pH, the His-Tag can be removed by the action of a specific protease whose recognition sequence separates the $(His)_6$ sequence from the rest of the protein.

D | Electrophoresis Separates Molecules According to Charge and Size

Electrophoresis, the migration of ions in an electric field, is described in Section 3-4B. **Polyacrylamide gel electrophoresis (PAGE)** of proteins is typically carried out in agarose or polyacrylamide gels with a characteristic pore size, so *the molecular separations are based on gel filtration (size and shape) as well as electrophoretic mobility (electric charge).* However, electrophoresis differs from gel filtration in that the electrophoretic mobility of smaller molecules is greater than the mobility of larger molecules

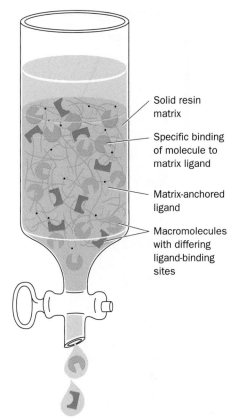

■ **Figure 5-8 | Affinity chromatography.** A ligand (shown here in *yellow*) is immobilized by covalently binding it to the chromatographic matrix. The cutout squares, semicircles, and triangles represent ligand-binding sites on macromolecules. Only certain molecules (represented by *orange circles*) specifically bind to the ligand. The other components are washed through the column.

Labels on figure:
Solid resin matrix
Specific binding of molecule to matrix ligand
Matrix-anchored ligand
Macromolecules with differing ligand-binding sites

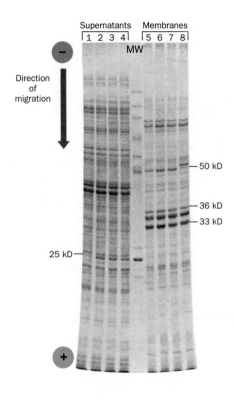

Supernatants Membranes
1 2 3 4 5 6 7 8
MW

Direction of migration

— 50 kD

— 36 kD
— 33 kD

25 kD—

■ **Figure 5-9** | **SDS-PAGE.** Samples of supernatants (*left*) and membrane fractions (*right*) from a preparation of the bacterium *Salmonella typhimurium* were electrophoresed in parallel lanes on a 35-cm-long by 0.8-mm-thick polyacrylamide slab. The lane marked MW contains molecular weight standards. [Courtesy of Giovanna F. Ames, University of California at Berkeley.]

with the same charge density. The pH of the gel is high enough (usually about pH 9) so that nearly all proteins have net negative charges and move toward the positive electrode when the current is switched on. Molecules of similar size and charge move as a band through the gel.

Following electrophoresis, the separated bands may be visualized in the gel by an appropriate technique, such as soaking the gel in a solution of a stain that binds tightly to proteins (e.g., Coomassie brilliant blue). If the proteins in a sample are radioactive, the gel can be dried and then clamped over a sheet of X-ray film. After a time, the film is developed and the resulting **autoradiograph** shows the positions of the radioactive components by a blackening of the film. If an antibody to a protein of interest is available, it can be used to specifically detect the protein on a gel in the presence of many other proteins, a process called **immunoblotting** or **Western blotting** that is similar to ELISA (Fig. 5-3). Depending on the dimensions of the gel and the visualization technique used, samples containing less than a nanogram of protein can be separated and detected by gel electrophoresis.

SDS-PAGE Separates Proteins by Mass. In one form of polyacrylamide gel electrophoresis, the detergent sodium dodecyl sulfate (SDS)

$$[CH_3-(CH_2)_{10}-CH_2-O-SO_3^-]Na^+$$

is used to denature proteins. Amphiphilic molecules (Section 2-1C) such as SDS interfere with the hydrophobic interactions that normally stabilize proteins. Proteins assume a rodlike shape in the presence of SDS. Furthermore, most proteins bind SDS in a ratio of about 1.4 g SDS per gram protein (about one SDS molecule for every two amino acid residues). The large negative charge that the SDS imparts masks the proteins' intrinsic charge. The net result is that SDS-treated proteins have similar shapes and charge-to-mass ratios. ***SDS-PAGE therefore separates proteins purely by gel filtration effects***, that is, according to molecular mass. Figure 5-9 is an example of the resolving power and the reproducibility of SDS-PAGE.

In SDS-PAGE, the relative mobilities of proteins vary approximately linearly with the logarithm of their molecular masses (Fig. 5-10). Consequently, the molecular mass of a protein can be determined with about 5 to 10% accuracy by electrophoresing it together with several "marker" proteins of known molecular masses that bracket that of the protein of interest. Because SDS disrupts noncovalent interactions between polypeptides, SDS-PAGE yields the molecular masses of the subunits of multisubunit proteins. The possibility that subunits are linked

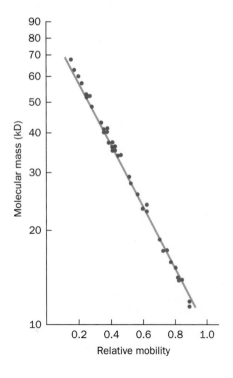

Molecular mass (kD)

90
80
70
60
50
40
30
20
10

0.2 0.4 0.6 0.8 1.0
Relative mobility

■ **Figure 5-10** | **Logarithmic relationship between the molecular mass of a protein and its electrophoretic mobility in SDS-PAGE.** The masses of 37 proteins ranging from 11 to 70 kD are plotted. [After Weber, K. and Osborn, M., *J. Biol. Chem.* **244**, 4406 (1969).]

by disulfide bonds can be tested by preparing samples for SDS-PAGE in the presence and absence of a reducing agent, such as **2-mercaptoethanol** (HSCH$_2$CH$_2$OH), that breaks these bonds (Section 5-3A).

Capillary Electrophoresis Rapidly Separates Charged Molecules. Although gel electrophoresis in its various forms is highly effective at separating charged molecules, it can require up to several hours and is difficult to quantitate and automate. These disadvantages are largely overcome through the use of **capillary electrophoresis (CE),** a technique in which electrophoresis is carried out in very thin capillary tubes (20- to 100-μm inner diameter). Such narrow capillaries rapidly dissipate heat and hence permit the use of very high electric fields, which reduces separation times to a few minutes. The CE techniques have extremely high resolution and can be automated in much the same way as is HPLC, that is, with automatic sample loading and on-line sample detection. Since CE can separate only small amounts of material, it is largely limited to use as an analytical tool.

Two-Dimensional Electrophoresis Resolves Complex Mixtures of Proteins. A protein has charged groups of both polarities and therefore has an isoelectric point, p*I*, at which it is immobile in an electric field. *If a mixture of proteins is electrophoresed through a solution or gel that has a stable pH gradient in which the pH smoothly increases from anode to cathode, each protein will migrate to the position in the pH gradient corresponding to its pI.* If a protein molecule diffuses away from this position, its net charge will change as it moves into a region of different pH and the resulting electrophoretic forces will move it back to its isoelectric position. Each species of protein is thereby "focused" into a narrow band about its p*I*. This type of electrophoresis is called **isoelectric focusing (IEF).**

IEF can be combined with SDS-PAGE in an extremely powerful separation technique named **two-dimensional (2D) gel electrophoresis.** First, a sample of proteins is subjected to IEF in one direction, and then the separated proteins are subjected to SDS-PAGE in the perpendicular direction. This procedure generates an array of spots, each representing a protein (Fig. 5-11). Up to 5000 proteins have been observed on a single two-dimensional electrophoretogram.

Two-dimensional gel electrophoresis is a valuable tool for **proteomics,** a field of study that involves cataloguing all of a cell's expressed proteins with emphasis on their quantitation, localization, modifications, interactions, and activities. Individual protein spots in a stained 2D gel can be excised with a scalpel, destained, and the protein eluted from the gel fragment for identification and/or characterization, often by mass spectrometry (Section 5-3D). 2D electrophoretograms can be analyzed by computer after they have been scanned and digitized. This facilitates the detection of variations in the positions and intensities of protein spots in samples obtained from different tissues or under different growth conditions. Numerous reference 2D gels are publicly available for this purpose in the Web-accessible databases listed at http://us.expasy.org/ch2d/. These databases contain images of 2D gels of a variety of organisms and tissues and identify many of their component proteins. Their use is illustrated in Bioinformatics Exercise 5-4 (www.wiley.com/college/voet).

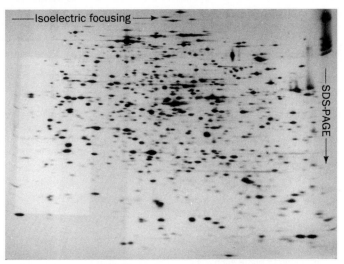

■ **Figure 5-11** | **Two-dimensional gel electrophoresis.** In this example, *E. coli* proteins that had been labeled with ^{14}C-amino acids were subjected to isoelectric focusing (horizontally) followed by SDS-PAGE (vertically). Over 1000 spots can be resolved in the autoradiogram shown here. [Courtesy of Patrick O'Farrell, University of California at San Francisco.]

■ **CHECK YOUR UNDERSTANDING**

What are some environmental conditions that must be controlled while purifying a protein?

Describe how a protein may be quantified by an assay or by absorbance spectroscopy.

Explain how salting out is used in protein fractionation.

Describe the basis for separating proteins by ion exchange, hydrophobic interaction, gel filtration, and affinity chromatography.

Describe the processes of gel electrophoresis, SDS-PAGE, and 2D gel electrophoresis.

LEARNING OBJECTIVES

■ Understand the steps required to sequence a protein, including N-terminal analysis, disulfide bond cleavage, chain fragmentation, Edman degradation (or mass spectrometry), and sequence reconstruction.
■ Understand the importance of protein sequence databases.

See Guided Exploration 4
Protein sequence determination.

3 Protein Sequencing

Once a pure sample of protein has been obtained, it may be used for a variety of purposes. But if the protein has not previously been characterized, the next step is often determining its sequence of amino acids. Frederick Sanger determined the first known protein sequence, that of bovine insulin, in 1953, thereby definitively establishing that proteins have unique covalent structures (Box 5-1). Since then, many additional proteins have been sequenced, and the sequences of many more proteins have been inferred from their DNA sequences. All told, the amino acid sequences of hundreds of thousands of polypeptides are now known. Such information is valuable for the following reasons:

1. Knowledge of a protein's amino acid sequence is prerequisite for determining its three-dimensional structure and is essential for understanding its molecular mechanism of action.

2. Sequence comparisons among analogous proteins from different species yield insights into protein function and reveal evolutionary relationships among the proteins and the organisms that produce them.

3. Many inherited diseases are caused by mutations that result in an amino acid change in a protein. Amino acid sequence analysis can assist in the development of diagnostic tests and effective therapies.

Sanger's determination of the sequence of insulin's 51 residues (Fig. 5-1) took about 10 years and required ~100 g of protein. Procedures for primary structure determination have since been so refined and automated that most proteins can be sequenced within a few hours or days using only a few micrograms of material. Regardless of the technique used, the basic approach for sequencing proteins is similar to the procedure developed by Sanger. *The protein must be broken down into fragments small enough to be individually sequenced, and the primary structure of the intact protein is then reconstructed from the sequences of overlapping fragments* (Fig. 5-12). Such a procedure, as we have seen (Section 3-4C), is also used to sequence DNA.

A | The First Step Is to Separate Subunits

The complete amino acid sequence of a protein includes the sequence of each of its subunits, if any, so the subunits must be identified and isolated before sequencing begins.

N-Terminal Analysis Reveals the Number of Different Types of Subunits. Each polypeptide chain (if it is not chemically blocked) has an N-terminal residue. *Identifying this "end group"*

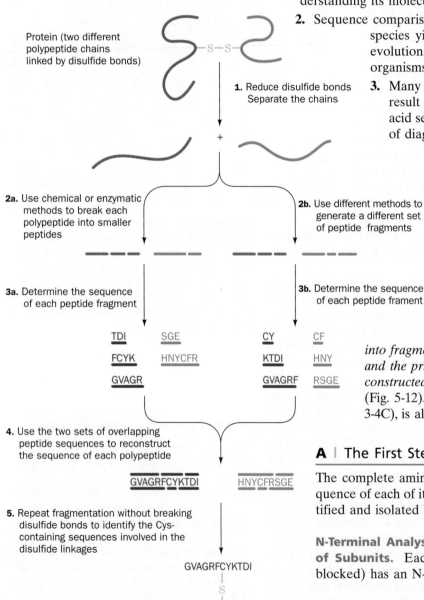

Protein (two different polypeptide chains linked by disulfide bonds)

1. Reduce disulfide bonds
Separate the chains

2a. Use chemical or enzymatic methods to break each polypeptide into smaller peptides

2b. Use different methods to generate a different set of peptide fragments

3a. Determine the sequence of each peptide fragment

3b. Determine the sequence of each peptide frament

TDI	SGE	CY	CF
FCYK	HNYCFR	KTDI	HNY
GVAGR		GVAGRF	RSGE

4. Use the two sets of overlapping peptide sequences to reconstruct the sequence of each polypeptide

GVAGRFCYKTDI   HNYCFRSGE

5. Repeat fragmentation without breaking disulfide bonds to identify the Cys-containing sequences involved in the disulfide linkages

GVAGRFCYKTDI
          |
          S
          |
          S
          |
HNYCFRSGE

■ **Figure 5-12** | **Overview of protein sequencing.**

BOX 5-1   PATHWAYS OF DISCOVERY

Frederick Sanger and Protein Sequencing

Frederick Sanger (1918–)

At one time, many biochemists believed that proteins were amorphous "colloids" of variable size, shape, and composition. This view was largely abandoned by the 1940s, when it became possible to determine the amino acid composition of a protein, that is, the number of each kind of constituent amino acid. However, such information revealed nothing about the order in which the amino acids were combined. In fact, skeptics still questioned whether proteins even had unique sequences. One plausible theory was that proteins were populations of related molecules that were probably assembled from shorter pieces. Some studies went so far as to describe the rules governing the relative stoichiometries and spacing of the various amino acids in proteins.

During the 1940s, the accuracy of amino acid analysis began to improve as a result of the development of chromatographic techniques for separating amino acids and the use of the reagent **ninhydrin,** which forms colored adducts with amino acids, to chemically quantify them (previous methods used cumbersome biological assays). Frederick Sanger, who began his work on protein sequencing in 1943, used these new techniques as well as classic organic chemistry. Sanger did not actually set out to sequence a protein; his first experiments were directed toward devising a better method for quantifying free amino groups such as the amino groups corresponding to the N-terminus of a polypeptide.

Sanger used the reagent 2,4-dinitrofluorobenzene, which forms a yellow dinitrophenyl (DNP) derivative at terminal amino groups without breaking any peptide bonds.

When the protein is subsequently hydrolyzed to break its peptide bonds, the N-terminal amino acid retains its DNP label and can be identified when the hydrolysis products are separated by chromatography. Sanger found that some DNP-amino acid derivatives were unstable during hydrolysis, so this step had to be shortened. In comparing the results of long and short hydrolysis times, Sanger observed extra yellow spots corresponding to dipeptides or other small peptides with intact peptide bonds. He could then isolate the dipeptides and identify the second residue. Sanger's genius was to recognize that by determining the sequences of overlapping small peptides from an incompletely hydrolyzed protein, the sequence of the intact protein could be determined.

An enormous amount of work was required to turn the basic principle into a sound laboratory technique for sequencing a protein. Sanger chose insulin as his subject, because it was one of the smallest known proteins. Insulin contains 51 amino acids in two polypeptide chains (called A and B). The sequence of the 30 residues in the B chain was completed in 1951, and the sequence of the A chain (21 residues) in 1953. Because the two chains are linked through disulfide bonds, Sanger also endeavored to find the optimal procedure for cleaving those bonds and then identifying their positions in the intact protein, a task he completed in 1955.

Sanger's work of over a decade, combining his expertise in organic chemistry (the cleavage and derivatization reactions) with the development of analytical tools for separating and identifying the reaction products, led to his winning a Nobel prize in 1958 [he won a second Nobel prize in 1980, for his invention of the chain-terminator method of nucleic acid sequencing (Section 3-4C)]. A testament to Sanger's brilliance is that his basic approaches to sequencing polypeptides and nucleic acids are still widely used.

Publication of the sequence of insulin in 1955 convinced skeptics that a protein has a unique amino acid sequence. Sanger's work also helped catalyze thinking about the existence of a genetic code that would link the amino acid sequence of a protein to the nucleotide sequence of DNA, a molecule whose structure had just been elucidated in 1953.

Sanger, F., Sequences, sequences, sequences, *Annu. Rev. Biochem.* **57,** 1–28 (1988). [A scientific autobiography that provides a glimpse of the early difficulties in sequencing proteins.]

Sanger, F., Thompson, E.O.P., and Kitai, R., The amide groups of insulin, *Biochem. J.* **59,** 509–518 (1955).

**2,4-Dinitrofluoro-   Polypeptide   DNP-Polypeptide
benzene (DNFB)**

---

can establish the number of chemically distinct polypeptides in a protein. For example, insulin has equal amounts of the N-terminal residues Gly and Phe, which indicates that it has equal numbers of two nonidentical polypeptide chains.

The N-terminus of a polypeptide can be determined by several methods. The fluorescent compound **5-dimethylamino-1-naphthalenesulfonyl chloride (dansyl chloride)** reacts with primary amines to yield dansylated polypeptides

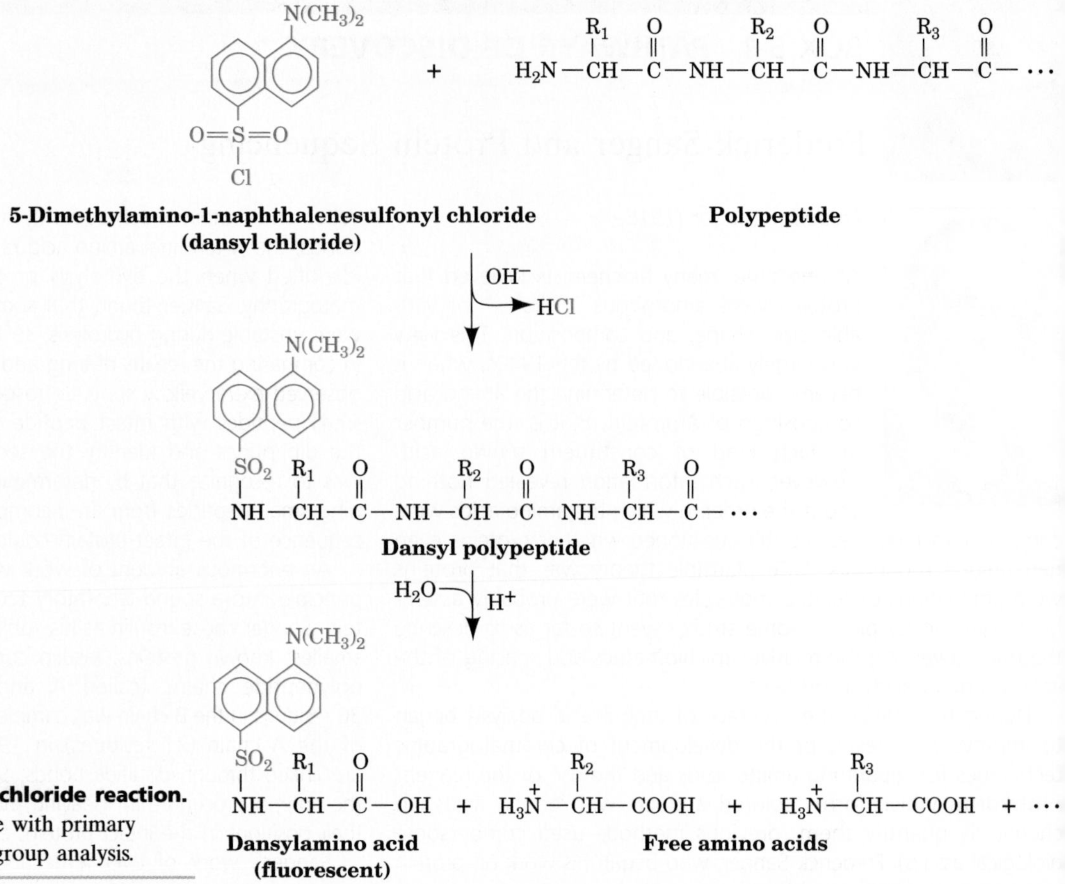

5-Dimethylamino-1-naphthalenesulfonyl chloride (dansyl chloride)

Polypeptide

Dansyl polypeptide

■ Figure 5-13 | The dansyl chloride reaction. The reaction of dansyl chloride with primary amino groups is used for end group analysis.

Dansylamino acid (fluorescent)

Free amino acids

(Fig. 5-13). The treatment of a dansylated polypeptide with aqueous acid at high temperature hydrolyzes its peptide bonds. This liberates the dansylated N-terminal residue, which can then be separated chromatographically from the other amino acids and identified by its intense yellow fluorescence. The N-terminal residue can also be identified by performing the first step of Edman degradation (Section 5-3C), a procedure that liberates amino acids one at a time from the N-terminus of a polypeptide.

Disulfide Bonds between and within Polypeptides Are Cleaved. Disulfide bonds between Cys residues must be cleaved to separate polypeptide chains—if they are disulfide-linked—and to ensure that polypeptide chains are fully linear (residues in polypeptides that are "knotted" with disulfide bonds may not be accessible to all the enzymes and reagents for sequencing). Disulfide bonds can be reductively cleaved by treating them with 2-mercaptoethanol or another **mercaptan** (compounds that contain an —SH group):

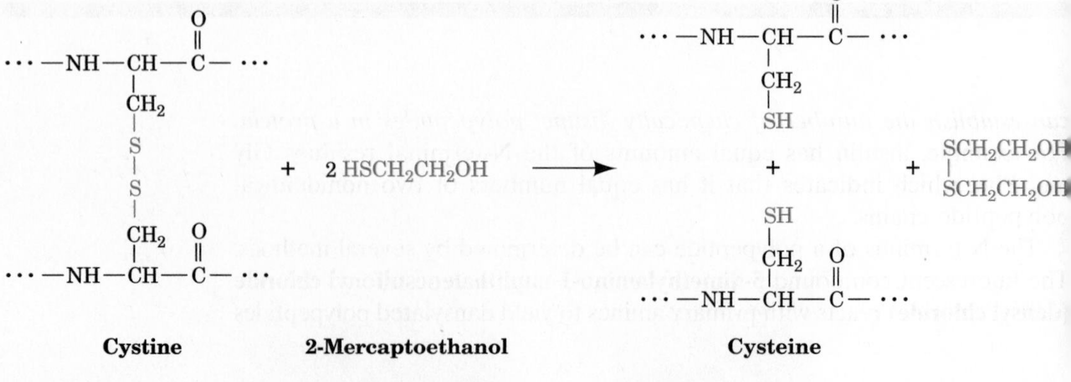

Cystine **2-Mercaptoethanol** **Cysteine**

The resulting free sulfhydryl groups are then alkylated, usually by treatment with **iodoacetate,** to prevent the re-formation of disulfide bonds through oxidation by O_2:

$$Cys—CH_2—SH \quad + \quad ICH_2COO^- \quad \longrightarrow \quad Cys—CH_2—S—CH_2COO^- \quad + \quad HI$$

| **Cysteine** | **Iodoacetate** | ***S*-Carboxymethylcysteine (CM-Cys)** |

B | The Polypeptide Chains Are Cleaved

Polypeptides that are longer than 40 to 100 residues cannot be directly sequenced and must therefore be cleaved, either enzymatically or chemically, to specific fragments that are small enough to be sequenced. Various **endopeptidases** (enzymes that catalyze the hydrolysis of internal peptide bonds, as opposed to **exopeptidases,** which catalyze the hydrolysis of N- or C-terminal residues) can be used to fragment polypeptides. Both endopeptidases and exopeptidases (which collectively are called **proteases**) have side chain requirements for the residues flanking the scissile peptide bond (i.e., the bond that is to be cleaved; Table 5-3). The digestive enzyme **trypsin** has the greatest specificity and is therefore the most valuable member of the arsenal of endopeptidases used to fragment polypeptides. It cleaves peptide bonds on the C side (toward the carboxyl terminus) of the positively charged residues Arg and Lys if the next residue is not Pro.

Table 5-3 Specificities of Various Endopeptidases

Enzyme	Source	Specificity	Comments
Trypsin	Bovine pancreas	R_{n-1} = positively charged residues: Arg, Lys; $R_n \neq$ Pro	Highly specific
Chymotrypsin	Bovine pancreas	R_{n-1} = bulky hydrophobic residues: Phe, Trp, Tyr; $R_n \neq$ Pro	Cleaves more slowly for R_{n-1} = Asn, His, Met, Leu
Elastase	Bovine pancreas	R_{n-1} = small neutral residues: Ala, Gly, Ser, Val; $R_n \neq$ Pro	
Thermolysin	*Bacillus thermoproteolyticus*	R_n = Ile, Met, Phe, Trp, Tyr, Val; $R_{n-1} \neq$ Pro	Occasionally cleaves at R_n = Ala, Asp, His, Thr; heat stable
Pepsin	Bovine gastric mucosa	R_n = Leu, Phe, Trp, Tyr; $R_{n-1} \neq$ Pro	Also others; quite nonspecific; pH optimum = 2
Endopeptidase V8	*Staphylococcus aureus*	R_{n-1} = Glu	

The other endopeptidases listed in Table 5-3 exhibit broader side chain specificities than trypsin and often yield a series of peptide fragments with overlapping sequences. However, through **limited proteolysis,** that is, by adjusting reaction conditions and limiting reaction times, these less specific endopeptidases can yield a set of discrete, nonoverlapping fragments.

Several chemical reagents promote peptide bond cleavage at specific residues. The most useful of these, **cyanogen bromide** (CNBr), cleaves on the C side of Met residues (Fig. 5-14).

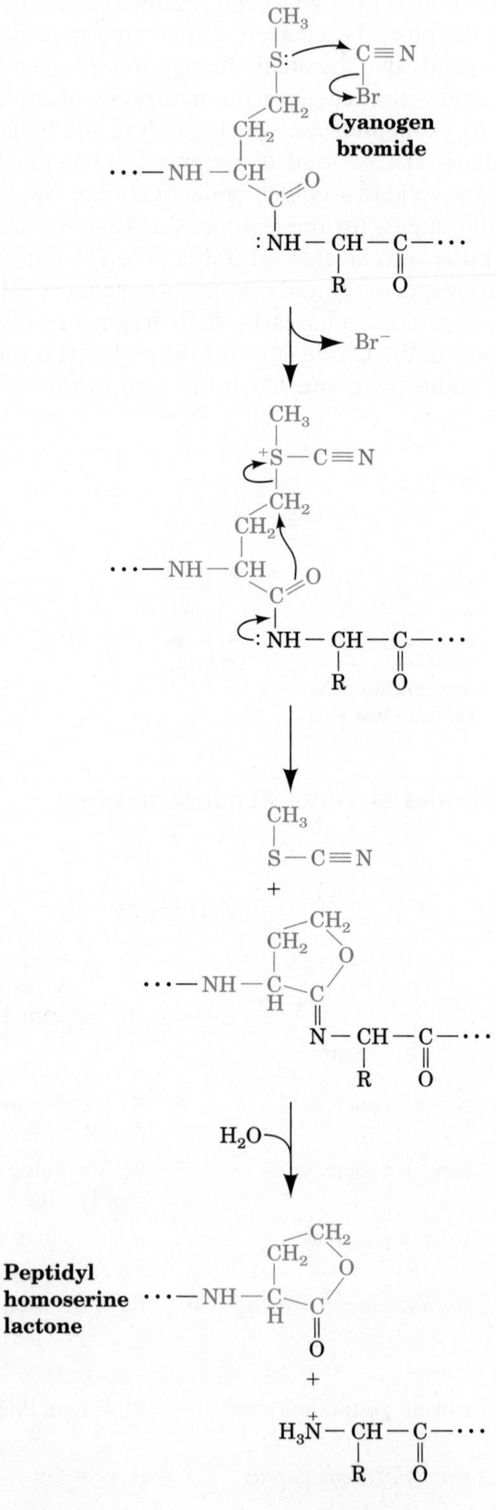

■ **Figure 5-14 | Cyanogen bromide cleavage of a polypeptide.** CNBr reacts specifically with Met residues, resulting in cleavage of the peptide bond on their C-terminal side. The newly formed C-terminal residue forms a cyclic structure known as a **peptidyl homoserine lactone.**

C | Edman Degradation Removes a Peptide's First Amino Acid Residue

Once the peptide fragments formed through specific cleavage reactions have been isolated, their amino acid sequences can be determined. This can be accomplished through repeated cycles of **Edman degradation.** In this process (named after its inventor, Pehr Edman), **phenylisothiocyanate** (**PITC;** also known as **Edman's reagent**) reacts with the N-terminal amino group of a polypeptide under mildly alkaline conditions to form a **phenylthiocarbamyl** (**PTC**) adduct (Fig. 5-15). This product is treated with anhydrous **trifluoroacetic acid,** which cleaves the N-terminal residue as a thiazolinone derivative but does not hydrolyze other peptide bonds. Edman degradation therefore releases the N-terminal amino acid residue but leaves intact the rest of the polypeptide chain. The thiazolinone-amino acid is selectively extracted into an organic solvent and is converted to the more stable **phenylthiohydantoin** (**PTH**) derivative by treatment with aqueous acid. This PTH-amino acid can later be identified by chromatography. Thus, *it is possible to determine the amino acid sequence of a polypeptide chain from the N-terminus inward by subjecting the polypeptide to repeated cycles of Edman degradation and, after every cycle, identifying the newly liberated PTH-amino acid.*

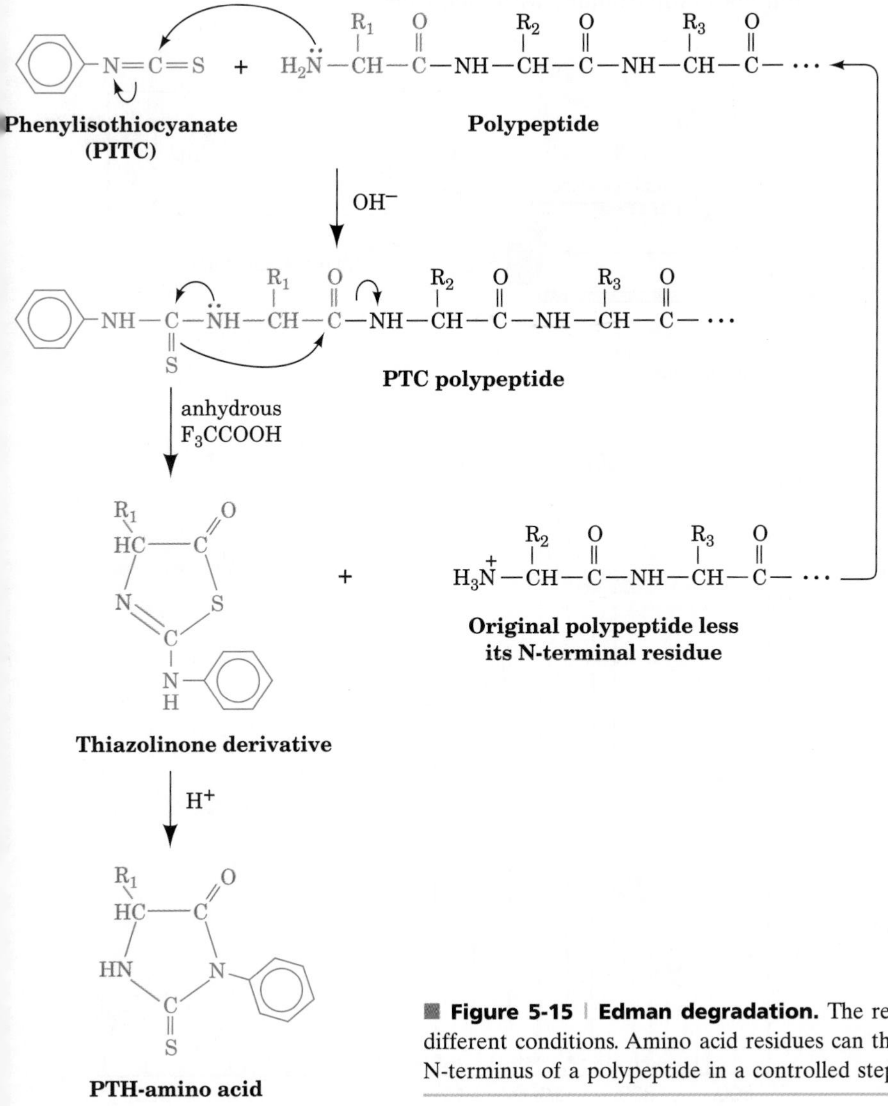

■ **Figure 5-15** | **Edman degradation.** The reaction occurs in three stages, each requiring different conditions. Amino acid residues can therefore be sequentially removed from the N-terminus of a polypeptide in a controlled stepwise fashion. **See the Animated Figures.**

The Edman degradation technique has been automated and refined, resulting in great savings of time and material. In modern instruments, the peptide sample is dried onto a disk of glass fiber paper, and accurately measured quantities of reagents are delivered and products removed as vapors in a stream of argon at programmed intervals. Up to 100 residues can be identified before the cumulative effects of incomplete reactions, side reactions, and peptide loss make further amino acid identification unreliable. Since less than a picomole of a PTH-amino acid can be detected and identified, sequence analysis can be carried out on as little as 5 to 10 pmol of a peptide (<0.1 μg—an invisibly small amount).

D | Mass Spectrometry Determines the Molecular Masses of Peptides

Mass spectrometry has emerged as an important technique for characterizing and sequencing polypeptides. Mass spectrometry accurately measures the mass-to-charge (m/z) ratio for ions in the gas phase (where m is the ion's mass and z is its charge). Until about 1985, macromolecules such as proteins and nucleic acids could not be analyzed by mass spectrometry. This was because macromolecules were destroyed during the production of gas-phase ions, which required vaporization by heating followed by ionization via bombardment with electrons.

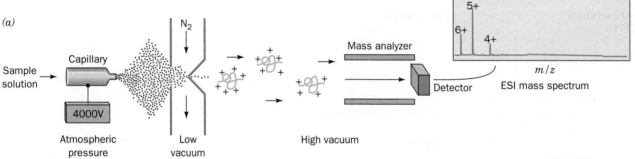

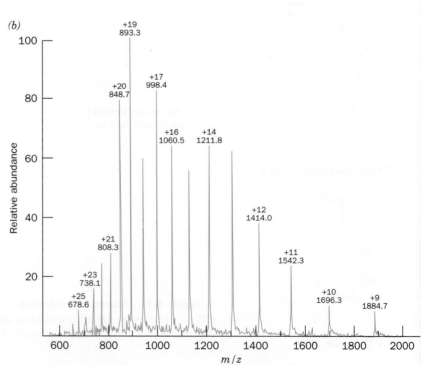

■ **Figure 5-16** | **Electrospray ionization mass spectrometry (ESI).** (*a*) Dry N_2 gas promotes the evaporation of solvent from charged droplets containing the protein of interest, leaving gas-phase ions, whose charge is due to the protonation of Arg and Lys residues. The mass spectrometer then determines the mass-to-charge ratio of these ions. The resulting mass spectrum consists of a series of peaks corresponding to ions that differ by a single ionic charge and the mass of one proton). [After Fitzgerald, M.C. and Siuzdak, G., *Chem. Biol.* **3,** 708 (1996).] (*b*) The ESI mass spectrum of horse heart **apomyoglobin** (myoglobin that lacks its Fe ion). The measured m/z ratios and the inferred charges for most of the peaks are indicated. The data provided by this spectrum permit the mass of the original molecule to be calculated (see Sample Calculation 5-1). [After Yates, J.R., *Methods Enzymol.* **271,** 353 (1996).]

Newer techniques have addressed this shortcoming. For example, in the **electrospray ionization (ESI)** technique, a solution of a macromolecule such as a peptide is sprayed from a narrow capillary tube maintained at high voltage ($\sim$4000 V), forming fine highly charged droplets from which the solvent rapidly evaporates (Fig. 5-16a). This yields a series of gas-phase macromolecular ions that typically have ionic charges in the range +0.5 to +2 per kilodalton. The charges result from the protonation of basic side chains such as Arg and Lys. The ions are directed into the mass spectrometer, which measures their m/z values with an accuracy of >0.01% (Fig. 5-16b). Consequently, determining an ion's z permits its molecular mass to be determined with far greater accuracy than by any other method.

Short polypeptides (<25 residues) can be directly sequenced though the use of a tandem mass spectrometer (Fig. 5-17; two mass spectrometers coupled in series). The first mass spectrometer functions to select and separate the peptide ion of interest from peptide ions of different masses as well as any contaminants that may be present. The selected peptide ion is then passed into a collision cell, where it collides with chemically inert atoms such as helium. The energy thereby imparted to the peptide ion causes it to fragment predominantly at only one of its several peptide bonds, thereby yielding one or two charged fragments per original ion. The molecular masses of the numerous charged fragments so produced are then determined by the second mass spectrometer.

By comparing the molecular masses of successively larger members of a family of fragments, the molecular masses and therefore the identities of the corresponding amino acid residues can be determined. The sequence of an entire polypeptide can thus be elucidated (although mass spectrometry cannot distinguish the isomeric residues Ile and Leu because they have exactly the same mass, and it cannot always reliably distinguish Gln and Lys residues because their molecular masses differ by only 0.036 D).

Computerization of the mass-comparison process has reduced the time required to sequence a short polypeptide to only a few minutes (one cycle of Edman degradation may take an hour). The reliability of this process has been increased through the computerized matching of a measured mass spectrum with those of peptides of known sequence as maintained in databases. Mass spectrometry can also be used to sequence peptides with chemically blocked N-termini (which prevents Edman degradation) and to characterize other posttranslational modifications such as the addition of phosphate or carbohydrate groups.

SAMPLE CALCULATION 5-1

An ESI mass spectrum such as that of apomyoglobin (Fig. 5-16b) contains a series of peaks, each corresponding to the m/z ratio of an $(M + nH)^{n+}$ ion. Two successive peaks in this mass spectrum have measured m/z ratios of 1414.0 and 1542.3. What is the molecular mass of the original apomyoglobin molecule, how does it compare with the value given for it in Table 5-1, and what are the charges of the ions causing these peaks?

The first peak ($p_1 = 1414.0$) arises from an ion with charge z and mass $M + z$, where M is the molecular mass of the original protein. Then the adjacent ($p_2 = 1542.3$) peak, which is due to an ion with one less proton, has charge $z - 1$ and mass $M + z - 1$. The m/z ratios for these ions, p_1 and p_2, are therefore given by the following expressions.

$$p_1 = (M + z)/z$$
$$p_2 = (M + z - 1)/(z - 1)$$

These two linear equations can readily be solved for their unknowns, M and z. Solve the first equation for M.

$$M = z(p_1 - 1)$$

Then plug this result into the second equation.

$$p_2 = \frac{z(p_1 - 1) + z - 1}{z - 1} = \frac{zp_1 - 1}{z - 1}$$
$$zp_2 - p_2 = zp_1 - 1$$
$$z = (p_2 - 1)/(p_2 - p_1)$$
$$M = (p_2 - 1)/(p_1 - 1)/(p_2 - p_1)$$

Plugging in the values for p_1 and p_2,

M = (1542.3 − 1)(1414.0 − 1)/(1542.3 − 1414.0)

$\quad$ = 16,975 D

which is only 0.14% larger than the 16,951 D for horse apomyoglobin given in Table 5-1. For the charge on ion 1,

$\quad z = (1542.3 - 1)/(1542.3 - 1414.0) = 12$

The ionic charge on ion 2 is 12 − 1 = 11.

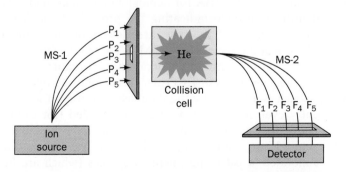

■ **Figure 5-17 | Tandem mass spectrometry in peptide sequencing.** Electrospray ionization (ESI), the ion source, generates gas-phase peptide ions, labeled P_1, P_2, etc., from a digest of the protein to be sequenced. These peptides are separated by the first mass spectrometer (MS-1) according to their m/z values, and one of them (here, P_3) is directed into the collision cell, where it collides with helium atoms. This treatment breaks the peptide into fragments (F_1, F_2, etc.), which are directed into the second mass spectrometer (MS-2) for determination of their m/z values. [After Biemann, K. and Scoble, H.A., *Science* **237**, 992 (1987).]

■ **Figure 5-18** | **Generating overlapping fragments to determine the amino acid sequence of a polypeptide.** In this example, two sets of overlapping peptide fragments are made by using trypsin to cleave the polypeptide after all its Arg and Lys residues and, in a separate reaction, using CNBr to cleave it after all its Met residues. ✌ **See the Animated Figures.**

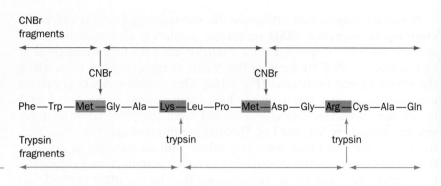

E | Reconstructed Protein Sequences Are Stored in Databases

After individual peptide fragments have been sequenced, their order in the original polypeptide must be elucidated. This is accomplished by conducting a second round of protein cleavage with a reagent of different specificity and then comparing the amino acid sequences of the overlapping sets of peptide fragments (Fig. 5-18).

The final step in an amino acid sequence analysis is to determine the positions (if any) of the disulfide bonds. This can be done by cleaving a sample of the protein, with its disulfide bonds intact, to yield pairs of peptide fragments, each containing a single Cys, that are linked by a disulfide bond. After isolating a disulfide-linked polypeptide fragment, the disulfide bond is cleaved and alkylated (Section 5-3A), and the sequences of the two peptides are determined (Fig. 5-19). The various pairs of such polypeptide fragments are identified by comparing their sequences with that of the protein, thereby establishing the locations of the disulfide bonds.

Sequences Are Recorded in Databases. After a protein's amino acid sequence has been determined, the information is customarily deposited in a public database. Databases for proteins as well as DNA sequences are accessible via the Internet (Table 5-4). Electronic links between databases allow rapid updates and cross-checking of sequence information.

Most sequence databases use similar conventions. For example, consider the annotated protein sequence database named UniProt. A sequence record in UniProt begins with the protein's ID code in the form X_Y, where X is a short mnemonic indicating the protein's name (for example, CYC for cytochrome c and HBA for hemoglobin α chain) and Y is a five-character identification code indicating the protein's biological source, which usually consists of the first three letters of the genus and the first two letters of the species [e.g., CANFA for *Canis familiaris* (dog)], although for most commonly encountered organisms, Y is self-explanatory (e.g., BOVIN or ECOLI). This is followed by an accession number, which is assigned by the database as a way of identifying an entry even if its ID code must be changed (for example, see Fig. 5-20). The entry continues with the date the sequence was entered into the database and when it was last modified and annotated, a list of pertinent references (which are linked to PubMed), a description of the protein, and its links to other databases. A Feature Table describes regions or sites of interest in the protein such as disulfide bonds, posttranslational modifications, binding sites, and conflicts between different references. The entry ends with the length of the peptide in residues, its molecular weight, and finally, its sequence using the one-letter amino acid code.

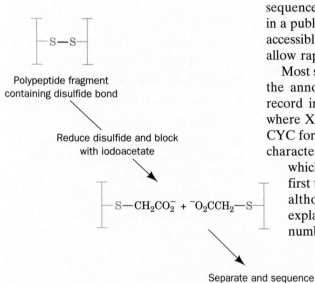

Polypeptide fragment containing disulfide bond

Reduce disulfide and block with iodoacetate

$-S-CH_2CO_2^- + {}^-O_2CCH_2-S-$

Separate and sequence the polypeptides

■ **Figure 5-19** | **Determining the positions of disulfide bonds.** In this method, disulfide-linked peptide fragments from a protein are reductively cleaved and separately sequenced to identify the positions of the disulfide bonds in the intact protein.

Table 5-4 Internet Addresses for the Major Protein and DNA Sequence Data Banks

Data Banks Containing Protein Sequences
ExPASy Proteomics Server: http://expasy.org/
Protein Information Resource (PIR): http://pir.georgetown.edu/
Protein Research Foundation (PRF): http://www4.prf.or.jp/
UniProt: http://www.ebi.uniprot.org/
Data Banks Containing Gene Sequences
GenBank: http://www.ncbi.nlm.nih.gov/Genbank/
European Bioinformatics Institute (EBI): http://www.ebi.ac.uk
DBGET/Integrated Database Retrieval System: GenomeNet@http://www.genome.jb/

Armed with the appropriate software (which is often publicly available at the database sites), a researcher can search a database to find proteins with similar sequences in various organisms. The sequence of even a short peptide fragment may be sufficient to "fish out" the parent protein or its counterpart from another species.

Amino acid sequence information is no less valuable when the nucleotide sequence of the corresponding gene is also known, because the protein sequence provides information about protein structure that is not revealed by nucleic acid sequencing (see Section 3-4). For example, only direct protein sequencing can reveal the locations of disulfide bonds in proteins. In addition, many proteins are modified after they are synthesized. For example, certain residues may be excised to produce the "mature" protein (insulin, shown in Fig. 5-1, is actually synthesized as an 84-residue polypeptide that is proteolytically processed to its smaller two-chain form). Amino acid side chains may also be modified by the addition of carbohydrates, phosphate groups, or acetyl groups, to name only a few. Although some of these modifications occur at characteristic amino acid sequences and are therefore identifiable in nucleotide sequences, only the actual protein sequence can confirm whether and where they occur.

■ CHECK YOUR UNDERSTANDING

Summarize the steps involved in sequencing a protein.

Why is it important to identify the N-terminal residue(s) of a protein?

What are some advantages of sequencing peptides by mass spectrometry rather than by Edman degradation?

What types of information can be retrieved from a protein sequence database?

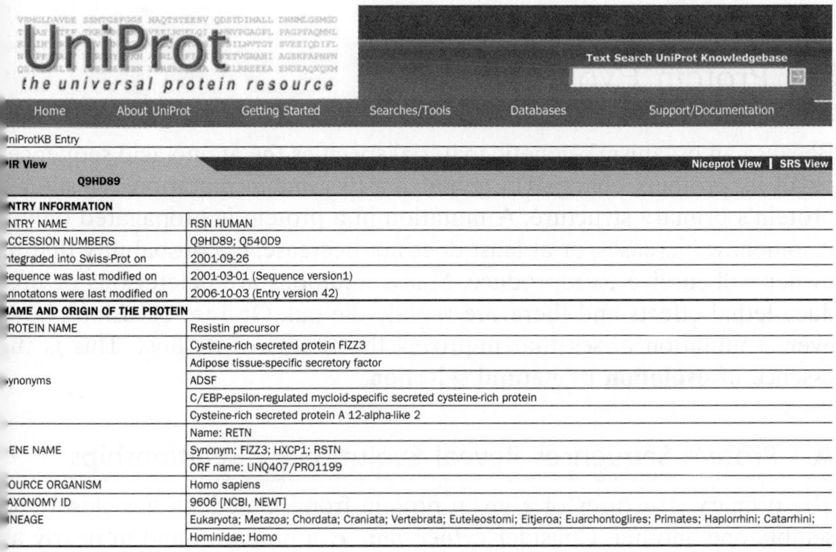

NTRY INFORMATION	
NTRY NAME	RSN HUMAN
CCESSION NUMBERS	Q9HD89; Q540D9
ntegraded into Swiss-Prot on	2001-09-26
equence was last modified on	2001-03-01 (Sequence version1)
nnotatons were last modified on	2006-10-03 (Entry version 42)
AME AND ORIGIN OF THE PROTEIN	
ROTEIN NAME	Resistin precursor
ynonyms	Cysteine-rich secreted protein FIZZ3
	Adipose tissue-specific secretory factor
	ADSF
	C/EBP-epsilon-regulated myeloid-specific secreted cysteine-rich protein
	Cysteine-rich secreted protein A 12-alpha-like 2
ENE NAME	Name: RETN
	Synonym: FIZZ3; HXCP1; RSTN
	ORF name: UNQ407/PRO1199
OURCE ORGANISM	Homo sapiens
AXONOMY ID	9606 [NCBI, NEWT]
INEAGE	Eukaryota; Metazoa; Chordata; Craniata; Vertebrata; Euteleostomi; Eitjeroa; Euarchontoglires; Primates; Haplorrhini; Catarrhini;
	Hominidae; Homo

■ Figure 5-20 | The initial portion of a UniProt entry. This information pertains to the protein **resistin,** which is produced by adipose (fat) tissue and may play a role in diabetes (Section 22-4B). The complete entry includes additional information and references as well as the protein's sequence. [From http://www.pir.uniprot.org/.]

Table 5-5 Amino Acid Sequences of Cytochromes *c* from 38 Species[a]

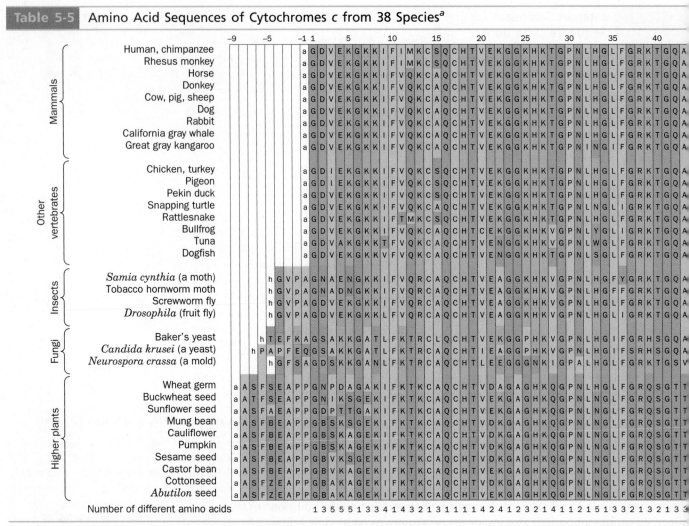

Number of different amino acids: 1 3 5 5 5 1 3 3 4 1 4 3 2 1 3 1 1 1 1 4 2 4 1 2 3 2 1 4 1 1 2 1 5 1 3 3 2 1 3 2 1 3 3

[a]The amino acid side chains have been shaded according to their polarity characteristics so that an invariant or conservatively substituted residue is identified by a vertical band of a single color. The letter a at the beginning of the chain indicates that the N-terminal amino group is acetylated; an h indi-cates that the acetyl group is absent.

Source: After Dickerson, R.E., *Sci. Am.* 226(4); 58–72 (1972), with corrections from Dickerson, R.E., and Timkovich, R., *in* Boyer, P.D. (Ed.), *The Enzymes* (3rd ed.), Vol. 11, pp. 421–422, Academic Press (1975). Table, Irving Geis/Geis Archives Trust, Copyright Howard Hughes Medical Institute. Reproduced with permission.

LEARNING OBJECTIVES

- Understand that sequence comparisons reveal the evolutionary relationships between proteins.
- Understand how protein families evolve by the duplication and divergence of genes encoding protein domains.
- Understand that the rate of evolution varies from protein to protein.

See Guided Exploration 5
Protein evolution.

4 Protein Evolution

Because an organism's genetic material specifies the amino acid sequence of all its proteins, changes in genes due to random mutation can alter a protein's primary structure. A mutation in a protein is propagated only if it somehow increases, or at least does not decrease, the probability that its owner will survive to reproduce. Many mutations are deleterious or produce lethal effects and therefore rapidly die out. On rare occasions, however, a mutation arises that improves the fitness of its host. This is the essence of **evolution** by **natural selection.**

A | Protein Sequences Reveal Evolutionary Relationships

The primary structures of a given protein from related species closely resemble one another. Consider **cytochrome *c*,** a protein found in nearly all eukaryotes. Cytochrome *c* is a component of the mitochondrial electron

Table 5-5	(continued)

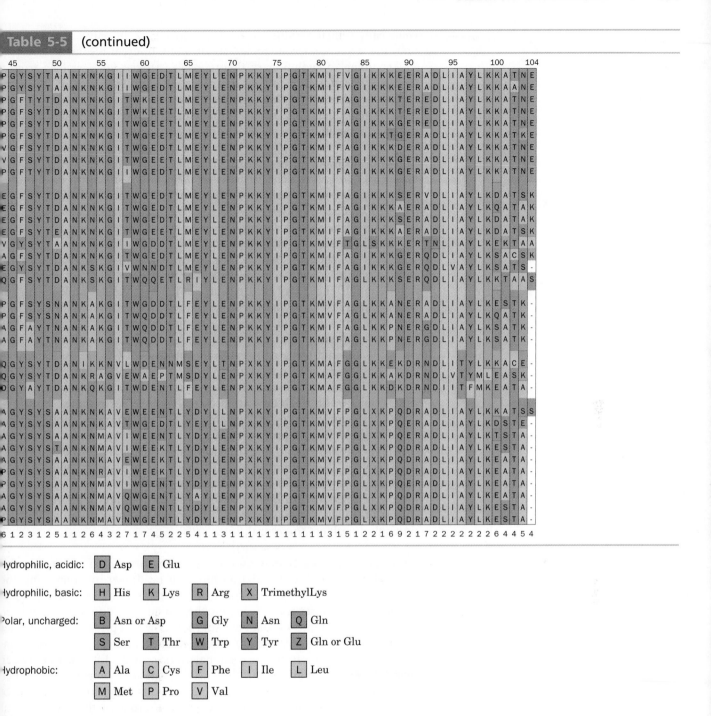

Hydrophilic, acidic: `D` Asp `E` Glu

Hydrophilic, basic: `H` His `K` Lys `R` Arg `X` TrimethylLys

Polar, uncharged: `B` Asn or Asp `G` Gly `N` Asn `Q` Gln
`S` Ser `T` Thr `W` Trp `Y` Tyr `Z` Gln or Glu

Hydrophobic: `A` Ala `C` Cys `F` Phe `I` Ile `L` Leu
`M` Met `P` Pro `V` Val

transport system (Section 18-2), which is believed to have taken its present form between 1.5 and 2 billion years ago, when organisms developed mechanisms for aerobic respiration. Emanuel Margoliash, Emil Smith, and others have elucidated the amino acid sequences of the cytochromes *c* from over 100 eukaryotic species ranging in complexity from yeast to humans. The cytochromes *c* from different species are single polypeptides of 104 to 112 residues. The sequences of 38 of these proteins are arranged in Table 5-5 to show the similarities between vertically aligned residues (the residues have been color-coded according to their physical properties). A survey of the aligned sequences (bottom line of Table 5-5) shows that at 38 positions (23 positions in the complete set of >100 sequences), the same amino acid appears in all species. Most of the remaining positions are occupied by chemically similar residues in different organisms. In only eight positions does the sequence accommodate six or more different residues.

According to evolutionary theory, *related species have evolved from a common ancestor, so it follows that the genes specifying each of their proteins must likewise have evolved from the corresponding gene in that ancestor.* The sequence of the ancestral cytochrome *c* is accessible only indirectly, by examining the sequences of extant proteins.

Sequence Comparisons Provide Information on Protein Structure and Function. *In general, comparisons of the primary structures of **homologous proteins** (evolutionarily related proteins) indicate which of the protein's residues are essential to its function, which are less significant, and which have little specific function.* Finding the same residue at a particular position in the amino acid sequence of a series of related proteins suggests that the chemical or structural properties of that so-called **invariant residue** uniquely suit it to some essential function of the protein. For example, its side chain may be necessary for binding another molecule or for participating in a catalytic reaction. Other amino acid positions may have less stringent side chain requirements and can therefore accommodate residues with similar characteristics (e.g., Asp or Glu, Ser or Thr, etc.); such positions are said to be **conservatively substituted.** On the other hand, a particular amino acid position may tolerate many different amino acid residues, indicating that the functional requirements of that position are rather nonspecific. Such a position is said to be **hypervariable.**

Why is cytochrome *c*—an ancient and essential protein—not identical in all species? Even a protein that is well adapted to its function, that is one that is not subject to physiological improvement, nevertheless continues evolving. The random nature of mutational processes will, in time, change such a protein in ways that do not significantly affect its function, a process called *neutral drift* (deleterious mutations are, of course, rapidly rejected through natural selection). Hypervariable residues are apparently particularly subject to neutral drift.

Phylogenetic Trees Depict Evolutionary History. Far-reaching conclusions about evolutionary relationships can be drawn by comparing the amino acid sequences of homologous proteins. The simplest way to assess evolutionary differences is to count the amino acid differences between proteins. For example, the data in Table 5-5 show that primate cytochromes *c* more nearly resemble those of other mammals than they do those of insects (8–12 differences among mammals versus 26–31 differences between mammals and insects). Similarly, the cytochromes *c* of fungi differ as much from those of mammals (45–51 differences) as they do from those of insects (41–47) or higher plants (47–54). The order of these differences largely parallels that expected from classical taxonomy, which is based primarily on morphological rather than molecular characteristics.

The sequences of homologous proteins can be analyzed by computer to construct a **phylogenetic tree,** a diagram that indicates the ancestral relationships among organisms that produce the protein. The phylogenetic tree for cytochrome *c* is sketched in Fig. 5-21. Similar trees have been derived for other proteins. Each branch point of the tree represents a putative common ancestor for all the organisms above it. The distances between branch points are expressed as the number of amino acid differences per 100 residues of the protein. Such trees present a more quantitative measure of the degree of relatedness of the various species than macroscopic taxonomy can provide.

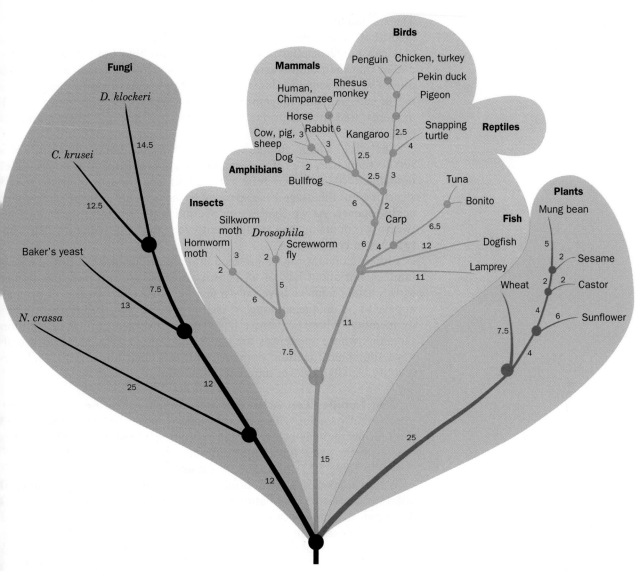

Figure 5-21 | Phylogenetic tree of cytochrome c. Each branch point represents an organism ancestral to the species connected above it. The number beside each branch indicates the number of inferred differences per 100 residues between the cytochromes c of the flanking branch points or species. [After Dayhoff, M.O., Park, C.M., and McLaughlin, P.J., *in* Dayhoff, M.O. (Ed.), *Atlas of Protein Sequence and Structure*, p. 8, National Biomedical Research Foundation (1972).]

Note that the evolutionary distances from all modern cytochromes c to the lowest point, the earliest common ancestor producing this protein, are approximately the same. Thus, "lower" organisms do not represent life-forms that appeared early in history and ceased to evolve further. The cytochromes c of all the species included in Fig. 5-21—whether called "primitive" or "advanced"—have evolved to about the same extent.

Proteins Evolve by the Duplication of Genes or Gene Segments

The effort to characterize protein evolution and create databases of related proteins was pioneered by Margaret Dayhoff beginning in the 1960s. Since then, around one million protein sequences have been catalogued as the result of direct protein sequencing or DNA sequencing projects.

This has led to the development of mathematically sophisticated computer algorithms to identify similarities between sequences. These search protocols can detect similarities between proteins that have evolved to the extent that their amino acid sequences are <20% identical and have acquired several sequence insertions and/or deletions of various lengths. The use of such sequence alignment programs, which are publicly available, is demonstrated in Bioinformatics Exercises 5-1 and 5-2 (www.wiley.com/college/voet).

Analysis of a large number of proteins indicates that evolutionarily conserved sequences are often segments of about 40 to 200 residues, called **domains.** Originally, this term referred to a portion of discrete protein structure, but the usage has expanded to include the corresponding amino acid sequence. As we shall see in Section 6-20, structural similarities between two domains may be apparent even when the sequences have few residues in common.

Protein domains can be grouped into an estimated 1000–1400 different families, but about half of all known domains fall into just 200 families. Most protein families have only a few members, and 10–20% of proteins appear to be unique, although it is also possible that they represent family members whose sequences have simply diverged beyond recognition. Domains whose sequences are more than about 40% identical usually have the same function; domains with less than about 25% sequence identity usually perform different roles.

Protein Families Can Arise through Gene Duplication. It is not surprising that proteins with similar functions have similar sequences; such proteins presumably evolved from a common ancestor. Homologous proteins with the same function in different species (e.g., the cytochromes shown in Table 5-5) are said to be **orthologous.**

Within a species, similar proteins arise through **gene duplication,** an aberrant genetic recombination event in which one member of a chromosome pair acquires both copies of the primordial gene (genetic recombination is discussed in Section 25-6). Following duplication, the sequences may diverge as mutations occur over time. *Gene duplication is a particularly efficient mode of evolution because one copy of the gene evolves a new function through natural selection while its counterpart continues to direct the synthesis of the original protein.* Two independently evolving genes that are derived from a duplication event are said to be **paralogous.** In prokaryotes, approximately 60% of protein domains have been duplicated; in many eukaryotes the figure is ~90%, and in humans, ~98%.

The **globin family** of proteins provides an excellent example of evolution through gene duplication and divergence. **Hemoglobin,** which transports O_2 from the lungs (or gills or skin) to the tissues, is a tetramer with the subunit composition $\alpha_2\beta_2$ (i.e., two α polypeptides and two β polypeptides). The sequences of the α and β subunits are similar to each other and to the sequence of the protein **myoglobin,** which facilitates oxygen diffusion through muscle tissue (hemoglobin and myoglobin are discussed in more detail in Chapter 7). The primordial globin probably functioned simply as an oxygen-storage protein. Gene duplication allowed one globin to evolve into a monomeric hemoglobin α chain. Duplication of the α chain gene gave rise to the paralogous gene for the β chain. Other members of the globin family include the β-like γ chain that is present in fetal hemoglobin, an $\alpha_2\gamma_2$ tetramer, and the β-like ε and α-like ζ chains that appear together early in embryogenesis as $\zeta_2\varepsilon_2$ hemoglobin. Primates contain a relatively recently duplicated globin, the β-like δ chain, which appears as a minor component (~1%) of adult hemoglobin. Although the $\alpha_2\delta_2$ hemoglobin has no known unique function, perhaps it may eventually evolve one. The genealogy of the members of the globin family is diagrammed in Fig. 5-22. The human genome also contains the relics of globin genes that are not expressed. These **pseudogenes** can be considered the dead ends of protein evolution. Note that a duplicated and therefore initially superfluous gene has only a limited time to evolve a new functionality that provides a selective advantage to its host before it is inactivated through mutation, that is, becomes a pseudogene.

The Rate of Sequence Divergence Varies. The sequence differences between orthologous proteins can be plotted against the time when, according to the fossil record, the species producing the proteins diverged. The plot for a given protein is essentially linear, indicating that its mutations accumulate at a constant rate over a geological time scale. However, rates of evolution vary among proteins (Fig. 5-23). This does not imply that the rates of mutation of the DNAs specifying those proteins differ, but rather that *the rate at which mutations are accepted into a protein varies.*

A major contributor to the rate at which a protein evolves is the effect of amino acid changes on the protein's function. For example, Fig. 5-23 shows that **histone H4,** a protein that binds to DNA in eukaryotes (Section 24-5A), is among the most highly conserved proteins (the histones H4 from peas and cows, species that diverged 1.2 billion years ago, differ by only two conservative changes in their 102 residues). Evidently, histone H4 is so finely tuned to its function of packaging DNA in cells that it is extremely intolerant of any mutations. Cytochrome *c* is only slightly more tolerant. It is a relatively small protein that binds to several other proteins. Hence, any changes in its amino acid sequence must be compatible with all its binding partners (or they would have to simultaneously mutate to accommodate the altered cytochrome *c,* an unlikely event). Hemoglobin, which functions as a free-floating molecule, is subject to less selective pressure than histone H4 or cytochrome *c,* so its surface residues are more easily substituted by other amino acids. The **fibrinopeptides** are ~20-residue fragments that are cleaved from the vertebrate protein **fibrinogen** to induce blood clotting. Once they have been removed, the fibrinopeptides are discarded, so that they are subject to little selective pressure to maintain their amino acid sequences.

The rate of protein evolution also depends on the protein's structural stability. For example, a mutation that slowed the rate at which a newly synthesized polypeptide chain folds into its functional three-dimensional shape could affect the cell's survival, even if the protein ultimately functioned normally. Such mutations would be especially critical for proteins that are produced at high levels, since the not-yet-folded proteins could swamp the cell's protein-folding mechanisms. In fact, the genes for highly expressed proteins appear to evolve more slowly than the genes for rarely expressed proteins.

Mutational changes in proteins do not account for all evolutionary changes among organisms. The DNA sequences that control the expression of proteins (Chapters 26, 27, and 28) are also subject to mutation. These sequences control where, when, and how much of the corresponding protein is made. Thus, although the proteins of humans and chimpanzees are >99% identical on average (e.g., their cytochromes *c* are

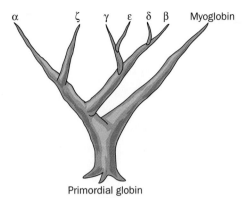

■ **Figure 5-22** | **Genealogy of the globin family.** Each branch point represents a gene duplication event. Myoglobin is a single-chain protein. The globins identified by Greek letters are subunits of hemoglobins.

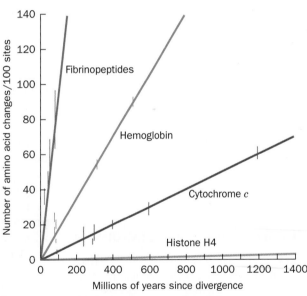

■ **Figure 5-23** | **Rates of evolution of four proteins.** The graph was constructed by plotting the number of different amino acid residues in the proteins on two sides of a branch point of a phylogenetic tree versus the time, according to the fossil record, since the corresponding species diverged from their common ancestor. [Illustration, Irving Geis/Geis Archives Trust. Copyright Howard Hughes Medical Institute. Reproduced with permission.]

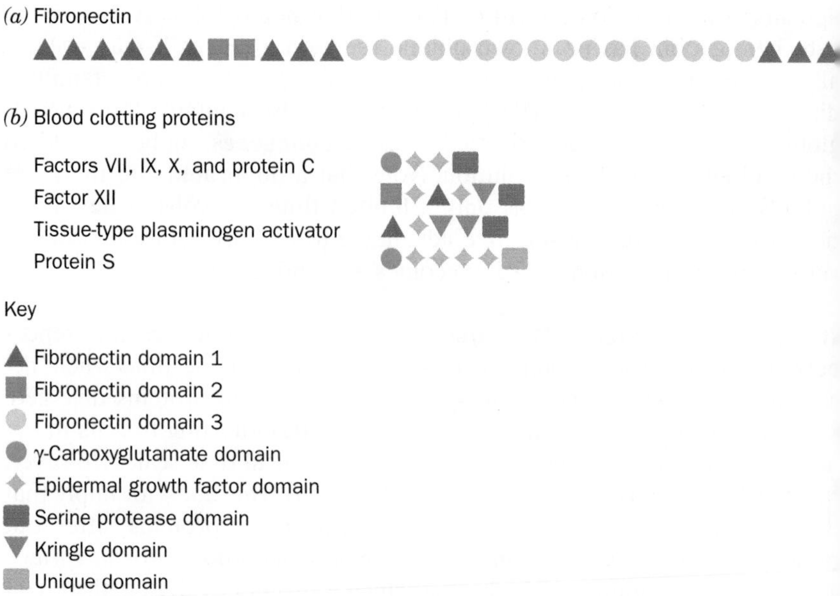

(a) Fibronectin

(b) Blood clotting proteins

Factors VII, IX, X, and protein C	●◆◆■
Factor XII	■◆▲◆▼■
Tissue-type plasminogen activator	▲◆▼▼■
Protein S	●◆◆◆◆■

Key

▲ Fibronectin domain 1
■ Fibronectin domain 2
● Fibronectin domain 3
● γ-Carboxyglutamate domain
◆ Epidermal growth factor domain
■ Serine protease domain
▼ Kringle domain
■ Unique domain

■ **Figure 5-24** | **Construction of some multidomain proteins.** Each shape represents a segment of ~40–100 residues that appears, with some sequence variation, several times in the same protein or in a number of related proteins. *(a)* **Fibronectin,** an ~500-kD protein of the extracellular matrix, is composed mostly of repeated domains of three types. *(b)* Some of the proteins that participate in blood clotting are built from a small set of domains. (The epidermal growth factor domain is so named because it was first observed as a component of **epidermal growth factor.**) [After Baron, M., Norman, D.G., and Campbell, I.D., *Trends Biochem. Sci.* **16,** 14 (1991).]

identical), their anatomical and behavioral differences are so great that they are classified as belonging to different families.

Many Proteins Contain Domains That Occur in Other Proteins. Gene duplication is not the only mechanism that generates new proteins. Analysis of protein sequences has revealed that many proteins, particularly those made by eukaryotes, are mosaics of sequence motifs or domains of about 40–100 amino acid residues. These domains occur in several other proteins in the same organism and may be repeated numerous times within a given protein (Fig. 5-24*a*). For example, most of the proteins involved in blood clotting are composed of sets of smaller domains (Fig. 5-24*b*). The sequence identity between homologous domains is imperfect since each domain evolves independently. The functions of individual domains are not always known: Some appear to have discrete activities such as catalyzing a certain chemical reaction or binding a particular molecule, but others may merely be spacers or scaffolding for other domains.

We shall see in Section 25-6C how gene segments encoding protein domains are copied and inserted into other positions in a genome to generate new genes that encode proteins with novel sequences. Such domain shuffling is a much faster process than the duplication of an entire gene followed by its evolution of a new functionality. Nevertheless, both mechanisms have played important roles in the evolution of proteins.

■ **CHECK YOUR UNDERSTANDING**

How can sequence comparisons reveal which amino acid residues are essential for a protein's function?

Explain how the number of amino acid differences between homologous proteins can be used to construct a phylogenetic tree.

Explain the origin of orthologous proteins, paralogous proteins, and multidomain proteins.

Why do different proteins appear to evolve at different rates?

SUMMARY

1. The properties of proteins depend largely on the sizes and sequences of their component polypeptides.

2. Protein purification requires controlled conditions such as pH and temperature, and a means to quantify the protein (an assay).

3. Fractionation procedures are used to purify proteins on the basis of solubility, charge, polarity, size, and binding specificity.

4. Differences in solubility permit proteins to be concentrated and purified by salting out.

5. Chromatography, the separation of soluble substances by their rate of movement through an insoluble matrix, is a technique for purifying molecules by charge (ion exchange chromatography), hydrophobicity (hydrophobic interaction chromatography), size (gel filtration chromatography), and binding specificity (affinity chromatography). Binding and elution often depend on the salt concentration and pH.

6. Electrophoresis separates molecules by charge and size; SDS-PAGE separates them primarily by size. 2D electrophoresis can resolve thousands of proteins.

7. Analysis of a protein's sequence begins with end group analysis, to determine the number of different subunits, and the cleavage of disulfide bonds.

8. Polypeptides are cleaved into fragments suitable for sequencing by Edman degradation, in which residues are removed, one at a time, from the N-terminus. Peptides can also be sequenced by mass spectrometry.

9. A protein's sequence is reconstructed from the sequences of overlapping peptide fragments and from information about the locations of disulfide bonds. The sequences of numerous proteins are archived in publicly available databases.

10. Proteins evolve through changes in primary structure. Protein sequences can be compared to construct phylogenetic trees and to identify essential amino acid residues.

11. New proteins arise as a result of the duplication of genes or gene segments specifying protein domains, followed by their divergence.

KEY TERMS

primary structure **92**
peptide **92**
multisubunit protein **92**
subunit **92**
denaturation **94**
protease **95**
nuclease **95**
assay **95**
coupled enzymatic reaction **95**
immunoassay **95**
antibody **95**
antigen **95**
RIA **95**
ELISA **95**
Beer–Lambert law **95**
absorbance (*A*) **95**
absorptivity (*ε*) **95**

chromophore **96**
Bradford assay **96**
fractionation procedure **97**
salting in **97**
salting out **97**
chromatography **98**
HPLC **98**
ion exchange chromatography **98**
anion exchanger **98**
cation exchanger **98**
polyelectrolyte **98**
elution **99**
eluant **99**
hydrophobic interaction chromatography **99**
gel filtration chromatography **100**

affinity chromatography **101**
ligand **101**
immunoaffinity chromatography **101**
metal chelate affinity chromatography **101**
PAGE **101**
autoradiography **102**
immunoblot (Western blot) **102**
SDS-PAGE **102**
capillary electrophoresis **103**
IEF **103**
two-dimensional (2D) gel electrophoresis **103**
proteomics **103**
mercaptan **106**
endopeptidase **107**

exopeptidase **107**
limited proteolysis **108**
Edman degradation **109**
mass spectrometry **110**
ESI **111**
homologous proteins **116**
invariant residue **116**
conservative substitution **116**
hypervariable residue **116**
neutral drift **116**
phylogenetic tree **116**
domain **118**
orthologous proteins **118**
gene duplication **118**
paralogous proteins **118**
pseudogenes **119**

PROBLEMS

1. Which peptide has greater absorbance at 280 nm?
   A. Gln–Leu–Glu–Phe–Thr–Leu–Asp–Gly–Tyr
   B. Ser–Val–Trp–Asp–Phe–Gly–Tyr–Trp–Ala

2. Protein X has an absorptivity of 0.4 mL·mg^{-1}·cm^{-1} at 280 nm. What is the absorbance at 280 nm of a 2.0 mg·mL^{-1} solution of protein X? (Assume the light path is 1 cm.)

3. You are using ammonium sulfate to purify protein Q (p*I* = 5.0) by salting out from a solution at pH 7.0. How should you adjust the pH of the mixture to maximize the amount of protein Q that precipitates?

4. (a) In what order would the amino acids Arg, His, and Leu be eluted from a carboxymethyl column at pH 6? (b) In what

order would Glu, Lys, and Val be eluted from a diethyl-aminoethyl column at pH 8?

5. Consult Table 5-1 to complete the following: (a) On a plot of absorbance at 280 nm versus elution volume, sketch the results of gel filtration of a mixture containing human cytochrome c and bacteriophage T7 RNA polymerase and identify each peak. (b) Sketch the results of SDS-PAGE of the same protein mixture showing the direction of migration and identifying each band.

6. Explain why a certain protein has an apparent molecular mass of 90 kD when determined by gel filtration and 60 kD when determined by SDS-PAGE in the presence or absence of 2-mercaptoethanol. Which molecular mass determination is more accurate?

7. Determine the subunit composition of a protein from the following information:

Molecular mass by gel filtration: 200 kD

Molecular mass by SDS-PAGE: 100 kD

Molecular mass by SDS-PAGE with 2-mercaptoethanol: 40 kD and 60 kD

8. What fractionation procedure could be used to purify protein 1 from a mixture of three proteins whose amino acid compositions are as follows?

1. 25% Ala, 20% Gly, 20% Ser, 10% Ile, 10% Val, 5% Asn, 5% Gln, 5% Pro

2. 30% Gln, 25% Glu, 20% Lys, 15% Ser, 10% Cys

3. 25% Asn, 20% Gly, 20% Asp, 20% Ser, 10% Lys, 5% Tyr

All three proteins are similar in size and pI, and there is no antibody available for protein 1.

9. Purification of Myoglobin (Mb). Purification tables are often used to keep track of the yield and purification of a protein. The specific activity is a ratio of the amount of the protein of interest, in this case Mb, obtained at a given step (μmol or enzyme units) divided by the amount (mg) of total protein. The yield is the ratio of the amount of the protein of interest obtained at a given step (μmol or enzyme units) divided by the original amount present in the crude extract, often converted to percent yield by multiplying by 100. The fold purification is the ratio of the specific activity of the purified protein to that of the crude preparation.

(a) For the purification table below, calculate the specific activity, % yield, and fold purification for the empty cells.

(b) Which step—DEAE or affinity chromatography—causes the greatest loss of Mb?

(c) Which step causes the greater purification of Mb?

(d) If you wanted to use only one purification step, which technique would you choose?

10. Explain why the dansyl chloride treatment of a single polypeptide chain followed by its complete acid hydrolysis yields several dansylated amino acids.

11. Identify the first residue obtained by Edman degradation of cytochrome c from (a) *Drosophila*, (b) baker's yeast, and (c) wheat germ (see Table 5-5).

12. You must cleave the following peptide into smaller fragments. Which of the proteases listed in Table 5-3 would be likely to yield the most fragments? The fewest?

NMTQGRCKPVNTFVHEPLVDVQNVCFKE

13. Electrospray ionization mass spectrometry (ESI-MS) of proteins involves creating positively charged ions of the protein and separating them according to their mass-to-charge ratio (m/z).

(a) What causes the different positive charges on different particles of the protein?

(b) The amino acid composition (in numbers of residues per chain) of hen egg-white lysozyme (HEWL) is as follows:

P	2	Y	3	N	14	H	1
D	7	M	2	L	8	E	2
C	8	R	11	G	12	F	3
A	12	I	6	K	6	V	6
S	10	W	6	T	7	Q	3

What is the maximum positive charge that can be present on a HEWL ion?

(c) The ESI-MS spectrum below was obtained for HEWL.

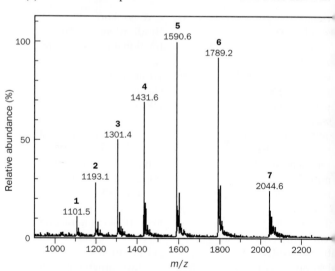

Using peaks 5 and 6, calculate the molecular mass of HEWL (see Sample Calculation 5-1). [Spectrum obtained from http://www.astbury.leeds.ac.uk/facil/MStut/mstutorial.htm]

(d) What is the charge on the ion that makes peak 5?

Purification Table for Problem 9

Purification step	mg total protein	μmol Mb	Specific activity (μmol Mb/mg total protein)	% yield	fold purification
1. Crude extract	1550	0.75		100	1
2. DEAE-cellulose chromatography	550	0.35			
3. Affinity chromatography	5.0	0.28			

4. You wish to determine the sequence of a short peptide. Cleavage with trypsin yields three smaller peptides with the sequences Leu–Glu, Gly–Tyr–Asn–Arg, and Gln–Ala–Phe–Val–Lys. Cleavage with chymotrypsin yields three peptides with the sequences Gln–Ala–Phe, Asn–Arg–Leu–Glu, and Val–Lys–Gly–Tyr. What is the sequence of the intact peptide?

5. Separate cleavage reactions of a polypeptide by CNBr and chymotrypsin yield fragments with the following amino acid sequences. What is the sequence of the intact polypeptide?

CNBr treatment

1. Arg–Ala–Tyr–Gly–Asn
2. Leu–Phe–Met
3. Asp–Met

Chymotrypsin

4. Met–Arg–Ala–Tyr
5. Asp–Met–Leu–Phe
6. Gly–Asn

6. You wish to determine the sequence of a polypeptide that has the following amino acid composition.

1 Ala 4 Arg 2 Asn 3 Asp 4 Cys 3 Gly 1 Gln 4 Glu
1 His 1 Lys 1 Met 1 Phe 2 Pro 4 Ser 2 Tyr 1 Trp

(a) What is the maximum number of peptides you can expect if you cleave the polypeptide with cyanogen bromide?

(b) What is the maximum number of peptides you can expect if you cleave the polypeptide with chymotrypsin?

(c) Analysis of the intact polypeptide reveals that there are no free sulfhydryl groups. How many disulfide bonds are likely to be present?

(d) How many different arrangements of disulfide bonds are possible?

7. Treatment of a polypeptide with 2-mercaptoethanol yields two polypeptides:

1. Ala–Val–Cys–Arg–Thr–Gly–Cys–Lys–Asn--Phe–Leu
2. Tyr–Lys–Cys–Phe–Arg–His–Thr–Lys–Cys–Ser

Treatment of the intact polypeptide with trypsin yields fragments with the following amino acid compositions:

3. (Ala, Arg, Cys$_2$, Ser, Val)
4. (Arg, Cys$_2$, Gly, Lys, Thr, Phe)
5. (Asn, Leu, Phe)
6. (His, Lys, Thr)
7. (Lys, Tyr)

Indicate the positions of the disulfide bonds in the intact polypeptide.

18. You wish to sequence the light chain of a protease inhibitor from the *Brassica nigra* plant. Cleavage of the light chain by trypsin and chymotrypsin yields the following fragments. What is the sequence of the light chain?

Chymotrypsin

1. Leu–His–Lys–Gln–Ala–Asn–Gln–Ser–Gly–Gly–Gly–Pro–Ser
2. Gln–Gln–Ala–Gln–His–Leu–Arg–Ala–Cys–Gln–Gln–Trp
3. Arg–Ile–Pro–Lys–Cys–Arg–Lys–Phe

Trypsin

4. Arg
5. Ala–Cys–Gln–Gln–Trp–Leu–His–Lys
6. Cys–Arg
7. Gln–Ala–Asn–Gln–Ser–Gly–Gly–Gly–Pro–Ser
8. Phe–Gln–Gln–Ala–Gln–His–Leu–Arg
9. Ile–Pro–Lys
10. Lys

19. In site-directed mutagenesis experiments, Gly is often successfully substituted for Val, but Val can rarely substitute for Gly. Explain.

20. Below is a list of the first 10 residues of the B helix in myoglobin from different organisms.

Position	1	2	3	4	5	6	7	8	9	10
Human	D	I	P	G	H	G	Q	E	V	L
Chicken	D	I	A	G	H	G	H	E	V	L
Alligator	K	L	P	E	H	G	H	E	V	I
Turtle	D	L	S	A	H	G	Q	E	V	I
Tuna	D	Y	T	T	M	G	G	L	V	L
Carp	D	F	E	G	T	G	G	E	V	L

Based on this information, which positions (a) appear unable to tolerate substitutions, (b) can tolerate conservative substitution, and (c) are highly variable?

CASE STUDY

Case 2 (available at www.wiley.com/college/voet)
Histidine–Proline-Rich Glycoprotein as a Plasma pH Sensor

Focus concept: A histidine–proline-rich glycoprotein may serve as a plasma sensor and regulate local pH in extracellular fluid during ischemia or metabolic acidosis.

Prerequisites: Chapters 4 and 5

• Acidic/basic properties of amino acids
• Amino acid structure and protein structure

BIOINFORMATICS EXERCISES

Bioinformatics Exercises are available at www.wiley.com/college/voet.

Chapter 5

Using Databases to Compare and Identify Related Protein Sequences

1. **Obtaining Sequences from BLAST.** Using a known protein sequence, find and retrieve the sequences of related proteins from other organisms.
2. **Multiple Sequence Alignment.** Examine the various sequences for similarities.
3. **Phylogenetic Trees.** Set up and interpret phylogenetic trees to explore the evolutionary relationships between related protein sequences.

4. **Interpreting Mass Spectral Data.** Learn about different types of mass spectrometry and how to correctly interpret the data they generate.
5. **One-Dimensional Electrophoresis.** Perform an SDS-PAGE electrophoresis simulation with known and unknown proteins.
6. **Two-Dimensional Electrophoresis.** Explore the predicted and observed electrophoretic parameters (pI, molecular mass, and fragmentation pattern) for a known protein.

REFERENCES

Protein Purification

Boyer, R.F., *Biochemistry Laboratory: Modern Theory and Techniques*, Benjamin Cummings (2006).

Janson, J.-C. (Ed.), *Protein Purification: Principles, High Resolution Methods, and Applications* (3rd ed.), Wiley (2007). [Contains detailed discussions of a variety of chromatographic and electrophoretic separation techniques.]

Tanford, C. and Reynolds, J., *Nature's Robots: A History of Proteins,* Oxford University Press (2001). [Descriptions of some early discoveries related to the nature of proteins and their purification and analysis.]

Wilson, K. and Walker, J.M. (Eds.), *Principles and Techniques of Biochemistry and Molecular Biology* (6th ed.), Cambridge University Press (2005). [Includes reviews of spectroscopy, electrophoresis, and chromatography.]

Protein Sequencing

Aebersold, R. and Mann, M., Mass spectrometry-based proteomics, *Nature* **422,** 198–207 (2003). [Describes some of the methods of mass spectrometric analysis of proteins as well as current and potential applications.]

Findlay, J.B.C. and Geisow, M.J. (Eds.), *Protein Sequencing. A Practical Approach,* IRL Press (1989).

Galperin, M.Y., The molecular biology database collection: 200 update, *Nucleic Acids Res.* **35,** Database issue D3–D4 (2007) [This and other articles in this Database Issue describe the features and potential uses of various protein and DNA sequence databases. Freely available at http://nar.oxfordjournals.org.]

Protein Evolution

Baxevanis, A.D. and Ouellette, B.F.F. (Eds.), *Bioinformatics, A Practical Guide to the Analysis of Genes and Proteins* (3rd ed.), Wiley-Interscience (2005).

Doolittle, R.F., Feng, D.-F., Tsang, S., Cho, G., and Little, E., Determining divergence times of the major kingdoms of living organisms with a protein clock, *Science* **271,** 470–477 (1996) [Demonstrates how protein sequences can be used to draw phylogenetic trees.]

Mount, D.W., *Bioinformatics: Sequence and Genome Analysis* (2nd ed.), Cold Spring Harbor Laboratory Press (2004).

Pál, C., Papp, B., and Lercher, M.J., An integrated view of protein evolution, *Nature Reviews Genetics* **7,** 337–348 (2006). [Discusses some of the factors that contribute to the variable rate of evolution among proteins, including protein dispensability and expression level.]

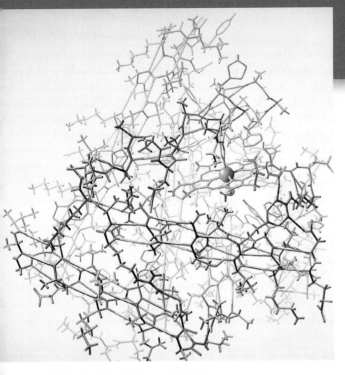

6

Proteins: Three-Dimensional Structure

The atomic structure of myoglobin, is drawn here as a stick model. Noncovalent forces stabilize its three-dimensional structure. [Illustration, Irving Geis. Image from the Irving Geis Collection/Howard Hughes Medical Institute. Rights owned by HHMI. Reproduction by permission only.]

■ MEDIA RESOURCES

(Available at www.wiley.com/college/voet)

Guided Exploration 6. Stable helices in proteins: the α helix
Guided Exploration 7. Hydrogen bonding in β sheets
Guided Exploration 8. Secondary structures in proteins
Interactive Exercise 2. Glyceraldehyde-3-phosphate dehydrogenase
Animated Figure 6-7. The α helix
Animated Figure 6-9. β sheets
Animated Figure 6-34. Symmetry in oligomeric proteins
Animated Figure 6-42. Mechanism of protein disulfide isomerase
Kinemage 3-1. The peptide group
Kinemage 3-2. The α helix
Kinemage 3-3. β sheets
Kinemage 3-4. Reverse turns
Kinemage 4-1, 4-2. Coiled coils
Kinemage 4-3, 4-4. Collagen
Kinemage 5. Cytochrome *c*
Case Study 4. The Structure of Insulin
Case Study 5. Characterization of Subtilisin from the Antarctic Psychrophile *Bacillus* TA41
Case Study 6. A Collection of Collagen Cases
Bioinformatics Exercises. Chapter 6. Visualizing Three-Dimensional Protein Structures

■ CHAPTER CONTENTS

1 Secondary Structure

  A. The Planar Peptide Group Limits Polypeptide Conformations

  B. The Most Common Regular Secondary Structures Are the α Helix and the β Sheet

  C. Fibrous Proteins Have Repeating Secondary Structures

  D. Most Proteins Include Nonrepetitive Structure

2 Tertiary Structure

  A. Most Protein Structures Are Determined by X-Ray Crystallography or Nuclear Magnetic Resonance

  B. Side Chain Location Varies with Polarity

  C. Tertiary Structures Contain Combinations of Secondary Structure

  D. Structure Is Conserved More than Sequence

  E. Structural Bioinformatics Provides Tools for Storing, Visualizing, and Comparing Protein Structural Information

3 Quaternary Structure and Symmetry

4 Protein Stability

  A. Proteins Are Stabilized by Several Forces

  B. Proteins Can Undergo Denaturation and Renaturation

5 Protein Folding

  A. Proteins Follow Folding Pathways

  B. Molecular Chaperones Assist Protein Folding

  C. Some Diseases Are Caused by Protein Misfolding

For many years, it was thought that proteins were colloids of random structure and that the enzymatic activities of certain crystallized proteins were due to unknown entities associated with an inert protein carrier. In 1934, J.D. Bernal and Dorothy Crowfoot Hodgkin showed that a crystal of the protein **pepsin** yielded a discrete diffraction pattern when placed in an X-ray beam. This result provided convincing evidence that pepsin was not a random colloid but an ordered array of atoms organized into a large yet uniquely structured molecule.

Even relatively small proteins contain thousands of atoms, almost all of which occupy definite positions in space. The first X-ray structure of a protein, that of sperm whale myoglobin, was reported in 1958 by John Kendrew and co-workers. At the time—only 5 years after James Watson and Francis Crick had elucidated the simple and elegant structure of DNA (Section 3-2B)—protein chemists were chagrined by the complexity and apparent lack of regularity in the structure of myoglobin. In retrospect, such irregularity seems essential for proteins to fulfill their diverse biological roles. However, comparisons of the nearly 50,000 protein structures now known have revealed that proteins actually exhibit a remarkable degree of structural regularity.

As we saw in Section 5-1, the primary structure of a protein is its linear sequence of amino acids. In discussing protein structure, three further levels of structural complexity are customarily invoked:

- **Secondary structure** is the local spatial arrangement of a polypeptide's backbone atoms without regard to the conformations of its side chains.
- **Tertiary structure** refers to the three-dimensional structure of an entire polypeptide, including its side chains.
- Many proteins are composed of two or more polypeptide chains, loosely referred to as subunits. A protein's **quaternary structure** refers to the spatial arrangement of its subunits.

The four levels of protein structure are summarized in Fig. 6-1.

In this chapter, we explore secondary through quaternary structure, including examples of proteins that illustrate each of these levels. We also discuss the process of protein folding and the forces that stabilize folded proteins.

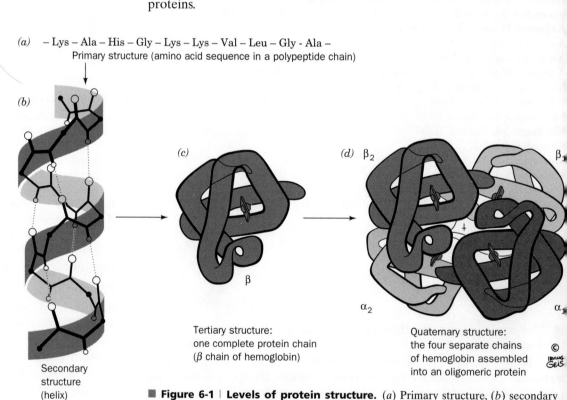

(a) – Lys – Ala – His – Gly – Lys – Lys – Val – Leu – Gly - Ala –
Primary structure (amino acid sequence in a polypeptide chain)

(b)

(c)

(d) β₂   β₁

α₂   α₁

Secondary structure (helix)

Tertiary structure:
one complete protein chain
(β chain of hemoglobin)

Quaternary structure:
the four separate chains
of hemoglobin assembled
into an oligomeric protein

© IRVING GEIS

■ **Figure 6-1** | **Levels of protein structure.** (*a*) Primary structure, (*b*) secondary structure, (*c*) tertiary structure, and (*d*) quaternary structure. [Illustration, Irving Geis. Image from the Irving Geis Collection/Howard Hughes Medical Institute. Rights owned by HHMI. Reproduction by permission only.]

1 Secondary Structure

Protein secondary structure includes the regular polypeptide folding patterns such as helices, sheets, and turns. However, before we discuss these basic structural elements, we must consider the geometric properties of peptide groups, which underlie all higher order structures.

A | The Planar Peptide Group Limits Polypeptide Conformations

Recall from Section 4-1B that a polypeptide is a polymer of amino acid residues linked by amide (peptide) bonds. In the 1930s and 1940s, Linus Pauling and Robert Corey determined the X-ray structures of several amino acids and dipeptides in an effort to elucidate the conformational constraints on a polypeptide chain. These studies indicated that *the peptide group has a rigid, planar structure as a consequence of resonance interactions that give the peptide bond ~40% double-bond character:*

This explanation is supported by the observations that a peptide group's C—N bond is 0.13 Å shorter than its N—C$_\alpha$ single bond and that its C=O bond is 0.02 Å longer than that of aldehydes and ketones. The planar conformation maximizes π-bonding overlap, which accounts for the peptide group's rigidity.

Peptide groups, with few exceptions, assume the **trans conformation,** in which successive C$_\alpha$ atoms are on opposite sides of the peptide bond joining them (Fig. 6-2). The **cis conformation,** in which successive C$_\alpha$ atoms are on the same side of the peptide bond, is ~8 kJ · mol^{-1} less stable than the trans conformation because of steric interference between neighboring side chains. However, this steric interference is reduced in peptide bonds to Pro residues, so *~10% of the Pro residues in proteins follow a cis peptide bond.*

Torsion Angles between Peptide Groups Describe Polypeptide Chain Conformations. The **backbone** or **main chain** of a protein refers to the atoms that participate in peptide bonds, ignoring the side chains of the amino acid residues. The backbone can be drawn as a linked sequence of rigid planar peptide groups (Fig. 6-3). *The conformation of the backbone*

LEARNING OBJECTIVES

■ Understand that the planar character of the peptide group limits the conformational flexibility of the polypeptide chain.
■ Become familiar with the α helix and the β sheet.
■ Understand the structures of the fibrous proteins α keratin and collagen.

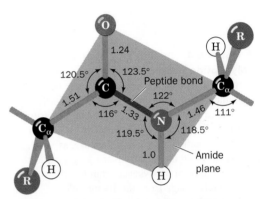

■ **Figure 6-2 | The trans peptide group.** The bond lengths (in angstroms) and angles (in degrees) are derived from X-ray crystal structures. [After Marsh, R.E. and Donohue, J., *Adv. Protein Chem.* **22,** 249 (1967).]
🔗 **See Kinemage Exercise 3-1.**

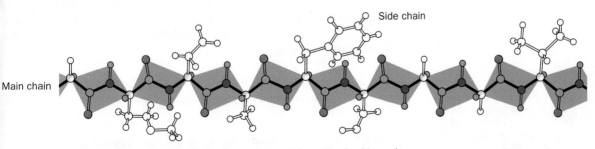

■ **Figure 6-3 | Extended conformation of a polypeptide.** The backbone is shown as a series of planar peptide groups. [Illustration, Irving Geis. Image from the Irving Geis Collection/Howard Hughes Medical Institute. Rights owned by HHMI. Reproduction by permission only.]

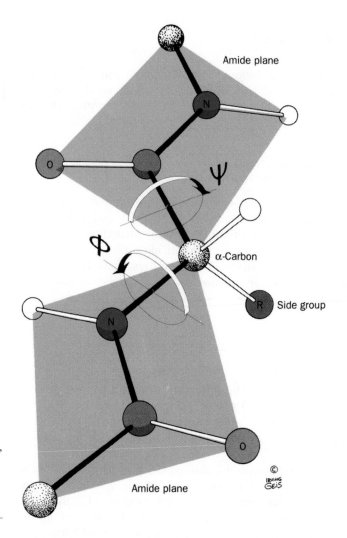

Figure 6-4 | Torsion angles of the polypeptide backbone. Two planar peptide groups are shown. The only reasonably free movements are rotations around the C_α—N (measured as ϕ) and the C_α—C bond (measured as ψ). By convention, both ϕ and ψ are 180° in the conformation shown and increase, as indicated, when the peptide plane is rotated in the clockwise direction as viewed from C_α. [Illustration, Irving Geis. Image from the Irving Geis Collection/Howard Hughes Medical Institute. Rights owned by HHMI. Reproduction by permission only.] **See Kinemage Exercise 3-1.**

can therefore be described by the **torsion angles** *(also called* **dihedral angles** *or rotation angles) around the C_α—N bond (ϕ) and the C_α—C bond (ψ) of each residue* (Fig. 6-4). These angles, ϕ and ψ, are both defined as 180° when the polypeptide chain is in its fully extended conformation and increase clockwise when viewed from C_α.

The conformational freedom and therefore the torsion angles of a polypeptide backbone are sterically constrained. Rotation around the C_α—N and C_α—C bonds to form certain combinations of ϕ and ψ angles will cause the amide hydrogen, the carbonyl oxygen, or the substituents of C_α of adjacent residues to collide (e.g., Fig. 6-5). Certain conformations of longer polypeptides can similarly produce collisions between residues that are far apart in sequence.

The Ramachandran Diagram Indicates Allowed Conformations of Polypeptides. The sterically allowed values of ϕ and ψ can be calculated.

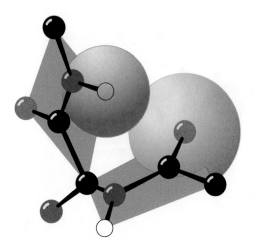

Figure 6-5 | Steric interference between adjacent peptide groups. Rotation can result in a conformation in which the amide hydrogen of one residue and the carbonyl oxygen of the next are closer than their van der Waals distance. [Illustration, Irving Geis. Image from the Irving Geis Collection/Howard Hughes Medical Institute. Rights owned by HHMI. Reproduction by permission only.] **See Kinemage Exercise 3-1.**

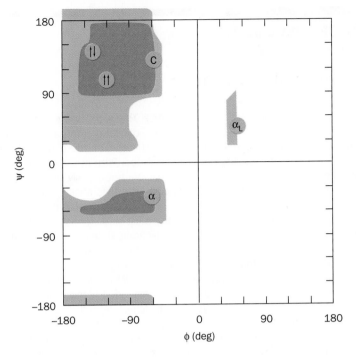

■ **Figure 6-6** | **The Ramachandran diagram.**
The blue-shaded regions indicate the sterically
allowed ϕ and ψ angles for all residues except Gly
and Pro. The green-shaded regions indicate the
more crowded (outer limit) ϕ and ψ angles. The
orange circles represent conformational angles of
several secondary structures: α, right-handed α
helix; ↑↑, parallel β sheet; ↑↓, antiparallel β sheet;
C, collagen helix; α_L, left-handed α helix.

Sterically forbidden conformations, such as the one shown in Fig. 6-5,
have ϕ and ψ values that would bring atoms closer than the corresponding van der Waals distance (the distance of closest contact between nonbonded atoms). Such information is summarized in a **Ramachandran
diagram** (Fig. 6-6), which is named after its inventor, G. N. Ramachandran.

Most areas of the Ramachandran diagram (most combinations of ϕ and
ψ) represent forbidden conformations of a polypeptide chain. Only three
small regions of the diagram are physically accessible to most residues. The
observed ϕ and ψ values of accurately determined structures nearly always
fall within these allowed regions of the Ramachandran plot. There are,
however, some notable exceptions:

1. The cyclic side chain of Pro limits its range of ϕ values to angles of
   around $-60°$, making it, not surprisingly, the most conformationally
   restricted amino acid residue.

2. Gly, the only residue without a C_β atom, is much less sterically hin-
   dered than the other amino acid residues. Hence, its permissible
   range of ϕ and ψ covers a larger area of the Ramachandran diagram.
   At Gly residues, polypeptide chains often assume conformations that
   are forbidden to other residues.

B | The Most Common Regular Secondary Structures Are the α Helix and the β Sheet

A few elements of protein secondary structure are so widespread that they
are immediately recognizable in proteins with widely differing amino acid
sequences. Both the **α helix** and the **β sheet** are such elements; they are
called **regular secondary structures** because they are composed of sequences of residues with repeating ϕ and ψ values.

The α Helix Is a Coil. Only one polypeptide helix has both a favorable
hydrogen bonding pattern and ϕ and ψ values that fall within the fully allowed regions of the Ramachandran diagram: the α helix. Its discovery by

See Guided Exploration 6
Stable helices in proteins: the α helix.

BOX 6-1 **PATHWAYS OF DISCOVERY**

Linus Pauling and Structural Biochemistry

(Linus Pauling, 1901–1994)

Linus Pauling, the only person to have been awarded two unshared Nobel prizes, is clearly the dominant figure in twentieth-century chemistry and one of the greatest scientific figures of all time. He received his B.Sc. in chemical engineering from Oregon Agricultural College (now Oregon State University) in 1922 and his Ph.D. in chemistry from the California Institute of Technology in 1925, where he spent most of his career.

The major theme throughout Pauling's long scientific life was the study of molecular structures and the nature of the chemical bond. He began this career by using the then recently invented technique of X-ray crystallography to determine the structures of simple minerals and inorganic salts. At that time, methods for solving the phase problem (Box 7-2) were unknown, so X-ray structures could only be determined using trial-and-error techniques. This limited the possible molecules that could be effectively studied to those with few atoms and high symmetry such that their atomic coordinates could be fully described by only a few parameters (rather than the three-dimensional coordinates of each of its atoms). Pauling realized that the positions of atoms in molecules were governed by fixed atomic radii, bond distances, and bond angles and used this information to make educated guesses about molecular structures. This greatly extended the complexity of the molecules whose structures could be determined.

In his next major contribution, occurring in 1931, Pauling revolutionized the way that chemists viewed molecules by applying the then infant field of quantum mechanics to chemistry. Pauling formulated the theories of orbital hybridization, electron-pair bonding, and resonance and thereby explained the nature of covalent bonds. This work was summarized in his highly influential monograph, *The Nature of the Chemical Bond*, which was first published in 1938.

In the mid-1930s, Pauling turned his attention to biological chemistry. He began these studies in collaboration with his colleague, Robert Corey, by determining the X-ray structures of several amino acids and dipeptides. At that time, the X-ray structural determination of even such small molecules required around a year of intense effort, largely because the numerous calculations required to solve a structure had to be made by hand (electronic computers had yet to be invented). Nevertheless, these studies led Pauling and Corey to the conclusions that the peptide bond is planar, which Pauling explained from resonance considerations (Section 6-1A), and that hydrogen bonding plays a central role in maintaining macromolecular structures.

In the 1940s, Pauling made several unsuccessful attempts to determine whether polypeptides have any preferred conformations. Then, in 1948, while visiting Oxford University, he was confined to bed by a cold. He eventually tired of reading detective stories and science fiction and again turned his attention to proteins. By folding drawings of polypeptides in various ways, he discovered the α helix, whose existence was rapidly confirmed by X-ray studies of α

keratin (Section 6-1C). This work was reported in 1951, and later that year Pauling and Corey also proposed both the parallel and antiparallel β pleated sheets. For these ground-breaking insights, Pauling received the Nobel Prize in Chemistry in 1954, although α helices and β sheets were not actually visualized until the first X-ray structures of proteins were determined, five to ten years later.

Pauling made numerous additional pioneering contributions to biological chemistry, most notably that the heme group in hemoglobin changes its electronic state on binding oxygen (Section 7-1A), that vertebrate hemoglobins are $\alpha_2\beta_2$ heterotetramers (Section 7-1B), that the denaturation of proteins is caused by the unfolding of their polypeptide chains, that sickle-cell anemia is caused by a mutation in the β chain of normal adult hemoglobin (the first so-called molecular disease to be characterized; Section 7-1E), that molecular complementarity plays an important role in antibody–antigen interactions (Section 7-3B) and by extension all macromolecular interactions, that enzymes catalyze reactions by preferentially binding their transition states (Section 11-3E), and that the comparison of the sequences of the corresponding proteins in different organisms yields evolutionary insights (Section 5-4).

Pauling was also a lively and stimulating lecturer who for many years taught a general chemistry course [which one of the authors of this textbook (DV) had the privilege of taking]. His textbook *General Chemistry*, revolutionized the way that introductory chemistry was taught by presenting it as a subject that could be understood in terms of atomic physics and molecular structure. For a book of such generality, an astounding portion of its subject matter had been elucidated by its author. Pauling's amazing grasp of chemistry was demonstrated by the fact that he dictated each chapter of the textbook in a single sitting.

By the late 1940s, Pauling became convinced that the possibility of nuclear war posed an enormous danger to humanity and calculated that the radioactive fallout from each aboveground test of a nuclear bomb would ultimately cause cancer in thousands of people. He therefore began a campaign to educate the public about the hazards of bomb testing and nuclear war. The political climate in the United States at the time was such that the government considered Pauling to be subversive and his passport was revoked (and only returned two weeks before he was to leave for Sweden to receive his first Nobel prize). Nevertheless, Pauling persisted in this campaign, which culminated, in 1962, with the signing of the first Nuclear Test Ban Treaty. For his efforts, Pauling was awarded the 1962 Nobel Peace Prize.

Pauling saw science as the search for the truth, which included politics and social causes. In his later years, he became a vociferous promoter of what he called orthomolecular medicine, the notion that large doses of vitamins could ward off and cure many human diseases, including cancer. In the best known manifestation of this concept, Pauling advocated taking large doses of vitamin C to prevent the common cold and lessen its symptoms, advice still followed by millions of people, although the medical evidence supporting this notion is scant. It should be noted, however, that Pauling, who followed his own advice, remained active until he died in 1994 at the age of 93.

Linus Pauling in 1951, through model building, ranks as one of the land-marks of structural biochemistry (Box 6-1).

The α helix (Fig. 6-7) is right-handed; that is, it turns in the direction that the fingers of a right hand curl when its thumb points in the direction that the helix rises (Fig. 3-7). The α helix has 3.6 residues per turn and a **pitch** (the distance the helix rises along its axis per turn) of 5.4 Å. The α helices of proteins have an average length of ~12 residues, which corresponds to over three helical turns, and a length of ~18 Å.

In the α helix, the backbone hydrogen bonds are arranged such that the peptide C=O bond of the nth residue points along the helix axis toward the peptide N—H group of the (n + 4)th residue. This results in a strong

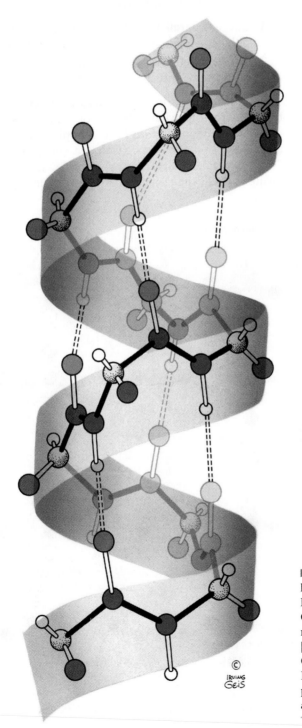

■ **Figure 6-7** | **The α helix.** This right-handed helical conformation has 3.6 residues per turn. Dashed lines indicate hydrogen bonds between C=O groups and N—H groups that are four residues farther along the polypeptide chain. [Illustration, Irving Geis. Image from the Irving Geis Collection/Howard Hughes Medical Institute. Rights owned by HHMI. Reproduction by permission only.] ✑ **See Kinemage Exercise 3-2 and the Animated Figures.**

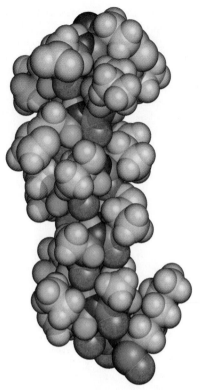

■ **Figure 6-8** | **Space-filling model of an α helix.** The backbone atoms are colored according to type with C green, N blue, O red, and H cyan. The side chains (*gold*) project away from the helix. This α helix is a segment of sperm whale myoglobin. [Based on an X-ray structure by Ilme Schlichting, Max Planck Institut für Molekulare Physiologie, Dortmund, Germany. PDBid 1A6M (for the definition of "PDBid" see Section 6-2E).]

> **See Guided Exploration 7**
> Hydrogen bonding in β sheets.

■ **Figure 6-9** | **β Sheets.** Dashed lines indicate hydrogen bonds between polypeptide strands. Side chains are omitted for clarity. (*a*) An antiparallel β sheet. (*b*) A parallel β sheet. [Illustration, Irving Geis. Image from the Irving Geis Collection/ Howard Hughes Medical Institute. Rights owned by HHMI. Reproduction by permission only.]
🖎 **See Kinemage Exercise 3-3 and the Animated Figures.**

hydrogen bond that has the nearly optimum N···O distance of 2.8 Å. Amino acid side chains project outward and downward from the helix (Fig. 6-8), thereby avoiding steric interference with the polypeptide backbone and with each other. The core of the helix is tightly packed; that is, its atoms are in van der Waals contact.

β Sheets Are Formed from Extended Chains. In 1951, the same year Pauling proposed the α helix, Pauling and Corey postulated the existence of a different polypeptide secondary structure, the β sheet. Like the α helix, the β sheet uses the full hydrogen-bonding capacity of the polypeptide backbone. *In β sheets, however, hydrogen bonding occurs between neighboring polypeptide chains rather than within one* as in an α helix.

Sheets come in two varieties:

1. The **antiparallel β sheet,** in which neighboring hydrogen-bonded polypeptide chains run in opposite directions (Fig. 6-9*a*).

2. The **parallel β sheet,** in which the hydrogen-bonded chains extend in the same direction (Fig. 6-9*b*).

The conformations in which these β structures are optimally hydrogen bonded vary somewhat from that of the fully extended polypeptide shown in Fig. 6-3. They therefore have a rippled or pleated edge-on appearance (Fig. 6-10) and for that reason are sometimes called "pleated sheets." Successive side chains of a polypeptide chain in a β sheet extend to opposite sides of the sheet with a two-residue repeat distance of 7.0 Å.

(*a*) **Antiparallel**

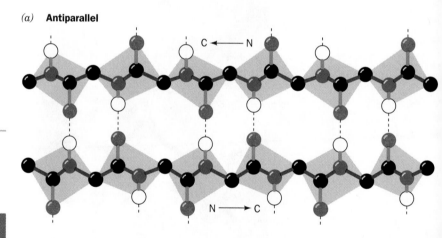

(*b*) **Parallel**

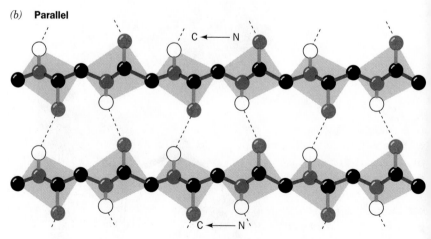

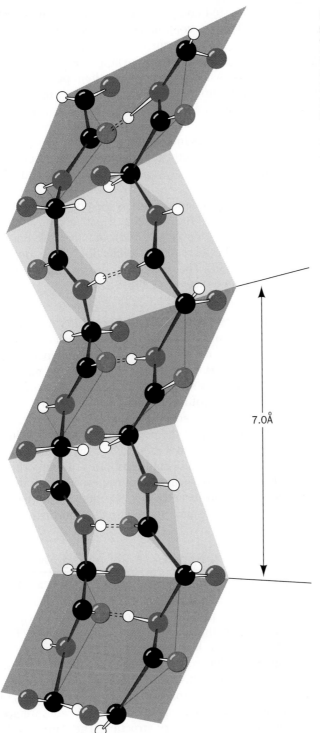

7.0Å

■ **Figure 6-10 | Pleated appearance of a β sheet.** Dashed lines indicate hydrogen bonds. The R groups (*purple*) on each polypeptide chain alternately extend to opposite sides of the sheet and are in register on adjacent chains. [Illustration, Irving Geis. Image from the Irving Geis Collection/ Howard Hughes Medical Institute. Rights owned by HHMI. Reproduction by permission only.] ♒ **See Kinemage Exercise 3-3.**

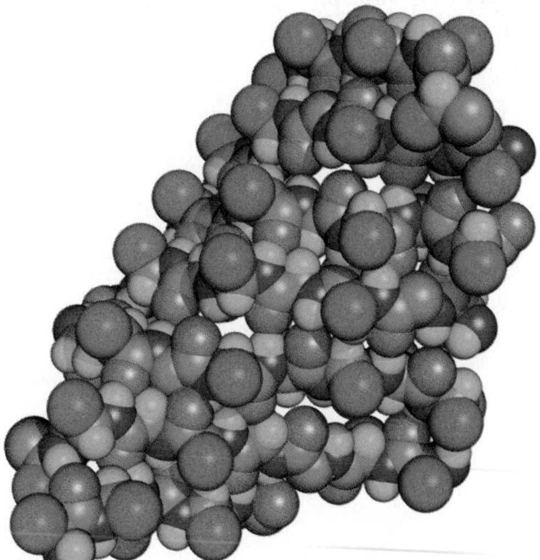

■ **Figure 6-11 | Space-filling model of a β sheet.** The backbone atoms are colored according to type with C green, N blue, O red, and H cyan. The R groups are represented by large magenta spheres. This seven-stranded antiparallel β sheet, which is shown with its polypeptide strands approximately horizontal, is from the jack bean protein **concanavalin A.** [Based on an X-ray structure by Gerald Edelman, The Rockefeller University. PDBid 2CNA.] ♒ **See Kinemage Exercise 3-3.**

β Sheets in proteins contain 2 to as many as 22 polypeptide strands, with an average of 6 strands. Each strand may contain up to 15 residues, the average being 6 residues. A seven-stranded antiparallel β sheet is shown in Fig. 6-11.

Parallel β sheets containing fewer than five strands are rare. This observation suggests that parallel β sheets are less stable than antiparallel β sheets, possibly because the hydrogen bonds of parallel sheets are

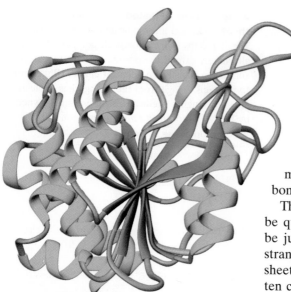

■ **Figure 6-12** | **X-Ray structure of bovine carboxypeptidase A.** The polypeptide backbone is drawn in ribbon form with α helices depicted as cyan coils, the strands of the β sheet represented by green arrows pointing toward the C-terminus, and its remaining portions portrayed by orange worms. Side chains are not shown. The eight-stranded β sheet forms a saddle-shaped curved surface with a right-handed twist. [Based on an X-ray structure by William Lipscomb, Harvard University. PDBid 3CPA.]

distorted compared to those of the antiparallel sheets (Fig. 6-9) β Sheets containing mixtures of parallel and antiparallel strand frequently occur.

β Sheets almost invariably exhibit a pronounced right-hande twist when viewed along their polypeptide strands (Fig. 6-12) Conformational energy calculations indicate that the twist is a consequence of interactions between chiral L-amino acid residue in the extended polypeptide chains. The twist distorts and weaken the β sheet's interchain hydrogen bonds. The geometry of a partic ular β sheet is thus a compromise between optimizing the confor mational energies of its polypeptide chains and preserving its hydroge bonding.

The **topology** (connectivity) of the polypeptide strands in a β sheet ca be quite complex. The connection between two antiparallel strands ma be just a small loop (Fig. 6-13a), but the link between tandem paralle strands must be a crossover connection that is out of the plane of the β sheet (Fig. 6-13b). The connecting link in either case can be extensive, of ten containing helices (e.g., Fig. 6-12).

Turns Connect Some Units of Secondary Structure. Polypeptide seg ments with regular secondary structure such as α helices or the strands o β sheets are often joined by stretches of polypeptide that abruptly change direction. Such **reverse turns** or **β bends** (so named because they ofte connect successive strands of antiparallel β sheets; Fig. 6-13a) almost al ways occur at protein surfaces. They usually involve four successive amino acid residues arranged in one of two ways, Type I and Type II, tha differ by a 180° flip of the peptide unit linking residues 2 and 3 (Fig. 6-14) Both types of turns are stabilized by a hydrogen bond, although deviations from these ideal conformations often disrupt this hydrogen bond. In Type II turns, the oxygen atom of residue 2 crowds the C_β atom of residue 3 which is therefore usually Gly. Residue 2 of either type of turn is often Pro since it can assume the required conformation.

C | Fibrous Proteins Have Repeating Secondary Structures

Proteins have historically been classified as either **fibrous** or **globular,** de pending on their overall morphology. This dichotomy predates methods for determining protein structure on an atomic scale and does not do jus tice to proteins that contain both stiff, elongated, fibrous regions as wel as more compact, highly folded, globular regions. Nevertheless, the divi sion helps emphasize the properties of fibrous proteins, which often have a protective, connective, or supportive role in living organisms. The two well-characterized fibrous proteins we discuss here—keratin and collagen—are highly elongated molecules whose shapes are dominated by a single type of secondary structure. They are therefore useful examples of these structural elements.

α Keratin Is a Coiled Coil. **Keratin** is a mechanically durable and rela tively unreactive protein that occurs in all higher vertebrates. It is the prin cipal component of their horny outer epidermal layer and its related appendages such as hair, horn, nails, and feathers. Keratins have been clas sified as either α keratins, which occur in mammals, or β keratins, which occur in birds and reptiles. Humans have over 50 keratin genes that are expressed in a tissue-specific manner.

(a)   *(b)*

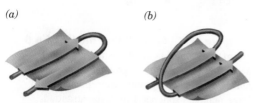

■ **Figure 6-13** | **Connections between adjacent strands in β sheets.** (a) Antiparallel strands may be connected by a small loop. (b) Parallel strands require a more extensive crossover connection. [After Richardson, J.S., *Adv. Protein Chem.* **34,** 196 (1981).]

(a) **Type I**   (b) **Type II**

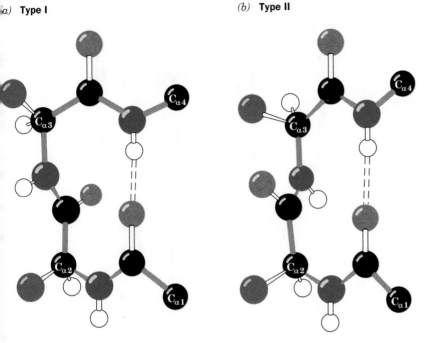

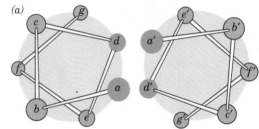

■ **Figure 6-14** | **Reverse turns in polypeptide chains.** Dashed lines represent hydrogen bonds. (*a*) Type I. (*b*) Type II. [Illustration, Irving Geis. Image from the Irving Geis Collection/Howard Hughes Medical Institute. Rights owned by HHMI. Reproduction by permission only.]
🔎 **See Kinemage Exercise 3-4.**

The X-ray diffraction pattern of α keratin resembles that expected for an α helix (hence the name α keratin). However, α keratin exhibits a 5.1-Å spacing rather than the 5.4-Å distance corresponding to the pitch of the α helix. This discrepancy is the result of *two α keratin polypeptides, each of which forms an α helix, twisting around each other to form a left-handed coil.* The normal 5.4-Å repeat distance of each α helix in the pair is thereby tilted relative to the axis of this assembly, yielding the observed 5.1-Å spacing. The assembly is said to have a **coiled coil** structure because each α helix itself follows a helical path.

The conformation of α keratin's coiled coil is a consequence of its primary structure: The central ~310-residue segment of each polypeptide chain has a 7-residue pseudorepeat, *a-b-c-d-e-f-g*, with nonpolar residues predominating at positions *a* and *d*. Since an α helix has 3.6 residues per turn, α keratin's *a* and *d* residues line up along one side of each α helix (Fig. 6-15a). The hydrophobic strip along one helix associates with the hydrophobic strip on another helix. Because the 3.5-residue repeat in α keratin is slightly smaller than the 3.6 residues per turn of a standard α helix, the two keratin helices are inclined about 18° relative to one another, resulting in the coiled coil arrangement (Fig. 6-15b). Coiled coils also occur in numerous other proteins, some of which are globular rather than fibrous.

The higher order structure of α keratin is not well understood. The N- and C-terminal domains of each polypeptide facilitate the assembly of

■ **Figure 6-15** | **A coiled coil.** (*a*) View down the coil axis showing the alignment of nonpolar residues along one side of each α helix. The helices have the pseudo-repeating sequence *a-b-c-d-e-f-g* in which residues *a* and *d* are predominately nonpolar. [After McLachlan, A.D. and Stewart, M., *J. Mol. Biol.* **98**, 295 (1975).] (*b*) Side view of the polypeptide backbones in stick form (*left*) and of the entire polypeptides in space-filling form (*right*). The atoms are colored according to type with C green in one chain and cyan in the other, N blue, O red, and S yellow. The 81-residue chains are parallel with their N-terminal ends above. Note that in the space-filling model the side chains of the two polypeptides contact each other. This coiled coil is a portion of the muscle protein tropomyosin (Section 7-2A). [Based on an X-ray structure by Carolyn Cohen, Brandeis University. PDBid 1IC2.] 🔎 **See Kinemage Exercises 4-1 and 4-2.**

(a)

(b)

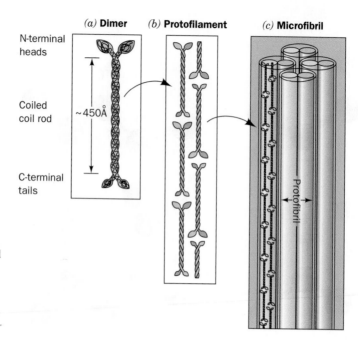

(a) **Dimer**   *(b)* **Protofilament**   *(c)* **Microfibril**

N-terminal heads

Coiled coil rod   ~450Å

C-terminal tails

Protofibril

■ **Figure 6-16 | Higher order α keratin structure.** (*a*) Two keratin polypeptides form a dimeric coiled coil. (*b*) Protofilaments are formed from two staggered rows of head-to-tail associated coiled coils. (*c*) Protofilaments dimerize to form a protofibril, four of which form a microfibril. The structures of the latter assemblies are poorly characterized.

coiled coils (dimers) into protofilaments, two of which constitute a protofibril (Fig. 6-16). Four protofibrils constitute a microfibril, which associates with other microfibrils to form a macrofibril. A single mammalian hair consists of layers of dead cells, each of which is packed with parallel macrofibrils.

α Keratin is rich in Cys residues, which form disulfide bonds that crosslink adjacent polypeptide chains. The α keratins are classified as "hard" or "soft" according to whether they have a high or low sulfur content. Hard keratins, such as those of hair, horn, and nail, are less pliable than soft keratins, such as those of skin and callus, because the disulfide bonds resist deformation. The disulfide bonds can be reductively cleaved by disulfide interchange with mercaptans (Section 5-3A). Hair so treated can be curled and set in a "permanent wave" by applying an oxidizing agent that reestablishes the disulfide bonds in the new "curled" conformation. Conversely, curly hair can be straightened by the same process.

The springiness of hair and wool fibers is a consequence of the coiled coil's tendency to recover its original conformation after being untwisted by stretching. If some of its disulfide bonds have been cleaved, however, an α keratin fiber can be stretched to over twice its original length. At this point, the polypeptide chains assume a β sheet conformation. β Keratin, such as that in feathers, exhibits a β-like pattern in its native state.

Collagen Is a Triple Helix. **Collagen,** which occurs in all multicellular animals, is the most abundant vertebrate protein. Its strong, insoluble fibers are the major stress-bearing components of connective tissues such as bone, teeth, cartilage, tendon, and the fibrous matrices of skin and blood vessels. A single collagen molecule consists of three polypeptide chains. Mammals have at least 33 genetically distinct chains that are assembled into at least 20 collagen varieties found in different tissues in the same individual. One of the most common collagens, called Type I, consists of two $\alpha_1(I)$ chains and one $\alpha_2(I)$ chain. It has a molecular mass of ~285 kD, a width of ~14 Å, and a length of ~3000 Å.

Collagen has a distinctive amino acid composition: Nearly one-third of its residues are Gly; another 15 to 30% of its residues are Pro and

4-hydroxyprolyl (Hyp). 3-Hydroxyprolyl and 5-hydroxylysyl (Hyl) residues also occur in collagen, but in smaller amounts.

4-Hydroxyprolyl residue (Hyp) **3-Hydroxyprolyl residue** **5-Hydroxylysyl residue (Hyl)**

These nonstandard residues are formed after the collagen polypeptides are synthesized. For example, Pro residues are converted to Hyp in a reaction catalyzed by **prolyl hydroxylase.** This enzyme requires **ascorbic acid (vitamin C)** to maintain its activity.

Ascorbic acid (vitamin C)

The disease **scurvy** results from the dietary deficiency of vitamin C (Box 6-2).

The amino acid sequence of a typical collagen polypeptide consists of monotonously repeating triplets of sequence Gly-X-Y over a segment of

BOX 6-2 BIOCHEMISTRY IN HEALTH AND DISEASE

Collagen Diseases

Some collagen diseases have dietary causes. In scurvy (caused by vitamin C deficiency), Hyp production decreases because prolyl hydroxylase requires vitamin C. Thus, in the absence of vitamin C, newly synthesized collagen cannot form fibers properly, resulting in skin lesions, fragile blood vessels, poor wound healing, and, ultimately, death. Scurvy was common in sailors whose diets were devoid of fresh foods on long voyages. The introduction of limes to the diet of the British navy by the renowned explorer Captain James Cook alleviated scurvy and led to the nickname "limey" for the British sailor.

The disease **lathyrism** is caused by regular ingestion of the seeds from the sweet pea *Lathyrus odoratus,* which contain a compound that specifically inactivates lysyl oxidase (see below). The resulting reduced cross-linking of collagen fibers produces serious abnormalities of the bones, joints, and large blood vessels.

Several rare heritable disorders of collagen are known. Mutations of Type I collagen, which constitutes the major structural protein in most human tissues, usually result in **osteogenesis imperfecta** (brittle bone disease). The severity of this disease varies

with the nature and position of the mutation: Even a single amino acid change can have lethal consequences. For example, the central Gly → Ala substitution in the model polypeptide shown in Fig. 6-18 locally distorts the already internally crowded collagen helix. This ruptures the hydrogen bond from the backbone N—H of each Ala (normally Gly) to the carbonyl group of the adjacent Pro in a neighboring chain, thereby reducing the stability of the collagen structure. Mutations may affect the structure of the collagen molecule or how it forms fibrils. These mutations tend to be dominant because they affect either the folding of the triple helix or fibril formation even when normal chains are also involved.

Many collagen disorders are characterized by deficiencies in the amount of a particular collagen type synthesized, or by abnormal activities of collagen-processing enzymes such as lysyl hydroxylase and lysyl oxidase. One group of at least 10 different collagen-deficiency diseases, the **Ehlers–Danlos syndromes,** are all characterized by the hyperextensibility of the joints and skin. The "India-rubber man" of circus fame had an Ehlers–Danlos syndrome.

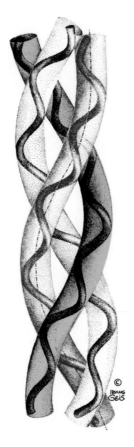

■ **Figure 6-17** | **The collagen triple helix.** Left-handed polypeptide helices are twisted together to form a right-handed superhelical structure. [Illustration, Irving Geis. Image from the Irving Geis Collection/Howard Hughes Medical Institute. Rights owned by HHMI. Reproduction by permission only.]

~1000 residues, where X is often Pro and Y is often Hyp. Hy[sometimes appears at the Y position. Collagen's Pro residues prevent i[from forming an α helix (Pro residues cannot assume the α-helical back[bone conformation and lack the backbone N—H groups that form the intrahelical hydrogen bonds shown in Fig. 6-7). Instead, *the collagen polypeptide assumes a left-handed helical conformation with about three residues per turn. Three parallel chains wind around each other with a gentle, right-handed, ropelike twist to form the triple-helical structure of a collagen molecule* (Fig. 6-17).

This model of the collagen structure has been confirmed by Barbara Brodsky and Helen Berman, who determined the X-ray crystal structure of a collagen-like model polypeptide. Every third residue of each polypeptide chain passes through the center of the triple helix, which is so crowded that only a Gly side chain can fit there. This crowding explains the absolute requirement for a Gly at every third position of a collagen polypeptide chain. The three polypeptide chains are staggered so that a Gly, X, and Y residue occurs at each level along the triple helix axis (Fig. 6-18a). The peptide groups are oriented such that the N—H of each Gly makes a strong hydrogen bond with the carbonyl oxygen of an X (Pro) residue on a neighboring chain (Fig. 6-18b). The bulky and relatively inflexible Pro and Hyp residues confer rigidity on the entire assembly.

■ **Figure 6-18** | **Structure of a collagen model peptide.** In this X-ray structure of (Pro-Hyp-Gly)$_{10}$, the fifth Gly of each peptide has been replaced by Ala. (*a*) A stick model of the middle portion of the triple helix oriented with its N-termini at the bottom. The C atoms of the three chains are colored orange, magenta, and gray. The N and O atoms on all chains are blue and red. Note how the replacement of Gly with the bulkier Ala (C atoms green) distorts the triple helix. (*b*) This view from the N-terminus down the helix axis shows the interchain hydrogen-bonding associations. Three consecutive residues from each chain are shown in stick form (C atoms green). Hydrogen bonds are represented by dashed lines from Gly N atoms to Pro O atoms in adjacent chains. Dots represent the van der Waals surfaces of the backbone atoms of the central residue in each chain. Note the close packing of the atoms along the triple helix axis. [Based on an X-ray structure by Helen Berman, Rutgers University, and Barbara Brodsky, UMDNJ–Robert Wood Johnson Medical School. PDBid 1CAG.]

🖙 **See Kinemage Exercises 4-3 and 4-4.**

(a) *(b)*

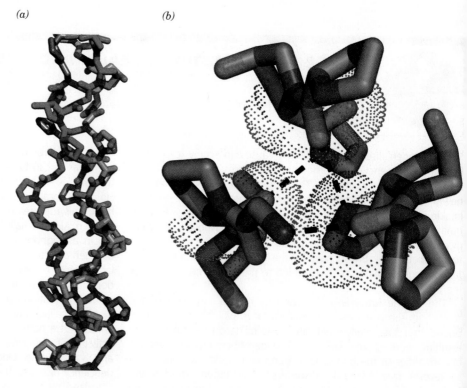

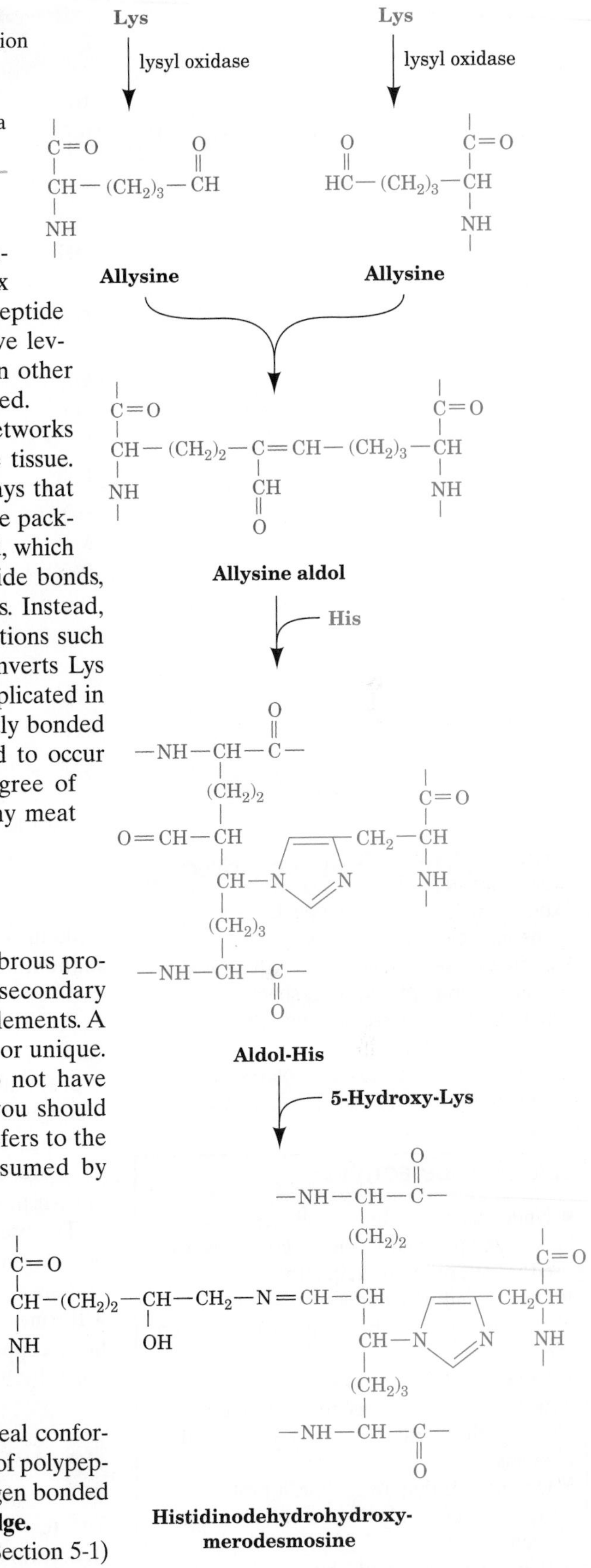

■ **Figure 6-19 | A reaction pathway for cross-linking side chains in collagen.** The first step is the lysyl oxidase–catalyzed oxidative deamination of Lys to form the aldehyde allysine. Two allysines then undergo an aldol condensation to form allysine aldol. This product can react with His to form aldol histidine, which can in turn react with 5-hydroxylysine to form a Schiff base (an imine bond), thereby cross-linking four side chains.

Collagen's well-packed, rigid, triple-helical structure is responsible for its characteristic tensile strength. The twist in the helix cannot be pulled out under tension because its component polypeptide chains are twisted in the opposite direction (Fig. 6-17). Successive levels of fiber bundles in high-quality ropes and cables, as well as in other proteins such as keratin (Fig. 6-16), are likewise oppositely twisted.

Several types of collagen molecules assemble to form loose networks or thick fibrils arranged in bundles or sheets, depending on the tissue. The collagen molecules in fibrils are organized in staggered arrays that are stabilized by hydrophobic interactions resulting from the close packing of triple-helical units. Collagen is also covalently cross-linked, which accounts for its poor solubility. The cross-links cannot be disulfide bonds, as in keratin, because collagen is almost devoid of Cys residues. Instead, the cross-links are derived from Lys and His side chains in reactions such as those shown in Fig. 6-19. **Lysyl oxidase,** the enzyme that converts Lys residues to those of the aldehyde **allysine,** is the only enzyme implicated in this cross-linking process. Up to four side chains can be covalently bonded to each other. The cross-links do not form at random but tend to occur near the N- and C-termini of the collagen molecules. The degree of cross-linking in a particular tissue increases with age. This is why meat from older animals is tougher than meat from younger animals.

D | Most Proteins Include Nonrepetitive Structure

The majority of proteins are globular proteins that, unlike the fibrous proteins discussed above, may contain several types of regular secondary structure, including α helices, β sheets, and other recognizable elements. A significant portion of a protein's structure may also be irregular or unique. Segments of polypeptide chains whose successive residues do not have similar ϕ and ψ values are sometimes called coils. However, you should not confuse this term with the appellation **random coil,** which refers to the totally disordered and rapidly fluctuating conformations assumed by **denatured** (fully unfolded) proteins in solution. In **native** (folded) proteins, *nonrepetitive structures are no less ordered than are helices or β sheets; they are simply irregular and hence more difficult to describe.*

Sequence Affects Secondary Structure. *Variations in amino acid sequence as well as the overall structure of the folded protein can distort the regular conformations of secondary structural elements.* For example, the α helix frequently deviates from its ideal conformation in the initial and final turns of the helix. Similarly, a strand of polypeptide in a β sheet may contain an "extra" residue that is not hydrogen bonded to a neighboring strand, producing a distortion known as a **β bulge.**

Many of the limits on amino acid composition and sequence (Section 5-1) may be due in part to conformational constraints in the three-dimensional structure of proteins. For example, a Pro residue produces a

Lys — lysyl oxidase → Allysine; Lys — lysyl oxidase → Allysine

Two Allysines → Allysine aldol

Allysine aldol — His → **Aldol-His**

Aldol-His — 5-Hydroxy-Lys → **Histidinodehydrohydroxy-merodesmosine**

Table 6-1	Propensities of Amino Acid Residues for α Helical and β Sheet Conformations	
Residue	P_α	P_β
Ala	1.42	0.83
Arg	0.98	0.93
Asn	0.67	0.89
Asp	1.01	0.54
Cys	0.70	1.19
Gln	1.11	1.10
Glu	1.51	0.37
Gly	0.57	0.75
His	1.00	0.87
Ile	1.08	1.60
Leu	1.21	1.30
Lys	1.16	0.74
Met	1.45	1.05
Phe	1.13	1.38
Pro	0.57	0.55
Ser	0.77	0.75
Thr	0.83	1.19
Trp	1.08	1.37
Tyr	0.69	1.47
Val	1.06	1.70

Source: Chou, P.Y. and Fasman, G.D., *Annu. Rev. Biochem.* **47,** 258 (1978).

■ **CHECK YOUR UNDERSTANDING**

Explain why the conformational freedom of peptide bonds is limited.

Summarize the features of an α helix and a parallel and antiparallel β sheet.

What distinguishes regular and irregular secondary structure?

What properties do fibrous proteins confer on substances such as hair and bones?

LEARNING OBJECTIVES

■ Understand how the techniques of X-ray crystallography and NMR spectroscopy are used to determine protein structure.

■ Understand why nonpolar residues occur in the protein interior and polar residues on the exterior.

■ Understand that a protein's tertiary structure consists of secondary structural elements that combine to form motifs and domains.

■ Understand that, over time, a protein's structure is more highly conserved than its sequence.

■ Become familiar with the type of information that is available from bioinformatics databases and programs.

kink in an α helix or β sheet. Similarly, steric clashes between several sequential amino acid residues with large branched side chains (e.g., Ile and Tyr) can destabilize α helices.

Analysis of known protein structures by Peter Chou and Gerald Fasman revealed the propensity P of a residue to occur in an α helix or a β sheet (Table 6-1). Chou and Fasman also discovered that certain residues not only have a high propensity for a particular secondary structure but they tend to disrupt or break other secondary structures. Such data are useful for predicting the secondary structures of proteins with known amino acid sequences.

The presence of certain residues outside of α helices or β sheets may also be nonrandom. For example, α helices are often flanked by residues such as Asn and Gln, whose side chains can fold back to form hydrogen bonds with one of the four terminal residues of the helix, a phenomenon termed **helix capping.** Recall that the four residues at each end of an α helix are not fully hydrogen bonded to neighboring backbone segments (Fig. 6-7).

2 Tertiary Structure

The tertiary structure of a protein describes the folding of its secondary structural elements and specifies the positions of each atom in the protein, including its side chains. This information is deposited in a database and is readily available via the Internet, which allows the tertiary structures of a variety of proteins to be analyzed and compared. The common

(a)   *(b)*   *(c)*

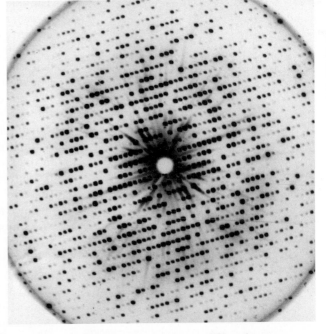

(d)   *(e)*   *(f)*

■ **Figure 6-20** | **Protein crystals.** (*a*) Azurin from *Pseudomonas aeruginosa*, (*b*) flavodoxin from *Desulfovibrio vulgaris*, (*c*) rubredoxin from *Clostridium pasteurianum*, (*d*) azidomet myohemerythrin from the marine worm *Siphonosoma funafuti*, (*e*) lamprey hemoglobin, and (*f*) bacteriochlorophyll *a* protein from *Prosthecochloris aestuarii*. These crystals are colored because the proteins contain light-absorbing groups; proteins are colorless in the absence of such groups. [Parts *a–c* courtesy of Larry Siecker, University of Washington; Parts *d* and *e* courtesy of Wayne Hendrikson, Columbia University; and Part *f* courtesy of John Olsen, Brookhaven National Laboratories, and Brian Matthews, University of Oregon.]

features of protein tertiary structures reveal much about the biological functions of proteins and their evolutionary origins.

A | Most Protein Structures Are Determined by X-Ray Crystallography or Nuclear Magnetic Resonance

X-Ray crystallography is a technique that directly images molecules. X-Rays must be used to do so because, according to optical principles, the uncertainty in locating an object is approximately equal to the wavelength of the radiation used to observe it (covalent bond distances and the wavelengths of the X-rays used in structural studies are both ~1.5 Å; individual molecules cannot be seen in a light microscope because visible light has a minimum wavelength of 4000 Å). There is, however, no such thing as an X-ray microscope because there are no X-ray lenses. Rather, a crystal of the molecule to be imaged (e.g., Fig. 6-20) is exposed to a collimated beam of X-rays and the resulting **diffraction pattern,** which arises from the regularly repeating positions of atoms in the crystal, is recorded by a radiation detector or, now infrequently, on photographic film (Fig. 6-21). The X-rays used in structural studies are produced by laboratory X-ray generators or, now commonly, by **synchrotrons,** particle accelerators that produce X-rays of far greater intensity. The intensities of the diffraction maxima (darkness of the spots on a film) are then used to construct mathematically the three-dimensional image of the crystal structure through methods that are beyond the scope of this text. In what follows, we discuss some of the special problems associated with interpreting the X-ray crystal structures of proteins.

X-Rays interact almost exclusively with the electrons in matter, not the nuclei. An X-ray structure is therefore an image of the **electron density** of the object under study. Such **electron density maps** are usually presented with the aid of computer graphics as one or more sets of **contours,** in

■ **Figure 6-21** | **An X-ray diffraction photograph of a crystal of sperm whale myoglobin.** The intensity of each diffraction maximum (the darkness of each spot) is a function of the crystal's electron density. [Courtesy of John Kendrew, Cambridge University, U.K.]

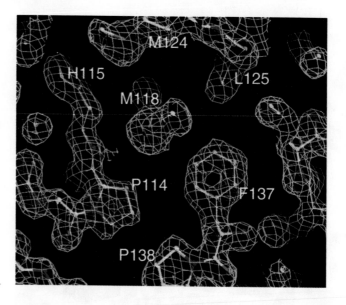

■ **Figure 6-22** | **A thin section through a 1.5-Å-resolution electron density map of a protein that is contoured in three dimensions.** Only a single contour level (*cyan*) is shown, together with a ball-and-stick model of the corresponding polypeptide segments colored according to atom type with C yellow, N blue, and O red. A water molecule is represented by a red sphere. [Courtesy of Xinhua Ji, NCI–Frederick Cancer Research and Development Center, Frederick, Maryland.]

which a contour represents a specific level of electron density in the same way that a contour on a topographic map indicates locations that have a particular altitude. A portion of an electron density map of a protein is shown in Fig. 6-22.

Most Protein Crystal Structures Exhibit Less Than Atomic Resolution. The molecules in protein crystals, as in other crystalline substances, are arranged in regularly repeating three-dimensional lattices. Protein crystals, however, differ from those of most small organic and inorganic molecules in being highly hydrated; they are typically 40 to 60% water by volume. The aqueous solvent of crystallization is necessary for the structural integrity of the protein crystals, because water is required for the structural integrity of native proteins themselves (Section 6-4).

The large solvent content of protein crystals gives them a soft, jellylike consistency so that their molecules usually lack the rigid order characteristic of crystals of small molecules such as NaCl or glycine. The molecules in a protein crystal are typically disordered by more than an angstrom, so the corresponding electron density map lacks information concerning structural details of smaller size. The crystal is therefore said to have a resolution limit of that size. Protein crystals typically have resolution limits in the range 1.5 to 3.0 Å, although some are better ordered (have higher resolution, that is, a lesser resolution limit) and many are less ordered (have lower resolution).

Since an electron density map of a protein must be interpreted in terms of its atomic positions, the accuracy and even the feasibility of a crystal structure analysis depends on the crystal's resolution limit. Indeed, the inability to obtain crystals of sufficiently high resolution is a major limiting factor in determining the X-ray crystal structure of a protein or other macromolecule. Figure 6-23 indicates how the quality (degree of focus) of an electron density map varies with its resolution limit. At 6-Å resolution, the presence of a molecule the size of diketopiperazine is difficult to discern. At 2.0-Å resolution, its individual atoms cannot yet be distinguished, although its molecular shape has become reasonably evident. At 1.5-Å resolution, which roughly corresponds to a bond distance, individual atoms become partially resolved. At 1.1-Å resolution, atoms are clearly visible.

Most protein crystal structures are too poorly resolved for their electron density maps to reveal clearly the positions of individual atoms (e.g.,

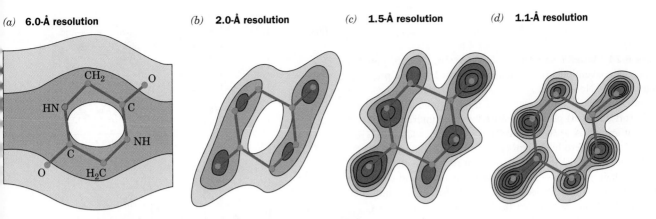

(a) **6.0-Å resolution**   *(b)* **2.0-Å resolution**   *(c)* **1.5-Å resolution**   *(d)* **1.1-Å resolution**

■ **Figure 6-23 | Electron density maps of diketopiperazine at different resolution levels.** Hydrogen atoms are not visible in these maps because of their low electron density. [After Hodgkin, D.C., *Nature* **188,** 445 (1960).]

Fig. 6-23). Nevertheless, the distinctive shape of the polypeptide backbone usually permits it to be traced, which, in turn, allows the positions and orientations of its side chains to be deduced (e.g., Fig. 6-22). Yet side chains of comparable size and shape, such as those of Leu, Ile, Thr, and Val, cannot always be differentiated (hydrogen atoms, having just one electron, are visible only if the resolution limit is less than ~1.2 Å). Consequently, a protein structure cannot be elucidated from its electron density map alone, but knowing the primary structure of the protein permits the sequence of amino acid residues to be fitted to the electron density map. Mathematical refinement can then reduce the uncertainty in the crystal structure's atomic positions to as little as 0.1 Å.

Most Crystalline Proteins Maintain Their Native Conformations. Does the structure of a protein in a crystal accurately reflect the structure of the protein in solution, where globular proteins normally function? Several lines of evidence indicate that *crystalline proteins assume very nearly the same structures that they have in solution:*

1. A protein molecule in a crystal is essentially in solution because it is bathed by solvent of crystallization over all of its surface except for the few, generally small patches that contact neighboring protein molecules.

2. In cases where different crystal forms of a protein have been analyzed, or when a crystal structure has been compared to a solution structure (determined by NMR; see below), the molecules have virtually identical conformations. Evidently, crystal packing forces do not greatly perturb the structures of protein molecules.

3. Many enzymes are catalytically active in the crystalline state. Since the activity of an enzyme is very sensitive to the positions of the groups involved in binding and catalysis (Chapter 11), the crystalline enzymes must have conformations that closely resemble their solution conformations.

Protein Structures Can Be Determined by NMR. The basis of **nuclear magnetic resonance (NMR)** is the observation that an atomic nucleus, such as a proton (a hydrogen nucleus), resonates in an applied magnetic field in a way that is sensitive to its electronic environment and its interactions with nearby nuclei. The development of NMR techniques, since the mid-1980s,

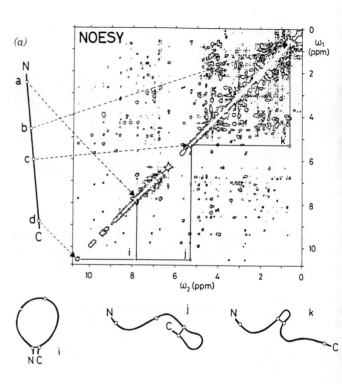

■ **Figure 6-24 | NOESY spectrum of a protein.** The diagonal represents the conventional one-dimensional NMR spectrum presented as a contour plot. Note that it is too crowded with peaks to be directly interpretable (even a small protein has hundreds of protons). The cross (off-diagonal) peaks each arise from the interaction of two protons that are <5 Å apart in space (their one-dimensional NMR peaks are located where horizontal and vertical lines intersect the diagonal). The line to the left of the spectrum represents the extended polypeptide chain with its N- and C-termini labeled N and C and the positions of four protons labeled a to d. The dashed arrows indicate the diagonal NMR peaks to which these protons give rise. Cross peaks, such as i, j, and k, each located at the intersection of the corresponding horizontal and vertical lines, show that two protons are <5 Å apart. These distance relationships are schematically drawn as three looped structures of the polypeptide chain below the spectrum. The assignment of a distance relationship between two protons in a polypeptide requires that the NMR peaks to which they give rise and their positions in the polypeptide be known, which requires that the polypeptide's amino acid sequence has been previously determined. [After Wüthrich, K., *Science* **243**, 45 (1989).]

in large part by Kurt Wüthrich, has made it possible to determine the three-dimensional structures of small globular proteins in aqueous solution.

A protein's conventional (one-dimensional) NMR spectrum is crowded with overlapping peaks, since even a small protein has hundreds of protons. This problem is addressed by **two-dimensional (2D) NMR spectroscopy,** which yields additional peaks arising from the interactions of protons that are less than 5 Å apart. Correlation spectroscopy (COSY) provides interatomic distances between protons that are covalently connected through one or two other atoms, such as the H atoms attached to the N and C_α of the same amino acid (corresponding to the ϕ torsion angle). Nuclear Overhauser spectroscopy (NOESY) provides interatomic distances for protons that are close in space although they may be far apart in the protein sequence. An example of a NOESY spectrum is shown in Fig. 6-24.

Interatomic distance measurements, along with knowledge of the protein's sequence and known geometric constraints such as covalent bond distances and angles, group planarity, chirality, and van der Waals radii, are used to compute the protein's three-dimensional structure. However, since interproton distance measurements are imprecise, they cannot imply a unique structure but rather are consistent with an ensemble of closely related structures. Consequently, an NMR structure of a protein (or another macromolecule) is often presented as a sample of structures that are consistent with the data (e.g., Figure 6-25). The "tightness" of a bundle of such structures is indicative both of the accuracy with which the structure is known, which in the most favorable cases is roughly comparable to that of an X-ray crystal structure with a resolution of 2 to 2.5 Å, and of the conformational fluctuations that the protein undergoes (Section 6-4A). Although present NMR methods are limited to determining the structures of macromolecules with molecular masses no greater than ~40 kD, recent advances in NMR technology suggest that this limit may soon increase to ~100 kD or more.

NMR methods, besides validating the structures of proteins analyzed by X-ray crystallography (or in some cases identifying protein residues that

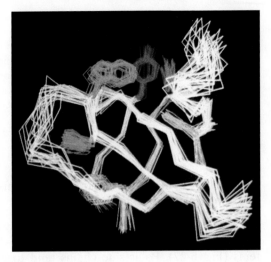

■ **Figure 6-25** | **The NMR structure of a protein.** The drawing represents 20 superimposed structures of a 64-residue polypeptide comprising the **Src protein SH3 domain** (Section 13-1B). The polypeptide backbone (its connected C_α atoms) is white, and its Phe, Tyr, and Trp side chains are yellow, red, and blue, respectively. The polypeptide backbone folds into two 3-stranded antiparallel β sheets that form a sandwich. [Courtesy of Stuart Schreiber, Harvard University.]

are perturbed by crystallization), can determine the structures of proteins and other macromolecules that fail to crystallize. Moreover, since NMR can probe motions over time scales spanning 10 orders of magnitude, it can also be used to study protein folding and dynamics (Section 6-5).

Proteins Can Be Depicted in Different Ways. The huge number of atoms in proteins makes it difficult to visualize them using the same sorts of models employed for small organic molecules. Ball-and-stick representations showing all or most atoms in a protein (as in Figs. 6-7 and 6-10) are exceedingly cluttered, and space-filling models (as in Figs. 6-8 and 6-11) obscure the internal details of the protein. Accordingly, computer-generated or artistic renditions (e.g., Fig. 6-12) are often more useful for representing protein structures. The course of the polypeptide chain can be followed by tracing the positions of its C_α atoms or by representing helices as helical ribbons or cylinders and β sheets as sets of flat arrows pointing from the N- to the C-termini.

B | Side Chain Location Varies with Polarity

In the years since Kendrew solved the structure of myoglobin, nearly 50,000 protein structures have been reported. No two are exactly alike, but they exhibit remarkable consistencies. The primary structures of globular proteins generally lack the repeating sequences that support the regular conformations seen in fibrous proteins. However, *the amino acid side chains in globular proteins are spatially distributed according to their polarities:*

1. The nonpolar residues Val, Leu, Ile, Met, and Phe occur mostly in the interior of a protein, out of contact with the aqueous solvent. The hydrophobic effects that promote this distribution are largely responsible for the three-dimensional structure of native proteins.

2. The charged polar residues Arg, His, Lys, Asp, and Glu are usually located on the surface of a protein in contact with the aqueous solvent. This is because immersing an ion in the virtually anhydrous interior of a protein is energetically unfavorable.

3. The uncharged polar groups Ser, Thr, Asn, Gln, and Tyr are usually on the protein surface but also occur in the interior of the molecule. When buried in the protein, these residues are almost always hydrogen bonded to other groups; in a sense, the formation of a hydrogen

(a)

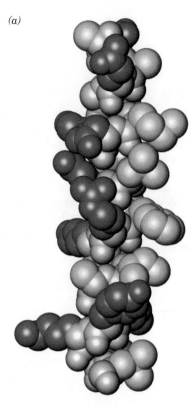

■ **Figure 6-26** | **Side chain locations in an α helix and a β sheet.** In these space-filling models, the main chain is gray, nonpolar side chains are gold, and polar side chains are magenta. (a) An α helix from sperm whale myoglobin. Note that the nonpolar residues are primarily on one side of the helix. (b) An antiparallel β sheet from concanavalin A (*side view*). The protein interior is to the right and the exterior is to the left. [Based on X-ray structures by Ilme Schlichting, Max Planck Institut für Molekulare Physiologie, Dortmund, Germany, and Gerald Edelman, The Rockefeller University. PDBids 1A6M and 2CNA.]

bond "neutralizes" their polarity. This is also the case with the polypeptide backbone.

These general principles of side chain distribution are evident in individual elements of secondary structure (Fig. 6-26) as well as in whole proteins (Fig. 6-27). Polar side chains tend to extend toward—and thereby help form—the protein's surface, whereas nonpolar side chains largely extend toward—and thereby occupy—its interior. Turns and loops joining secondary structural elements usually occur at the protein surface.

Most proteins are quite compact, with their interior atoms packed together even more efficiently than the atoms in a crystal of small organic molecules. Nevertheless, the atoms of protein side chains almost invariably have low-energy arrangements. Evidently, interior side chains adopt relaxed conformations despite the profusion of intramolecular interactions. Closely packed protein interiors generally exclude water. When water molecules are present, they often occupy specific positions where they can form hydrogen bonds, sometimes acting as a bridge between two hydrogen-bonding protein groups.

C | Tertiary Structures Contain Combinations of Secondary Structure

Globular proteins—each with a unique tertiary structure—are built from combinations of secondary structural elements. The proportions of α helices and β sheets and the order in which they are connected provide an informative way of classifying and analyzing protein structure.

Certain Combinations of Secondary Structure Form Motifs. Groupings of secondary structural elements, called **supersecondary structures** or **motifs,** occur in many unrelated globular proteins:

1. The most common form of supersecondary structure is the **βαβ motif,** in which an α helix connects two parallel strands of a β sheet (Fig. 6-28a).

2. Another common supersecondary structure, the **β hairpin** motif, consists of antiparallel strands connected by relatively tight reverse turns (Fig. 6-28b).

3. In an **αα motif,** two successive antiparallel α helices pack against each other with their axes inclined. This permits energetically favorable intermeshing of their contacting side chains (Fig. 6-28c). Similar associations stabilize the coiled coil conformation of α keratin and tropomyosin (Fig. 6-15b), although their helices are parallel rather than antiparallel.

4. In the **Greek key motif** (Fig. 6-28d; named after an ornamental design commonly used in ancient Greece; see inset), a β hairpin is folded over to form a 4-stranded antiparallel β sheet.

(b)

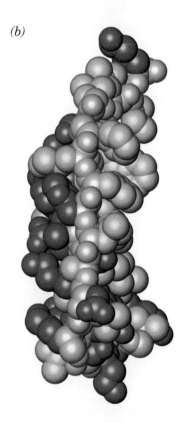

See Guided Exploration 8
Secondary structures in proteins.

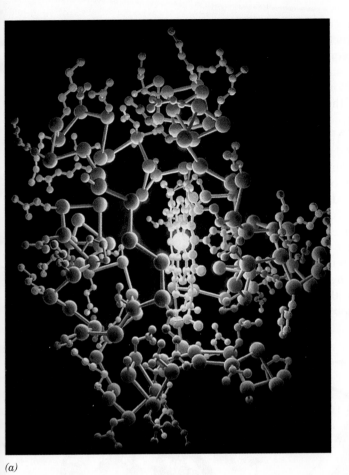

(a)

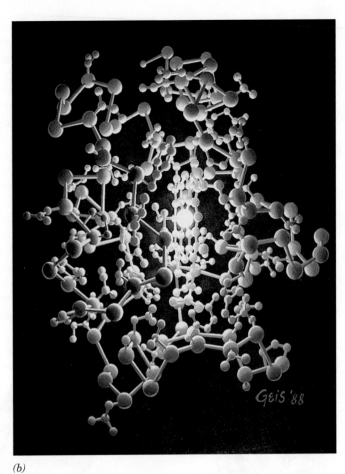

(b)

■ **Figure 6-27** | **Side chain distribution in horse heart cytochrome c.** In these paintings, based on an X-ray structure determined by Richard Dickerson, the protein is illuminated by its single iron atom centered in a heme group. Hydrogen atoms are not shown. In (a) the hydrophilic side chains are green, and in (b) the hydrophobic side chains are orange. [Illustration, Irving Geis. Image from the Irving Geis Collection/Howard Hughes Medical Institute. Rights owned by HHMI. Reproduction by permission only.] 🔗 **See Kinemage Exercise 5.**

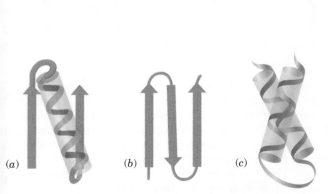

(a)   (b)   (c)

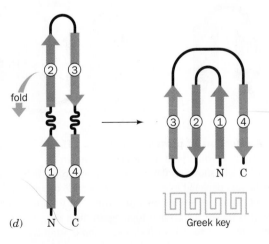

(d)

Greek key

■ **Figure 6-28** | **Schematic diagrams of supersecondary structures.** (a) A βαβ motif, (b) a β hairpin motif, (c) an αα motif, and (d) a Greek key motif, showing how it is constructed from a folded-over β hairpin. The polypeptide backbones are drawn as ribbons, with β strands shown as flat arrows pointing from N- to C-terminus, and α helices represented by cylinders.

Most Proteins Can Be Classified as α, β, or α/β. The major types of secondary structural elements occur in globular proteins in varying proportions and combinations. Some proteins, such as *E. coli* **cytochrome b_{562}** (Fig. 6-29*a*), consist only of α helices spanned by short connecting links and are therefore classified as **α proteins.** Others, such as immunoglobulins, contain the **immunoglobulin fold** (Fig. 6-29*b*), and are called **β proteins** because they have a large proportion of β sheets and are devoid of α helices. Most proteins, however, including **lactate dehydrogenase** (Fig. 6-29*c*) and carboxypeptidase A (Fig. 6-12), are known as **α/β proteins** because they largely consist of mixtures of both types of secondary structure (proteins, on average contain ~31% α helix and ~28% β sheet).

The α, β, and α/β classes of proteins can be further subdivided by their **topology,** that is, according to how their secondary structural elements are connected. For example, extended β sheets often roll up to form **β barrels.** Three different types of 8-stranded β barrels, each with a different topology, are shown in Fig. 6-30. Two of these (Fig. 6-30*a* and *b*) are all-β structures containing multiple β hairpin motifs. The third, known as an **α/β barrel** (Fig. 6-30*c*), can be considered as a set of overlapping βαβ motifs (and is a member of the α/β class of proteins).

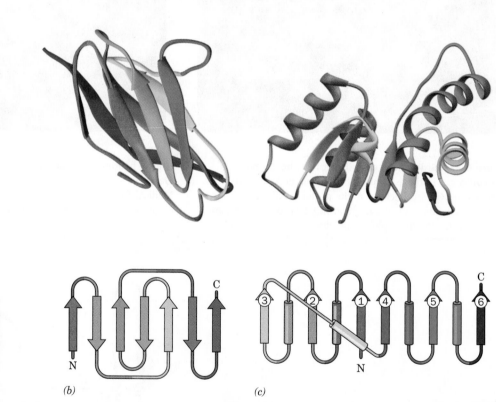

(a)   *(b)*   *(c)*

■ **Figure 6-29 | A selection of protein structures.** The proteins are represented by their peptide backbones, drawn in ribbon form, with β strands shown as flat arrows pointing from N- to C-terminus and α-helices depicted as coils. The polypeptide chain is colored, from N- to C-terminus, in rainbow order from red to blue. Below each drawing is the corresponding topological diagram indicating the connectivity of its helices (cylinders) and β strands (flat arrows). (*a*) *E. coli* **cytochrome b_{562}** (106 residues), which forms an up–down–up–down 4-helix bundle. Its bound heme group is shown in ball-and-stick form with C magenta, N blue, O red, and Fe orange. (*b*) The N-terminal domain of the human immunoglobulin fragment **Fab New** (103 residues) showing its immunoglobulin fold. The polypeptide chain is folded into a sandwich of 3- and 4-stranded antiparallel β sheets. (*c*) The N-terminal domain of dogfish lactate dehydrogenase (163 residues). It contains a 6-stranded parallel β sheet in which the crossovers between β strands all contain an α helix that forms a right-handed helical turn with its flanking β strands. [Based on X-ray structures by (*a*) F. Scott Matthews, Washington University School of Medicine; (*b*) Roberto Poljak, The Johns Hopkins School of Medicine; and (*c*) Michael Rossmann, Purdue University. PDBids (*a*) 256B, (*b*) 7FAB, and (*c*) 6LDH.]

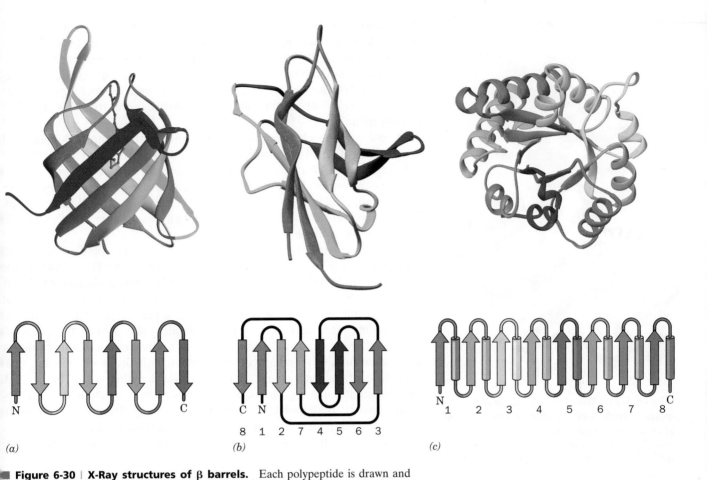

(a)   *(b)*   *(c)*

■ **Figure 6-30** │ **X-Ray structures of β barrels.** Each polypeptide is drawn and colored and accompanied by its corresponding topological diagram as is described in the legend to Fig. 6-29. (*a*) Human **retinol binding protein** showing its 8-stranded up-and-down β barrel (residues 1–142 of the 182-residue protein). Note that each β strand is linked via a short loop to its clockwise-adjacent strand as seen from the top. The protein's bound retinol molecule is represented by a gray ball-and-stick model. (*b*) **Peptide-N^4-(N-acetyl-β-D-glucosaminyl)asparagine amidase F** from *Flavobacterium meningosepticum* (residues 1–140 of the 340-residue enzyme). Note how its 8-stranded β barrel is formed by rolling up a 4-segment β hairpin. Here the two β strands in each segment of the β hairpin are colored alike with strands 1 and 8 (the N- and C-terminal strands) red, strands 2 and 7 orange, strands 3 and 6 cyan, and strands 4 and 5 blue. This motif, which is known as a **jelly roll** or **Swiss roll barrel,** is so named because of its topological resemblance to the rolled-up pastries. (*c*) Chicken muscle **triose phosphate isomerase** (**TIM;** 247 residues) forms a so-called **α/β barrel** in which 8 pairs of alternating β strands and α helices roll up to form an inner barrel of 8 parallel β strands surrounded by an outer barrel of 8 parallel α helices. The protein is viewed approximately along the axis of the α/β barrel. Note that the α/β barrel is essentially a series of linked βαβ motifs. [Based on X-ray structures by (a) T. Alwyn Jones, Biomedical Center, Uppsala, Sweden; (b) Patrick Van Roey, New York State Department of Health, Albany, New York; and (c) David Phillips, Oxford University, Oxford, U.K. PDBids (a) 1RBP, (b) 1PNG, and (c) 1TIM.]

Large Polypeptides Form Domains. Polypeptide chains containing more than ~200 residues usually fold into two or more globular clusters known as **domains,** which give these proteins a bi- or multilobal appearance. Each subunit of the enzyme **glyceraldehyde-3-phosphate dehydrogenase,**

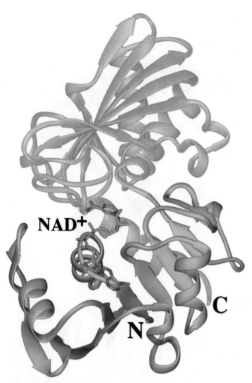

■ Figure 6-31 | The two-domain protein glyceraldehyde-3-phosphate dehydrogenase.
The N-terminal domain (*light blue*) binds NAD$^+$ (drawn in stick form and colored according to atom type with C green, N blue, O red, and P magenta), and the C-terminal domain (*orange*) binds glyceraldehyde-3-phosphate (not shown). [Based on an X-ray structure by Alan Wonacott, Imperial College, London, U.K. PDBid 1GD1.]
See Interactive Exercise 2.

for example, has two distinct domains (Fig. 6-31). Most domains consist of 40 to 200 amino acid residues and have an average diameter of ~25 Å. An inspection of the various protein structures diagrammed in this chapter reveals that domains consist of two or more layers of secondary structural elements. The reason for this is clear: At least two such layers are required to seal off a domain's hydrophobic core from its aqueous environment.

A polypeptide chain wanders back and forth within a domain, but neighboring domains are usually connected by only one or two polypeptide segments. *Consequently, many domains are structurally independent units that have the characteristics of small globular proteins.* Nevertheless, the domain structure of a protein is not necessarily obvious since its domains may make such extensive contacts with each other that the protein appears to be a single globular entity.

Domains often have a specific function such as the binding of a small molecule. In Fig. 6-31, for example, the dinucleotide NAD$^+$ (nicotinamide adenine dinucleotide; Fig. 11-4) binds to the N-terminal domain of glyceraldehyde-3-phosphate dehydrogenase. Michael Rossmann has shown that a βαβαβ unit, in which the β strands form a parallel sheet with α helical connections, often acts as a nucleotide-binding site. Two of these βαβαβ units combine to form a domain known as a **dinucleotide-binding fold,** or **Rossmann fold.** Glyceraldehyde-3-phosphate dehydrogenase's N-terminal domain contains such a fold, as does lactate dehydrogenase (Fig. 6-29c). In some multidomain proteins, binding sites occupy the clefts between domains; that is, small molecules are bound by groups from two domains. In such cases, the relatively pliant covalent connection between the domains allows flexible interactions between the protein and the small molecule.

D | Structure Is Conserved More than Sequence

The many thousands of known protein structures, comprising an even greater number of separate domains, can be grouped into families by examining the overall paths followed by their polypeptide chains. Although it is estimated that there are as many as 1400 different protein domain families, approximately 200 different folding patterns account for about half of all known protein structures. As described in Section 5-4B, the domain is the fundamental unit of protein evolution. Apparently, the most common protein domains are evolutionary sinks—domains that arose and persisted because of their ability (1) to form stable folding patterns; (2) to tolerate amino acid deletions, substitutions, and insertions, thereby making them more likely to survive evolutionary changes; and/or (3) to support essential biological functions.

Polypeptides with similar sequences tend to adopt similar backbone conformations. This is certainly true for evolutionarily related proteins that carry out similar functions. For example, the cytochromes *c* of different species are highly conserved proteins with closely similar sequences (Table 5-5) and three-dimensional structures.

Cytochrome *c* occurs only in eukaryotes, but prokaryotes contain proteins, known as ***c*-type cytochromes,** which perform the same general function (that of an electron carrier). The *c*-type cytochromes from different species exhibit only low degrees of sequence similarity to each other and to eukaryotic cytochromes *c*. Yet their X-ray structures are clearly similar, particularly in polypeptide chain folding and side chain packing in the protein interior (Fig. 6-32). The major structural differences among *c*-type cytochromes lie in the various polypeptide loops on their surfaces. The

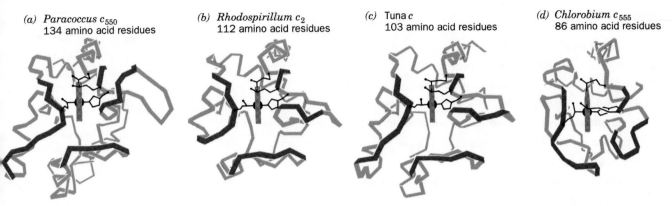

(a) *Paracoccus* c_{550}
134 amino acid residues

(b) *Rhodospirillum* c_2
112 amino acid residues

(c) Tuna c
103 amino acid residues

(d) *Chlorobium* c_{555}
86 amino acid residues

▌ **Figure 6-32** | **Three-dimensional structures of c-type cytochromes.** The polypeptide backbones (*blue*) are shown in analogous orientations such that their heme groups (*red*) are viewed edge-on. The Cys, Met, and His side chains that covalently link the heme to the protein are also shown. (a) Cytochrome c_{550} from *Paracoccus denitrificans*, (b) cytochrome c_2 from *Rhodospirillum rubrum*, (c) cytochrome c from tuna, and (d) cytochrome c_{555} from *Chlorobium limicola*. [Illustration, Irving Geis. Image from the Irving Geis Collection/Howard Hughes Medical Institute. Rights owned by HHMI. Reproduction by permission only.] ⚛ **See Kinemage Exercise 5.**

sequences of the *c*-type cytochromes have diverged so far from one another that, in the absence of their X-ray structures, they can be properly aligned only through the use of mathematically sophisticated computer programs. Thus, *it appears that the essential structural and functional elements of proteins, rather than their amino acid residues, are conserved during evolution.*

E | Structural Bioinformatics Provides Tools for Storing, Visualizing, and Comparing Protein Structural Information

The data obtained by X-ray crystallography, NMR spectroscopy, and certain other techniques take the form of three-dimensional coordinates describing the spatial positions of atoms in molecules. This kind of information can be easily stored, displayed, and compared, much like sequence information obtained by nucleotide or protein sequencing methods (see Sections 3-4 and 5-3). **Bioinformatics** is the rapidly growing discipline that deals with the burgeoning amount of information related to molecular sequences and structures. **Structural bioinformatics** is a branch of bioinformatics that is concerned with how macromolecular structures are displayed and compared. Some of the databases and analytical tools that are used in structural bioinformatics are listed in Table 6-2.

The Protein Data Bank Is the Repository for Structural Information. The atomic coordinates of nearly 50,000 macromolecular structures, including proteins, nucleic acids, and carbohydrates, are archived in the **Protein Data Bank (PDB).** Indeed, most scientific journals that publish macromolecular structures require that authors deposit their structure's coordinates in the PDB.

Each independently determined structure in the PDB is assigned a unique four-character identifier (its PDBid). For example, the PDBid for the structure of sperm whale myoglobin is 1MBO. A coordinate file begins with information that identifies the macromolecule, its source (the organism from which it was obtained), the author(s) who determined the structure, and key journal references. The file continues with a synopsis of how the structure was determined together with indicators of its accuracy.

Table 6-2	Structural Bioinformatics Internet Addresses

Structural Databases

Protein Data Bank (PDB): http://www.rcsb.org/pdb/

Nucleic Acid Database: http://ndbserver.rutgers.edu/

Molecular Modeling Database (MMDB): http://www.ncbi.nlm.nih.gov/Structure/index.shtml

Most Representative NMR Structure in an Ensemble: http://pqs.ebi.ac.uk/pqs-nmr.html

PQS Protein Quaternary Structure Query Form at the EBI: http://pqs.ebi.ac.uk/

Molecular Graphics Programs

Cn3D: http://www.ncbi.nlm.nih.gov/Structure/CN3D/cn3d.shtml

Jmol: http://jmol.sourceforge.net/

KiNG: http://kinemage.biochem.duke.edu/

FirstGlance: http:// molvis.sdsc.edu/fgij/index.htm

Swiss-PDB Viewer (Deep View): http://us.expasy.org/spdbv/

Structural Classification Algorithms

CATH (*C*lass, *A*rchitecture, *T*opology, and *H*omologous superfamily): http://www.cathdb.info/latest/index.html

CE (*C*ombinatorial *E*xtension of optimal pathway): http://cl.sdsc.edu/

FSSP (*F*amily of *S*tructurally *S*imilar *P*roteins): http://www.ebi.ac.uk/dali/

SCOP (*S*tructural *C*lassification *O*f *P*roteins): http://scop.mrc-lmb.cam.ac.uk/scop/

VAST (*V*ector *A*lignment *S*earch *T*ool): http://www.ncbi.nlm.nih.gov/Structure/VAST/vast.shtml

The sequences of the structure's various chains are then listed together with the descriptions and formulas of its so-called HET (for heterogen) groups, which are molecular entities that are not among the "standard" amino acid or nucleotide residues (for example, organic molecules, nonstandard residues such as Hyp, metal ions, and bound water molecules). The positions of the structure's secondary structural elements and its disulfide bonds are then provided.

The bulk of a PDB file consists of a series of records (lines), each of which provides the three-dimensional (x, y, z) coordinates in angstroms of one atom in the structure. All atoms are labeled either ATOM (for a "standard" amino acid or nucleotide residue) or HETATM (for any other atom). Each atom is identified by a serial number, an atom name (for example, C and O for an amino acid residue's carbonyl C and O atoms, CA and CB for C_α and C_β atoms), the name of the residue, and a letter to identify the chain to which it belongs (for structures that have more than one chain). For NMR-based structures, the PDB file contains a full set of records for each member of the ensemble of structures (the most representative member of such a coordinate set can be obtained from another database; see Table 6-2).

A particular PDB file may be located according to its PDBid or, if this is unknown, by searching with a variety of criteria including a protein's name, its source, the author(s), key words, and/or the experimental technique used to determine the structure. Selecting a particular macromolecule in the PDB initially displays a summary page with options for viewing the structure (either statically or interactively), for viewing or downloading the coordinate file, and for classifying or analyzing the structure in terms of its geometric properties and sequence. The **Nucleic Acid Database (NDB)** archives the atomic coordinates of structures that contain nucleic acids, using roughly the same format as PDB files.

Molecular Graphics Programs Interactively Show Macromolecules in Three Dimensions. The most informative way to examine a macromolecular structure is through the use of molecular graphics programs that permit the user to interactively rotate a macromolecule and thereby perceive its three-dimensional structure. This impression may be further enhanced by simultaneously viewing the macromolecule in stereo. Most molecular graphics programs use PDB files as input. The programs described here can be downloaded from the Internet addresses listed in Table 6-2, some of which also provide instructions for the program's use.

Jmol, which functions as both a Web browser–based applet or as a standalone program, allows the user to display user-selected macromolecules in a variety of colors and formats (e.g., wire frame, ball-and-stick, backbone, space-filling, and cartoons). The Interactive Exercises on the website that accompanies this textbook (http://wiley.com/college/voet/) all use Jmol. **FirstGlance** uses Jmol to display macromolecules via a user-friendly interface. **KiNG,** which also has Web browser–based and standalone versions, displays the so-called **Kinemages** on this textbook's accompanying website. KiNG provides a generally more author-directed user environment than does Jmol. Macromolecules can be displayed directly from their corresponding PDB page using either Jmol or KiNG. The **Swiss-PDB Viewer** (also called **Deep View**), in addition to displaying molecular structures, provides tools for basic model building, homology modeling, energy minimization, and multiple sequence alignment. One advantage of the Swiss-PDB Viewer is that it allows users to easily superimpose two or more models.

Structure Comparisons Reveal Evolutionary Relationships. Most proteins are structurally related to other proteins, since *evolution tends to conserve the structures of proteins rather than their sequences*. The computational tools described below facilitate the classification and comparison of protein structures. These programs can be accessed directly via their Internet addresses and in some cases through the PDB. Studies using these programs yield functional insights, reveal distant evolutionary relationships that are not apparent from sequence comparisons, generate libraries of unique folds for structure prediction, and provide indications as to why certain types of structures are preferred over others.

1. ***CATH*** (for *C*lass, *A*rchitecture, *T*opology, and *H*omologous superfamily), as its name suggests, categorizes proteins in a four-level structural hierarchy: (1) Class, the highest level, places the selected protein in one of four levels of gross secondary structure (e.g., Mainly α, Mainly β, α/β, and Few Secondary Structures); (2) Architecture, the gross arrangement of secondary structure; (3) Topology, which depends on both the overall shape of the protein domain and the connectivity of its secondary structural elements; and (4) Homologous Superfamily, which identifies the protein as a member of a group that shares a common ancestor.

2. ***CE*** (for *C*ombinatorial *E*xtension of the optimal path) finds all proteins in the PDB that can be structurally aligned with the query structure to within user-specified geometric criteria. CE can optimally align and display two user-selected structures.

3. ***FSSP*** (*F*amily of *S*tructurally *S*imilar *P*roteins) lists the protein structures that, at least in part, structurally resemble the query protein. It is based on continuously updated all-against-all comparisons of the protein structures in the PDB, using a program called **Dali.**

■ **CHECK YOUR UNDERSTANDING**

List some of the relative advantages and disadvantages of using X-ray crystallography and NMR spectroscopy to determine the structure of a protein.

Why do turns and loops most often occur on the protein surface? Which side chains usually occur on a protein's surface? in its interior?

Describe some of the common protein structural motifs.

Explain why a protein's sequence evolves faster than its structure.

Summarize the types of information provided in a PDB file.

Why is it useful to compare protein structures in addition to protein sequences?

LEARNING OBJECTIVES

■ Understand that some proteins contain multiple subunits, usually arranged symmetrically.

4. **SCOP** (Structural Classification Of Proteins) classifies protein structures based mainly on manually generated topological considerations according to a six-level hierarchy: Class (e.g., all-α, all-β, α/β), Fold (based on the arrangement of secondary structural elements), Superfamily (indicative of distant evolutionary relationships based on structural criteria and functional features), Family (indicative of near evolutionary relationships based on sequence as well as on structure), Protein, and Species. SCOP permits the user to navigate through its treelike hierarchical organization and lists the known members of any particular branch.

5. **VAST** (Vector Alignment Search Tool), a component of the National Center for Biotechnology Information (NCBI) Entrez system, reports a precomputed list of proteins of known structure that structurally resemble the query protein ("structure neighbors"). The VAST system uses the **Molecular Modeling Database (MMDB),** an NCBI-generated database that is derived from PDB coordinates but in which molecules are represented by connectivity graphs rather than sets of atomic coordinates. VAST displays the superposition of the query protein in its structural alignment with up to five other proteins using the molecular graphics program **Cn3D.** VAST also reports a precomputed list of proteins that are similar to the query protein in sequence ("sequence neighbors").

3 Quaternary Structure and Symmetry

Most proteins, particularly those with molecular masses >100 kD, consist of more than one polypeptide chain. These polypeptide subunits associate with a specific geometry. The spatial arrangement of these subunits is known as a protein's quaternary structure.

There are several reasons why multisubunit proteins are so common. In large assemblies of proteins, such as collagen fibrils, the advantages of subunit construction over the synthesis of one huge polypeptide chain are analogous to those of using prefabricated components in constructing a building: Defects can be repaired by simply replacing the flawed subunit; the site of subunit manufacture can be different from the site of assembly into the final product; and the only genetic information necessary to specify the entire edifice is the information specifying its few different self-assembling subunits. In the case of enzymes, increasing a protein's size tends to better fix the three-dimensional positions of its reacting groups. *Increasing the size of an enzyme through the association of identical subunits is more efficient than increasing the length of its polypeptide chain since each subunit has an active site. More importantly, the subunit construction of many enzymes provides the structural basis for the regulation of their activities* (Sections 7-3B and 12-3).

Subunits Usually Associate Noncovalently. A multisubunit protein may consist of identical or nonidentical polypeptide chains. Hemoglobin, for example, has the subunit composition $\alpha_2\beta_2$ (Fig. 6-33). Proteins with more than one subunit are called **oligomers,** and their identical units are called **protomers.** A protomer may therefore consist of one polypeptide chain or several unlike polypeptide chains. In this sense, hemoglobin is a dimer of αβ protomers.

The contact regions between subunits resemble the interior of a single-subunit protein: They contain closely packed nonpolar side chains, hydrogen bonds involving the polypeptide backbones and their side chains, and, in some cases, interchain disulfide bonds. However, the subunit interfaces of proteins that dissociate *in vivo* have lesser hydrophobicities than do permanent interfaces.

Subunits Are Symmetrically Arranged. In the vast majority of oligomeric proteins, the protomers are symmetrically arranged; that is, each protomer occupies a geometrically equivalent position in the oligomer. Proteins cannot have inversion or mirror symmetry, however, because bringing the protomers into coincidence would require converting chiral L residues to D residues. Thus, *proteins can have only **rotational symmetry.***

In the simplest type of rotational symmetry, **cyclic symmetry,** protomers are related by a single axis of rotation (Fig. 6-34*a*). Objects with two-, three-, or *n*-fold rotational axes are said to have C_2, C_3, or C_n symmetry, respectively. C_2 symmetry is the most common; higher cyclic symmetries are relatively rare.

Dihedral symmetry (D_n), a more complicated type of rotational symmetry, is generated when an *n*-fold rotation axis intersects a twofold rotation axis at right angles (Fig. 6-34*b*). An oligomer with D_n symmetry consists of 2*n* protomers. D_2 symmetry is the most common type of dihedral symmetry in proteins.

Other possible types of rotational symmetry are those of a tetrahedron, cube, and icosahedron (Fig. 6-34*c*). Some multienzyme complexes and spherical viruses are built on these geometric plans.

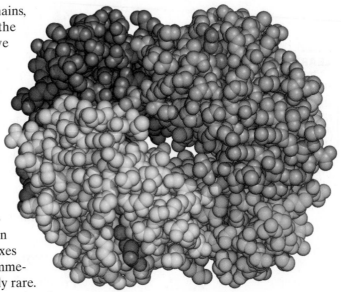

■ **Figure 6-33 | Quaternary structure of hemoglobin.** In this space-filling model, the α_1, α_2, β_1, and β_2 subunits are colored yellow, green, cyan, and blue, respectively. Heme groups are red. [Based on an X-ray structure by Max Perutz, MRC Laboratory of Molecular Biology, Cambridge, U.K. PDBid 2DHB.]

■ **CHECK YOUR UNDERSTANDING**

List the advantages of multiple subunits in proteins.
Why can't proteins have mirror symmetry?

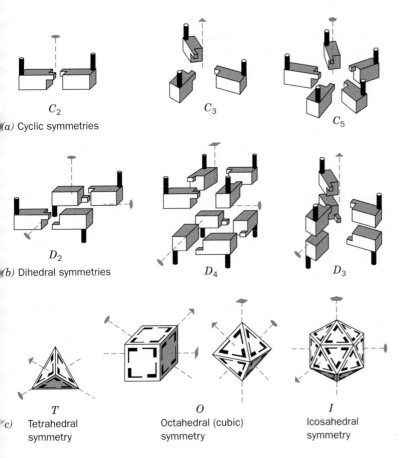

(a) Cyclic symmetries

(b) Dihedral symmetries

(c) Tetrahedral symmetry / Octahedral (cubic) symmetry / Icosahedral symmetry

■ **Figure 6-34 | Symmetries of oligomeric proteins.** The oval, the triangle, the square, and the pentagon at the ends of the dashed green lines indicate, respectively, the unique twofold, threefold, fourfold, and fivefold rotational axes of the objects shown. (*a*) Assemblies with cyclic symmetry. (*b*) Assemblies with dihedral symmetry. In these objects, a twofold axis is perpendicular to another rotational axis. (*c*) Assemblies with the rotational symmetries of a tetrahedron, a cube or octahedron, and an icosahedron. [Illustration, Irving Geis. Image from the Irving Geis Collection/Howard Hughes Medical Institute. Rights owned by HHMI. Reproduction by permission only.]
🐾 **See the Animated Figures.**

LEARNING OBJECTIVES

■ Understand that protein stability depends primarily on hydrophobic effects and secondarily on electrostatic interactions.

■ Understand that a protein that has been denatured may undergo renaturation.

Table 6-3	Hydropathy Scale for Amino Acid Side Chains

Side Chain	Hydropathy
Ile	4.5
Val	4.2
Leu	3.8
Phe	2.8
Cys	2.5
Met	1.9
Ala	1.8
Gly	−0.4
Thr	−0.7
Ser	−0.8
Trp	−0.9
Tyr	−1.3
Pro	−1.6
His	−3.2
Glu	−3.5
Gln	−3.5
Asp	−3.5
Asn	−3.5
Lys	−3.9
Arg	−4.5

Source: Kyte, J. and Doolittle, R.F., *J. Mol. Biol.* **157**, 110 (1982).

4 Protein Stability

Incredible as it may seem, thermodynamic measurements indicate that *native proteins are only marginally stable under physiological conditions.* The free energy required to denature them is ~0.4 kJ·mol⁻¹ per amino acid residue, so a fully folded 100-residue protein is only about 40 kJ·mol⁻¹ more stable than its unfolded form (for comparison, the energy required to break a typical hydrogen bond is ~20 kJ·mol⁻¹). The various noncovalent influences on proteins—hydrophobic effects, electrostatic interactions, and hydrogen bonding—each have energies that may total thousands of kilojoules per mole over an entire protein molecule. Consequently, a protein structure is the result of a delicate balance among powerful countervailing forces.

A | Proteins Are Stabilized by Several Forces

Protein structures are governed primarily by hydrophobic effects and, to a lesser extent, by interactions between polar residues, and by other types of bonds.

The Hydrophobic Effect Has the Greatest Influence on Protein Stability. *The hydrophobic effect, which causes nonpolar substances to minimize their contacts with water* (Section 2-1C), *is the major determinant of native protein structure.* The aggregation of nonpolar side chains in the interior of a protein is favored by the increase in entropy of the water molecules that would otherwise form ordered "cages" around the hydrophobic groups. The combined hydrophobic and hydrophilic tendencies of individual amino acid residues in proteins can be expressed as **hydropathies** (Table 6-3). The greater a side chain's hydropathy, the more likely it is to occupy the interior of a protein and vice versa. Hydropathies are good predictors of which portions of a polypeptide chain are inside a protein, out of contact with the aqueous solvent, and which portions are outside (Fig. 6-35).

Site-directed mutagenesis experiments in which individual interior residues have been replaced by a number of others suggest that the factors that affect stability are, in order, the hydrophobicity of the substituted residue, its steric compatibility, and, last, the volume of its side chain.

Electrostatic Interactions Contribute to Protein Stability. In the closely packed interiors of native proteins, van der Waals forces, which are relatively weak (Section 2-1A), are nevertheless an important stabilizing influence. This is because these forces only act over short distances and hence are lost when the protein is unfolded.

Perhaps surprisingly, *hydrogen bonds, which are central features of protein structures, make only minor contributions to protein stability.* This is because hydrogen-bonding groups in an unfolded protein form hydrogen bonds with water molecules. Thus the contribution of a hydrogen bond to the stability of a native protein is the small difference in hydrogen bonding free energies between the native and unfolded states (−2 to 8 kJ·mol⁻¹ as determined by site-directed mutagenesis studies). Nevertheless, hydrogen bonds are important determinants of native protein structures, because if a protein folded in a way that prevented a hydrogen bond from forming, the stabilizing energy of that hydrogen bond would be lost. Hydrogen bonding therefore fine-tunes tertiary structure by "selecting"

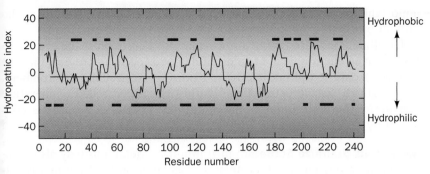

■ **Figure 6-35** | **A hydropathic index plot for bovine chymotrypsinogen.** The sum of the hydropathies of nine consecutive residues is plotted versus residue sequence number. A large positive hydropathic index indicates a hydrophobic region of the polypeptide, whereas a large negative value indicates a hydrophilic region. The upper bars denote the protein's interior regions, as determined by X-ray crystallography, and the lower bars denote the protein's exterior regions. [After Kyte, J. and Doolittle, R.F., *J. Mol. Biol.* **157**, 111 (1982).]

the unique native structure of a protein from among a relatively small number of hydrophobically stabilized conformations.

The association of two ionic protein groups of opposite charge (e.g., Lys and Asp) is known as an **ion pair** or **salt bridge.** About 75% of the charged residues in proteins are members of ion pairs that are located mostly on the protein surface (Fig. 6-36). Despite the strong electrostatic attraction between the oppositely charged members of an ion pair, these interactions contribute little to the stability of a native protein. This is because the free energy of an ion pair's charge–charge interactions usually fails to compensate for the loss of entropy of the side chains and the loss of solvation free energy when the charged groups form an ion pair. This accounts for the observation that ion pairs are poorly conserved among homologous proteins.

Disulfide Bonds Cross-Link Extracellular Proteins. Disulfide bonds (Fig. 4-6) within and between polypeptide chains form as a protein folds to its native conformation. Some polypeptides whose Cys residues have been derivatized or mutagenically replaced to prevent disulfide bond formation can still assume their fully active conformations, suggesting that disulfide bonds are not essential stabilizing forces. They may, however, be

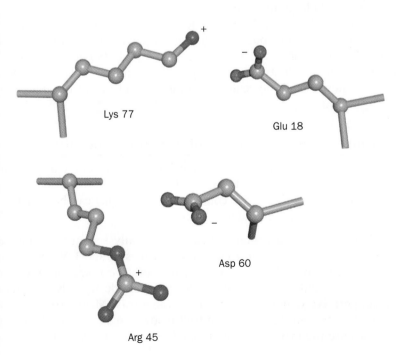

■ **Figure 6-36** | **Examples of ion pairs in myoglobin.** In each case, oppositely charged side chain groups from residues far apart in sequence closely approach each other through the formation of ion pairs.

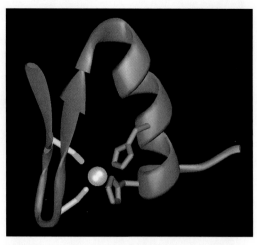

■ **Figure 6-37 | A zinc finger motif.** This structure, from the DNA-binding protein **Zif268**, is known as a Cys$_2$–His$_2$ zinc finger because the zinc atom (*silver sphere*) is coordinated by two Cys residues (*yellow*) and two His residues (*cyan*). [Based on an X-ray structure by Carl Pabo, MIT. PDBid 1ZAA.]

important for "locking in" a particular backbone folding pattern as the protein proceeds from its fully extended state to its mature form.

Disulfide bonds are rare in intracellular proteins because the cytoplasm is a reducing environment. Most disulfide bonds occur in proteins that are secreted from the cell into the more oxidizing extracellular environment. The relatively hostile extracellular world (e.g., uncontrolled temperature and pH) apparently requires the additional structural constraints conferred by disulfide bonds.

Metal Ions Stabilize Some Small Domains. Metal ions may also function to internally cross-link proteins. For example, at least ten motifs collectively known as **zinc fingers** have been described in nucleic acid–binding proteins. These structures contain about 25–60 residues arranged around one or two Zn^{2+} ions that are tetrahedrally coordinated by the side chains of Cys, His, and occasionally Asp or Glu (Fig. 6-37). The Zn^{2+} ion allows relatively short stretches of polypeptide chain to fold into stable units that can interact with nucleic acids. Zinc fingers are too small to be stable in the absence of Zn^{2+}. Zinc is ideally suited to its structural role in intracellular proteins: Its filled *d* electron shell permits it to interact strongly with a variety of ligands (e.g., sulfur, nitrogen, or oxygen) from different amino acid residues. In addition, zinc has only one stable oxidation state (unlike, for example, copper and iron), so it does not undergo oxidation–reduction reactions in the cell.

Proteins Are Dynamic Structures. The plethora of forces acting to stabilize proteins as well as the static way that their structures are usually portrayed may leave the false impression that proteins have fixed and rigid structures. In fact, proteins are flexible and rapidly fluctuating molecules whose structural mobilities are functionally significant. Groups ranging in size from individual side chains to entire domains or subunits may be displaced by up to several angstroms through random intramolecular movements or in response to a trigger such as the binding of a small molecule. Extended side chains, such as Lys, and the N- and C-termini of polypeptide chains are especially prone to wave around in solution because there are few forces holding them in place.

Theoretical calculations by Martin Karplus indicate that a protein's native structure probably consists of a large collection of rapidly interconverting conformations that have essentially equal stabilities (Fig. 6-38). Conformational flexibility, or **breathing,** with structural displacement of up to ~2 Å, allows small molecules to diffuse in and out of the interior of certain proteins.

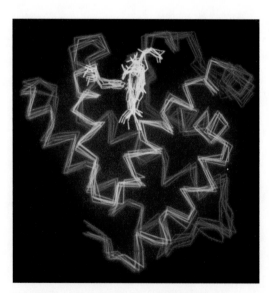

■ **Figure 6-38 | Molecular dynamics of myoglobin.** Several "snapshots" of the protein calculated at intervals of 5×10^{-12} s are superimposed. The backbone is blue, the heme group is yellow, and the His side chain linking the heme to the protein is orange. [Courtesy of Martin Karplus, Harvard University.]

B | Proteins Can Undergo Denaturation and Renaturation

The low conformational stabilities of native proteins make them easily susceptible to denaturation by altering the balance of the weak nonbonding forces that maintain the native conformation. Proteins can be denatured by a variety of conditions and substances:

1. Heating causes a protein's conformationally sensitive properties such as optical rotation (Section 4-2), viscosity, and UV absorption to change abruptly over a narrow temperature range. Such a sharp transition indicates that the entire polypeptide unfolds or "melts" **cooperatively,** that is, nearly simultaneously. Most proteins have melting temperatures that are well below 100°C. Among the exceptions are the proteins of thermophilic bacteria (Box 6-3).

BOX 6-3 PERSPECTIVES IN BIOCHEMISTRY

Thermostable Proteins

Certain species of bacteria known as **hyperthermophiles** grow at temperatures near 100°C. They live in such places as hot springs and submarine hydrothermal vents, with the most extreme, the archaebacterium *Pyrolobus fumarii*, able to grow at temperatures as high as 113°C. These organisms have many of the same metabolic pathways as do **mesophiles** (organisms that grow at "normal" temperatures). Yet most mesophilic proteins denature at temperatures where hyperthermophiles thrive. What is the structural basis for the thermostability of hyperthermophilic proteins?

The difference in the thermal stabilities of the corresponding (hyper)thermophilic and mesophilic proteins does not exceed ~100 kJ·mol^{-1}, the equivalent of a few noncovalent interactions. This is probably why comparisons of the X-ray structures of hyperthermophilic enzymes with their mesophilic counterparts have failed to reveal any striking differences between them. These proteins exhibit some variations in secondary structure but no more than would be expected for homologous proteins from distantly related mesophiles. However, several of these thermostable enzymes have a superabundance of salt bridges on their surfaces, many of which are arranged in extensive networks containing up to 18 side chains.

The idea that salt bridges can stabilize a protein structure appears to contradict the conclusion of Section 6-4A that ion pairs are, at best, marginally stable. The key to this apparent paradox is

that *the salt bridges in thermostable proteins form networks.* Thus, the gain in charge–charge free energy on associating a third charged group with an ion pair is comparable to that between the members of this ion pair, whereas the free energy lost on desolvating and immobilizing the third side chain is only about half that lost in bringing together the first two side chains. The same, of course, is true for the addition of a fourth, fifth, etc., side chain to a salt bridge network.

Not all thermostable proteins have such a high incidence of salt bridges. Structural comparisons suggest that these proteins are stabilized by a combination of small effects, the most important of which are an increased size of the protein's hydrophobic core, an increased size in the interface between its domains and/or subunits, and a more tightly packed core as evidenced by a reduced surface-to-volume ratio.

The fact that the proteins of hyperthermophiles and mesophiles are homologous and carry out much the same functions indicates that mesophilic proteins are by no means maximally stable. This, in turn, strongly suggests *that the marginal stability of most proteins under physiological conditions (averaging ~0.4 kJ·mol^{-1} of amino acid residues) is an essential property that has arisen through natural selection.* Perhaps this marginal stability helps confer the structural flexibility that many proteins require to carry out their physiological functions.

---

2. pH variations alter the ionization states of amino acid side chains, thereby changing protein charge distributions and hydrogen-bonding requirements.

3. Detergents associate with the nonpolar residues of a protein, thereby interfering with the hydrophobic interactions responsible for the protein's native structure.

4. The **chaotropic agents** guanidinium ion and urea,

$$
\begin{array}{cc}
\overset{\displaystyle NH_2^+}{\underset{\displaystyle \|}{}} & \overset{\displaystyle O}{\underset{\displaystyle \|}{}} \\
H_2N\!-\!C\!-\!NH_2 & H_2N\!-\!C\!-\!NH_2 \\
\textbf{Guanidinium ion} & \textbf{Urea}
\end{array}
$$

in concentrations in the range 5 to 10 M, are the most commonly used protein denaturants. Chaotropic agents are ions or small organic molecules that increase the solubility of nonpolar substances in water. Their effectiveness as denaturants stems from their ability to disrupt hydrophobic interactions, although their mechanism of action is not well understood.

Many Denatured Proteins Can Be Renatured. In 1957, the elegant experiments of Christian Anfinsen on **ribonuclease A (RNase A)** showed that proteins can be denatured reversibly. RNase A, a 124-residue single-chain protein, is completely unfolded and its four disulfide bonds reductively

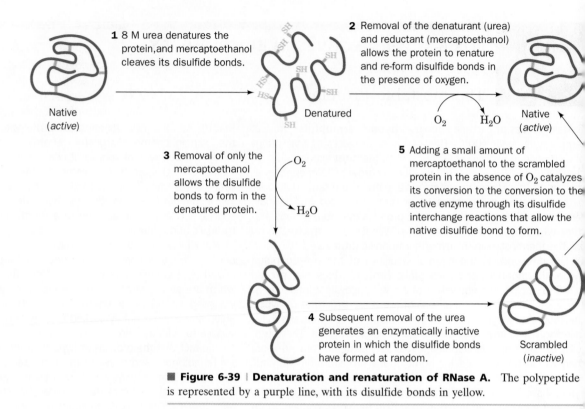

1 8 M urea denatures the protein, and mercaptoethanol cleaves its disulfide bonds.

2 Removal of the denaturant (urea) and reductant (mercaptoethanol) allows the protein to renature and re-form disulfide bonds in the presence of oxygen.

Native (*active*)

Denatured

O_2 H_2O

Native (*active*)

3 Removal of only the mercaptoethanol allows the disulfide bonds to form in the denatured protein.

O_2

H_2O

5 Adding a small amount of mercaptoethanol to the scrambled protein in the absence of O_2 catalyzes its conversion to the conversion to the active enzyme through its disulfide interchange reactions that allow the native disulfide bond to form.

4 Subsequent removal of the urea generates an enzymatically inactive protein in which the disulfide bonds have formed at random.

Scrambled (*inactive*)

■ **Figure 6-39** | **Denaturation and renaturation of RNase A.** The polypeptide is represented by a purple line, with its disulfide bonds in yellow.

cleaved in an 8 M urea solution containing 2-mercaptoethanol. Dialyzing away the urea and reductant and exposing the resulting solution to O_2 at pH 8 (which oxidizes the SH groups to form disulfides) yields a protein that is virtually 100% enzymatically active and physically indistinguishable from native RNase A (Fig. 6-39). The protein must therefore **renature** spontaneously.

The renaturation of RNase A demands that its four disulfide bonds re-form. The probability of one of the eight Cys residues randomly forming a disulfide bond with its proper mate among the other seven Cys residues is 1/7; that of one of the remaining six Cys residues then randomly forming its proper disulfide bond is 1/5; etc. Thus the overall probability of RNase A re-forming its four native disulfide links at random is

$$\frac{1}{7} \times \frac{1}{5} \times \frac{1}{3} \times \frac{1}{1} = \frac{1}{105}$$

Clearly, the disulfide bonds do not randomly re-form under renaturing conditions, since, if they did, only 1% of the refolded protein would be catalytically active. Indeed, if the RNase A is reoxidized in 8 M urea so that its disulfide bonds re-form while the polypeptide chain is a random coil, then after removal of the urea, the RNase A is, as expected, only ~1% active (Fig. 6-39, Steps 3–4). This "scrambled" protein can be made fully active by exposing it to a trace of 2-mercaptoethanol, which breaks the improper disulfide bonds and allows the proper bonds to form. *Anfinsen's work demonstrated that proteins can fold spontaneously into their native conformations under physiological conditions. This implies that a protein's primary structure dictates its three-dimensional structure.*

■ **CHECK YOUR UNDERSTANDING**

Describe the forces that stabilize proteins, and rank their relative importance.
Summarize the results of Anfinsen's experiment with RNase A.

5 Protein Folding

LEARNING OBJECTIVES

■ Understand that a folding protein follows a pathway from high energy and high entropy to low energy and low entropy.
■ Understand that molecular chaperones assist protein folding via an ATP-dependent bind-and-release mechanism.
■ Understand how amyloid diseases result from protein misfolding.

Studies of protein stability and renaturation suggest that protein folding is directed largely by the residues that occupy the interior of the folded protein. But *how* does a protein fold to its native conformation? One might guess that this process occurs through the protein's random exploration of all the conformations available to it until it eventually stumbles onto the correct one. A simple calculation first made by Cyrus Levinthal, however, convincingly demonstrates that this cannot possibly be the case: Assume that an *n*-residue protein's 2^n torsion angles, ϕ and ψ, each have three stable conformations. This yields $3^{2n} \approx 10^n$ possible conformations for the protein (a gross underestimate because we have completely neglected its side chains). Then, if the protein could explore a new conformation every 10^{-13} s (the rate at which single bonds reorient), the time t, in seconds, required for the protein to explore all the conformations available to it is

$$t = \frac{10^n}{10^{13}}$$

For a small protein of 100 residues, $t = 10^{87}$ s, which is immensely greater than the apparent age of the universe (20 billion years, or 6×10^{17} s). Clearly, proteins must fold more rapidly than this.

A | Proteins Follow Folding Pathways

Experiments have shown that many proteins fold to their native conformations in less than a few seconds. This is because *proteins fold to their native conformations via directed pathways rather than stumbling on them through random conformational searches.* Thus, as a protein folds, its conformational stability increases sharply (i.e., its free energy decreases sharply), which makes folding a one-way process. A hypothetical folding pathway is diagrammed in Fig. 6-40.

Experimental observations indicate that protein folding begins with the formation of local segments of secondary structure (α helices and β sheets). This early stage of protein folding is extremely rapid, with much of the native secondary structure in small proteins appearing within 5 ms of the initiation of folding. Since native proteins contain compact hydrophobic cores, it is likely that the driving force in protein folding is what has been termed a **hydrophobic collapse.** The collapsed state is known as a **molten globule,** a species that has much of the secondary structure of the native protein but little of its tertiary structure. Theoretical studies suggest that helices and sheets form in part because they are particularly compact ways of folding a polypeptide chain.

Over the next 5 to 1000 ms, the secondary structure becomes stabilized and tertiary structure begins to form. During this intermediate stage, the nativelike elements are thought to take the form of subdomains that are not yet properly docked to form domains. In the final stage of folding, which for small single-domain proteins occurs over the next few seconds, the protein undergoes a series of complex motions in which it attains its

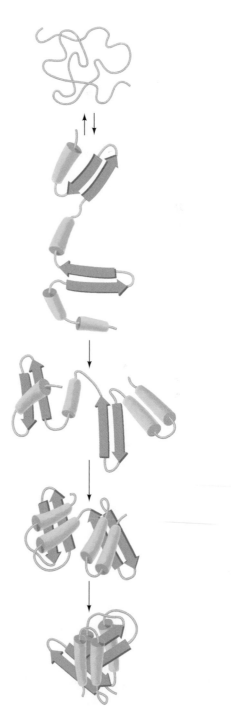

Figure 6-40 | Hypothetical protein folding pathway. This example shows a linear pathway for folding a two-domain protein. [After Goldberg, M.E., *Trends Biochem. Sci.* **10,** 389 (1985).]

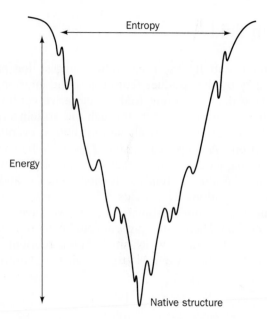

■ **Figure 6-41** | **Energy–entropy diagram for protein folding.** The width of
the diagram represents entropy, and the depth, the energy. The unfolded polypeptide
proceeds from a high-entropy, disordered state (*wide*) to a single low-entropy
(*narrow*), low-energy native conformation. [After Onuchic, J.N., Wolynes, P.G.,
Luthey-Schulten, Z., and Socci, N.D., *Proc. Natl. Acad. Sci.* **92,** 3626 (1995).]

relatively stable internal side chain packing and hydrogen bonding while
it expels the remaining water molecules from its hydrophobic core.

In multidomain and multisubunit proteins, the respective units then assemble in a similar manner, with a few slight conformational adjustments
required to produce the protein's native tertiary or quaternary structure.
Thus, *proteins appear to fold in a hierarchical manner, with small local elements of structure forming and then coalescing to yield larger elements,
which coalesce with other such elements to form yet larger elements, etc.*

Folding, like denaturation, appears to be a cooperative process, with
small elements of structure accelerating the formation of additional structures. A folding protein must proceed from a high-energy, high-entropy
state to a low-energy, low-entropy state. This energy–entropy relationship,
which is diagrammed in Fig. 6-41, is known as a **folding funnel.** An
unfolded polypeptide has many possible conformations (high entropy). As
it folds into an ever-decreasing number of possible conformations, its entropy and free energy decrease. The energy–entropy diagram is not a
smooth valley but a jagged landscape. Minor clefts and gullies represent
conformations that are temporarily trapped until, through random thermal activation, they overcome a slight "uphill" free energy barrier and can
then proceed to a lower energy conformation. Evidently, *proteins have
evolved to have efficient folding pathways as well as stable native
conformations.*

Understanding the process of protein folding as well as the forces that
stabilize folded proteins is essential for elucidating the rules that govern
the relationship between a protein's amino acid sequence and its three-
dimensional structure. Such information will prove useful in predicting the
structures of the hundreds of thousands of proteins that are known only
from their sequences (Box 6-4).

BOX 6-4 PERSPECTIVES IN BIOCHEMISTRY

Protein Structure Prediction and Protein Design

Around one million protein sequences are known, yet the structures of only ~50,000 of these proteins have been determined. Consequently, there is a need to develop robust techniques for predicting a protein's structure from its amino acid sequence. This represents a formidable challenge but promises great rewards in terms of understanding protein function, identifying diseases related to abnormal protein sequences, and designing drugs to alter protein structure or function.

There are several major approaches to protein structure prediction. The simplest and most reliable approach, **homology modeling,** aligns the sequence of interest with the sequence of a homologous protein or domain of known structure—compensating for amino acid substitutions, insertions, and deletions—through modeling and energy minimization calculations. This method yields reliable models for proteins that have as little as 25% sequence identity with a protein of known structure, although, of course, the accuracy of the model increases with the degree of sequence identity. The emerging field of **structural genomics,** which seeks to determine the X-ray structures of all representative domains, is aimed at expanding this predictive technique. The identification of structural homology is likely to provide clues as to a protein's function even with imperfect structure prediction.

Distantly related proteins may be structurally similar even though they have diverged to such an extent that their sequences show no obvious resemblance. **Threading** is a computational technique that attempts to determine the unknown structure of a protein by ascertaining whether it is consistent with a known protein structure. It does so by placing (threading) the unknown protein's residues along the backbone of a known protein structure and then determining whether the amino acid side chains of the unknown protein are stable in that arrangement. This method is not yet reliable, although it has yielded encouraging results.

Empirical methods based on experimentally determined statistical information such as the α helix and β sheet propensities deduced by Chou and Fasman (Table 6-1) have been moderately successful in predicting the secondary structures of proteins. Their main drawback is that neighboring residues in a polypeptide sometimes exert strong influence on a given residue's tendency to form a particular secondary structure.

Since the native structure of a protein ultimately depends on its amino acid sequence, it should be possible, in principle, to predict the structure of a protein based only on its chemical and physical properties (e.g., the hydrophobicity, size, hydrogen-bonding propensity, and charge of each of its amino acid residues). Such **ab initio** (from the beginning) methods are still only moderately successful in predicting the structures of small polypeptides.

Protein design, the experimental inverse of protein structure prediction, has provided insights into protein folding and stability. Protein design attempts to construct an amino acid sequence that will form a structure such as a sandwich of β sheets or a bundle of α helices. The designed polypeptide is then chemically or biologically synthesized, and its structure is determined. Experimental results suggest that the greatest challenge of protein design may lie not in getting the polypeptide to fold to the desired conformation but in preventing it from folding into other unwanted conformations. In this respect, science lags far behind nature.

The first wholly successful *de novo* (beginning anew) protein design, accomplished by Stephen Mayo, was for a 28-residue ββα motif that has a backbone conformation designed to resemble a zinc finger (Fig. 6-37) but that contains no stabilizing metal ions. A computational design process considered the interactions among side chain and backbone atoms, screened all possible amino acid sequences, and, in order to take into account side chain flexibility, tested all sets of energetically allowed torsion angles for each side chain. The number of amino acid sequences to be tested was limited to 1.9×10^{27}, representing 1.1×10^{62} possible conformations! The design process yielded an optimal sequence of 28 residues, which was chemically synthesized and its structure determined by NMR spectroscopy. The designed protein, called FSD-1, closely resembled its predicted structure, and its backbone conformation (blue) was nearly superimposable on that of a known zinc finger motif (red). Although FSD is relatively small, it folds into a unique stable structure, thereby demonstrating the power of protein design techniques.

[Photo courtesy of Stephen Mayo, California Institute of Technology.]

Protein Disulfide Isomerase Acts During Protein Folding. Even under optimal experimental conditions, proteins often fold more slowly *in vitro* than they fold *in vivo*. One reason is that folding proteins often

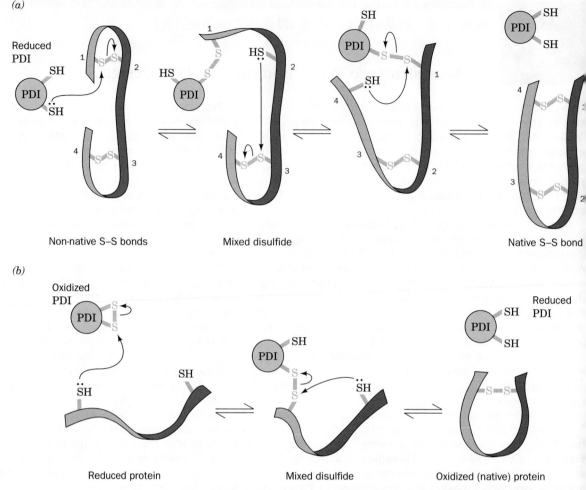

(a)

Reduced PDI

Non-native S–S bonds   Mixed disulfide   Native S–S bond

(b)

Oxidized PDI

Reduced PDI

Reduced protein   Mixed disulfide   Oxidized (native) protein

■ **Figure 6-42** | **Mechanism of protein disulfide isomerase.** (*a*) Reduced (SH-containing) PDI catalyzes the rearrangement of a polypeptide's non-native disulfid bonds via disulfide interchange reactions to yield native disulfide bonds. (*b*) Oxidized (disulfide-containing) PDI catalyzes the initial formation of a polypeptide's disulfide bonds through the formation of a mixed disulfide. Reduced PDI can then react with a cellular oxidizing agent to regenerate oxidized PDI. 🔁 **See the Animated Figures.**

form disulfide bonds not present in the native proteins, and then slowl form native disulfide bonds through the process of disulfide interchange **Protein disulfide isomerase (PDI)** catalyzes this process. Indeed, the ob servation that RNase A folds so much faster *in vivo* than *in vitro* le Anfinsen to discover this enzyme.

PDI binds to a wide variety of unfolded polypeptides via a hydropho bic patch on its surface. A Cys—SH group on reduced (SH-containing PDI reacts with a disulfide group on the polypeptide to form a mixe disulfide and a Cys—SH group on the polypeptide (Fig. 6-42*a*). Anothe disulfide group on the polypeptide, brought into proximity by the sponta neous folding of the polypeptide, is attacked by this Cys—SH group. Th newly liberated Cys—SH group then repeats this process with anothe disulfide bond, and so on, ultimately yielding the polypeptide containin only native disulfide bonds, along with regenerated PDI.

Oxidized (disulfide-containing) PDI also catalyzes the initial formatio of a polypeptide's disulfide bonds by a similar mechanism (Fig. 6-42*b*). I

his case, the reduced PDI reaction product must be reoxidized by cellu-
ar oxidizing agents in order to repeat the process.

Molecular Chaperones Assist Protein Folding

Proteins begin to fold as they are being synthesized, so the renaturation
of a denatured protein *in vitro* may not entirely mimic the folding of a
protein *in vivo*. In addition, proteins fold *in vivo* in the presence of ex-
remely high concentrations of other proteins with which they can poten-
ially interact. *Molecular chaperones are essential proteins that bind to
unfolded and partially folded polypeptide chains to prevent the improper
association of exposed hydrophobic segments that might lead to non-native
folding as well as polypeptide aggregation and precipitation.* This is especially important for multidomain and multisubunit proteins, whose components must fold fully before they can properly associate with each other.
Molecular chaperones also induce misfolded proteins to refold to their native conformations.

Many molecular chaperones were first described as **heat shock proteins
(Hsp)** because their rate of synthesis is increased at elevated temperatures.
Presumably, the additional chaperones are required to recover heat-dena-
tured proteins or to prevent misfolding under conditions of environmental stress.

Chaperone Activity Requires ATP. There are several classes of molecular
chaperones in both prokaryotes and eukaryotes, including (1) the **Hsp70**
family of proteins, which function as monomers; (2) the **chaperonins,** which
are large multisubunit proteins; (3) the **Hsp90** proteins, which are mainly involved with the folding of proteins involved with signal transduction such as
steroid receptors (Section 28-3B); and (4) **trigger factor,** which associates with
the ribosome to prevent the improper folding of polypeptides as they are
being synthesized (Section 27-5A). All of these molecular chaperones operate by binding to an unfolded or aggregated polypeptide's solvent-exposed
hydrophobic surface and subsequently releasing it, often repeatedly, in a
manner that facilitates its proper folding. Molecular chaperones are **ATPases,**
that is, enzymes that catalyze the hydrolysis of ATP (adenosine triphosphate)
to ADP (adenosine diphosphate) and P_i (inorganic phosphate):

$$ATP + H_2O \rightarrow ADP + P_i$$

The favorable free energy change of ATP hydrolysis drives the
chaperone's bind-and-release reaction cycle.

Hsp70 proteins are highly conserved 70-kD proteins in both prokaryotes and eukaryotes. An Hsp70 chaperone, which functions in association
with the **cochaperone** protein **Hsp40,** appears to bind to a newly synthesized polypeptide as it emerges from the ribosome. The chaperone changes
its shape so that it binds the polypeptide loosely or tightly depending on
whether ATP is bound (before the hydrolysis reaction) or ADP is bound
(after hydrolysis). The repeated binding and release of small hydrophobic regions on the new polypeptide may prevent its premature folding. Other chaperones apparently complete the job begun by the Hsp70 proteins. The Hsp70
proteins also function to unfold proteins in preparation for their transport
through membranes (Section 9-4D) and to subsequently refold them.

**The GroEL/ES Chaperonin Forms Closed Chambers in Which Proteins
Fold.** The chaperonins in *E. coli* consist of two types of subunits named
GroEL and **GroES.** The X-ray structure of a GroEL–GroES–(ADP)$_7$

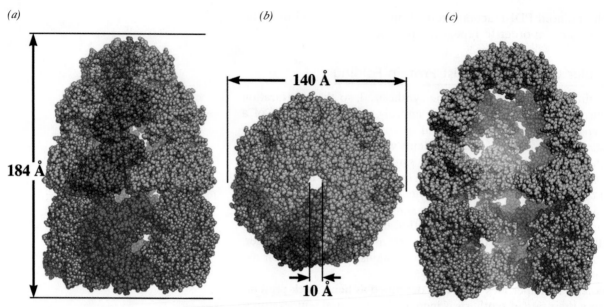

(a)   (b)   (c)

184 Å   140 Å   10 Å

■ **Figure 6-43** | **X-Ray structure of the GroEL–GroES–(ADP)$_7$ complex.** (*a*) A space-filling drawing as viewed perpendicularly to the complex's sevenfold axis with the GroES ring orange, the cis ring of GroEL green, and the trans ring of GroEL red with one subunit of each ring shaded more brightly. The dimensions of the complex are indicated. Note the different conformations of the two GroEL rings. The ADPs, whose binding sites are in the base of each cis ring GroEL subunit, are not seen because they are surrounded by protein. (*b*) As in Part *a* but viewed along the sevenfold axis. (*c*) As in Part *a* but with the two GroEL subunits closest to the viewer in both the cis and trans rings removed to expose the interior of the complex. The level of fog increases with the distance from the viewer. Note the much larger size of the cavity formed by the cis ring and GroES in comparison to that of the trans ring. [Based on an X-ray structure by Paul Sigler, Yale University. PDBid 1AON.]

complex (Fig. 6-43), determined by Arthur Horwich and Paul Sigler, reveals fourteen identical 549-residue GroEL subunits arranged in two stacked rings of seven subunits each. This complex is capped at one end by a domelike heptameric ring of 97-residue GroES subunits to form a bullet-shaped complex with C_7 symmetry. The two GroEL rings each enclose a central chamber with a diameter of ~45 Å in which partially folded proteins fold to their native conformations. A barrier in the center of the complex (Fig. 6-43*c*) prevents a folding protein from passing between the two GroEL chambers. The GroEL ring that contacts the GroES heptamer is called the cis ring; the opposing GroEL ring is known as the trans ring.

ATP Binding and Hydrolysis Drive the Conformational Changes in GroEL/ES. Each GroEL subunit has a binding pocket for ATP that catalyzes the hydrolysis of its bound ATP to ADP + P_i. When the cis ring subunits hydrolyze their bound ATP molecules and release the product P_i, the protein undergoes a conformational change that widens and elongates the cis inner cavity so as to more than double its volume from 85,000 Å^3 to 175,000 Å^3. (In the structure shown in Fig. 6-43, the cis ring has already hydrolyzed its seven molecules of ATP to ADP.) The expanded cavity can enclose a partially folded substrate protein of at least 70 kD. *All seven subunits of the GroEL ring act in concert; that is, they are mechanically linked such that they change their conformations simultaneously.*

The cis and trans GroEL rings undergo conformational changes in a reciprocating fashion, with events in one ring influencing events in the other ring. The entire GroEL/ES chaperonin complex functions as follows (Fig. 6-44):

1. One GroEL ring that has bound 7 ATP also binds an improperly folded substrate protein, which associates with hydrophobic patches

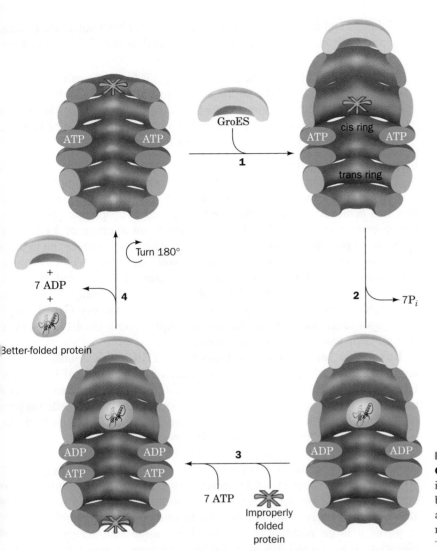

■ **Figure 6-44** **Reaction cycle of the GroEL/ES chaperonin.** The protein complex is drawn in cutaway form with the rings formed by each subunit's equatorial, intermediate, and apical domains colored blue, green, and red, respectively. See the text for an explanation.

that line the inner wall of the GroEL chamber. The GroES cap then binds to the GroEL ring like a lid on a pot, thereby inducing a conformational change in the resulting cis ring that buries the hydrophobic patches, thereby depriving the substrate protein of its binding sites. This releases the substrate protein into the now enlarged and closed cavity, where it commences folding. The cavity, which is now lined only with hydrophilic groups, provides the substrate protein with an isolated microenvironment that prevents it from nonspecifically aggregating with other misfolded proteins. Moreover, the conformational change that buries GroEL's hydrophobic patches stretches and thereby partially unfolds the improperly folded substrate protein before it is released. This rescues the substrate protein from a local energy minimum in which it had become trapped (Fig. 6-41) thereby permitting it to continue its conformational journey down the folding funnel toward its native state (the state of lowest free energy.

2. Within ~13 s (the time the substrate protein has to fold), the cis ring catalyzes the hydrolysis of its 7 bound ATPs to ADP + P_i and the P_i is released. The absence of ATP's γ phosphate group weakens the interactions that bind GroES to GroEL.

3. A second molecule of improperly folded substrate protein binds to the trans ring followed by 7 ATP. Conformational linkages between the cis and trans rings prevent the binding of both substrate protein and ATP to the trans ring until the ATP in the cis ring has been hydrolyzed.

4. The binding of substrate protein and ATP to the trans ring conformationally induces the cis ring to release its bound GroES, 7 ADP and the presumably now better-folded substrate protein. This leaves ATP and substrate protein bound only to the trans ring of GroEL which now becomes the cis ring as it binds GroES.

Steps 1 through 4 are then repeated. The GroEL/ES system expends 7 ATPs per folding cycle. If the released substrate protein has not achieved its native state, it may subsequently rebind to GroEL (a substrate protein that has achieved its native fold lacks exposed hydrophobic groups and hence cannot rebind to GroEL). It requires an average of 24 folding cycles for a protein to attain its native state, which necessitates the hydrolysis of 168 ATPs (which appears to be a profligate use of ATP but constitutes only a small fraction of the thousands of ATPs that must be hydrolyzed to synthesize a typical polypeptide and its component amino acids). Because protein folding occurs alternately in the two GroEL rings, the proper functioning of the chaperonin requires both GroEL rings, even though their two cavities are unconnected.

Eukaryotic cells contain the chaperonin **TRiC,** with double rings of eight nonidentical subunits, each of which resembles a GroEL subunit. However, the TRiC proteins contain an additional segment that acts as a built-in lid, so the complex encloses a polypeptide chain and mediates protein folding without the assistance of a GroES-like cap. Like its bacterial counterpart, TRiC operates in an ATP-dependent fashion.

Experiments indicate that the GroEL/ES system interacts with only a subset of *E. coli* proteins, most with molecular masses in the range 20 to 60 kD. These proteins tend to contain two or more α/β domains that mainly consist of open β sheets. Such proteins are expected to fold only slowly to their native state because the formation of hydrophobic β sheets requires a large number of specific long-range interactions. Proteins dissociate from GroEL/ES after folding, but some frequently revisit the chaperonin, apparently because they are structurally labile or prone to aggregate and must return to GroEL for periodic maintenance.

C | Some Diseases Are Caused by Protein Misfolding

Most proteins in the body maintain their native conformations or, if they become partially denatured, are either renatured through the auspices of molecular chaperones or are proteolytically degraded (Section 21-1). However, at least 20 different—and usually fatal—human diseases are associated with the extracellular deposition of normally soluble proteins in certain tissues in the form of insoluble fibrous aggregates (Table 6-4). The aggregates are known as **amyloids,** a term that means starchlike because it was originally thought that the material resembled starch.

The diseases known as **amyloidoses** are a set of relatively rare inherited diseases in which mutant forms of normally occurring proteins [e.g., **lysozyme,** an enzyme that hydrolyzes bacterial cell walls (Section 11-4), and **fibrinogen,** a blood plasma protein that is the precursor of **fibrin,** which forms blood clots (Box 11-4)] accumulate in a variety of tissues as amyloids. The symptoms of amyloidoses usually do not become apparent until the third to seventh decade of life and typically progress over 5 to 15 years, ending in death.

Table 6-4	Some Protein Misfolding Diseases
Disease	**Defective Protein**
Alzheimer's disease	Amyloid-β protein
Amyotrophic lateral sclerosis	Superoxide dismutase
Huntington's disease	Huntingtin with polyglutamate expansion
Lysozyme amyloidosis	Lysozyme
Hereditary renal amyloidosis	Fibrinogen
Parkinson's disease	α-Synuclein
Transmissible spongiform encephalopathies (TSEs)	Prion protein

Amyloid-β Protein Accumulates in Alzheimer's Disease. **Alzheimer's disease,** a neurodegenerative condition that strikes mainly the elderly, causes devastating mental deterioration and eventual death (it affects ~10% of those over 65 and ~50% of those over 85). It is characterized by brain tissue containing abundant amyloid **plaques** (deposits) surrounded by dead and dying neurons (Fig. 6-45). The amyloid plaques consist mainly of fibrils of a 40- to 42-residue protein named **amyloid-β protein (Aβ).** Aβ is a fragment of a 770-residue membrane protein called the **Aβ precursor protein (βPP),** whose normal function is unknown. Aβ is excised from βPP in a multistep process through the actions of two proteolytic enzymes dubbed **β-** and **γ-secretases.** The neurotoxic effects of Aβ begin even before significant amyloid deposits appear (see below).

The age dependence of Alzheimer's disease suggests that Aβ deposition is an ongoing process. Indeed, several rare mutations in the βPP gene that increase the rate of Aβ production result in the onset of Alzheimer's disease as early as the fourth decade of life. A similar phenomenon occurs in individuals with **Down's syndrome,** a condition characterized by mental retardation and a distinctive physical appearance caused by the trisomy (3 copies per cell) of chromosome 21 rather than the normal two copies. These individuals invariably develop Alzheimer's disease by their 40th year because the gene encoding βPP is located on chromosome 21 and hence individuals with Down's syndrome produce βPP and presumably Aβ at an accelerated rate. Consequently, a promising strategy for halting the progression of Alzheimer's disease is to develop drugs that inhibit the action of the β- and/or γ-secretases so as to decrease the rate of Aβ production.

Prion Diseases Are Infectious. Certain diseases that affect the mammalian central nervous system were originally thought to be caused by "slow viruses" because they take months, years, or even decades to develop. Among them are **scrapie** (a neurological disorder of sheep and goats), **bovine spongiform encephalopathy (BSE** or **mad cow disease),** and **kuru** (a degenerative brain disease in humans that was transmitted by ritual cannibalism among the Fore people of Papua New Guinea; *kuru* means "trembling"). There is also a sporadic (spontaneously arising) human disease with similar symptoms, **Creutzfeldt–Jakob disease (CJD),** which strikes one person per million per year and which may

■ **Figure 6-45** | **Brain tissue from an individual with Alzheimer's disease.** The two circular objects in this photomicrograph are plaques that consist of amyloid deposits of Aβ protein surrounded by a halo of neurites (axons and dendrites) from dead and dying neurons. [Courtesy of Dennis Selkoe and Marcia Podlisny, Harvard University Medical School.]

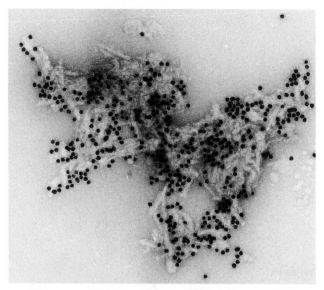

■ Figure 6-46 | Electron micrograph of a cluster of partially proteolyzed prion rods. The black dots are colloidal gold beads that are coupled to anti-PrP antibodies adhering to the PrP. [Courtesy of Stanley Pruisner, University of California at San Francisco Medical Center.]

be identical to kuru. In all of these invariably fatal diseases, neurons develop large vacuoles that give brain tissue a spongelike microscopic appearance. Hence the diseases are collectively known as **transmissible spongiform encephalopathies (TSEs).**

Unlike other infectious diseases, *the TSEs are not caused by a virus or microorganism.* Indeed, extensive investigations have failed to show that they are associated with any nucleic acid. Instead, as Stanley Pruisner demonstrated for scrapie, the infectious agent is a protein called a **prion** (for *pro*teinaceous *in*fectious particle that lacks nucleic acid) and hence TSEs are alternatively called **prion diseases.** The scrapie prion, which is named **PrP** (for *Pr*ion *P*rotein), consists of 208 mostly hydrophobic residues. This hydrophobicity causes partially proteolyzed PrP to aggregate as clusters of rodlike particles that closely resemble the amyloid fibrils seen on electron microscopic examination of prion-infected brain tissue (Fig. 6-46). These fibrils presumably form the amyloid plaques that accompany the neuronal degeneration in TSEs.

How are prion diseases transmitted? PrP is the product of a normal cellular gene that has no known function (genetically engineered mice that fail to express PrP appear to be normal). Infection of cells by prions somehow alters the PrP protein. Various methods have demonstrated that the scrapie form of PrP (PrP^{Sc}) is identical to normal cellular PrP (PrP^C) in sequence but differs in secondary and/or tertiary structure. This suggests that *PrP^{Sc} induces PrP^C to adopt the conformation of PrP^{Sc}*; that is, a small amount of PrP^{Sc} triggers the formation of additional PrP^{Sc} from PrP^C, which triggers more PrP^{Sc} to form, and so on. This accounts for the observation that mice that do not express the gene encoding PrP cannot be infected with scrapie.

Human PrP^C consists of a disordered (and hence unseen) 99-residue N-terminal "tail" and a 110-residue C-terminal globular domain containing three α helices and a short two-stranded antiparallel β sheet (Fig. 6-47a). Unfortunately, the insolubility of PrP^{Sc} has precluded its structural

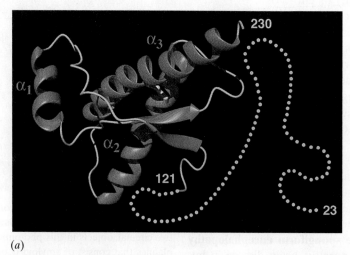

(a)

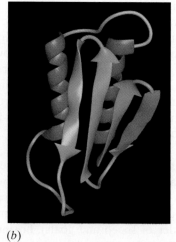

(b)

■ Figure 6-47 | Prion protein conformations. (*a*) The NMR structure of human prion protein (PrP^C). Its flexibly disordered N-terminal "tail" (residues 23–121) is represented by yellow dots (the protein's N-terminal 22 residues have been posttranslationally excised). (*b*) A plausible model for the structure of PrP^{Sc}. [Part *a* courtesy of Kurt Wüthrich, Eidgenössische Technische Hochschule, Zurich, Switzerland. Part *b* courtesy of Fred Cohen University of California at San Francisco.]

determination, but spectroscopic methods indicate that it has a lower α helix content and a higher β sheet content than PrP^C. This suggests that the protein has refolded (Fig. 6-47b). The high β sheet content of PrP^{Sc} presumably facilitates the aggregation of PrP^{Sc} as amyloid fibrils (see below).

Prion diseases can be transmitted by the consumption of nerve tissue from infected individuals, as illustrated by the incidence of BSE. This disease was unknown before 1985 but reached epidemic proportions among cattle in the U.K. in 1993. The rise in BSE reflects the practice, beginning in the 1970s, of feeding cattle preparations of meat-and-bone meal that were derived from other animals by a method that failed to inactivate prions. The BSE epidemic abated due to the banning of such feeding in 1988, together with the slaughter of a large number of animals at risk for having BSE. However, it is now clear that BSE was transmitted to humans who ate meat from BSE-infected cattle: Some 160 cases of so-called **new variant CJD** have been reported to date, almost entirely in the U.K., many of which occurred in teenagers and young adults. Yet before 1994, CJD under the age of 40 was extremely rare. It should be noted that the transmission of BSE from cattle to humans was unexpected: Scrapie-infected sheep have long been consumed worldwide and yet the incidence of CJD in mainly meat-eating countries such as the U.K. (in which sheep are particularly abundant) was no greater than that in largely vegetarian countries such as India.

Amyloid Fibrils Are β Sheet Structures. The amyloid fibers that characterize the amyloidoses, Alzheimer's disease, and the TSEs are built from proteins that exhibit no structural or functional similarities in their native states. In contrast, the appearance of their fibrillar forms is strikingly similar. Spectroscopic analysis of amyloid fibrils indicates that they are rich in β structure, with individual β strands oriented perpendicular to the fiber axis (Fig. 6-48). Furthermore, the ability to form amyloid fibrils is not unique to the small set of proteins associated with specific diseases. Under the appropriate conditions, almost any protein can be induced to aggregate. Thus, *the ability to form amyloid may be an intrinsic property of all polypeptide chains.*

A variety of experiments indicate that amyloidogenic mutant proteins are significantly less stable than their wild-type counterparts (e.g., they have significantly lower melting temperatures). This suggests that the partially unfolded, aggregation-prone forms are in equilibrium with the native conformation even under conditions in which the native state is thermodynamically stable [keep in mind that the equilibrium ratio of unfolded (U) to native (N) protein molecules in the reaction N ⇌ U is governed by Eq. 1-17: $K_{eq} = [U]/[N] = e^{-\Delta G°'/RT}$, where $\Delta G°'$ is the standard free energy of unfolding,

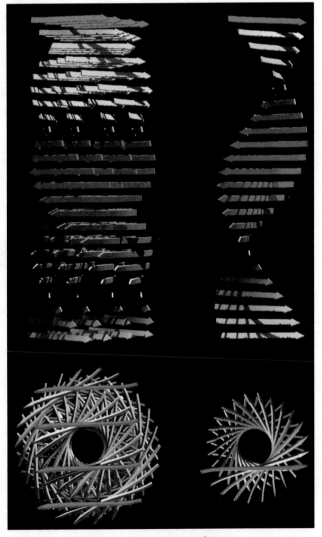

Figure 6-48 | Model of an amyloid fibril. (*a*) The model, based on X-ray fiber diffraction measurements, is viewed normal to the fibril axis (*above*) and along the fibril axis (*below*). The arrowheads indicate the path but not necessarily the direction of the β strands. (*b*) A single β sheet, which is shown for clarity. The loop regions connecting the β strands have unknown structure. [Courtesy of Colin Blake, Oxford University, Oxford, U.K., and Louise Serpell, University of Cambridge, U.K.]

(*a*)   (*b*)

so that as $\Delta G^{\circ\prime}$ decreases, the equilibrium proportion of U increases]. It i therefore likely that fibril formation is initiated by the association of th β domains of two or more partially unfolded amyloidogenic proteins t form a more extensive β sheet. This would provide a template or nucleu for the recruitment of additional polypeptide chains to form the growin; fibril. Since most amyloid diseases require several decades to becom symptomatic, the development of an amyloid nucleus must be a rare event Once an amyloid fiber begins to grow, however, its development is mor rapid.

The factors that trigger amyloid formation remain obscure, even whe mutations (in the case of hereditary amyloidoses) or infection (in the cas of TSEs) appear to be the cause. After it has formed, an amyloid fibril i virtually indestructible under physiological conditions, possibly due to th large number of main-chain hydrogen bonds that must be broken in or der to separate the individual polypeptide strands (side chain interaction are less important in stabilizing β sheets). It seems likely that protein fold ing pathways have evolved not only to allow polypeptides to assume sta ble native structures but also to avoid forming interchain hydrogen bond that would lead to fibril formation.

Are fibrillar deposits directly responsible for the neurodegeneratio seen in many amyloid diseases? A growing body of evidence suggests tha cellular damage begins when the misfolded proteins first aggregate but ar still soluble. For example, in mouse models of Alzheimer's disease, cogni tive impairment is evident before amyloid plaques develop. Other exper iments show that the most infectious prion preparations contain just 14–2{ PrP^{Sc} molecules, that is, a nucleus for a fibril, not the fibril itself. Even modest number of misfolded protein molecules could be toxic if they pre vented the cell's chaperones from assisting other more critical proteins t fold. The appearance of extracellular—and sometimes intracellular—amy loid fibrils may simply represent the accumulation of protein that ha overwhelmed the cellular mechanisms that govern protein folding or th disposal of misfolded proteins.

■ **CHECK YOUR UNDERSTANDING**

Describe the energy and entropy changes that occur during protein folding.

How does protein renaturation *in vitro* differ from protein folding *in vivo*?

Explain the role of ATP in the action of Hsp70 and GroEL/ES.

What are amyloid fibrils, what is their origin, and why are they harmful?

SUMMARY

1. Four levels of structural complexity are used to describe the three-dimensional shapes of proteins.

2. The conformational flexibility of the peptide group is described by its ϕ and ψ torsion angles.

3. The α helix is a regular secondary structure in which hydrogen bonds form between backbone groups four residues apart. In the β sheet, hydrogen bonds form between the backbones of separate polypeptide segments.

4. Fibrous proteins are characterized by a single type of secondary structure: α keratin is a left-handed coil of two α helices, and collagen is a left-handed triple helix with three residues per turn.

5. The structures of proteins have been determined mainly by X-ray crystallography and NMR spectroscopy.

6. The nonpolar side chains of a globular protein tend to occupy the protein's interior, whereas the polar side chains tend to define its surface.

7. Protein structures can be classified on the basis of motifs, sec ondary structure content, topology, or domain architecture Structural elements are more likely to be evolutionarily con served than are amino acid sequences.

8. The field of structural bioinformatics is concerned with th storage, visualization, analysis, and comparison of macromol ecular structures.

9. The individual subunits of multisubunit proteins are usuall symmetrically arranged.

10. Native protein structures are only slightly more stable tha their denatured forms. The hydrophobic effect is the primar determinant of protein stability. Hydrogen bonding and ior pairing contribute relatively little to a protein's stability.

11. Studies of protein denaturation and renaturation indicate tha the primary structure of a protein determines its three-dimen sional structure.

12. Proteins fold to their native conformations via directe

pathways in which small elements of structure coalesce into larger structures.

13. Molecular chaperones facilitate protein folding *in vivo* by repeatedly binding and releasing a polypeptide in an ATP-dependent manner and providing it with an isolated microenvironment in which to fold.

14. Diseases caused by protein misfolding include the amyloidoses, Alzheimer's disease, and the transmissible spongiform encephalopathies (TSEs).

KEY TERMS

secondary structure 126
tertiary structure 126
quaternary structure 126
peptide group 127
trans conformation 127
cis conformation 127
backbone 127
torsion (dihedral) angle 128
ϕ 128
ψ 128
Ramachandran diagram 129
α helix 129
regular secondary
    structure 129
pitch 131
antiparallel β sheet 132
parallel β sheet 132
topology 134

reverse turn (β bend) 134
fibrous protein 134
globular protein 134
coiled coil 135
random coil 139
denaturation 139
native structure 139
β bulge 139
helix cap 140
X-ray crystallography 141
diffraction pattern 141
electron density 141
contour map 141
NMR 143
supersecondary structure
    (motif) 146
$\beta\alpha\beta$ motif 146
β hairpin 146

$\alpha\alpha$ motif 146
β barrel 148
α/β barrel 148
domain 149
dinucleotide-binding
    (Rossmann) fold 150
structural bioinformatics 151
oligomer 154
protomer 154
rotational symmetry 155
cyclic symmetry 155
dihedral symmetry 155
hydropathy 156
ion pair (salt bridge) 157
zinc finger 158
breathing 158
cooperativity 158
chaotropic agent 159

renaturation 160
hydrophobic collapse 161
molten globule 161
homology modeling 163
threading 163
ab initio 163
molecular chaperone 165
heat shock protein 165
chaperonin 165
ATPase 165
amyloid 168
Alzheimer's disease 169
transmissible spongiform
    encephalopathies
    (TSEs) 169
Creutzfeldt–Jakob
    disease 169
prion 170

PROBLEMS

1. Draw a cis peptide bond and identify the groups that experience steric interference.

2. Helices can be described by the notation n_m, where n is the number of residues per helical turn and m is the number of atoms, including H, in the ring that is closed by the hydrogen bond. (a) What is this notation for the α helix? (b) Is the 3_{10} helix steeper or shallower than the α helix?

3. Calculate the length in angstroms of a 100-residue segment of the α keratin coiled coil.

4. Hydrophobic residues usually appear at the first and fourth positions in the seven-residue repeats of polypeptides that form coiled coils. (a) Why do polar or charged residues usually appear in the remaining five positions? (b) Why is the sequence Ile–Gln–Glu–Val–Glu–Arg–Asp more likely than the sequence Trp–Gln–Glu–Tyr–Glu–Arg–Asp to appear in a coiled coil?

5. Globular proteins are typically constructed from several layers of secondary structure, with a hydrophobic core and a hydrophilic surface. Is this true for a fibrous protein such as α keratin?

6. The digestive tract of the larvae of clothes moths is a strongly reducing environment. Why is this beneficial to the larvae?

7. Describe the primary, secondary, tertiary, and quaternary structures of collagen.

8. Explain why gelatin, which is mostly collagen, is nutritionally inferior to other types of protein.

9. Is it possible for a native protein to be entirely irregular, that is, without α helices, β sheets, or other repetitive secondary structure?

10. (a) Is Trp or Gln more likely to be on a protein's surface? (b) Is Ser or Val less likely to be in the protein's interior? (c) Is Leu or Ile less likely to be found in the middle of an α helix? (d) Is Cys or Ser more likely to be in a β sheet?

11. What types of rotational symmetry are possible for a protein with (a) four or (b) six identical subunits?

12. You are performing site-directed mutagenesis to test predictions about which residues are essential for a protein's function. Which of each pair of amino acid substitutions listed below would you expect to disrupt protein structure the most? Explain.

    (a) Val replaced by Ala or Phe.

    (b) Lys replaced by Asp or Arg.

    (c) Gln replaced by Glu or Asn.

    (d) Pro replaced by His or Gly.

13. Laboratory techniques for randomly linking together amino acids typically generate an insoluble polypeptide, yet a naturally occurring polypeptide of the same length is usually soluble. Explain.

14. Given enough time, can all denatured proteins spontaneously renature?

15. Describe the intra- and intermolecular bonds or interactions that are broken or retained when collagen is heated to produce gelatin.

16. Under physiological conditions, polylysine assumes a random coil conformation. Under what conditions might it form an α helix?

17. It is often stated that proteins are quite large compared to the molecules they bind. However, what constitutes a large number depends on your point of view. Calculate the ratio of the volume of a hemoglobin molecule (65 kD) to that of the four O_2 molecules that it binds and the ratio of the volume of a typical office ($4 \times 4 \times 3$ m) to that of the typical (70-kg) office worker that occupies it. Assume that the molecular volumes of hemoglobin and O_2 are in equal proportions to their molecular masses and that the office worker has a density of 1.0 g/cm^3. Compare these ratios. Is this the result you expected?

18. Which of the following polypeptides is most likely to form an α helix? Which is least likely to form a β strand?
    (a) CRAGNRKIVLETY
    (b) SEDNFGAPKSILW
    (c) QKASVEMAVRNSG

19. The X-ray crystallographic analysis of a protein often fails to reveal the positions of the first few and/or the last few residues of a polypeptide chain. Explain.

CASE STUDIES

Case 4 (available at www.wiley.com/college/voet)
The Structure of Insulin

Focus concept: The primary structure of insulin is examined, and the sequences of various animal insulins are compared.

Prerequisites: Chapters 4, 5, and 6
• Amino acid structure
• Protein architecture
• Basic immunology

Case 5
Characterization of Subtilisin from the Antarctic Psychrophile Bacillus TA41

Focus concept: The structural features involved in protein adaptation to cold temperatures are explored.

Prerequisite: Chapter 6
• Protein architecture
• Principles of protein folding

Case 6
A Collection of Collagen Cases

Focus concept: Factors important in the stability of collagen are examined.

Prerequisites: Chapters 4, 5, and 6
• Amino acid structures and properties
• Primary and secondary structure
• Basic collagen structure

BIOINFORMATICS EXERCISES

Bioinformatics Exercises are available at www.wiley.com/college/voet.

Chapter 6
Visualizing Three-Dimensional Protein Structures
1. **Obtaining Structural Information.** Compare different secondary structure predictions for a given protein sequence, then inspect its X-ray crystallographic structure.
2. **Exploring the Protein Data Bank.** Learn how to locate and download specific protein structure files, sequences, and images. Explore additional educational resources such as Molecule of the Month and links to additional structural biology resources.
3. **Using RasMmol and PyMol.** Examine a protein structure file and use basic molecular modeling programs to visualize the protein and highlight selected features.
4. **Protein Families.** Identify homologous proteins in other structural databases.

REFERENCES

General
Bourne, P.E. and Weissig, H. (Eds.), *Structural Bioinformatics*, Wiley-Liss (2003).

Branden, C. and Tooze, J., *Introduction to Protein Structure* (2nd ed.), Garland Publishing (1999). [A well-illustrated book with chapters introducing amino acids and protein structure, plus chapters on specific proteins categorized by their structure and function.]

Goodsell, D.S., Visual methods from atoms to cells, *Structure* **13,** 347–454 (2005). [Discusses several ways of depicting different features of molecular structures.]

Goodsell, D.S. and Olson, J., Structural symmetry and protein function, *Annu. Rev. Biophys. Biomol. Struct.* **29,** 105–153 (2000).

Lesk, A.M., *Introduction to Protein Science*, Oxford University Press (2004).

Petsko, G.A. and Ringe, D., *Protein Structure and Function,* New Science Press (2004).

Fibrous Proteins

Brodsky, B. and Persikov, A.V., Molecular structure of the collagen triple helix, *Adv. Protein Chem.* **70,** 301–339 (2005).

Macromolecular Structure Determination

McPherson, A., *Macromolecular Crystallography,* Wiley (2002).

Rhodes, G., *Crystallography Made Crystal Clear: A Guide for Users of Macromolecular Models* (3rd ed.), Academic Press (2006). [Includes overviews, methods, and discussions of model quality.]

Wider, G. and Wüthrich, K., NMR spectroscopy of large molecules and multimolecular assemblies in solution, *Curr. Opin. Struct. Biol.* **9,** 594–601 (1999).

Protein Stability

Fersht, A., *Structure and Mechanism in Protein Science,* Chapter 11, Freeman (1999).

Karplus, M. and McCammon, J.A., Molecular dynamics simulations of biomolecules, *Nature Struct. Biol.* **9,** 646–652 (2002).

Protein Folding

Fitzkee, N.C., Fleming, P.J., Gong, H., Panasik, N., Jr., Street, T.O., and Rose, G.D., Are proteins made from a limited parts list? *Trends Biochem. Sci.* **30,** 73–80 (2005).

Onuchic, J.N. and Wolynes, P.G., Theory of protein folding, *Curr. Opin. Struct. Biol.* **14,** 70–75 (2004).

Schueler-Furman, O., Wang, C., Bradley, P., Misura, K., and Baker, D., Progress in modeling of protein structures and interactions, *Science* **310,** 638–642 (2005).

Young, J.C., Agashe, V.R., Siegers, K., and Hartl, F.U., Pathways of chaperone-mediated protein folding in the cytosol, *Nature Reviews Mol. Cell Biol.* **5,** 781–791 (2004). [Summarizes the types and activities of chaperones that function in prokaryotes and eukaryotes.]

Protein Misfolding Diseases

Dobson, C.M., Protein folding and misfolding, *Nature* **426,** 884–890 (2003).

Selkoe, D.J., Cell biology of protein misfolding: the examples of Alzheimer's and Parkinson's diseases, *Nature Cell Biol.* **6,** 1054–1061 (2004). [Describes the relationship between protein misfolding and cellular pathology.]

Weissmann, C., The state of the prion, *Nature Reviews Microbiol.* **2,** 861–862 (2004).

7

Protein Function: Myoglobin and Hemoglobin, Muscle Contraction, and Antibodies

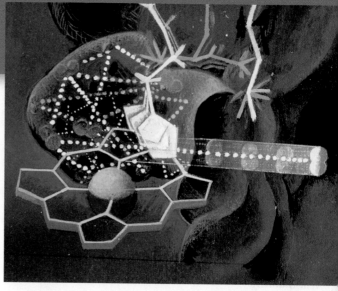

The structure of a protein determines its biological role. The oxygen-binding site of myoglobin is structured so that O_2 can bind or, as pictured here, escape from the protein. [Illustration, Irving Geis. Image from the Irving Geis Collection/Howard Hughes Medical Institute. Rights owned by HHMI. Reproduction by permission only.]

■ **CHAPTER CONTENTS**

1 Oxygen Binding to Myoglobin and Hemoglobin

  A. Myoglobin Is a Monomeric Oxygen-Binding Protein

  B. Hemoglobin Is a Tetramer with Two Conformations

  C. Oxygen Binds Cooperatively to Hemoglobin

  D. Hemoglobin's Two Conformations Exhibit Different Affinities for Oxygen

  E. Mutations May Alter Hemoglobin's Structure and Function

2 Muscle Contraction

  A. Muscle Consists of Interdigitated Thick and Thin Filaments

  B. Muscle Contraction Occurs When Myosin Heads Walk Up Thin Filaments

  C. Actin Forms Microfilaments in Nonmuscle Cells

3 Antibodies

  A. Antibodies Have Constant and Variable Regions

  B. Antibodies Recognize a Huge Variety of Antigens

■ **MEDIA RESOURCES**

(available at www.wiley.com/college/voet)

Interactive Exercise 3. Structure of a mouse antibody

Animated Figure 7-6. Oxygen-binding curve of hemoglobin

Animated Figure 7-8. Movements of heme and F helix in hemoglobin

Animated Figure 7-11. The Bohr effect

Animated Figure 7-13. Effect of BPG and CO_2 on hemoglobin

Animated Figure 7-32. Mechanism of force generation in muscle

Kinemage 6-1. Myoglobin structure

Kinemage 6-2, 6-3. Hemoglobin structure

Kinemage 6-3. BPG binding to hemoglobin

Kinemage 6-4. Conformational changes in hemoglobin

Kinemage 6-5. Changes at $\alpha_1–\beta_2/\alpha_2–\beta_1$ interfaces in hemoglobin

Case Study 8. Hemoglobin, the Oxygen Carrier

Case Study 9. Allosteric Interactions in Crocodile Hemoglobin

Case Study 10. The Biological Roles of Nitric Oxide

The preceding two chapters have painted a broad picture of the chemical and physical properties of proteins but have not delved deeply into their physiological functions. Nevertheless, it should come as no surprise that the structural complexity and variety of proteins allow them to carry out an enormous array of specialized biological tasks. For example, the enzyme catalysts of virtually all metabolic reactions are proteins (we consider enzymes in detail in Chapters 11 and 12). Genetic information would remain locked in DNA were it not for the proteins that participate in decoding and transmitting that information. Remarkably, the thousands of proteins that participate in building, supporting, recognizing, transporting, and transforming cellular components act with incredible speed and accuracy and in many cases are subject to multiple regulatory mechanisms.

The specialized functions of proteins, from the fibrous proteins we examined in Section 6-1C to the precisely regulated metabolic enzymes we discuss in later chapters, can all be understood in terms of how proteins bind to and interact with other components of living systems. In this chapter, we focus on three sets of proteins: the oxygen-binding proteins myoglobin and hemoglobin, the actin and myosin proteins responsible for muscle contraction, and antibody molecules. The molecular structures and physiological roles of these proteins are known in detail, and their proper functioning is vital for human health. In addition, these proteins serve as models for many of the proteins we will examine later when we discuss metabolism and the management of genetic information.

1 Oxygen Binding to Myoglobin and Hemoglobin

We begin our study of protein function with two proteins that reversibly bind molecular oxygen (O_2). **Myoglobin,** the first protein whose structure was determined by X-ray crystallography, is a small protein with relatively simple oxygen-binding behavior. **Hemoglobin,** a tetramer of myoglobin-like polypeptides, is a more complicated protein that functions as a sophisticated system for delivering oxygen to tissues throughout the body. The efficiency with which hemoglobin binds and releases O_2 is reminiscent of the specificity and efficiency of metabolic enzymes. It is worthwhile to study hemoglobin's structure and function because many of the theories formulated to explain O_2 binding to hemoglobin also explain the control of enzyme activity.

A | Myoglobin Is a Monomeric Oxygen-Binding Protein

Myoglobin is a small intracellular protein in vertebrate muscle. Its X-ray structure, determined by John Kendrew in 1959, revealed that most of myoglobin's 153 residues are members of eight α helices (traditionally labeled A through H) that are arranged to form a globular protein with approximate dimensions $44 \times 44 \times 25$ Å (Fig. 7-1).

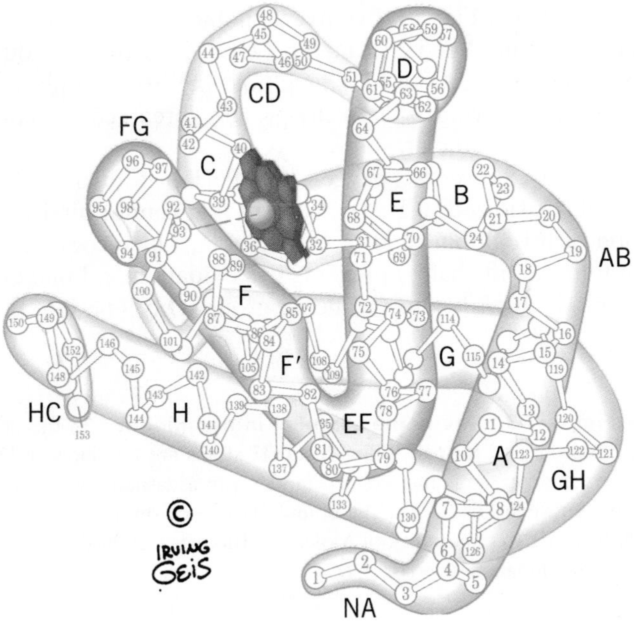

LEARNING OBJECTIVES

- Understand that myoglobin, with its single heme prosthetic group, exhibits a hyperbolic O_2-binding curve.
- Understand that hemoglobin can adopt the deoxy (T) or oxy (R) conformation, which differ in their O_2-binding affinity.
- Understand that oxygen binding triggers conformational changes in hemoglobin so that oxygen binds to the protein cooperatively, yielding a sigmoidal binding curve.
- Understand how the Bohr effect and BPG alter oxygen binding and transport by hemoglobin *in vivo*.
- Understand that amino acid mutations in hemoglobin can alter oxygen binding and cause disease.

■ **Figure 7-1 | Structure of sperm whale myoglobin.** This 153-residue monomeric protein consists of eight α helices, labeled A through H, that are connected by short polypeptide links (the last half of what was originally thought to be the EF corner has been shown to form a short helix that is designated the F′ helix). The heme group is shown in red. [Illustration, Irving Geis. Image from the Irving Geis Collection/Howard Hughes Medical Institute. Rights owned by HHMI. Reproduction by permission only.] **See Kinemage Exercise 6-1.**

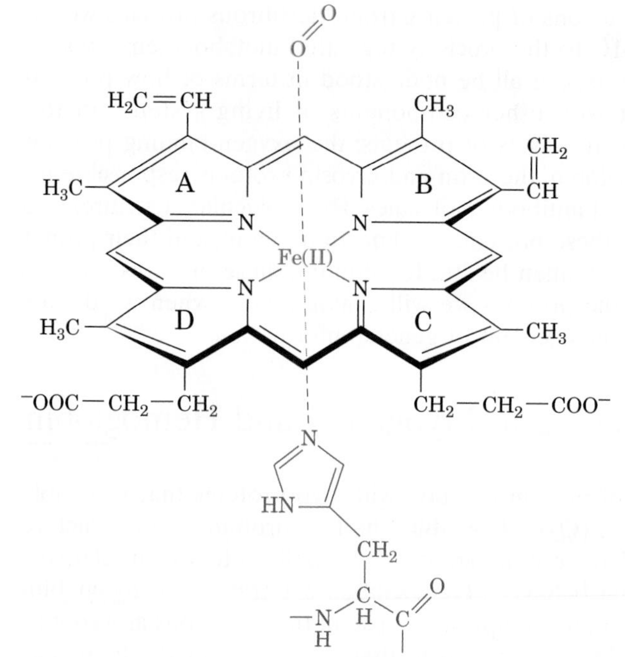

Figure 7-2 | The heme group. The central Fe(II) atom is shown liganded to four N atoms of the porphyrin ring, whose pyrrole groups are labeled A–D. The heme is a conjugated system, so all the Fe—N bonds are equivalent. The Fe(II) is also liganded to a His side chain and, when it is present, to O_2. The six ligands are arranged at the corners of an octahedron centered on the Fe ion (octahedral geometry).

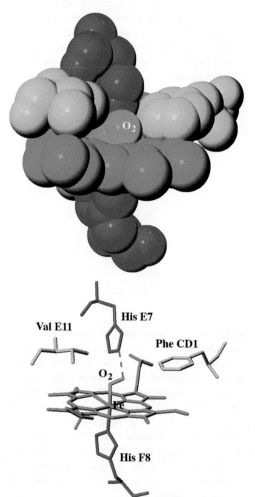

Myoglobin Contains a Heme Prosthetic Group. Myoglobin, other members of the globin family of proteins (Section 5-4B), and a variety of other proteins such as cytochrome *c* (Sections 5-4A and 6-2D) all contain a single **heme** group (Fig. 7-2). The heme is tightly wedged in a hydrophobic pocket between the E and F helices in myoglobin. The heterocyclic ring system of heme is a **porphyrin** derivative containing four **pyrrole** groups (labeled A–D) linked by methene bridges (other porphyrins vary in the substituents attached to rings A–D). The Fe(II) atom at the center of heme is coordinated by the four porphyrin N atoms and one N from a His side chain (called, in a nomenclature peculiar to myoglobin and hemoglobin, His F8 because it is the eighth residue of the F helix). A molecule of oxygen (O_2) can act as a sixth ligand to the iron atom. His E7 (the seventh residue of helix E) hydrogen bonds to the O_2 with the geometry shown in Fig. 7-3. Two hydrophobic side chains on the O_2-binding side of the heme, Val E11 and Phe CD1 (the first residue in the segment between helices C and D), help hold the heme in place. These side chains presumably swing aside as the protein "breathes" (Section 6-4A), allowing O_2 to enter and exit.

When exposed to oxygen, the Fe(II) atom of isolated heme is irreversibly oxidized to Fe(III), a form that cannot bind O_2. The protein portion of myoglobin (and of hemoglobin, which contains four heme groups in four globin chains) prevents this oxidation and makes it possible for O_2 to bind reversibly to the heme group. **Oxygenation** alters the electronic

Figure 7-3 | The heme complex in myoglobin. In the upper drawing, atoms are represented in space-filling form (H atoms are not shown). The lower drawing shows the corresponding skeletal model with a dashed line representing the hydrogen bond between His E7 and the bound O_2. [Based on an X-ray structure by Simon Phillips, MRC Laboratory of Molecular Biology, Cambridge, U.K. PDBid 1MBO.]
See Kinemage Exercise 6-1.

tate of the Fe(II)–heme complex, as indicated by its color change from dark purple (the color of hemoglobin in venous blood) to brilliant scarlet the color of hemoglobin in arterial blood). Under some conditions, the Fe(II) of myoglobin or hemoglobin becomes oxidized to Fe(III) to form **netmyoglobin** or **methemoglobin,** respectively; these proteins are responsible for the brown color of old meat and dried blood.

In addition to O_2, certain other small molecules such as CO, NO, and H_2S can bind to heme groups in proteins. These other compounds bind with much higher affinity than O_2, which accounts for their toxicity. CO, or example, has 200-fold greater affinity for hemoglobin than does O_2.

Myoglobin Binds O_2 to Facilitate Its Diffusion. Although myoglobin was originally thought to be only an oxygen-storage protein, it is now apparent that *its major physiological role is to facilitate oxygen diffusion in muscle* (the most rapidly respiring tissue under conditions of high exertion). The rate at which O_2 can diffuse from the capillaries to the tissues is limited by its low solubility in aqueous solution ($\sim 10^{-4}$ M in blood). Myoglobin increases the effective solubility of O_2 in muscle cells, acting as a kind of molecular bucket brigade to boost the O_2 diffusion rate. The oxygen-storage function of myoglobin is probably significant only in aquatic mammals such as seals and whales, whose muscle myoglobin concentrations are around 10-fold greater than those in terrestrial mammals (which is one reason why Kendrew chose the sperm whale as a source of myoglobin for his X-ray crystallographic studies). Nevertheless, mice in which the gene for myoglobin has been "knocked out" are apparently normal, although their muscles are lighter in color than those of wild-type mice. This experiment suggests that myoglobin is not required by muscles under normal metabolic conditions. In contrast, a recently discovered myoglobin-like protein in the brain, dubbed **neuroglobin,** may be essential for boosting O_2 concentrations in neural tissues, which are metabolically highly active. For example, the brain constitutes only about 2% of the mass of a human body, but it consumes about 20% of the available oxygen.

Myoglobin's Oxygen-Binding Curve Is Hyperbolic. The reversible binding of O_2 to myoglobin **(Mb)** is described by a simple equilibrium reaction:

$$Mb + O_2 \rightleftharpoons MbO_2$$

The dissociation constant, K, for the reaction is

$$K = \frac{[Mb][O_2]}{[MbO_2]} \qquad [7\text{-}1]$$

Note that biochemists usually express equilibria in terms of dissociation constants, the reciprocal of the association constants favored by chemists. The O_2 dissociation of myoglobin can be characterized by its **fractional saturation, Y_{O_2},** which is defined as the fraction of O_2-binding sites occupied by O_2:

$$Y_{O_2} = \frac{[MbO_2]}{[Mb] + [MbO_2]} \qquad [7\text{-}2]$$

Y_{O_2} ranges from zero (when no O_2 is bound to the myoglobin molecules) to one (when the binding sites of all the myoglobin molecules are occupied). Equation 7-1 can be rearranged to

$$[MbO_2] = \frac{[Mb][O_2]}{K} \qquad [7\text{-}3]$$

When this expression for $[MbO_2]$ is substituted into Eq. 7-2, the fractional saturation becomes

$$Y_{O_2} = \frac{\dfrac{[Mb][O_2]}{K}}{[Mb] + \dfrac{[Mb][O_2]}{K}} \qquad [7\text{-}4]$$

Factoring out the $[Mb]/K$ term in the numerator and denominator gives

$$Y_{O_2} = \frac{[O_2]}{K + [O_2]} \qquad [7\text{-}5]$$

Since O_2 is a gas, its concentration is conveniently expressed by its **partial pressure, pO_2** (also called the oxygen tension). Equation 7-5 can therefore be expressed as

$$Y_{O_2} = \frac{pO_2}{K + pO_2} \qquad [7\text{-}6]$$

This equation describes a rectangular **hyperbola** *and is identical in form to the equations that describe a hormone binding to its cell-surface receptor or a small molecular substrate binding to the active site of an enzyme.* This hyperbolic function can be represented graphically as shown in Fig. 7-4. At low pO_2, very little O_2 binds to myoglobin (Y_{O_2} is very small). As the pO_2 increases, more O_2 binds to myoglobin. At very high pO_2, virtually all the O_2-binding sites are occupied and myoglobin is said to be **saturated** with O_2.

The steepness of the hyperbola for a simple binding event, such as O_2 binding to myoglobin, increases as the value of K decreases. This means that *the lower the value of K, the tighter is the binding*. K is equivalent to the concentration of ligand at which half of the binding sites are occupied. In other words, when $pO_2 = K$, myoglobin is half-saturated with oxygen. This can be shown algebraically by substituting pO_2 for K in Eq. 7-6:

$$Y_{O_2} = \frac{pO_2}{K + pO_2} = \frac{pO_2}{2pO_2} = 0.5 \qquad [7\text{-}7]$$

Thus, K can be operationally defined as the value of pO_2 at which $Y = 0.5$ (Fig. 7-4).

It is convenient to define K as p_{50}, that is, the oxygen pressure at which myoglobin is 50% saturated. The p_{50} for myoglobin is 2.8 torr (760 torr = 1 atm). Over the physiological range of pO_2 in the blood (100 torr in arterial blood and 30 torr in venous blood), myoglobin is almost fully saturated with oxygen; for example, $Y_{O_2} = 0.97$ at $pO_2 = 100$ torr and 0.91 at 30 torr. Consequently, *myoglobin efficiently relays oxygen from the capillaries to muscle cells.*

Myoglobin, a single polypeptide chain with one heme group and hence one oxygen-binding site, is a useful model for other binding proteins. Even proteins with multiple binding sites for the same small molecule, or **ligand,** may generate hyperbolic binding curves like myoglobin's. *A hyperbolic binding curve occurs when ligands interact independently with their binding sites.* In practice, the affinity of a ligand for its binding protein may not be known. Constructing a binding curve such as the one shown in Fig. 7-4 may provide this information.

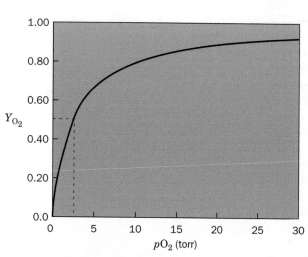

pO_2 (torr)

■ **Figure 7-4 | Oxygen-binding curve of myoglobin.** Myoglobin is half-saturated with O_2 ($Y_{O_2} = 0.5$) at an oxygen partial pressure (pO_2) of 2.8 torr (*dashed lines*). The hyperbolic shape of myoglobin's binding curve is typical of the simple binding of a small molecule to a protein. The background is shaded to indicate the color change that myoglobin undergoes as it binds O_2.

B | Hemoglobin Is a Tetramer with Two Conformations

Hemoglobin, the intracellular protein that gives red blood cells their color, is one of the best-characterized proteins and was one of the first proteins to be associated with a specific physiological function (oxygen transport). Animals that are too large (>1 mm thick) for simple diffusion to deliver sufficient oxygen to their tissues have circulatory systems containing hemoglobin or a protein of similar function that does so (Box 7-1).

Mammalian hemoglobin, as we saw in Fig. 6-33, is an $\alpha_2\beta_2$ tetramer (a dimer of $\alpha\beta$ protomers). The α and β subunits are structurally and evolutionarily related to each other and to myoglobin. The structure of hemoglobin was determined by Max Perutz (Box 7-2). Only about 18% of the residues are identical in myoglobin and in the α and β subunits of hemoglobin, but the three polypeptides have remarkably similar tertiary structures (hemoglobin subunits follow the myoglobin helix-labeling system, although

---

BOX 7-1   PERSPECTIVES IN BIOCHEMISTRY

Other Oxygen-Transport Proteins

The presence of O_2 in the earth's atmosphere and its utility in the oxidation of metabolic fuels have driven the evolution of various mechanisms for storing and transporting oxygen. Small organisms rely on diffusion to supply their respiratory oxygen needs. However, since the rate at which a substance diffuses varies inversely with the square of the distance it must diffuse, organisms of >1-mm thickness overcome the constraints of diffusion with circulatory systems and boost the limited solubility of O_2 in water with specific O_2-transport proteins.

Many invertebrates, and even some plants and bacteria, contain heme-based O_2-binding proteins. Single-subunit and multimeric hemoglobins are found both as intracellular proteins and as extracellular components of blood and other body fluids. The existence of hemoglobin-like proteins in some species of bacteria is evidence of gene transfer from animals to bacteria at one or more points during evolution. In bacteria, these proteins may function as sensors of environmental conditions such as local O_2 concentration. In some leguminous plants, the so-called **leghemoglobins** bind O_2 that would otherwise interfere with nitrogen fixation carried out by bacteria that colonize plant root nodules (Section 21-7). The **chlorocruorins,** which occur in some annelids (e.g., earthworms), contain a somewhat differently derivatized porphyrin than that in hemoglobin, which accounts for the green color of chlorocruorins.

The two other types of O_2-binding proteins, **hemerythrin** and **hemocyanin** (neither of which contains heme groups), occur only in invertebrate animals. Hemerythrin, which occurs in only a few species of marine worms, is an intracellular protein with a subunit mass of ~13 kD. It contains two Fe atoms liganded by His and acidic residues. It is violet-pink when oxygenated and colorless when deoxygenated.

Hemocyanins, which are exclusively extracellular, transport O_2 in mollusks and arthropods. The molluscan and arthropod hemocyanins are large multimeric proteins that differ in their primary

through quaternary structures. However, their oxygen-binding sites are highly similar, consisting of a pair of copper atoms, each liganded by three His residues.

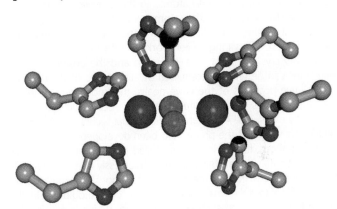

[Figure based on an X-ray structure by Wim Hol, University of Washington School of Medicine. PDBid 1OXY.]

In this model of the O_2-binding site of hemocyanin from the horseshoe crab *Limulus polyphemus,* atoms are colored according to type with C gray, N blue, O red, and Cu purple. The otherwise colorless complex turns blue when it binds O_2.

Hemocyanins must be present at high concentrations in order to function efficiently as oxygen carriers. For example, octopus **hemolymph** (its equivalent of blood) contains about 100 mg/mL hemocyanin. In order to minimize the osmotic pressure of so much protein, hemocyanins form multimeric structures with masses as great as 9×10^6 D in some species. Hemocyanins are often the predominant extracellular protein and may therefore have additional functions as buffers against pH changes and osmotic fluctuations. In some invertebrates, hemocyanins may serve as a nutritional reserve, for example, during metamorphosis or molting.

BOX 7-2 PATHWAYS OF DISCOVERY

Max Perutz and the Structure and Function of Hemoglobin

Max Perutz (1914–2002)

The determination of the three-dimensional structures of proteins has become so commonplace that it is difficult to appreciate the challenges that faced the first protein crystallographers. Max Perutz was a pioneer in this area, spending many years determining the structure of hemoglobin at atomic resolution and then using this information to explain the physiological function of the protein.

In 1934, two years before Perutz began his doctoral studies in Cambridge, J.D. Bernal and Dorothy Crowfoot Hodgkin had placed a crystal of the protein pepsin in an X-ray beam and obtained a diffraction pattern. Perutz tried the same experiment with hemoglobin, chosen because of its abundance, ease of crystallization, and obvious physiological importance. Hemoglobin crystals yielded diffraction patterns with thousands of diffraction maxima (called reflections), the result of X-ray scattering by the thousands of atoms in each protein molecule. At the time, X-ray crystallography had been used to determine the structures of molecules containing no more than around 40 atoms, so the prospect of using the technique to determine the atomic structure of hemoglobin seemed impossible. Nevertheless, Perutz took on the challenge and spent the rest of his long career working with hemoglobin.

In X-ray crystallography, the intensities and the positions of the reflections can be readily determined but the values of their phases (the relative positions of the wave peaks, the knowledge of which is as important as wave amplitude for image reconstruction) cannot be directly measured. Although computational techniques for determining the values of the phases had been developed for small molecules, methods for solving this so-called phase problem for such complex entities as proteins seemed hopelessly out of reach. In 1952, Perutz realized that the method of isomorphous replacement might suffice to solve the phase problem for hemoglobin. In this method, a heavy atom such as an Hg^{2+} ion, which is rich in electrons (the particles that scatter X-rays), must bind to specific sites on the protein without significantly disturbing its structure (which

would change the positions of the reflections). If this causes measurable changes in the intensities of the reflections, these differences would provide the information to determine their phases. With trepidation followed by jubilation, Perutz observed that Hg-doped hemoglobin crystals indeed yielded reflections with measurable changes in intensity but no changes in position. Still, it took another 5 years to obtain the three-dimensional structure of hemoglobin at low (5.5-Å) resolution and it was not until 1968, some 30 years after he began the project, that he determined the structure of hemoglobin at near atomic (2.8-Å) resolution. In the meantime, Perutz's colleague John Kendrew used the method of isomorphous replacement to solve the structure of myoglobin, a smaller and simpler relative of hemoglobin. For their groundbreaking work, Perutz and Kendrew were awarded the 1962 Nobel Prize in Chemistry.

For Perutz, obtaining the structure of hemoglobin was only part of his goal of understanding hemoglobin. For example, functional studies indicated that the four oxygen-binding sites of hemoglobin interacted, as if they were in close contact, but Perutz's structure showed that the binding sites lay in deep and widely separated pockets. Perutz was also intrigued by the fact that crystals of hemoglobin prepared in the absence of oxygen would crack when they were exposed to air (the result, it turns out, of a dramatic conformational change). Although many other researchers also turned their attention to hemoglobin, Perutz was foremost among them in ascribing oxygen-binding behavior to protein structural features. He also devoted considerable effort to relating functional abnormalities in mutant hemoglobins to structural changes.

Perutz's groundbreaking work on the X-ray crystallography of proteins paved the way for other studies. For example, the first X-ray structure of an enzyme, lysozyme, was determined in 1965. The nearly 50,000 macromolecular structures that have been obtained since then owe a debt to Perutz and his decision to pursue an "impossible" task and to follow through on his structural work to the point where he could use his results to explain biological phenomena.

Perutz, M.F., Rossmann, M.G., Cullis, A.F., Muirhead, H., Will, G., and North, A.C.T., Structure of haemoglobin: A three-dimensional Fourier synthesis at 5.5 Å resolution, obtained by X-ray analysis. *Nature* **185,** 416–422 (1960).

the α chain has no D helix). The αβ protomers of hemoglobin are symmetrically related by a twofold rotation (i.e., a rotation of 180° brings the protomers into coincidence). In addition, hemoglobin's structurally similar α and β subunits are related by an approximate twofold rotation (pseudosymmetry) whose axis is perpendicular to that of the exact twofold rotation. Thus, hemoglobin has exact C_2 symmetry and pseudo-D_2 symmetry (Section 6-3; objects with D_2 symmetry have the rotational symmetry of a tetrahedron). The hemoglobin molecule has overall dimensions of about $64 \times 55 \times 50$ Å.

Oxygen binding alters the structure of the entire hemoglobin tetramer, so the structures of **deoxyhemoglobin** (Fig. 7-5*a*) and **oxyhemoglobin** (Fig. 7-5*b*) are noticeably different. In both forms of hemoglobin, the α and β subunits form extensive contacts: Those at the α₁–β₁ interface (and its α₂–β₂ symmetry equivalent) involve 35 residues, and those at the α₁–β₂ (and α₂–β₁) interface involve 19 residues. These associations are predominantly hydrophobic, although numerous hydrogen bonds and several ion pairs are also involved. Note, however, that the α₁–α₂ and β₁–β₂ interactions are tenuous at best because these subunit pairs are separated by an

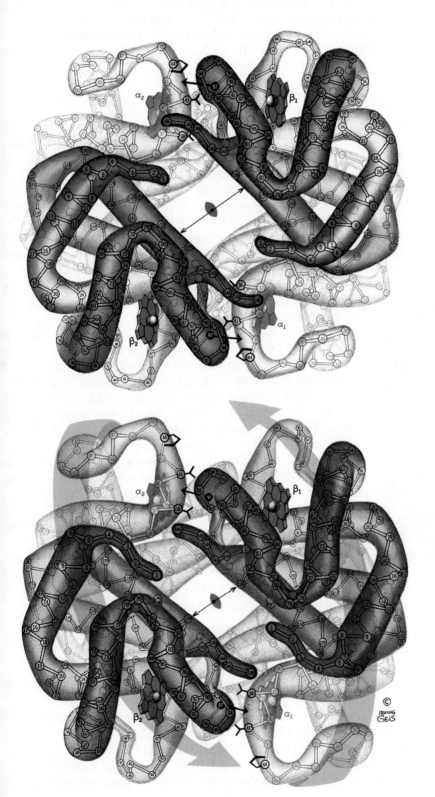

■ **Figure 7-5 | Hemoglobin structure.**
(a) Deoxyhemoglobin and (b) oxyhemoglobin. The α₁β₁ protomer is related to the α₂β₂ protomer by a twofold axis of symmetry (*lenticular symbol*), which is perpendicular to the page. Oxygenation causes one protomer to rotate ~15° relative to the other, bringing the β chains closer together (compare the lengths of the double-headed arrows) and shifting the contacts between subunits at the α₁–β₂ and α₂–β₁ interfaces (some of the relevant side chains are drawn in black). The large gray arrows in *b* indicate the molecular movements that accompany oxygenation. [Illustration, Irving Geis. Image from the Irving Geis Collection/Howard Hughes Medical Institute. Rights owned by HHMI. Reproduction by permission only.]
🔁 **See Kinemage Exercises 6-2 and 6-3.**

~20-Å-diameter solvent-filled channel that parallels the 50-Å length of hemoglobin's exact twofold axis (Fig. 7-5).

When oxygen binds to hemoglobin, the α_1–β_2 (and α_2–β_1) contacts shift, producing a change in quaternary structure. Oxygenation rotates one $\alpha\beta$ dimer ~15° with respect to the other $\alpha\beta$ dimer (gray arrows in Fig. 7-5b), which brings the β subunits closer together and narrows the solvent-filled central channel (Fig. 7-5). Some atoms in the α_1–β_2 and α_2–β_1 interfaces shift by as much as 6 Å (oxygenation causes such extensive quaternary structural changes that crystals of deoxyhemoglobin shatter on exposure to O_2). This structural rearrangement is a crucial element of hemoglobin's oxygen-binding behavior.

C | Oxygen Binds Cooperatively to Hemoglobin

Hemoglobin has a p_{50} of 26 torr (i.e., hemoglobin is half-saturated with O_2 at an oxygen partial pressure of 26 torr), which is nearly 10 times greater than the p_{50} of myoglobin. Moreover, hemoglobin does not exhibit a myoglobin-like hyperbolic oxygen-binding curve. Instead, O_2 binding to hemoglobin is described by a **sigmoidal** (S-shaped) **curve** (Fig. 7-6). *This permits the blood to deliver much more O_2 to the tissues than if hemoglobin had a hyperbolic curve with the same p_{50}* (dashed line in Fig. 7-6). For example, hemoglobin is nearly fully saturated with O_2 at arterial oxygen pressures ($Y_{O_2} = 0.95$ at 100 torr) but only about half-saturated at venous oxygen pressures ($Y_{O_2} = 0.55$ at 30 torr). This 0.40 difference in oxygen saturation, a measure of hemoglobin's ability to deliver O_2 from the lungs to the tissues, would be only 0.25 if hemoglobin exhibited hyperbolic binding behavior.

In any binding system, a sigmoidal curve is diagnostic of a **cooperative** *interaction between binding sites.* This means that the binding of a ligand to one site affects the binding of additional ligands to the other sites. In the case of hemoglobin, O_2 binding to one subunit increases the O_2 affinity of the remaining subunits. The initial slope of the oxygen-binding curve (Fig. 7-6) is low, as hemoglobin subunits independently compete for the first O_2. However, an O_2 molecule bound to one of hemoglobin's subunits increases the O_2-binding affinity of its other subunits, thereby accounting for the increasing slope of the middle portion of the sigmoidal curve.

The Hill Equation Describes Hemoglobin's O_2-Binding Curve. The earliest attempt to analyze hemoglobin's sigmoidal O_2 dissociation curve was formulated by Archibald Hill in 1910. Hill assumed that hemoglobin **(Hb)** bound n molecules of O_2 in a single step,

$$\text{Hb} + n\text{O}_2 \rightarrow \text{Hb}(\text{O}_2)_n$$

that is, with infinite cooperativity. Thus, in analogy with the derivation of Eq. 7-6,

$$Y_{O_2} = \frac{(pO_2)^n}{(p_{50})^n + (pO_2)^n} \qquad [7\text{-}8]$$

which is known as the **Hill equation.** Like Eq. 7-6, it describes the degree of saturation of hemoglobin as a function of pO_2.

Infinite O_2 binding cooperativity, as Hill assumed, is a physical impossibility. Nevertheless, n may be taken to be a nonintegral parameter related to the degree of cooperativity among interacting hemoglobin

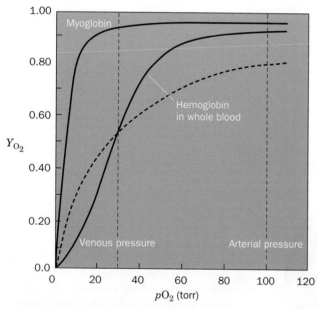

■ **Figure 7-6** | **Oxygen-binding curve of hemoglobin.** In whole blood, hemoglobin is half-saturated at an oxygen pressure of 26 torr. The normal sea level values of human arterial and venous pO_2 are indicated (atmospheric pO_2 is 160 torr at sea level). The O_2-binding curve for myoglobin is included for comparison. The dashed line is a hyperbolic O_2-binding curve with the same p_{50} as hemoglobin. The background is shaded to indicate the color change that hemoglobin undergoes as it binds O_2. ✒ **See the Animated Figures.**

ubunits rather than the number of subunits hat bind O_2 in one step. The Hill equation an then be taken as a useful empirical curve-fitting relationship rather than as an indicator of a particular model of ligand binding.

The quantity n, the **Hill constant,** *increases with the degree of cooperativity of a reaction and therefore provides a convenient although simplistic characterization of a ligand-binding reaction.* If $n = 1$, Eq. 7-8 describes a hyperbola as does Eq. 7-6 for myoglobin, and the O_2-binding reaction is said to be **noncooperative.** If $n > 1$, the reaction is described as being **positively cooperative,** because O_2 binding increases the affinity of hemoglobin for further O_2 binding (cooperativity is infinite in the limit that $n = 4$, the number of O_2 binding sites in hemoglobin). Conversely, if $n < 1$, the reaction is said to be **negatively cooperative,** because O_2 binding would then reduce the affinity of hemoglobin for subsequent O_2 binding.

The Hill coefficient, n, and the value of p_{50} that best describe hemoglobin's saturation curve can be graphically determined by rearranging Eq. 7-8. First, divide both sides by $1 - Y_{O_2}$:

$$\frac{Y_{O_2}}{1 - Y_{O_2}} = \frac{\dfrac{(pO_2)^n}{(p_{50})^n + (pO_2)^n}}{1 - Y_{O_2}} = \frac{\dfrac{(pO_2)^n}{(p_{50})^n + (pO_2)^n}}{1 - \dfrac{(pO_2)^n}{(p_{50})^n + (pO_2)^n}} \qquad [7\text{-}9]$$

Factoring out the $[(p_{50})^n + (pO_2)^n]$ term gives

$$\frac{Y_{O_2}}{1 - Y_{O_2}} = \frac{(pO_2)^n}{[(p_{50})^n + (pO_2)^n] - (pO_2)^n} = \frac{(pO_2)^n}{(p_{50})^n} \qquad [7\text{-}10]$$

Taking the log of both sides yields a linear equation:

$$\log\left(\frac{Y_{O_2}}{1 - Y_{O_2}}\right) = n\log pO_2 - n\log p_{50} \qquad [7\text{-}11]$$

The linear plot of $\log[Y_{O_2}/(1 - Y_{O_2})]$ versus $\log pO_2$, the **Hill plot,** has a slope of n and an intercept on the $\log pO_2$ axis of $\log p_{50}$ (recall that the linear equation $y = mx + b$ describes a line with a slope of m and an x intercept of $-b/m$).

Figure 7-7 shows the Hill plots for myoglobin and purified hemoglobin. For myoglobin, the plot is linear with a slope of 1, as expected. Although all subunits of hemoglobin do not bind O_2 in a single step as was assumed in deriving the Hill equation, its Hill plot is essentially linear for values of Y_{O_2} between 0.1 and 0.9. When $pO_2 = p_{50}$, $Y_{O_2} = 0.5$, and

$$\frac{Y_{O_2}}{1 - Y_{O_2}} = \frac{0.5}{1 - 0.5} = 1.0 \qquad [7\text{-}12]$$

As can be seen in Fig. 7-7, this is the region of maximum slope, whose value is customarily taken to be the Hill coefficient, n. For normal human hemoglobin, the Hill coefficient is between 2.8 and 3.0; that is, hemoglobin's

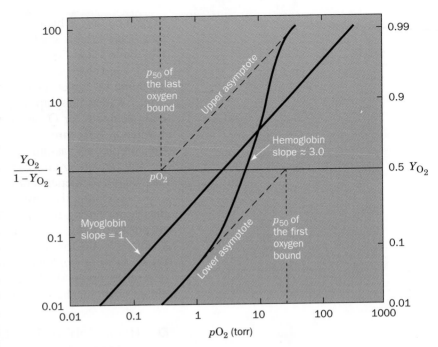

■ **Figure 7-7 | Hill plots for myoglobin and purified hemoglobin.** Note that this is a log–log plot. At $pO_2 = p_{50}$, $Y_{O_2}/(1 - Y_{O_2}) = 1$. [The p_{50} for hemoglobin *in vivo* is higher than the p_{50} of purified hemoglobin due to its binding of certain substances present in the red cell (see below).]

oxygen binding is highly, but not infinitely, cooperative. Many abnormal hemoglobins exhibit smaller Hill coefficients (Section 7-1E), indicating that they have a less than normal degree of cooperativity.

At Y_{O_2} values near zero, when few hemoglobin molecules have bound even one O_2 molecule, the Hill plot for hemoglobin assumes a slope of 1 (Fig. 7-7, lower asymptote) because the hemoglobin subunits independently compete for O_2 as do molecules of myoglobin. At Y_{O_2} values near 1, when at least three of hemoglobin's four O_2-binding sites are occupied, the Hill plot also assumes a slope of 1 (Fig. 7-7, upper asymptote) because the few remaining unoccupied sites are on different molecules and therefore bind O_2 independently.

Extrapolating the lower asymptote in Fig. 7-7 to the horizontal axis indicates, according to Eq. 7-11, that $p_{50} = 30$ torr for binding the first O_2 to purified hemoglobin. Likewise, extrapolating the upper asymptote yields $p_{50} = 0.3$ torr for binding hemoglobin's fourth O_2. Thus, *the fourth O_2 binds to hemoglobin with 100-fold greater affinity than the first.* This difference, as we shall see below, is entirely due to the influence of the globin chain on the O_2 affinity of heme.

D | Hemoglobin's Two Conformations Exhibit Different Affinities for Oxygen

The cooperativity of oxygen binding to hemoglobin arises from the effect of the ligand-binding state of one heme group on the ligand-binding affinity of another. Yet the hemes are 25 to 37 Å apart—too far to interact electronically. Instead, information about the O_2-binding status of a heme group is mechanically transmitted to the other heme groups by motions of the protein. These movements are responsible for the different quaternary structures of oxy- and deoxyhemoglobin depicted in Fig. 7-5.

Oxygen Binding to Hemoglobin Triggers a Conformational Change from T to R. On the basis of the X-ray structures of oxy- and deoxyhemoglobin, Perutz formulated a mechanism for hemoglobin oxygenation. *In the **Perutz mechanism**, hemoglobin has two stable conformational states, the **T state** (the conformation of deoxyhemoglobin) and the **R state** (the conformation of oxyhemoglobin).* The conformations of all four subunits in T-state hemoglobin differ from those in the R state. Oxygen binding initiates a series of coordinated movements that result in a shift from the T state to the R state within a few microseconds:

1. In the T state, the Fe(II) in each of the four hemes is situated ~0.6 Å out of the heme plane because of a pyramidal doming of the porphyrin group toward His F8 (Fig. 7-8). O_2 binding changes the heme's electronic state, which shortens the Fe—N$_{porphyrin}$ bonds by ~0.1 Å and causes the porphyrin doming to subside. Consequently, during the T → R transition, the Fe(II) moves into the center of the heme plane.

2. The Fe(II) drags the covalently linked His F8 along with it. However, the direct movement of His F8 by 0.6 Å toward the heme plane would cause it to collide with the heme. To avoid this steric clash, the attached F helix tilts and translates by ~1 Å across the heme plane.

3. The changes in tertiary structure are coupled to a shift in the arrangement of hemoglobin's four subunits. The largest change produced by the T → R transition is the result of movements of residues at the α_1–β_2 and α_2–β_1 interfaces; in other words, at the interface between the two protomeric units of hemoglobin. In the T state, His

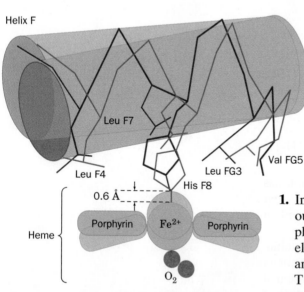

Figure 7-8 | Movements of the heme and the F helix during the T → R transition in hemoglobin. In the T form (*blue*), the Fe is 0.6 Å above the center of the domed porphyrin ring. On assuming the R form (*red*), the Fe moves into the plane of the now undomed porphyrin, where it can more tightly bind O_2, and, in doing so, pulls His F8 and its attached F helix with it. ◈ **See Kinemage Exercise 6-4 and the Animated Figures.**

97 in the β chain contacts Thr 41 in the α chain (Fig. 7-9a). In the R state, His 97 contacts Thr 38, which is positioned one turn back along the C helix (Fig. 7-9b). In both conformations, the "knobs" on one

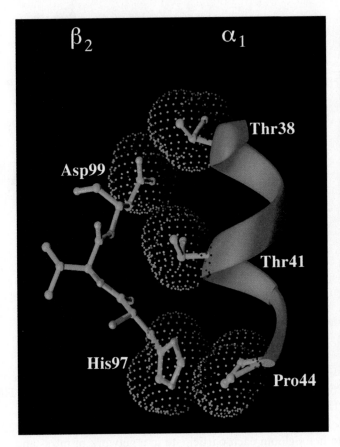
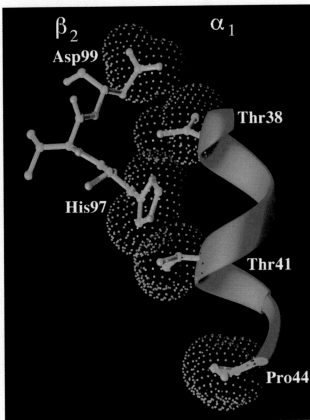

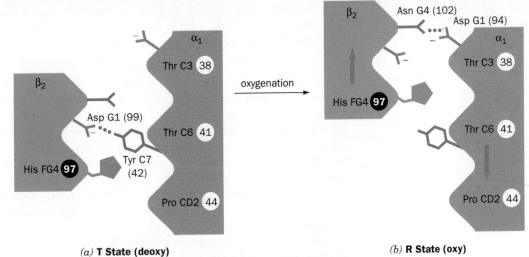

(a) **T State (deoxy)**   (b) **R State (oxy)**

■ **Figure 7-9 | Changes at the α₁–β₂ interface during the T → R transition in hemoglobin.** (a) The T state and (b) the R state. In the upper drawings, the C helix is represented by a purple ribbon, the contacting residues forming the α₁C–β₂FG contact are shown in ball-and-stick form colored by atom type (C green, N blue, and O red), and their van der Waals surfaces are outlined by like-colored dots. The lower drawings are the corresponding schematic diagrams of the α₁C–β₂FG contact. Upon a T → R transformation, the β₂FG region shifts by one turn along the α₁C

helix with no stable intermediate (note how in both conformations, the knobs formed by the side chains of His 97β and Asp 99β fit between the grooves on the C helix formed by the side chains of Thr 38α, Thr 41α, and Pro 44α). The subunits are joined by different hydrogen bonds in the two quaternary states. Figure 7-5 provides another view of these interactions. [Based on X-ray structures by Giulio Fermi, Max Perutz, and Boaz Shaanan, MRC Laboratory of Molecular Biology, Cambridge, U.K. PDBids (a) 2HHB and (b) 1HHO.] 🔎 **See Kinemage Exercise 6-5.**

(a) α Chains

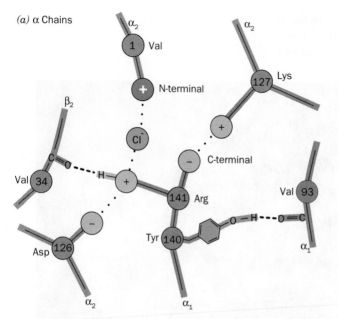

(b) β Chains

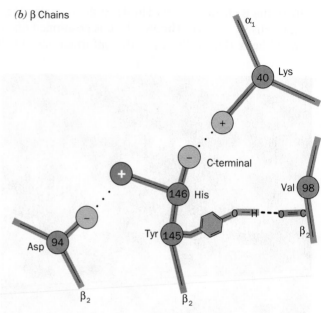

■ **Figure 7-10 | Networks of ion pairs and hydrogen bonds in deoxyhemoglobin.** These bonds, which involve the last two residues of (*a*) the α chains and (*b*) the β chains, are ruptured in the T → R transition. Two groups that become partially deprotonated in the R state (part of the Bohr effect) are indicated by white plus signs. [Illustration, Irving Geis. Image from the Irving Geis Collection/Howard Hughes Medical Institute. Rights owned by HHMI. Reproduction by permission only.]

subunit mesh nicely with the "grooves" on the other. An intermediate position would be severely strained because it would bring His 97 and Thr 41 too close together (i.e., knobs on knobs).

4. The C-terminal residues of each subunit (Arg 141α and His 146β) in T-state hemoglobin each participate in a network of intra- and intersubunit ion pairs (Fig. 7-10) that stabilize the T state. However, the conformational shift in the T → R transition tears away these ion pairs in a process that is driven by the energy of formation of the Fe—O_2 bonds.

The essential feature of hemoglobin's T → R transition is that *its subunits are so tightly coupled that large tertiary structural changes within one subunit cannot occur without quaternary structural changes in the entire tetrameric protein.* Hemoglobin is limited to only two quaternary forms, T and R, because the intersubunit contacts shown in Fig. 7-9 act as a binary switch that permits only two stable positions of the subunits relative to each other. The inflexibility of the $α_1$–$β_1$ and $α_2$–$β_2$ interfaces requires that the T → R shift occur simultaneously at both the $α_1$–$β_2$ and $α_2$–$β_1$ interfaces. No one subunit or dimer can greatly change its conformation independently of the others.

We are now in a position to structurally rationalize the cooperativity of oxygen binding to hemoglobin. The T state of hemoglobin has low O_2 affinity, mostly because of the 0.1 Å greater length of its Fe—O_2 bond relative to that of the R state (e.g., the blue structure shown in Fig. 7-8). Experimental evidence indicates that when at least one O_2 has bound to each αβ dimer, the strain in the T-state hemoglobin molecule is sufficient to tear away the C-terminal ion pairs, thereby snapping the protein into the R state. All the subunits are thereby simultaneously converted to the R-state conformation whether or not they have bound O_2. Unliganded subunits in the R-state conformation have increased oxygen affinity because hey are already in the O_2-binding conformation. This accounts or the high O_2 affinity of nearly saturated hemoglobin.

The Bohr Effect Enhances Oxygen Transport. The conformaional changes in hemoglobin that occur on oxygen binding decrease the pK's of several groups. Recall that the tendency for a group to ionize depends on its microenvironment, which may include other ionizable groups. For example, in T-state hemoglobin, the N-terminal amino groups of the α subunits and the C-terminal His of the β subunits are positively charged and participate in ion pairs (see Fig. 7-10). The formation of ion pairs increases the pK values of these groups (makes them less acidic and therefore less likely to give up their protons). In R-state hemoglobin, these ion pairings are absent, and the pK's of the groups decrease (making them more acidic and more likely to give up protons). Consequently, under physiological conditions, hemoglobin releases ~0.6 protons for each O_2 it binds. Conversely, increasing the pH, that is, removing protons, stimulates hemoglobin to bind more O_2 at lower oxygen pressures (Fig. 7-11). This phenomenon is known as the **Bohr effect** after Christian Bohr (father of the physicist Niels Bohr), who first reported it in 1904.

The Bohr effect has important physiological functions in transporting O_2 from the lungs to respiring tissue and in transporting the CO_2 produced by respiration back to the lungs (Fig. 7-12). The CO_2 produced by respiring tissues diffuses from the tissues to the capillaries. This dissolved CO_2 forms bicarbonate (HCO_3^-) only very slowly, by the reaction

$$CO_2 + H_2O \rightleftharpoons H^+ + HCO_3^-$$

However, in the **erythrocyte** (red blood cell; from the Greek: *erythrose*, red + *kytos*, a hollow vessel), the enzyme **carbonic anhydrase** greatly accelerates this reaction. Accordingly, most of the CO_2 in the blood is carried in the form of bicarbonate (in the absence of carbonic anhydrase, bubbles of CO_2 would form in the blood).

In the capillaries, where pO_2 is low, the H^+ generated by bicarbonate formation is taken up by hemoglobin in forming the ion pairs of the T

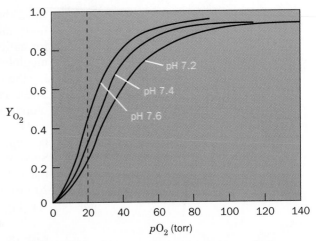

■ **Figure 7-11** | **The Bohr effect.** The O_2 affinity of hemoglobin increases with increasing pH. The dashed line indicates the pO_2 in actively respiring muscle. [After Benesch, R.E. and Benesch, R., *Adv. Protein Chem.* **28**, 212 (1974).]
🔁 **See the Animated Figures.**

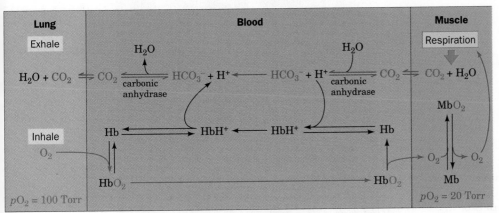

■ **Figure 7-12** | **The roles of hemoglobin and myoglobin in O_2 and CO_2 transport.** Oxygen is inhaled into the lungs at high pO_2, where it binds to hemoglobin in the blood. The O_2 is then transported to respiring tissue, where the pO_2 is low. The O_2 therefore dissociates from the Hb and diffuses into the tissues, where it is used to oxidize metabolic fuels to CO_2 and H_2O. In rapidly respiring muscle tissue, the O_2 first binds to myoglobin (whose oxygen affinity is higher than that of hemoglobin). This increases the rate at which O_2 can diffuse from the capillaries to the tissues by, in effect, increasing its solubility. The Hb and CO_2 (mostly as HCO_3^-) are then returned to the lungs, where the CO_2 is exhaled.

state, thereby inducing hemoglobin to unload its bound O_2. This H^+ up take, moreover, facilitates CO_2 transport by stimulating bicarbonate formation. Conversely, in the lungs, where pO_2 is high, O_2 binding by he moglobin disrupts the T-state ion pairs to form the R state, thereby releas ing the Bohr protons, which recombine with bicarbonate to drive off CO_2 These reactions are closely matched, so they cause very little change in blood pH (see Box 2-1).

The Bohr effect provides a mechanism whereby additional oxygen can be supplied to highly active muscles, where the pO_2 may be <20 torr Such muscles generate lactic acid (Section 15-3A) so fast that they lower the pH of the blood passing through them from 7.4 to 7.2. At a pO_2 of 20 torr, hemoglobin releases ~10% more O_2 at pH 7.2 than it does at pH 7.4 (Fig. 7-11).

CO_2 also modulates O_2 binding to hemoglobin by combining reversibly with the N-terminal amino groups of blood proteins to form **carbamates**:

$$R-NH_2 + CO_2 \rightleftharpoons R-NH-COO^- + H^+$$

The T (deoxy) form of hemoglobin binds more CO_2 as carbamate than does the R (oxy) form. When the CO_2 concentration is high, as it is in the capillaries, the T state is favored, stimulating hemoglobin to release its bound O_2. The protons released by carbamate formation further promote O_2 release through the Bohr effect. Although the difference in CO_2 bind ing between the oxy and deoxy states of hemoglobin accounts for only ~5% of the total blood CO_2, it is nevertheless responsible for around half the CO_2 transported by the blood. This is because only ~10% of the to tal blood CO_2 is lost through the lungs in each circulatory cycle.

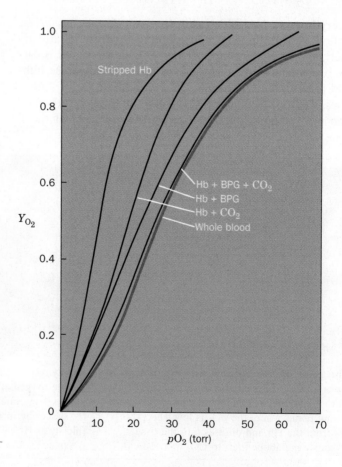

■ **Figure 7-13** | **The effects of BPG and CO₂ on hemoglobin's O₂ dissociation curve.** Stripped hemoglobin (*left*) has higher O_2 affinity than whole blood (*red curve*). Adding BPG or CO_2 or both to hemoglobin shifts the dissociation curve back to the right (lowers hemoglobin's O_2 affinity). [After Kilmartin, J.V. and Rossi-Bernardi, L., *Physiol. Rev.* **53**, 884 (1973).] ✑ **See the Animated Figures.**

Bisphosphoglycerate Binds to Deoxyhemoglobin. Highly purified "stripped") hemoglobin has a much greater oxygen affinity than hemoglobin in whole blood (Fig. 7-13). This observation led Joseph Barcroft, in 1921, to speculate that blood contains some other substance besides CO_2 that affects oxygen binding to hemoglobin. This compound is **D-2,3-bisphosphoglycerate (BPG).**

$$
\begin{array}{c}
{}^{-}\text{O} \diagdown \quad \diagup \text{O} \\
\text{C} \\
| \\
\text{H} - \text{C} - \text{OPO}_3^{2-} \\
| \\
\text{H} - \text{C} - \text{OPO}_3^{2-} \\
| \\
\text{H}
\end{array}
$$

D-2,3-Bisphosphoglycerate (BPG)

BPG binds tightly to deoxyhemoglobin but only weakly to oxyhemoglobin. *The presence of BPG in mammalian erythrocytes therefore decreases hemoglobin's oxygen affinity by keeping it in the deoxy conformation.* In other vertebrates, different phosphorylated compounds elicit the same effect.

BPG has an indispensable physiological function: In arterial blood, where pO_2 is ~100 torr, hemoglobin is ~95% saturated with O_2, but in venous blood, where pO_2 is ~30 torr, it is only 55% saturated (Fig. 7-6). Consequently, in passing through the capillaries, hemoglobin unloads ~40% of its bound O_2. In the absence of BPG, little of this bound O_2 would be released since hemoglobin's O_2 affinity is increased, thus shifting its O_2 dissociation curve significantly toward lower pO_2 (Fig. 7-13, *left*). BPG also plays an important role in adaptation to high altitudes (Box 7-3).

The X-ray structure of a BPG–deoxyhemoglobin complex shows that BPG binds in the central cavity of deoxyhemoglobin (Fig. 7-14). The anionic groups of BPG are within hydrogen-bonding and ion-pairing distances of the N-terminal amino groups of both β subunits. The T → R transformation brings the two βH helices together, which narrows the central cavity (compare Figs. 7-5a and 7-5b) and expels the BPG. It also widens the distance between the β N-terminal amino groups from 16 to 20 Å, which prevents their simultaneous hydrogen bonding with BPG's phosphate groups. BPG therefore binds to and stabilizes only the T conformation of hemoglobin by cross-linking its β subunits. This shifts the T $\rightleftharpoons$ R equilibrium toward the T state, which lowers hemoglobin's O_2 affinity.

Fetal Hemoglobin Has Low BPG Affinity. The effects of BPG also help supply the fetus with oxygen. A fetus obtains its O_2 from the maternal circulation via the placenta. The concentration of BPG is the same in adult and fetal erythrocytes, but BPG binds more tightly to adult hemoglobin than to fetal hemoglobin. The higher oxygen affinity of fetal hemoglobin facilitates the transfer of O_2 to the fetus.

Fetal hemoglobin has the subunit composition $\alpha_2\gamma_2$ in which the γ subunit is a variant of the β chain (Section 5-4B). Residue 143 of the β chain of adult hemoglobin has a cationic His residue, whereas the γ chain has an uncharged Ser residue. The absence of this His eliminates a pair of interactions that stabilize the BPG–deoxyhemoglobin complex (Fig. 7-14).

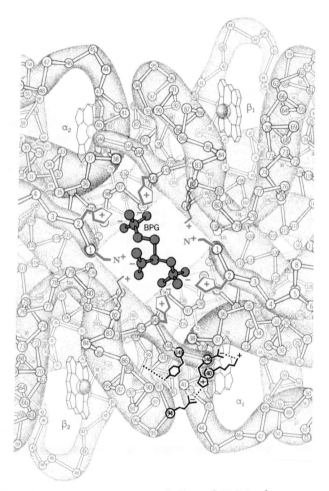

■ **Figure 7-14 | Binding of BPG to deoxyhemoglobin.** BPG (*red*) binds in hemoglobin's central cavity. The BPG, which has a charge of −5 under physiological conditions, is surrounded by eight cationic groups (*blue*) extending from the two β subunits. In the R state, the central cavity is too narrow to contain BPG. Some of the ion pairs and hydrogen bonds that help stabilize the T state (Fig. 7-10b) are indicated at the lower right. [Illustration, Irving Geis. Image from the Irving Geis Collection/Howard Hughes Medical Institute. Rights owned by HHMI. Reproduction by permission only.] *See Kinemage Exercise 6-3.*

BOX 7-3 BIOCHEMISTRY IN HEALTH AND DISEASE

High-Altitude Adaptation

Atmospheric pressure decreases with altitude, so that the oxygen pressure at 3000 m (10,000 feet) is only ~110 torr, 70% of its sea-level pressure. A variety of physiological responses are required to maintain normal oxygen delivery (without adaptation, pO_2 levels of 85 torr or less result in mental impairment).

High-altitude adaptation is a complex process that involves increases in the number of erythrocytes and the amount of hemoglobin per erythrocyte. It normally requires several weeks to complete. Yet, as is clear to anyone who has climbed to high altitude, even a 1-day stay there results in a noticeable degree of adaptation. This effect results from a rapid increase in the amount of BPG synthesized in erythrocytes (from ~4 mM to ~8 mM; BPG cannot cross the erythrocyte membrane). As illustrated by plots of Y_{O_2} versus pO_2, the high altitude–induced increase in BPG causes the O_2-binding curve of hemoglobin to shift from its sea-level position (*black line*) to a lower affinity position (*red line*). At sea level, the difference between arterial and venous pO_2 is 70 torr (100 torr − 30 torr), and hemoglobin unloads 38% of its bound O_2. However, when the arterial pO_2 drops to 55 torr, as it does at an altitude of 4500 m, hemoglobin would be able to unload only 30% of its O_2. High-altitude adaptation (which decreases the amount of O_2 that hemoglobin can bind in the lungs but, to a greater extent, increases the amount of O_2 it releases at the tissues) allows hemoglobin to deliver a near-normal 37% of its bound O_2. BPG concentrations also increase in individuals suffering from disorders that limit the oxygenation of the blood (**hypoxia**), such as various anemias and cardiopulmonary insufficiency.

The BPG concentration in erythrocytes can be adjusted more rapidly than hemoglobin can be synthesized (Box 15-2; erythrocytes lack nuclei and therefore cannot synthesize proteins). An altered BPG level is also a more sensitive regulator of oxygen delivery than an altered respiratory rate. Hyperventilation, another early response to high altitude, may lead to respiratory alkalosis (Box 2-1). Interestingly, individuals in long-established Andean and Himalayan populations exhibit high lung capacity, along with high

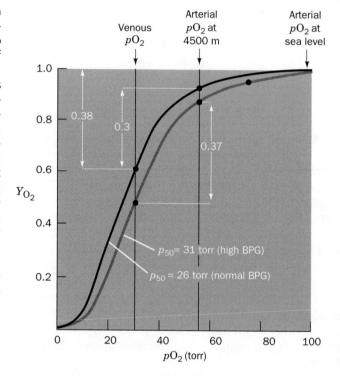

hemoglobin levels and, often, enlarged right ventricles (reflecting increased cardiac output), compared to individuals from low-altitude populations.

In contrast to the mechanism of human adaptation to high altitude, most mammals that normally live at high altitudes (e.g. the llama) have genetically altered hemoglobins that have higher O_2-binding affinities than do their sea-level cousins. Thus, both raising and lowering hemoglobin's p_{50} can provide high-altitude adaptation.

Hemoglobin Is a Model Allosteric Protein. The cooperativity of oxygen binding to hemoglobin is a classic model for the behavior of many other multisubunit proteins (including many enzymes) that bind small molecules. In some cases, binding of a ligand to one site increases the affinity of other binding sites on the same protein (as in O_2 binding to hemoglobin). In other cases, a ligand decreases the affinity of other binding sites (as when BPG binding decreases the O_2 affinity of hemoglobin). All these effects are the result of **allosteric interactions** (Greek: *allos*, other + *stereos*, solid or space). *Allosteric effects, in which the binding of a ligand at one site affects the binding of another ligand at another site, generally require interactions among subunits of oligomeric proteins.* The T → R transition in hemoglobin subunits explains the difference in the oxygen affinities of oxy- and deoxyhemoglobin. Other proteins exhibit similar

■ Figure 7-15 | The symmetry model of allosterism. Squares and circles represent T- and R-state subunits, respectively, of a tetrameric protein. The T and R states are in equilibrium regardless of the number of ligands (represented by S) that have bound to the protein. All the subunits must be in either the T or the R form; the model does not allow combinations of T- and R-state subunits in the same protein.

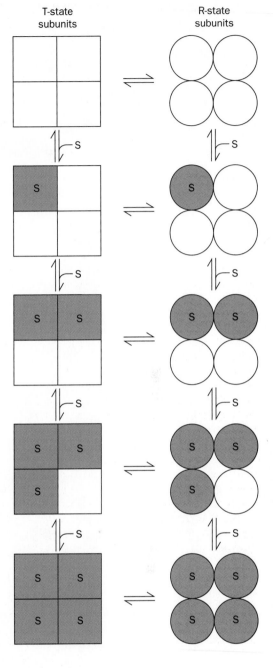

conformational shifts, although the molecular mechanisms that underlie these phenomena are not completely understood.

Two models that account for cooperative ligand binding have received the most attention. One of them, the **symmetry model** of allosterism, formulated in 1965 by Jacques Monod, Jeffries Wyman, and Jean-Pierre Changeux, is defined by the following rules:

1. An allosteric protein is an oligomer of symmetrically related subunits (although the α and β subunits of hemoglobin are only pseudosymmetrically related).

2. Each oligomer can exist in two conformational states, designated R and T; these states are in equilibrium.

3. The ligand can bind to a subunit in either conformation. *Only the conformational change alters the affinity for the ligand.*

4. *The molecular symmetry of the protein is conserved during the conformational change.* The subunits must therefore change conformation in a concerted manner; in other words, there are no oligomers that simultaneously contain R- and T-state subunits.

The symmetry model is diagrammed for a tetrameric binding protein in Fig. 7-15. If a ligand binds more tightly to the R state than to the T state, ligand binding will promote the T → R shift, thereby increasing the affinity of the unliganded subunits for the ligand.

One major objection to the symmetry model is that it is difficult to believe that oligomeric symmetry is perfectly preserved in all proteins, that is, that the T → R shift occurs simultaneously in all subunits regardless of the number of ligands bound. In addition, the symmetry model can account only for positive cooperativity, although some proteins exhibit negative cooperativity.

An alternative to the symmetry model is the **sequential model** of allosterism, proposed by Daniel Koshland. According to this model, ligand binding induces a conformational change in the subunit to which it binds, and cooperative interactions arise through the influence of those conformational changes on neighboring subunits. The conformational changes occur sequentially as more ligand-binding sites are occupied (Fig. 7-16). The ligand-binding affinity of a subunit varies with its conformation and may be higher or lower than that of the subunits in the ligand-free protein.

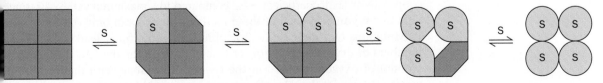

■ Figure 7-16 | The sequential model of allosterism. Ligand binding progressively induces conformational changes in the subunits, with the greatest changes occurring in those subunits that have bound ligand. The symmetry of the oligomeric protein is not preserved in this process as it is in the symmetry model.

Thus, proteins that follow the sequential model of allosterism may be positively or negatively cooperative.

If the mechanical coupling between subunits in the sequential model is particularly strong, the conformational changes occur simultaneously and the oligomer retains its symmetry, as in the symmetry model. Thus, the symmetry model of allosterism may be considered to be an extreme case of the more general sequential model.

Oxygen binding to hemoglobin exhibits features of both models. The quaternary T → R conformational change is concerted, as the symmetry model requires. Yet ligand binding to the T state does cause small tertiary structural changes, as the sequential model predicts. These minor conformational shifts are undoubtedly responsible for the buildup of strain that eventually triggers the T → R transition. It therefore appears that the complexity of ligand–protein interactions in hemoglobin and other proteins allows binding processes to be fine-tuned to the needs of the organism under changing internal and external conditions. We shall revisit allosteric effects when we discuss enzymes in Chapter 12.

E | Mutations May Alter Hemoglobin's Structure and Function

Before the advent of recombinant DNA techniques, mutant hemoglobins provided what was an almost unique opportunity to study structure–function relationships in proteins. This is because, for many years, hemoglobin was the only protein of known structure that had a large number of well-characterized naturally occurring **variants.** The examination of individuals with physiological disabilities, together with the routine electrophoretic screening of human blood samples, has led to the discovery of nearly 950 variant hemoglobins, >90% of which result from single amino acid substitutions in a globin polypeptide chain. Indeed, about 5% of the world's human population are carriers of an inherited variant hemoglobin.

Not all hemoglobin variants produce clinical symptoms, but some abnormal hemoglobin molecules do cause debilitating diseases (~300,000 individuals with serious hemoglobin disorders are born every year; naturally occurring hemoglobin variants that are lethal are, of course, never observed). Table 7-1 lists several of these hemoglobin variants. Mutations that destabilize hemoglobin's tertiary or quaternary structure alter hemoglobin's oxygen-binding affinity (p_{50}) and reduce its cooperativity (Hill coefficient). Moreover, the unstable hemoglobins are degraded by the erythrocytes, and their degradation products often cause the erythrocytes to **lyse** (break open). The resulting **hemolytic anemia** (anemia is a deficiency of red blood cells) compromises O_2 delivery to tissues.

Certain mutations at the O_2-binding site of either the α or β chain favor the oxidation of Fe(II) to Fe(III). Individuals carrying the resulting methemoglobin subunit exhibit **cyanosis,** a bluish skin color, due to the presence of methemoglobin in their arterial blood. These hemoglobins have reduced cooperativity (Hill coefficient ~1.2 compared to a maximum value of 2, since only two subunits in each of these methemoglobins can bind oxygen).

Mutations that increase hemoglobin's oxygen affinity lead to increased numbers of erythrocytes in order to compensate for the less than normal amount of oxygen released in the tissues. Individuals with this condition, which is named **polycythemia,** often have a ruddy complexion.

A Single Amino Acid Change Causes Sickle-Cell Anemia. Most harmful hemoglobin variants occur in only a few individuals, in many of whom the mutation apparently originated. However, ~10% of African-

Table 7-1 Some Hemoglobin Variants

Name[a]	Mutation	Effect
Hammersmith	Phe CD1(42)β → Ser	Weakens heme binding
Bristol	Val E11(67)β → Asp	Weakens heme binding
Bibba	Leu H19(136)α → Pro	Disrupts the H helix
Savannah	Gly B6(24)β → Val	Disrupts the B–E helix interface
Philly	Tyr C1(35)β → Phe	Disrupts hydrogen bonding at the α_1–β_1 interface
Boston	His E7(58)α → Tyr	Promotes methemoglobin formation
Milwaukee	Val E11(67)β → Glu	Promotes methemoglobin formation
Iwate	His F8(87)α → Tyr	Promotes methemoglobin formation
Yakima	Asp G1(99)β → His	Disrupts a hydrogen bond that stabilizes the T conformation
Kansas	Asn G4(102)β → Thr	Disrupts a hydrogen bond that stabilizes the R conformation

[a]Hemoglobin variants are usually named after the place where they were discovered (e.g., hemoglobin Boston).

Americans and as many as 25% of black Africans carry a single copy of (are **heterozygous** for) the gene for **sickle-cell hemoglobin (hemoglobin S).** Individuals who carry two copies of (are **homozygous** for) the gene for hemoglobin S suffer from **sickle-cell anemia,** in which deoxyhemoglobin S forms insoluble filaments that deform erythrocytes (Fig. 7-17). In this painful, debilitating, and often fatal disease, the rigid, sickle-shaped cells cannot easily pass through the capillaries. Consequently, in a sickle-cell "crisis," the blood flow to some tissues may be completely blocked, resulting in tissue death. In addition, the mechanical fragility of the misshapen cells results in hemolytic anemia. Heterozygotes, whose hemoglobin is ~40% hemoglobin S, usually lead a normal life, although their erythrocytes have a shorter than normal lifetime.

In 1945, Linus Pauling hypothesized that sickle-cell anemia was the result of a mutant hemoglobin, and in 1949 he showed that the mutant hemoglobin had a less negative ionic charge than normal adult hemoglobin. This was the first evidence that a disease could result from an alteration in the molecular structure of a protein. Furthermore, since sickle-cell anemia is an inherited disease, a defective gene must be responsible for the abnormal protein. Nevertheless, the molecular defect in sickle-cell hemoglobin was not identified until 1956, when Vernon Ingram showed that hemoglobin S contains Val rather than Glu at the sixth position of each β chain. This was the first time an inherited disease was shown to arise from a specific amino acid change in a protein.

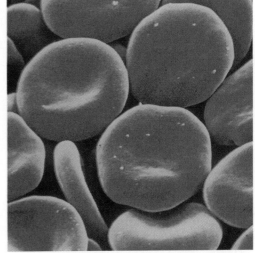

(a)

(b)

■ **Figure 7-17 | Scanning electron micrographs of human erythrocytes.** (a) Normal erythrocytes are flexible biconcave disks that can tolerate slight distortions as they pass through the capillaries (many of which have smaller diameters than erythrocytes). (b) Sickled erythrocytes from an individual with sickle-cell anemia are elongated and rigid and cannot easily pass through capillaries. [(a) David M. Phillips/Visuals Unlimited; (b) Bill Longcore/Photo Researchers, Inc.]

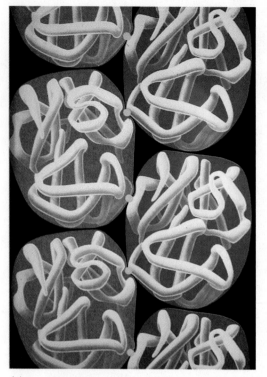

(a)

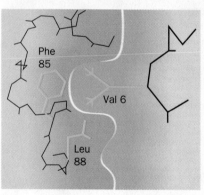

(b)

■ **Figure 7-18** | **Structure of a deoxyhemoglobin S fiber.** (*a*) The arrangement of deoxyhemoglobin S molecules in the fiber. Only three subunits of each deoxy-hemoglobin S molecule are shown. (*b*) The side chain of the mutant Val 6 in the β_2 chain of one hemoglobin S molecule (yellow knob in Part *a*) binds to a hydrophobic pocket on the β_1 subunit of a neighboring deoxyhemoglobin S molecule. [Illustration, Irving Geis. Image from the Irving Geis Collection/Howard Hughes Medical Institute. Rights owned by HHMI. Reproduction by permission only.]

The X-ray structure of deoxyhemoglobin S has revealed that one mutant Val side chain in each hemoglobin S tetramer nestles into a hydrophobic pocket on the surface of a β subunit in another hemoglobin tetramer (Fig. 7-18). This intermolecular contact allows hemoglobin S tetramers to form linear polymers. Aggregates of 14 strands that wind around each other form fibers extending throughout the length of the erythrocyte (Fig. 7-19). The hydrophobic pocket on the β subunit cannot accommodate the normally occurring Glu side chain, and the pocket is absent in oxyhemoglobin. Consequently, neither normal hemoglobin nor oxyhemoglobin S can polymerize. In fact, hemoglobin S fibers dissolve essentially instantaneously on oxygenation, so none are present in arterial blood. The danger of sickling is greatest when erythrocytes pass through the capillaries, where deoxygenation occurs. The polymerization of hemoglobin S molecules is time and concentration dependent, which explains why blood flow blockage occurs only sporadically (in a sickle-cell "crisis").

Interestingly, many hemoglobin S homozygotes have only a mild form of sickle-cell anemia because they express relatively high levels of fetal hemoglobin, which contains γ chains rather than the defective β chains. The fetal hemoglobin dilutes the hemoglobin S, making it more difficult for hemoglobin S to aggregate during the 10–20 s it takes for an erythrocyte to travel from the tissues to the lungs for reoxygenation. The administration of **hydroxyurea,**

$$H_2N{-}\overset{\overset{\displaystyle O}{\|}}{C}{-}NH{-}OH$$

Hydroxyurea

the first and as yet the only effective treatment for sickle-cell anemia, ameliorates the symptoms of sickle-cell anemia by increasing the fraction of cells containing fetal hemoglobin (although the mechanism whereby hydroxyurea acts is unknown).

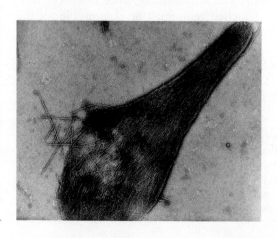

■ **Figure 7-19** | **Electron micrograph of deoxyhemoglobin S fibers spilling out of a ruptured erythrocyte.** [Courtesy of Robert Josephs, University of Chicago.]

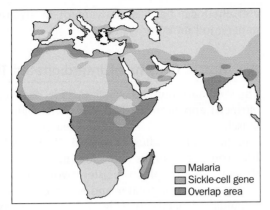

■ **Figure 7-20** | **Correspondence between malaria and the sickle-cell gene.** The blue areas of the map indicate regions where malaria is or was prevalent. The pink areas represent the distribution of the gene for hemoglobin S. Note the overlap (*purple*) of the distributions.

Hemoglobin S Protects Against Malaria. Before the advent of modern palliative therapies, individuals with sickle-cell anemia rarely survived to maturity. Natural selection has not minimized the prevalence of the hemoglobin S variant, however, because heterozygotes are more resistant to **malaria,** an often lethal infectious disease. Of the 2.5 billion people living within malaria-endemic areas, 100 million are clinically ill with the disease at any given time and around 1 million, mostly very young children, die from it each year. Malaria is caused by the mosquito-borne protozoan *Plasmodium falciparum,* which resides within an erythrocyte during much of its 48-h life cycle. Infected erythrocytes adhere to capillary walls, causing death when cells impede blood flow to a vital organ.

The regions of equatorial Africa where malaria is a major cause of death coincide closely with those areas where the sickle-cell gene is prevalent (Fig. 7-20), thereby suggesting that the sickle-cell gene confers resistance to malaria. How does it do so? Plasmodia increase the acidity of infected erythrocytes by ~0.4 pH units. The lower pH favors the formation of deoxyhemoglobin via the Bohr effect, thereby increasing the likelihood of sickling in erythrocytes that contain hemoglobin S. Erythrocytes damaged by sickling are normally removed from the circulation by the spleen. During the early stages of a malarial infection, parasite-enhanced sickling probably allows the spleen to preferentially remove infected erythrocytes. In the later stages of infection, when the parasitized erythrocytes attach to the capillary walls (presumably to prevent the spleen from removing them from the circulation), sickling may mechanically disrupt the parasite. Consequently, heterozygous carriers of hemoglobin S in a malarial region have an adaptive advantage: They are more likely to survive to maturity than individuals who are homozygous for normal hemoglobin. Thus, in malarial regions, the fraction of the population who are heterozygotes for the sickle-cell gene increases until their reproductive advantage is balanced by the correspondingly increased proportion of homozygotes (who, without modern medical treatment, die in childhood).

2 Muscle Contraction

One of the most striking characteristics of living things is their capacity for organized movement. Such phenomena occur at all structural levels and include such diverse vectorial processes as the separation of replicated chromosomes during cell division, the beating of flagella and cilia, and, most obviously, muscle contraction. In this section, we consider the structural

■ **CHECK YOUR UNDERSTANDING**

Describe the O_2-binding behavior of myoglobin in terms of pO_2 and K. How is K defined?

Explain the structural basis for cooperative oxygen binding to hemoglobin.

Describe how myoglobin and hemoglobin function in delivering O_2 from the lungs to respiring tissues.

What is the physiological relevance of the Bohr effect and BPG?

Explain why mutations can increase or decrease the oxygen affinity and cooperativity of hemoglobin. How can the body compensate for these changes?

LEARNING OBJECTIVES

■ Understand that myosin is a motor protein that undergoes conformational changes as it hydrolyzes ATP.

■ Understand how the sliding filament model of muscle contraction describes the movement of thick filaments relative to thin filaments.

■ Understand how the globular protein actin can form structures such as microfilaments and the thin filaments of muscle.

■ **Figure 7-21** | **Photomicrograph of a muscle fiber.** The longitudinal axis of the fiber is horizontal (perpendicular to the striations). The alternating pattern of dark A bands and light I bands from multiple in-register myofibrils is clearly visible. [J.C. Revy, CNRI/Photo Researchers.]

and chemical basis of movement in **striated muscle,** one of the best understood mobility systems.

A | Muscle Consists of Interdigitated Thick and Thin Filaments

The voluntary muscles, which include the skeletal muscles, have a striated (striped) appearance when viewed by light microscopy (Fig. 7-21). Such muscles consist of long multinucleated cells (the muscle fibers) that contain parallel bundles of **myofibrils** (Greek: *myos,* muscle; Fig. 7-22). Electron micrographs show that muscle striations arise from the banded structure of multiple in-register myofibrils. The bands are formed by alternating regions of greater and lesser electron density called **A bands** and **I bands,** respectively (Fig. 7-23). The myofibril's repeating unit, the **sarcomere** (Greek: *sarkos,* flesh), is bounded by **Z disks** at the center of each I band. The A band is centered on the **H zone,** which in turn is centered on the **M disk.** The A band contains 150-Å-diameter **thick filaments** and the I band contains 70-Å-diameter **thin filaments.** The two sets of filaments are linked by cross-bridges where they overlap.

A contracted muscle can be as much as one-third shorter than its fully extended length. The contraction results from a decrease in the length of the sarcomere, caused by reductions in the lengths of the I band and the H zone (Fig. 7-24a). These observations, made by Hugh Huxley in 1954

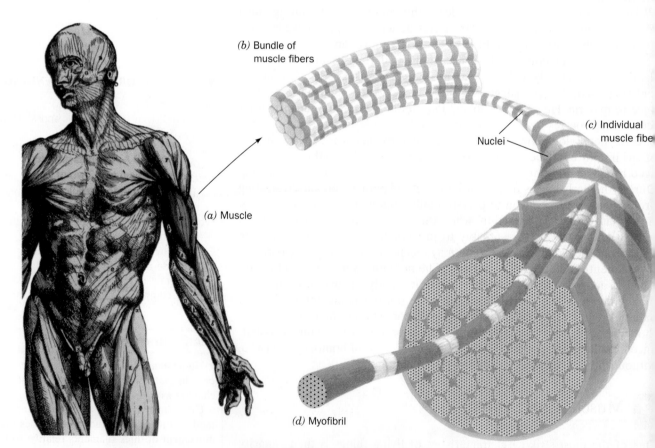

(b) Bundle of muscle fibers

(c) Individual muscle fiber

Nuclei

(a) Muscle

(d) Myofibril

■ **Figure 7-22** | **Skeletal muscle organization.** A muscle (a) consists of bundles of muscle fibers (b), each of which is a long, thin, multinucleated cell (c) that may run the length of the muscle. Muscle fibers contain bundles of laterally aligned myofibrils (d), which in turn consist of bundles of alternating thick and thin filaments.

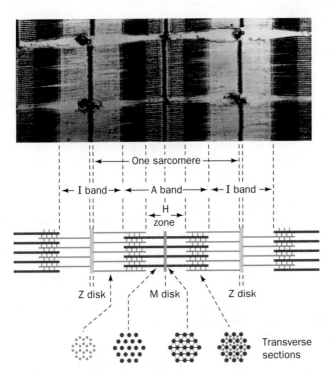

■ Figure 7-23 | Anatomy of the myofibril. The electron micrograph shows parts of three myofibrils, which are separated by horizontal gaps. The accompanying interpretive drawing shows the major features of the myofibril: the light I band, which contains only thin filaments; the A band, whose dark H zone contains only thick filaments and whose darker outer segments contain overlapping thick and thin filaments; the Z disk, to which the thin filaments are anchored; and the M disk, which arises from a bulge at the center of each thick filament. The myofibril's functional unit, the sarcomere, is the region between two successive Z disks. [Courtesy of Hugh Huxley, Brandeis University.]

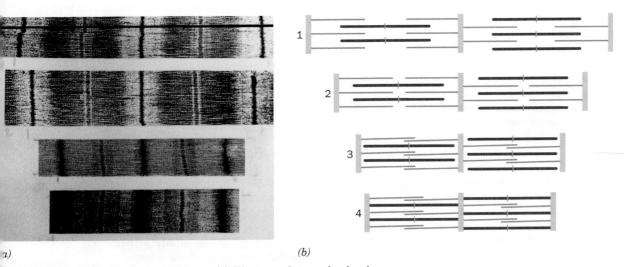

■ Figure 7-24 | Myofibril contraction. (a) Electron micrographs showing myofibrils in progressively more contracted states. The lengths of the I band and H zone decrease on contraction, whereas the lengths of the thick and thin filaments remain constant. (b) Interpretive drawings showing interpenetrating sets of thick and thin filaments sliding past each other. [Courtesy of Hugh Huxley, Brandeis University.]

BOX 7-4 **PATHWAYS OF DISCOVERY**

Hugh Huxley and the Sliding Filament Model

Hugh Huxley (1924–)

The mechanism of muscle action has fascinated scientists for hundreds if not thousands of years. The first close look at muscle fibers came in 1682, when Antoni van Leeuwenhoek's early microscope revealed a pattern of thin longitudinal fibers. In the modern era, research on muscle has followed one of two approaches. First, it is possible to study muscle as an energy-transducing system, in which metabolic energy is generated and consumed. This line of research received a tremendous boost in the 1930s with the discovery that ATP is the energy source for muscle contraction. The second approach involves treating muscle as a mechanical system, that is, sorting out its rods and levers. Ultimately, a molecular approach united the mechanical and energetic aspects of muscle research. The insights of Hugh Huxley made this possible.

The molecular characterization of muscle did not occur overnight. In 1859, Willi Kühne isolated a proteinaceous substance from muscle tissue that he named "myosin" (almost certainly a mixture of many proteins), but it tended to aggregate and was therefore not as popular a study subject as the more soluble proteins such as hemoglobin. A major breakthrough in muscle protein chemistry came in 1941, when the Hungarian biochemist Albert Szent-Györgyi showed that two types of protein could be extracted from ground muscle by a solution with high salt concentration (Szent-Györgyi also contributed to the elucidation of the citric acid cycle; Box 17-1). Extraction for 20 minutes yielded a protein he named myosin A but which is now called myosin. However, extraction overnight yielded a second protein which he named myosin B but is now called actomyosin. It soon became apparent that myosin B was a mixture of two proteins, myosin and a new protein which was named actin. Further work showed that threads of actomyosin contracted to ~10% of their original length in the presence of ATP. Since actin and myosin alone do not contract in the presence of ATP, the contraction must have resulted from their interaction. However, it took another decade to develop a realistic model of how myosin and actin interact.

A number of theories had been advanced to explain muscle contraction. According to one theory, the cytoplasm of muscle cells moved like that of an amoeba. Other theories proposed that muscle fibers took up and gave off water or repelled and attracted other fibers electrostatically. Linus Pauling, who had recently discovered the structures of the α helix and β sheet (Box 6-1), ventured that myosin could change its length by shifting between the two protein conformations. Huxley formulated an elegant—and correct—explanation in his sliding filament model for muscle contraction.

In 1948, Huxley began his doctoral research at Cambridge University in the United Kingdom, in the laboratory of John Kendrew (who 10 years later determined the first X-ray structure of a protein, that of myoglobin; Section 7-1A). There, through X-ray studies on frog muscle fibers, Huxley established that the X-ray diffraction pattern changes with the muscle's physiological state. Furthermore, he showed that muscle contained two sets of parallel fibers, rather than one, and that these fibers were linked together by multiple cross-links. These observations became the germ for further research which he carried out at MIT in 1953 and 1954. He teamed up with Jean Hanson, a Briton who was also working at MIT. Hanson made good use of her knowledge of muscle physiology and her expertise in phase-contrast microscopy, a technique that could visualize the banded patterns of muscle fibers. Huxley and Hanson observed rabbit muscle fibers under different experimental conditions, making precise measurements of the width of the A and I bands in sarcomeres (Fig. 7-23). In one experiment, they extracted myosin from the muscle fiber, noted the loss of the dark A band, and concluded that the A band consists of myosin. When they extracted both actin and myosin, all identifiable structure was lost, and they concluded that actin is present throughout the sarcomere.

When ATP was added, the muscle slowly contracted, and Huxley and Hanson were able to measure the shortening of the I band. The A band maintained a constant length but became darker. A muscle fiber under the microscope could also be stretched by pulling on the coverslip. As the muscle "relaxed," the I band increased in width and the A band became less dense. Measurements were made for muscle fibers contracted to 60% of their original length and stretched to 120% of their original length.

The key to the sliding filament model that Huxley described and subsequently refined is that the individual molecules (that is, their observable fibrous forms) do not shrink or extend but instead slide past each other. During contraction, actin filaments (thin filaments) in the I band are drawn into the A band, which consists of stationary myosin-containing filaments (thick filaments). During stretching, the actin filaments withdraw from the A band. Similar conclusions were reached by the team of Andrew Huxley (no relation to Hugh) and Rolf Niedergerke, who were examining the contraction of living frog muscle fibers. Both groups published their work in back-to-back papers in *Nature* in 1954.

Hugh Huxley went on to supply additional details to his sliding filament model. For example, he showed that myosin forms cross bridges with actin fibers. However, these bridges are asymmetric, pointing in opposite directions in the two halves of the sarcomere. This arrangement allows myosin to pull thin filaments in opposite directions toward the center of the sarcomere (Fig. 7-24).

While Huxley was describing the mechanism of muscle contraction, Watson and Crick discovered the structure of DNA, and Max Perutz made a decisive breakthrough in the use of heavy metal atoms to solve the phase problem in his X-ray studies of hemoglobin (Box 7-2). Collectively, these discoveries indicated the tremendous potential for describing biological phenomena in molecular terms. Subsequent studies of muscle contraction have used electron microscopy, X-ray crystallography, and enzymology to probe the fine details of the sliding filament model, including the structure of myosin's lever arm, the composition of the thin filament, and the exact role of ATP in triggering conformational changes that generate mechanical force.

Huxley, H.E. and Hanson, J., Changes in the cross-striations of muscle during contraction and stretch and their structural interpretation, *Nature* **173**, 973–976 (1954).

Box 7-4), are explained by the **sliding filament model** in which interdigitated thick and thin filaments slide past each other (Fig. 7-24b). Thus, during a contraction, a muscle becomes shorter, and because its total volume does not change, it also becomes thicker.

Thick Filaments Consist Mainly of Myosin. Vertebrate thick filaments are composed almost entirely of a single type of protein, **myosin**, which consists of six polypeptide chains: two 220-kD **heavy chains** and two pairs of different **light chains,** the so-called **essential** and **regulatory light chains (ELC** and **RLC)** that vary in size between 15 and 22 kD, depending on their source. X-Ray structure determinations by Ivan Rayment and Hazel Holden of the N-terminal half of the myosin heavy chain, the so-called **myosin head,** reveals that it forms an elongated (55 × 165 Å) globular head to which one subunit each of ELC and RLC bind (Fig. 7-25a). The C-terminal half of the heavy chain forms a long fibrous α-helical tail, two of which associate to form a left-handed coiled coil. Thus, *myosin consists of a 1600-Å-long rodlike segment with two globular heads* (Fig. 7-25b). The

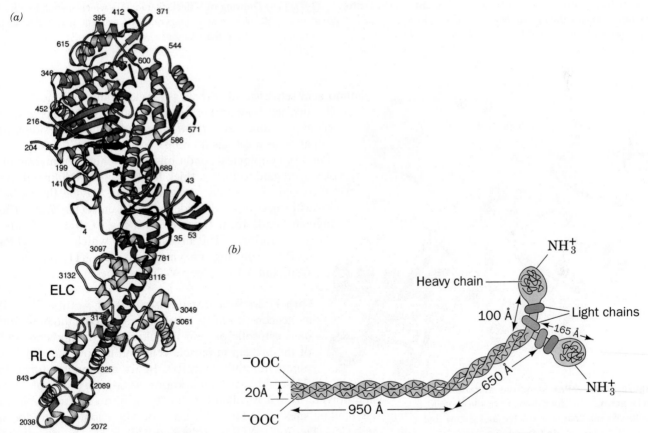

Figure 7-25 | Structure of myosin. (*a*) A ribbon diagram of the myosin head from chicken muscle. The heavy chain's 25-, 50-, and 20-kD segments are green, red, and blue, respectively, and its essential and regulatory light chains, RLC and ELC, are magenta and yellow. Residue numbers are indicated at various positions, with 2000 and 3000 being added to those of the RLC and ELC to distinguish them from the heavy chain. A sulfate ion, shown in space-filling form (*red*), is bound near the confluence of the three heavy chain segments, where it occupies the binding site of ATP's β-phosphate group. An RLC-bound Ca^{2+} ion (*lower left*) is represented by a gray ball. [Courtesy of Ivan Rayment and Hazel Holden, University of Wisconsin. PDBid 2MYS.] (*b*) Diagram of the myosin molecule. Its two identical heavy chains (*green and orange*) each have an N-terminal globular head and an α-helical tail. Between the head and tail is an α helix, the lever arm, that associates with the two kinds of light chains (*light blue and lavender*). The tails wind around each other to form a 1600-Å-long parallel coiled coil.

(a)

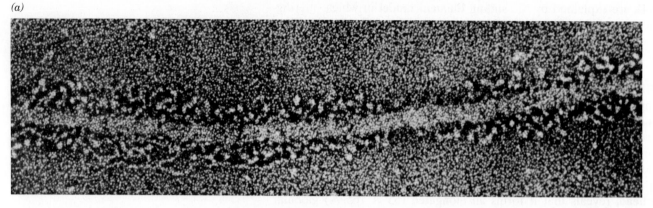

(b)

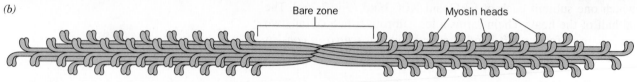

■ **Figure 7-26 │ Structure of the thick filament.** (*a*) Electron micrograph showing the myosin heads projecting from the thick filament. [From Trinick, J. and Elliott, A., *J. Mol. Biol.* **131,** 135 (1977).] (*b*) Drawing of a thick filament, in which several hundred myosin molecules form a staggered array with their globular heads pointing away from the filament.

amino acid sequence of myosin's α-helical tail is characteristic of coils such as those in keratin (Section 6-1C): It has a seven-residue pseudorepeat, *a-b-c-d-e-f-g,* with nonpolar residues predominating at positions *a* and *d.*

Under physiological conditions, several hundred myosin molecules aggregate to form a thick filament. The rodlike tails pack end to end in a regular staggered array, leaving the globular heads projecting to the sides on both ends (Fig. 7-26). These myosin heads form the cross-bridges to thin filaments in intact myofibrils. The myosin head, which is an **ATPase** (ATP-hydrolyzing enzyme), has its ATP-binding site located in a 13-Å-deep V-shaped pocket.

Thin Filaments Consist Mainly of Actin. Thin filaments consist mainly of polymers of **actin,** the most abundant cytosolic protein in eukaryotes (comprising ~20% of the protein in muscle cells and up to 15% of the protein in nonmuscle cells). In its monomeric form, this ~375-residue protein is known as **G-actin** (G for globular) when polymerized, it is called **F-actin** (F for fibrous). Each actin subunit has binding sites for ATP and a Ca^{2+} or Mg^{2+} ion that are located in a deep cleft (Fig. 7-27). ATP hydrolysis to ADP + P_i is not required for actin polymerization but occurs afterward (Section 7-2C).

The fibrous nature of F-actin and its variable fiber lengths has thwarted its crystallization in a manner suitable for X-ray crystallographic analysis Consequently, our current understanding of the atomic structure of F-actin is based on electron micrographs (Fig. 7-28*a*) together with low resolution models based on X-ray studies of oriented gels of F-actin into which high resolution atomic models of G-actin have been fitted (Fig. 7-28*b*). These models indicate that the actin polymer is a double-stranded helix of subunits in which each subunit contacts four others. Each actin subunit has

■ **Figure 7-27 │ X-Ray structure of rabbit muscle actin.** The four domains of the protein are colored cyan, magenta, orange, and yellow, and the N- and C-termini are labeled. A nonhydrolyzable ATP analog, adenosine-5'-(β,γ-imido)triphosphate, drawn in stick form and colored according to atom type (C green, N blue, O red, and P gold), binds at the bottom of a deep cleft between the domains. The Ca^{2+} ion is represented by a light green sphere. [Based on an X-ray structure by Roberto Dominguez, Boston Biomedical Research Institute, Watertown, Massachusetts. PDBid 1NWK.]

Figure 7-28 | Structure of the actin filament. (*a*) Cryoelectron microscopy–based image. The tropomyosin binding sites (see below) are blue. [Courtesy of Daniel Safer, University of Pennsylvania, and Ronald Milligan, The Scripps Research Institute, La Jolla, California.] (*b*) Model based on fitting the known X-ray structure of the actin monomer to the X-ray fiber diffraction pattern of F-actin. Actin monomers are shown in space-filling representation, in alternating blue, red, and white, with each amino acid residue represented by a sphere. The lowest monomer shown is oriented identically to that in Fig. 7-27. The residues that cross-linking studies indicate form the myosin-binding site (see below) are green. [Courtesy of Wolfgang Kabsch and Kenneth Holmes, Max-Planck-Institute für medizinische Forschung, Heidleberg, Germany.]

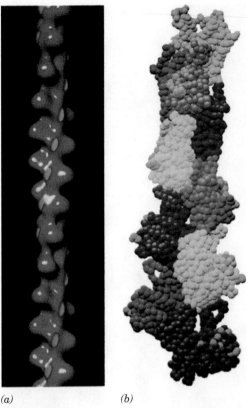

(*a*)   (*b*)

the same head-to-tail orientation (e.g., all the nucleotide-binding clefts open upward in Fig. 7-28*b*), so the assembled fiber has a distinct polarity. The end of the fiber toward which the nucleotide-binding sites open is known as the **(−) end,** and its opposite end is the **(+) end.** The (+) ends of the thin filaments bind to the Z disk (Fig. 7-23).

Each of muscle F-actin's monomeric units can bind a single myosin head (Fig. 7-29), probably by ion pairing and by the association of hydrophobic patches on each protein. Electron micrographs indicate that the myosin heads bound to an F-actin filament all have the same orientation

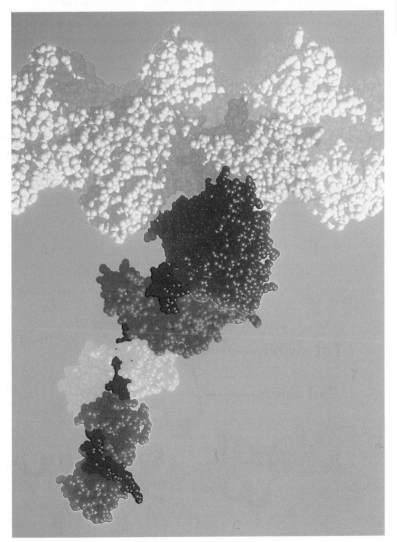

Figure 7-29 | Model of the myosin–actin interaction. This space-filling model was constructed from the X-ray structures of actin and the myosin head and electron micrographs of their complex. The actin filament is at the top. The myosin head globular regions are red and green, its α-helical lever arm is blue, and the light chains are yellow and purple. The coiled-coil tail is not shown. An ATP-binding site is located in a cleft in the red domain of the myosin head. In a myofibril, every actin monomer has the potential to bind a myosin head, and the thick filament has many myosin heads projecting from it. [Courtesy of Ivan Rayment and Hazel Holden, University of Wisconsin.]

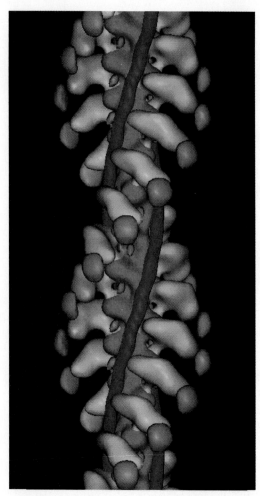

■ **Figure 7-30** | **Cryoelectron microscopy–based image at <25-Å resolution of a thin filament decorated with myosin heads.** F-actin is red, tropomyosin is blue, the myosin motor domain is yellow, yellow, and the essential light chain is green. The helical filament has a pitch (rise per turn) of 370 Å. [Courtesy of Ronald Milligan, The Scripps Research Institute, La Jolla, California.]

(Fig. 7-30) and that in thin filaments that are still attached to the Z disk the myosin heads all point away from the Z disk.

Tropomyosin and Troponin Are Thin Filament Components. Myosin and actin, the major components of muscle, account for 60 to 70% and 20 to 25% of total muscle protein, respectively. Of the remainder, two proteins that are associated with the thin filaments are particularly prominent.

1. **Tropomyosin,** a homodimer whose two 284-residue α-helical subunits wrap around each other to form a parallel coiled coil that extends nearly the entire 400-Å length of the molecule (a portion of which is shown in Fig. 6-15b). Multiple copies of these rod-shaped proteins are joined head-to-tail to form cables wound in the grooves of the F-actin helix such that each tropomyosin molecule contacts seven consecutive actin subunits in a quasi-equivalent manner (Fig. 7-30).

2. **Troponin,** which consists of three subunits: **TnC,** a Ca^{2+}-binding protein; **TnI,** which binds to actin; and **TnT,** an elongated molecule, which binds to tropomyosin at its head-to-tail junctions. The X-ray structure of troponin in complex with four Ca^{2+} ions (Fig. 7-31), determined by Robert Fletterick, reveals that TnI closely resembles the myosin light chains and that the inhibitory segment of TnI binds to TnC's rigid central helix in this Ca^{2+}-activated state.

The tropomyosin–troponin complex, as we shall see below, regulates muscle contraction by controlling the access of the myosin heads to their binding site on actin.

Muscle Contains Numerous Minor Proteins That Organize Its Structure. Other proteins serve to form the Z disk and the M disk and to organize the arrays of thick and thin filaments. For instance, **α-actinin,** a rodlike homodimeric protein that cross-links F-actin filaments, is localized in the Z disk's interior and is therefore thought to attach oppositely oriented thin filaments to the Z disk.

One of the more unusual muscle proteins, **titin,** the longest known polypeptide chain (34,350 residues), is composed of ~300 repeating

■ **Figure 7-31** | **X-Ray structure of chicken skeletal muscle troponin.** TnC is red, TnI is blue, and TnT is gold. The four Ca^{2+} ions bound by TnC are represented by cyan spheres. [Based on an X-ray structure by Robert Fletterick, University of California at San Francisco. PDBid 1YTZ.]

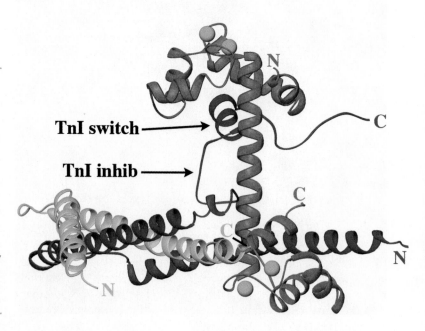

lobular domains. Three to six titin molecules associate with each thick filament, spanning the 1-μm distance between the M and Z disks. Titin is believed to function as a molecular bungee cord to keep the thick filament centered on the sarcomere: During muscle contraction, it compresses as the sarcomere shortens, but when the muscle relaxes, titin resists sarcomere extension past the starting point.

Nebulin, which is also extremely large (6669 residues), is a mainly α-helical protein that is associated with the thin filament. It is thought to set the length of the thin filament by acting as a template for actin polymerization. This length is held constant by **tropomodulin,** which caps the (−) end of the thin filament (the end not attached to the Z disk), thereby preventing further actin polymerization and depolymerization. **CapZ** (also called **β-actinin**) is an α-actinin-associated heterodimer that similarly caps the (+) end of F-actin.

The M disk (Fig. 7-23) arises from the local enlargement of in-register thick filaments. Two proteins that are associated with this structure, **myomensin** and **M-protein,** bind to titin and are therefore likely to participate in thick filament assembly, as does the thick filament–associated **myosin-binding protein C.**

Duchenne muscular dystrophy (DMD) and the less severe **Becker muscular dystrophy (BMD)** are both sex-linked muscle-wasting diseases. In DMD, which has an onset age of 2 to 5 years, muscle degeneration exceeds muscle regeneration, causing progressive muscle weakness and ultimately death, typically due to respiratory disorders or heart failure, usually by age 25. In BMD, the onset age is 5 to 10 years and there is an overall less progressive course of muscle degeneration and a longer (sometimes normal) life span than in individuals with DMD.

The gene responsible for DMD/BMD encodes a 3685-residue protein named **dystrophin,** which has a normal abundance in muscle tissue of 0.002%. Individuals with DMD usually have no detectable dystrophin in their muscles, whereas those with BMD mostly have dystrophins of altered sizes. Evidently, the dystrophins of individuals with DMD are rapidly degraded, whereas those of individuals with BMD are semifunctional.

Dystrophin is a member of a family of flexible rod-shaped proteins that includes other actin-binding cytoskeletal components. Dystrophin associates on the inner surface of the muscle plasma membrane with a transmembrane glycoprotein complex, where it helps anchor F-actin to the extracellular matrix and thereby protects the plasma membrane from being torn by the mechanical stress of muscle contraction. Although such small tears are common in muscle cells, they occur much more frequently in dystrophic cells, leading to a greatly increased rate of cell death.

Muscle Contraction Occurs When Myosin Heads Walk Up Thin Filaments

In order to complete our description of muscle contraction we must determine how ATP hydrolysis is coupled to the sliding filament model. If the sliding filament model is correct then it would be impossible for a myosin cross-bridge to remain attached to the same point on a thin filament during muscle contraction. Rather, it must repeatedly detach and then reattach itself at a new site further along the thin filament toward the Z disk. This, in turn, suggests that *muscular tension is generated through the interaction of myosin cross-bridges with thin filaments.* The actual contractile force is provided by ATP hydrolysis. Thus, myosin is a **motor protein** that converts the chemical energy of ATP hydrolysis to the mechanical energy of movement. Edwin Taylor formulated a model fc myosin-mediated ATP hydrolysis, which has been refined by the structur₂ studies of Rayment, Holden, and Ronald Milligan as follows (Fig. 7-32):

1. ATP binds to a myosin head in a manner that causes myosin's actir binding site to open up and release its bound actin.

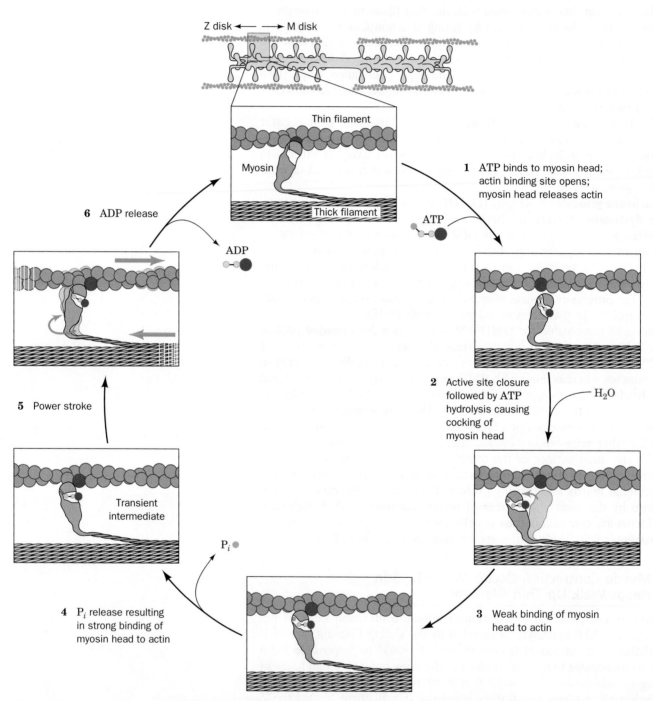

■ **Figure 7-32** | **Mechanism of force generation in muscle.** The myosin head "walks" up the actin thin filament through a unidirectional cyclic process that is driven by ATP hydrolysis to ADP and P_i. Only one myosin head is shown. The actin monomer to which the myosin head is bound at the beginning of the cycle is more darkly colored for reference. [After Rayment, I. and Holden, H., *Curr. Opin. Struct. Biol.* **3**, 949 (1993).] ✑ **See the Animated Figures.**

2. Myosin's active site (distinct from its actin-binding site) closes around the ATP. The resulting hydrolysis of the ATP to ADP + P_i "cocks" the myosin head, that is, puts it into its "high energy" conformation in which it is approximately perpendicular to the thick filament.

3. The myosin head binds weakly to an actin monomer that is closer to the Z disk than the one to which it had been bound previously.

4. Myosin releases P_i, which causes its actin-binding site to close, thereby increasing its affinity for actin.

5. The resulting transient state is immediately followed by the power stroke, a conformational shift that sweeps the myosin head's C-terminal tail by an estimated ~100 Å toward the Z disk relative to the actin-binding site on its head, thus translating the attached thin filament by this distance toward the M disk.

6. ADP is released, thereby completing the cycle.

Because the reaction cycle involves several steps, some of which are irreversible (e.g., ATP hydrolysis and P_i release), the entire cycle is unidirectional. The ~500 myosin heads on every thick filament asynchronously cycle through this reaction sequence about five times each per second during a strong muscular contraction. *The myosin heads thereby "walk" or "row" up adjacent thin filaments toward the Z disk with the concomitant contraction of the muscle.* Although myosin is dimeric, its two heads function independently.

Calcium Triggers Muscle Contraction. Highly purified actin and myosin can contract regardless of the Ca^{2+} concentration, but preparations containing intact thin filaments contract only in the presence of Ca^{2+}, due to the regulatory action of troponin C (Fig. 7-31). Stimulation of a myofibril by a nerve impulse results in the release of Ca^{2+} from the **sarcoplasmic reticulum** (a system of flattened vesicles derived from the endoplasmic reticulum). As a result, the intracellular $[Ca^{2+}]$ increases from ~10^{-7} to ~10^{-5} M. The higher calcium concentration triggers the conformational change in the troponin–tropomyosin complex that exposes the site on actin where the myosin head binds (Fig. 7-33). When the myofibril $[Ca^{2+}]$ is low (Ca^{2+} is rapidly pumped back into the sarcoplasmic reticulum by ATP-requiring Ca^{2+} pumps; Section 10-3B), the troponin–tropomyosin complex assumes its resting conformation, blocking myosin binding to actin and causing the muscle to relax.

C | Actin Forms Microfilaments in Nonmuscle Cells

Although actin and myosin are most prominent in muscle, they also occur in other tissues. In fact, actin is ubiquitous and is usually the most abundant cytoplasmic protein in eukaryotic cells, typically accounting for 5 to 10% of their total protein. Nonmuscle actin forms ~70-Å-diameter fibers known as **microfilaments** that can be visualized by **immunofluorescence microscopy** (in which a fluorescent-tagged antibody is used to "stain" the

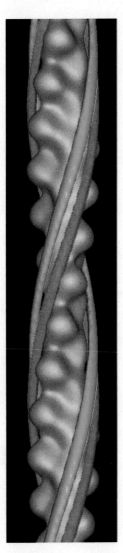

Figure 7-33 | **Comparison of the positions of tropomyosin on the thin filament in the absence and presence of Ca^{2+}.** In this superposition of cryoelectron microscopy–based images, the F-actin filament is gold, the tropomyosin in the absence of Ca^{2+} is red, and that in the presence of Ca^{2+} is green. [Courtesy of William Lehman, Boston University School of Medicine.]

■ **Figure 7-34** | **Actin microfilaments.** The microfilaments in a fibroblast resting on the surface of a culture dish are revealed by immunofluorescence microscopy using a fluorescently labeled antibody to actin. When the cell begins to move, the filaments disassemble. [Courtesy of John Victor Small, Austrian Academy of Sciences, Salzburg.]

actin to which it binds; Fig. 7-34). In nonmuscle cells, actin plays an essential role in many processes, including changes in cell shape, cell division, endocytosis, and organelle transport.

Microfilament Treadmilling Can Mediate Locomotion. ATP–G-actin binds to both ends of an F-actin filament but with a greater affinity for its (+) end (hence its name). This polymerization activates F-actin subunits to hydrolyze their bound ATP to ADP + P_i with the subsequent dissociation of P_i. The resulting conformation change reduces the affinity of an ADP–F-actin subunit for its neighboring subunits relative to that of ATP–F-actin. Since F-actin–catalyzed ATP hydrolysis occurs more slowly than actin polymerization and F-actin's bound nucleotide does not exchange with those in solution (its nucleotide-binding site is blocked by its associated subunits), F-actin's more recently polymerized and hence predominantly ATP-containing subunits occur largely at its (+) end, whereas its (−) end consists mainly of less recently polymerized and hence predominantly ADP-containing subunits. The lesser affinity of ADP-containing actin subunits for F-actin results in their net dissociation from the (−) end of the polymer.

The steady state (when the microfilament maintains a constant length) occurs when the net rate of addition of subunits at the (+) end matches the net rate of dissociation of subunits at the (−) end. Then, *subunits that have added to the (+) end move toward the (−) end where they dissociate, a process called* **treadmilling** (Fig. 7-35). Thus, a fluorescently labeled actin monomer is seen to move from the (+) end of the microfilament toward its (−) end. Treadmilling is driven by the free energy of ATP hydrolysis and hence is not at equilibrium.

The directional growth of actin filaments exerts force against the plasma membrane, allowing a cell to extend its cytoplasm in one direction. If the cytoplasmic protrusion anchors itself to the underlying surface, then the cell can use the adhesion point for traction in order to advance further.

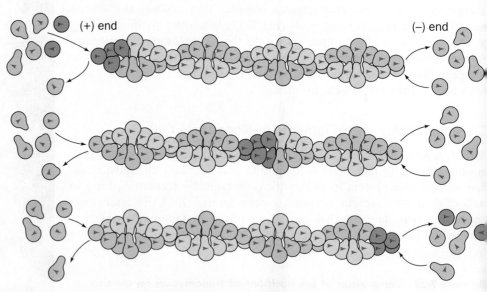

■ **Figure 7-35** | **Microfilament treadmilling.** In the steady state, actin monomers continually add to the (+) end of the filament (*left*) but dissociate at the same rate from the (−) end (*right*). The filament thereby maintains a constant length while its component monomers translocate from left to right.

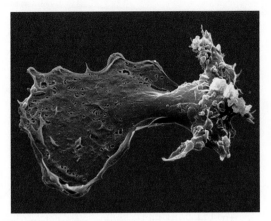

■ **Figure 7-36** | **Scanning electron micrograph of a crawling cell.** The leading edge of the cell (*left*) is ruffled where it has become detached from the surface and is in the process of extending. The cell's trailing edge or tail (*right*), which is still attached to the surface, is gradually pulled toward the leading edge. The rate of actin polymerization is greatest at the leading edge. [© David Phillips/Visuals Unlimited.]

In order for the cell to crawl, however, the trailing edge of the cell must release its contacts with the surface while newer contacts are being made at the leading edge (Fig. 7-36). In addition, as microfilament polymerization proceeds at the leading edge, depolymerization must occur elsewhere in the cell, since the pool of G-actin is limited. A variety of actin-binding proteins modulate the rate of actin depolymerization and repolymerization *in vivo.*

Actin-mediated cell locomotion, that is, amoeboid motion, is the most primitive mechanism of cell movement. Nevertheless, virtually all eukaryotic cells undertake some version of it, even if it involves just a small patch of actin near the cell surface. More extensive microfilament rearrangements are essential for cells such as neutrophils (a type of white blood cell) that travel relatively long distances to sites of infection or inflammation.

■ **CHECK YOUR UNDERSTANDING**

Explain how myosin structure relates to its function as a motor protein.

Draw a diagram of the components of a sarcomere.

Explain the molecular basis of the sliding filament model of muscle contraction.

Describe the process of treadmilling in a microfilament.

How does a microfilament differ from the thin filament in a myofibril?

3 Antibodies

All organisms are continually subject to attack by other organisms, including disease-causing microorganisms and viruses. In higher animals, these **pathogens** may penetrate the physical barrier presented by the skin and mucous membranes (a first line of defense) only to be identified as foreign invaders and destroyed by the **immune system.** Two types of immunity have been distinguished:

LEARNING OBJECTIVES

■ Understand the overall structure of immunoglobulins,

■ Understand how the immune system generates a diversity of antibodies to bind a variety of different antigens.

1. **Cellular immunity,** which guards against virally infected cells, fungi, parasites, and foreign tissue, is mediated by **T lymphocytes** or **T cells,** so called because they develop in the thymus.

2. **Humoral immunity** (*humor* is an archaic term for fluid), which is most effective against bacterial infections and the extracellular phases of viral infections, is mediated by an enormously diverse collection of related proteins known as **antibodies** or **immunoglobulins.** Antibodies are produced by **B lymphocytes** or **B cells,** which in mammals mature in the bone marrow.

In this section we focus on the structure, function, and generation of antibodies.

The immune response is triggered by the presence of a foreign macromolecule, often a protein or carbohydrate, known as an antigen. B cells display immunoglobulins on their surfaces. If a B cell encounters an antigen that binds to its particular immunoglobulin, it engulfs the antigen–antibody complex, degrades it, and displays the antigen fragments on the cell surface.

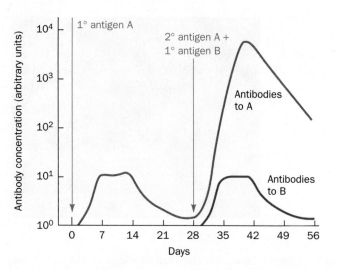

T cells then stimulate the B cell to proliferate. Most of the B cell progeny are circulating cells that secrete large amounts of the antigen-specific antibody. These antibodies can bind to additional antigen molecules, thereby marking them for destruction by other components of the immune system. Although most B cells live only a few days unless stimulated by their corresponding antigen, a few long-lived **memory B cells** can recognize antigen several weeks or even many years later and can mount a more rapid and massive immune response (called a secondary response) than B cells that have not yet encountered their antigen (Fig. 7-37).

A | Antibodies Have Constant and Variable Regions

The immunoglobulins form a related but enormously diverse group of proteins. All immunoglobulins contain at least four subunits: two identical ~23-kD **light chains (L)** and two identical 53- to 75-kD **heavy chains (H)**. These subunits associate by disulfide bonds and by noncovalent interactions to form a roughly Y-shaped symmetric molecule with the formula $(LH)_2$ (Fig. 7-38).

The five classes of immunoglobulin **(Ig)** differ in the type of heavy chain they contain and, in some cases, in their subunit structure (Table 7-2). For example, **IgM** consists of five Y-shaped molecules arranged around a central **J subunit; IgA** occurs as monomers, dimers, and trimers. The various immunoglobulin classes also have different physiological functions. IgM is most effective against microorganisms and is the first immunoglobulin to

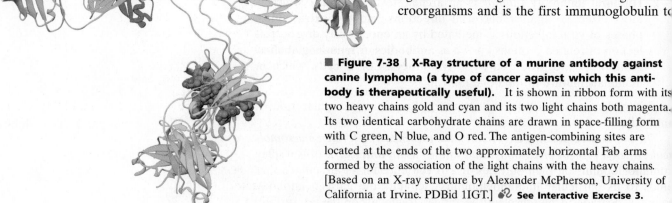

■ **Figure 7-38** | **X-Ray structure of a murine antibody against canine lymphoma (a type of cancer against which this antibody is therapeutically useful).** It is shown in ribbon form with its two heavy chains gold and cyan and its two light chains both magenta. Its two identical carbohydrate chains are drawn in space-filling form with C green, N blue, and O red. The antigen-combining sites are located at the ends of the two approximately horizontal Fab arms formed by the association of the light chains with the heavy chains. [Based on an X-ray structure by Alexander McPherson, University of California at Irvine. PDBid 1IGT.] 🖱 **See Interactive Exercise 3.**

Table 7-2	Classes of Human Immunoglobulins			
Class	Heavy Chain	Light Chain	Subunit Structure	Molecular Mass (kD)
IgA	α	κ or λ	$(\alpha_2\kappa_2)_nJ^a$ or $(\alpha_2\lambda_2)_nJ^a$	360–720
IgD	δ	κ or λ	$\delta_2\kappa_2$ or $\delta_2\lambda_2$	160
IgE	ε	κ or λ	$\varepsilon_2\kappa_2$ or $\varepsilon_2\lambda_2$	190
IgG[b]	γ	κ or λ	$\gamma_2\kappa_2$ or $\gamma_2\lambda_2$	150
IgM	μ	κ or λ	$(\mu_2\kappa_2)_5J$ or $(\mu_2\lambda_2)_5J$	950

n = 1, 2, or 3.

IgG has four subclasses, IgG1, IgG2, IgG3, and IgG4, which differ in their γ chains.

be secreted in response to an antigen. **IgG,** the most common immunoglobulin, is equally distributed between the blood and the extravascular fluid. IgA occurs predominantly in the intestinal tract and defends against pathogens by adhering to their antigenic sites so as to block their attachment to epithelial (outer) surfaces. **IgE,** which is normally present in the blood in minute concentrations, protects against parasites and has been implicated in allergic reactions. **IgD,** which is also present in small amounts, has no clearly known function. Our discussion of antibody structure will focus on IgG.

IgG can be cleaved through limited proteolysis with the enzyme **papain** into three ~50-kD fragments: two identical **Fab fragments** and one **Fc fragment.** The Fab fragments are the "arms" of the Y-shaped antibody and contain an entire L chain and the N-terminal half of an H chain (Fig. 7-39). These fragments contain IgG's antigen-binding sites (the "ab" in Fab

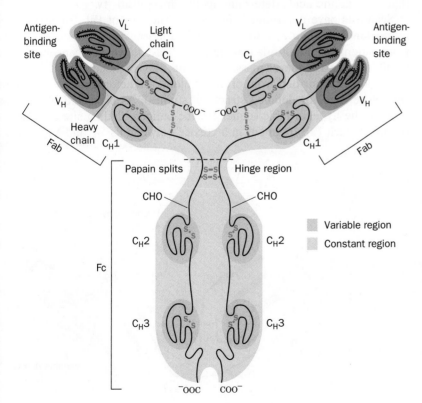

■ **Figure 7-39** | **Diagram of human immunoglobulin G (IgG).** Each light chain contains a variable (V_L) and a constant (C_L) region, and each heavy chain contains one variable (V_H) and three constant (C_H1, C_H2, and C_H3) regions. Each of the variable and constant domains contains a disulfide bond, and the four polypeptide chains are linked by disulfide bonds. The proteolytic enzyme papain cleaves IgG at the hinge region to yield two Fab fragments and one Fc fragment. CHO represents carbohydrate chains. [Illustration, Irving Geis. Image from Irving Geis Collection/Howard Hughes Medical Institute. Rights owned by HHMI. Reproduction by permission only.]

stands for *a*ntigen *b*inding). The Fc portion ("c" because it *c*rystallize easily) derives from the "stem" of the antibody and consists of the C-ter minal halves of two H chains. The arms of the Y are connected to the stem by a flexible hinge region. The hinge angles may vary, so an antibody mol ecule may not be perfectly symmetrical (e.g., Fig. 7-38).

Although all IgG molecules have the same overall structure, IgGs that recognize different antigens have different amino acid sequences. The light chains of different antibodies differ mostly in their N-terminal halves. These polypeptides are therefore said to have a **variable region, V_L** (residues 1 to 108), and a **constant region, C_L** (residues 109 to 214). Comparisons of H chains, which have 446 residues, reveal that H chains also have a variable region, V_H, and a constant region, C_H. As indicated in Fig. 7-39, the C_H region consists of three ~110-residue segments, C_H1, C_H2, and C_H3, which are homologous to each other and to C_L. In fact, all the constant and variable regions resemble each other in sequence and in disulfide-bonding pattern. These similarities suggest that the six different homology units of an IgG evolved through the duplication of a primor dial gene encoding an ~110-residue protein.

B | Antibodies Recognize a Huge Variety of Antigens

The immunoglobulin homology units all have the same characteristic **immunoglobulin fold:** a sandwich composed of three- and four-stranded antiparallel β sheets that are linked by a disulfide bond (Fig. 6-29b). Nevertheless, the basic immunoglobulin structure must accommodate an enormous variety of antigens. The ability to recognize antigens resides in three loops in the variable domain (Fig. 7-40). Most of the amino acid vari ation among antibodies is concentrated in these three short segments called **hypervariable** sequences. As hypothesized by Elvin Kabat, the hy pervariable sequences line an immunoglobulin's antigen-binding site, so that their amino acids determine its binding specificity.

Scientists have determined the X-ray structures of Fab fragments from **monoclonal antibodies** (Box 7-5) and monospecific antibodies isolated from patients with **multiple myeloma** (a disease in which a cancerous B cell proliferates and produces massive amounts of a single immunoglobulin; im munoglobulins purified from ordinary blood are heterogeneous and hence cannot be used for detailed structural studies). As predicted by the posi tions of the hypervariable sequences, the antigen-binding site is located at the tip of each Fab fragment in a crevice between its V_L and V_H domains.

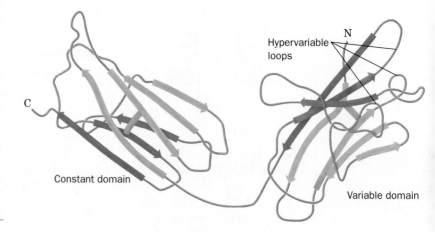

■ **Figure 7-40** | **Immunoglobulin folds in a light chain.** Both the constant and variable domains consist of a sandwich of a four-stranded antiparallel β sheet (*blue*) and a three-stranded antiparallel β sheet (*orange*) that are linked by a disulfide bond (*yellow*). The positions of the three hypervariable sequences in the variable domain are indicated. [After Schiffer, M., Girling, R.L., Ely, K.R., and Edmundson, A.B., *Biochemistry* **12,** 4628 (1973).]

BOX 7-5 PERSPECTIVES IN BIOCHEMISTRY

Monoclonal Antibodies

Introducing a foreign molecule into an animal induces the synthesis of large amounts of antigen-specific but heterogeneous antibodies. One might expect that a single lymphocyte from such an animal could be cloned (allowed to reproduce) to yield a harvest of homogeneous immunoglobulin molecules. Unfortunately, lymphocytes do not grow continuously in culture. In the late 1970s, however, César Milstein and Georges Köhler developed a technique for immortalizing such cells so that they can grow continuously and secrete virtually unlimited quantities of a specific antibody. Typically, lymphocytes from a mouse that has been immunized with a particular antigen are harvested and fused with mouse myeloma cells (a type of blood system cancer), which can multiply indefinitely (see figure). The cells are then incubated in a selective medium that inhibits the synthesis of purines, which are essential for myeloma growth [the myeloma cells lack the enzyme **hypoxanthine phosphoribosyl transferase (HPRT),** which could otherwise participate in a purine nucleotide salvage pathway; Section 23-1D]. The only cells that can grow in the selective medium are fused cells, known as **hybridoma cells,** that combine the missing HPRT (it is supplied by the lymphocyte) with the immortal attributes of the myeloma cells. Clones derived from single fused cells are then screened for the presence of antibodies to the original antigen. Antibody-producing cells can be grown in large quantities in tissue culture or as semisolid tumors in mouse hosts.

Monoclonal antibodies are used to purify macromolecules (Section 5-2), to identify infectious diseases, and to test for the presence of drugs and other substances in body tissues. Because of their purity and specificity and, to some extent, their biocompatibility, monoclonal antibodies also hold considerable promise as therapeutic agents against cancer and other diseases. In fact, the monoclonal antibody known as **Herceptin** binds specifically to the growth factor receptor **HER2** that is overexpressed in about one-quarter of breast cancers. Herceptin binding to HER2 blocks its growth-signaling activity, thereby causing the tumor to stop growing or even regress.

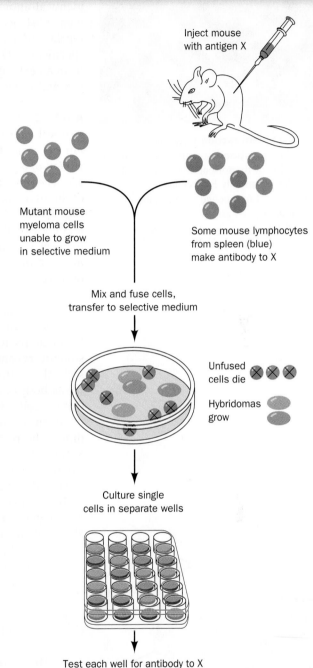

The association between antibodies and their antigens involves van der Waals, hydrophobic, hydrogen bonding, and ionic interactions. Their dissociation constants range from 10^{-4} to 10^{-10} M, comparable (or even greater) in strength to the associations between enzymes and their substrates. The specificity and strength of an antigen–antibody complex are a function of the exquisite structural complementarity between the antigen and the

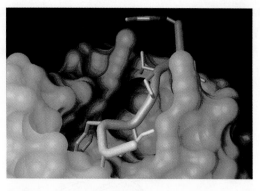

■ **Figure 7-41** | **Interaction between an antibody.** This X-ray structure shows a portion of the solvent-accessible surface of a monoclonal antibody Fab fragment (*green*) with a stick model of a bound nine-residue fragment of its peptide antigen (*lavender*). [Courtesy of Ian Wilson, The Scripps Research Institute, La Jolla, California. PDBid 1HMM.]

antibody (e.g., Fig. 7-41). These are also the features that make antibodie such useful laboratory reagents (Fig. 5-3, for example).

Most immunoglobulins are divalent molecules; that is, they can bind two identical antigens simultaneously (IgM and IgA are multivalent). A for eign substance or organism usually has multiple antigenic regions, and typical immune response generates a mixture of antibodies with differen specificities. Divalent binding allows antibodies to cross-link antigens t form an extended lattice (Fig. 7-42), which hastens the removal of the anti gen and triggers B cell proliferation.

Antibody Diversity Results from Gene Rearrangement and Mutation

A novel antigen does not direct a B cell to begin manufacturing a new im munoglobulin to which it can bind. Rather, *an antigen stimulates the prolif eration of a preexisting B cell whose antibodies happen to recognize the anti gen.* The immune system has the potential to produce an enormous numbe of different antibodies, probably $>10^{18}$. Even though this number is so larg that an individual can synthesize only a small fraction of its potentia immunoglobulin repertoire during its lifetime, this fraction is still sufficien to react with almost any antigen the individual might encounter. Yet th number of immunoglobulin genes is far too small to account for th observed level of antibody diversity. The diversity in antibody sequence arises instead from genetic changes during B lymphocyte development.

Each chain of an immunoglobulin molecule is encoded by multipl DNA segments: V, J, and C segments for the light chains, and V, D, J, an C segments for heavy chains. These segments are joined together b **somatic recombination** during B cell development before being tran scribed and translated into protein. The process is called somatic (Greek *soma,* body) to distinguish it from the recombination that occurs in repro ductive cells. Because there are multiple versions of the V, D, J, and C seg ments in the genome, the combinatorial possibilities are enormous. In ad dition, the recombination process sometimes adds or deletes nucleotide at the junctions between gene segments, further contributing to the diver sity of the encoded protein. The generation of antibody diversity is furthe discussed in Section 28-3D.

Additional changes can occur after a B cell has encountered its antigen and begun secreting antibody molecules. As the antibody-producing B cell divide, their rate of immunoglobulin gene mutation increases dramatically favoring the substitution of one nucleotide for another and leading t an average of one amino acid change for every cell generation. Thi process, which is called **somatic hypermutation,** permits the anti gen specificity of the antibody to be fine-tuned over many cel generations, because the rate of B cell proliferation increase with the antigen-binding affinity of the antibody it produces.

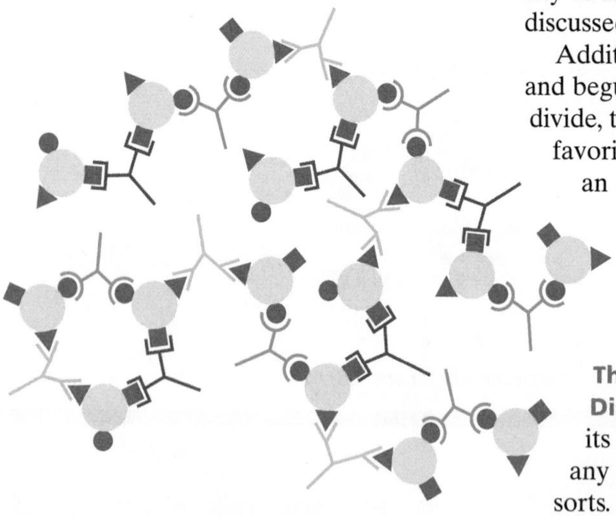

The Immune System Loses Its Tolerance in Autoimmun Diseases. Another remarkable property of the immune system is tha its power is unleashed only against foreign substances and not agains any of the tens of thousands of endogenous (self) molecules of variou sorts. Virtually all macromolecules are potentially antigenic, as can b demonstrated by transplanting tissues from one individual to another, eve within a species. This incompatibility presents obvious challenges for ther apies ranging from routine blood transfusions to multiple organ transplants

The mechanism whereby an individual's immune system distinguishe self from non-self is poorly understood. It begins to operate around th time of birth and must be ongoing, since new lymphocytes arise throughou

■ **Figure 7-42** | **Antigen cross-linking by antibodies.** A mixture of divalent antibodies that recognizes the several different antigenic regions of an intruding particle such as a toxin molecule or a bacterium can form an extensive lattice of antigen and antibody molecules.

Table 7-3	Some Autoimmune Diseases	
Disease	**Target Tissue**	**Major Symptoms**
Addison's disease	Adrenal cortex	Low blood glucose, muscle weakness, Na^+ loss, K^+ retention, increased susceptibility to stress
Crohn's disease	Intestinal lining	Intestinal inflammation, chronic diarrhea
Graves' disease	Thyroid gland	Oversecretion of thyroid hormone resulting in increased appetite accompanied by weight loss
Insulin-dependent diabetes mellitus	Pancreatic β cells	Loss of ability to make insulin
Multiple sclerosis	Myelin sheath of nerve fibers in brain and spinal cord	Progressive loss of motor control
Myasthenia gravis	Acetylcholine receptors at nerve–muscle synapses	Progressive muscle weakness
Psoriasis	Epidermis	Hyperproliferation of the skin
Rheumatoid arthritis	Connective tissue	Inflammation and degeneration of the joints
Systemic lupus erythematosus	DNA, phospholipids, other tissue components	Rash, joint and muscle pain, anemia, kidney damage, mental dysfunction

an individual's lifetime. Occasionally, the immune system loses tolerance to some of its self-antigens, resulting in an **autoimmune disease.**

All the body's organ systems are theoretically susceptible to attack by an immune system that has lost its self-tolerance, but some tissues are attacked more often than others. Some of the most common autoimmune diseases are listed in Table 7-3. The symptoms of a particular disease reflect the type of tissue with which the autoantibodies react. In general, autoimmune diseases are chronic, often with periods of remission, and their clinical severity may differ among individuals.

The loss of tolerance to one's own antigens may result from an innate malfunctioning of the mechanism by which the immune system distinguishes self from non-self, possibly precipitated by an event, such as trauma or infection, in which tissues that are normally sequestered from the immune system are exposed to lymphocytes. For example, breaching the blood–brain barrier may allow lymphocytes access to the brain or spinal cord, and injury may allow access to the spaces at joints, which are not normally served by blood vessels. There is also evidence that some autoimmune diseases are caused by antibodies to certain viral or bacterial antigens that cross-react with endogenous substances because of chance antigenic similarities. Some diseases, such as systemic lupus erythematosus, represent a more generalized breakdown of the immune system, so that antibodies to many endogenous substances (e.g., DNA and phospholipids) may be generated.

■ CHECK YOUR UNDERSTANDING

Identify the domains of an immunoglobulin molecule.
What is the source of antibody diversity?
How do autoimmune diseases arise?

SUMMARY

1. Myoglobin, a monomeric heme-containing muscle protein, reversibly binds a single O_2 molecule.

2. Hemoglobin, a tetramer with pseudo-D_2 symmetry, has distinctly different conformations in its oxy and deoxy states.

3. Oxygen binds to hemoglobin in a sigmoidal fashion, indicating cooperative binding.

4. O_2 binding to a heme group induces a conformational change in the entire hemoglobin molecule that includes movements

at the subunit interfaces and the disruption of ion pairs. The result is a shift from the T to the R state.

5. CO_2 promotes O_2 dissociation from hemoglobin through the Bohr effect. BPG decreases hemoglobin's O_2 affinity by binding to deoxyhemoglobin.

6. The symmetry and sequential models of allosterism explain how binding of a ligand at one site affects binding of another ligand at a different site.

7. Hemoglobin variants have revealed structure–function relationships. Hemoglobin S produces the symptoms of sickle-cell anemia by forming rigid fibers in its deoxy form.

8. The thick filaments of a sarcomere are composed of the motor protein myosin and the thin filaments are composed mainly of actin.

9. The heads of myosin molecules in thick filaments form bridges to actin in thin filaments such that the detachment

and reattachment of the myosin heads cause the thick and thin filaments to slide past each other during muscle contraction. The contractile force derives from conformational changes in myosin that are triggered by ATP hydrolysis.

10. In nonmuscle cells, actin forms microfilaments, which are components of the cytoskeleton. Microfilaments are dynamic structures whose growth and regression are responsible for certain types of cell movement.

11. The immune system responds to foreign macromolecules through the production of antibodies (immunoglobulins).

12. The Y-shaped IgG molecule consists of two heavy and two light chains. The two antigen-binding sites are formed by the hypervariable sequences in the variable domains at the ends of a heavy and a light chain.

13. Antibody diversity results from somatic recombination during B cell development and from somatic hypermutation.

KEY TERMS

heme **178**
oxygenation **178**
Y_{O_2} **179**
pO_2 **180**
hyperbolic curve **180**
saturation **180**
p_{50} **180**
ligand **180**
sigmoidal curve **184**
cooperative binding **184**
Hill equation **184**
Hill coefficient **185**
noncooperative binding **185**
positive cooperativity **185**
negative cooperativity **185**
Perutz mechanism **186**

T state **186**
R state **186**
Bohr effect **189**
erythrocyte **189**
allosteric interaction **192**
symmetry model **193**
sequential model **193**
variant **194**
lyse **194**
anemia **194**
cyanosis **194**
polycythemia **194**
heterozygote **195**
homozygote **195**
sickle-cell anemia **195**
striated muscle **198**

myofibril **198**
sarcomere **198**
thick filament **198**
thin filament **198**
sliding filament model **201**
(−) end **203**
(+) end **203**
motor protein **205**
microfilament **207**
treadmilling **208**
pathogen **209**
immune system **209**
cellular immunity **209**
lymphocyte **209**
humoral immunity **209**
immunoglobulin (Ig) **209**

antigen **209**
memory B cell **210**
Fab fragment **211**
Fc fragment **211**
variable region **212**
constant region **212**
immunoglobulin fold **212**
hypervariability **212**
monoclonal antibody **212**
multiple myeloma **212**
somatic recombination **214**
somatic hypermutation **214**
autoimmune disease **215**

PROBLEMS

1. Estimate K from the following data describing ligand binding to a protein.

[Ligand] (mM)	Y
0.25	0.30
0.50	0.45
0.80	0.56
1.4	0.66
2.2	0.80
3.0	0.83
4.5	0.86
6.0	0.93

2. Which set of binding data is likely to represent cooperative ligand binding to an oligomeric protein?

(a) [Ligand] (mM)	Y	(b) [Ligand] (mM)	Y
0.1	0.3	0.2	0.1
0.2	0.5	0.3	0.3
0.4	0.7	0.4	0.6
0.7	0.9	0.6	0.8

3. In active muscles, the pO_2 may be 10 torr at the cell surface and 1 torr at the mitochondria (the organelles where oxidative metabolism occurs). Use Eq. 7-6 to show how myoglobin ($p_{50} = 2.8$ torr) facilitates the diffusion of O_2 through these cells.

4. In humans, the urge to breathe results from high concentrations of CO_2 in the blood; there are no direct physiological sensors of blood pO_2. Skindivers often hyperventilate (breathe rapidly and deeply for several minutes) just before making a dive in the belief that this will increase the O_2 content of their blood. (a) Does it do so? (b) Use your knowledge of hemoglobin function to evaluate whether this practice is useful.

5. Drinking a few drops of a commercial preparation called "vitamin O," which consists of oxygen and sodium chloride dissolved in water, is claimed to increase the concentration of oxygen in the body. (a) Use your knowledge of oxygen transport to evaluate this claim. (b) Would vitamin O be more or less effective if it were infused directly into the bloodstream?

6. Is the p_{50} higher or lower than normal in (a) hemoglobin Yakima and (b) hemoglobin Kansas? Explain.

7. Hemoglobin S homozygotes who are severely anemic often have elevated levels of BPG in their erythrocytes. Is this a beneficial effect?

8. In hemoglobin Rainier, Tyr 145β is replaced by Cys, which forms a disulfide bond with another Cys residue in the same subunit. This prevents the formation of ion pairs that normally stabilize the T state. How does hemoglobin Rainier differ from normal hemoglobin with respect to (a) oxygen affinity, (b) the Bohr effect, and (c) the Hill coefficient?

9. The crocodile, which can remain under water without breathing for up to 1 h, drowns its air-breathing prey and then dines at its leisure. An adaptation that aids the crocodile in doing so is that it can utilize virtually 100% of the O_2 in its blood whereas humans, for example, can extract only ~65% of the O_2 in their blood. Crocodile Hb does not bind BPG. However, crocodile deoxyHb preferentially binds HCO_3^-. How does this help the crocodile obtain its dinner?

10. Some primitive animals have a hemoglobin that consists of two identical subunits.

   (a) Sketch an oxygen-binding curve for this protein.

   (b) What is the likely range of the Hill coefficient for this hemoglobin?

11. Is myosin a fibrous protein or a globular protein? Explain.

12. A myosin head can undergo five ATP hydrolysis cycles per second, each of which moves an actin monomer by ~100 Å. How is it possible for an entire sarcomere to shorten by 1000 Å in this same period?

13. **Rigor mortis,** the stiffening of muscles after death, is caused by depletion of cellular ATP. Describe the molecular basis of rigor.

14. Explain why a microfilament is polar whereas a filament of keratin is not.

15. Give the approximate molecular masses of an immunoglobulin G molecule analyzed by (a) gel filtration chromatography, (b) SDS-PAGE, and (c) SDS-PAGE in the presence of 2-mercaptoethanol.

16. Explain why the variation in V_L and V_H domains of immunoglobulins is largely confined to the hypervariable loops.

17. Why do antibodies raised against a native protein sometimes fail to bind to the corresponding denatured protein?

18. Antibodies raised against a macromolecular antigen usually produce an antigen–antibody precipitate when mixed with that antigen. Explain why no precipitate forms when (a) Fab fragments from those antibodies are mixed with the antigen; (b) antibodies raised against a small antigen are mixed with that small antigen; and (c) the antibody is in great excess over the antigen and vice versa.

CASE STUDIES

Case 8 (available at www.wiley.com/college/voet)
Hemoglobin, the Oxygen Carrier

Focus concept: A mutation in the gene for hemoglobin results in an altered protein responsible for the disease sickle-cell anemia. An understanding of the biochemistry of the disease may suggest possible treatments.

Prerequisite: Chapter 7

• Hemoglobin structure and function

Case 9
Allosteric Interactions in Crocodile Hemoglobin

Focus concept: The effect of allosteric modulators on oxygen affinity for crocodile hemoglobin differs from that of other species.

Prerequisite: Chapter 7

• Hemoglobin structure and function

Case 10
The Biological Roles of Nitric Oxide

Focus concept: Nitric oxide, a small lipophilic molecule, acts as a second messenger in blood vessels.

Prerequisite: Chapter 7

• Hemoglobin structure and function

REFERENCES

Myoglobin and Hemoglobin

Ackers, G.K. and Holt, J.M., Asymmetric cooperativity in a symmetric tetramer: human hemoglobin, *J. Biol. Chem.* **281,** 11441–11443 (2006). [A brief review of hemoglobin's allosteric behavior.]

Allison, A.C., The discovery of resistance to malaria of sickle-cell heterozygotes, *Biochem. Mol. Biol. Educ.* **30,** 279–287 (2002).

Dickerson, R.E. and Geis, I., *Hemoglobin,* Benjamin/Cummings (1983). [A beautifully written and lavishly illustrated treatise on the structure, function, and evolution of hemoglobin.]

Hsia, C.C.W., Respiratory function of hemoglobin, *New Engl. J. Med.* **338,** 239–247 (1998). [A short review of hemoglobin's physiological role.]

Judson, H.F., *The Eighth Day of Creation* (Expanded edition), Chapters 9 and 10, Cold Spring Harbor Laboratory Press (1996). [Includes a fascinating historical account of how our present perception of hemoglobin structure and function came about.]

Nagel, R.L., Haemoglobinopathies due to structural mutations, *in* Provan, D. and Gribben, J. (Eds.), *Molecular Haematology,* pp. 121–133, Blackwell Science (2000).

Perutz, M.F., Wilkinson, A.J., Paoli, M., and Dodson, G.G., The stereochemical mechanism of the cooperative effects in hemoglobin revisited, *Annu. Rev. Biophys. Biomol. Struct.* **27,** 1–34 (1998).

Strasser, B.J., Sickle-cell anemia, a molecular disease, *Science* **286,** 1488–1490 (1999). [A short history of Pauling's characterization of sickle-cell anemia.]

Actin and Myosin

Cooper, J.A. and Schafer, D.A., Control of actin assembly and disassembly at filament ends, *Curr. Opin. Cell Biol.* **12,** 97–103 (2000). [Provides an overview of the principles of microfilament dynamics and some of the key protein players.]

Craig, R. and Woodhead, J.L., Structure and function of myosin filaments, *Curr. Opin. Struct. Biol.* **16,** 204–212 (2006). [Includes details of myosin and thick filament structure, including its arrangement in the sarcomere.]

Schliwa, M. and Woehlke, G., Molecular motors, *Nature* **422,** 759–765 (2003). [Includes reviews of myosin and other motor proteins.]

Spudich, J.A., The myosin swinging cross-bridge model, *Nature Rev. Mol. Cell Biol.* **2,** 387–391 (2001). [Summarizes the history and current state of models for myosin action.]

Antibodies

Davies, D.R. and Cohen, G.H., Interactions of protein antigens with antibodies, *Proc. Natl. Acad. Sci.* **93,** 7–12 (1996).

Harris, L.J., Larson, S.B., Hasel, K.W., Day, J., Greenwood, A., and McPherson, A., The three-dimensional structure of an intact monoclonal antibody for canine lymphoma, *Nature* **360** 369–372 (1992). [The first high-resolution X-ray structure of an intact IgG.]

Janeway, C.A., Jr., Travers, P., Walport, M., and Shlomchik, M.J. *Immunobiology 6: The Immune System in Health and Disease* Garland Science (2004).

Marrack, P., Kappler, J., and Kotzin, B.L., Autoimmune disease why and where it occurs, *Nature Medicine* **7,** 899–905 (2001).

Carbohydrates

Sugars are relatively simple molecules that can be linked together in various ways to form larger molecules, for example, starch. This storage form of carbohydrate is the primary source of energy in many foods, including bread, rice, and pasta. [Charles D. Winters/ Photo Researchers.]

■ **CHAPTER CONTENTS**

1 Monosaccharides

  A. Monosaccharides Are Aldoses or Ketoses

  B. Monosaccharides Vary in Configuration and Conformation

  C. Sugars Can Be Modified and Covalently Linked

2 Polysaccharides

  A. Lactose and Sucrose Are Disaccharides

  B. Cellulose and Chitin Are Structural Polysaccharides

  C. Starch and Glycogen Are Storage Polysaccharides

  D. Glycosaminoglycans Form Highly Hydrated Gels

3 Glycoproteins

  A. Proteoglycans Contain Glycosaminoglycans

  B. Bacterial Cell Walls Are Made of Peptidoglycan

  C. Many Eukaryotic Proteins Are Glycosylated

  D. Oligosaccharides May Determine Glycoprotein Structure, Function, and Recognition

■ **MEDIA RESOURCES**

(available at www.wiley.com/college/voet)

Kinemage 7-1. D-Glucopyranose, α and β anomers

Kinemage 7-2. Sucrose

Kinemage 7-3. Hyaluronate

Kinemage 7-4. Structure of a complex carbohydrate

Carbohydrates or **saccharides** (Greek: *sakcharon,* sugar) are the most abundant biological molecules. They are chemically simpler than nucleotides or amino acids, containing just three elements—carbon, hydrogen, and oxygen—combined according to the formula $(C \cdot H_2O)_n$, where $n \geq 3$. The basic carbohydrate units are called **monosaccharides.** There are numerous different types of monosaccharides, which, as we discuss below, differ in their number of carbon atoms and in the arrangement of the H and O atoms attached to the carbons. Furthermore, monosaccharides can be strung together in almost limitless ways to form **polysaccharides.**

Until the 1960s, carbohydrates were thought to have only passive roles as energy sources (e.g., glucose and starch) and as structural materials (e.g., cellulose). Carbohydrates, as we shall see, do not catalyze complex chemical reactions as do proteins, nor do carbohydrates replicate themselves as do nucleic acids. And because polysaccharides are not built according to a genetic "blueprint," as are nucleic acids and proteins, they tend to be much more heterogeneous—both in size and in composition—than other biological molecules.

However, it has become clear that the innate structural variation in carbohydrates is fundamental to their biological activity. The apparently haphazard arrangements of carbohydrates on proteins and on the surfaces of cells are the key to many recognition events between proteins and between cells. An understanding of carbohydrate structure, from the simplest monosaccharides to the most complex branched polysaccharides, is essential for appreciating the varied functions of carbohydrates in biological systems.

1 Monosaccharides

Monosaccharides, or simple sugars, are synthesized from smaller precur
sors that are ultimately derived from CO_2 and H_2O by photosynthesis.

A | Monosaccharides Are Aldoses or Ketoses

*Monosaccharides are aldehyde or ketone derivatives of straight-chain poly
hydroxy alcohols containing at least three carbon atoms.* They are classified
according to the chemical nature of their carbonyl group and the number
of their C atoms. If the carbonyl group is an aldehyde, the sugar is an
aldose. If the carbonyl group is a ketone, the sugar is a **ketose.** The
smallest monosaccharides, those with three carbon atoms, are **trioses**

LEARNING OBJECTIVES

■ Be able to recognize monosaccharides and
their derivatives.
■ Understand how monosaccharides cyclize
to form two different anomers.
■ Understand that a glycosidic bond links
two monosaccharides.

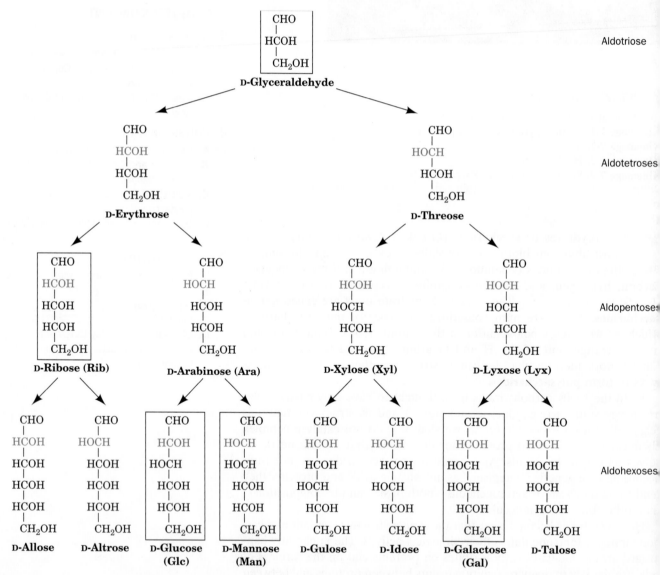

■ **Figure 8-1** | **The D-aldoses with three to six carbon atoms.**
The arrows indicate stereochemical relationships (not biosynthetic
pathways). The configuration around C2 (*red*) distinguishes the
members of each pair of monosaccharides. The L counterparts of
these 15 sugars are their mirror images. The biologically most
common aldoses are boxed.

Those with four, five, six, seven, etc. C atoms are, respectively, **tetroses, pentoses, hexoses, heptoses,** etc.

The aldohexose **D-glucose** has the formula $(C \cdot H_2O)_6$:

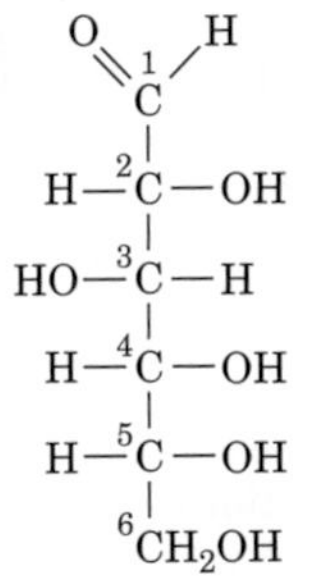

$$
\begin{array}{c}
\overset{1}{C} \underset{\diagdown H}{\overset{O}{\diagup}} \\
H-\overset{2}{C}-OH \\
HO-\overset{3}{C}-H \\
H-\overset{4}{C}-OH \\
H-\overset{5}{C}-OH \\
\overset{6}{C}H_2OH
\end{array}
$$

D-Glucose

All but two of its six C atoms, C1 and C6, are chiral centers, so D-glucose is one of $2^4 = 16$ possible stereoisomers. The stereochemistry and nomenclature of the D-aldoses are presented in Fig. 8-1. The assignment of D or L is made according to the Fischer convention (Section 4-2): *D sugars have the same absolute configuration at the asymmetric center farthest from their carbonyl group as does D-glyceraldehyde* (i.e., the —OH at C5 of D-glucose is on the right in a Fischer projection). The L sugars are the mirror images of their D counterparts. Because L sugars are biologically much less abundant than D sugars, the D prefix is often omitted.

Sugars that differ only by the configuration around one C atom are known as **epimers** of one another. Thus, D-glucose and **D-mannose** are epimers with respect to C2. The most common aldoses include the six-carbon sugars glucose, mannose, and **galactose.** The pentose **ribose** is a component of the ribonucleotide residues of RNA. The triose **glyceraldehyde** occurs in several metabolic pathways.

The most common ketoses are those with their ketone function at C2 (Fig. 8-2). The position of their carbonyl group gives ketoses one less asymmetric center than their isomeric aldoses, so a ketohexose has only $2^3 = 8$ possible stereoisomers (4 D sugars and 4 L sugars). The most common ketoses are **dihydroxyacetone, ribulose,** and **fructose,** which we shall encounter in our studies of metabolism.

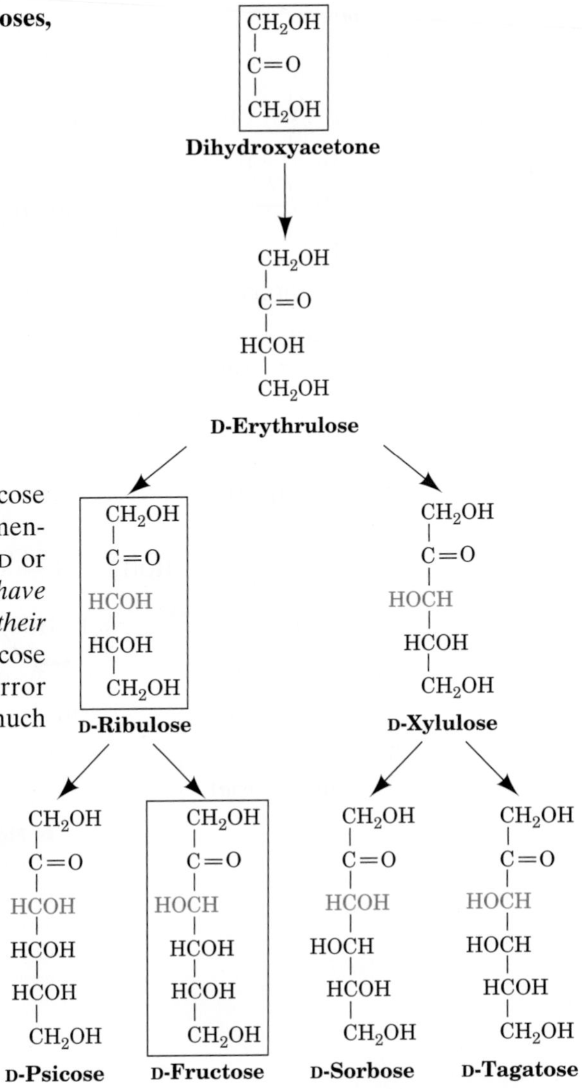

■ **Figure 8-2 | The D-ketoses with three to six carbon atoms.** The configuration around C3 (*red*) distinguishes the members of each pair. The biologically most common ketoses are boxed.

B | Monosaccharides Vary in Configuration and Conformation

Alcohols react with the carbonyl groups of aldehydes and ketones to form **hemiacetals** and **hemiketals,** respectively:

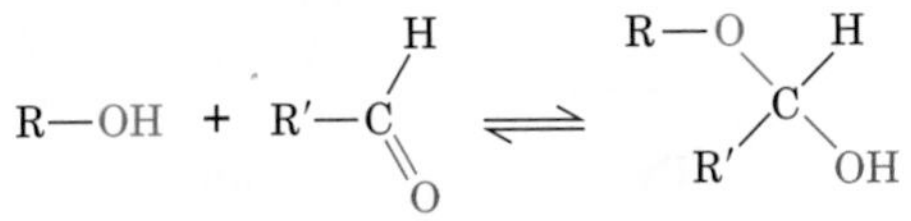

Alcohol Aldehyde Hemiacetal

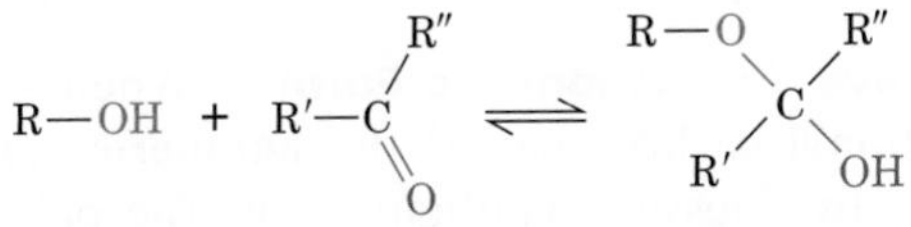

Alcohol Ketone Hemiketal

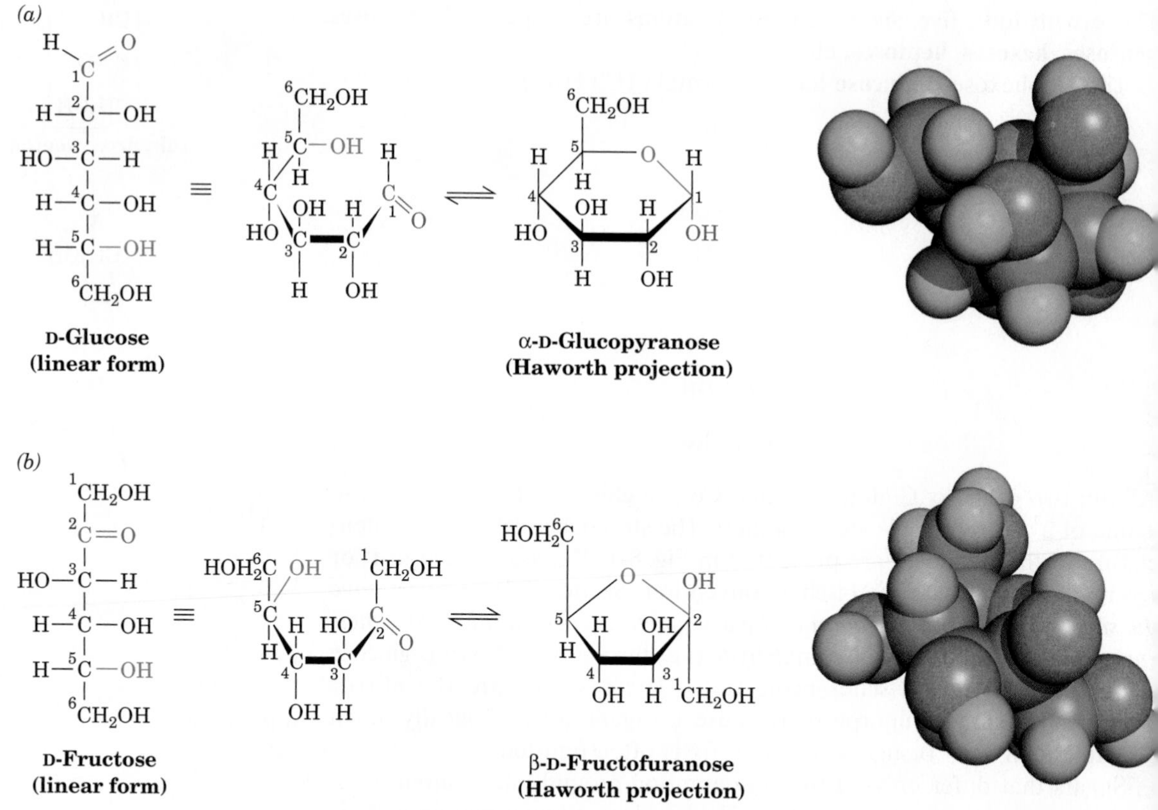

(a)

D-Glucose
(linear form)

α-D-Glucopyranose
(Haworth projection)

(b)

D-Fructose
(linear form)

β-D-Fructofuranose
(Haworth projection)

■ **Figure 8-3** | **Cyclization of glucose and fructose.** (*a*) The linear form of
D-glucose yielding the cyclic hemiacetal α-D-glucopyranose. (*b*) The linear form of
D-fructose yielding the hemiketal β-D-fructofuranose. The cyclic sugars are shown
as both Haworth projections and space-filling models with C green, H cyan, and
O red.

The hydroxyl and either the aldehyde or the ketone functions of monosaccharides can likewise react intramolecularly to form cyclic hemiacetals
and hemiketals (Fig. 8-3). The configurations of the substituents of each
carbon atom in these sugar rings are conveniently represented by their
Haworth projections, in which the heavier ring bonds project in front of
the plane of the paper and the lighter ring bonds project behind it.

A sugar with a six-membered ring is known as a **pyranose** in analogy
with **pyran,** the simplest compound containing such a ring. Similarly, sugars
with five-membered rings are designated **furanoses** in analogy with **furan:**

Pyran   **Furan**

The cyclic forms of glucose and fructose with six- and five-membered rings
are therefore known as **glucopyranose** and **fructofuranose,** respectively.

Cyclic Sugars Have Two Anomeric Forms. When a monosaccharide
cyclizes, the carbonyl carbon, called the **anomeric carbon,** becomes a
chiral center with two possible configurations. The pair of stereoisomers
that differ in configuration at the anomeric carbon are called **anomers.** In

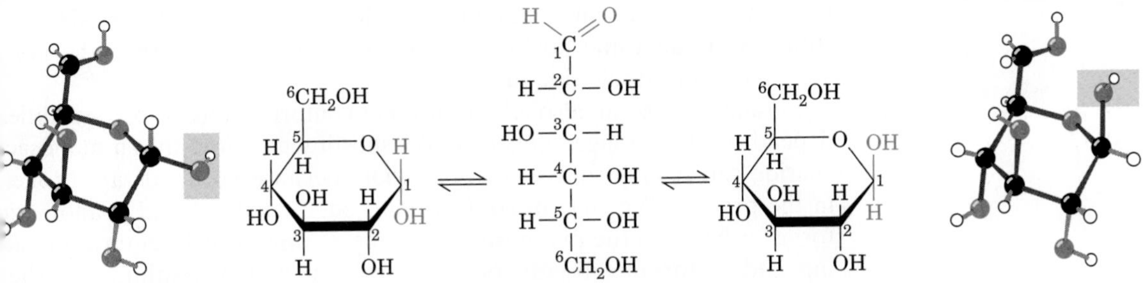

α-D-Glucopyranose   D-Glucose (linear form)   β-D-Glucopyranose

Figure 8-4 | α and β anomers. The monosaccharides α-D-glucopyranose and β-D-glucopyranose, drawn as Haworth projections and ball-and-stick models, interconvert through the linear form. They differ only by their configuration about the anomeric carbon, C1. ✷ **See Kinemage Exercise 7-1.**

the **α anomer,** the OH substituent of the anomeric carbon is on the opposite side of the sugar ring from the CH$_2$OH group at the chiral center that designates the D or L configuration (C5 in hexoses). The other form is known as the **β anomer** (Fig. 8-4).

The two anomers of D-glucose have slightly different physical and chemical properties, including different optical rotations (Section 4-2). *The anomers freely interconvert in aqueous solution,* so at equilibrium, D-glucose is a mixture of the β anomer (63.6%) and the α anomer (36.4%). The linear form is normally present in only minute amounts.

Sugars Can Adopt Different Conformations. A given hexose or pentose can assume pyranose or furanose forms. In principle, hexoses and larger sugars can form rings of seven or more atoms, but such rings are rarely observed because of the greater stabilities of the five- and six-membered rings. The internal strain of three- and four-membered rings makes them less stable than the linear forms.

The use of Haworth formulas may lead to the erroneous impression that furanose and pyranose rings are planar. This cannot be the case, however, because all the atomic orbitals in the ring atoms are tetrahedrally (sp^3) hybridized. The pyranose ring, like the cyclohexane ring, can assume a chair conformation, in which the substituents of each atom are arranged tetrahedrally. Of the two possible chair conformations, the one that predominates is the one in which the bulkiest ring substituents occupy **equatorial** positions rather than the more crowded **axial** positions (Fig. 8-5).

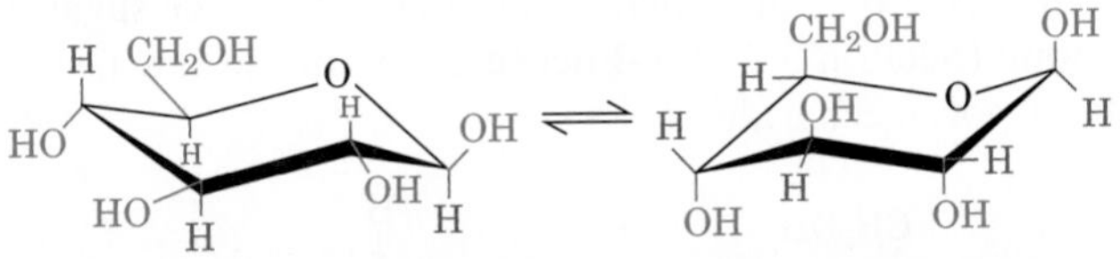

Figure 8-5 | The two chair conformations of β-D-glucopyranose. In the conformation on the left, which predominates, the relatively bulky OH and CH$_2$OH substituents all occupy equatorial positions, where they extend alternately above and below the ring. In the conformation on the right (drawn in ball-and-stick form in Fig. 8-4, *right*), the bulky groups occupy the more crowded axial (vertical) positions. ✷ **See Kinemage Exercise 7-1.**

Only β-D-glucose can simultaneously have all five of its non-H sub stituents in equatorial positions. Perhaps this is why glucose is the mos abundant monosaccharide in nature.

Furanose rings can also adopt different conformations, whose stabilitie depend on the arrangements of bulky substituents. Note that a monosac charide can readily shift its *conformation,* because no bonds are broken in the process. The shift in *configuration* between the α and β anomeri forms or between the pyranose and furanose forms, which requires break ing and re-forming bonds, occurs slowly in aqueous solution. Othe changes in configuration, such as **epimerization,** do not occur under phys iological conditions without the appropriate enzyme.

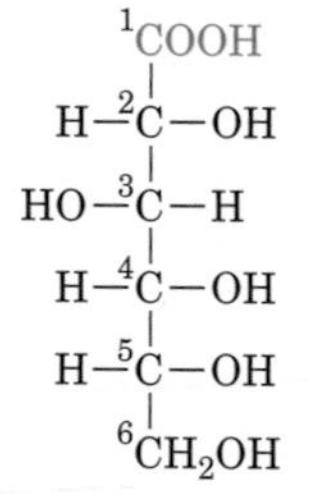

D-Gluconic acid

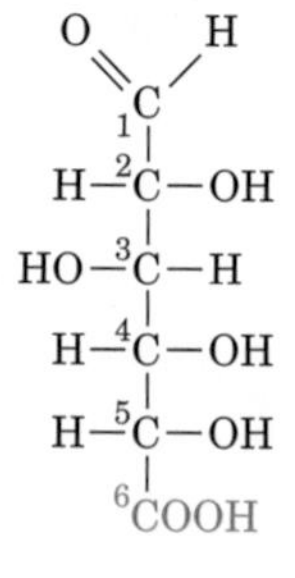

D-Glucuronic acid

C | Sugars Can Be Modified and Covalently Linked

Because the cyclic and linear forms of aldoses and ketoses do intercon vert, these sugars undergo reactions typical of aldehydes and ketones.

1. Oxidation of an aldose converts its aldehyde group to a carboxyli acid group, thereby yielding an **aldonic acid** such as **gluconic acid** *(a left)*. Aldonic acids are named by appending the suffix *-onic acid* tc the root name of the parent aldose.

2. Oxidation of the primary alcohol group of aldoses yields **uroni acids,** which are named by appending *-uronic acid* to the root name of the parent aldose, for example, **D-glucuronic acid** *(at left)*. Uronic acids can assume the pyranose, furanose, and linear forms.

3. Aldoses and ketoses can be reduced under mild conditions, for ex ample, by treatment with $NaBH_4$, to yield polyhydroxy alcohols known as **alditols,** which are named by appending the suffix *-itol* to the root name of the parent aldose. **Ribitol** is a component of flavin coenzymes (Fig. 14-12), and **glycerol** and the cyclic polyhydroxy alcohol *myo*-**inositol** are important lipid components (Section 9-1). **Xylitol** is a sweetener that is used in "sugarless" gum and candies:

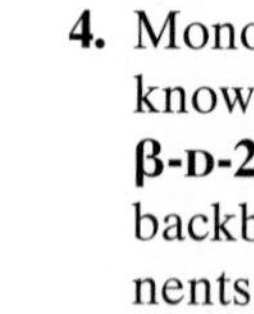

Ribitol 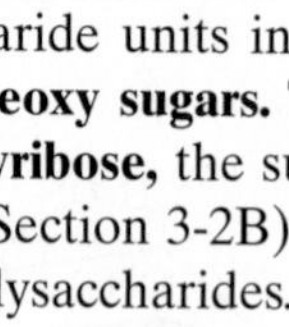   **Xylitol** 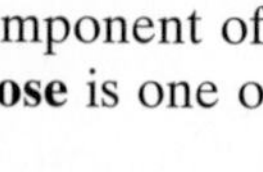   **Glycerol** 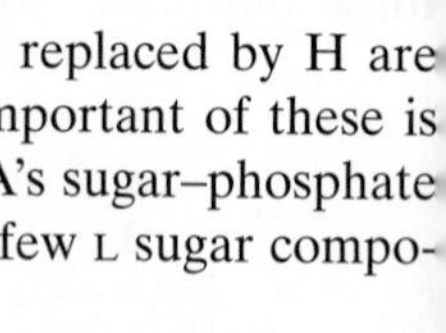   *myo*-**Inositol**

4. Monosaccharide units in which an OH group is replaced by H are known as **deoxy sugars.** The biologically most important of these is **β-D-2-deoxyribose,** the sugar component of DNA's sugar–phosphate backbone (Section 3-2B). **L-Fucose** is one of the few L sugar compo nents of polysaccharides.

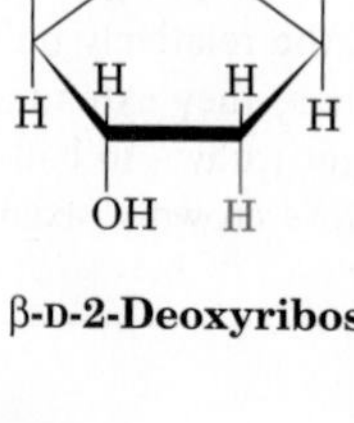

β-D-2-Deoxyribose 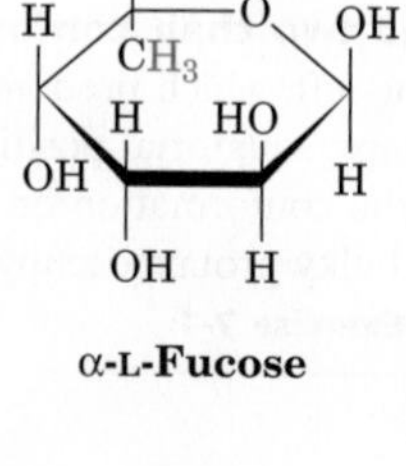   **α-L-Fucose**

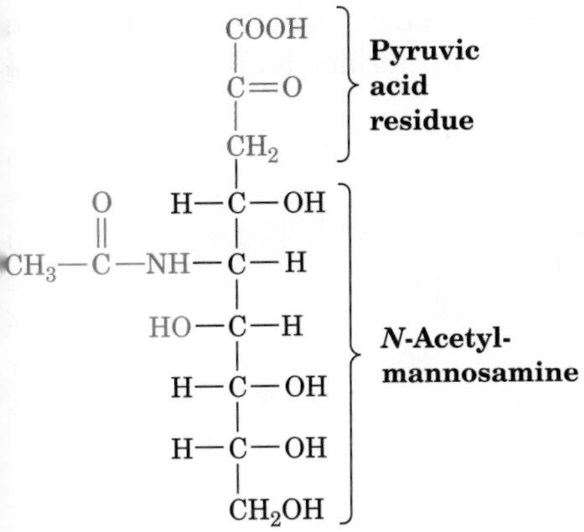

N-Acetylneuraminic acid
(linear form)

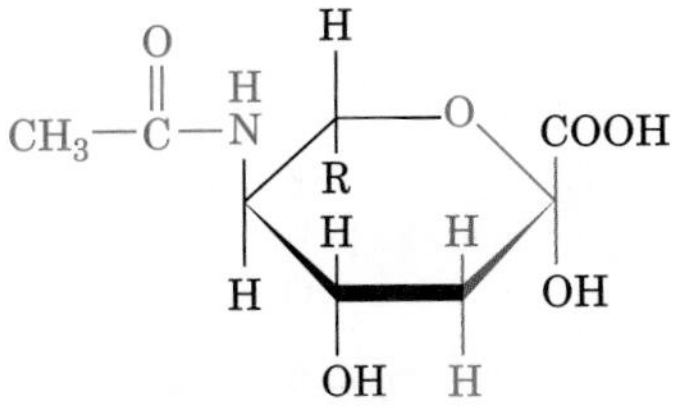

N-Acetylneuraminic acid
(pyranose form)

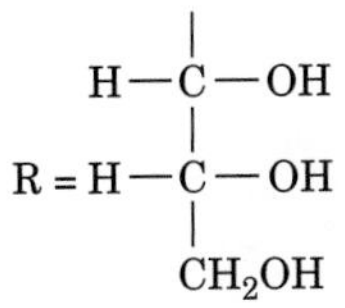

■ **Figure 8-6** | *N*-**Acetylneuraminic acid.** In the cyclic form of this nine-carbon monosaccharide, the pyranose ring incorporates the pyruvic acid residue (*blue*) and part of the mannose moiety.

5. In **amino sugars,** one or more OH groups have been replaced by an amino group, which is often acetylated. **D-Glucosamine** and **D-galactosamine** are the most common:

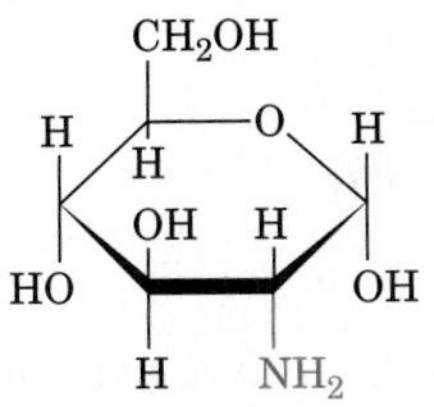

α-D-Glucosamine
(2-amino-2-deoxy-
α-D-glucopyranose)

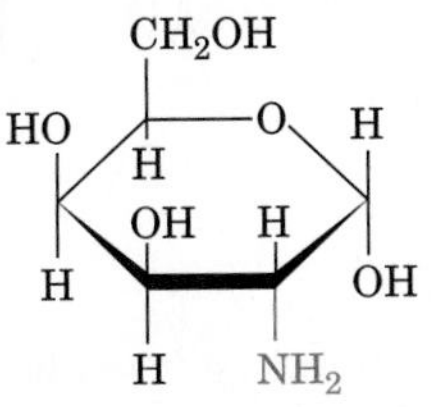

α-D-Galactosamine
(2-amino-2-deoxy-
α-D-galactopyranose)

N-**Acetylneuraminic acid,** which is derived from *N*-**acetylmannosamine** and **pyruvic acid** (Fig. 8-6), is an important constituent of **glycoproteins** and **glycolipids** (proteins and lipids with covalently attached carbohydrate). *N*-Acetylneuraminic acid and its derivatives are often referred to as **sialic acids.**

Glycosidic Bonds Link the Anomeric Carbon to Other Compounds. The anomeric group of a sugar can condense with an alcohol to form **α-** and **β-glycosides** (Greek: *glykys,* sweet; Fig. 8-7). The bond connecting the anomeric carbon to the alcohol oxygen is termed a **glycosidic bond.**

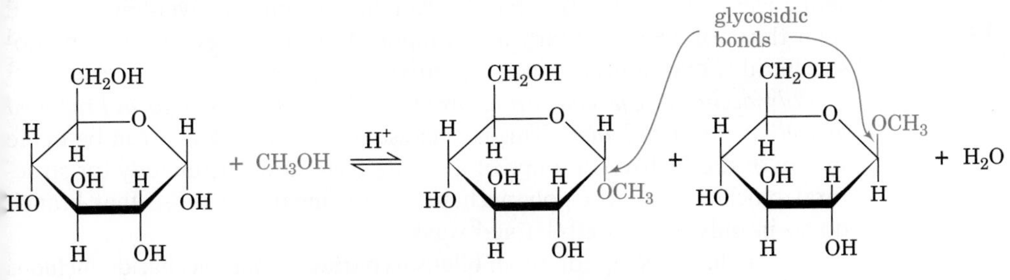

α-D-Glucose

Methyl-α-D-glucoside

Methyl-β-D-glucoside

■ **Figure 8-7** | **Formation of glycosides.** The acid-catalyzed condensation of α-D-glucose with methanol yields an anomeric pair of **methyl-D-glucosides.**

N-Glycosidic bonds, which form between the anomeric carbon and an amine, are the bonds that link D-ribose to purines and pyrimidines in nucleic acids:

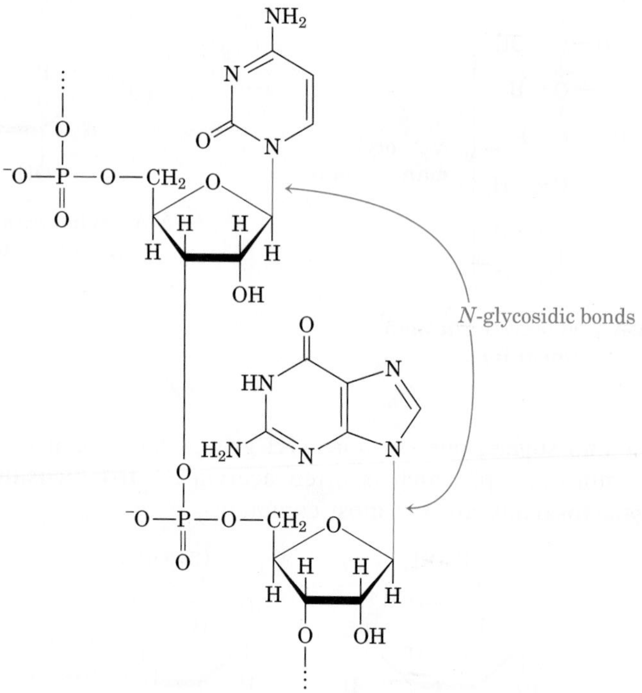

N-glycosidic bonds

■ **CHECK YOUR UNDERSTANDING**

How does an aldose differ from a ketose?

Show how aldoses and ketoses can form five- and six-membered rings.

Explain why anomers of a monosaccharide can interconvert whereas epimers cannot.

Describe aldonic acids, uronic acids, alditols, deoxy sugars, and amino sugars.

Explain why a sugar can form at least two different glycosides.

LEARNING OBJECTIVES

■ Be able to describe the monosaccharide units and their linkages in the common polysaccharides.

■ Understand how the physical properties of polysaccharides relate to their biological functions.

Like peptide bonds, glycosidic bonds hydrolyze extremely slowly under physiological conditions in the absence of appropriate hydrolytic enzymes. Consequently, an anomeric carbon that is involved in a glycosidic bond cannot freely convert between its α and β anomeric forms. Saccharides bearing anomeric carbons that have not formed glycosides are termed **reducing sugars,** because the free aldehyde group that is in equilibrium with the cyclic form of the sugar reduces mild oxidizing agents. Identification of a sugar as **nonreducing** is evidence that it is a glycoside.

2 Polysaccharides

Polysaccharides, which are also known as **glycans,** *consist of monosaccharides linked together by glycosidic bonds.* They are classified as **homopolysaccharides** or **heteropolysaccharides** if they consist of one type or more than one type of monosaccharide. Although the monosaccharide sequences of heteropolysaccharides can, in principle, be even more varied than those of proteins, many are composed of only a few types of monosaccharides that alternate in a repetitive sequence.

Polysaccharides, in contrast to proteins and nucleic acids, form branched as well as linear polymers. This is because glycosidic linkages can be made to any of the hydroxyl groups of a monosaccharide. Fortunately for structural biochemists, most polysaccharides are linear and those that branch do so in only a few well-defined ways.

A complete description of an **oligosaccharide** or polysaccharide includes the identities, anomeric forms, and linkages of all its component monosaccharide units. Some of this information can be gathered through the use of specific **exoglycosidases** and **endoglycosidases,** enzymes that hydrolyze monosaccharide units in much the same way that exopeptidases and endopeptidases cleave amino acid residues from polypeptides (Section 5-3B). NMR measurements are also invaluable in determining both sequences and conformations of polysaccharides.

A | Lactose and Sucrose Are Disaccharides

Oligosaccharides containing three or more residues are relatively rare, occurring almost entirely in plants. **Disaccharides,** the simplest polysaccharides, are more common. Many occur as the hydrolysis products of larger molecules. However, two disaccharides are notable in their own right. **Lactose** *(at right)*, for example, occurs naturally only in milk, where its concentration ranges from 0 to 7% depending on the species (Box 8-1). The systematic name for lactose, *O*-β-D-galactopyranosyl-(1→4)-D-glucopyranose, specifies its monosaccharides, their ring types, and how they are linked together. The symbol (1→4) combined with the β in the prefix indicates that the glycosidic bond links C1 of the β anomer of galactose to O4 of glucose. Note that lactose has a free anomeric carbon on its glucose residue and is therefore a reducing sugar.

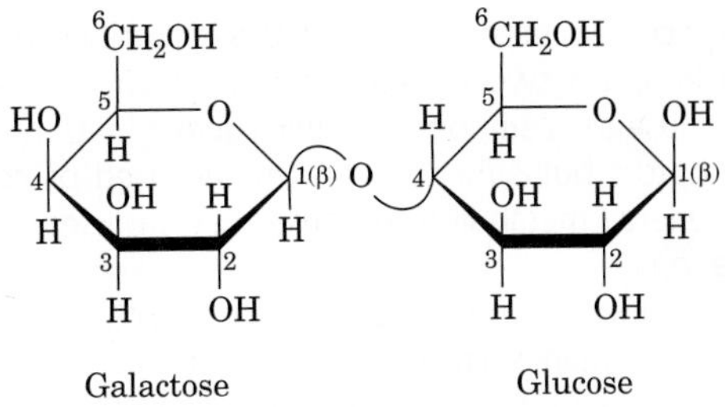

The most abundant disaccharide is **sucrose,**

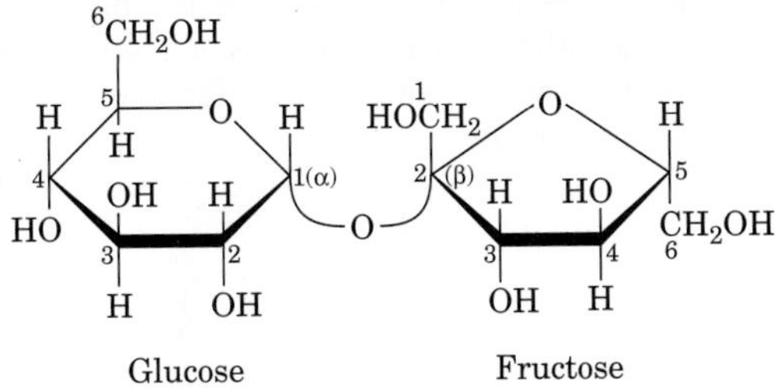

Lactose

the major form in which carbohydrates are transported in plants. Sucrose is familiar to us as common table sugar (🔎 **see Kinemage Exercise 7-2).** The systematic name for sucrose, *O*-α-D-glucopyranosyl-(1→2)-β-D-fructofuranoside, indicates that the anomeric carbon of each sugar (C1 in glucose and C2 in fructose) participates in the glycosidic bond and hence sucrose is not a reducing sugar. Noncarbohydrate molecules that mimic the taste of sucrose are used as sweetening agents in foods and beverages (Box 8-2).

Sucrose

BOX 8-1 BIOCHEMISTRY IN HEALTH AND DISEASE

Lactose Intolerance

In infants, lactose (also known as milk sugar) is hydrolyzed by the intestinal enzyme **β-D-galactosidase** (or **lactase)** to its component monosaccharides for absorption into the bloodstream. The galactose is enzymatically converted (epimerized) to glucose, which is the primary metabolic fuel of many tissues.

Since mammals are unlikely to encounter lactose after they have been weaned, most adult mammals have low levels of β-galactosidase. Consequently, much of the lactose they might ingest moves through their digestive tract to the colon, where bacterial fermentation generates large quantities of CO_2, H_2, and

irritating organic acids. These products cause the embarrassing and often painful digestive upset known as **lactose intolerance.**

Lactose intolerance, which was once considered a metabolic disturbance, is actually the norm in adult humans, particularly those of African and Asian descent. Interestingly, however, β-galactosidase levels decrease only mildly with age in descendants of populations that have historically relied on dairy products for nutrition throughout life. Modern food technology has come to the aid of milk lovers who develop lactose intolerance: Milk in which the lactose has been hydrolyzed enzymatically is widely available.

BOX 8-2 PERSPECTIVES IN BIOCHEMISTRY

Artificial Sweeteners

Artificial sweeteners are added to processed foods and beverages to impart a sweet taste without adding calories. This is possible because the compounds mimic sucrose in its interactions with taste receptors but either are not metabolized or contribute very little to energy metabolism because they are used at such low concentrations.

Naturally occurring saccharides, such as fructose, are slightly sweeter than sucrose. Honey, which contains primarily fructose, glucose, and maltose (a glucose disaccharide), is about 1.5 times as sweet as sucrose. How is sweetness measured? There is no substitute for the human sense of taste, so a panel of individuals sample solutions of a compound and compare them to a reference solution containing sucrose. The very sweet compounds listed below must be diluted significantly before testing in this manner.

Compound	Sweetness Relative to Sucrose
Acesulfame	200
Alitame	2000
Aspartame	180
Saccharin	350
Sucralose	600

One of the oldest artificial sweeteners is saccharin, discovered in 1879 and commonly consumed as Sweet'N Low®. In the 1970s, extremely high doses of saccharin were found to cause cancer in laboratory rats. Such doses are now considered to be so far outside of the range used for sweetening as to be of insignificant concern to users.

Saccharin

Aspartame, the active ingredient in NutraSweet® and Equal®, was approved for human use in 1981 and is currently the market leader:

Aspartylphenylalanine methyl ester (aspartame)

Unlike saccharin, which is not metabolized by the human body, aspartame is broken down into its components: aspartate (*green*), phenylalanine (*red*), and methanol (*blue*). The Asp and Phe, like all amino acids, can be metabolized, so aspartame is not calorie-free. Methanol in large amounts is toxic; however, the amount derived from an aspartame-sweetened drink is comparable to the amount naturally present in the same volume of fruit juice. Individuals with the genetic disease **phenylketonuria,** who are unable to metabolize phenylalanine, are advised to avoid ingesting excess Phe in the form of aspartame (or any other polypeptide). The greatest drawback of aspartame may be its instability to heat, which makes it unsuitable for baking. In addition, aspartame in soft drinks hydrolyzes over a period of months and hence loses its flavor.

Acesulfame is sometimes used in combination with aspartame, since the two compounds act synergistically (i.e., their sweetness when combined is greater than the sum of their individual sweetnesses).

Acesulfame

Other artificial sweeteners are derivatives of sugars, such as sucralose (Splenda®; see Problem 8-9), or of aspartame (e.g., alitame). Some plant extracts (e.g., *Stevia*) are also used as artificial sweeteners.

The market for artificial sweeteners is worth several billion dollars annually. But surprisingly, the most successful sweetening agents have not been the result of dedicated research efforts. Instead, they were discovered by chance or mishap. For example, aspartame was discovered in 1965 by a synthetic chemist who unknowingly got a small amount of the compound on his fingers and happened to lick them. Sucralose came to light in 1975 when a student was asked to "test" a compound and misunderstood the directions as "taste" the compound.

B | Cellulose and Chitin Are Structural Polysaccharides

Plants have rigid cell walls that can withstand osmotic pressure differences between the extracellular and intracellular spaces of up to 20 atm. In large plants, such as trees, the cell walls also have a load-bearing function.

Cellulose, the primary structural component of plant cell walls (Fig. 8-8), accounts for over half of the carbon in the biosphere: Approximately 10^{15} kg of cellulose is estimated to be synthesized and degraded annually.

Cellulose is a linear polymer of up to 15,000 D-glucose residues linked by β(1→4) glycosidic bonds:

Cellulose

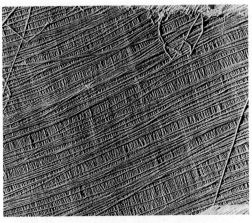

■ **Figure 8-8** | **Electron micrograph of cellulose fibers.** The cellulose fibers in this sample of cell wall from the alga *Chaetomorpha* are arranged in layers. [Biophoto Associates/Photo Researchers.]

X-Ray and other studies of cellulose fibers reveal that cellulose chains are flat ribbons in which successive glucose rings are turned over 180° with respect to each other. This permits the C3—OH group of each glucose residue to form a hydrogen bond with the ring oxygen (O5) of the next residue. Parallel cellulose chains form sheets with interchain hydrogen bonds, including O2—H⋯O6 and O6—H⋯O3 bonds (Fig. 8-9). Stacks of these sheets are held together by hydrogen bonds and van der Waals interactions. This highly cohesive structure gives cellulose fibers exceptional strength and makes them water insoluble despite their hydrophilicity. In plant cell walls, the cellulose fibers are embedded in and cross-linked by a matrix containing other polysaccharides and **lignin,** a plasticlike phenolic

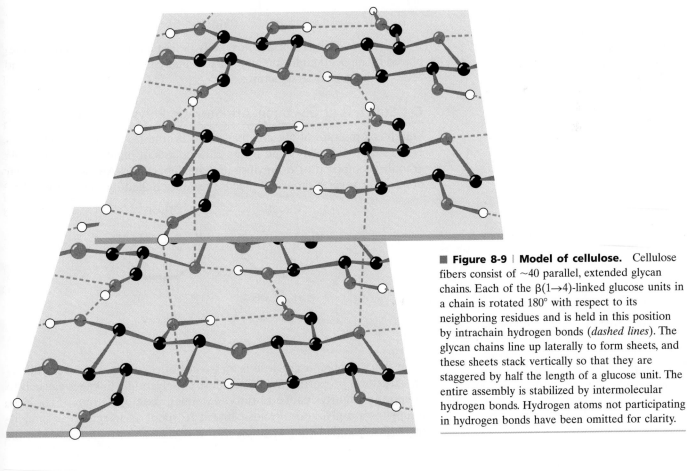

■ **Figure 8-9** | **Model of cellulose.** Cellulose fibers consist of ~40 parallel, extended glycan chains. Each of the β(1→4)-linked glucose units in a chain is rotated 180° with respect to its neighboring residues and is held in this position by intrachain hydrogen bonds (*dashed lines*). The glycan chains line up laterally to form sheets, and these sheets stack vertically so that they are staggered by half the length of a glucose unit. The entire assembly is stabilized by intermolecular hydrogen bonds. Hydrogen atoms not participating in hydrogen bonds have been omitted for clarity.

polymer. The resulting composite material can withstand large stresses because the matrix evenly distributes the stresses among the cellulose reinforcing elements.

Although vertebrates themselves do not possess an enzyme capable of hydrolyzing the $\beta(1\rightarrow4)$ linkages of cellulose, the digestive tracts of herbivores contain symbiotic microorganisms that secrete a series of enzymes, collectively known as **cellulases,** that do so. The same is true of termites. Nevertheless, the degradation of cellulose is a slow process because its tightly packed and hydrogen-bonded glycan chains are not easily accessible to cellulase and do not separate readily even after many of their glycosidic bonds have been hydrolyzed. Thus, cows must chew their cud, and the decay of dead trees by fungi and other organisms generally takes many years.

Chitin is the principal structural component of the exoskeletons of invertebrates such as crustaceans, insects, and spiders and is also present in the cell walls of most fungi and many algae. It is therefore almost as abundant as cellulose. Chitin is a homopolymer of $\beta(1\rightarrow4)$-linked *N*-acetyl-D-glucosamine residues:

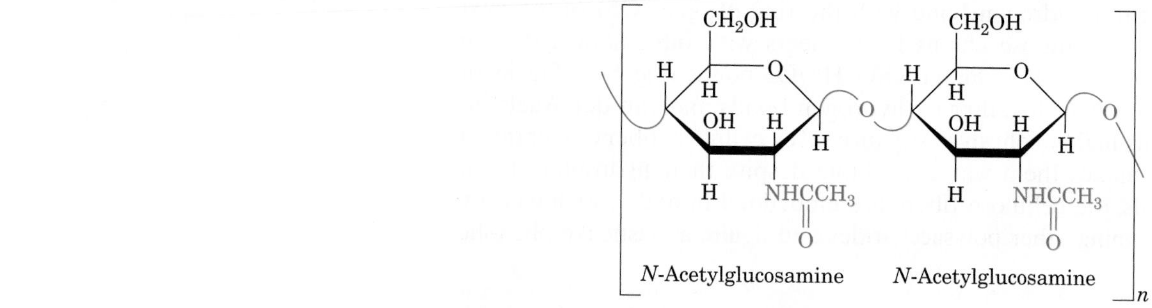

Chitin

It differs chemically from cellulose only in that each C2—OH group is replaced by an acetamido function. X-Ray analysis indicates that chitin and cellulose have similar structures.

C | Starch and Glycogen Are Storage Polysaccharides

Starch is a mixture of glycans that plants synthesize as their principal energy reserve. It is deposited in the chloroplasts of plant cells as insoluble granules composed of **α-amylose** and **amylopectin.** α-Amylose is a linear polymer of several thousand glucose residues linked by $\alpha(1\rightarrow4)$ bonds:

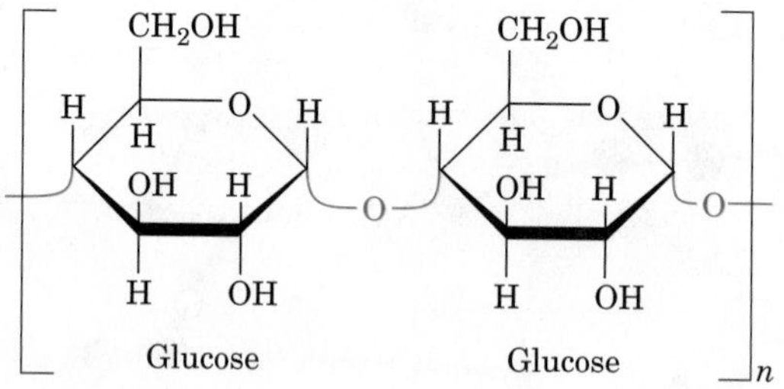

α-Amylose

Note that although α-amylose is an isomer of cellulose, it has very different structural properties. While cellulose's β-glycosidic linkages cause it to assume a tightly packed, fully extended conformation (Fig. 8-9), α-amylose's α-glycosidic bonds cause it to adopt an irregularly aggregating helically coiled conformation (Fig. 8-10).

Figure 8-10 | α-Amylose. This regularly repeating polymer forms a left-handed helix. Note the great differences in structure and properties that result from changing α-amylose's α(1→4) linkages to the β(1→4) linkages of cellulose (Fig. 8-9). [Illustration, Irving Geis/Geis Archives Trust. Copyright Howard Hughes Medical Institute. Reproduced with permission.]

Amylopectin consists mainly of α(1→4)-linked glucose residues but is a branched molecule with α(1→6) branch points every 24 to 30 glucose residues on average:

$$CH_2OH$$

α(1→6) branch point

$$CH_2$$

Amylopectin

Amylopectin molecules contain up to 10^6 glucose residues, making them some of the largest molecules in nature. The storage of glucose as starch greatly reduces the large intracellular osmotic pressure that would result from its storage in monomeric form, because osmotic pressure is proportional to the number of solute molecules in a given volume (Section 2-1D). Starch is a reducing sugar, although it has only one residue, called the **reducing end,** that lacks a glycosidic bond.

The digestion of starch, the main carbohydrate source in the human diet, begins in the mouth. Saliva contains an **amylase,** which randomly hydrolyzes the α(1→4) glycosidic bonds of starch. Starch digestion continues in the small intestine under the influence of pancreatic amylase, which degrades starch to a mixture of small oligosaccharides. Further hydrolysis by an **α-glucosidase,** which removes one glucose residue at a time, and by a **debranching enzyme,** which hydrolyzes α(1→6) as well as α(1→4) bonds, produces monosaccharides that are absorbed by the intestine and transported to the bloodstream.

Glycogen, the storage polysaccharide of animals, is present in all cells but is most prevalent in skeletal muscle and in liver, where it occurs as cytoplasmic granules (Fig. 8-11). The primary structure of glycogen resembles that of amylopectin, but glycogen is more highly branched, with branch points occurring every 8 to 14 glucose residues. In the cell, glycogen is degraded for metabolic use by **glycogen phosphorylase,** which phosphorolytically cleaves glycogen's α(1→4) bonds sequentially inward from its nonreducing ends. *Glycogen's highly branched structure, which has many nonreducing ends, permits the rapid mobilization of glucose in times of metabolic need.* The α(1→6) branches of glycogen are cleaved by **glycogen debranching enzyme** (glycogen breakdown is discussed further in Section 16-1).

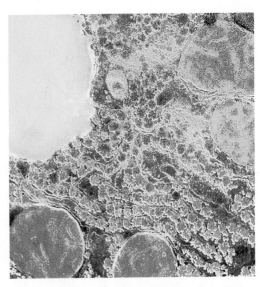

Figure 8-11 | Glycogen granules in a liver cell. In this photomicrograph, glycogen granules are pink, the greenish objects are mitochondria, and the yellow object is a fat globule. The glycogen content of liver may reach 10% of its net weight. [CNRI/Science Photo Library/Photo Researchers.]

D | Glycosaminoglycans Form Highly Hydrated Gels

The extracellular spaces, particularly those of connective tissues such as cartilage, tendon, skin, and blood vessel walls, contain collagen (Section 6-1C) and other proteins embedded in a gel-like matrix that is composed largely of **glycosaminoglycans.** These unbranched polysaccharides consist of alternating uronic acid and hexosamine residues. Solutions of glycosaminoglycans have a slimy, mucuslike consistency that results from their high viscosity and elasticity.

Hyaluronate Acts as a Shock Absorber and Lubricant. **Hyaluronic acid (hyaluronate)** is an important glycosaminoglycan component of connective tissue, synovial fluid (the fluid that lubricates joints), and the vitreous humor of the eye. Hyaluronate molecules are composed of 250 to 25,000 β(1→4)-linked disaccharide units that consist of D-glucuronic acid and **N-acetyl-D-glucosamine (GlcNAc)** linked by a β(1→3) bond (Fig. 8-12). Hyaluronate is an extended, rigid molecule whose numerous repelling anionic groups bind cations and water molecules. In solution, hyaluronate occupies a volume ~1000 times that in its dry state.

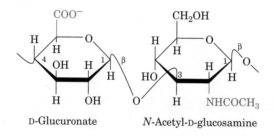

D-Glucuronate   *N*-Acetyl-D-glucosamine

Hyaluronate

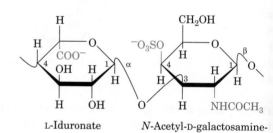

L-Iduronate   *N*-Acetyl-D-galactosamine-4-sulfate

Dermatan sulfate

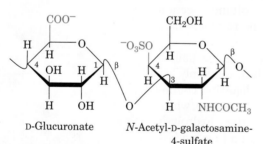

D-Glucuronate   *N*-Acetyl-D-galactosamine-4-sulfate

Chondroitin-4-sulfate

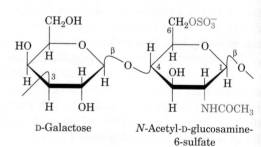

D-Galactose   *N*-Acetyl-D-glucosamine-6-sulfate

Keratan sulfate

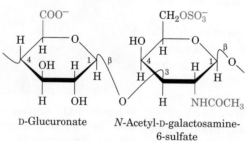

D-Glucuronate   *N*-Acetyl-D-galactosamine-6-sulfate

Chondroitin-6-sulfate

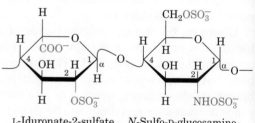

L-Iduronate-2-sulfate   *N*-Sulfo-D-glucosamine-6-sulfate

Heparin

■ **Figure 8-12** | **Repeating disaccharide units of some glycosaminoglycans.** The anionic groups are shown in red and the *N*-acetylamido groups are shown in blue. ✎ **See Kinemage Exercise 7-3.**

Hyaluronate solutions have a viscosity that is shear dependent (an object under shear stress has equal and opposite forces applied across its opposite faces). At low shear rates, hyaluronate molecules form tangled masses that greatly impede flow; that is, the solution is quite viscous. As the shear stress increases, the stiff hyaluronate molecules tend to line up with the flow and thus offer less resistance to it. This viscoelastic behavior makes hyaluronate solutions excellent biological shock absorbers and lubricants.

Some Glycosaminoglycans Are Sulfated. The other common glycosaminoglycans shown in Fig. 8-12 consist of 50 to 1000 sulfated disaccharide units. **Chondroitin-4-sulfate** and **chondroitin-6-sulfate** differ only in the sulfation of their *N*-acetylgalactosamine (GalNAc) residues. **Dermatan sulfate** is derived from chondroitin by enzymatic epimerization of the C5 of glucuronate residues to form **iduronate** residues. **Keratan sulfate** (not to be confused with the fibrous protein keratin; Section 6-1C) is the most heterogeneous of the major glycosaminoglycans in that its sulfate content is variable and it contains small amounts of fucose, mannose, GlcNAc, and sialic acid. **Heparin** is also variably sulfated, with an average of 2.5 sulfate residues per disaccharide unit, which makes it the most highly charged polymer in mammalian tissues (Fig. 8-13).

In contrast to the other glycosaminoglycans, heparin is not a constituent of connective tissue but occurs almost exclusively in the intracellular granules of the mast cells that occur in arterial walls. It inhibits the clotting of blood, and its release, through injury, is thought to prevent runaway clot formation. Heparin is therefore in wide clinical use to inhibit blood clotting, for example, in postsurgical patients.

Heparan sulfate, a ubiquitous cell-surface component as well as an extracellular substance in blood vessel walls and brain, resembles heparin but has a far more variable composition with fewer *N*- and *O*-sulfate groups and more *N*-acetyl groups. Heparan sulfate plays a critical role in development and in wound healing. Various **growth factors** bind to heparan sulfate, and the formation of complexes of the glycosaminoglycan, the growth factor, and the growth factor receptor is required to initiate cell differentiation and proliferation. Specific sulfation patterns on heparan sulfate are required for the formation of these ternary complexes.

Plants Produce Pectin. Plants do not synthesize glycosaminoglycans, but the **pectins,** which are major components of cell walls, may function similarly as shock absorbers. Pectins are heterogeneous polysaccharides with a core of α(1→4)-linked galacturonate residues interspersed with the hexose **rhamnose:**

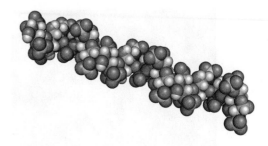

■ **Figure 8-13** | **NMR structure of heparin.** The polymer shown here in space-filling form contains six pairs of iduronate and glucosamine residues. Atoms are colored according to type with iduronate C green, glucosamine C cyan, H white, N blue, O red, and S yellow. Note the high density of anionic sulfate groups. [Based on an NMR structure by Barbara Mulloy and Mark Forster, National Institute for Biological Standards and Control, Herts, U.K. PDBid 1HPN.]

Rhamnose

The galacturonate residues may be modified by the addition of methyl and acetyl groups. Other polysaccharide chains, some containing the pentoses arabinose and xylose and other sugars, are attached to the galacturonate. The aggregation of pectin molecules to form bundles requires divalent cations (usually Ca^{2+}), which form cross-links between the anionic carboxylate groups of neighboring galacturonate residues. The tendency for

■ **Figure 8-14** | **A *Pseudomonas aeruginosa* biofilm.** Bacterial colonies growing on the surface of an agar plate form a biofilm with complex architecture. [Courtesy of Roberto Kolter, Harvard Medical School,]

■ **CHECK YOUR UNDERSTANDING**

Compare and contrast the structures and functions of cellulose, chitin, starch, and glycogen.

How do the physical properties of glycosaminoglycans and similar molecules relate to their biological roles?

LEARNING OBJECTIVES

■ Understand that proteoglycans are large, glycosaminoglycan-containing proteins.

■ Understand that bacterial cell walls consist of glycan chains cross-linked by peptides.

■ Understand that the oligosaccharide chains covalently attached to eukaryotic glycoproteins may play a role in protein structure and recognition.

pectin to form highly hydrated gels is exploited in the manufacture of jams and jellies, to which pectin is often added to augment the endogenous pectin content of the fruit.

Bacterial Biofilms Are a Type of Extracellular Matrix. Outside the laboratory, bacteria are most often found growing on surfaces as a **biofilm,** an association of cells in a semisolid matrix (Fig. 8-14). The extracellular material of the biofilm consists mostly of highly hydrated polysaccharides such as anionic poly-D-glucuronate, poly-N-acetylglucosamine, cellulose-like molecules, and acetylated glycans. A biofilm is difficult to characterize, as it typically houses a mixture of species, and the proportions of its component polysaccharides can vary over time and space.

The gel-like consistency of a biofilm, for example, the plaque that forms on teeth, prevents bacterial cells from being washed away and protects them from desiccation. Biofilms that develop on medical apparatus, such as catheters, are problematic because they offer a foothold for pathogenic organisms and create a barrier to soluble antimicrobial agents.

3 Glycoproteins

Many proteins are actually glycoproteins, with carbohydrate contents varying from <1% to >90% by weight. Glycoproteins occur in all forms of life and have functions that span the entire spectrum of protein activities, including those of enzymes, transport proteins, receptors, hormones, and structural proteins. The polypeptide chains of glycoproteins, like those of all proteins, are synthesized under genetic control. Their carbohydrate chains, in contrast, are enzymatically generated and covalently linked to the polypeptide without the rigid guidance of nucleic acid templates. For this reason, glycoproteins tend to have variable carbohydrate composition, a phenomenon known as **microheterogeneity.** Characterizing the structures of carbohydrates—and their variations—is one goal of the field of **glycomics,** which complements the studies of genomics (for DNA) and proteomics (for proteins).

A | Proteoglycans Contain Glycosaminoglycans

Proteins and glycosaminoglycans in the extracellular matrix aggregate covalently and noncovalently to form a diverse group of macromolecules known as **proteoglycans.** Electron micrographs (Fig. 8-15a) and other evidence indicate that proteoglycans have a bottlebrush-like molecular architecture, with "bristles" noncovalently attached to a filamentous hyaluronate "backbone." The bristles consist of a **core protein** to which glycosaminoglycans, most often keratan sulfate and chondroitin sulfate, are covalently linked (Fig. 8-15b). The interaction between the core protein and the hyaluronate is stabilized by a **link protein.** Smaller oligosaccharides are usually attached to the core protein near its site of attachment to hyaluronate. These oligosaccharides are glycosidically linked to the protein via the amide N of specific Asn residues (and are therefore known as **N-linked oligosaccharides;** Section 8-3C). The keratan

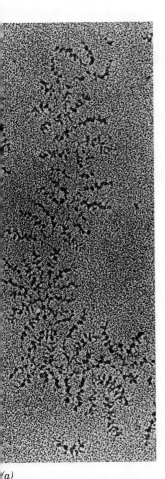

(a)

■ **Figure 8-15** | **A proteoglycan.** (*a*) Electron micrograph showing a central strand of hyaluronate, which supports numerous projections. [From Caplan, A.I., *Sci. Am.* **251**(4), 87 (1984). Copyright © Scientific American, Inc. Used by permission.] (*b*) Bottlebrush model of the proteoglycan shown in Part *a*. Numerous core proteins are noncovalently linked to the central hyaluronate strand. Each core protein has three saccharide-binding regions.

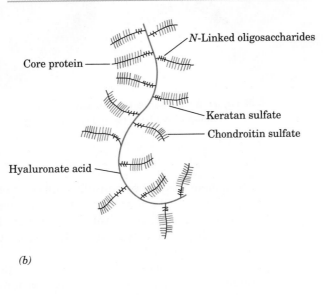

(b)

sulfate and chondroitin sulfate chains are glycosidically linked to the core protein via oligosaccharides that are covalently bonded to side chain O atoms of specific Ser or Thr residues (i.e., **O-linked oligosaccharides**).

Altogether, a central strand of hyaluronate, which varies in length from 4000 to 40,000 Å, can have up to 100 associated core proteins, each of which binds ~50 keratan sulfate chains of up to 250 disaccharide units and ~100 chondroitin sulfate chains of up to 1000 disaccharide units each. This accounts for the enormous molecular masses of many proteoglycans, which range up to tens of millions of daltons.

The extended brushlike structure of proteoglycans, together with the polyanionic character of their keratan sulfate and chondroitin sulfate components, cause these complexes to be highly hydrated. Cartilage, which consists of a meshwork of collagen fibrils that is filled in by proteoglycans, is characterized by its high resilience: The application of pressure on cartilage squeezes water away from the charged regions of its proteoglycans until charge–charge repulsions prevent further compression. When the pressure is released, the water returns. Indeed, the cartilage in the joints, which lacks blood vessels, is nourished by this flow of liquid brought about by body movements. This explains why long periods of inactivity cause cartilage to become thin and fragile.

B | Bacterial Cell Walls Are Made of Peptidoglycan

Bacteria are surrounded by rigid cell walls (Fig. 1-6) that give them their characteristic shapes (Fig. 1-7) and permit them to live in **hypotonic** (less than intracellular salt concentration) environments that would otherwise

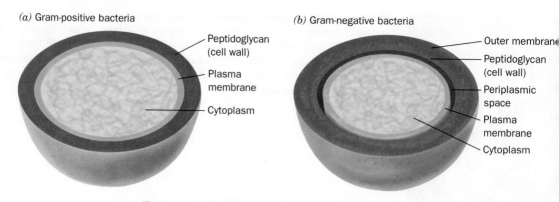

(a) Gram-positive bacteria

Peptidoglycan
(cell wall)

Plasma
membrane

Cytoplasm

(b) Gram-negative bacteria

Outer membrane

Peptidoglycan
(cell wall)

Periplasmic
space

Plasma
membrane

Cytoplasm

■ **Figure 8-16** | **Bacterial cell walls.** This diagram compares the cell envelopes of *(a)* gram-positive bacteria and *(b)* gram-negative bacteria.

cause them to swell osmotically until their plasma (cell) membranes lysed (burst). Bacterial cell walls are of considerable medical significance because they are, in part, responsible for bacterial **virulence** (disease-evoking power). In fact, the symptoms of many bacterial diseases can be elicited in animals merely by injecting bacterial cell walls. Furthermore, bacterial cell wall components are antigenic (Section 7-3B), so such injections often invoke immunity against these bacteria.

Bacteria are classified as **gram-positive** or **gram-negative** according to whether or not they take up Gram stain (a procedure developed in 1884 by Christian Gram in which heat-fixed cells are successively treated with the dye crystal violet and iodine and then destained by ethanol or acetone). Gram-positive bacteria (Fig. 8-16a) have a thick cell wall (~250 Å) surrounding their plasma membrane, whereas gram-negative bacteria (Fig. 8-16b) have a thin cell wall (~30 Å) covered by a complex outer membrane. This outer membrane functions, in part, to exclude substances toxic to the bacterium, including Gram stain. This accounts for the observation that gram-negative bacteria are more resistant to antibiotics than are gram-positive bacteria.

The cell walls of bacteria consist of covalently linked polysaccharide and polypeptide chains, which form a baglike macromolecule that completely encases the cell. This framework, whose structure was elucidated in large part by Jack Strominger, is known as a **peptidoglycan.** Its polysaccharide component consists of linear chains of alternating β(1→4)-linked GlcNAc and **N-acetylmuramic acid** (Latin: *murus,* wall). The lactic acid group of *N*-acetylmuramic acid forms an amide bond with a D-amino acid–containing tetrapeptide to form the peptidoglycan repeating unit (Fig. 8-17). Neighboring parallel peptidoglycan chains are covalently cross-linked through their tetrapeptide side chains, although only ~40% of possible cross-links are made.

In the bacterium *Staphylococcus aureus,* whose tetrapeptide has the sequence L-Ala-D-isoglutamyl-L-Lys-D-Ala, the cross-link consists of a pentaglycine chain that extends from the terminal carboxyl group of one tetrapeptide to the ε-amino group of the Lys in a neighboring tetrapeptide. A model based on the NMR structure of a synthetic segment of peptidoglycan suggests that in the bacterial cell, the glycan chains are perpendicular to the plasma membrane and, with their peptide cross-links, form a honeycomb-like structure with spaces that could accommodate proteins that are known to penetrate the cell wall (Fig. 8-18).

(a)

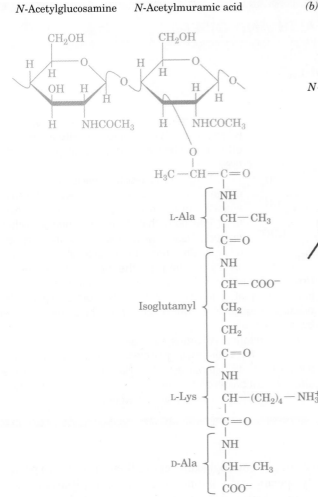

(b)

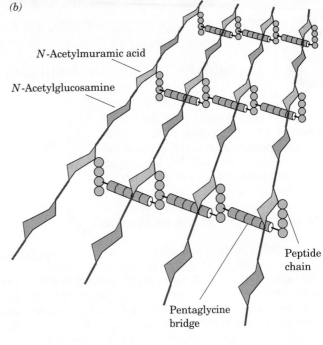

■ **Figure 8-17** | **Peptidoglycan.** (*a*) The repeating unit of peptidoglycan is an *N*-acetylglucosamine–*N*-acetylmuramic acid disaccharide whose lactyl side chain forms an amide bond with a tetrapeptide. The tetrapeptide of *S. aureus* is shown. The isoglutamyl residue is so designated because it forms a peptide link via its γ-carboxyl group. (*b*) The *S. aureus* bacterial cell wall peptidoglycan, showing its pentaglycine connecting bridges (*purple*).

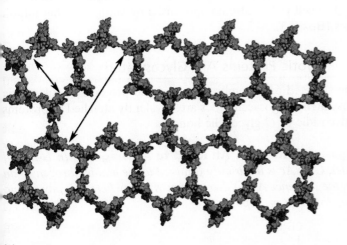

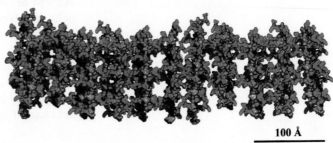

(a)

(b)

■ **Figure 8-18** | **Model of a bacterial cell wall.** The glycan chains, each consisting of eight disaccharide repeats, are orange, and their peptide extensions are green (the pentaglycine cross-links are not included in this model). (*a*) Top view, showing pores (indicated by arrows) that could accommodate peptidoglycan-synthesizing enzymes or other proteins. (*b*) Side view, parallel to the plane of the plasma membrane. [Courtesy of Shahriar Mobashery, University of Notre Dame.]

BOX 8-3 BIOCHEMISTRY IN HEALTH AND DISEASE

Peptidoglycan-Specific Antibiotics

In 1928, Alexander Fleming noticed that the chance contamination of a bacterial culture plate with the mold *Penicillium notatum* resulted in the lysis of the bacteria in the vicinity of the mold. This was caused by the presence of **penicillin,** an antibiotic secreted by the mold. Penicillin contains a thiazolidine ring (*red*) fused to a β-lactam ring (*blue*). A variable R group is bonded to the β-lactam ring via a peptide link.

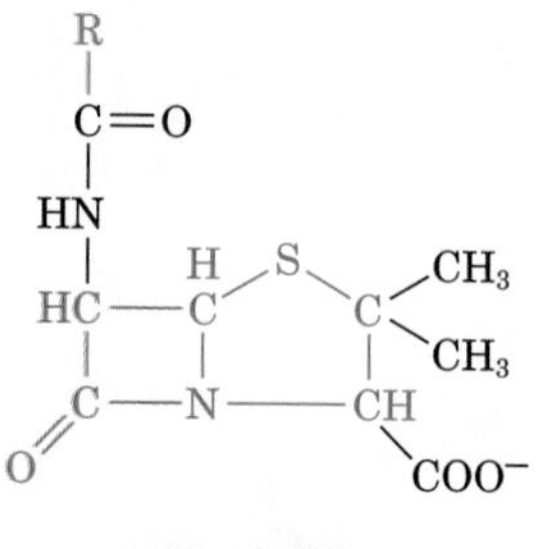

Penicillin specifically binds to and inactivates enzymes that cross-link the peptidoglycan strands of bacterial cell walls. Since cell wall expansion in growing cells requires that their rigid cell walls be opened up for the insertion of new cell wall material, exposure of growing bacteria to penicillin results in cell lysis. However, since no human enzyme binds penicillin specifically, it is not toxic to humans and is therefore therapeutically useful.

Most bacteria that are resistant to penicillin secrete the enzyme **penicillinase** (also called **β-lactamase**), which inactivates penicillin by cleaving the amide bond of its β-lactam ring. Attempts to over-

Penicillin

come this resistance have led to the development of β-lactamase inhibitors such as **sulbactam** that are often prescribed as mixtures with penicillin derivatives.

Multiple drug resistant bacteria are a growing problem. For many years, **vancomycin,** the so-called antibiotic of last resort, has been used to treat bacterial infections that do not succumb to other antibiotics. Vancomycin inhibits the transpeptidation (cross-linking) reaction of bacterial cell wall synthesis by binding to the peptidoglycan precursor. However, bacteria can become resistant to vancomycin by acquiring a gene that allows cell wall synthesis from a slightly different precursor sequence, to which vancomycin binds much less effectively.

One limitation of drugs such as vancomycin and penicillin particularly for slow-growing bacteria, is that the drug may halt bacterial growth without actually killing the cells. For this reason effective antibacterial treatments may require combinations of antibiotics over a course of several weeks.

The D-amino acids of peptidoglycans render them resistant to proteases, which are mostly specific for L-amino acids. However, **lysozyme,** an enzyme that is present in tears, mucus, and other vertebrate body secretions, as well as in egg whites, catalyzes the hydrolysis of the β(1→4) glycosidic linkage between *N*-acetylmuramic acid and *N*-acetylglucosamine (the structure and mechanism of lysozyme are examined in detail in Section 11-4). The cell wall is also compromised by antibiotics that inhibit its biosynthesis (Box 8-3).

C | Many Eukaryotic Proteins Are Glycosylated

Almost all the secreted and membrane-associated proteins of eukaryotic cells are **glycosylated.** Oligosaccharides are covalently attached to proteins by either *N*-glycosidic or *O*-glycosidic bonds.

N-Linked Oligosaccharides Are Attached to Asparagine. *In N-linked oligosaccharides, GlcNAc is invariably β-linked to the amide nitrogen of an Asn residue in the sequence Asn-X-Ser or Asn-X-Thr, where X is any amino acid except possibly Pro or Asp:*

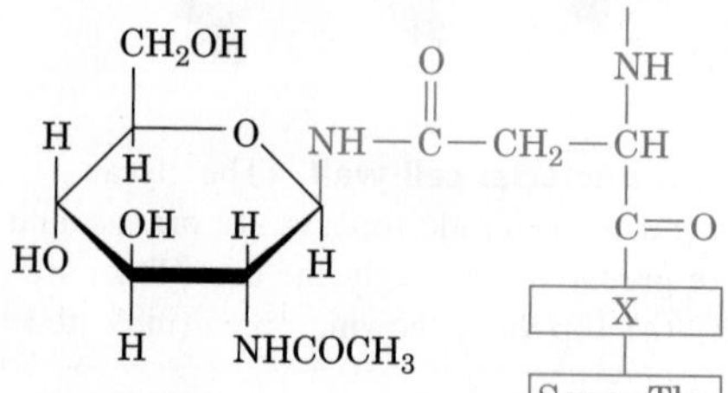

GlcNAc   **Asn**

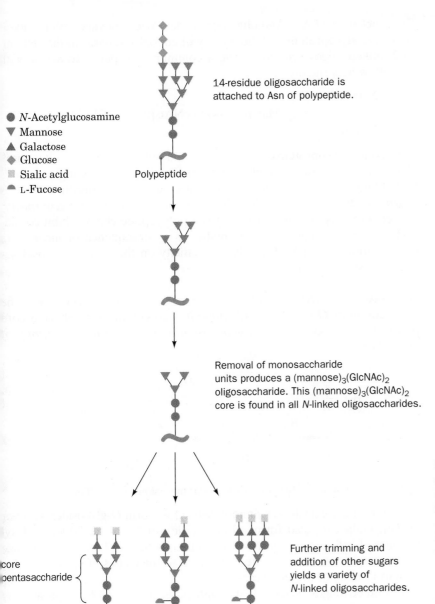

14-residue oligosaccharide is attached to Asn of polypeptide.

● N-Acetylglucosamine
▼ Mannose
▲ Galactose
◆ Glucose
■ Sialic acid
▬ L-Fucose

Polypeptide

Removal of monosaccharide units produces a (mannose)$_3$(GlcNAc)$_2$ oligosaccharide. This (mannose)$_3$(GlcNAc)$_2$ core is found in all N-linked oligosaccharides.

core pentasaccharide

Further trimming and addition of other sugars yields a variety of N-linked oligosaccharides.

■ **Figure 8-19** | **Synthesis of N-linked oligosaccharides.** The addition of a (mannose)$_9$(glucose)$_3$(GlcNAc)$_2$ oligosaccharide is followed by removal of monosaccharides as catalyzed by glycosidases, and the addition of other monosaccharides as catalyzed by glycosyltransferases. The core pentasaccharide occurs in all N-linked oligosaccharides. [Adapted from Kornfeld, R. and Kornfeld, S., *Annu. Rev. Biochem.* **54**, 640 (1985).] ✆ **See Kinemage Exercise 7-4.**

N-Glycosylation occurs **cotranslationally,** that is, while the polypeptide is being synthesized. Proteins containing N-linked oligosaccharides typically are glycosylated and then processed as elucidated, in large part, by Stuart Kornfeld (Fig. 8-19):

1. An oligosaccharide containing 9 mannose residues, 3 glucose residues, and 2 GlcNAc residues is attached to the Asn of a growing polypeptide chain that is being synthesized by a ribosome associated with the endoplasmic reticulum (Section 16-5).

2. Some of the sugars are removed during processing, which begins in the lumen (internal space) of the endoplasmic reticulum and continues in the Golgi apparatus (Fig. 1-8). Enzymatic trimming is accomplished by glucosidases and mannosidases.

3. Additional monosaccharide residues, including GlcNAc, galactose, fucose, and sialic acid, are added by the action of specific **glycosyltransferases** in the Golgi apparatus.

The exact steps of *N*-linked oligosaccharide processing vary with the identity of the glycoprotein and the battery of endoglycosidases in the cell, but all *N*-linked oligosaccharides have a common core pentasaccharide with the following structure:

$$\begin{array}{c} \text{Man } \alpha(1\rightarrow6) \\ \\ \text{Man } \alpha(1\rightarrow3) \end{array} \Bigg\rangle \text{Man } \beta(1\rightarrow4) \text{ GlcNAc } \beta(1\rightarrow4) \text{ GlcNAc}\text{—}$$

In some glycoproteins, processing is limited, leaving "high-mannose" oligosaccharides; in other glycoproteins, extensive processing generates large oligosaccharides containing several kinds of sugar residues. *There is enormous diversity among the oligosaccharides of N-linked glycoproteins.* Indeed, even glycoproteins with a given polypeptide chain exhibit considerable microheterogeneity, presumably as a consequence of incomplete glycosylation and lack of absolute specificity on the part of glycosidases and glycosyltransferases.

O-Linked Oligosaccharides Are Attached to Serine or Threonine. The most common *O*-glycosidic attachment involves the disaccharide core *β-galactosyl-(1→3)-α-N-acetylgalactosamine linked to the OH group of either Ser or Thr:*

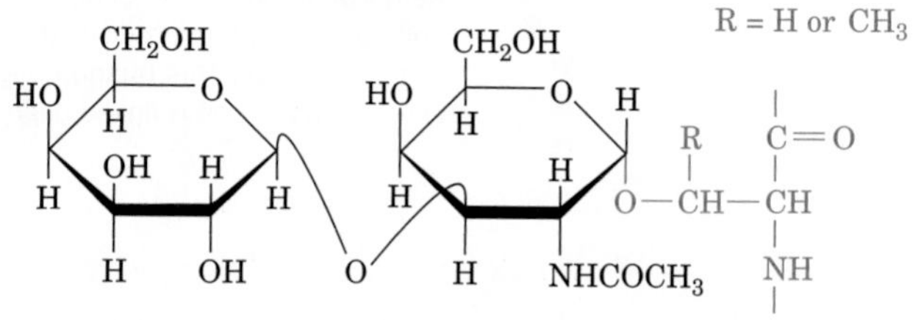

β-Galactosyl-(1→3)-α-*N*-acetylgalactosaminyl-Ser/Thr

Less commonly, galactose, mannose, and xylose form *O*-glycosides with Ser or Thr. Galactose also forms *O*-glycosidic bonds to the 5-hydroxylysyl residues of collagen (Section 6-1C). *O*-Linked oligosaccharides vary in size from a single galactose residue in collagen to the chains of up to 1000 disaccharide units in proteoglycans.

O-Linked oligosaccharides are synthesized in the Golgi apparatus by the serial addition of monosaccharide units to a completed polypeptide chain. Synthesis starts with the transfer of GalNAc to a Ser or Thr residue on the polypeptide. *N*-Linked oligosaccharides are transferred to an Asn in a specific amino acid sequence, but *O*-glycosylated Ser and Thr residues are not members of any common sequence. Instead, the locations of glycosylation sites are specified only by the secondary or tertiary structure of the polypeptide. *O*-Glycosylation continues with stepwise addition of sugars by the corresponding glycosyltransferases. The energetics and enzymology of oligosaccharide synthesis are discussed further in Section 16-5.

D | Oligosaccharides May Determine Glycoprotein Structure, Function, and Recognition

A single protein may contain several *N*- and *O*-linked oligosaccharide chains, although different molecules of the same glycoprotein may differ in the sequences, locations, and numbers of covalently attached carbohydrates (the variant species of a glycoprotein are known as its **glycoforms**). This heterogeneity makes it difficult to assign discrete biological functions o oligosaccharide chains. In fact, certain glycoproteins synthesized by cells that lack particular oligosaccharide-processing enzymes appear to function normally despite abnormal or absent glycosylation. In other cases, however, glycosylation may affect a protein's structure, stability, or activity.

Oligosaccharides Help Define Protein Structure. Oligosaccharides are usually attached to proteins at sequences that form surface loops or turns. Since sugars are hydrophilic, the oligosaccharides tend to project away from the protein surface. Because carbohydrate chains are often conformationally mobile, oligosaccharides attached to proteins can occupy time-averaged volumes of considerable size (Fig. 8-20). In this way, an oligosaccharide can shield a protein's surface, possibly modifying its activity or protecting it from proteolysis.

In addition, some oligosaccharides may play structural roles by limiting the conformational freedom of their attached polypeptide chains. Since N-linked oligosaccharides are added as the protein is being synthesized, the attachment of an oligosaccharide may help determine how the protein folds. In addition, the oligosaccharide may help stabilize the folded conformation of a polypeptide by reducing backbone flexibility. In particular, O-linked oligosaccharides, which are usually clustered in heavily glycosylated segments of a protein, may help stiffen and extend the polypeptide chain.

Oligosaccharides Mediate Recognition Events. The many possible ways that carbohydrates can be linked together to form branched structures gives them the potential to carry more biological information than either nucleic acids or proteins of similar size. For example, two different nucleotides can make only two distinct dinucleotides, but two different hexoses can combine in 36 different ways (although not all possibilities are necessarily realized in nature).

The first evidence that unique combinations of carbohydrates might be involved in intercellular communication came with the discovery that all cells are coated with sugars in the form of **glycoconjugates** such as glycoproteins and glycolipids. The oligosaccharides of glycoconjugates form a fuzzy layer up to 1400 Å thick in some cells (Fig. 8-21).

Additional evidence that cell-surface carbohydrates have recognition functions comes from **lectins** (proteins that bind carbohydrates), which are ubiquitous in nature and frequently appear on the surfaces of cells. Lectins are exquisitely specific: They can recognize individual monosaccharides in particular linkages to other sugars in an oligosaccharide (this property also makes lectins useful laboratory tools for isolating glycoproteins and oligosaccharides). Protein–carbohydrate interactions are typically characterized by extensive hydrogen bonding (often including bridging water molecules) and the van der Waals packing of hydrophobic sugar faces against aromatic side chains (Fig. 8-22).

Proteins known as **selectins** mediate the attachment between **leukocytes** (circulating white blood cells) and the surfaces of endothelial cells (the

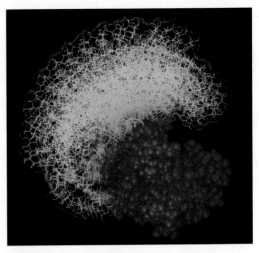

■ **Figure 8-20** | **Model of oligosaccharide dynamics.** The allowed conformations of a $(GlcNAc)_2(mannose)_{5-9}$ oligosaccharide (*yellow*) attached to the bovine pancreatic enzyme **ribonuclease B** (*purple*) are shown in superimposed "snapshots." [Courtesy of Raymond Dwek, Oxford University, U.K.]

■ **Figure 8-21** | **Electron micrograph of the erythrocyte surface.** Its thick (up to 1400 Å) carbohydrate coat, which is called the **glycocalyx,** consists of closely packed oligosaccharides attached to cell-surface proteins and lipids. [Courtesy of Harrison Latta, UCLA.]

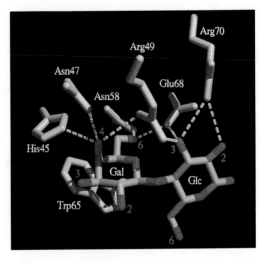

■ **Figure 8-22** | **Carbohydrate binding by a lectin.** Human **galectin-2** binds β-galactosides, such as lactose, primarily through their galactose residue. The galactose and glucose residues are shown in green (with red O atoms), and the lectin amino acid side chains are shown in violet. Hydrogen bonds between the side chains and the sugar residues are shown as dashed yellow lines. [Courtesy of Hakon Leffler, University of California at San Francisco. PDBid 1HLC.]

Table 8-1	Structures of the A, B, and H Antigenic Determinants in Erythrocytes

Type	Antigen[a]
H	Galβ(1→4)GlcNAc··· ↑1,2 L-Fucα
A	GalNAcα(1→3)Galβ(1→4)GlcNAc··· ↑1,2 L-Fucα
B	Galα(1→3)Galβ(1→4)GlcNAc··· ↑1,2 L-Fucα

[a]Gal, Galactose; GalNAc, *N*-acetylgalactosamine; GlcNAc, *N*-acetylglucosamine; L-Fuc, L-fucose.

■ **CHECK YOUR UNDERSTANDING**

Describe the general structures of proteoglycans, peptidoglycans, and glycosylated proteins.

List the major biological functions of proteoglycans and peptidoglycans.

Explain the difference between *N*- and *O*-linked oligosaccharides.

How do oligosaccharides participate in biological recognition?

cells that line blood vessels). Leukocytes constitutively (continually) express selectins on their surface; endothelial cells transiently display their own selectins in response to tissue damage from infection or mechanical injury. The selectins recognize and bind specific oligosaccharides on cell surface glycoproteins. Reciprocal selectin–oligosaccharide interactions between the two cell types allow the endothelial cells to "capture" circulating leukocytes, which then crawl past the endothelial cells on their way to eliminate the infection or help repair damaged tissues.

Other cell–cell recognition phenomena depend on oligosaccharides. For example, proteins on the surface of mammalian spermatozoa recognize GlcNAc or galactose residues on the glycoproteins of the ovum as part of the binding and activation events during fertilization. Many viruses, bacteria, and eukaryotic parasites invade their target tissues by first binding to cell-surface carbohydrates.

Oligosaccharides Are Antigenic Determinants. The carbohydrates on cell surfaces are some of the best known immunochemical markers. For example, the **ABO blood group antigens** are oligosaccharide components of glycoproteins and glycolipids on the surfaces of an individual's cells (not just red blood cells). Individuals with type A cells have A antigens on their cell surfaces and carry anti-B antibodies in their blood; those with type B cells, which bear B antigens, carry anti-A antibodies; those with type AB cells, which have both A and B antigens, carry neither anti-A nor anti-B antibodies; and type O individuals, whose cells bear neither antigen, carry both anti-A and anti-B antibodies. Consequently, the transfusion of type A blood into a type B individual, for example, results in an anti-A antibody–A antigen reaction, which agglutinates (clumps together) the transfused erythrocytes, resulting in an often fatal blockage of blood vessels.

Table 8-1 lists the oligosaccharides found in the **A, B,** and **H antigens** (type O individuals have the H antigen). These occur at the nonreducing ends of the oligosaccharides. The H antigen is the precursor oligosaccharide of A and B antigens. Type A individuals have a 303-residue glycosyltransferase that specifically adds a GalNAc residue to the terminal position of the H antigen. In type B individuals, this enzyme, which differs by four amino acid residues from that of type A individuals, instead adds a galactose residue. In type O individuals, the enzyme is inactive because its synthesis terminates after its 115th residue.

SUMMARY

1. Monosaccharides, the simplest carbohydrates, are classified as aldoses or ketoses.

2. The cyclic hemiacetal and hemiketal forms of monosaccharides have either the α or β configuration at their anomeric carbon but are conformationally variable.

3. Monosaccharide derivatives include aldonic acids, uronic acids, alditols, deoxy sugars, amino sugars, and α- and β-glycosides.

4. Polysaccharides consist of monosaccharides linked by glycosidic bonds.

5. Cellulose and chitin are polysaccharides whose β(1 → 4) linkages cause them to adopt rigid and extended structures.

6. The storage polysaccharides starch and glycogen consist of α-glycosidically linked glucose residues.

7. Glycosaminoglycans are unbranched polysaccharides containing uronic acid and amino sugars that are often sulfated.

8. Proteoglycans are enormous molecules consisting of hyaluronate with attached core proteins that bear numerous glycosaminoglycans and oligosaccharides.

9. Bacterial cell walls are made of peptidoglycan, a network of polysaccharide and polypeptide chains.

10. Glycosylated proteins may contain *N*-linked oligosaccharides (attached to Asn) or *O*-linked oligosaccharides (attached to Ser or Thr) or both. Different molecules of a glycoprotein may contain different sequences and locations of oligosaccharides.

11. Oligosaccharides play important roles in determining protein structure and in cell-surface recognition phenomena.

KEY TERMS

carbohydrate **219**	aldonic acid **224**	oligosaccharide **226**	gram-positive **236**
monosaccharide **219**	uronic acid **224**	exoglycosidase **226**	gram-negative **236**
polysaccharide **219**	alditol **224**	endoglycosidase **226**	peptidoglycan **236**
aldose **220**	deoxy sugar **224**	disaccharide **227**	glycosylation **238**
ketose **220**	amino sugar **225**	starch **230**	oligosaccharide
epimer **221**	glycoprotein **225**	glycogen **231**	processing **240**
hemiacetal **221**	glycolipid **225**	growth factor **233**	glycoforms **240**
hemiketal **221**	α-glycoside **225**	glycosaminoglycan **233**	glycoconjugate **241**
Haworth projection **222**	β-glycoside **225**	biofilm **234**	lectin **241**
pyranose **222**	glycosidic bond **225**	microheterogeneity **234**	leukocyte **241**
furanose **222**	reducing sugar **226**	glycomics **234**	ABO blood group
anomeric carbon **222**	glycan **226**	proteoglycan **234**	antigens **242**
α anomer **223**	homopolysaccharide **226**	*N*-linked oligosaccharide **234**	
β anomer **223**	heteropolysaccharide **226**	*O*-linked oligosaccharide **235**	

PROBLEMS

1. How many stereoisomers are possible for (a) a ketopentose, (b) a ketohexose, and (c) a ketoheptose?

2. Which of the following pairs of sugars are epimers of each other?

   (a) D-sorbose and D-psicose

   (b) D-sorbose and D-fructose

   (c) D-fructose and L-fructose

   (d) D-arabinose and D-ribose

   (e) D-ribose and D-ribulose

3. The sucrose substitute tagatose (Fig. 8-2) is produced by hydrolyzing lactose and then chemically converting one of the two resulting aldoses to a ketose. Which residue of lactose gives rise to tagatose?

4. Draw the furanose and pyranose forms of D-ribose.

5. Are (a) D-glucitol, (b) D-galactitol, and (c) D-glycerol optically active?

6. Draw a Fischer projection of L-fucose. L-Fucose is the 6-deoxy form of which L-hexose?

7. (a) Deduce the structure of the disaccharide trehalose from the following information: Complete hydrolysis yields only D-glucose; it is hydrolyzed by α-glucosidase but not β-glucosidase; and it does not reduce Cu^{2+} to Cu^+. (b) When exposed to dehydrating conditions, many plants and invertebrates synthesize large amounts of trehalose, which enables them to survive prolonged desiccation. What properties of the trehalose molecule might allow it to act as a water substitute?

8. How many different disaccharides of D-glucopyranose are possible?

9. The artificial sweetener sucralose is a derivative of sucrose with the formal name 1,6-dichloro-1,6-dideoxy-β-D-fructofuranosyl-4-chloro-4-deoxy-α-D-galactopyranoside. Draw its structure.

10. How many reducing ends are in a molecule of glycogen that contains 10,000 residues with a branch every 10 residues?

11. Is amylose or amylopectin more likely to be a long-term storage polysaccharide in plants?

12. "Nutraceuticals" are products that are believed to have some beneficial effect but are not strictly defined as either food or drug. Why might an individual suffering from osteoarthritis be tempted to consume the nutraceutical glucosamine?

13. Calculate the net charge of a chondroitin-4-sulfate molecule containing 100 disaccharide units.

14. The core of pectin molecules is a polymer of α(1→4)-linked D-galacturonate. Draw one of its residues.

15. Draw the structure of the O-type oligosaccharide (the H antigen, described in Table 8-1).

16. Glycogen is treated with dimethyl sulfate, which adds a methyl group to every free OH group. Next, the molecule is hydrolyzed to break all the glycosidic bonds between glucose residues. The reaction products are then chemically analyzed.

    (a) How many different types of methylated glucose molecules are obtained?

    (b) Draw the structure of the one that is most abundant.

REFERENCES

Branda, S.S., Vik, A., Friedman, L., and Kolter, R., Biofilms: the matrix revisited, *Trends Microbiol.* **13,** 20–26 (2005). [Summarizes the general features of biofilms and ways of studying them.]

Esko, J.D. and Lindahl, U., Molecular diversity of heparan sulfate, *J. Clin. Invest.* **108,** 169–173 (2001). [Reviews the structure, function, and biosynthesis of heparan sulfate–containing proteoglycans.]

Meroueh, S.O., Bencze, K.Z., Hesek, D., Lee, M., Fisher, J.F., Stemmler, T.L., and Mobashery, S., Three-dimensional structure of the bacterial cell wall peptidoglycan, *Proc. Natl. Acad. Sci.* **103,** 4404–4409 (2006).

Mitra, N., Sinha, S., Ramya, T.N.C., and Surolia, A., *N*-Linked oligosaccharides as outfitters for glycoprotein folding, form and function, *Trends Biochem. Sci.* **31,** 156–163 and 251 (2006).

[Summarizes the ways in which oligosaccharides can influence glycoprotein structure.]

Sharon, N. and Lis, H., History of lectins: from hemagglutinin to biological recognition molecules, *Glycobiology* **14** 53R–62R (2004). [A historical account of lectin research and applications.]

Spiro, R.G., Protein glycosylation: nature, distribution, enzymatic formation, and disease implications of glycopeptide bonds, *Glycobiology* **12,** 43R–56R (2002). [Catalogs the various ways in which saccharides are linked to proteins, and describes the enzymes involved in glycoprotein synthesis.]

Varki, A., Cummings, R., Esko, J., Freeze, H., Hart, G., and Marth, J. (Eds.), *Essentials of Glycobiology,* Cold Spring Harbor Laboratory Press (1999).

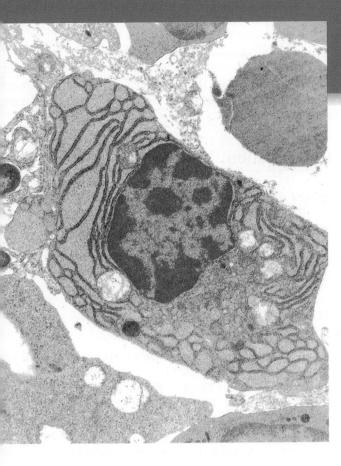

9

Lipids and Biological Membranes

Due to their hydrophobicity, lipids do not mix freely with the aqueous phase but instead can form bilayers. Membranes, which consist of a lipid bilayer and the proteins embedded in it, surround the cytoplasm of all cells and delineate discrete metabolic compartments within cells. [©ISM/Phototake.]

■ CHAPTER CONTENTS

1 Lipid Classification
- **A.** The Properties of Fatty Acids Depend on Their Hydrocarbon Chains
- **B.** Triacylglycerols Contain Three Esterified Fatty Acids
- **C.** Glycerophospholipids Are Amphiphilic
- **D.** Sphingolipids Are Amino Alcohol Derivatives
- **E.** Steroids Contain Four Fused Rings
- **F.** Other Lipids Perform a Variety of Metabolic Roles

2 Lipid Bilayers
- **A.** Bilayer Formation Is Driven by the Hydrophobic Effect
- **B.** Lipid Bilayers Have Fluidlike Properties

3 Membrane Proteins
- **A.** Integral Membrane Proteins Interact with Hydrophobic Lipids
- **B.** Lipid-Linked Proteins Are Anchored to the Bilayer
- **C.** Peripheral Proteins Associate Loosely with Membranes

4 Membrane Structure and Assembly
- **A.** The Fluid Mosaic Model Accounts for Lateral Diffusion
- **B.** The Membrane Skeleton Helps Define Cell Shape
- **C.** Membrane Lipids Are Distributed Asymmetrically
- **D.** The Secretory Pathway Generates Secreted and Transmembrane Proteins
- **E.** Intracellular Vesicles Transport Proteins
- **F.** Proteins Mediate Vesicle Fusion

■ MEDIA RESOURCES

(available at www.wiley.com/college/voet)

Guided Exploration 9. Membrane structure and the fluid mosaic model
Interactive Exercise 4. Model of phospholipase A_2 and glycerophospholipid
Animated Figure 9-35. Secretory pathway
Kinemage 8-1. Bacteriorhodopsin
Kinemage 8-3. OmpF porin

Lipids (Greek: *lipos,* fat) are the fourth major group of molecules found in all cells. Unlike nucleic acids, proteins, and polysaccharides, lipids are not polymeric. However, they do aggregate, and it is in this state that they perform their most obvious function as the structural matrix of biological membranes.

Lipids exhibit greater structural variety than the other classes of biological molecules. To a certain extent, lipids constitute a catchall category of substances that are similar only in that they are largely hydrophobic and only sparingly soluble in water. In general, lipids perform three biological functions (although certain lipids apparently serve more than one purpose in some cells):

1. Lipid molecules in the form of lipid bilayers are essential components of biological membranes.

2. Lipids containing hydrocarbon chains serve as energy stores.

3. Many intra- and intercellular signaling events involve lipid molecules.

In this chapter we examine the structures and physical properties of the most common types of lipids. Next, we look at the properties of the lipid bilayer and the proteins that are situated within it. Finally, we explore current models of membrane structure. The following chapter examines membrane transport phenomena. The participation of lipids in intracellular signaling is discussed in Section 13-4.

1 Lipid Classification

Lipids are substances of biological origin that are soluble in organic solvents such as chloroform and methanol. Hence, they are easily separated from other biological materials by extraction into organic solvents. Fats, oils, certain vitamins and hormones, and most nonprotein membrane components are lipids. In this section, we discuss the structures and physical properties of the major classes of lipids.

A | The Properties of Fatty Acids Depend on Their Hydrocarbon Chains

Fatty acids are carboxylic acids with long-chain hydrocarbon side groups (Fig. 9-1). They usually occur in esterified form as major components of the various lipids described in this chapter. The more common biological fatty acids are listed in Table 9-l. In higher plants and animals, the predominant fatty acid residues are those of the C_{16} and C_{18} species: **palmitic, oleic, linoleic,** and **stearic acids.** Fatty acids with <14 or >20 carbon atoms are uncommon. Most fatty acids have an even number of carbon

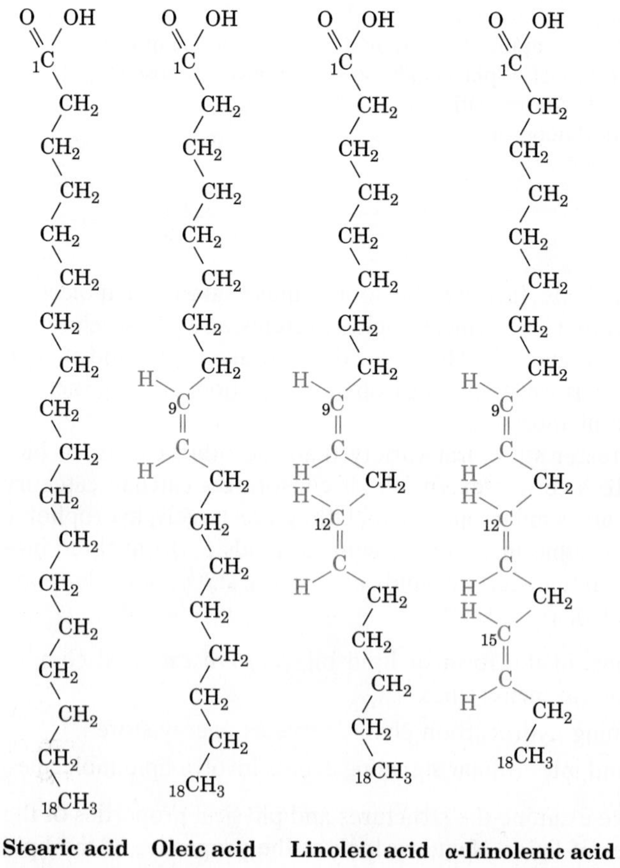

LEARNING OBJECTIVES

- Become familiar with the structures and nomenclature of the major classes of lipids, including fatty acids, triacylglycerols, glycerophospholipids, sphingolipids, and steroids.
- Understand how hydrocarbon chain length affects a lipid's physical properties.
- Understand the physiological roles of lipids as membrane components, energy-storage molecules, and signaling molecules.

■ **Figure 9-1** | **The structural formulas of some C_{18} fatty acids.** The double bonds all have the cis configuration.

Stearic acid   Oleic acid   Linoleic acid   α-Linolenic acid

Table 9-1 The Common Biological Fatty Acids

Symbol[a]	Common Name	Systematic Name	Structure	mp (°C)
Saturated fatty acids				
12:0	Lauric acid	Dodecanoic acid	$CH_3(CH_2)_{10}COOH$	44.2
14:0	Myristic acid	Tetradecanoic acid	$CH_3(CH_2)_{12}COOH$	53.9
16:0	Palmitic acid	Hexadecanoic acid	$CH_3(CH_2)_{14}COOH$	63.1
18:0	Stearic acid	Octadecanoic acid	$CH_3(CH_2)_{16}COOH$	69.6
20:0	Arachidic acid	Eicosanoic acid	$CH_3(CH_2)_{18}COOH$	77
22:0	Behenic acid	Docosanoic acid	$CH_3(CH_2)_{20}COOH$	81.5
24:0	Lignoceric acid	Tetracosanoic acid	$CH_3(CH_2)_{22}COOH$	88
Unsaturated fatty acids (all double bonds are cis)				
16:1*n*–7	Palmitoleic acid	9-Hexadecanoic acid	$CH_3(CH_2)_5CH{=}CH(CH_2)_7COOH$	−0.5
18:1*n*–9	Oleic acid	9-Octadecanoic acid	$CH_3(CH_2)_7CH{=}CH(CH_2)_7COOH$	12
18:2*n*–6	Linoleic acid	9,12-Octadecadienoic acid	$CH_3(CH_2)_4(CH{=}CHCH_2)_2(CH_2)_6COOH$	−5
18:3*n*–3	α-Linolenic acid	9,12,15-Octadecatrienoic acid	$CH_3CH_2(CH{=}CHCH_2)_3(CH_2)_6COOH$	−11
18:3*n*–6	γ-Linolenic acid	6,9,12-Octadecatrienoic acid	$CH_3(CH_2)_4(CH{=}CHCH_2)_3(CH_2)_3COOH$	−11
20:4*n*–6	Arachidonic acid	5,8,11,14-Eicosatetraenoic acid	$CH_3(CH_2)_4(CH{=}CHCH_2)_4(CH_2)_2COOH$	−49.5
20:5*n*–3	EPA	5,8,11,14,17-Eicosapentaenoic acid	$CH_3CH_2(CH{=}CHCH_2)_5(CH_2)_2COOH$	−54
22:6*n*–3	DHA	4,7,10,13,16,19-Docosohexenoic acid	$CH_3CH_2(CH{=}CHCH_2)_6CH_2COOH$	−44
24:1*n*–9	Nervonic acid	15-Tetracosenoic acid	$CH_3(CH_2)_7CH{=}CH(CH_2)_{13}COOH$	39

[a] Number of carbon atoms:Number of double bonds. For unsaturated fatty acids, the quantity "*n*–*x*" indicates the position of the last double bond in the fatty acid, where *n* is its number of C atoms, and *x* is the position of the last double-bonded C atom counting from the methyl-terminal (ω) end.

Source: LipidBank (http://www.lipidbank.jp)

atoms because they are biosynthesized by the concatenation of C_2 units Section 20-4).

Over half of the fatty acid residues of plant and animal lipids are **unsaturated** (contain double bonds) and are often **polyunsaturated** (contain two or more double bonds). Bacterial fatty acids are rarely polyunsaturated but are commonly branched, hydroxylated, or contain cyclopropane rings.

Table 9-1 indicates that the first double bond of an unsaturated fatty acid commonly occurs between its C9 and C10 atoms counting from the carboxyl C atom. This bond is called a Δ^9- or 9-double bond. In polyunsaturated fatty acids, the double bonds tend to occur at every third carbon atom (e.g., —CH=CH—CH₂—CH=CH—) and so are not conjugated (as in —CH=CH—CH=CH—). Two important classes of polyunsaturated fatty acids are designated as ω-3 or ω-6 fatty acids, a nomenclature that identifies the last double-bonded carbon atom as counted from the methyl terminal (ω) end of the chain. α-**Linolenic acid** and linoleic acid (Fig. 9-1) are examples of such fatty acids.

Saturated fatty acids (which are fully reduced or "saturated" with hydrogen) are highly flexible molecules that can assume a wide range of conformations because there is relatively free rotation around each of their C—C bonds. Nevertheless, their lowest energy conformation is the fully extended conformation, which has the least amount of steric interference between neighboring methylene groups. The melting points (mp) of saturated fatty acids, like those of most substances, increase with their molecular mass (Table 9-1).

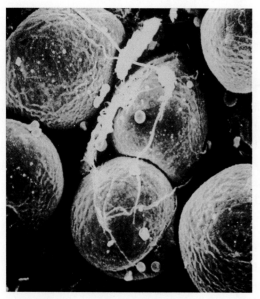

■ **Figure 9-2** | **Scanning electron micrograph of adipocytes.** Each adipocyte contains a fat globule that occupies nearly the entire cell. [Fred E. Hossler/Visuals Unlimited.]

Fatty acid double bonds almost always have the cis configuratio. (Fig. 9-1). This puts a rigid 30° bend in the hydrocarbon chair Consequently, unsaturated fatty acids pack together less efficiently that saturated fatty acids. The reduced van der Waals interactions of unsaturate fatty acids cause their melting points to decrease with the degree of unsat uration. The fluidity of lipids containing fatty acid residues likewise in creases with the degree of unsaturation of the fatty acids. This phenome non, as we shall see, has important consequences for biological membrane:

B | Triacylglycerols Contain Three Esterified Fatty Acids

The fats and oils that occur in plants and animals consist largely of mix tures of **triacylglycerols** (also called **triglycerides**). These nonpolar, wate insoluble substances are fatty acid triesters of **glycerol:**

$$
\begin{array}{cc}
{}^1CH_2\!-\!OH & {}^1CH_2\!-\!O\!-\!\overset{\displaystyle O}{\overset{\|}{C}}\!-\!R_1 \\[2pt]
{}^2CH\!-\!OH & {}^2CH\;-\!O\!-\!\overset{\displaystyle O}{\overset{\|}{C}}\!-\!R_2 \\[2pt]
{}^3CH_2\!-\!OH & {}^3CH_2\!-\!O\!-\!\overset{\displaystyle O}{\overset{\|}{C}}\!-\!R_3 \\
\end{array}
$$

Glycerol   **Triacylglycerol**

Triacylglycerols function as energy reservoirs in animals and are therefor their most abundant class of lipids even though they are not component of cellular membranes.

Triacylglycerols differ according to the identity and placement o their three fatty acid residues. Most triacylglycerols contain two or three different types of fatty acid residues and are named according to thei placement on the glycerol moiety, for example, **1-palmitoleoyl-2 linoleoyl-3-stearoylglycerol** *(at left).* Note that the *-ate* ending of th name of the fatty acid becomes *-oyl* in the fatty acid ester. **Fats and oil** (which differ only in that fats are solid and oils are liquid at room tem perature) are complex mixtures of triacylglycerols whose fatty acid com positions vary with the organism that produced them. Plant oils are usu ally richer in unsaturated fatty acid residues than animal fats, as the lowe melting points of oils imply.

Triacylglycerols Function as Energy Reserves. Fats are a highly effi cient form in which to store metabolic energy. This is because triacylglyc erols are less oxidized than carbohydrates or proteins and hence yield sig nificantly more energy per unit mass on complete oxidation. Furthermore triacylglycerols, which are nonpolar, are stored in anhydrous form, wherea glycogen (Section 8-2C), for example, binds about twice its weight of wate under physiological conditions. *Fats therefore provide about six times th metabolic energy of an equal weight of hydrated glycogen.*

In animals, **adipocytes** (fat cells; Fig. 9-2) are specialized for the synthe sis and storage of triacylglycerols. Whereas other types of cells have only a few small droplets of fat dispersed in their cytosol, adipocytes may b almost entirely filled with fat globules. **Adipose tissue** is most abundant i a subcutaneous layer and in the abdominal cavity. The fat content of nor mal humans (21% for men, 26% for women) allows them to survive star vation for 2 or 3 months. In contrast, the body's glycogen supply, whicl functions as a short-term energy store, can provide for the body's energ needs for less than a day. The subcutaneous fat layer also provides ther mal insulation, which is particularly important for warm-blooded aquati

$$
\begin{array}{ccc}
{}^1CH_2 & \!\!-\!{}^2CH\!-\!\! & {}^3CH_2 \\
| & | & | \\
O & O & O \\
| & | & | \\
C_1\!\!=\!\!O & C_1\!\!=\!\!O & C_1\!\!=\!\!O \\
| & | & | \\
CH_2 & CH_2 & CH_2 \\
| & | & | \\
CH_2 & CH_2 & CH_2 \\
| & | & | \\
CH_2 & CH_2 & CH_2 \\
| & | & | \\
CH_2 & CH_2 & CH_2 \\
| & | & | \\
CH_2 & CH_2 & CH_2 \\
| & | & | \\
CH_2 & CH_2 & CH_2 \\
| & | & | \\
CH_2 & CH_2 & CH_2 \\
| & | & | \\
CH & CH & CH_2 \\
\|^9 & \|^9 & | \\
CH & CH & CH_2 \\
| & | & | \\
CH_2 & CH_2 & CH_2 \\
| & | & | \\
CH_2 & CH & CH_2 \\
| & \|^{12} & | \\
CH_2 & CH & CH_2 \\
| & | & | \\
CH_2 & CH_2 & CH_2 \\
| & | & | \\
CH_2 & CH_2 & CH_2 \\
| & | & | \\
{}_{16}CH_3 & CH_2 & CH_2 \\
& | & | \\
& CH_2 & CH_2 \\
& | & | \\
& {}_{18}CH_3 & {}_{18}CH_3 \\
\end{array}
$$

**1-Palmitoleoyl-2-linoleoyl-
3-stearoylglycerol**

Figure 9-3 | **Structure of glycerophospholipids.** (*a*) The backbone,
L-glycerol-3-phosphate. (*b*) The general formula of the glycerophospholipids. R$_1$ and
R$_2$ are the long-chain hydrocarbon tails of fatty acids, and X is derived from a polar
alcohol (Table 9-2). Note that glycerol-3-phosphate and glycerophospholipid are
chiral compounds.

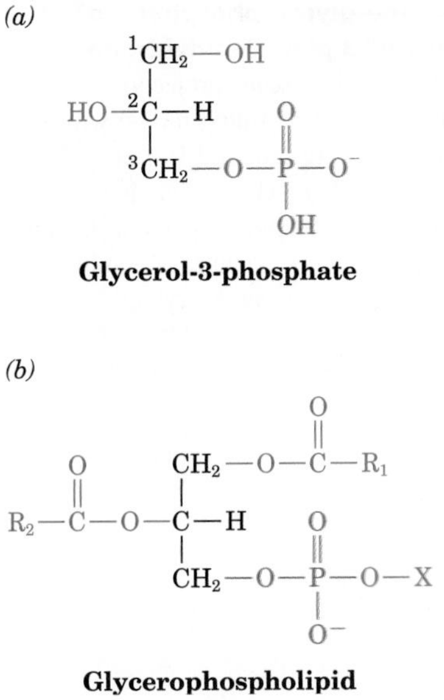

(*a*)

Glycerol-3-phosphate

animals, such as whales, seals, geese, and penguins, which are routinely
exposed to low temperatures.

C | Glycerophospholipids Are Amphiphilic

Glycerophospholipids (or **phosphoglycerides**) are the major lipid components of biological membranes. They consist of **glycerol-3-phosphate**
whose C1 and C2 positions are esterified with fatty acids. In addition, the
phosphoryl group is linked to another usually polar group, X (Fig. 9-3).
*Glycerophospholipids are therefore amphiphilic molecules with nonpolar
aliphatic (hydrocarbon) "tails" and polar phosphoryl-X "heads."*

The simplest glycerophospholipids, in which X = H, are **phosphatidic
acids;** they are present in only small amounts in biological membranes. In
the glycerophospholipids that commonly occur in biological membranes,
the head groups are derived from polar alcohols (Table 9-2). Saturated C$_{16}$
or C$_{18}$ fatty acids usually occur at the C1 position of the glycerophospholipids,

(*b*)

Glycerophospholipid

Table 9-2 The Common Classes of Glycerophospholipids

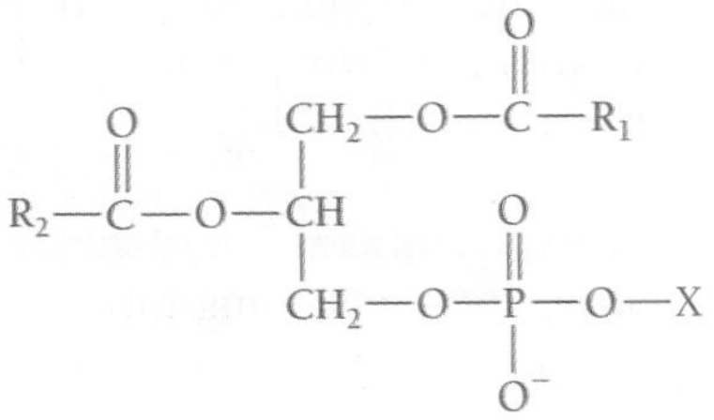

Name of X—OH	Formula of —X	Name of Phospholipid
Water	—H	Phosphatidic acid
Ethanolamine	—CH$_2$CH$_2$NH$_3^+$	Phosphatidylethanolamine
Choline	—CH$_2$CH$_2$N(CH$_3$)$_3^+$	Phosphatidylcholine (lecithin)
Serine	—CH$_2$CH(NH$_3^+$)COO$^-$	Phosphatidylserine
myo-Inositol	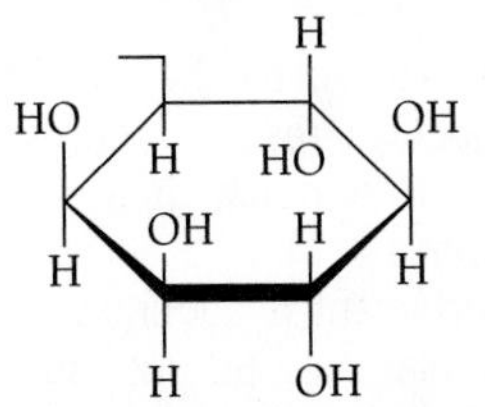	Phosphatidylinositol
Glycerol	—CH$_2$CH(OH)CH$_2$OH	Phosphatidylglycerol
Phosphatidylglycerol	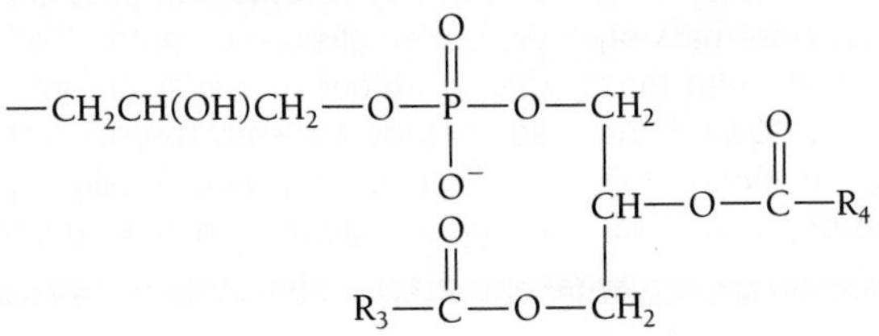	Diphosphatidylglycerol (cardiolipin)

■ **Figure 9-4** | **The glycerophospholipid 1-stearoyl-2-oleoyl-3-phosphatidylcholine.** (*a*) Molecular formula in Fischer projection. (*b*) Energy-minimized space-filling model with C green, H white, N blue, O red, and P orange. Note how the unsaturated oleoyl chain (*left*) is bent compared to the saturated stearoyl chain. [Based on coordinates provided by Richard Venable and Richard Pastor, NIH, Bethesda, Maryland.]

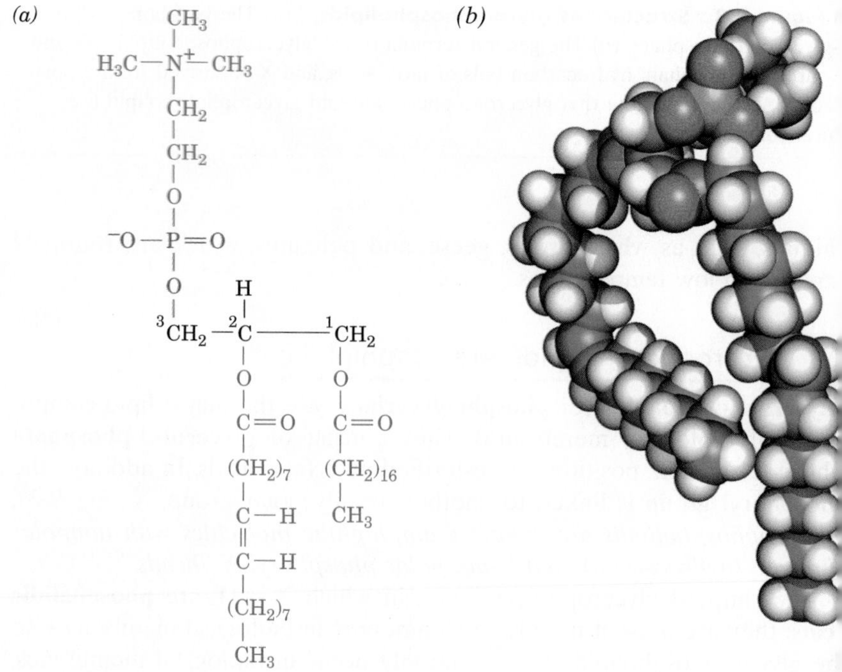

(*a*)

(*b*)

1-Stearoyl-2-oleoyl-3-phosphatidylcholine

and the C2 position is often occupied by an unsaturated C_{16} to C_2 fatty acid. Individual glycerophospholipids are named according to the identities of these fatty acid residues (e.g., Fig. 9-4). A glycerophospholipid containing two palmitoyl chains is an important component of **lung surfactant** (Box 9-1).

Phospholipases Hydrolyze Glycerophospholipids. The chemical structures—including fatty acyl chains and head groups—of glycerophos

BOX 9-1 BIOCHEMISTRY IN HEALTH AND DISEASE

Lung Surfactant

Dipalmitoyl phosphatidylcholine (DPPC) is the major lipid of lung surfactant, the protein–lipid mixture that is essential for normal pulmonary function. The surfaces of the cells that form the alveoli (small air spaces of the lung) are coated with surfactant, which decreases the alveolar surface tension. Lung surfactant contains 80 to 90% phospholipid by weight, and 70 to 80% of the phospholipid is phosphatidylcholine, mostly the dipalmitoyl species.

Because the palmitoyl chains of DPPC are saturated, they tend to extend straight out without bending. This allows close packing of DPPC molecules, which are oriented in a single layer with their nonpolar tails toward the air and their polar heads toward the alveolar cells. When air is expired from the lungs, the volume and surface area of the alveoli decrease. The collapse of the alveolar

space is prevented by the surfactant, because the closely packed DPPC molecules resist compression. Reopening a collapsed air space requires a much greater force than expanding an already open air space.

Lung surfactant is continuously synthesized, secreted, and recycled by alveolar cells. Because surfactant production is low until just before birth, premature infants are at risk of developing **respiratory distress syndrome,** which is characterized by difficulty in breathing due to alveolar collapse. The syndrome can be treated by introducing exogenous surfactant into the lungs. A related condition in adults **(adult respiratory distress syndrome)** is characterized by insufficient surfactant, usually secondary to other lung injury. This condition, too, can be treated with exogenous surfactant.

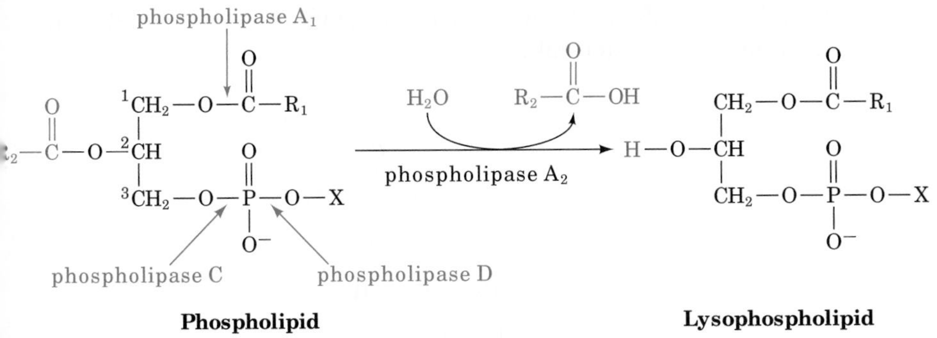

phospholipase A_1

$$\overset{1}{C}H_2-O-\overset{\overset{\displaystyle O}{\|}}{C}-R_1$$

$$R_2-\overset{\overset{\displaystyle O}{\|}}{C}-O-\overset{2}{C}H$$

$$\overset{3}{C}H_2-O-\overset{\overset{\displaystyle}{|}}{\underset{\underset{\displaystyle O^-}{|}}{P}}-O-X$$

phospholipase C   phospholipase D

Phospholipid

H_2O $R_2-\overset{\overset{\displaystyle O}{\|}}{C}-OH$

$\xrightarrow{\quad\text{phospholipase } A_2\quad}$

$$CH_2-O-\overset{\overset{\displaystyle O}{\|}}{C}-R_1$$

$$H-O-CH$$

$$CH_2-O-\overset{\overset{\displaystyle}{|}}{\underset{\underset{\displaystyle O^-}{|}}{P}}-O-X$$

Lysophospholipid

Figure 9-5 | Action of phospholipases. Phospholipase A_2 hydrolytically excises the C2 fatty acid residue from a triacylglycerol to yield the corresponding lysophospholipid. The bonds hydrolyzed by other types of phospholipases, which are named according to their specificities, are also indicated.

pholipids can be determined from the products of the hydrolytic reactions catalyzed by enzymes known as **phospholipases.** For example, **phospholipase A_2** hydrolytically excises the fatty acid residue at C2, leaving a **lysophospholipid** (Fig. 9-5). Lysophospholipids, as their name implies, are powerful detergents that disrupt cell membranes, thereby lysing cells. Bee and snake venoms are rich sources of phospholipase A_2. Other types of phospholipases act at different sites in glycerophospholipids, as shown in Fig. 9-5.

Enzymes that act on lipids have fascinated biochemists because the enzymes must gain access to portions of the lipids that are buried in a nonaqueous environment. Phospholipases A_2, which constitute some of the best understood lipid-specific enzymes, are relatively small proteins (~14 kD, ~125 amino acid residues). The X-ray structure of phospholipase A_2 from cobra venom suggests that the enzyme binds a glycerophospholipid molecule such that its polar head group fits into the enzyme's active site, whereas the hydrophobic tails, which extend beyond the active site, interact with several aromatic side chains (Fig. 9-6).

Lipases specific for triacylglycerols and membrane lipids catalyze their degradation *in vivo*. Occasionally, the hydrolysis products are not destined for further degradation but instead serve as intra- and extracellular signal molecules. For example, **lysophosphatidic acid (1-acyl-glycerol-3-phosphate),** which is not actually lytic since it has a small head group (an unsubstituted phosphate group), is produced by hydrolysis of membrane lipids in blood platelets and injured cells and stimulates cell growth as part of the wound-repair process. **1,2-Diacylglycerol,** derived from membrane lipids by the action of **phospholipase C,** is an intracellular signal molecule that activates a **protein kinase** (Section 13-4C; kinases catalyze ATP-dependent phosphoryl-transfer reactions).

Plasmalogens Contain an Ether Linkage. Plasmalogens are glycerophospholipids in which the C1 substituent of the glycerol moiety is

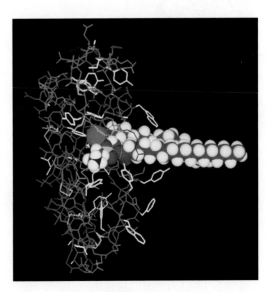

Figure 9-6 | Model of phospholipase A_2 and a glycerophospholipid. The X-ray structure of the enzyme from cobra venom is shown with a space-filling model of dimyristoyl phosphatidylethanolamine in its active site as located by NMR methods. A Ca^{2+} ion in the active site is shown in magenta. [Courtesy of Edward A. Dennis, University of California at San Diego.] **See Interactive Exercise 4.**

linked via an α,β-unsaturated ether linkage in the cis configuration rather than through an ester linkage:

$$
\begin{array}{c}
X \\
| \\
O \\
| \\
O=P-O^- \\
| \\
O \\
| \\
CH_2-CH-CH_2 \\
| \quad\quad | \\
O \quad\quad O \\
| \quad\quad | \\
CH \quad C=O \\
|| \quad\quad | \\
CH \quad R_2 \\
| \\
R_1
\end{array}
$$

A plasmalogen

Ethanolamine, choline, and serine (Table 9-2) form the most common plasmalogen head groups. The functions of most plasmalogens are not well understood. Because the vinyl ether group is easily oxidized, plasmalogens may react with oxygen free radicals, by-products of normal metabolism, thereby preventing free-radical damage to other cell constituents.

D | Sphingolipids Are Amino Alcohol Derivatives

Sphingolipids are also major membrane components. Their function in cells was at first mysterious, so they were named after the Sphinx. Most sphingolipids are derivatives of the C_{18} amino alcohol **sphingosine,** whose double bond has the trans configuration. The *N*-acyl fatty acid derivatives of sphingosine are known as **ceramides:**

(a)

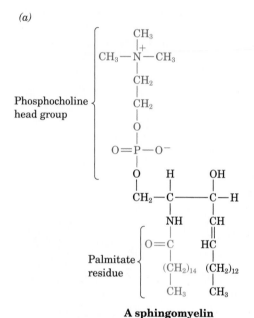

A sphingomyelin

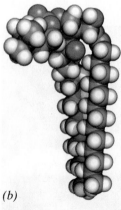

(b)

■ **Figure 9-7** | **A sphingomyelin.** (*a*) Molecular formula. (*b*) Energy-minimized space-filling model with C green, H white, N blue, O red, and P orange. [Based on coordinates provided by Richard Venable and Richard Pastor, NIH, Bethesda, Maryland.]

Sphingosine   **A ceramide**

Ceramides are the parent compounds of the more abundant sphingolipids:

1. **Sphingomyelins,** the most common sphingolipids, are ceramides bearing either a phosphocholine (Fig. 9-7) or a phosphoethanolamine head group, so they can also be classified as **sphingophospholipids.** They typically make up 10 to 20 mol % of plasma membrane lipids. *Although sphingomyelins differ chemically from phosphatidylcholine and phosphatidylethanolamine, their conformations and charge distributions are quite similar* (compare Figs. 9-4 and 9-7). The membranous myelin sheath that surrounds and electrically insulates many nerve cell axons is particularly rich in sphingomyelins (Fig. 9-8).

2. **Cerebrosides** are ceramides with head groups that consist of a single sugar residue. These lipids are therefore **glycosphingolipids.** **Galactocerebrosides** and **glucocerebrosides** are the most prevalent

Cerebrosides, in contrast to phospholipids, lack phosphate groups and hence are nonionic.

3. *Gangliosides* are the most complex glycosphingolipids. They are ceramides with attached oligosaccharides that include at least one sialic acid residue. The structures of **gangliosides G_{M1}, G_{M2}, and G_{M3},** three of the over 60 that are known, are shown in Fig. 9-9. Gangliosides are primarily components of cell-surface membranes and constitute a significant fraction (6%) of brain lipids.

Gangliosides have considerable physiological and medical significance. Their complex carbohydrate head groups, which extend beyond the surfaces of cell membranes, act as specific receptors for certain pituitary glycoprotein hormones that regulate a number of important physiological functions. Gangliosides are also receptors for certain bacterial protein toxins such as **cholera toxin.** There is considerable evidence that gangliosides are specific determinants of cell–cell recognition, so they probably have an important role in the growth and differentiation of tissues as well as in carcinogenesis. Disorders of ganglioside breakdown are responsible for several hereditary **sphingolipid storage diseases,** such as **Tay-Sachs disease,** which are characterized by an invariably fatal neurological deterioration in early childhood.

Sphingolipids, like glycerophospholipids, are a source of smaller lipids that have discrete signaling activity. Sphingomyelin itself, as well as the ceramide portions of more complex sphingolipids, appear to specifically modulate the activities of protein kinases and **protein phosphatases** (enzymes that remove phosphoryl groups from proteins) that are involved in regulating cell growth and differentiation.

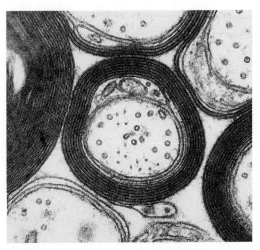

■ **Figure 9-8** | **Electron micrograph of myelinated nerve fibers.** This cross-sectional view shows the spirally wrapped membranes around each nerve axon. The myelin sheath may be 10–15 layers thick. Its high lipid content makes it an electrical insulator. [Courtesy of Cedric S. Raine, Albert Einstein College of Medicine.]

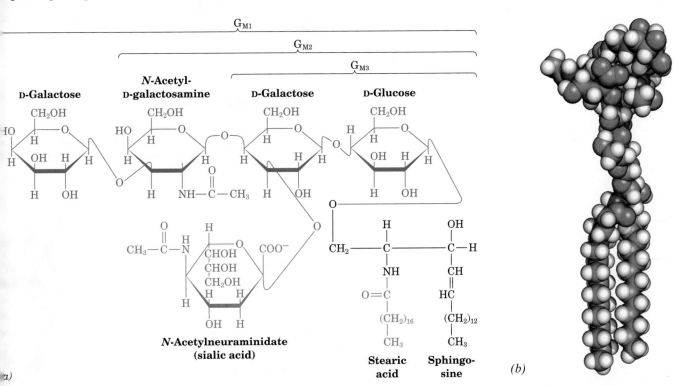

■ **Figure 9-9** | **Gangliosides.** (*a*) Structural formula of gangliosides G_{M1}, G_{M2}, and G_{M3}. Gangliosides G_{M2} and G_{M3} differ from G_{M1} only by the sequential absences of the terminal D-galactose and N-acetyl-D-galactosamine residues. Other gangliosides have different oligosaccharide head groups. (*b*) Energy-minimized space-filling model of G_{M1} with C green, H white, N blue, and O red. [Based on coordinates provided by Richard Venable and Richard Pastor, NIH, Bethesda, Maryland.]

E | Steroids Contain Four Fused Rings

Steroids, which are mostly of eukaryotic origin, are derivatives o
cyclopentanoperhydrophenanthrene,

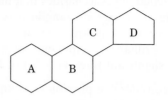

Cyclopentanoperhydrophenanthrene

a compound that consists of four fused, nonplanar rings (labeled A–D
The much maligned **cholesterol,** which is the most abundant steroid in an
imals, is further classified as a **sterol** because of its C3-OH group (Fig. 9-10
Cholesterol is a major component of animal plasma membranes, typicall
constituting 30 to 40 mol % of plasma membrane lipids. Its polar OI
group gives it a weak amphiphilic character, whereas its fused ring syster
provides it with greater rigidity than other membrane lipids. Cholestero
can also be esterified to long-chain fatty acids to form **cholesteryl ester**
for example:

Cholesteryl stearate

Plants contain little cholesterol but synthesize other sterols. Yeast and fung
also synthesize sterols, which differ from cholesterol in their aliphatic sid
chains and number of double bonds. Prokaryotes contain little, if any, stero

(a)

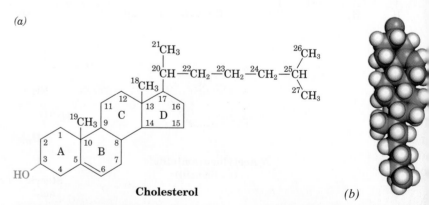

Cholesterol (b)

■ **Figure 9-10** | **Cholesterol.** (a) Structural formula with the standard numbering
system. (b) Energy-minimized space-filling model with C green, H white, and O red.
[Based on coordinates provided by Richard Venable and Richard Pastor, NIH,
Bethesda, Maryland.]

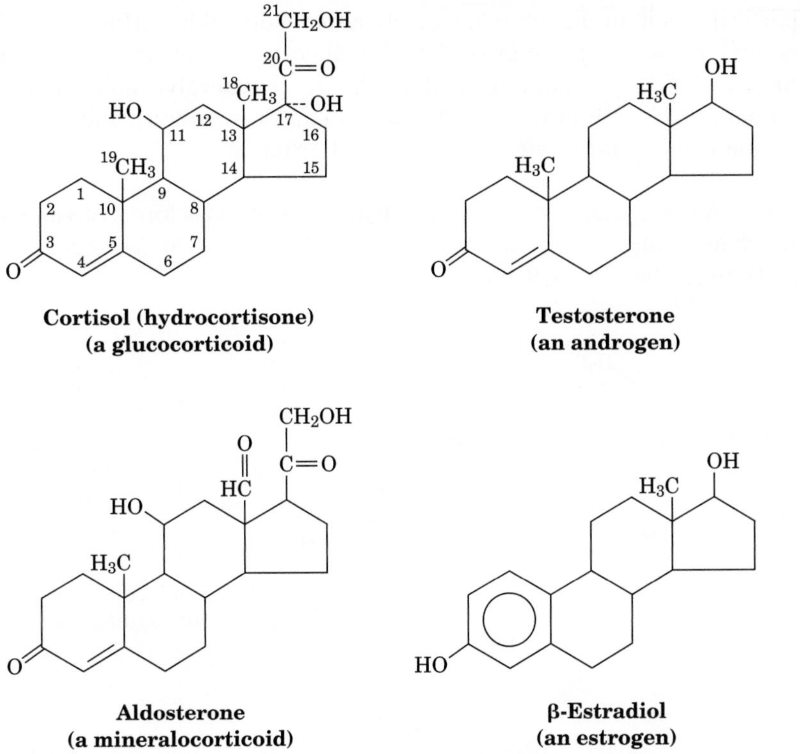

Cortisol (hydrocortisone)
(a glucocorticoid)

Testosterone
(an androgen)

Aldosterone
(a mineralocorticoid)

β-Estradiol
(an estrogen)

Figure 9-11 | Some representative steroid hormones.

In mammals, cholesterol is the metabolic precursor of **steroid hormones,** substances that regulate a great variety of physiological functions. The structures of some steroid hormones are shown in Fig. 9-11. Steroid hormones are classified according to the physiological responses they evoke:

1. The **glucocorticoids,** such as **cortisol** (a C_{21} compound), affect carbohydrate, protein, and lipid metabolism and influence a wide variety of other vital functions, including inflammatory reactions and the capacity to cope with stress.
2. **Aldosterone** and other **mineralocorticoids** regulate the excretion of salt and water by the kidneys.
3. The **androgens** and **estrogens** affect sexual development and function. **Testosterone,** a C_{19} compound, is the prototypic androgen (male sex hormone), whereas **β-estradiol,** a C_{18} compound, is an estrogen (female sex hormone).

Glucocorticoids and mineralocorticoids are synthesized by the cortex (outer layer) of the adrenal gland. Both androgens and estrogens are synthesized by testes and ovaries (although androgens predominate in testes and estrogens predominate in ovaries) and, to a lesser extent, by the adrenal cortex. Because steroid hormones are water insoluble, they bind to proteins for transport through the blood to their target tissues.

Impaired adrenocortical function, either through disease or trauma, results in **Addison's disease,** which is characterized by **hypoglycemia** (decreased amounts of glucose in the blood), muscle weakness, Na^+ loss, K^+ retention, impaired cardiac function, and greatly increased susceptibility to stress. The victim, unless treated by the administration of glucocorticoids and mineralocorticoids, slowly languishes and dies without any particular pain or distress. Conversely, adrenocortical hyperfunction, whic[h] is often caused by a tumor of the adrenal cortex, results in **Cushing's syn**-**drome,** which is characterized by fatigue, **hyperglycemia** (increase[d] amount of glucose in the blood), **edema** (water retention), and a redistri[-]bution of body fat to yield a characteristic "moon face."

Vitamin D Regulates Ca²⁺ Metabolism. The various forms of **vitamin** D, which are really hormones, are sterol derivatives in which the steroid B rin[g] is disrupted between C9 and C10:

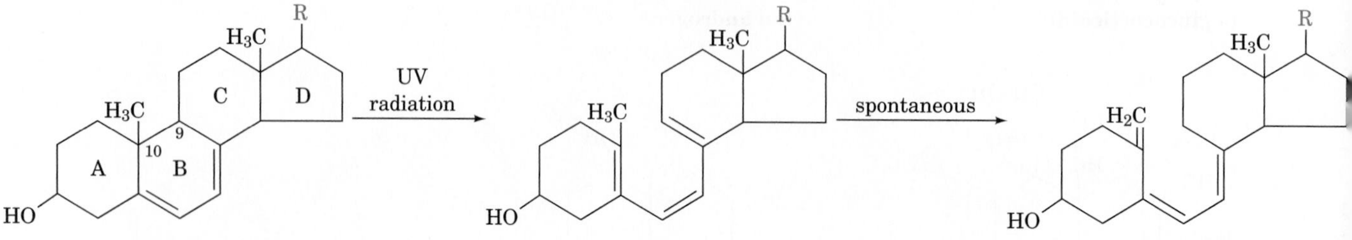

R = X **7-Dehydrocholesterol**
R = Y **Ergosterol**

R = X **Vitamin D₃ (cholecalcifero**[l])
R = Y **Vitamin D₂ (ergocalciferol**[)]

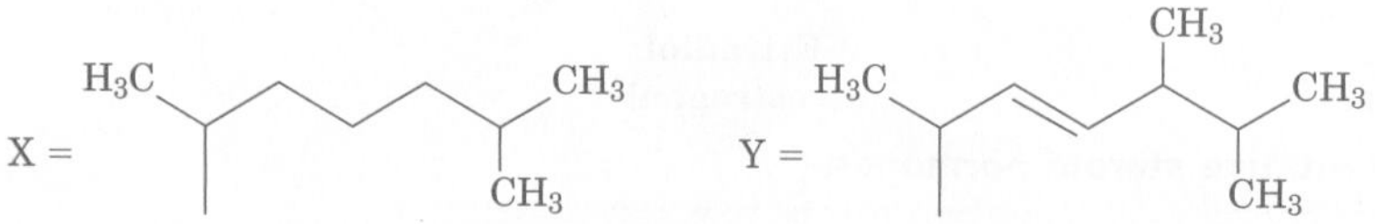

Vitamin D₂ (ergocalciferol) is nonenzymatically formed in the skin of an[-]imals through the photolytic action of UV light on the plant sterol **ergos**-**terol,** a common milk additive, whereas the closely related **vitamin D**[₃] **(cholecalciferol)** is similarly derived from **7-dehydrocholesterol** (hence th[e] saying that sunlight provides vitamin D).

Vitamins D₂ and D₃ are inactive; the active forms are produce[d] through their enzymatic hydroxylation (addition of an OH group[)] carried out by the liver (at C25) and by the kidney (at C1) to yield **1α,25**-**dihydroxycholecalciferol:**

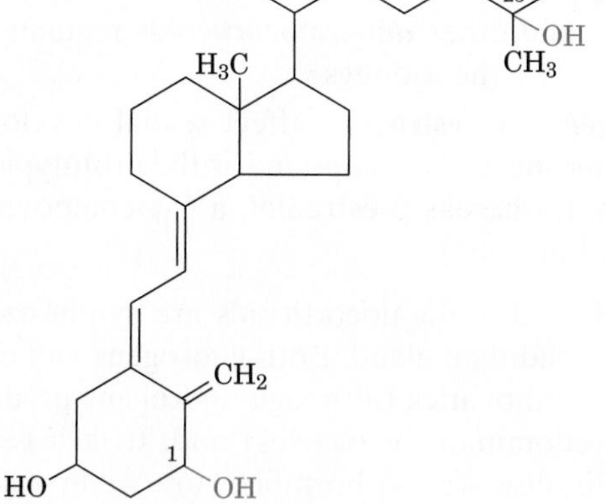

1α,25-Dihydroxycholecalciferol

Active vitamin D increases serum [Ca²⁺] by promoting the intestinal ab[-]sorption of dietary Ca²⁺. This increases the deposition of Ca²⁺ in bone[s] and teeth. Vitamin D deficiency produces **rickets** in children, a diseas[e] characterized by stunted growth and deformed bones caused by insuffi[-]cient bone mineralization. Although rickets was first described in 1645, i[t] was not until the early twentieth century that eating animal fats, particularly fish liver oils, was shown to prevent this deficiency disease. Rickets can also be prevented by exposing children to sunlight or just UV light in the wavelength range 230 to 313 nm, regardless of their diets.

Since vitamin D is water insoluble, it can accumulate in fatty tissues. Excessive intake of vitamin D over long periods results in **vitamin D intoxication.** The consequent high serum $[Ca^{2+}]$ results in aberrant calcification of soft tissues and in the development of kidney stones, which can cause kidney failure. The observation that the level of skin pigmentation in indigenous human populations tends to increase with their proximity to the equator is explained by the hypothesis that skin pigmentation functions to prevent vitamin D intoxication by filtering out excessive solar radiation.

Other Lipids Perform a Variety of Metabolic Roles

In addition to the well-characterized lipids that are found in large amounts in cellular membranes, many organisms synthesize compounds that are not membrane components but are classified as lipids on the basis of their physical properties. For example, lipids occur in the waxy coatings of plants, where they protect cells from desiccation by creating a water-impermeable barrier.

Isoprenoids Are Built from Five-Carbon Units. Among the compounds that are not structural components of membranes—although they are soluble in the lipid bilayer—are the **isoprenoids,** which are built from five-carbon units with the same carbon skeleton as **isoprene.**

Isoprene

For example, the isoprenoid **ubiquinone** (also known as **coenzyme Q**) is reversibly reduced and oxidized in the mitochondrial membrane (its activity is described in more detail in Section 18-2C). Mammalian ubiquinone consists of 10 isoprenoid units.

Coenzyme Q (CoQ) or ubiquinone

The plant kingdom is rich in isoprenoid compounds, which serve as pigments, molecular signals (hormones and pheromones), and defensive agents. Indeed, over 25,000 isoprenoids (also known as **terpenoids**), which are mostly of plant, fungal, and bacterial origin, have been characterized. During the course of evolution, vertebrate metabolism has co-opted several of these compounds for other purposes. Some of these compounds (e.g., vitamin D) are known as **fat-soluble vitamins** (**vitamins** are organic substances that an animal requires in small amounts but cannot synthesize and hence must acquire in its diet).

Vitamin A, or **retinol** (*at right*), is derived mainly from plant products such as **β-carotene** [a red pigment that is present in green vegetables as well as carrots (after which it is named) and tomatoes; Section 19-1B]. Retinol is oxidized to its corresponding aldehyde, **retinal,** which functions

X = CH₂OH   **Retinol (vitamin A)**
X = CHO   **Retinal**

as the eye's photoreceptor at low light intensities. Light causes the retinal to isomerize, triggering, via a complex signaling pathway, an impulsthrough the optic nerve. A severe deficiency of vitamin A can lead tblindness. Retinoic acid also has hormonelike properties in that it stimulates tissue repair. It is used to treat severe acne and skin ulcers anis also used cosmetically to eliminate wrinkles.

Vitamin K is a lipid synthesized by plants (as **phylloquinone**) and bacteria (as **menaquinone**):

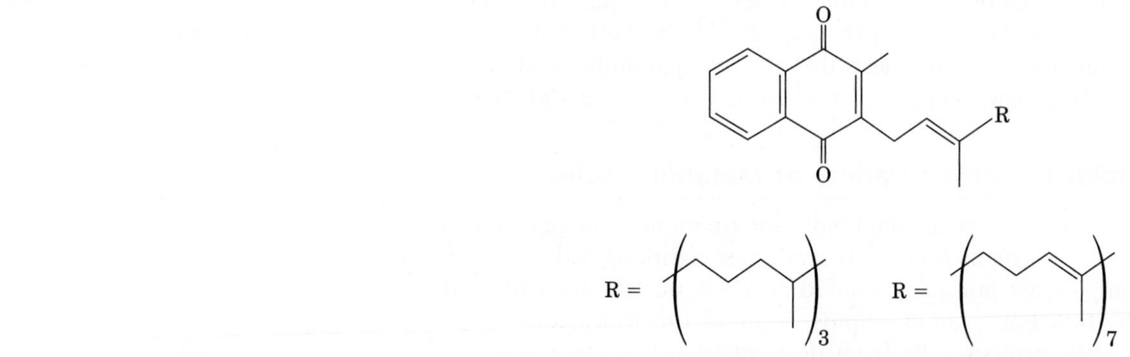

Phylloquinone
(vitamin K₁)

Menaquinone
(vitamin K₂)

About half of the daily requirement for humans is supplied by intestinbacteria. Vitamin K participates in the carboxylation of Glu residues isome of the proteins involved in blood clotting (vitamin K is named fcthe Danish word *Koagulation*). Vitamin K deficiency prevents this caboxylation, and the resulting inactive clotting proteins lead to excessivbleeding. Compounds that interfere with vitamin K function are the active ingredients in some rodent poisons.

Vitamin E is actually a group of compounds whose most abundarmember is **α-tocopherol:**

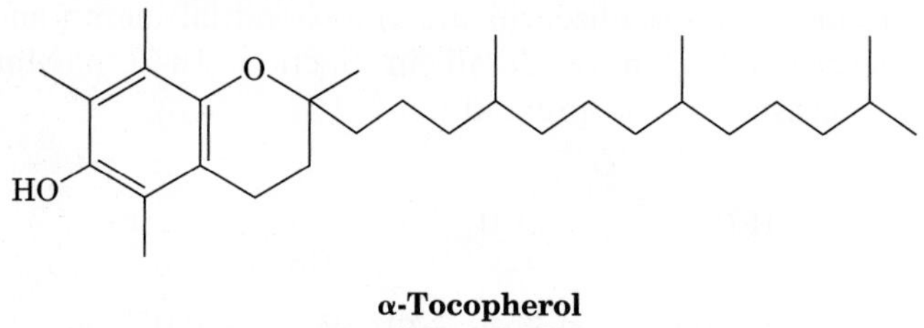

α-Tocopherol
(vitamin E)

This highly hydrophobic molecule is incorporated into cell membranewhere it functions as an antioxidant that prevents oxidative damage tmembrane proteins and lipids. A deficiency of vitamin E elicits a varietof nonspecific symptoms, which makes the deficiency difficult to detecThe popularity of vitamin E supplements rests on the hypothesis that vitamin E protects against oxidative damage to cells and hence reduces theffects of aging.

Eicosanoids Are Derived from Arachidonic Acid. Other less commolipids are derived from relatively abundant membrane lipids. **Prostaglandin**(e.g., Fig. 9-12) were discovered in the 1930s by Ulf von Euler, who thoughthey were produced by the prostate gland. Prostaglandins and relatecompounds—**prostacyclins, thromboxanes, leukotrienes,** and **lipoxins**—arknown collectively as **eicosanoids** because they are all C_{20} compound(Greek: *eikosi*, twenty). *The eicosanoids act at very low concentrations an*

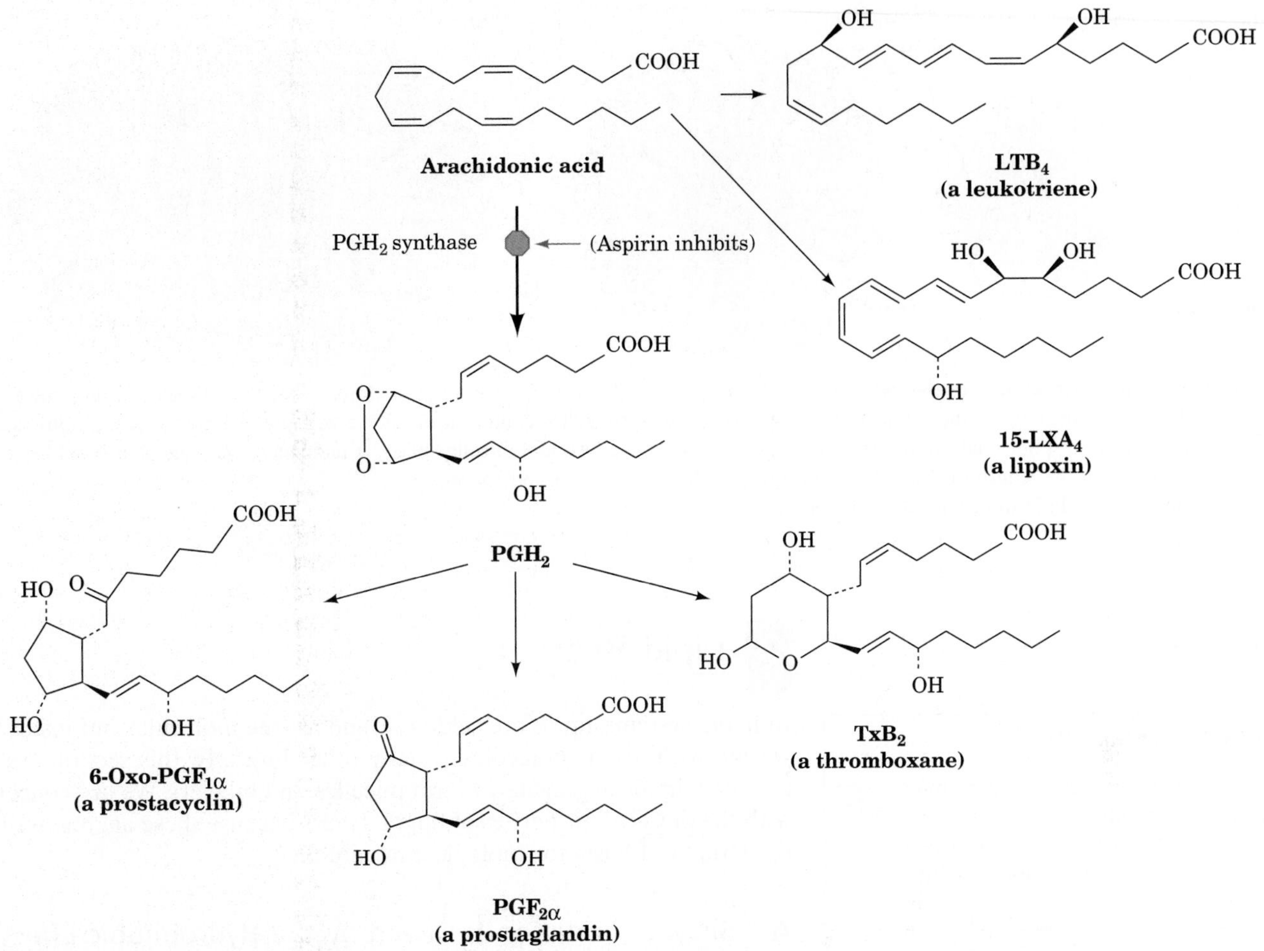

Figure 9-12 | Eicosanoids. Arachidonate is the precursor of prostaglandins (PG), prostacyclins, thromboxanes (Tx), and lipoxins (LX). Arachidonate also leads to leukotrienes. Although only a single example of each type of eicosanoid is shown, each has numerous physiologically significant derivatives, which are designated by letters and subscripts (e.g., **PGH$_2$** for **prostaglandin H$_2$**).

---

are involved in the production of pain and fever, and in the regulation of blood pressure, blood coagulation, and reproduction. Unlike most other types of hormones, eicosanoids are not transported by the bloodstream to their sites of action but tend to act locally, close to the cells that produced them. In fact, most eicosanoids decompose within seconds or minutes, which limits their effects on nearby tissues. The synthesis of the eicosanoids is discussed in Section 20-6C.

In humans, the most important eicosanoid precursor is **arachidonic acid,** a polyunsaturated fatty acid with four double bonds (Table 9-1). Arachidonate is stored in cell membranes as the C2 ester of **phosphatidylinositol** (Table 9-2) and other phospholipids. The fatty acid residue is released by the action of phospholipase A$_2$ (Fig. 9-5).

The specific products of arachidonate metabolism are tissue-dependent. For example, platelets produce thromboxanes almost exclusively, but endothelial cells (which line the walls of blood vessels) predominantly synthesize prostacyclins. Interestingly, thromboxanes stimulate vasoconstriction and platelet aggregation (which helps initiate blood clotting), while prostacyclins elicit the opposite effects. Thus, the two substances act in opposition to maintain a balance in the cardiovascular system.

■ CHECK YOUR UNDERSTANDING

How do lipids differ from the three other major classes of biological molecules?

How does unsaturation affect the physical properties of fatty acids or the membrane lipids to which they are esterified?

Compare the structures and physical properties of triacylglycerols, glycerophospholipids, and sphingolipids.

Summarize the functions of steroids and eicosanoids.

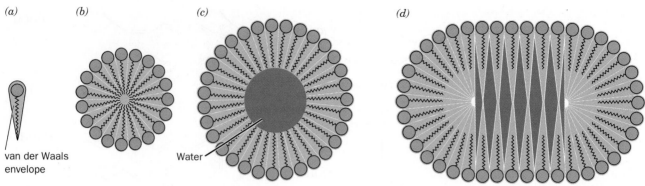

(a)   (b)   (c)   (d)

van der Waals
envelope

Water

■ **Figure 9-13 | Aggregates of single-tailed lipids.** The tapered van der Waals envelope of these lipids (*a*) permits them to pack efficiently to form a spheroidal micelle (*b*). The diameter of the micelles depends on the length of the tails. Spheroidal micelles composed of many more lipid molecules than the optimal number

(*c*) would have an unfavorable water-filled center (*blue*). Such micelles could flatten out to collapse the hollow center, but as these ellipsoidal micelles become elongated (*d*), they also develop water-filled spaces.

LEARNING OBJECTIVES

■ Understand why certain amphiphilic molecules form bilayers.
■ Understand that the bilayer is a fluid structure in which lipids rapidly diffuse laterally.

2 Lipid Bilayers

In living systems, lipids are seldom found as free molecules but instead associate with other molecules, usually other lipids. In this section, we discuss how lipids aggregate to form micelles and bilayers. We are concerned with the physical properties of lipid bilayers because these aggregates form the structural basis for biological membranes.

A | Bilayer Formation Is Driven by the Hydrophobic Effect

In aqueous solutions, amphiphilic molecules such as soaps and detergents form micelles (globular aggregates whose hydrocarbon groups are out of contact with water; Section 2-1C). This molecular arrangement eliminates unfavorable contacts between water and the hydrophobic tails of the amphiphiles and yet permits the solvation of the polar head groups.

The approximate size and shape of a micelle can be predicted from geometrical considerations. Single-tailed amphiphiles, such as soap anions, form spheroidal or ellipsoidal micelles because of their tapered shape (their hydrated head groups are wider than their tails; Fig. 9-13*a,b*). The number of molecules in such a micelle depends on the amphiphile, but for many substances it is on the order of several hundred. Too few lipid molecules would expose the hydrophobic core of the micelle to water, whereas too many would give the micelle an energetically unfavorable hollow center (Fig. 9-13*c*). Of course, a large micelle could flatten out to eliminate this hollow center, but the resulting decrease of curvature at the flattened surfaces would also generate empty spaces (Fig. 9-13*d*).

The two hydrocarbon tails of glycerophospholipids and sphingolipids give these amphiphiles a somewhat rectangular cross section (Fig. 9-14*a*). The steric requirements of packing such molecules together yields large disklike micelles (Fig. 9-14*b*) that are really extended bimolecular leaflets. These **lipid bilayers** are ~60 Å thick, as measured by electron microscopy and X-ray diffraction techniques, the value expected for more or less fully extended hydrocarbon tails.

A suspension of phospholipids (glycerophospholipids or sphingomyelins) can form **liposomes**—closed, self-sealing solvent-filled

(a)   (b)

■ **Figure 9-14 | Bilayer formation by phospholipids.** The cylindrical van der Waals envelope of these lipids (*a*) causes them to form extended disklike micelles (*b*) that are better described as lipid bilayers.

Figure 9-15 | **Electron micrograph of a liposome.** Its wall, as the
accompanying diagram indicates, consists of a lipid bilayer. [Courtesy of Walther
Stoeckenius, University of California at San Francisco.]

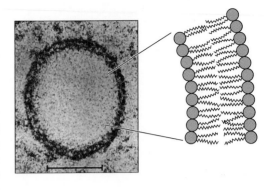

vesicles that are bounded by only a single bilayer (Fig. 9-15). They typically have diameters of several hundred angstroms and, in a given
preparation, are rather uniform in size. Once formed, liposomes are quite
stable and can be purified by dialysis, gel filtration chromatography, or
centrifugation. Liposomes whose internal environment differs from the
surrounding solution can therefore be readily prepared. Liposomes serve
as models of biological membranes and also hold promise as vehicles for
drug delivery since they are absorbed by many cells through fusion with
the plasma membrane.

| Lipid Bilayers Have Fluidlike Properties

*The transfer of a lipid molecule across a bilayer (Fig. 9-16a), a process
termed* **transverse diffusion** *or a* **flip-flop,** *is an extremely rare event.* This
is because a flip-flop requires the hydrated, polar head group of the lipid
to pass through the anhydrous hydrocarbon core of the bilayer. The flip-
flop rates of phospholipids have half-times of several days or more. In contrast to their low flip-flop rates, *lipids are highly mobile in the plane of the
bilayer* (**lateral diffusion;** Fig. 9-16b). It has been estimated that lipids in a
membrane can diffuse the 1-μm length of a bacterial cell in ~1 s. Because
of the mobilities of the lipids, the lipid bilayer can be considered to be a
two-dimensional fluid.

The interior of the lipid bilayer is in constant motion due to rotations
around the C—C bonds of the lipid tails. Various physical measurements
suggest that the interior of the bilayer has the viscosity of light machine
oil. This feature of the bilayer core is evident in **molecular dynamics simulations,** in which the time-dependent positions of atoms are predicted
from calculations of the forces acting on them (Fig. 9-17). The viscosity of
the bilayer increases dramatically closer to the lipid head groups, whose
rotation is limited and whose lateral mobility is more constrained by interactions between other polar or charged head groups.

(a) Transverse diffusion (flip-flop)

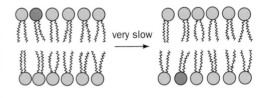

(b) Lateral diffusion

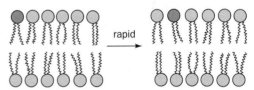

■ **Figure 9-16** | **Phospholipid diffusion in a
lipid bilayer.** (*a*) Transverse diffusion (a flip-
flop) is defined as the transfer of a phospholipid
molecule from one bilayer leaflet to the other.
(*b*) Lateral diffusion is defined as the pairwise
exchange of neighboring phospholipid molecules
in the same bilayer leaflet.

■ **Figure 9-17** | **Model (snapshot) of a
lipid bilayer at an instant in time.** The
conformations of dipalmitoyl phosphatidylcholine
molecules in a bilayer surrounded by water were
modeled by computer. Atom colors are chain and
glycerol C gray except terminal methyl C yellow,
ester O red, phosphate P and O green, and
choline C and N magenta. Water molecules are
represented by translucent blue spheres (those
near the bilayer appear dark because they overlap
head group atoms). [Courtesy of Richard Pastor
and Richard Venable, NIH, Bethesda, Maryland.]

Note that the hydrophobic tails of the lipids shown in Fig. 9-17 are no stiffly regimented as Fig. 9-16 might suggest, but instead bend and interdig itate. A typical biological membrane includes many different lipid mole cules, some of whose tails are of different lengths or are kinked due to th presence of double bonds. Under physiological conditions, highly mobil chains fill any gaps that might form between lipids in the bilayer interior

The model bilayer shown in Fig. 9-17 indicates that the phospholipic bob up and down to some degree. This is also the case in naturally occur ring membranes, which contain a variety of different lipid head groups tha must nestle among each other. The polar nature of the outer surface c the bilayer extends from the head groups to the carbonyl groups of th ester and amide bonds that link the fatty acyl chains. Consequently, wate molecules penetrate a lipid bilayer to a depth of up to 15 Å, avoiding onl the central ~30 Å hydrocarbon core.

The Fluidity of a Lipid Bilayer Is Temperature-Dependent. *As a lipi bilayer cools below a characteristic* **transition temperature,** *it undergoes sort of phase change in which it becomes a gel-like solid; that is, it loses it fluidity* (Fig. 9-18). Above the transition temperature, the highly mobil lipids are in a state known as a **liquid crystal** because they are ordered i some directions but not in others. The bilayer is thicker in the gel stat than in the liquid crystal state due to the stiffening of the hydrocarbo tails at lower temperatures.

The transition temperature of a bilayer increases with the chain lengt and the degree of saturation of its component fatty acid residues for th same reasons that the melting points of fatty acids increase with these quan tities. The transition temperatures of most biological membranes are in th range 10 to 40°C. Bacteria and cold-blooded animals such as fish modif (through lipid synthesis and degradation) the fatty acid compositions c their membrane lipids with ambient temperature so as to maintain a con stant level of fluidity. Thus, the fluidity of biological membranes is one o their important physiological attributes.

Cholesterol, which by itself does not form a bilayer, decreases membran fluidity because its rigid steroid ring system interferes with the motions o

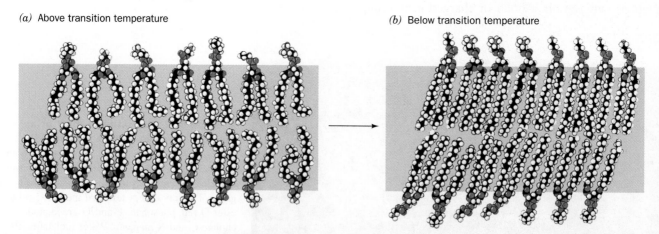

(a) Above transition temperature   *(b)* Below transition temperature

■ **Figure 9-18** | **Phase transition in a lipid bilayer.** (*a*) Above the transition temperature, both the lipid molecules as a whole and their nonpolar tails are highly mobile in the plane of the bilayer. (*b*) Below the transition temperature, the lipid molecules form a much more orderly array to yield a gel-like solid. [After Robertson R.N., *The Lively Membranes,* pp. 69–70, Cambridge University Press (1983).]

he fatty acid side chains in other membrane lipids. It also broadens the temperature range of the phase transition. This is because cholesterol inhibits the ordering of fatty acid side chains by fitting in between them. Thus, cholesterol functions as a kind of membrane plasticizer.

3 Membrane Proteins

Biological membranes contain proteins as well as lipids. The exact lipid and protein components and the ratio of protein to lipid varies with the identity of the membrane. For example, the lipid-rich myelinated membranes that surround and insulate certain nerve axons (Fig. 9-8) have a protein-to-lipid ratio of 0.23, whereas the protein-rich inner membrane of mitochondria, which mediates numerous chemical reactions, has a protein-to-lipid ratio of 3.2. Eukaryotic plasma membranes are typically ~50% protein.

Membrane proteins catalyze chemical reactions, mediate the flow of nutrients and wastes across the membrane, and participate in relaying information about the extracellular environment to various intracellular components. Such proteins carry out their functions in association with the lipid bilayer. They must therefore interact to some degree with the hydrophobic core and/or the polar surface of the bilayer. In this section, we examine the structures of some membrane proteins, which are classified by their mode of interaction with the membrane.

A | Integral Membrane Proteins Interact with Hydrophobic Lipids

Integral or **intrinsic proteins** (Fig. 9-19) associate tightly with membranes through hydrophobic effects and can be separated from membranes only by treatment with agents that disrupt membranes. For example, detergents such as sodium dodecyl sulfate (Section 5-2D) solubilize membrane proteins by replacing the membrane lipids that normally surround the protein. The hydrophobic portions of the detergent molecules coat the hydrophobic regions of the protein, and the polar head groups render the detergent–protein complex soluble in water. Chaotropic agents such as guanidinium ion and urea (Section 6-4B) disrupt water structure, thereby reducing the hydrophobic effect, the primary force stabilizing the association of the protein with the membrane. Some integral proteins bind lipids so tenaciously that they can be freed from them only under denaturing conditions.

■ **Figure 9-19 | Structure of the integral membrane protein aquaporin-0 (AQP0) in association with lipids.** The protein is represented by its surface diagram, which is colored according to charge (red negative, blue positive, and white uncharged). Tightly bound molecules of dimyristoylphosphatidylcholine are drawn in space-filling form with O red, P orange, and C gray. Note how the lipid tails closely conform to the nonpolar surface of the protein, thereby solvating it. The arrangement of the two rows of lipid molecules, with phosphate–phosphate distances of ~35 Å, matches the dimensions of a lipid bilayer. [Courtesy of Anthony Lee, University of Southampton, Southampton, U.K. Based on an electron crystallography structure by Stephen Harrison and Thomas Walz, Harvard Medical School.]

■ **CHECK YOUR UNDERSTANDING**

Why do glycerophospholipids—but not fatty acids—form bilayers?
Explain why lateral diffusion of membrane lipids is faster than transverse diffusion.
What factors influence the fluidity of a bilayer?

LEARNING OBJECTIVES

■ Understand that integral membrane proteins contain a transmembrane structure consisting of α helices or a β barrel with a hydrophobic surface.
■ Understand that lipid-linked proteins have a covalently attached prenyl group, fatty acyl group, or glycosylphosphatidylinositol group.
■ Understand that peripheral membrane proteins interact with proteins or lipids at the membrane surface.

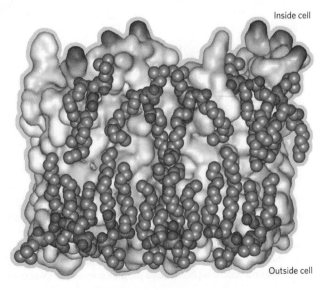

Inside cell

Outside cell

Once they have been solubilized, integral proteins can be purified by many of the protein fractionation methods described in Section 5-2. Since these proteins tend to aggregate and precipitate in aqueous solution, their solubility frequently requires the presence of detergents or water-miscible organic solvents such as butanol or glycerol.

Integral Proteins Are Asymmetrically Oriented Amphiphiles. *Integral proteins are amphiphiles; the protein segments immersed in a membrane's nonpolar interior have predominantly hydrophobic surface residues, whereas those portions that extend into the aqueous environment are by and large sheathed with polar residues.* This was first demonstrated through **surface labeling,** a technique employing agents that react with proteins but cannot penetrate membranes. For example, the extracellular domain of an integral protein binds antibodies elicited against it, but its cytoplasmic domain will do so only if the membrane has been ruptured. Membrane-impermeable protein-specific reagents that are fluorescent or radioactively labeled can be similarly employed. Alternatively, proteases, which digest only the solvent-exposed portions of an integral protein, may be used to identify the membrane-immersed portions of the protein. These techniques revealed, for example, that the erythrocyte membrane protein **glycophorin A** has three domains (Fig. 9-20): (1) a 72-residue externally

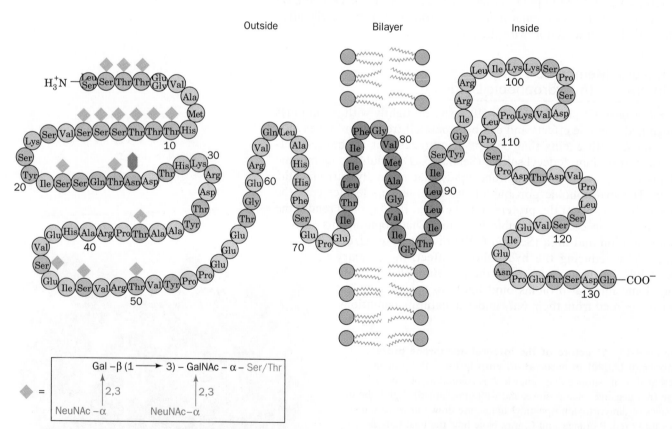

■ **Figure 9-20 | Human erythrocyte glycophorin A.** The protein bears 15 *O*-linked oligosaccharides (*green diamonds*) and one that is *N*-linked (*dark green hexagon*) on its extracellular domain. The predominant sequence of the *O*-linked oligosaccharides is also shown (NeuNAc = *N*-acetylneuraminic acid). The protein's transmembrane portion (*brown and purple*) consists of 19 sequential predominantly hydrophobic residues. Its C-terminal portion, which is located on the membrane's cytoplasmic face, is rich in anionic (*pink*) and cationic (*blue*) residues. There are two common genetic variants of glycophorin A: Glycophorin A^M has Ser and Gly at positions 1 and 5, whereas glycophorin A^N has Leu and Glu at these positions. [After Marchesi, V.T., *Semin. Hematol.* **16,** 8 (1979).]

located N-terminal domain that bears 16 carbohydrate chains; (2) a 19-residue sequence, consisting almost entirely of hydrophobic residues, that spans the erythrocyte cell membrane; and (3) a 40-residue cytoplasmic C-terminal domain that has a high proportion of charged and polar residues. Thus, glycophorin A is a **transmembrane (TM) protein;** that is, it completely spans the membrane.

Studies of a variety of biological membranes have established that *biological membranes are asymmetric in that a particular membrane protein is invariably located on only one particular face of a membrane, or in the case of a transmembrane protein, oriented in only one direction with respect to the membrane.* However, no protein is known to be completely buried in a membrane; that is, all membrane-associated proteins are at least partially exposed to the aqueous environment.

Transmembrane Proteins May Contain α Helices. In order for a polypeptide chain to penetrate or span the lipid bilayer, it must have hydrophobic side chains that contact the lipid tails and it must shield its polar backbone groups. This second requirement is met by the formation of secondary structure that satisfies the hydrogen-bonding capabilities of the polypeptide backbone. Consequently, all known TM segments of integral membrane proteins consist of either α helices or β sheets. For example, glycophorin A's 19-residue TM sequence almost certainly forms an α helix. The existence of such a TM helix can be predicted by comparing the free energy change in transferring α-helical polypeptide segments from the nonpolar interior of a membrane to water (Fig. 9-21). Alternatively, a potential TM sequence can be identified by reference to hydropathy indices such as those in Table 6-3. Methods for predicting the position of a TM α helix are useful because the difficulty in crystallizing integral membrane proteins has permitted relatively few of their X-ray structures to be determined.

Nigel Unwin and Richard Henderson used **electron crystallography** (Box 9-2) to determine the structure of the integral membrane protein **bacteriorhodopsin.** This 247-residue homotrimeric protein, which is produced by the halophilic (salt-loving) archaebacterium *Halobacterium salinarum* (it grows best in 4.3 M NaCl), is a light-driven proton pump: It generates a proton concentration gradient across the cell membrane that powers ATP synthesis by a mechanism discussed in Section 18-3B. A covalently bound retinal (Section 9-1F) is the protein's light-absorbing group. Bacteriorhodopsin consists largely of a bundle of seven ~25-residue α-helical rods that span the lipid bilayer in directions almost perpendicular to the bilayer plane (Fig. 9-22). As expected, the amino acid side chains that contact the lipid tails are highly hydrophobic. Successive membrane-spanning helices are connected in head-to-tail fashion by hydrophilic loops of varying size. This arrangement places the protein's charged residues near the surfaces of the membrane in contact with the aqueous environment.

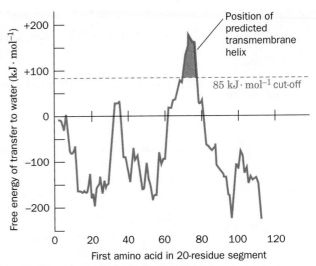

■ **Figure 9-21 | Identification of glycophorin A's transmembrane domain.** The calculated free energy change in transferring 20-residue-long α-helical segments from the interior of a membrane to water is plotted against the position of the segment's first residue. Peaks higher than +85 kJ · mol⁻¹ indicate a transmembrane helix. [After Engelman, D.M., Steitz, T.A., and Goldman, A., *Annu. Rev. Biophys. Biophys. Chem.* **15,** 343 (1986).]

■ **Figure 9-22 | The structure of bacteriorhodopsin.** The protein is shown in ribbon form as viewed from within the membrane plane and colored in rainbow order from its N-terminus (*blue*) to its C-terminus (*red*). Its covalently bound retinal is drawn in stick form (*magenta*). [Based on an X-ray structure by Nikolaus Grigorieff and Richard Henderson, MRC Laboratory of Molecular Biology, Cambridge, U.K. PDBid 2BRD.] 🔗 **See Kinemage Exercise 8-1.**

BOX 9-2 **PATHWAYS OF DISCOVERY**

Richard Henderson and the Structure of Bacteriorhodopsin

Richard Henderson (1945–)

Richard Henderson, like a number of other pioneering structural biologists, began his career as a physicist. He turned his attention to membrane proteins because of their importance in cellular metabolic, transport, and signaling phenomena. Unlike globular proteins, which are soluble in aqueous solution from which they can often be crystallized, integral membrane proteins aggregate in aqueous solution and hence can only be kept in solution by the presence of a suitable detergent. In spite of this, such solubilized proteins rarely crystallize in a manner suitable for X-ray analysis (and none had been made to do so at the time that Henderson began his studies). To circumvent this obstacle, Henderson adapted the technique of electron crystallography to macromolecules, using the membrane protein bacteriorhodopsin as his subject.

Bacteriorhodopsin was discovered in 1967, and its function as a proton pump was described shortly thereafter. The protein is synthesized by halophilic archaebacteria such as *H. salinarum* (formerly known as *H. halobium*). In addition to bacteriorhodopsin, the archaeal rhodopsin family includes chloride-pumping and sensory proteins. Similar proteins have also been identified in eubacteria and in unicellular eukaryotes. What made bacteriorhodopsin attractive as a research subject is its relatively small size (248 residues), its stability, and—most importantly—its unusual proclivity to form ordered two-dimensional arrays in the bacterial cell membrane. In *H. salinarum,* such arrays, which occur as 0.5-μm-wide patches, are known as purple membranes due to the color of the protein's bound retinal molecule. Each purple membrane patch, which is essentially a two-dimensional crystal, consists of 75% bacteriorhodopsin and 25% lipid.

At the time that Henderson began his structural studies of bacteriorhodopsin, the X-ray structures of only around a dozen different globular proteins had been reported. Henderson, working with Nigel Unwin, adapted the principles of X-ray crystallography to the two-dimensional bacteriorhodopsin crystals by measuring the diffraction intensities generated by the electron beam from an electron microscope impinging on a purple membrane patch (as explained by the wave–particle duality, electrons, like all particles, have wavelike properties with a wavelength, $\lambda = h/mv$, where h is Planck's constant, m is the particle mass, and v is its velocity). It was necessary to use an electron beam rather than X-rays because the electron microscope can focus its electron beam on the microscopically small purple membrane patches. Nevertheless, only very low electron beam intensities could be used because other-

wise the resulting radiation damage would destroy the purple membrane. Consequently, to obtain diffraction data of sufficiently high signal-to-noise ratio, the diffraction patterns of around one hundred or more purple membrane samples had to be averaged.

Working at the limits of the available technology, Henderson and Unwin, in 1975, published a low-resolution model for the structure of bacteriorhodopsin. This was the first glimpse of an integral membrane protein. Its seven transmembrane helices were clearly visible as columns of electron density that were approximately perpendicular to the plane of the membrane. However, to obtain three-dimensional diffraction data, a two-dimensional crystal must be systematically tilted relative to the electron beam. Mechanical limitations that prevented the sample from being tilted to the degree necessary to obtain a full three-dimensional data set as well as other technical difficulties therefore yielded a model that had a resolution of 7 Å in the plane of the membrane, but only 14 Å in a perpendicular direction. Consequently, the polypeptide loops connecting the seven helices could not be discerned, nor were the protein's associated retinal molecule or any of its side chains visible. However, over the next 15 years, developments in electron microscopy, such as the use of better electron sources and liquid-helium temperatures to minimize radiation damage to the sample, permitted Henderson to extend the resolution of the bacteriorhodopsin structure to 3.5 Å in the plane of the membrane and 10 Å in the perpendicular direction. The resulting electron density map clearly revealed the positions of several bulky aromatic residues and the bound retinal and permitted the loops connecting the transmembrane helices to be visualized. Thus, electron crystallography has become a useful tool for determining the structures of a variety of proteins that can be induced to form two-dimensional arrays as well as those that form very thin three-dimensional crystals.

Henderson's groundbreaking work on bacteriorhodopsin made a seminal contribution to the growing body of biochemical, genetic, spectroscopic, and structural studies of bacteriorhodopsin. This information, together with more recent high-resolution X-ray structures derived from three-dimensional crystals of bacteriorhodopsin, obtained by crystallizing the protein in a lipid matrix, have led to a detailed understanding of the mechanism of the light-induced structural changes through which bacteriorhodopsin pumps protons out of the bacterial cell.

Henderson, R. and Unwin, P.N., Three-dimensional model of purple membrane obtained by electron microscopy, *Nature* **257**, 28–32 (1975).

Henderson, R., Baldwin, J.M., Ceska, T.A., Zemlin, F., Beckmann, E., and Downing, K.H., Model for the structure of bacteriorhodopsin based on high resolution electron cryo-microscopy, *J. Mol. Biol.* **213**, 899–929 (1990).

Hydrophobic effects, as we saw in Section 6-4A, are the dominant forces stabilizing the three-dimensional structures of water-soluble globular proteins. However, since the TM regions of integral membrane proteins are nmersed in nonpolar environments, what stabilizes their structures? Analysis of integral protein structures indicates that their interior residues have hydrophobicities comparable to those of water-soluble proteins. However, the membrane-exposed residues of these proteins, on average, are even more hydrophobic than their interior residues. Thus, *the difference between integral proteins and water-soluble proteins is only skin-deep: their interiors are similar, but their surface polarities are consistent with the polarities of their environments.*

Some Transmembrane Proteins Contain β Barrels. A protein segment immersed in the nonpolar interior of a membrane must fold so that it satisfies the hydrogen-bonding potential of its polypeptide backbone. An α helix can do so as can an antiparallel β sheet that rolls up to form a barrel (a β barrel; Section 6-2C). Transmembrane β barrels of known structure consist of 8 to 22 strands. The number of strands must be even to permit the β sheet to close up on itself with all strands antiparallel.

β Barrels occur in **porins,** which are channel-forming proteins in the outer membrane of gram-negative bacteria (Section 8-3B). The outer membrane protects the bacteria from hostile environments while the porins permit the entry of small polar solutes such as nutrients. Porins also occur in eukaryotes in the outer membranes of mitochondria and chloroplasts (consistent with the descent of these organelles from free-living gram-negative bacteria; Section 1-2C).

Bacterial porins are monomers or trimers of identical 30- to 50-kD subunits. X-Ray structural studies show that most porin subunits consist largely of at least a 16-stranded antiparallel β barrel that forms a solvent-accessible central channel with a length of ~55 Å and a minimum diameter of ~7 Å (Fig. 9-23). As expected, the side chains of the protein's membrane-exposed surface are nonpolar, thereby forming a ~27-Å-high hydrophobic band encircling the trimer (Fig. 9-23c). This band is flanked by more polar aromatic side chains (Table 6-3) that form interfaces with the head groups of the lipid bilayer (Fig. 9-23c). In contrast, the side chains at the solvent-exposed surface of the protein, including those lining the walls of the aqueous channel, are polar. Possible mechanisms for the solute selectivity of porins are discussed in Section 10-2B.

B | Lipid-Linked Proteins Are Anchored to the Bilayer

Some membrane-associated proteins contain covalently attached lipids that anchor the protein to the membrane. The lipid group, like any modifying group, may also mediate protein–protein interactions or modify the structure and activity of the protein to which it is attached. **Lipid-linked**

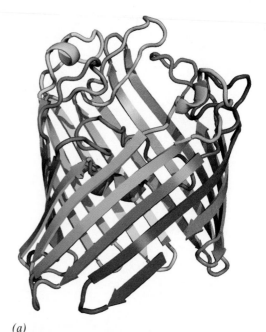

(a)

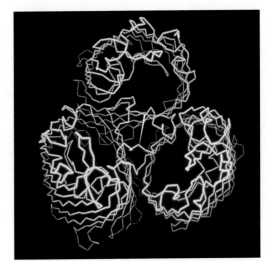

(b)

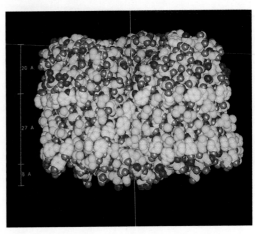

(c)

◀ **Figure 9-23 | X-Ray structure of the *E. coli* OmpF porin.** (*a*) A ribbon diagram of the 16-stranded monomer colored in rainbow order from its N-terminus (*blue*) to its C-terminus (*red*). (*b*) The C$_\alpha$ backbone of the trimer viewed ~30° from its threefold axis of symmetry, showing the pore through each subunit. (*c*) A space-filling model of the trimer viewed perpendicular to its threefold axis (*vertical green line*). N atoms are blue, O atoms are red, and C atoms are yellow, except those in the side chains of aromatic residues, which are white. The aromatic groups appear to delimit an ~27-Å-high hydrophobic band (*scale at left*) that is immersed in the nonpolar portion of the bacterial outer membrane (with the cell's exterior at the tops of Parts *a* and *c*). [Part *a* based on an X-ray structure by and Parts *b* and *c* courtesy of Tilman Schirmer and Johan Jansonius, University of Basel, Switzerland. PDBid 1OPF.] 🞊 **See Kinemage Exercise 8-3.**

proteins come in three varieties: prenylated proteins, fatty acylated proteins, and glycosylphosphatidylinositol-linked proteins. A single protein may contain more than one covalently linked lipid group.

Prenylated proteins have covalently attached lipids that are built from isoprene units (Section 9-1F). The most common isoprenoid groups are the C_{15} **farnesyl** and C_{20} **geranylgeranyl** residues:

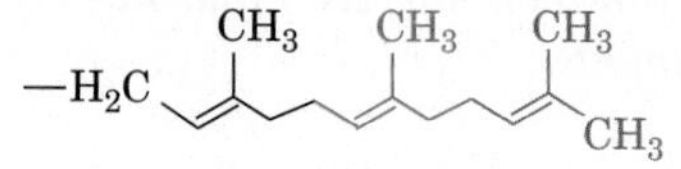

Farnesyl residue

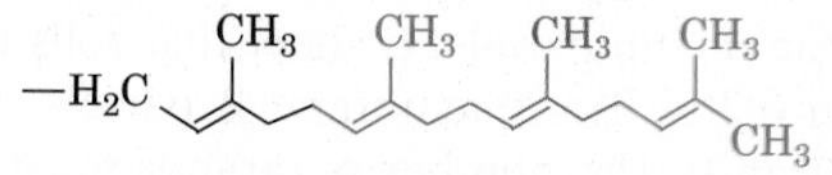

Geranylgeranyl residue

The most common prenylation site in proteins is the C-terminal tetrapeptide C-X-X-Y, where C is Cys and X is often an aliphatic amino acid residue. Residue Y influences the type of prenylation: Proteins are farnesylated when Y is Ala, Met, or Ser and geranylgeranylated when Y is Leu. In both cases, the prenyl group is enzymatically linked to the Cys sulfur atom via a thioether linkage. The X-X-Y tripeptide is then proteolytically excised, and the newly exposed terminal carboxyl group is esterified with a methyl group, producing a C-terminus with the structure

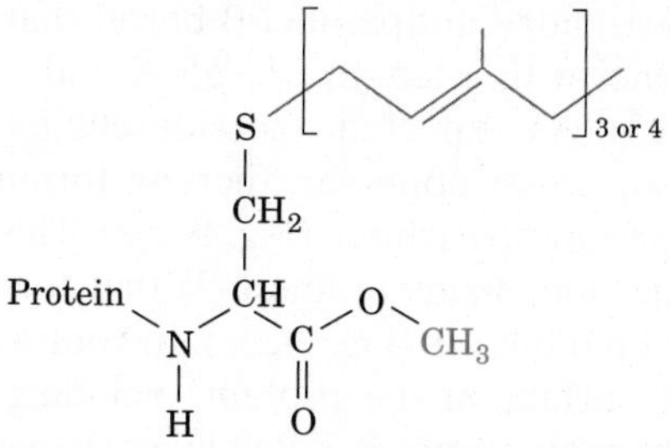

Two kinds of fatty acids, myristic acid and palmitic acid, are linked to membrane proteins. Myristic acid, a biologically rare saturated C_{14} fatty acid, is appended to a protein via an amide linkage to the α-amino group of an N-terminal Gly residue. **Myristoylation** is stable: The fatty acyl group remains attached to the protein throughout its lifetime. Myristoylated proteins are located in a number of subcellular compartments, including the cytosol, endoplasmic reticulum, plasma membrane, and the nucleus.

In **palmitoylation,** the saturated C_{16} fatty acid palmitic acid is joined in thioester linkage to a specific Cys residue. Palmitoylated proteins occur almost exclusively on the cytoplasmic face of the plasma membrane, where many participate in transmembrane signaling. The palmitoyl group can be removed by the action of **palmitoyl thioesterases,** suggesting that reversible palmitoylation may regulate the association of the protein with the membrane and thereby modulate the signaling processes.

Glycosylphosphatidylinositol-linked proteins (GPI-linked proteins) occur in all eukaryotes but are particularly abundant in some parasitic protozoa which contain relatively few membrane proteins anchored by transmembrane polypeptide segments. Like glycoproteins and glycolipids, GPI-linked proteins are located only on the exterior surface of the plasma membrane.

The core structure of the GPI group consists of phosphatidylinositol (Table 9-2) glycosidically linked to a linear tetrasaccharide composed of

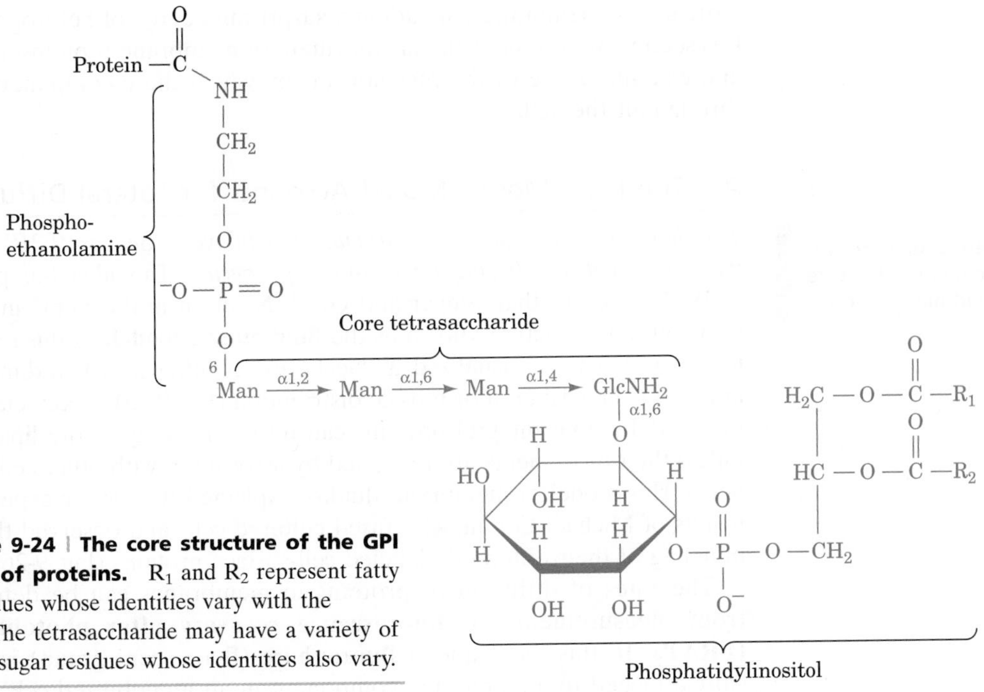

Figure 9-24 | The core structure of the GPI anchors of proteins. R_1 and R_2 represent fatty acid residues whose identities vary with the protein. The tetrasaccharide may have a variety of attached sugar residues whose identities also vary.

three mannose residues and one glucosaminyl residue (Fig. 9-24). The mannose at the nonreducing end of this assembly forms a phosphodiester bond with a phosphoethanolamine residue that is amide-linked to the protein's C-terminal carboxyl group. The core tetrasaccharide is generally substituted with a variety of sugar residues that vary with the identity of the protein. There is likewise considerable diversity in the fatty acid residues of the phosphatidylinositol group.

C | Peripheral Proteins Associate Loosely with Membranes

Peripheral or **extrinsic proteins,** unlike integral membrane proteins or lipid-linked proteins, can be dissociated from membranes by relatively mild procedures that leave the membrane intact, such as exposure to high ionic strength salt solutions or pH changes. Peripheral proteins do not bind lipid and, once purified, behave like water-soluble proteins. They associate with membranes by binding at their surfaces, most likely to certain lipids or integral proteins, through electrostatic and hydrogen-bonding interactions. Cytochrome *c* (Sections 5-4A, 6-2D, and 18-2E) is a peripheral membrane protein that is associated with the outer surface of the inner mitochondrial membrane. At physiological pH, cytochrome *c* is cationic and can interact with negatively charged phospholipids such as phosphatidylserine and phosphatidylglycerol.

4 Membrane Structure and Assembly

Membranes were once thought to consist of a phospholipid bilayer sandwiched between two layers of unfolded polypeptide. This sandwich model, which is improbable on thermodynamic grounds, was further discredited by electron microscopic visualization of membranes and other experimental approaches. More recent studies have revealed insights into the fine

■ CHECK YOUR UNDERSTANDING

Explain the differences between integral and peripheral membrane proteins.

What are the two types of secondary structures that occur in transmembrane proteins?

Describe the covalent modifications of lipid-linked proteins.

LEARNING OBJECTIVES

■ Understand how the arrangement and interactions of membrane lipids and proteins are described by the fluid mosaic model.

■ Understand that the membrane skeleton gives the cell shape yet is flexible.

■ Understand that lipids are not distributed uniformly throughout a membrane.

■ Understand how the secretory pathway describes the transmembrane passage of membrane and secreted proteins.

■ Understand that different types of coated vesicles transport proteins between cellular compartments.

■ Understand the role of SNAREs in vesicle fusion.

structure of membranes, including a surprising degree of heterogeneity. In this section, we consider the arrangement of membrane proteins and lipids and examine some of the mechanisms by which these components move throughout the cell.

A | The Fluid Mosaic Model Accounts for Lateral Diffusion

See Guided Exploration 9
Membrane structure and the fluid mosaic model.

The demonstrated fluidity of artificial lipid bilayers (Section 9-2B) suggests that biological membranes have similar properties. This idea was proposed in 1972 by S. Jonathan Singer and Garth Nicolson in their unifying theory of membrane structure known as the **fluid mosaic model.** In this model, integral proteins are visualized as "icebergs" floating in a two-dimensional lipid "sea" in a random or mosaic distribution (Fig. 9-25). A key element of the model is that integral proteins can diffuse laterally in the lipid matrix unless their movements are restricted by association with other cell components. This model of membrane fluidity explained the earlier experimental results of Michael Edidin, who fused cultured cells and observed the intermingling of their differently labeled cell-surface proteins (Fig. 9-26).

The rates of diffusion of proteins in membranes can be determined from measurements of **fluorescence recovery after photobleaching (FRAP).** In this technique, a **fluorophore** (fluorescent group) is specifically attached to a membrane component in an immobilized cell or in an artificial membrane system. An intense laser pulse focused on a very small area ($\sim$3 μm^2) destroys (bleaches) the fluorophore there (Fig. 9-27). The rate at which the bleached area recovers its fluorescence, as monitored by fluorescence microscopy, indicates the rate at which unbleached and bleached fluorophore-labeled molecules laterally diffuse into and out of the bleached area.

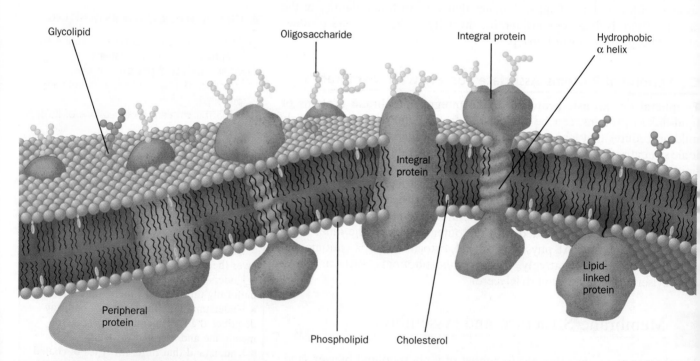

Glycolipid — Oligosaccharide — Integral protein — Hydrophobic α helix

Integral protein

Peripheral protein — Phospholipid — Cholesterol — Lipid-linked protein

■ **Figure 9-25 | Diagram of a plasma membrane.** Integral proteins (*orange*) are embedded in a bilayer composed of phospholipids (*blue head groups attached to wiggly tails*) and cholesterol (*yellow*). The carbohydrate components (*green and yellow beads*) of glycoproteins and glycolipids occur on only the external face of the membrane. Most membranes contain a higher proportion of protein than is depicted here.

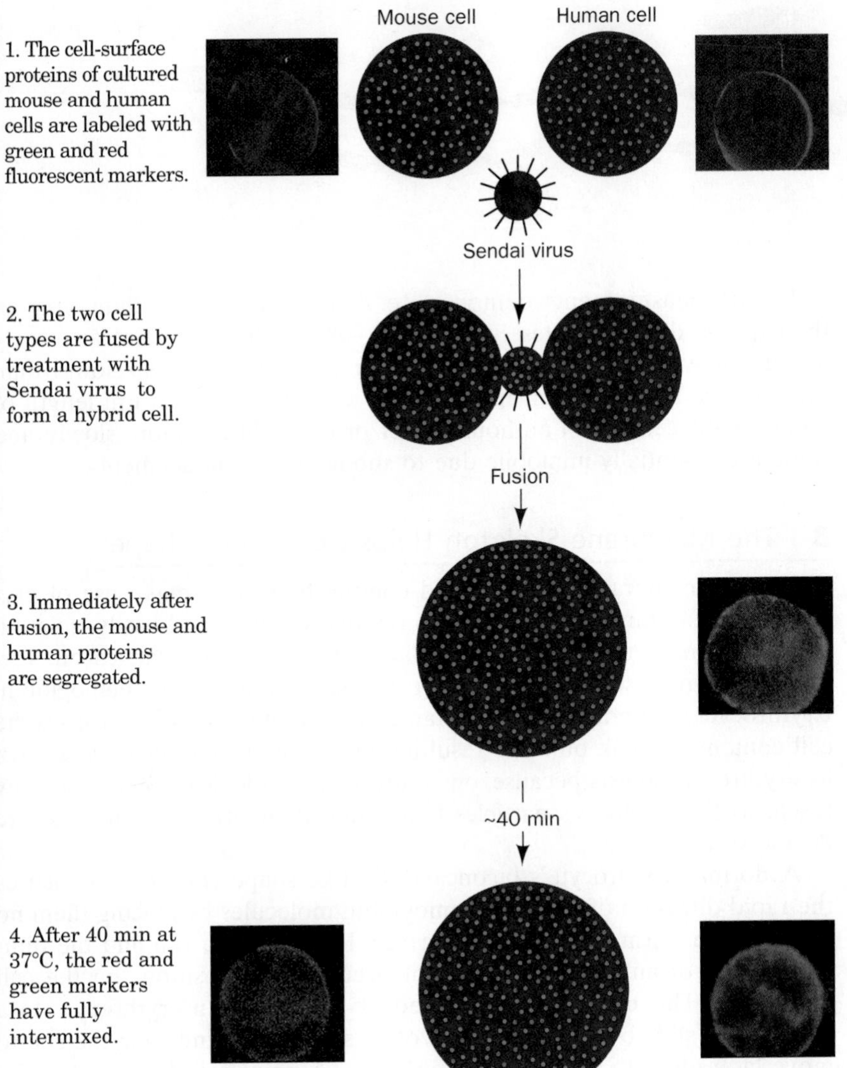

1. The cell-surface proteins of cultured mouse and human cells are labeled with green and red fluorescent markers.

Mouse cell   Human cell

Sendai virus

■ **Figure 9-26** | **Fusion of mouse and human cells.** The accompanying photomicrographs (in square boxes) were taken through filters that allowed only red or green light to reach the camera. [Immunofluorescence photomicrographs courtesy of Michael Edidin, The Johns Hopkins University.]

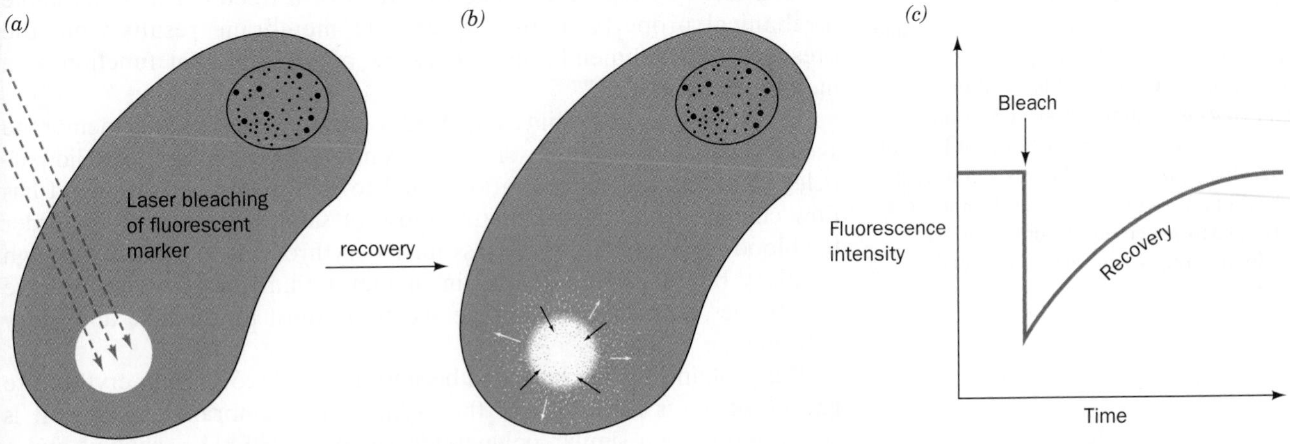

2. The two cell types are fused by treatment with Sendai virus to form a hybrid cell.

Fusion

3. Immediately after fusion, the mouse and human proteins are segregated.

~40 min

4. After 40 min at 37°C, the red and green markers have fully intermixed.

(a)

Laser bleaching of fluorescent marker

recovery

(b)

(c)

Bleach

Fluorescence intensity

Recovery

Time

■ **Figure 9-27** | **The fluorescence recovery after photobleaching (FRAP) technique.** (*a*) An intense laser light pulse bleaches the fluorescent markers (*green*) from a small region of an immobilized cell that has a fluorophore-labeled membrane component. (*b*) The fluorescence of the bleached area recovers as the bleached molecules laterally diffuse out of it and intact fluorescent molecules diffuse into it. (*c*) The fluorescence recovery rate depends on the diffusion rate of the labeled molecule.

(a)

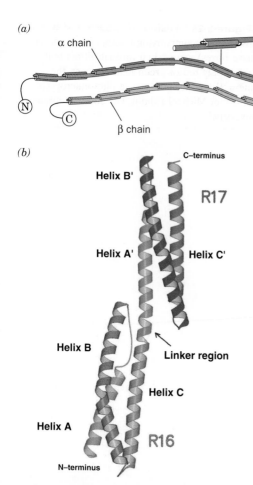

(b)

Figure 9-28 | Structure of spectrin.
(a) Structure of an αβ dimer. Both of these antiparallel polypeptides contain multiple 106-residue repeats, which are thought to form flexibly connected triple-helical bundles. Two of these heterodimers join, head to head, to form an (αβ)₂ heterotetramer. [After Speicher, D.W. and Marchesi, V. *Nature* **311**, 177 (1984).] (b) The X-ray structure of two consecutive repeats of chicken brain α-spectrin. Each of these 106-residue repeats consists of an up–down–up triple-helical bundle in which the C-terminal helix of the first repeat (*red*) is continuous, via a 5-residue helical linker (*green*), with the N-terminal helix of the second repeat (*blue*). The helices within each triple-helical bundle wrap around each other in a gentle left-handed supercoil. [Courtesy of Alfonso Mondragón, Northwestern University. PDBid 1CUN.]

FRAP measurements demonstrate that membrane proteins vary in their lateral diffusion rates. Some 30 to 90% of these proteins are freely mobile; they diffuse at rates only an order of magnitude or so slower than those of the much smaller lipids, so they can diffuse the 20-μm length of a eukaryotic cell within an hour. Other proteins diffuse more slowly, and some are essentially immobile due to submembrane attachments.

B | The Membrane Skeleton Helps Define Cell Shape

Studies of membrane structure and composition often make use of erythrocyte membranes, since these are relatively simple and easily isolated. A mature mammalian erythrocyte lacks organelles and carries out few metabolic processes; it is essentially a membranous bag of hemoglobin. Erythrocyte membranes can be obtained by osmotic lysis, which causes the cell contents to leak out. The resulting membranous particles are known as erythrocyte **ghosts** because, on return to physiological conditions, they reseal to form colorless particles that retain their original shape but are devoid of cytoplasm.

A normal erythrocyte's biconcave disklike shape (Fig. 7-17a) ensures the rapid diffusion of O₂ to its hemoglobin molecules by placing them no further than 1 μm from the cell surface. However, the rim and the dimple regions of an erythrocyte do not occupy fixed positions on the cell membrane. This can be demonstrated by anchoring an erythrocyte to a microscope slide by a small portion of its surface and inducing the cell to move laterally with a gentle flow of buffer. A point originally on the rim of the erythrocyte will move across the dimple to the rim on the opposite side of the cell. Evidently, the membrane rolls across the cell while maintaining its shape, much like the tread of a tractor. This remarkable mechanical property of the erythrocyte membrane results from the presence of a submembranous network of proteins that function as a membrane "skeleton."

The fluidity and flexibility imparted to an erythrocyte by its membrane skeleton have important physiological consequences. A slurry of solid particles of a size and concentration equal to that of red cells in blood has flow characteristics approximating those of sand. Consequently, in order for blood to flow at all, much less for its erythrocytes to squeeze through capillary blood vessels smaller in diameter than they are, erythrocyte membranes, with their membrane skeletons, must be fluidlike and easily deformable.

The protein **spectrin,** so called because it was discovered in erythrocyte ghosts, accounts for ~75% of the erythrocyte membrane skeleton. It is composed of two similar polypeptide chains, a 280-kD α subunit and a 246-kD β subunit, which each consist of repeating 106-residue segments that fold into triple-stranded α-helical coiled coils (Fig. 9-28). These large polypeptides are loosely intertwined to form a flexible wormlike αβ dimer that is ~1000 Å long. Two such heterodimers further associate in a head-

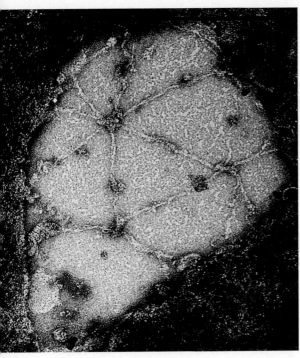

(a)

■ **Figure 9-29** | **The human erythrocyte membrane skeleton.** (a) An electron micrograph of an erythrocyte membrane skeleton that has been stretched to an area 9 to 10 times greater than that of the native membrane. Stretching makes it possible to obtain clear images of the membrane skeleton, which in its native state is densely packed and irregularly flexed. Note the predominantly hexagonal network composed of spectrin tetramers. [Courtesy of Daniel Branton, Harvard University.] (b) A model of the erythrocyte membrane skeleton with an inset showing its relationship to the intact erythrocyte. The junctions between spectrin tetramers include actin and tropomyosin (Section 7-2) and **band 4.1 protein** (named after its position in an SDS-PAGE electrophoretogram). [After Goodman, S.R., Krebs, K.E., Whitfield, C.F., Riederer, B.M., and Zagen, I.S., *CRC Crit. Rev. Biochem.* **23,** 196 (1988).]

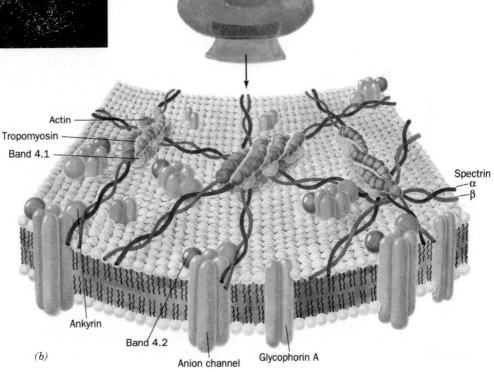

(b)

Actin
Tropomyosin
Band 4.1
Spectrin
—α
—β
Ankyrin
Band 4.2
Anion channel
Glycophorin A

to-head manner to form an $(\alpha\beta)_2$ tetramer. Spectrin is a homolog of dystrophin, the muscle protein that is defective in muscular dystrophy (Section 7-2A).

There are ~100,000 spectrin tetramers per cell, and they are cross-linked at both ends by attachments to other cytoskeletal proteins. Together, these proteins form a dense and irregular protein meshwork that underlies the erythrocyte plasma membrane (Fig. 9-29). A defect or deficiency in spectrin synthesis causes **hereditary spherocytosis,** in which erythrocytes are spheroidal and relatively fragile and inflexible. Individuals with the disease suffer from anemia due to erythrocyte lysis and the removal of spherocytic cells by the spleen (which normally functions to

■ **Figure 9-30** | **The X-ray structure of human ankyrin repeats 13 to 24.** The individual repeats are colored in rainbow order with repeat 13 red and repeat 24 violet. [Courtesy of Peter Michaely, University of Texas Southwestern Medical Center, Dallas, Texas. PDBid 1N11.]

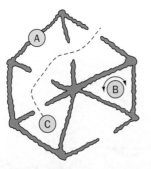

■ **Figure 9-31** | **Model rationalizing the various mobilities of membrane proteins.** Protein A, which interacts tightly with the underlying cytoskeleton, is immobile. Protein B is free to rotate within the confines of the cytoskeletal "fences." Protein C diffuses by traveling through "gates" in the cytoskeleton. The diffusion of some membrane proteins is not affected by the cytoskeleton. [After Edidin, M., *Trends Cell Biol.* **2,** 378 (1992).]

filter out aged and hence inflexible erythrocytes from the blood at the end of their ~120-day lifetimes).

Spectrin also associates with an 1880-residue protein known as **ankyrin** which binds to an integral membrane ion channel protein. This attachment anchors the membrane skeleton to the membrane. Immunochemical studies have revealed spectrin-like and ankyrin-like proteins in a variety of tissues, in addition to erythrocytes. Ankyrin's N-terminal 798-residue segment consists almost entirely of 24 tandem ~33-residue repeats known as **ankyrin repeats** (Fig. 9-30), which also occur in a variety of other proteins. Each ankyrin repeat consists of two short (8- or 9-residue) antiparallel α helices followed by a long loop. These structures are arranged in a right-handed helical stack. The entire assembly forms an elongated concave surface that is postulated to bind various integral proteins as well as spectrin.

The interaction of membrane components with the underlying skeleton helps explain why integral membrane proteins exhibit different degrees of mobility within the membrane: Some integral proteins are firmly attached to elements of the cytoskeleton or are trapped within the spaces defined by those "fences." Other membrane proteins may be able to squeeze through gaps or "gates" between cytoskeletal components, whereas still other proteins can diffuse freely without interacting with the cytoskeleton at all (Fig. 9-31). Support for this **gates and fences model** comes from the finding that partial destruction of the cytoskeleton results in freer protein diffusion.

C | Membrane Lipids Are Distributed Asymmetrically

The lipid and protein components of membranes do not occur in equal proportions on the two sides of biological membranes. For example, *membrane glycoproteins and glycolipids are invariably oriented with their carbohydrate moieties facing the cell's exterior.* The asymmetric distribution of certain membrane lipids between the inner and outer leaflets of a membrane was first established through the use of phospholipases (Section 9-1C). Phospholipases cannot pass through membranes, so phospholipids on only the external surface of intact cells are susceptible to hydrolysis by these enzymes. Such studies reveal that lipids in biological membranes are asymmetrically distributed (e.g., Fig. 9-32). How does this asymmetry arise?

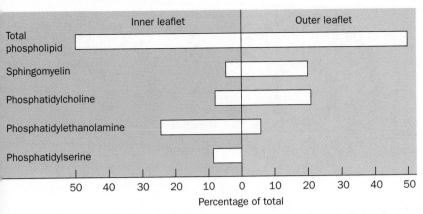

■ **Figure 9-32 │ Asymmetric distribution of membrane phospholipids in the human erythrocyte membrane.** The phospholipid content is expressed as mol %. [After Rothman, J.E. and Lenard, J., *Science* **194**, 1744 (1977).]

In eukaryotes, the enzymes that synthesize membrane lipids are mostly integral membrane proteins of the **endoplasmic reticulum (ER;** the interconnected membranous vesicles that occupy much of the cytosol; Fig. 1-8), whereas in prokaryotes, lipids are synthesized by integral membrane proteins in the plasma membrane. Hence, membrane lipids are fabricated on site. Eugene Kennedy and James Rothman demonstrated this to be the case in bacteria through the use of selective labeling. They gave growing bacteria a 1-minute pulse of $^{32}PO_4^{3-}$ in order to radioactively label the phosphoryl groups of only the newly synthesized phospholipids. Immediately afterward, they added **trinitrobenzenesulfonic acid (TNBS),** a membrane-impermeable reagent that combines with phosphatidylethanolamine (**PE;** Fig. 9-33). Analysis of the resulting doubly labeled membranes showed that none of the TNBS-labeled PE was

Phosphatidylethanolamine (PE)

Trinitrobenzenesulfonic acid (TNBS)

H_2SO_3

■ **Figure 9-33 │ The reaction of TNBS with phosphatidylethanolamine.**

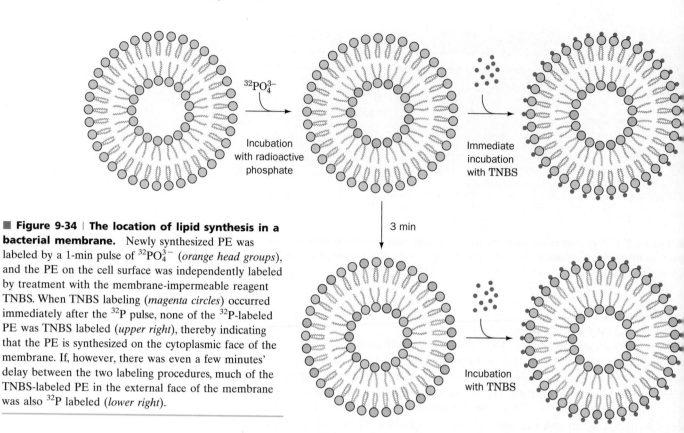

■ Figure 9-34 │ The location of lipid synthesis in a bacterial membrane. Newly synthesized PE was labeled by a 1-min pulse of $^{32}PO_4^{3-}$ (*orange head groups*), and the PE on the cell surface was independently labeled by treatment with the membrane-impermeable reagent TNBS. When TNBS labeling (*magenta circles*) occurred immediately after the ^{32}P pulse, none of the ^{32}P-labeled PE was TNBS labeled (*upper right*), thereby indicating that the PE is synthesized on the cytoplasmic face of the membrane. If, however, there was even a few minutes' delay between the two labeling procedures, much of the TNBS-labeled PE in the external face of the membrane was also ^{32}P labeled (*lower right*).

radioactively labeled. This observation indicates that *newly made PE is synthesized on the cytoplasmic face of the membrane* (Fig. 9-34, *upper right*).

However, if an interval of only 3 minutes was allowed to elapse between the $^{32}PO_4^{3-}$ pulse and the TNBS addition, about half of the ^{32}P-labeled PE was also TNBS labeled (Fig. 9-34, *lower right*). This observation indicates that the flip-flop rate of PE in the bacterial membrane is ~100,000-fold greater than it is in bilayers consisting of only phospholipids (where the flip-flop rates have half-times of many days).

How do phospholipids synthesized on one side of the membrane reach its other side so quickly? Phospholipid flip-flops in bacteria as well as eukaryotes appear to be facilitated in two ways:

1. Membrane proteins known as **flipases** catalyze the flip-flops of specific phospholipids. These proteins tend to equilibrate the distribution of their corresponding phospholipids across a bilayer; that is, the net transport of a phospholipid is from the side of the bilayer with the higher concentration of the phospholipid to the opposite side. Such a process, as we shall see in Section 10-1, is a form of **facilitated diffusion.**

2. Membrane proteins known as **phospholipid translocases** transport specific phospholipids across a bilayer in a process that is driven by ATP hydrolysis. These proteins can transport certain phospholipids from the side of a bilayer that has the lower concentration of the phospholipid to the opposite side, thereby establishing a nonequilibrium distribution of the phospholipid. Such a process, as we shall see in Section 10-3, is a form of **active transport.**

The observed distribution of phospholipids across membranes (e.g., Fig. 9-32) therefore appears to arise from the membrane orientations of the enzymes that synthesize phospholipids combined with the countervailing tendencies of ATP-dependent phospholipid translocases that generate asymmetric phospholipid distributions and flipases that equilibrate these distributions. The importance of these lipid transport systems is demonstrated by the observation that the presence of phosphatidylserine on the exteriors of many cells induces blood clotting (i.e., it is an indication of tissue damage) and, in erythrocytes, marks the cell for removal from the circulation.

In all cells, *new membranes are generated by the expansion of existing membranes*. In eukaryotic cells, lipids synthesized on the cytoplasmic face of the ER are transported to other parts of the cell by membranous vesicles that bud off from the ER and fuse with other cellular membranes. These vesicles also carry membrane proteins.

Lipid Rafts Are Membrane Subdomains. *Lipids and proteins in membranes can also be laterally organized.* Thus the plasma membranes of many eukaryotic cells have two or more distinct domains that have different functions. For example, the plasma membranes of epithelial cells (the cells lining body cavities and free surfaces) have an **apical domain,** which faces the lumen (interior) of the cavity and often has a specialized function (such as the absorption of nutrients in intestinal brush border cells), and a **basolateral domain,** which covers the remainder of the cell. These two domains, which do not intermix, have different compositions of both lipids and proteins.

In addition, the hundreds of different lipids and proteins within a given plasma membrane domain may not be uniformly mixed but instead often segregate to form **microdomains** that are enriched in certain lipids and proteins. This may result from specific interactions between integral membrane proteins and particular types of membrane lipids. Divalent metal ions, notably Ca^{2+}, which bind to negatively charged lipid head groups such as those of phosphatidylserine, may also cause clustering of these lipids.

One type of microdomain, termed a **lipid raft,** appears to consist of closely packed glycosphingolipids (which occur only in the outer leaflet of the plasma membrane) and cholesterol. By themselves, glycosphingolipids cannot form bilayers because their large head groups prevent the requisite close packing of their predominantly saturated hydrophobic tails. Conversely, cholesterol by itself does not form a bilayer due to its small head group. It is therefore likely that *the glycosphingolipids in lipid rafts associate laterally via weak interactions between their carbohydrate head groups, and the voids between their tails are filled in by cholesterol.*

Owing to the close packing of their component lipids and the long, saturated sphingolipid tails, sphingolipid–cholesterol rafts have a more ordered or crystalline arrangement than other regions of the membrane and are more resistant to solubilization by detergents. The rafts may diffuse laterally within the membrane. Certain proteins preferentially associate with the rafts, including many GPI-linked proteins and some of the proteins that participate in transmembrane signaling processes (Chapter 13). This suggests that lipid rafts, which are probably present in all cell types, function as platforms for the assembly of complex intercellular signaling systems. Several viruses, including influenza virus, measles virus, Ebola virus, and HIV, localize to lipid rafts, which therefore appear to be the sites from which these viruses enter uninfected cells and bud from infected cells. It should be noted that lipid rafts are highly dynamic structures that rapidly exchange both proteins and lipids with their surrounding membrane as a consequence of the weak and transient interactions between membrane components.

Caveolae (Latin for small caves), which are ~75-nm-diameter flask shaped invaginations (infoldings) on the plasma membrane, are specialized forms of lipid rafts that are associated with ~21-kD integral proteins named **caveolins.** Caveolae, which occur mainly on muscle and epithelial cells, participate in **endocytosis** (the internalization of receptor-bound ligands; Section 20-1B) as well as intercellular signaling.

D | The Secretory Pathway Generates Secreted and Transmembrane Proteins

In contrast to membrane lipids, membrane proteins do not change their orientation in the membrane after they are synthesized. Membrane proteins, like all proteins, are ribosomally synthesized under the direction of messenger RNA templates (translation is discussed in Chapter 27). The polypeptide grows from its N-terminus to its C-terminus by the stepwise addition of amino acid residues. Ribosomes may be free in the cytosol or bound to the ER to form the **rough endoplasmic reticulum (RER,** so called because of the knobby appearance its bound ribosomes give it; Fig. 1-8). *Free ribosomes synthesize mostly soluble and mitochondrial proteins, whereas membrane-bound ribosomes manufacture transmembrane proteins and proteins destined for secretion, operation within the ER, and incorporation into* **lysosomes** (Fig. 1-8; membranous vesicles containing a battery of hydrolytic enzymes that degrade and recycle cell components). The latter proteins initially appear in the ER.

Secreted and Transmembrane Proteins Pass through the ER Membrane. How are RER-destined proteins differentiated from other proteins? And how do these large, relatively polar molecules pass through the RER membrane? These processes occur via the **secretory pathway,** which was first described by Günter Blobel, Cesar Milstein, and David Sabatini around 1975. Since ~25% of the various proteins synthesized by all types of cells are integral proteins and many others are secreted, *~40% of the various types of proteins that a cell synthesizes must be processed via the secretory pathway or some other protein targeting pathway.* Here we outline the secretory pathway, which is diagrammed in Fig. 9-35:

1. *All secreted, ER-resident, and lysosomal proteins, as well as many TM proteins, are synthesized with leading (N-terminal) 13- to 36-residue* **signal peptides.** These signal peptides consist of a 6- to 15-residue hydrophobic core flanked by several relatively hydrophilic residues that usually include one or more basic residues near the N-terminus (Fig. 9-36). Signal peptides otherwise have little sequence similarity. However, a variety of evidence indicates they form α helices in nonpolar environments.

2. When the signal peptide first protrudes beyond the ribosomal surface (when the polypeptide is at least ~40 residues long), the **signal recognition particle (SRP),** a 325-kD complex of six different polypeptides and a 300-nucleotide RNA molecule, binds to both the signal peptide and the ribosome (Section 27-5B). At the same time, the SRP's bound **guanosine diphosphate (GDP;** the guanine analog of ADP) is replaced by **guanosine triphosphate (GTP;** the guanine analog of ATP). The resulting conformational change in the SRP causes the ribosome to arrest further polypeptide growth, thereby preventing the RER-destined protein from being released into the cytosol.

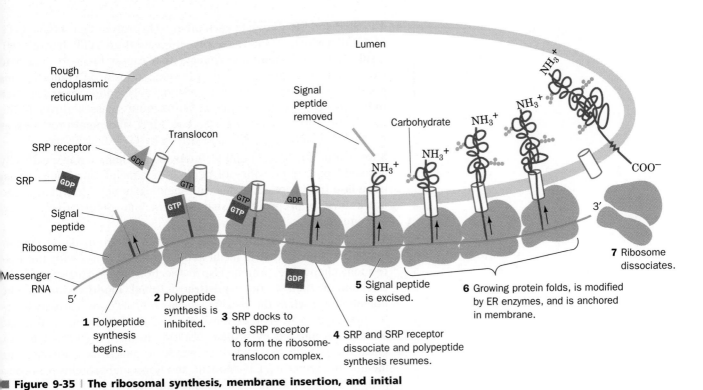

Figure 9-35 | **The ribosomal synthesis, membrane insertion, and initial glycosylation of an integral protein via the secretory pathway.** Details are given in the text. 🔁 **See the Animated Figures.**

3. The SRP–ribosome complex diffuses to the RER surface, where it binds to the **SRP receptor (SR;** also called **docking protein)** in complex with the **translocon,** a protein pore in the ER membrane through which the growing polypeptide will be extruded. In forming the SR–translocon complex, the SR's bound GDP is replaced by GTP.

			Signal peptidase cleavage site
Bovine growth hormone	M M A A G P R T S	L L L A F A L L C L P	W T Q V V G	A F P
Bovine proalbumin	M K W V T	F I S L L L L L F	S S A Y S	R G V
Human proinsulin	M A L W M R	L L P L L A L L A L	W G P D P A A A	F V N
Human interferon-γ	M K Y T S Y	I L A F Q L C I Y L	G S L G	C Y C
Human α-fibrinogen	M F S M R	I V C L V L S V V G	T A W T	A D S
Human IgG heavy chain	M E F G L S W	L F L V A I L	K G V Q C	E V Q
Rat amylase	M K	F V L L L S L I G F	C W A	Q Y D
Murine α-fetoprotein	M K W I T P A S	L I L L L L	H F A A S K	A L H
Chicken lysozyme	M R S	L L I L V L C F L P L A A L	G	K V F
Zea mays rein protein 22.1	M A T K	I L A L L A L L A L L V	S A T N A	F I I

Figure 9-36 | **The N-terminal sequences of some eukaryotic preproteins.** The hydrophobic cores (*brown*) of most signal peptides are preceded by basic residues (*blue*). [After Watson, M.E.E., *Nucleic Acids Res.* **12,** 5147–5156 (1984).]

4. The SRP and SR stimulate each other to hydrolyze their bound GTP to GDP (which is energetically equivalent to ATP hydrolysis) resulting in conformational changes that causes them to dissociate from each other and from the ribosome–translocon complex. This permits the bound ribosome to resume polypeptide synthesis such that the growing polypeptide's N-terminus passes through the translocon into the lumen of the ER. Most ribosomal processes, as we shall see in Section 27-4, are driven by GTP hydrolysis.

5. Shortly after the signal peptide enters the ER lumen, it is specifically cleaved from the growing polypeptide by a membrane-bound **signal peptidase** (polypeptide chains with their signal peptide still attached are known as **preproteins;** signal peptides are alternatively called **presequences**).

6. The nascent (growing) polypeptide starts to fold to its native conformation, a process that is facilitated by its interaction with the ER-resident chaperone protein Hsp70 (Section 6-5B). Enzymes in the ER lumen then initiate **posttranslational modification** of the polypeptide, such as the specific attachments of "core" carbohydrates to form glycoproteins (Section 8-3C) and the formation of disulfide bonds as facilitated by protein disulfide isomerase (Section 6-5A). Once the protein has folded, it cannot be pulled back through the membrane. Secretory, ER-resident, and lysosomal proteins pass completely through the RER membrane into the lumen. TM proteins, in contrast, contain one or more hydrophobic ~20-residue **membrane anchor** sequences that remain embedded in the membrane.

7. When the synthesis of the polypeptide is completed, it is released from both the ribosome and the translocon. The ribosome detaches from the RER, and its two subunits dissociate.

The secretory pathway also functions in prokaryotes for the insertion of certain proteins into the cell membrane (whose exterior is equivalent to the ER lumen). Indeed, all forms of life yet tested have homologous SRPs, SRs, and translocons. Nevertheless, it should be noted that cells have several mechanisms for installing proteins in or transporting them through membranes. For example, cytoplasmically synthesized proteins that reside in the mitochondrion reach their destinations via mechanisms that are substantially different from that of the secretory pathway.

The Translocon Is a Multifunctional Transmembrane Pore. In 1975, Blobel postulated that protein transport through the RER membrane is mediated by an aqueous TM channel. However, it was not until 1991 that he was able to experimentally demonstrate its existence. These channels, now called translocons, enclose aqueous pores that completely span the ER membrane, as shown by linking nascent polypeptide chains to fluorescent dyes whose fluorescence is sensitive to the polarity of their environment. The channel-forming component of the translocon is a heterotrimeric protein named **Sec61** in mammals and **SecY** in prokaryotes. This protein is conserved throughout all kingdoms of life and hence is likely to have a similar structure and function in all organisms.

The X-ray structure of the SecY complex from the archaeon *Methanococcus jannaschii* reveals that the α, β, and γ subunits, respectively, have 10, 1, and 1 TM α helices (Fig. 9-37). The α subunit's TM helices are wrapped around an hourglass-shaped channel whose minimum diameter is ~3 Å. The channel is blocked at its extracellular end by a short

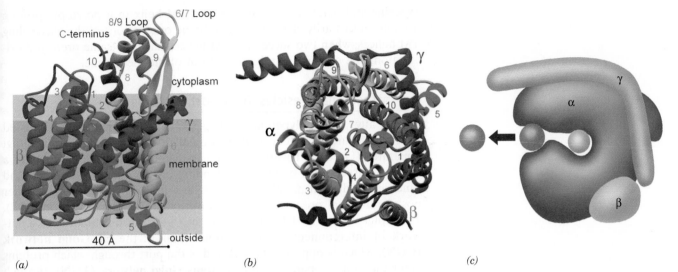

■ **Figure 9-37** | **Structure and function of the *M. jannaschii* SecY complex.** (*a*) X-Ray structure of the complex, with shading indicating the positions of membrane phospholipid head groups (*gray*) and hydrocarbon tails (*violet*). The α subunit of SecY is colored in rainbow order from its N-terminus (*dark blue*) to its C-terminus (*red-orange*), the β subunit is red, and the γ subunit is magenta. (*b*) View of SecY from the cytosol. The translocon's putative lateral gate is on the left between helices 2 and 7. (*c*) Model for the insertion of a TM helix into a membrane. The translocon (*blue*) is viewed as in Part *b*. A polypeptide chain (*yellow*) is shown bound in the translocon's pore during its translocation through the membrane, and a signal-anchor sequence (*red*) is shown passing through the translocon's lateral gate and being released into the membrane (*arrow*). [Parts *a* and *b* courtesy of Stephen Harrison and Tom Rapoport, Harvard Medical School. PDBid 1RH5. Part *c* after a drawing by Dobberstein, B. and Sinning, I., *Science* **303**, 320 (2004).]

relatively hydrophilic helix (blue unnumbered helix in Figs. 9-37*a* and *b*). It is proposed that an incoming signal peptide pushes this helix aside and hence that the helix functions as a plug to prevent small molecules from leaking across the membrane in the absence of a translocating polypeptide. The maximum diameter of an extended polypeptide is ~12 Å and that of an α helix is ~14 Å. In order for SecY to function as a channel for translocating polypeptides, the central pore must expand, a structural change that would require relatively simple hingelike motions involving conserved Gly residues.

In addition to forming a conduit for soluble proteins to pass through the membrane, *the translocon must mediate the insertion of an integral protein's TM segments into the membrane.* The X-ray structure of SecY suggests that this occurs by the opening of the C-shaped α subunit, as is diagramed in Fig. 9-37*c*, to permit the lateral installation of the TM segment into the membrane.

The signal peptides of many TM proteins are not cleaved by signal peptidase but, instead, are inserted into the membrane. Such so-called **signal-anchor sequences** *may be oriented with either their N- or C-termini in the cytosol.* If the N-terminus is installed in the cytosol, then the polypeptide must have looped around before being inserted into the membrane. Moreover, for **polytopic** (multispanning) TM proteins such as the SecY α subunit itself, this must occur for each successive TM helix. Since it seems unlikely that the SecY channel could expand to simultaneously accommodate numerous TM helices, these helices are probably installed in the membrane one or two at a time. The mechanisms by which the translocon recognizes TM segments are not well understood. For example, the experimental deletion or insertion of a TM helix in a polytopic protein does not necessarily change the membrane orientations of the succeeding TM helices; when two successive TM helices have the same preferred orientation, one of them may be forced out of the membrane.

E | Intracellular Vesicles Transport Proteins

Shortly after their polypeptide synthesis is completed, partially processed transmembrane, secretory, and lysosomal proteins appear in the Golgi apparatus (Fig. 1-8). This 0.5- to 1.0-μm-diameter organelle consists of a stack of three to six or more (depending on the species) flattened and functionally distinct membranous sacs known as **cisternae,** where further posttranslational processing, mainly glycosylation, occurs (Section 8-3C). The Golgi stack (Fig. 9-38) has two distinct faces, each composed of a network of interconnected membranous tubules: the **cis Golgi network (CGN),** which is opposite the ER and is the port through which proteins enter the Golgi apparatus; and the **trans Golgi network (TGN),** through which processed proteins exit to their final destinations. The intervening Golgi stack contains at least three different types of sacs, the **cis, medial,** and **trans cisternae,** each of which contains different sets of glycoprotein-processing enzymes.

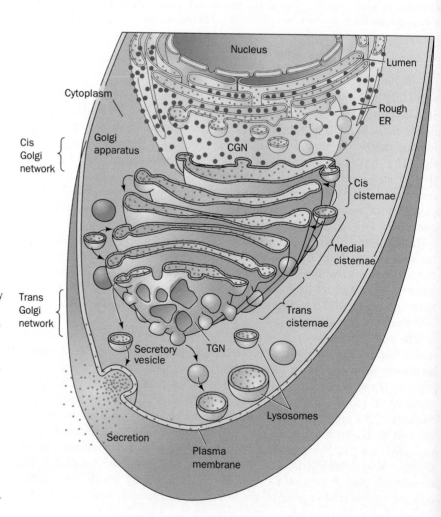

■ **Figure 9-38 | The posttranslational processing of proteins.** Membrane, secretory, and lysosomal proteins are synthesized by RER-associated ribosomes (*blue dots; top*). As they are synthesized, the proteins (*red dots*) are either injected into the lumen of the ER or inserted into its membrane. After initial processing in the ER, the proteins are encapsulated in vesicles that bud off from the ER membrane and subsequently fuse with the cis Golgi network (CGN). The proteins are progressively processed in the cis, medial, and trans cisternae of the Golgi. Finally, in the trans Golgi network (TGN; *bottom*), the completed glycoproteins are sorted for delivery to their final destinations: the plasma membrane, **secretory vesicles,** or lysosomes, to which they are transported by yet other vesicles.

Proteins transit from one end of the Golgi stack to the other while be-ing modified in a stepwise manner. The proteins are transported via two mechanisms:

1. They are conveyed between successive Golgi compartments in the cis to trans direction as cargo within membranous vesicles that bud off of one compartment and fuse with a successive compartment, a process known as forward or **anterograde transport.**

2. They are carried as passengers in Golgi compartments that transit the Golgi stack; that is, the cis cisternae eventually become trans cisternae, a process called **cisternal progression** or **maturation.** (Golgi-resident proteins may migrate backward by **retrograde transport** from one com-partment to the preceding one via membranous vesicles.)

Upon reaching the trans Golgi network, the now mature proteins are sorted and sent to their final cellular destinations.

Membrane, Secretory, and Lysosomal Proteins Are Transported in Coated Vesicles. The vehicles in which proteins are transported between the RER, the different compartments of the Golgi apparatus, and their final destinations are known as **coated vesicles** (Fig. 9-39). This is because these 60- to 150-nm-diameter membranous sacs are initially encased on their outer (cytosolic) faces by specific proteins that act as flexible scaf-folding in promoting vesicle formation. A vesicle buds off from its membrane

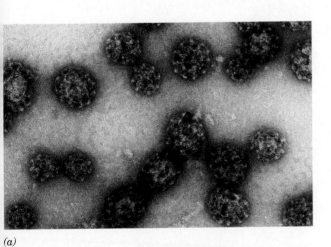

(a)

■ **Figure 9-39** | **Electron micrographs of coated vesicles.**
(*a*) Clathrin-coated vesicles. Note their polyhedral character.
[Courtesy of Barbara Pearse, Medical Research Council, U.K.]
(*b*) COPI-coated vesicles. (*c*) COPII-coated vesicles. The inserts in Parts *b* and *c* show the respective vesicles at higher magnification.
[Courtesy of Lelio Orci, University of Geneva, Switzerland.]

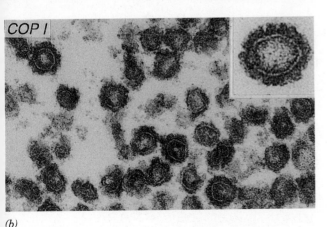

(b)

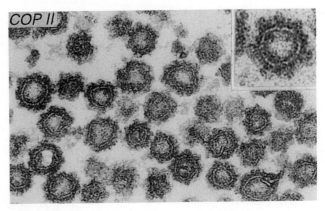

(c)

of origin and later fuses to its target membrane. *This process preserves the orientation of the transmembrane protein (Fig. 9-40), because the lumens of the ER and the Golgi cisternae are topologically equivalent to the outside of the cell.* This explains why the carbohydrate moieties of integral glycoproteins and the GPI anchors of GPI-linked proteins occur only on the external surfaces of plasma membranes.

The three known types of coated vesicles are characterized by their protein coats:

1. **Clathrin** (Fig. 9-39a), a protein that forms a polyhedral framework around vesicles that transport TM, GPI-linked, and secreted proteins from the Golgi to the plasma membrane (see below).

2. **COPI** protein (Fig. 9-39b; COP for *coat* protein), which forms a fuzzy rather than a polyhedral coating about vesicles that carry out both the anterograde and retrograde transport of proteins between successive Golgi compartments. In addition, COPI-coated vesicles

■ **Figure 9-40** | **Fusion of a vesicle with the plasma membrane.** The inside of the vesicle and the exterior of the cell are topologically equivalent. Fusion of the vesicle with the plasma membrane preserves the orientation of the integral proteins embedded in the vesicle bilayer because the same side of the protein is always immersed in the cytosol. Note that soluble proteins packaged inside a secretory vesicle that fuses with the plasma membrane would be released outside the cell.

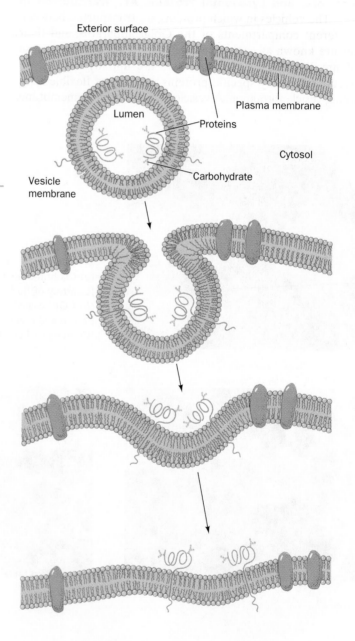

return escaped ER-resident proteins from the Golgi back to the ER (see below). The COPI protomer, which contains seven different subunits, is named **coatomer.**

3. **COPII** protein (Fig. 9-39c), which transports proteins from the ER to the Golgi. The COPII vesicle components are then returned to the ER by COPI-coated vesicles (the COPI vesicle components entering the ER are presumably recycled by COPII-coated vesicles). The COPII coat consists of two conserved protein heterodimers.

All of the above coated vesicles also bear receptors that bind the proteins being transported, as well as proteins that mediate the fusion of these vesicles with their target membranes (Section 9-4F).

Clathrin Forms Flexible Cages. Clathrin-coated vesicles are structurally better characterized than those coated with COPI or COPII. The clathrin network is built from proteins known as **triskelions** (Fig. 9-41), which consist of three heavy chains (190 kD) that each bind one of two homologous light chains (24–27 kD). The triskelions assemble to form a polyhedral cage in which each vertex is the center (hub) of a triskelion and the ~150-Å-long edges are formed by the overlapping legs of four triskelions (Fig. 9-42). The clathrin light chains are not required for clathrin cage assembly. In fact, they inhibit heavy chain polymerization *in vitro*, suggesting that they play a regulatory role in clathrin cage formation in the cytosol.

A clathrin polyhedron, which has 12 pentagonal faces and a variable number of hexagonal faces, is the most parsimonious way of enclosing a spheroidal object in a polyhedral cage. The volume enclosed by a clathrin polyhedron increases with the number of hexagonal faces. The structure shown in Fig. 9-42a is ~600 Å in diameter. *In vivo*, clathrin-coated vesicles are typically at least ~1200 Å in diameter.

The triskelion legs, which have a total length of ~450 Å, exhibit considerable flexibility (Fig. 9-41). This is a functional necessity for the

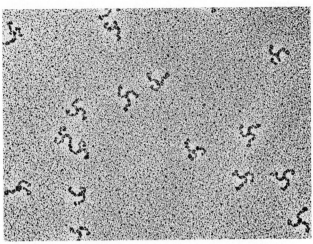

■ **Figure 9-41 | An electron micrograph of triskelions.** The variable orientations of their legs is indicative of their flexibility. [Courtesy of Daniel Branton, Harvard University.]

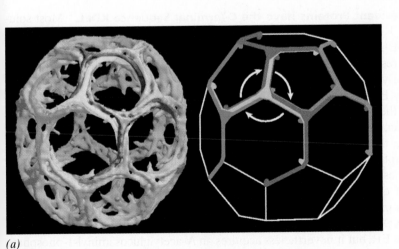

(a)

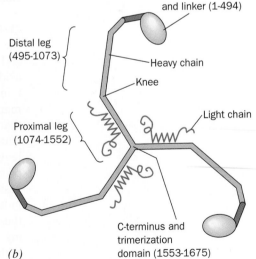

N-terminal domain and linker (1-494)

Distal leg (495-1073)

Heavy chain

Knee

Light chain

Proximal leg (1074-1552)

C-terminus and trimerization domain (1553-1675)

(b)

■ **Figure 9-42 | The anatomy of a clathrin-coated vesicle.** (a) A cryoelectron microscopy–based image of a clathrin cage at 21 Å resolution with its triskelions differently colored. As the accompanying diagram (*right*) indicates, a triskelion is centered on each of this polyhedral cage's 36 vertices, its edges are formed by the legs of adjacent triskelions, and the linker and N-terminal domains of each clathrin heavy chain project inward. [Electron micrograph by Barbara Pearse and courtesy of H.T. McMahon, MRC Laboratory for Molecular Biology, Cambridge, U.K.] (b) Schematic diagram of a triskelion indicating its structural subdivisions.

formation of different-sized vesicles as well as for the budding of a vesicle from a membrane surface, which requires a large change in its curvature. The clathrin heavy chains appear to flex mainly along a segment of the knee (Fig. 9-42b) between the proximal and distal legs that is free of contacts with other molecules in clathrin cages.

In addition to transporting membrane and secretory proteins between the Golgi apparatus and the plasma membrane, clathrin-coated vesicles participate in **endocytosis.** In this process (discussed in Section 20-1B), a portion of the plasma membrane invaginates to form a clathrin-coated vesicle that engulfs specific proteins from the extracellular medium and then transports them to intracellular destinations.

Proteins Are Directed to the Lysosome by Carbohydrate Recognition Markers. The signals that direct particular proteins to the various types of coated vesicles for transport between cellular compartments are not entirely understood. However, the trafficking of lysosomal proteins is known to depend on their oligosaccharides. A clue to the nature of this process was provided by the human hereditary defect known as **I-cell disease** (alternatively, **mucolipidosis II**) which, in homozygotes, is characterized by severe progressive psychomotor retardation, skeletal deformities, and death by age 10. The lysosomes in the connective tissue of I-cell disease victims contain large inclusions (after which the disease is named) of glycosaminoglycans and glycolipids as a result of the absence of several lysosomal hydrolases. These enzymes are synthesized on the RER with their correct amino acid sequences, but rather than being dispatched to the lysosomes, are secreted into the extracellular medium. This misdirection results from the absence of a mannose-6-phosphate recognition marker on the carbohydrate moieties of these hydrolases because of a deficiency of an enzyme required for mannose phosphorylation of the lysosomal proteins. The mannose-6-phosphate residues are normally bound by a receptor in the coated vesicles that transports lysosomal hydrolases from the Golgi apparatus to the lysosomes. No doubt, other glycoproteins are directed to their intracellular destinations by similar carbohydrate markers.

ER-Resident Proteins Have the C-Terminal Sequence KDEL. Most soluble ER-resident proteins in mammals have the C-terminal sequence KDEL (HDEL in yeast), KKXX, or KXKXXX (where X represents any amino acid residue), whose alteration results in the secretion of the resulting protein. By what means are these proteins selectively retained in the ER? Since many ER-resident proteins freely diffuse within the ER, it seems unlikely that they are immobilized by membrane-bound receptors within the ER. Rather, ER-resident proteins, like secretory and lysosomal proteins, readily leave the ER via COPII-coated vesicles, but ER-resident proteins are promptly retrieved from the Golgi and returned to the ER in COPI-coated vesicles. Indeed, coatomer binds the Lys residues in the C-terminal KKXX motif of transmembrane proteins, which presumably permits it to gather these proteins into COPI-coated vesicles. Furthermore, genetically appending KDEL to the lysosomal protease **cathepsin D** causes it to accumulate in the ER, but it nevertheless acquires an N-acetylglucosaminyl-1-phosphate group, a modification that is made in an early Golgi compartment. Presumably, a membrane-bound receptor in a post-ER compartment binds the KDEL signal and the resulting complex is returned to the ER in a COPI-coated vesicle. **KDEL receptors** have, in fact, been identified in yeast and humans. However, the observation that former KDEL proteins whose KDEL sequences have been deleted are, nevertheless, secreted relatively slowly suggests that there are mechanisms for retaining these proteins in the

ER by actively withholding them from the bulk flow of proteins through the secretory pathway.

F | Proteins Mediate Vesicle Fusion

In all cells, *new membranes are generated by the expansion of existing membranes.* In eukaryotes, this process occurs mainly via vesicle trafficking in which a vesicle buds off from one membrane (e.g., that of the Golgi apparatus) and fuses to a different membrane (e.g., the plasma membrane or that of the lysosome), thereby transferring both lipids and proteins from the parent to the target membrane.

On arriving at its target membrane, a vesicle fuses with it, thereby releasing its contents on the opposite side of the target membrane (Fig. 9-40). We have already seen how proteins are transported from the ER through the Golgi apparatus and secreted by this mechanism. Other substances are also secreted in this way. For example (Fig. 9-43), when a nerve impulse in a presynaptic cell reaches a **synapse** [the junction between neurons (nerve cells) or between neurons and muscles], it triggers the fusion of **neurotransmitter**-containing **synaptic vesicles** with the **presynaptic membrane** (a specialized section of the neuron's plasma membrane). This releases the neurotransmitter (a small molecule) into the ~200-Å-wide **synaptic cleft** (the process whereby membranous vesicles fuse with the plasma membrane to release their contents outside the cell is called **exocytosis**). In less than 0.1 ms, the neurotransmitter diffuses across the synaptic cleft to the **postsynaptic membrane,** where it binds to specific receptors that then trigger the continuation of the nerve impulse or muscle contraction in the postsynaptic cell.

Biological membranes do not spontaneously fuse. Indeed, being negatively charged, they strongly repel each other at short distances. This repulsive force must be overcome if biological membranes are to fuse. How do vesicles fuse and why do they fuse only with their target membranes?

Extensive investigations, in large part by James Rothman, have identified numerous proteins that mediate vesicle fusion with their target membranes. Among these are integral or lipid-linked proteins known as **SNAREs. R-SNAREs** (which contain conserved Arg residues) usually associate with vesicle membranes, and **Q-SNAREs** (which contain conserved Gln residues) usually associate with target membranes. Interactions among these proteins, as we shall see, firmly anchor the vesicle to the target membrane, a process called docking.

The X-ray structure of a core SNARE complex is shown in Fig. 9-44. Four parallel ~65-residue α helices wrap around each other with a gentle left-handed twist. For the most part,

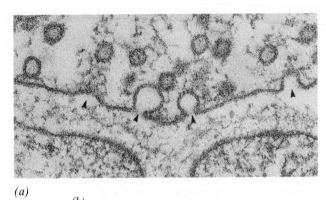

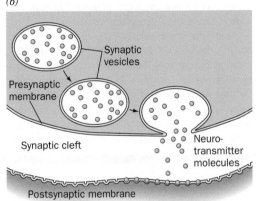

(a)

(b)

■ Figure 9-43 | Vesicle fusion at a synapse. (*a*) An electron micrograph of a frog neuromuscular synapse. Synaptic vesicles are undergoing fusion (*arrows*) with the presynaptic plasma membrane (*top*). [Courtesy of John Heuser, Washington University School of Medicine, St. Louis, Missouri.] (*b*) This process discharges the neurotransmitter contents of the synaptic vesicles into the synaptic cleft, the space between the neuron and the muscle cell (the postsynaptic cell).

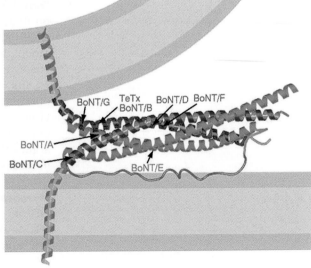

■ Figure 9-44 | X-Ray structure of a SNARE complex modeled between two membranes. The complex includes an R-SNARE (**syntaxin**, *red*) and two Q-SNARES (**synaptobrevin**, *blue,* and **SNAP-25,** *green,* a two-Q-domain–containing Q-SNARE) for a total of four helices, which are shown here as ribbons. The transmembrane C-terminal extensions of syntaxin and synaptobrevin are modeled as helices (*yellow-green*). The peptide segment connecting the two Q-domain helices of SNAP-25 is speculatively represented as an unstructured loop (*brown*). The loop is anchored to the membrane via Cys-linked palmitoyl groups (*not shown*). The cleavage sites for various clostridial neurotoxins (causing tetanus and botulism; Box 9-3) are indicated by the arrows. [Courtesy of Axel Brünger, Yale University. PDBid 1SFC.]

BOX 9-3 BIOCHEMISTRY IN HEALTH AND DISEASE

Tetanus and Botulinum Toxins Specifically Cleave SNAREs

The frequently fatal infectious diseases **tetanus** (which arises from wound contamination) and **botulism** (a type of food poisoning) are caused by certain anaerobic bacteria of the genus *Clostridium*. These bacteria produce extremely potent protein neurotoxins that inhibit the release of neurotransmitters into synapses. In fact, botulinum toxins are the most powerful known toxins; they are ~10 million times more toxic than cyanide.

There are seven serologically distinct types of botulinum neurotoxins, designated **BoNT/A** through **BoNT/G,** and one type of tetanus neurotoxin, **TeTx.** Each of these homologous proteins is synthesized as a single ~150-kD polypeptide chain that is cleaved by host proteases to yield an ~50-kD light chain and an ~100-kD heavy chain. The heavy chains bind to specific types of neurons and facilitate the uptake of the light chain by endocytosis. *Each light chain is a protease that cleaves its target SNARE at a specific*

site (see Fig. 9-44). SNARE cleavage prevents the formation of the core complex and thereby halts the exocytosis of synaptic vesicles. The heavy chain of TeTx specifically binds to inhibitory neurons (which function to moderate excitatory nerve impulses) and is thereby responsible for the spastic paralysis characteristic of tetanus. The heavy chains of the BoNTs instead bind to motor neurons (which innervate muscles) and thus cause the flaccid paralysis characteristic of botulism.

The administration of carefully controlled quantities of botulinum toxin ("Botox") is medically useful in relieving the symptoms of certain types of chronic muscle spasms. Moreover, this toxin is being used cosmetically: Its injection into the skin relaxes the small muscles causing wrinkles and hence these wrinkles disappear for ~3 months.

the sequence of each helix has the expected seven-residue repeat, $(a\text{-}b\text{-}c\text{-}d\text{-}e\text{-}f\text{-}g)_n$, with residues a and d hydrophobic (Section 6-1C). However, the central layer of side chains along the length of the four-helix bundle includes an Arg residue from the R-SNARE that is hydrogen bonded to three Gln side chains, one from each of the Q-SNARE helices. These highly conserved polar residues are sealed off from the aqueous environment so that their interactions serve to bring the four helices into proper register. Since cells contain numerous different R-SNAREs and Q-SNAREs, it seems likely that their interactions are at least partially responsible for the specificity that vesicles exhibit in fusing with their target membranes. Bacterial proteases that cleave SNAREs interfere with vesicle fusion, with serious consequences (Box 9-3).

SNAREs Facilitate the Fusion of Membranes by Bringing Them Together. The association of an R-SNARE on a vesicle with Q-SNAREs on its target membrane brings the two bilayers into close proximity. But what induces the fusion of the juxtaposed lipid bilayers? According to one model, mechanical stresses arising from the formation of SNARE complexes expel lipid molecules from their bilayer. This, it is hypothesized, results in the formation of a transient structure with lipids from the opposing bilayer, a process that culminates in bilayer fusion (Fig. 9-45). However, *in vitro*, this process takes 30 to 40 minutes, whereas the fusion of a synaptic vesicle with the presynaptic membrane requires ~0.3 ms. This argues that other proteins also participate in inducing bilayer fusion and, indeed, several other proteins have been implicated.

Membrane-Enveloped Viruses Infect Their Target Cells Using Viral Fusion Proteins. Many viruses, including those causing influenza and AIDS, arise by budding from the plasma membrane of a virus-infected cell, much like the budding of a vesicle from a membrane. In order to

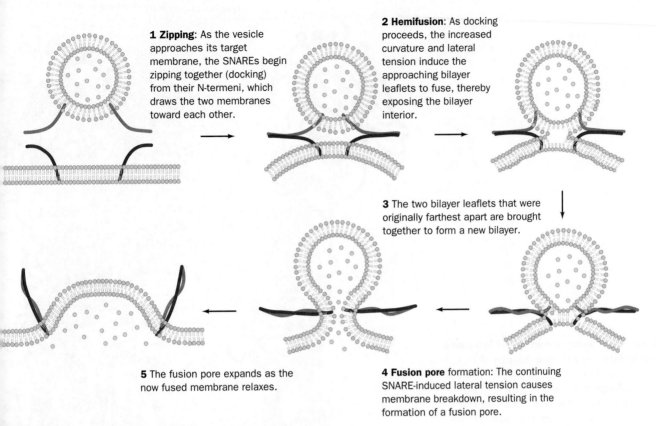

1 Zipping: As the vesicle approaches its target membrane, the SNAREs begin zipping together (docking) from their N-termeni, which draws the two membranes toward each other.

2 Hemifusion: As docking proceeds, the increased curvature and lateral tension induce the approaching bilayer leaflets to fuse, thereby exposing the bilayer interior.

3 The two bilayer leaflets that were originally farthest apart are brought together to form a new bilayer.

5 The fusion pore expands as the now fused membrane relaxes.

4 Fusion pore formation: The continuing SNARE-induced lateral tension causes membrane breakdown, resulting in the formation of a fusion pore.

Figure 9-45 | A model for SNARE-mediated vesicle fusion. Here R-SNAREs and Q-SNAREs are schematically represented by red and blue worms. [After a drawing by Chen, Y.A. and Scheller, R.H., *Nature Rev. Mol. Cell Biol.* **2**, 98 (2001).]

infect a new cell, the membrane of the resulting **membrane-enveloped virus** must fuse with a membrane in its target cell so as to deposit the virus' cargo of nucleic acid in the cell's cytoplasm. Such membrane fusion events are mediated by protein systems that differ from those responsible for the vesicle fusion events we discussed above. As an example, let us discuss how **influenza virus** mediates membrane fusion (other membrane-enveloped viruses use similar systems). Virus-mediated membrane fusion occurs in three stages:

1. Host cell recognition by the virus.
2. Activation of the viral membrane fusion machinery.
3. Fusion of the viral membrane with a host cell membrane so as to release the viral genome into the host cell cytoplasm.

The major integral protein component of the membrane that envelops influenza virus is named **hemagglutinin (HA)** because it causes erythrocytes to agglutinate (clump together). HA, a so-called **viral fusion protein,** mediates influenza host cell recognition by binding to specific glycoproteins that act as cell-surface receptors. These glycoproteins (glycophorin A in erythrocytes; Section 9-3A) bear terminal *N*-acetylneuraminic acid (sialic acid; Fig. 8-6) residues on their carbohydrate groups. HA is synthesized as a homotrimer of 550-residue subunits that are each anchored to

(a)   (b)

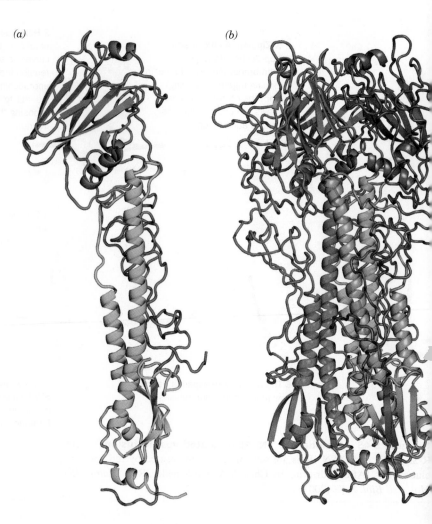

■ **Figure 9-46** | **X-Ray structure of influenza hemagglutinin.** (*a*) Ribbon diagram of the BHA monomer. HA1 is green and HA2 is cyan. (*b*) Ribbon diagram of the BHA trimer. Each HA1 and HA2 chain is drawn in a different color. The orientations of the green HA1 and the cyan HA2 are the same as in Part *a*. [Based on an X-ray structure by John Skehel, National Institute for Medical Research, London, U.K., and Don Wiley, Harvard University. PDBid 4HMG.]

the membrane by a single transmembrane helix (residues 524–540). However, HA's Arg 329 is posttranslationally excised by host cell proteases to yield two peptides, designated HA1 and HA2, that remain linked by a disulfide bond.

After binding to the plasma membrane of its host cell, an influenza virus particle is taken into the cell by the invagination of the membrane via a process known as **receptor-mediated endocytosis** (Section 20-1B) that superficially resembles the reverse of the fusion of a vesicle with a membrane (Fig. 9-40). The resulting intracellular vesicle with the virus bound to its inner surface then fuses with a vesicle known as an **endosome** that has an internal pH of ∼5. The consequent drop in pH triggers a conformational change in which the N-terminal end of HA2, a conserved, hydrophobic, ∼24-residue segment known as a **fusion peptide,** inserts into the host cell's endosomal membrane, thereby tightly linking it to the viral membrane preparatory to their fusion.

Our understanding of how HA mediates the fusion of viral and host cell membranes is based largely on X-ray structural studies by Don Wiley and John Skehel. HA's hydrophobic membrane anchor interferes with its crystallization. However, the proteolytic removal of HA's transmembrane helix yields a crystallizable protein named BHA, whose X-ray structure reveals that it consists of a globular region that is perched on a long fibrous stalk projecting from the viral membrane surface (Fig. 9-46*a*). The globular region contains the sialic acid–binding pocket, whereas the

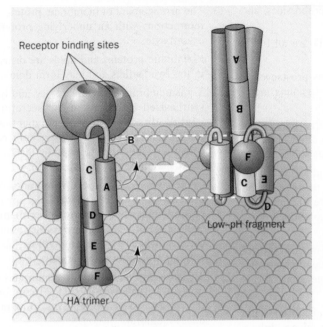

■ Figure 9-47 | Schematic drawing comparing the structures of BHA and TBHA2. This drawing indicates the positions and heights above the viral membrane surface of TBHA2's various structural elements in the HA trimer (*left*) and in its low-pH form (*right*). In the low-pH form, the fusion peptide would protrude well above the receptor-binding heads where it would presumably insert itself into the endosomal membrane.

fibrous stalk includes a remarkable 76-Å-long (53 residues in 14 turns) α helix. The dominant interaction stabilizing BHA's trimeric structure is a triple-stranded coiled coil consisting of the long α helices from each of its protomers (Fig. 9-46b). Curiously, BHA's fusion peptides are buried in its hydrophobic interior, ~100 Å from the sialic acid–binding sites at the "top" of the protein.

In the endosome, HA undergoes a dramatic conformational change (Fig. 9-47), the nature of which was elucidated by the X-ray structure of a portion of BHA named TBHA2 that consists of BHA's long helix and some of its flanking regions. In this conformational change, segments A and B at the N-terminus of TBHA2 (the red and orange segments in Fig. 9-47) undergo a jackknife-like movement of ~100 Å in a way that extends the top of the long helix by ~10 helical turns toward the endosomal membrane. This translocates the fusion peptide (which is absent in TBHA2 but would extend beyond its N-terminus at the top of segment A) by at least 100 Å above its position in BHA, thereby allowing it to insert into the host membrane. At the same time, the long helix is shortened from the bottom by similar shifts of segments D and E (green and blue in Fig. 9-47). These conformational changes, which simultaneously occur in several closely spaced HA molecules in the viral membrane, draw together the viral and host membranes so as to facilitate their fusion in a manner similar to that postulated for SNARE complexes.

■ CHECK YOUR UNDERSTANDING

Describe the fluid mosaic model.

Explain how the membrane skeleton influences membrane protein distribution.

What are the functions of flipases and phospholipid translocases?

Describe the structure of a lipid raft.

Summarize the steps of the secretory pathway, including the function of the translocon.

Describe how a membrane protein, a secreted protein, and a lysosomal protein are transported from the RER to their final destination.

Describe how SNAREs and viral fusion proteins such as hemagglutinin act to bring specific membranes close together and trigger their fusion.

SUMMARY

1. Lipids are a diverse group of molecules that are soluble in organic solvents and, in contrast to other major types of biomolecules, do not form polymers.

2. Fatty acids are carboxylic acids whose chain lengths and degrees of unsaturation vary.

3. Adipocytes and other cells contain stores of triacylglycerols, which consist of three fatty acids esterified to glycerol.

4. Glycerophospholipids are amphiphilic molecules that contain two fatty acid chains and a polar head group.

5. The sphingolipids include sphingomyelins, cerebrosides, and gangliosides.

6. Cholesterol, steroid hormones, and vitamin D are all based on a four-ring structure.

7. The arachidonic acid derivatives prostaglandins, prostacyclins, thromboxanes, leukotrienes, and lipoxins are signaling molecules that have diverse physiological roles.

8. Glycerophospholipids and sphingolipids form bilayers in which their nonpolar tails associate with each other and their polar head groups are exposed to the aqueous solvent.

9. Although the transverse diffusion of a lipid across a bilayer is extremely slow, lipids rapidly diffuse in the plane of the bilayer. Bilayer fluidity varies with temperature and with the chain lengths and degree of saturation of its component fatty acid residues.

10. The proteins of biological membranes include integral (intrinsic) proteins that contain one or more transmembrane α helices or a β barrel. In all cases, the membrane-exposed surface of the protein is hydrophobic.

11. Other membrane-associated proteins may be anchored to the membrane via isoprenoid, fatty acid, or glycosylphosphatidylinositol (GPI) groups. Peripheral (extrinsic) proteins are loosely associated with the membrane surface.

12. The fluid mosaic model of membrane structure accounts for the lateral diffusion of membrane proteins and lipids.

13. The arrangement of membrane proteins may depend on their interactions with an underlying protein skeleton, as in the erythrocyte.

14. Membrane proteins and lipids are distributed asymmetrically in the two leaflets and may form domains such as lipid rafts.

15. Transmembrane (TM), secretory, and lysosomal proteins are synthesized by means of the secretory pathway. A signal peptide directs a growing polypeptide chain through the RER membrane via a protein pore called the translocon, which also functions to laterally install TM proteins into the RER membrane.

16. Coated vesicles transport membrane-embedded and luminal proteins from the ER to the Golgi apparatus for further processing, and from there to other membranes. The proteins coating these vesicles may consist largely of clathrin, which forms polyhedral cages, or COPI or COPII, which form coats with an amorphous appearance.

17. The fusion of vesicles with membranes occurs via a complex process that involves SNAREs. These form four-helix bundles that bring two membranes into proximity, which in turn induces membrane fusion.

18. Viral fusion proteins mediate the fusion of membrane-enveloped viruses such as influenza virus with their host cell membranes so as to release the viral nucleic acids into the host cell cytoplasm.

KEY TERMS

lipid 245
fatty acid 246
saturation 247
triacylglycerol 248
fats 248
oils 248
adipocyte 248
glycerophospholipid 249
phosphatidic acid 249
phospholipase 251
lysophospholipid 251
plasmalogen 251
sphingolipid 252
ceramide 252
sphingomyelin 252
cerebroside 252

ganglioside 253
steroid 254
sterol 254
glucocorticoid 255
mineralocorticoid 255
androgen 255
estrogen 255
isoprenoid 257
vitamin 257
prostaglandin 258
eicosanoid 258
lipid bilayer 260
liposome 260
transverse diffusion 261
lateral diffusion 261
transition temperature 262

integral (intrinsic) protein 263
transmembrane (TM) protein 265
electron crystallography 265
prenylation 268
myristoylation 268
palmitoylation 268
GPI-linked protein 268
peripheral (extrinsic) protein 269
fluid mosaic model 270
fluorescence recovery after photobleaching (FRAP) 270
gates and fences model 274
flipase 276

lipid raft 277
endocytosis 278
secretory pathway 278
signal peptide 278
signal recognition particle (SRP) 278
SRP receptor (SR) 279
translocon 279
coated vesicles 283
clathrin 284
exocytosis 287
SNARE 287
membrane-enveloped virus 289
hemagglutinin 289
viral fusion protein 289

PROBLEMS

1. Does *trans*-oleic acid have a higher or lower melting point than *cis*-oleic acid? Explain.

2. How many different types of triacylglycerols could incorporate the fatty acids shown in Fig. 9-1?

3. Which triacylglycerol yields more energy on oxidation: one containing three residues of linolenic acid or three residues of stearic acid?

4. Draw the structure of a glycerophospholipid that has a saturated C_{16} fatty acyl group at position 1, a monounsaturated C_{18} fatty acyl group at position 2, and an ethanolamine head group.

5. What products are obtained when 1-palmitoyl-2-oleoyl-3-phosphatidylserine is hydrolyzed by (a) phospholipase A_1; (b) phospholipase A_2; (c) phospholipase C; (d) phospholipase D?

6. Which of the glycerophospholipid head groups listed in Table 9-2 can form hydrogen bonds?

7. Does the phosphatidylglycerol "head group" of cardiolipin (Table 9-2) project out of a lipid bilayer like other glycerophospholipid head groups?

8. In some autoimmune diseases, an individual develops antibodies that recognize cell constituents such as DNA and phospholipids. Some of the antibodies react with both DNA and phospholipids. What is the structural basis for this cross-reactivity?

9. Most hormones, such as peptide hormones, exert their effects by binding to cell-surface receptors. However, steroid hormones do so by binding to cytosolic receptors. How is this possible?

10. Animals cannot synthesize linoleic acid (a precursor of arachidonic acid) and therefore must obtain this **essential fatty acid** from their diet. Explain why cultured animal cells can survive in the absence of linoleic acid.

11. Why can't triacylglycerols be significant components of lipid bilayers?

12. Why would a bilayer containing only gangliosides be unstable?

13. When bacteria growing at 20°C are warmed to 30°C, are they more likely to synthesize membrane lipids with (a) saturated or unsaturated fatty acids, and (b) short-chain or long-chain fatty acids? Explain.

14. (a) How many turns of an α helix are required to span a lipid bilayer (~30 Å across)? (b) What is the minimum number of residues required? (c) Why do most transmembrane helices contain more than the minimum number of residues?

15. The distance between the C_α atoms in a β sheet is ~3.5 Å. Can a single 9-residue segment with a β conformation serve as the transmembrane portion of an integral membrane protein?

16. Are the following lipid samples likely to correspond to the inner or outer leaflet of a eukaryotic plasma membrane? (a) 20% phosphatidylcholine, 15% phosphatidylserine, 65% other lipids. (b) 35% phosphatidylcholine, 15% gangliosides, 5% cholesterol, 45% other lipids.

17. Describe the labeling pattern of glycophorin A when a membrane-impermeable protein-labeling reagent is added to (a) a preparation of solubilized erythrocyte proteins; (b) intact erythrocyte ghosts; and (c) erythrocyte ghosts that are initially leaky and then immediately sealed and transferred to a solution that does not contain the labeling reagent.

18. Predict the effect of a mutation in signal peptidase that narrows its specificity so that it cleaves only between two Leu residues.

19. Explain why a drug that interferes with the disassembly of a SNARE complex would block neurotransmission.

REFERENCES

Lipids and Membrane Structure

Edidin, M., Lipids on the frontier: a century of cell-membrane bilayers, *Nature Rev. Mol. Cell Biol.* **4**, 414–418 (2003). [A short account of the history of the study of membranes.]

Engelman, D.M., Membranes are more mosaic than fluid, *Nature* **438**, 578–580 (2005). [A brief review updating the classic model with more proteins and variable bilayer thickness.]

Gurr, M.I., Harwood, J.L., and Frayn, K.N., *Lipid Biochemistry: An Introduction* (5th ed.), Blackwell Science (2002).

Nagle, J.F. and Tristram-Nagle, S., Lipid bilayer structure, *Curr. Opin. Struct. Biol.* **10**, 474–480 (2000). [Explains why it is difficult to quantitatively describe the structure of the lipid bilayer.]

Vance, D.E. and Vance, J. (Eds.), *Biochemistry of Lipids, Lipoproteins, and Membranes* (4th ed.), Elsevier (2002).

Membrane Proteins

Fleishman, S.J., Unger, V.M., and Ben-Tal, N., Transmembrane protein structures without X-rays, *Trends Biochem. Sci.* **31**, 106–113 (2006). [Discusses how information about TM proteins can be obtained from a limited number of known protein structures.]

Grum, V.L., Li, D., MacDonald, R.I., and Mondragón, A., Structures of two repeats of spectrin suggest models of flexibility, *Cell* **98**, 523–535 (1999).

Popot, J.-L. and Engelman, D.M., Helical membrane protein folding, stability, and evolution, *Annu. Rev. Biochem.* **69**, 881–922

(2000). [Shows a number of protein structures and discusses many features of transmembrane proteins.]

Sharom, F.J., and Lehto, M.T., Glycosylphosphatidylinositol-anchored proteins: structure, function, and cleavage by phosphatidylinositol-specific phospholipase C, *Biochem. Cell Biol.* **80**, 535–549 (2002). [Includes a discussion of the GPI anchor and its importance for protein localization and function.]

Subramaniam, S., The structure of bacteriorhodopsin: an emerging consensus, *Curr. Opin. Struct. Biol.* **9**, 462–468 (1999). [Compares the six structures of bacteriorhodopsin that have been independently determined by electron or X-ray crystallography and finds them to be remarkably similar.]

Wimley, W.C., The versatile β-barrel membrane protein, *Curr. Opin. Struct. Biol.* **13**, 404–411 (2003). [Reviews the basic principles of construction for transmembrane β barrels.]

Zhang, F.L. and Casey, P.J., Protein prenylation: molecular mechanisms and functional consequences, *Annu. Rev. Biochem.* **65**, 241–269 (1996).

The Secretory Pathway

Alder, N.N. and Johnson, A.E., Cotranslational membrane protein biogenesis at the endoplasmic reticulum, *J. Biol. Chem.* **279**, 22787–22790 (2004).

Keenan, R.J., Fraymann, D.M., Stroud, R.M., and Walter, P., The signal recognition particle, *Annu. Rev. Biochem.* **70**, 755–775 (2001).

van den Berg, B., Clemons, W.M., Jr., Collinson, I., Modis, Y.,

Hartmann, E., Harrison, S.C., and Rapaport, T.A., X-Ray structure of a protein-conducting channel, *Nature* **427,** 36–44 (2004). [The X-ray structure of SecY.]

Vesicle Trafficking

Brodsky, F.M., Chen, C.-Y., Knuehl, C., Towler, M.C., and Wakeham, D.E., Biological basket weaving: formation and function of clathrin-coated vesicles, *Annu. Rev. Cell Dev. Biol.* **17,** 515–568 (2001).

Kirchhausen, T., Clathrin, *Annu. Rev. Biochem.* **69,** 677–706 (2000).

Membrane Fusion

Skehel, J.J and Wiley, D.C., Receptor binding and membrane fusion in virus entry: The influenza hemagglutinin, *Annu. Rev. Biochem.* **69,** 531–569 (2000).

Ungar, D. and Hughson, F.M., SNARE protein structure and function, *Annu. Rev. Cell Dev. Biol.* **19,** 493–517 (2003).

Ungermann, C. and Langosch, D., Functions of SNAREs in intracellular membrane fusion and lipid bilayer mixing. *J. Cell Sci* **118,** 3819–3828 (2005).

Membrane Transport

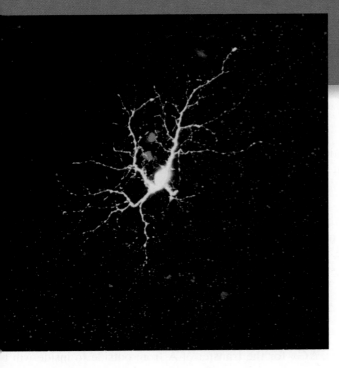

The impermeable membranes of cells, including those of neurons such as that pictured here, permit the establishment of a membrane potential, which changes when certain membrane proteins allow ions to flow into or out of the cell. [David Becker/Photo Researchers.]

■ **MEDIA RESOURCES**

(available at www.wiley.com/college/voet)

Interactive Exercise 5. The K$^+$ channel selectivity filter

Animated Figure 10-13. Model for glucose transport

Case Study 3. Carbonic Anhydrase II Deficiency

Case Study 14. Shavings from the Carpenter's Bench: The Biological Role of the Insulin C-peptide

Case Study 17. A Possible Mechanism for Blindness Associated with Diabetes: Na$^+$-Dependent Glucose Uptake by Retinal Cells

■ **CHAPTER CONTENTS**

1 Thermodynamics of Transport

2 Passive-Mediated Transport
- **A.** Ionophores Carry Ions across Membranes
- **B.** Porins Contain β Barrels
- **C.** Ion Channels Are Highly Selective
- **D.** Aquaporins Mediate the Transmembrane Movement of Water
- **E.** Transport Proteins Alternate between Two Conformations

3 Active Transport
- **A.** The (Na$^+$–K$^+$)–ATPase Transports Ions in Opposite Directions
- **B.** The Ca^{2+}–ATPase Pumps Ca^{2+} Out of the Cytosol
- **C.** ABC Transporters Are Responsible for Drug Resistance
- **D.** Active Transport May Be Driven by Ion Gradients

Cells are separated from their environments by plasma membranes. Eukaryotic cells, in addition, are compartmentalized by intracellular membranes that form the boundaries and internal structures of their various organelles. Biological membranes present formidable barriers to the passage of ionic and polar substances, so *these substances can traverse membranes only through the action of specific **transport proteins.*** Such proteins are therefore required to mediate the transmembrane movements of ions, such as Na$^+$, K$^+$, Ca^{2+}, and Cl$^-$, as well as metabolites such as pyruvate, amino acids, sugars, and nucleotides, and even water. Transport proteins are also responsible for all biological electrochemical phenomena such as neurotransmission. More complicated processes (e.g., endocytosis) are required to move larger substances such as proteins and macromolecular aggregates across membranes.

We begin our discussion of membrane transport by considering the thermodynamics of this process. We will then examine the structures and mechanisms of several different types of transport systems.

LEARNING OBJECTIVE

- Understand the thermodynamics of mediated and nonmediated membrane transport.

SAMPLE CALCULATION 10-1

Show that $\Delta G < 0$ when Ca^{2+} ions move from the endoplasmic reticulum (where $[Ca^{2+}] = 1$ mM) to the cytosol (where $[Ca^{2+}] = 0.1$ μM). Assume $\Delta \Psi = 0$. The cytosol is *in* and the endoplasmic reticulum is *out*.

$$\Delta G = RT \ln \frac{[Ca^{2+}]_{in}}{[Ca^{2+}]_{out}} = RT \ln \frac{10^{-7}}{10^{-3}}$$

$$= RT(-9.2)$$

Hence, ΔG is negative.

---

1 Thermodynamics of Transport

The diffusion of a substance between two sides of a membrane

$$A(out) \rightleftharpoons A(in)$$

thermodynamically resembles a chemical equilibration. We saw in Section 1-3D that the free energy of a solute, A, varies with its concentration.

$$\overline{G}_A = \overline{G}_A^{\circ\prime} = RT \ln [A] \qquad [10\text{-}1]$$

where $\overline{G}_A$ is the **chemical potential** (partial molar free energy) of A (the bar indicates quantity per mole) and $\overline{G}_A^{\circ\prime}$ is the chemical potential of its standard state. Thus, a difference in the concentrations of the substance on two sides of a membrane generates a **chemical potential difference:**

$$\Delta \overline{G}_A = \overline{G}_A(in) - \overline{G}_A(out) = RT \ln \left(\frac{[A]_{in}}{[A]_{out}} \right) \qquad [10\text{-}2]$$

Consequently, if the concentration of A outside the membrane is greater than that inside, $\Delta \overline{G}_A$ for the transfer of A from outside to inside will be negative and the spontaneous net flow of A will be inward. If, however [A] is greater inside than outside, $\Delta \overline{G}_A$ is positive and an inward net flow of A can occur only if an exergonic process, such as ATP hydrolysis, is coupled to it to make the overall free energy change negative (see Sample Calculation 10-1).

The transmembrane movement of ions also results in charge differences across the membrane, thereby generating an electrical potential difference $\Delta \Psi = \Psi(in) - \Psi(out)$, where $\Delta \Psi$ is termed the **membrane potential.** Consequently, if A is ionic, Eq. 10-2 must be amended to include the electrical work required to transfer a mole of A across the membrane from outside to inside:

$$\Delta \overline{G}_A = RT \ln \left(\frac{[A]_{in}}{[A]_{out}} \right) + Z_A \mathscr{F} \Delta \Psi \qquad [10\text{-}3]$$

where Z_A is the ionic charge of A; $\mathscr{F}$, the Faraday constant, is the charge of a mole of electrons (96,485 C · mol^{-1}; C is the symbol for coulomb); and $\overline{G}_A$ is now termed the **electrochemical potential** of A. The membrane potentials of living cells are commonly as large as -100 mV (inside negative; note that 1 V $= 1$ J · C^{-1}), which for a 50-Å-thick membrane corresponds to a voltage gradient of 200,000 V · cm^{-1}. Hence, the last term in Eq. 10-3 is often significant for ionic substances, particularly in mitochondria (Chapter 18) and in neurotransmission (Section 10-2C).

Transport May Be Mediated or Nonmediated. There are two types of transport processes: **nonmediated transport** and **mediated transport.** Nonmediated transport occurs through simple diffusion. In contrast, mediated transport occurs through the action of specific carrier proteins. The driving force for the nonmediated flow of a substance through a medium is its chemical potential gradient. Thus, *the substance diffuses in the direction that eliminates its concentration gradient, at a rate proportional to the magnitude of the gradient. The rate of diffusion of a substance also depends on its solubility in the membrane's nonpolar core.* Consequently, nonpolar molecules such as steroids and O_2 readily diffuse through biological membranes by nonmediated transport, according to their concentration gradients across the membranes.

Mediated transport is classified into two categories depending on the thermodynamics of the system:

1. **Passive-mediated transport,** or **facilitated diffusion,** in which a specific molecule flows from high concentration to low concentration.
2. **Active transport,** in which a specific molecule is transported from low concentration to high concentration, that is, against its concentration gradient. Such an endergonic process must be coupled to a sufficiently exergonic process to make it favorable (i.e., $\Delta G < 0$).

■ **CHECK YOUR UNDERSTANDING**

Explain why the free energy change of membrane transport depends on both the concentration and charge of the transported substance.
Explain the differences between mediated and nonmediated transport across membranes.

2 | Passive-Mediated Transport

Substances that are too large or too polar to diffuse across lipid bilayers on their own may be conveyed across membranes via proteins or other molecules that are variously called **carriers, permeases, channels,** and **transporters.** These transporters operate under the same thermodynamic principles but vary widely in structure and mechanism, particularly as it relates to their selectivity.

A | Ionophores Carry Ions across Membranes

Ionophores are organic molecules of diverse types, often of bacterial origin, that increase the permeability of membranes to ions. These molecules often exert an antibiotic effect by discharging the vital ion concentration gradients that cells actively maintain.

There are two types of ionophores:

1. *Carrier ionophores, which increase the permeabilities of membranes to their selected ion by binding it, diffusing through the membrane, and releasing the ion on the other side* (Fig. 10-1a). For net transport to occur, the uncomplexed ionophore must then return to the original side of the membrane ready to repeat the process. Carriers therefore share the common property that *their ionic complexes are soluble in nonpolar solvents.*
2. *Channel-forming ionophores, which form transmembrane channels or pores through which their selected ions can diffuse* (Fig. 10-1b).

Both types of ionophores transport ions at a remarkable rate. For example, a single molecule of the carrier ionophore **valinomycin** transports up to 10^4 K^+ ions per second across a membrane. However, *since ionophores*

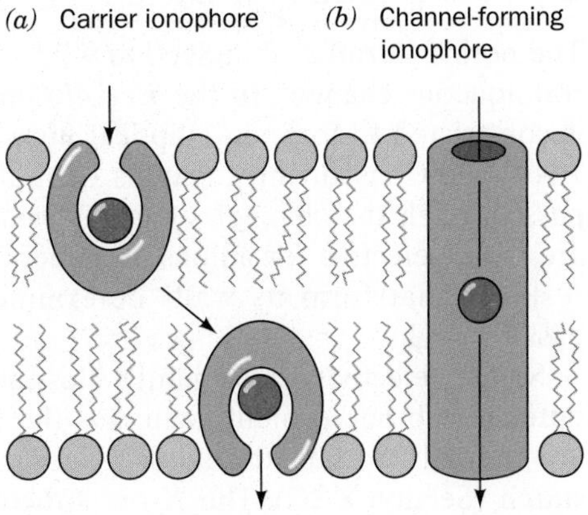

LEARNING OBJECTIVES

■ Understand the overall structure and mechanism of ionophores, porins, ion channels, aquaporins, and transport proteins.
■ Understand the protein features that make passive-mediated transport systems specific for a solute.
■ Understand the importance of gating in ion channels.
■ Understand that membrane proteins may mediate uniport, symport, and antiport transport.

(a) Carrier ionophore (b) Channel-forming ionophore

■ **Figure 10-1 | Ionophore action.** (a) Carrier ionophores transport ions by diffusing through the lipid bilayer. (b) Channel-forming ionophores span the membrane with a channel through which ions can diffuse.

(a)

L-Val   D-Hydroxy-   D-Val   L-Lactic
        isovaleric   acid
        acid

Valinomycin

(b)

■ **Figure 10-2** | **Valinomycin.** (a) This cyclic ionophore contains ester and amide bonds and D- as well as L-amino acids. (b) X-Ray structure of valinomycin in complex with a K^+ ion colored according to atom type (C green, H cyan, N blue, O red, and K^+ purple). Note that the K^+ ion is octahedrally coordinated by the carbonyl oxygen atoms of its six Val residues. [Based on an X-ray structure by Max Dobler, ETH, Zürich, Switzerland.]

passively permit ions to diffuse across a membrane in either direction, their effect can only be to equilibrate the concentrations of their selected ions across the membrane.

Valinomycin, which is one of the best characterized ionophores, specifically binds K^+. It is a cyclic molecule containing D- and L-amino acid residues that participate in ester linkages as well as peptide bonds (Fig. 10-2a). The X-ray structure of valinomycin's K^+ complex (Fig. 10-2b) indicates that the K^+ ion is octahedrally coordinated by the carbonyl groups of its six Val residues, and the cyclic valinomycin backbone surrounds the K^+ coordination shell. The methyl and isopropyl side chains project outward to provide the complex with a nonpolar exterior that makes it soluble in the hydrophobic cores of lipid bilayers.

The K^+ ion (ionic radius, $r = 1.33$ Å) fits snugly into valinomycin's coordination site, but the site is too large for Na^+ ($r = 0.95$ Å) or Li^+ ($r = 0.60$ Å) to coordinate with all six carbonyl oxygens. Valinomycin therefore has 10,000-fold greater binding affinity for K^+ than for Na^+. No other known substance discriminates better between Na^+ and K^+.

B | Porins Contain β Barrels

The porins, introduced in Section 9-3A, are β barrel structures with a central aqueous channel. In the *E. coli* OmpF porin (Fig. 9-23), the channel is constricted to form an elliptical pore with a minimum cross section of 7×11 Å. Consequently, solutes of more than ~600 D are too large to pass through the channel. OmpF is weakly cation selective; other porins are more selective for anions. In general, the size of the channel and the residues that form its walls determine what types of substances can pass through.

Solute selectivity is elegantly illustrated by **maltoporin.** This bacterial outer membrane protein facilitates the diffusion of **maltodextrins,** which are the $\alpha(1\rightarrow4)$-linked glucose oligosaccharide degradation products of starch (Section 8-2C). The X-ray structure of *E. coli* maltoporin reveals hat the protein is structurally similar to OmpF porin but is a homotrimer of 18-stranded rather than 16-stranded antiparallel β barrels. Three long oops from the extracellular face of each maltoporin subunit fold inward nto the barrel, thereby constricting the channel near the center of the nembrane to a diameter of ~5 Å and giving the channel an hourglass-ike cross section. The channel is lined on one side with a series of six con-iguous aromatic side chains arranged in a left-handed helical path that natches the left-hand helical curvature of α-amylose (Fig. 8-10). This so-alled greasy slide extends from one end of the channel, through its con-triction, to the other end (Fig. 10-3).

How does the greasy slide work? The hydrophobic faces of the mal-odextrin glucose residues stack on aromatic side chains, as is often ob-erved in complexes of sugars with proteins. The glucose hydroxyl groups, vhich are arranged in two strips along opposite edges of the maltodex-rins, form numerous hydrogen bonds with polar and charged side chains hat line the channel. Tyr 118, which protrudes into the channel opposite the greasy slide, apparently functions as a steric barrier that only permits the passage of near-planar groups such as glucosyl residues. Thus, the hook-shaped sucrose (a glucose–fructose disaccharide) passes only very slowly hrough the maltoporin channel.

At the start of the translocation process, the entering glucosyl residue nteracts with the readily accessible end of the greasy slide in the extra-cellular vestibule of the channel. Further translocation along the helical channel requires the maltodextrin to follow a screwlike path that main-ains the helical structure of the oligosaccharide, much like the movement of a bolt through a nut, thereby excluding molecules of comparable size hat have different shapes. *The translocation process is unlikely to en-counter any large energy barrier due to the smooth surface of the greasy slide and the multiple polar groups at the channel constriction that would permit the essentially continuous exchange of hydrogen bonds as a mal-odextrin moves through the constriction.*

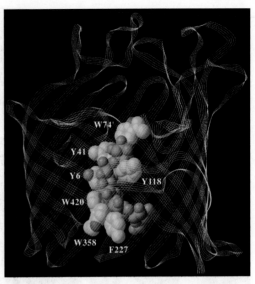

■ **Figure 10-3 | Structure of a maltoporin subunit in complex with a malto-dextrin of six glycosyl units.** The polypeptide backbone of this *E. coli* protein is represented by a cyan ribbon. Five glucose residues of maltodextrin and the aromatic side chains lining the transport channel are shown in space-filling form with N blue, O red, protein C gold, and glucosyl C green. The "greasy slide" consists of the aromatic side chains of six residues. Tyr 118, which projects into the channel, helps restrict passage to glucosyl residues. [Based on an X-ray structure by Tilman Schirmer, University of Basel, Basel, Switzerland. PDBid 1MPO.]

C | Ion Channels Are Highly Selective

All cells contain ion-specific channels that allow the rapid passage of ons such as Na^+, K^+, and Cl^-. The movement of these ions through such channels, along with their movement through active transporters discussed in Section 10-3), is essential for maintaining osmotic balance, or signal transduction (Section 13-4A), and for effecting changes in mem-brane potential that are responsible for neurotransmission. Mammalian cells, for example, maintain a nonequilibrium distribution of ions on either side of the plasma membrane: ~150 mM Na^+ and ~4 mM K^+ in the extracellular fluid, and ~12 mM Na^+ and ~140 mM K^+ inside the cell.

The Structure of the KcsA K^+ Channel Explains Its Selectivity and Speed. Potassium ions passively diffuse from the cytoplasm to the extra-cellular space through transmembrane proteins known as **K^+ channels.** Although there is a large diversity of K^+ channels, even within a single organism, all of them have similar sequences, exhibit comparable perme-ability characteristics, and most importantly, are at least 10,000-fold more permeable to K^+ than Na^+. Since this high selectivity (around the same as that of valinomycin; Section 10-2A) implies energetically strong inter-actions between K^+ and the protein, how can the K^+ channel maintain its observed nearly diffusion-limited throughput rate of up to 10^8 ions per second (a 10^4-fold greater rate than that of valinomycin)?

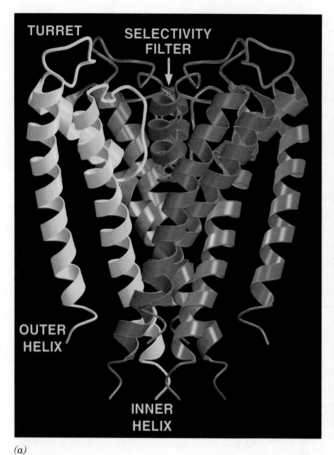

(a)

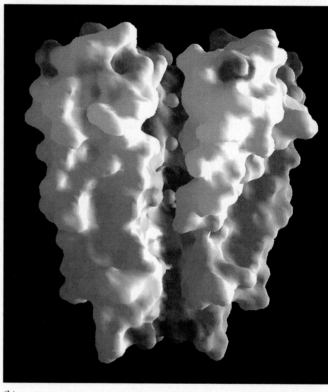

(b)

■ **Figure 10-4 ǀ X-Ray structure of the KcsA K⁺ channel.**
(a) Ribbon diagram of the tetramer as viewed from within the plane of the membrane, with the cytoplasm below and the extracellular region above. The protein's fourfold axis of rotation is vertical and each of its identical subunits is differently colored. Each subunit has an inner helix that forms part of the central pore, an outer helix that contacts the membrane interior, and a turret that projects out into the extracellular space. The selectivity filter at the extracellular end of the protein allows the passage of K^+ ions but not Na^+ ions. (b) Cutaway diagram viewed similarly to Part a in which the K^+ channel is represented by its solvent-accessible surface. The surface is colored according to its physical properties with negatively charged areas red, uncharged areas white, positively charged areas blue, and hydrophobic areas of the central pore yellow. K^+ ions are represented by green spheres. [Courtesy of Roderick MacKinnon, Rockefeller University. PDBid 1BL8.]

One of the best characterized ion channels is a K^+ channel from *Streptomyces lividans* named **KcsA.** This 158-residue integral membrane protein, like all known K^+ channels, functions as a homotetramer. The X-ray structure of KcsA's N-terminal 125-residue segment, determined by Roderick MacKinnon, reveals that each of its subunits contains two nearly parallel transmembrane helices plus a shorter helix (Fig. 10-4a). Four such subunits associate to form a fourfold symmetric assembly surrounding a central pore. The four inner helices, which largely form the pore, pack against each other near the cytoplasmic side of the membrane much like the poles of an inverted teepee. The four outer helices, which face the lipid bilayer, buttress the inner helices. The central pore can accommodate several K^+ ions (Fig. 10-4b).

The 45-Å-long central pore has variable width: It starts at its cytoplasmic side as an ~6-Å-diameter tunnel whose entrance is lined with four anionic side chains (red area at the bottom of Fig. 10-4b) that presumably attract cations and repel anions. The pore then widens to form an ~10-Å diameter cavity. These regions of the central pore are wide enough so that

K$^+$ ion could move through them in its hydrated state. However, the upper part of the pore, called the selectivity filter, narrows to 3 Å, thereby forcing a transiting K$^+$ ion to shed its waters of hydration. The walls of the pore and the cavity are lined with hydrophobic groups that interact minimally with diffusing ions (yellow area of the pore in Fig. 10-4b). However, the selectivity filter (red area of the pore at the top of Fig. 10-b) is lined with closely spaced main chain carbonyl oxygens of residues from a TVGYG "signature sequence" that is highly conserved in all K$^+$ channels.

How does the K$^+$ channel discriminate so acutely between K$^+$ and Na$^+$ ions? The main chain O atoms lining the selectivity filter form a stack of rings (Fig. 10-5, *top*) that provide a series of closely spaced sites of appropriate dimensions for coordinating dehydrated K$^+$ ions but not the smaller Na$^+$ ions. The structure of the protein surrounding the selectivity filter suggests that the diameter of the pore is rigidly maintained, thus making the energy of a dehydrated Na$^+$ in the selectivity filter considerably higher than that of hydrated Na$^+$ and thereby accounting for the K$^+$ channel's high selectivity for K$^+$ ions.

What is the function of the cavity? Energy calculations indicate that an ion moving through a narrow transmembrane pore must surmount an energy barrier that is maximal at the center of the membrane. The existence of the cavity reduces this electrostatic destabilization by surrounding the ion with polarizable water molecules (Fig. 10-5, *bottom*). The cavity holds ~40 additional water molecules, which are disordered and therefore not seen in the X-ray structure. Remarkably, the K$^+$ ion occupying the cavity is liganded by 8 ordered water molecules located at the corners of a square antiprism (a cube with one face twisted by 45° with respect to the opposite face). K$^+$ in aqueous solution is known to have such an inner hydration shell but it had never before been visualized.

How does KcsA support such a high throughput of K$^+$ ions (up to 10^8 ions per second)? Figure 10-5 shows a string of regularly spaced K$^+$ ions: four in the selectivity filter and two more just outside it on its extracellular (top) side. Such closely spaced positive ions would strongly repel one another and hence represent a high energy situation. However, the X-ray structure is an average of many KcsA molecules, and a variety of evidence indicates that within a single channel, the K$^+$ ions in the pore actually alternate with water molecules. This arrangement means that each K$^+$ ion is surrounded by O atoms (from H$_2$O or protein carbonyl groups) at each position along the selectivity filter. As a K$^+$ ion moves into the selectivity filter from the cavity, it exchanges some of its hydrating water molecules for protein ligands, then does the reverse to restore its hydration shell when it exits the selectivity filter to enter the extracellular solution. Within the selectivity filter, the ligands are spaced and oriented such that there is little free energy change (<12 kJ · mol^{-1}) as a K$^+$ ion moves to successive positions. This level free energy landscape allows the rapid movement of K$^+$ ions through the ion channel. In

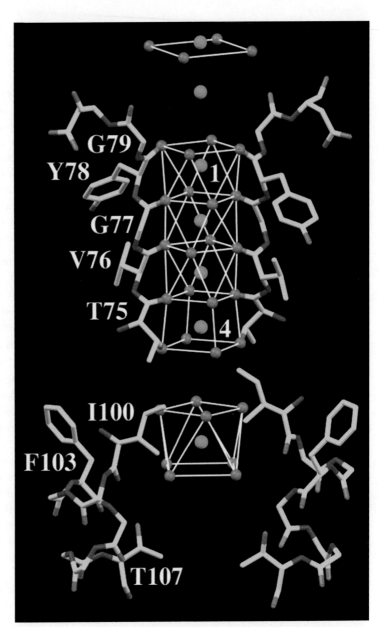

■ **Figure 10-5 | Portions of the KcsA K$^+$ channel responsible for its ion selectivity.** The protein is viewed similarly to Fig. 10-4 but with the front and back subunits omitted for clarity. The residues forming the cavity (*bottom*) and selectivity filter (*top*) are shown with atoms colored according to type (C yellow, N blue, O red, and K$^+$ ions represented by green spheres). The water and protein O atoms that ligand the K$^+$ ions, including those contributed by the front and back subunits, are represented by red spheres. The coordination polyhedra formed by these O atoms are outlined by thin white lines. [Based on an X-ray structure by Roderick MacKinnon, Rockefeller University. PDBid 1K4C.] ✍ **See Interactive Exercise 5.**

addition, mutual electrostatic repulsions between successive K^+ ions balance the attractive interactions holding these ions in the selectivity filter and hence further facilitate their rapid transit.

Ion Channels Are Gated. The physiological functions of ion channels depend not only on their exquisite ion specificity and speed of transport but also on their ability to be selectively opened or closed. For example, the ion gradients across cell membranes, which are generated by specific energy-driven pumps (Section 10-3), are discharged through Na^+ and K^+ channels. However, the pumps could not keep up with the massive fluxes of ions passing through the open channels, so *ion channels are normally shut and only open transiently to perform some specific task for the cell.* The opening and closing of ion channels, a process known as **gating,** can occur in response to a variety of stimuli:

1. **Mechanosensitive channels** open in response to local deformation in the lipid bilayer. Consequently, they respond to direct physical stimuli such as touch, sound, and changes in osmotic pressure.
2. **Ligand-gated channels** open in response to an extracellular chemical stimulus such as a neurotransmitter.
3. **Signal-gated channels** open on intracellularly binding a Ca^{2+} ion or some other signaling molecule (Section 13-4A).
4. **Voltage-gated channels** open in response to a change in membrane potential. Multicellular organisms contain numerous varieties of voltage-gated channels, including those responsible for generating nerve impulses.

Nerve Impulses Are Propagated by Action Potentials. As an example of the functions of voltage-gated channels, let us consider electrical signaling events in neurons (nerve cells). The stimulation of a neuron, a cell specialized for electrical signaling, causes Na^+ channels to open so that Na^+ ions spontaneously flow into the cell. The consequent local increase in membrane potential induces neighboring voltage-gated Na^+ channels to open. The resulting local **depolarization** of the membrane induces nearby voltage-gated K^+ channels to open. This allows K^+ ions to spontaneously flow out of the cell in a process called **repolarization** (Fig. 10-6). However, well before the distribution of Na^+ and K^+ ions across the membrane equilibrates, the Na^+ and K^+ channels spontaneously close. Yet, because depolarization of a membrane segment induces the voltage-gated Na^+ channels in a neighboring membrane segment to open, which induces their neighboring voltage-gated Na^+ channels to open, etc., a wave of transient change in the membrane potential, called an **action potential,** travels along the length of the nerve cell (which may be over 1 m long). The action potential, which travels at ~10 m/s, propagates in one direction only because after the ion channels have spontaneously closed, they resist reopening until the membrane potential has regained its resting value, which takes a few milliseconds (Fig. 10-6).

As an action potential is propagated along the length of a nerve cell, it is continuously renewed so that its signal strength remains constant (in contrast, an electrical impulse traveling down a wire dissipates as a consequence of resistive and capacitive effects). Nevertheless, the relative ion imbalance responsible for the resting membrane potential is small; only a tiny fraction of a nerve cell's Na^+–K^+ gradient (which is generated by ion pumps; Section 10-3A) is discharged by a single nerve impulse (only one K^+ ion per 3000–300,000 in the cytosol is exchanged for extracellular Na^+ as indicated by measurements with radioactive Na^+). A nerve cell can therefore

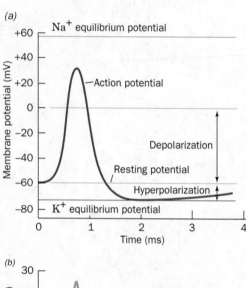

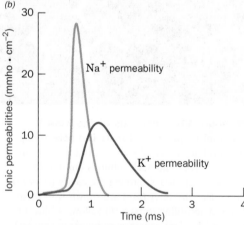

■ **Figure 10-6** | **Time course of an action potential.** (*a*) The neuron membrane undergoes rapid depolarization, followed by a nearly as rapid hyperpolarization and then a slow recovery to its resting potential. (*b*) The depolarization is caused by a transient increase in Na^+ permeability (conductance), whereas the hyperpolarization results from a more prolonged increase in K^+ permeability that begins a fraction of a millisecond later. [After Hodgkin, A.L. and Huxley, A.F., *J. Physiol.* **117,** 530 (1952).]

ransmit a nerve impulse every few milliseconds without letup. This capacity to fire rapidly is an essential feature of neuronal communications: Since action potentials all have the same amplitude, the magnitude of a stimulus is conveyed by the rate at which a nerve fires.

Voltage Gating in Kv Channels Is Triggered by the Motion of a Positively Charged Protein Helix. The subunits of all voltage-gated K^+ channels contain an ~220-residue N-terminal cytoplasmic domain, an ~250-residue transmembrane domain consisting of six helices, S1 to S6, and an ~150-residue C-terminal cytoplasmic domain (Fig. 10-7). S5 and S6 are respectively homologous to the outer and inner transmembrane helices of the KcsA channel (Fig. 10-4), and their intervening P-loop, which forms the selectivity filter, includes the same TVGYG signature sequence that occurs in KcsA. In the voltage-gated K^+ channels known as **Kv channels,** a conserved, cytoplasmic, ~100-residue so-called T1 domain precedes the transmembrane domain.

Kv channels closely resemble the KcsA channel in their tetrameric pore structure, but what is the nature of the gating machinery in the voltage-gated ion channels? The ~19-residue S4 helix, which contains around five positively charged side chains spaced about every three residues on an otherwise hydrophobic polypeptide, appears to act as a voltage sensor. Various experimental approaches indicate that when the membrane potential increases (the inside becomes less negative), the S4 helix is pulled toward the extracellular side of the membrane.

The X-ray structure of a Kv channel from rat brain named **Kv1.2** (Fig. 10-8) shows how gating might occur. As the membrane begins to depolarize, the four conserved Arg residues on the S4 helix are drawn

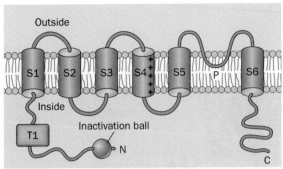

■ **Figure 10-7** | **Topology of voltage-gated K^+ channel subunits.**

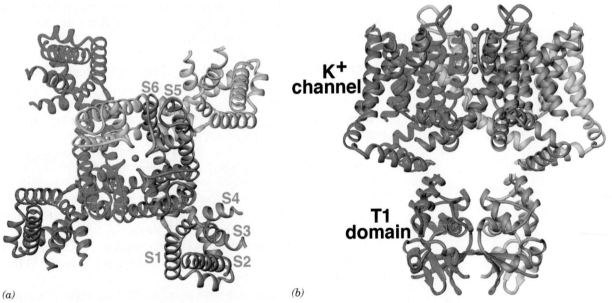

(a)   (b)

■ **Figure 10-8** | **X-Ray structure of the Kv1.2 voltage-gated K^+ channel.** (a) View along the tetrameric protein's fourfold axis from the extracellular side of the membrane in which it is embedded. Each of its four identical subunits is colored differently, and the T1 domain has been omitted for clarity. The fragmented appearance of the polypeptide chains is due to the high mobilities of the missing segments. The S5 and S6 helices with their intervening P loops form the pore for K^+ ions (delineated by green spheres). Helices S1 to S4 form a separate intramembrane voltage-sensing domain that associates with the S5 and S6 helices of the clockwise adjacent subunit. (b) View perpendicular to that in Part a with the extracellular side of the membrane above. The pore and voltage sensing domains span a distance of 30 Å, the thickness of the membrane's hydrophobic core. The T1 domain, which occupies the cytoplasm, forms the vestibule of the transmembrane K^+ channel. The four large openings between the T1 domain and the K^+ channel are the portals through which K^+ ions enter the K^+ channel. [Based on an X-ray structure by Roderick MacKinnon, Rockefeller University. PDBid 2A79.]

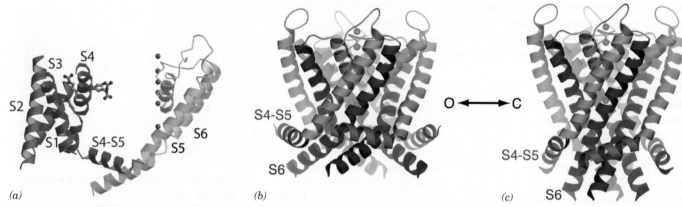

(a)　　　　　　　　　　　(b)　　　　　　　　　　　(c)

■ **Figure 10-9** | **Operation of the transmembrane domain of the Kv1.2 voltage-gated K⁺ channel.** (*a*) Side view of a single subunit with its extracellular side at the top. The pore-forming helices (S5 and S6) are gray, and the voltage-sensor domain (helices S1–S4) is blue. The S4–S5 linker helix (not drawn in Fig. 10-7), which is parallel to the membrane surface, connects the voltage-sensing domain to the domain forming the K⁺ pore (delineated by green spheres). Four Arg residues on S4 are shown in ball-and-stick form with C atoms gold and N atoms blue. Two of these residues interact with the protein, and two project into the lipid bilayer. (*b*) Side view of the channel tetramer in its open conformation. The S5 helices are gray, the S6 helices are blue, and the S4–S5 linker helix is red. (*c*) Hypothetical model of the channel in its closed conformation, colored as in Part *b*. The downward movement of the Arg-bearing S4 helix (not shown in this drawing) pushes down on the S4–S5 linker helix to pinch off the pore at its cytoplasmic end (*bottom*). [Courtesy of Roderick MacKinnon, Rockefeller University. PDBid 2A79.]

toward the extracellular surface (up in Fig. 10-9), pulling on the S4-S5 linker helix (not drawn in Fig. 10-7) and with it the S5 helix. This splays the ends of the S6 helices so as to enlarge the intracellular entrance to the K⁺ channel (Fig. 10-9*b*). During repolarization, as the cell interior becomes more negative, the positively charged S4 helix drops back toward the cytoplasmic side of the membrane, pressing down on the S4-S5 lever to close off the channel (Fig. 10-9*c*).

Ion Channels Have a Second Gate. Electrophysiological measurements indicate that Kv channels spontaneously close a few milliseconds after opening and do not reopen until after the membrane has regained its resting membrane potential. Evidently, *the Kv channel contains two voltage-sensitive gates, one to open the channel on an increase in membrane potential and one to inactivate it a short time later.* This inactivation of the Kv channel is abolished by proteolytically excising its N-terminal 20-residue segment, whose NMR structure is a ball-like assembly. In the intact Kv channel, this "inactivation ball" is tethered to the end of a flexible 65-residue peptide segment (Fig. 10-7), suggesting that channel inactivation normally occurs when the ball swings around to bind in the mouth of the open K⁺ pore, thereby blocking the passage of K⁺ ions. The mobility of this "ball and chain" is presumably why it is not visible in the X-ray structure of Kv1.2 (Fig. 10-8).

The T1 tetramer does not have an axial channel, so the inactivation ball must find its way to block the central pore through the side portals between the T1 tetramer and the central pore (Fig. 10-8*b*). These portals, which are 15 to 20 Å across, are lined with negatively charged groups that presumably attract K⁺ ions.

The cytoplasmic entrance to the K⁺ channel pore is only 6 Å in diameter, too narrow to admit the inactivation ball. Therefore, it appears that the ball peptide must unfold in order to enter the pore. The first 10 residues of the unfolded ball peptide are predominantly hydrophobic and presumably make contact with the hydrophobic residues lining the Kv channel pore. The next 10 residues, which are largely hydrophilic and contain several cationic groups, bind to anionic groups lining the entrance to the side portals in T1. Thus, the inactivation peptide acts more like a snake than a ball and chain. A Kv channel engineered so that only one subunit has an inactivation peptide still becomes inactivated but at one-fourth the rate of normal Kv channels. Apparently, any of the normal Kv channel's four inactivation peptides can block the channel and it is simply a matter of chance as to which one does so.

Other Voltage-Gated Cation Channels Contain a Central Pore. Voltage-gated Na^+ and Ca^{2+} channels appear to resemble K^+ channels, although rather than forming homotetramers, they are monomers of four consecutive domains, each of which is homologous to the K^+ channel, separated by often large cytoplasmic loops. These domains presumably assume a pseudotetrameric arrangement about a central pore resembling that of voltage-gated K^+ channels. This structural homology suggests that voltage-gated ion channels share a common architecture in which differences in ion selectivity arise from precise stereochemical variations within the central pore. However, outside of their conserved transmembrane core, voltage-gated ion channels with different ion selectivities are highly divergent. For example, the T1 domain of Kv channels is absent in other types of voltage-gated ion channels.

Cl^- Channels Differ from Cation Channels. **Cl^- channels,** which occur in all cell types, permit the transmembrane movement of chloride ions along their concentration gradient. In mammals, the extracellular Cl^- concentration is ~120 mM and the intracellular concentration is ~4 mM.

ClC Cl^- channels form a large family of anion channels that occur widely in both prokaryotes and eukaryotes. The X-ray structures of ClC Cl^- channels from two species of bacteria, determined by MacKinnon, reveal, as biophysical measurements had previously suggested, that ClC Cl^- channels are homodimers with each subunit forming an anion-selective pore (Fig. 10-10). Each subunit consists mainly of 18 mostly transmembrane α helices that are remarkably tilted with respect to the membrane plane and have variable lengths compared to the transmembrane helices in other integral proteins of known structures.

The specificity of the Cl^- channel results from an electrostatic field established by basic amino acids on the protein surface, which helps funnel anions toward the pore, and by a selectivity filter formed by the N-terminal ends of several α helices. Because the polar groups of an α helix are all aligned (Fig. 6-7), it forms a strong electrical dipole with its N-terminal end positively charged. This feature of the selectivity filter helps attract Cl^- ions, which are specifically coordinated by main chain amide nitrogens and side chain hydroxyls from Ser and Tyr residues. A positively charged residue such as Lys or Arg, if it were present in

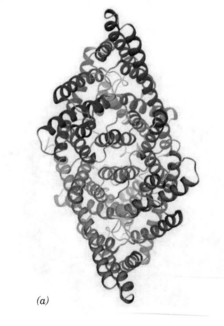

(a)

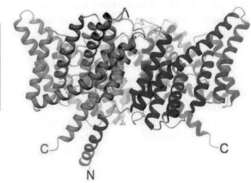

(b)

Figure 10-10 | X-Ray structure of the ClC Cl^- channel from _Salmonella typhimurium_. Each subunit of the homodimer contains 18 α helices of variable lengths. (*a*) View from the extracellular side of the membrane. The two subunits are colored blue and red. The green spheres represent Cl^- ions in the selectivity filter. (*b*) View from within the membrane with the extracellular surface above. The scale bar indicates the thickness of the membrane. [Courtesy of Roderick MacKinnon, Rockefeller University. PDBid 1KPL.]

35 Å

the selectivity filter, would probably bind a Cl^- ion too tightly to facilitate its rapid transit through the channel.

Unlike the K^+ channel, which has a central aqueous cavity (Fig. 10-4b), the Cl^- channel is hourglass-shaped, with its narrowest part in the center of the membrane and flanked by wider aqueous "vestibules." A conserved Glu side chain projects into the pore. This group would repel other anions, suggesting that rapid Cl^- flux requires a protein conformational change in which the Glu side chain moves aside. Another anion could push the Glu away, which explains why some Cl^- channels appear to be activated by Cl^- ions; that is, they open in response to a certain concentration of Cl^- in the extracellular fluid.

D | Aquaporins Mediate the Transmembrane Movement of Water

The observed rapid passage of water molecules across biological membranes had long been assumed to occur via simple diffusion that was made possible by the small size of water molecules and their high concentrations in biological systems. However, certain cells, such as those in the kidney, can sustain particularly rapid rates of water transport, which can be reversibly inhibited by mercuric ions. This suggested the existence of previously unrecognized protein pores that conduct water through biological membranes. The first of these elusive proteins was discovered in 1992 by Peter Agre, who named them **aquaporins.**

Aquaporins are widely distributed in nature; plants may have as many as 50 different aquaporins. The 11 mammalian aquaporins that have been identified are expressed at high levels in tissues that rapidly transport water, including kidneys, salivary glands, and lacrimal glands (which produce tears). Aquaporins permit the passage of water molecules at an extremely high rate ($\sim 3 \times 10^9$ per second) but do not permit the transport of solutes (e.g., glycerol or urea) or ions, including, most surprisingly, protons (really hydronium ions; H_3O^+), whose free passage would discharge the cell's membrane potential.

The most extensively characterized member of the aquaporin family, **AQP1,** is a homotetrameric glycoprotein. Its X-ray and electron crystallographic structures reveal that each of its subunits consists mainly of six transmembrane α helices plus two shorter helices that lie within the bilayer (Fig. 10-11). These helices are arranged so as to form an elongated hourglass-shaped central pore that, at its narrowest point, the so-called constriction region, is ~ 2.8 Å wide, which is the van der Waals diameter of a water molecule (Fig. 10-12). Much of the pore is lined with hydrophobic groups whose lack of strong interactions with water molecules hasten their passage through the pore. However, for a water molecule to transit the constriction region, it must shed its associated waters of hydration. This is facilitated by the side chains of highly conserved Arg and His residues as well as several backbone carbonyl groups that form hydrogen bonds to a transiting water molecule and hence readily displace its associated water molecules, much as occurs with K^+ in the selectivity filter of the KcsA channel (Section 10-2C).

If water were to pass through aquaporin as an uninterrupted chain of hydrogen-bonded molecules, then protons would pass even more rapidly through the channel via proton jumping (Fig. 2-15; in order for more than one such series of proton jumps to occur, each water molecule in the chain must reorient such that one of its protons forms a hydrogen bond to the next water molecule in the chain). However, aquaporin interrupts this

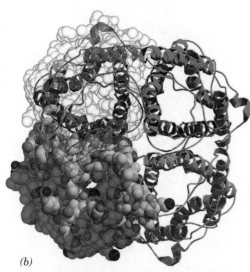

(a)

(b)

■ **Figure 10-11 | X-Ray structure of the aquaporin AQP1 from bovine erythrocytes.** (*a*) Superimposed ribbon and space-filling models of an aquaporin subunit as viewed from within the membrane with its extracellular surface above. The eight helical segments are drawn with different colors. (*b*) View of the aquaporin tetramer from the extracellular surface. Each subunit forms a water-transport channel, which is visible in the space-filling subunit model at the lower left. [Courtesy of Bing Jap, University of California at Berkeley. PDBid 1J4N.]

process by forming hydrogen bonds from the side chain NH_2 groups of two highly conserved Asn residues to a water molecule that is centrally located in the pore (Fig. 10-12). Consequently, although this central water molecule can readily donate hydrogen bonds to its neighboring water molecules in the hydrogen-bonded chain, it cannot accept one from them nor reorient, thereby severing the "proton-conducting wire."

E | Transport Proteins Alternate between Two Conformations

Up to this point, we have examined the structures and functions of membrane proteins that form a physical passageway for small molecules, ions, or water. Membrane proteins known as **connexins** also form such channels, in the form of **gap junctions** between cells (see Box 10-1). However, not all membrane transport proteins offer a discrete bilayer-spanning pore. Instead, some proteins undergo conformational changes to move substances from one side of the membrane to the other. The **erythrocyte glucose transporter** (also known as **GLUT1**) is such a protein.

Biochemical evidence indicates that GLUT1 has glucose-binding sites on both sides of the membrane. John Barnett showed that adding a propyl group to glucose C1 prevents glucose binding to the outer surface of the membrane, whereas adding a propyl group to C6 prevents binding to the inner surface. He therefore proposed that this transmembrane protein has two alternate conformations: one with the glucose site facing the external cell surface, requiring O1 contact and leaving O6 free, and the other with the glucose site facing the internal cell surface, requiring O6 contact and leaving O1 free. Transport apparently occurs as follows (Fig. 10-13):

1. Glucose binds to the protein on one face of the membrane.
2. A conformational change closes the first binding site and exposes the binding site on the other side of the membrane (transport).
3. Glucose dissociates from the protein.
4. The transport cycle is completed by the reversion of GLUT1 to its initial conformation in the absence of bound glucose (recovery).

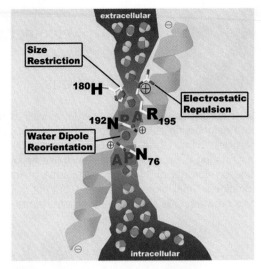

■ **Figure 10-12** | **Schematic drawing of the water-conducting pore of aquaporin AQP1.** The pore is viewed from within the membrane with the extracellular surface above. The positions of residues critical for preventing the passage of protons, other ions, and small molecule solutes are indicated. [Courtesy of Peter Agre, The Johns Hopkins School of Medicine.]

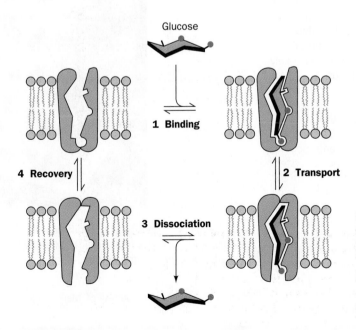

■ **Figure 10-13** | **Model for glucose transport.** The transport protein alternates between two mutually exclusive conformations. The glucose molecule (*red*) is not drawn to scale. [After Baldwin, S.A. and Lienhard, G.E., *Trends Biochem. Sci.* **6,** 210 (1981).] **♫ See the Animated Figures.**

BOX 10-1 PERSPECTIVES IN BIOCHEMISTRY

Gap Junctions

Most eukaryotic cells are in metabolic as well as physical contact with neighboring cells. This contact is brought about by tubular particles, named **gap junctions,** that join discrete regions of neighboring plasma membranes much like hollow rivets. The gap junction consists of two apposed plasma membrane–embedded complexes. Small molecules and ions, but not macromolecules, can pass between cells via the gap junction's central channel.

Cytoplasm

Cytoplasm

Ions, amino acids, sugars, nucleotides

Proteins, nucleic acids

Intercellular space

These intercellular channels are so widespread that many whole organs are continuous from within. Thus, *gap junctions are important intercellular communication channels.* For example, the synchronized contraction of heart muscle is brought about by flows of ions through gap junctions, and gap junctions serve as conduits for some of the substances that mediate embryonic development.

Mammalian gap junction channels are 16 to 20 Å in diameter, which Werner Loewenstein established by microinjecting single cells with fluorescent molecules of various sizes and observing with a fluorescence microscope whether the fluorescent probe passed into neighboring cells. The molecules and ions that can pass freely between neighboring cells are limited in molecular mass to a maximum of ~1000 D; macromolecules such as proteins and nucleic acids cannot leave a cell via this route.

The diameter of a gap junction channel varies with Ca^{2+} concentration: The channels are fully open when the Ca^{2+} level is $<10^{-7}$ M and become narrower as the Ca^{2+} concentration increases until, above 5×10^{-5} M, they close. This shutter system is thought to protect communities of interconnected cells from the otherwise catastrophic damage that would result from the death of even one of their members. Cells generally maintain very low cytosolic Ca^{2+} concentrations ($<10^{-7}$ M) by actively pumping Ca^{2+} out of the cell as well as into their mitochondria and endoplasmic reticulum (Section 10-3B). Ca^{2+} floods back into leaky or metabolically depressed cells, thereby inducing closure of their gap junctions and sealing them off from their neighbors.

Gap junctions are constructed from a single sort of protein subunit known as a **connexin.** A single gap junction consists of two hexagonal rings of connexins, called **connexons,** one from each of the adjoining plasma membranes. A given animal expresses numerous genetically distinct connexins, with molecular masses ranging from 25 to 50 kD. At least some connexons may be formed from two or more species of connexins, and the gap junctions joining two cells may consist of two different types of connexons. These various types of gap junctions presumably differ in their selectivities for the substances they transmit.

The structure of a cardiac gap junction, determined by electron crystallography, reveals a symmetrical assembly that has a diameter of ~70 Å, a length of ~150 Å, and encloses a central channel whose diameter varies from ~40 Å at its mouth to ~15 Å in its interior. The transmembrane portions of the gap junction each contain 24 rods of electron density that are arranged with hexagonal symmetry and which extend normal to the membrane plane.

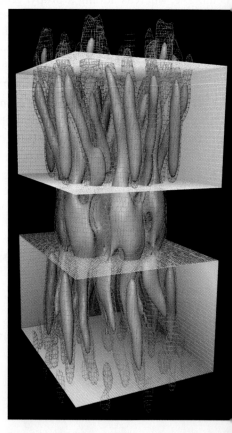

Here, the electron density at two different levels is represented by the solid and mesh contours (*gold*), whereas the white boxes indicate the positions of the cell membranes.

[Electron crystal structure courtesy of Mark Yeager, The Scripps Research Institute, La Jolla, California.]

BOX 10-2 PERSPECTIVES IN BIOCHEMISTRY

Differentiating Mediated and Nonmediated Transport

Glucose and many other compounds can enter cells by a non-mediated pathway; that is, they slowly diffuse into cells at a rate proportional to their membrane solubility and their concentrations on either side of the membrane. This is a linear process: the **flux** (rate of transport per unit area) of a substance across the membrane increases with the magnitude of its concentration gradient (the difference between its internal and external concentrations). If the same substance, say glucose, moves across a membrane by means of a transport protein, its flux is no longer linear. This is one of four characteristics that distinguish mediated from nonmediated transport:

1. **Speed and specificity.** The solubilities of the chemically similar sugars D-glucose and D-mannitol in a synthetic lipid bilayer are similar. However, the rate at which glucose moves through the erythrocyte membrane is four orders of magnitude faster than that of D-mannitol. The erythrocyte membrane must therefore contain a system that transports glucose and that can distinguish D-glucose from D-mannitol.

2. **Saturation.** The rate of glucose transport into an erythrocyte does not increase infinitely as the external glucose concentration increases: The rate gradually approaches a maximum. Such an observation is evidence that a specific number of sites on the membrane are involved in the transport of glucose. At high [glucose], the transporters become saturated, much like myoglobin becomes saturated with O_2 at high pO_2 (Fig. 7-4). As expected, the plot of glucose flux versus [glucose] (*above right*) is hyperbolic. The nonmediated glucose flux increases linearly with [glucose] but would not visibly depart from the baseline on the scale of the graph.

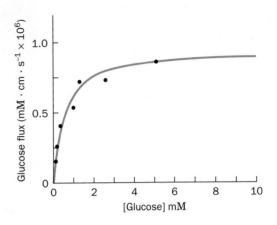

3. **Competition.** The above curve is shifted to the right in the presence of a substance that competes with glucose for binding to the transporter; for example, 6-O-benzyl-D-galactose has this effect. Competition is not a feature of nonmediated transport, since no transport protein is involved.

4. **Inactivation.** Reagents that chemically modify proteins and hence may affect their functions may eliminate the rapid, saturatable flux of glucose into the erythrocyte. The susceptibility of the erythrocyte glucose transport system to protein-modifying reagents is additional proof that it is a protein.

[Graph based on data from Stein, W.D., *Movement of Molecules across Membranes,* p. 134, Academic Press (1967).]

This transport cycle can occur in either direction, according to the relative concentrations of intracellular and extracellular glucose. GLUT1 provides a means of equilibrating the glucose concentration across the erythrocyte membrane without any accompanying leakage of small molecules or ions (as might occur through an always-open channel such as a porin).

All known transport proteins appear to be asymmetrically situated transmembrane proteins that alternate between two conformational states in which the ligand-binding sites are exposed, in turn, to opposite sides of the membrane. Such a mechanism is analogous to the T → R allosteric transition of proteins such as hemoglobin (Section 7-1B). In fact, many of the features of ligand-binding proteins such as myoglobin and hemoglobin also apply to transport proteins (Box 10-2).

Biochemical analyses indicate that GLUT1 has 12 membrane-spanning α helices and probably forms a tetramer in the membrane. This protein belongs to a large family of transporters whose structures have not been as well characterized as those of channel-type proteins. The 6.5-Å-resolution electron crystal structure of a bacterial **oxalate transporter** named **OxlT** reveals that its 12 transmembrane helices are arranged around a central

■ Figure 10-14 | Electron crystal structure of oxalate transporter OxlT from *Oxalobacter formigenes*. Twelve α helices have been fitted to the electron density map, which has a resolution of 6.5 Å. The green helices are nearly perpendicular to the plane of the membrane; yellow helices include a bend; and magenta helices are both bent and curved to match the electron density. Segments linking the helices are not resolved. [Courtesy of Sriram Subramaniam, NIH, Bethesda, Maryland.]

cavity, which presumably represents a substrate-binding site (Fig. 10-14) The protein exhibits a high degree of symmetry between its cytoplasmi and external halves, which is consistent with its ability to transport sub stances both into and out of the cell. The structure shown in Fig. 10-1 probably corresponds to a conformational intermediate that is not full accessible to either the cytoplasmic or extracellular face of the membrane

Some transporters can transport more than one substance. For exam ple, the bacterial oxalate transporter transports **oxalate** into the cell an transports **formate** out.

$$^-OOC-COO^- \qquad H-COO^-$$
Oxalate **Formate**

■ CHECK YOUR UNDERSTANDING

What are the similarities and differences among ionophores, porins, ion channels, and passive-mediated transport proteins? Explain how and why ion channels are gated. Use the terminology of allosteric proteins to discuss the operation of proteins that carry out uniport, symport, and antiport transport processes.

Some transport proteins move more than one substance at a time. Hence it is useful to categorize mediated transport according to the stoichiometr of the transport process (Fig. 10-15):

1. A **uniport** involves the movement of a single molecule at a time GLUT1 is a uniport system.
2. A **symport** simultaneously transports two different molecules in th same direction.
3. An **antiport** simultaneously transports two different molecules i opposite directions.

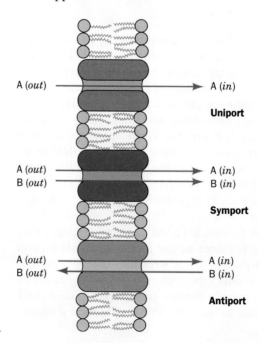

■ Figure 10-15 | Uniport, symport, and antiport translocation systems.

3 Active Transport

Passive-mediated transporters, including porins, ion channels, and proteins such as GLUT1, facilitate the transmembrane movement of substances according to the relative concentrations of the substance on either side of the membrane. For example, the glucose concentration in the blood plasma (~5 mM) is generally higher than in cells, so GLUT1 allows glucose to enter the erythrocyte to be metabolized. Many substances, however, are available on one side of a membrane in lower concentrations than are required on the other side of the membrane. Such substances must be actively and selectively transported across the membrane against their concentration gradients.

Active transport is an endergonic process that, in most cases, is coupled to the hydrolysis of ATP. Several families of ATP-dependent transporters have been identified:

1. **P-type ATPases** undergo phosphorylation as they transport cations such as Na^+, K^+, and Ca^{2+} across the membrane.
2. **F-type ATPases** are proton-transporting complexes located in mitochondria and bacterial membranes. Instead of using the free energy of ATP to pump protons against their gradient, these proteins operate in reverse in order to synthesize ATP, as we shall see in Section 18-3.
3. **V-type ATPases** resemble the F-type ATPases and occur in plant vacuoles and acidic vesicles such as animal lysosomes.
4. **A-type ATPases** transport anions across membranes.
5. **ABC transporters** are named for their *ATP*-*b*inding *c*assette and transport a wide variety of substances, including ions, small metabolites, and drug molecules.

In this section, we examine two P-type ATPases and an ABC transporter; these proteins carry out **primary active transport.** In **secondary active transport,** the free energy of the electrochemical gradient generated by another mechanism, such as an ion-pumping ATPase, is used to transport a neutral molecule against its concentration gradient.

LEARNING OBJECTIVES

■ Understand how pumps use the free energy of ATP to transport ions against their gradient.
■ Understand that ABC transporters move amphipathic substances from one side of the membrane to the other.
■ Understand the difference between primary and secondary active transport.

A | The (Na^+–K^+)–ATPase Transports Ions in Opposite Directions

One of the most thoroughly studied active transport systems is the **Na^+–K^+)–ATPase** in the plasma membranes of higher eukaryotes, which was first characterized by Jens Skou. This transmembrane protein consists of two types of subunits: a 110-kD nonglycosylated α subunit that contains the enzyme's catalytic activity and ion-binding sites, and a 55-kD glycoprotein β subunit of unknown function. Sequence analysis suggests that the α subunit has eight transmembrane α-helical segments and two large cytoplasmic domains. The β subunit has a single transmembrane helix and a large extracellular domain. The protein may function as an $(\alpha\beta)_2$ tetramer *in vivo* (Fig. 10-16).

The (Na^+–K^+)–ATPase is often called the **(Na^+–K^+) pump** because it pumps Na^+ out of and K^+ into the cell with the concomitant hydrolysis of intracellular ATP. The overall stoichiometry of the reaction is

$$3\,Na^+(in) + 2\,K^+(out) + ATP + H_2O \rightleftharpoons$$
$$3\,Na^+(out) + 2\,K^+(in) + ADP + P_i$$

The (Na^+–K^+)–ATPase is an antiport that generates a charge separation across the membrane, since three positive charges exit the cell for every two

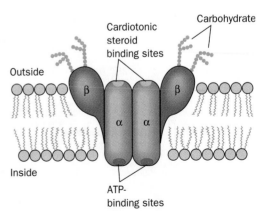

■ **Figure 10-16 | (Na^+–K^+)–ATPase.** This diagram shows the transporter's putative dimeric structure and its orientation in the plasma membrane. Cardiotonic steroids (Box 10-3) bind to the external surface of the transporter so as to inhibit transport.

that enter. This extrusion of Na$^+$ enables animal cells to control their water content osmotically; *without functioning (Na$^+$–K$^+$)–ATPases to maintain low internal [Na$^+$], water would osmotically rush in to such an extent the animal cells, which lack cell walls, would swell and burst.* The electrochemical gradient generated by the (Na$^+$–K$^+$)–ATPase is also responsible for the electrical excitability of nerve cells (Section 10-2C). In fact, all cells expend a large fraction of the ATP they produce (up to 70% in nerve cells) to maintain their required cytosolic Na$^+$ and K$^+$ concentrations.

The key to the (Na$^+$–K$^+$)–ATPase is the phosphorylation of a specific Asp residue of the transport protein. ATP phosphorylates the transporter only in the presence of Na$^+$, whereas the resulting aspartyl phosphate residue

$$\begin{array}{c} | \\ \text{C}=\text{O} \qquad\qquad \text{O} \\ | \qquad\qquad\qquad\quad \| \\ \text{CH}-\text{CH}_2-\text{C}-\text{OPO}_3^- \\ | \\ \text{NH} \\ | \end{array}$$

Aspartyl phosphate
residue

is subject to hydrolysis only in the presence of K$^+$. This suggests that the (Na$^+$–K$^+$)–ATPase has two conformational states (called E_1 and E_2) with different structures, different catalytic activities, and different ligand specificities. The protein appears to operate in the following manner (Fig. 10-17).

1. The transporter in the E_1 state binds three Na$^+$ ions inside the cell and then binds ATP to yield an $E_1 \cdot \text{ATP} \cdot 3\,\text{Na}^+$ complex.

2. ATP hydrolysis produces ADP and a "high-energy" aspartyl phosphate intermediate $E_1{\sim}\text{P} \cdot 3\,\text{Na}^+$ (here "$\sim$" indicates a "high-energy" bond).

3. This "high-energy" intermediate relaxes to its "low-energy" conformation, $E_2{-}\text{P} \cdot 3\,\text{Na}^+$, and releases its bound Na$^+$ outside the cell.

4. $E_2{-}\text{P}$ binds two K$^+$ ions from outside the cell to form an $E_2{-}\text{P} \cdot 2\,\text{K}^+$ complex.

5. The phosphate group is hydrolyzed, yielding $E_2 \cdot 2\,\text{K}^+$.

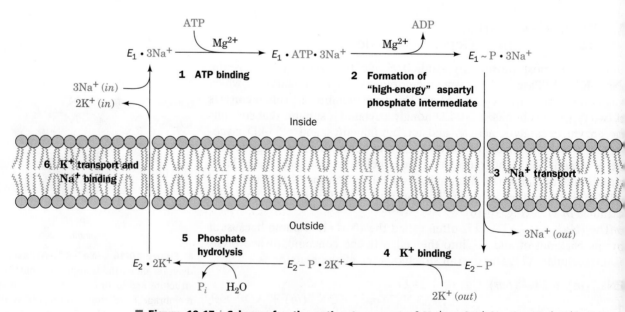

■ **Figure 10-17** | **Scheme for the active transport of Na$^+$ and K$^+$ by the (Na$^+$–K$^+$)–ATPase**

BOX 10-3 BIOCHEMISTRY IN HEALTH AND DISEASE

The Action of Cardiac Glycosides

The cardiac glycosides are natural products that increase the intensity of heart muscle contraction. Indeed, **digitalis,** an extract of purple foxglove leaves, which contains a mixture of cardiac glycosides including **digitalin** (see figure below), has been used to treat congestive heart failure for centuries. The cardiac glycoside **ouabain** (pronounced wabane), a product of the East African ouabio tree, has been long used as an arrow poison.

intracellular $[Na^+]$ stimulates the cardiac $(Na^+–Ca^{2+})$ antiport system, which pumps Na^+ out of and Ca^{2+} into the cell, ultimately boosting the $[Ca^{2+}]$ in the sarcoplasmic reticulum. Thus, the release of Ca^{2+} to trigger muscle contraction (Section 7-2B) produces a larger than normal increase in cytosolic $[Ca^{2+}]$, thereby intensifying the force of cardiac muscle contraction. Ouabain, which was once thought to be produced only by plants, has recently been

Digitalin

Ouabain

These two steroids, which are still among the most commonly prescribed cardiac drugs, inhibit the $(Na^+–K^+)$–ATPase by binding strongly to an externally exposed portion of the protein (Fig. 10-16) so as to block Step 5 in Fig. 10-17. The resultant increase in

discovered to be an animal hormone that is secreted by the adrenal cortex and functions to regulate cellular $[Na^+]$ and overall body salt and water balance.

---

6. $E_2 \cdot 2\,K^+$ changes conformation, releases its two K^+ ions inside the cell, and replaces them with three Na^+ ions, thereby completing the transport cycle.

Although each of the above reaction steps is individually reversible, the cycle, as diagramed in Fig. 10-17, circulates only in the clockwise direction under normal physiological conditions. This is because ATP hydrolysis and ion transport are coupled vectorial (unidirectional) processes. The vectorial nature of the reaction cycle results from the alternation of some of the steps of the exergonic ATP hydrolysis reaction (Steps 1 + 2 and Step 5) with some of the steps of the endergonic ion transport process (Steps 3 + 4 and Step 6). Thus, *neither reaction can go to completion unless the other one also does.* Study of the $(Na^+–K^+)$–ATPase has been greatly facilitated by the use of glycosides that inhibit the transporter (Box 10-3).

B | The Ca^{2+}–ATPase Pumps Ca^{2+} Out of the Cytosol

Transient increases in cytosolic $[Ca^{2+}]$ trigger numerous cellular responses including muscle contraction (Section 7-2B), the release of neurotransmitters,

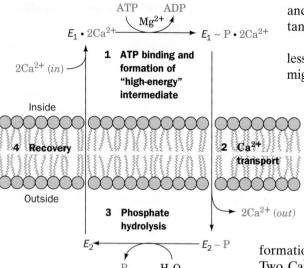

■ Figure 10-18 | Scheme for the active transport of Ca²⁺ by the Ca²⁺–ATPase. Here (*in*) refers to the cytosol and (*out*) refers to the outside of the cell for plasma membrane Ca²⁺–ATPase or the lumen of the endoplasmic reticulum (or sarcoplasmic reticulum) for the Ca²⁺–ATPase of that membrane.

and glycogen breakdown (Section 16-3). Moreover, Ca^{2+} is an important activator of oxidative metabolism (Section 18-4).

The $[Ca^{2+}]$ in the cytosol (~0.1 μM) is four orders of magnitude less than it is in the extracellular spaces [~1500 μM; intracellular Ca^{2+} might otherwise combine with phosphate to form $Ca_3(PO_4)_2$, which has a maximum solubility of only 65 μM]. This large concentration gradient is maintained by the active transport of Ca^{2+} across the plasma membrane and the endoplasmic reticulum (the sarcoplasmic reticulum in muscle) by a **Ca^{2+}–ATPase.** This Ca^{2+} **pump** actively pumps two Ca^{2+} ions out of the cytosol at the expense of ATP hydrolysis, while countertransporting two or three protons. The mechanism of the Ca^{2+}–ATPase (Fig. 10-18) resembles that of the $(Na^+–K^+)$–ATPase (Fig. 10-17).

The superimposed X-ray structures of the Ca^{2+}–ATPase from rabbit muscle sarcoplasmic reticulum in its E_1 and E_2 conformations, determined by Chikashi Toyoshima, are shown in Fig. 10-19. Two Ca^{2+} ions bind within a bundle of 10 transmembrane helices. Three additional domains form a large structure on the cytoplasmic side of the membrane. The differences between the Ca^{2+}-bound (E_1) and the Ca^{2+}-free (E_2) structures indicate that the transporter undergoes extensive rearrangements, particularly in the positions of the cytoplasmic domains but also in the Ca^{2+}-transporting membrane domain, during the reaction cycle. These changes apparently mediate communication between the Ca^{2+} binding sites and the ~80-Å-distant site where bound ATP is hydrolyzed.

C | ABC Transporters Are Responsible for Drug Resistance

The inability of anticancer drugs to kill cancer cells is frequently traced to the overexpression of a membrane protein known as **P-glycoprotein.** This member of the ABC class of transporters pumps a variety of amphiphilic substances—including many drugs—out of the cell, so that it is also called a **multidrug resistance (MDR) transporter.** Similar proteins in bacteria contribute to their antibiotic resistance.

The **ABC transporters,** which pump ions, sugars, amino acids, and other polar and nonpolar substances, are built from four modules: two highly conserved cytoplasmic nucleotide-binding domains, and two transmembrane domains that typically contain six transmembrane helices each. In bacteria, the four domains are contained on two or four separate polypeptides, and in eukaryotes, a single polypeptide includes all four domains. Bacterial ABC transporters mediate the uptake as well as the efflux of a variety of compounds, whereas their eukaryotic counterparts apparently

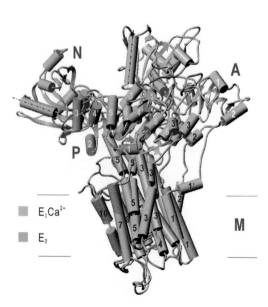

■ Figure 10-19 | X-Ray structures of the Ca²⁺-free and Ca²⁺-bound Ca²⁺–ATPase. The Ca^{2+}-free form, E_2, is green with black helix numbers, and the Ca^{2+}-bound form, E_1Ca^{2+}, is violet with yellow helix numbers. These proteins, which are superimposed on their transmembrane domains, are viewed from within the membrane with the cytosolic side up. Ten transmembrane helices form the M (for membrane) domain, ATP binds to the N (for nucleotide-binding) domain, the Asp residue that is phosphorylated during the reaction cycle is located on the P (for phosphorylation) domain, and the A (for actuator) domain is so named because it participates in the transmission of major conformational changes. Dashed lines highlight the orientations of a helix in the N domain in the two conformations and the horizontal lines delineate the membrane. [Courtesy of Chikashi Toyoshima, University of Tokyo, Japan. PDBids 1EUL and 1WIO.]

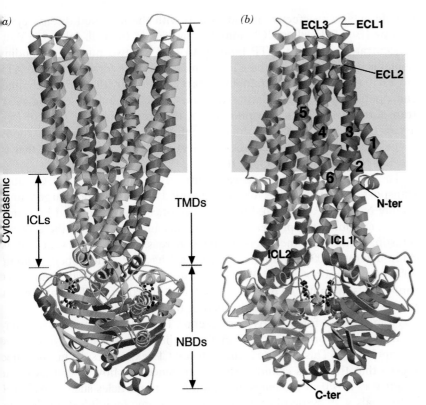

■ **Figure 10-20** | **X-Ray structure of the ABC transporter Sav1866 from *Staphylococcus aureus.*** (*a*) Ribbon diagram of the homodimeric protein in which its subunits are colored yellow-green and turquoise. The protein is viewed parallel to the membrane with its extracellular surface at the top. The transmembrane domains (TMDs), nucleotide-binding domains (NBDs), and intracellular loops (ICLs) are indicated, and the gray box marks the approximate location of the lipid bilayer. (*b*) Same model, rotated 90° around its vertical molecular twofold axis. Its bound ADP molecules are drawn in ball-and-stick form. The transmembrane helices of the turquoise subunit are numbered, and several extracellular loops (ECL) and intracellular loops (ICL) are indicated. [Courtesy of Kaspar Locher, ETH, Zurich, Switzerland. PDBid 2HYD.]

operate only as exporters that transport material out of the cell or into intracellular compartments such as the endoplasmic reticulum.

The X-ray structure of a bacterial ABC transporter called **Sav1866,** which shows significant homology to human P-glycoprotein, provides some clues about how the ABC transporters function. The two identical subunits of Sav1866 are extensively intertwined, with three helices from each subunit forming each of the two arms of the V-shaped transmembrane domain (Fig. 10-20*a*). Two ATP-binding sites are located at the interface between the subunits in the nucleotide-binding domains. Conformational changes resulting from ATP binding and hydrolysis in this part of the protein appear to be transmitted to the transmembrane domains via small movements in two short intracellular helices (ICL; Fig. 10-20*b*) that are oriented parallel to the membrane. These so-called coupling helices interact with the nucleotide-binding domain of the opposite subunit, permitting the two subunits of the transporter to move in concert.

In the nucleotide-bound state drawn in Fig. 10-20, the transmembrane domains define a cavity that is accessible to the outer leaflet of the bilayer and the extracellular space. ATP hydrolysis presumably triggers a conformational change that exposes the cavity to the cytosol and the inner leaflet. Thus, ATP-driven conformational changes would allow the transporter to bind a molecule from inside the cell or from the inner leaflet and release it outside the cell or into the outer leaflet (hence the transporter would operate as a flipase for lipid-soluble substances). In its outward-facing conformation, the cavity is lined primarily with polar and charged residues, which would favor the release of hydrophobic substances such as drug molecules.

CFTR Is an ABC Transporter. Only one of the thousands of known ABC transporters functions as an ion channel rather than a pump: the **cystic fibrosis transmembrane conductance regulator (CFTR).** This 1480-residue protein, which is defective in individuals with the inherited disease cystic fibrosis (Box 3-1), allows Cl⁻ ions to flow out of the cell, following their concentration gradient. ATP binding to CFTR's two nucleotide-binding domains appears to open the Cl⁻ channel, and the hydrolysis of one ATP closes it (the other ATP remains intact). However, the CFTR channel can open only if its regulatory domain (which is unique among ABC transporters) has been phosphorylated, thus regulating the flow of ions across the membrane. CFTR does not exhibit high specificity for Cl⁻ ions, suggesting that the channel lacks a selectivity filter analogous to that in the KcsA K⁺ channel (Section 10-2C).

The maintenance of electrical neutrality requires that the Cl⁻ ions transported by the CFTR be accompanied by positively charged ions, mainly Na⁺. The transported ions are osmotically accompanied by water, thus maintaining the proper level of fluidity in secretions of the airways, intestinal tract, and the ducts of the pancreas, testes, and sweat glands. Although over 1000 mutations of the CFTR have been described, in about 70% of cystic fibrosis cases, Phe 508 of the CFTR has been deleted. Even though this mutant CFTR is functional, it is improperly folded and hence is degraded before it can be installed in the plasma membrane.

Homozygotes for defective or absent CFTRs have problems in many of their above organs but especially in their lungs (heterozygotes are asymptomatic). This is because the reduced Cl⁻ export results in thickened mucus that the lungs cannot easily clear. Since the flow of mucus is the major way in which the lungs eliminate foreign particles such as bacteria, individuals with cystic fibrosis suffer from chronic lung infections leading to progressive lung damage and early death.

D | Active Transport May Be Driven by Ion Gradients

Systems such as the $(Na^+–K^+)$–ATPase generate electrochemical gradients across membranes. The free energy stored in an electrochemical gradient (Eq. 10-3) can be harnessed to power various endergonic physiological processes. For example, cells of the intestinal epithelium take up dietary glucose by Na⁺-dependent symport (Fig. 10-21). The immediate energy source for this "uphill" transport process is the Na⁺ gradient. This process is an example of secondary active transport because *the Na⁺ gradient in these cells is maintained by the $(Na^+–K^+)$–ATPase*. The Na⁺–glucose transport system concentrates glucose inside the cell. Glucose is then transported into the capillaries through a passive-mediated glucose uniport (which resembles GLUT1; Fig. 10-13). Thus, since glucose enhances Na⁺ resorption, which in turn enhances water resorption, glucose, in addition to salt and water, should be fed to individuals suffering from salt and water losses due to diarrhea.

Lactose Permease Requires a Proton Gradient. Gram-negative bacteria such as *E. coli* contain several active transport systems for concentrating sugars. One extensively studied system, **lactose permease** (also known as **galactoside permease**), *utilizes the proton gradient across the bacterial cell membrane to cotransport H⁺ and lactose*. The proton gradient is metabolically generated through oxidative metabolism in a manner similar to that in mitochondria (Section 18-2). The electrochemical potential gradient created by both these systems is used mainly to drive the synthesis of ATP.

Lactose permease is a 417-residue monomer that, like GLUT1 and the oxalate transporter (Section 10-2E), to which it is distantly related

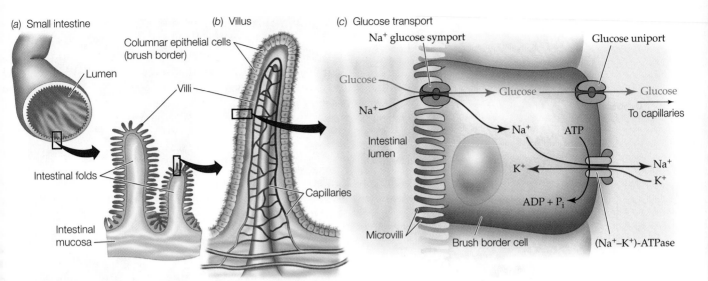

(a) Small intestine; (b) Villus; (c) Glucose transport

Figure 10-21 | Glucose transport in the intestinal epithelium. The brushlike villi lining the small intestine greatly increase its surface area (a), thereby facilitating the absorption of nutrients. The brush border cells from which the villi are formed (b) concentrate glucose from the intestinal lumen in symport with Na$^+$ (c), a process that is driven by the (Na$^+$–K$^+$)–ATPase, which is located on the capillary side of the cell and functions to maintain a low internal [Na$^+$]. The glucose is exported to the bloodstream via a separate passive-mediated uniport system similar to GLUT1.

consists largely of 12 transmembrane helices with its N- and C-termini in the cytoplasm. Like (Na$^+$–K$^+$)–ATPase, it has two major conformational states (Fig. 10-22):

1. E-1, which has a low-affinity lactose-binding site facing the interior of the cell.
2. E-2, which has a high-affinity lactose-binding site facing the exterior of the cell.

Ronald Kaback established that E-1 and E-2 can interconvert only when their H$^+$- and lactose-binding sites are either both filled or both empty. This prevents dissipation of the H$^+$ gradient without cotransport of lactose into the cell. It also prevents transport of lactose out of the cell since this would require cotransport of H$^+$ against its concentration gradient.

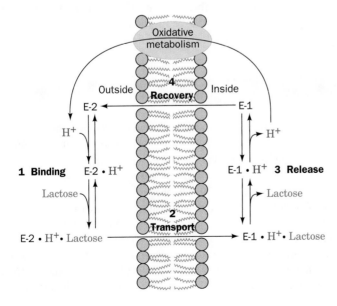

Figure 10-22 | Scheme for the cotransport of H$^+$ and lactose by lactose permease in E. coli. H$^+$ binds first to E-2 outside the cell, followed by lactose. They are sequentially released from E-1 inside the cell. E-2 must bind to lactose and H$^+$ in order to change conformation to E-1, thereby cotransporting these substances into the cell. E-1 changes conformation to E-2 when neither lactose nor H$^+$ is bound, thus completing the transport cycle.

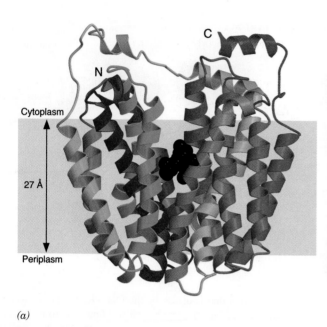

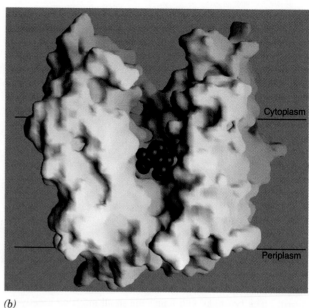

(a)

(b)

■ **Figure 10-23** | **X-Ray structure of lactose permease from**
E. coli. (*a*) Ribbon diagram as viewed from the membrane with
the cytoplasmic side up. The protein's 12 transmembrane helices are
colored in rainbow order from the N-terminus (*purple*) to the
C-terminus (*pink*). The bound lactose analog is represented by
black spheres. (*b*) Surface model viewed as in Part *a* but with the
two helices closest to the viewer in Part *a* removed to reveal the
lactose-binding cavity. The surface is colored according to its
electrostatic potential with positively charged areas blue, negatively
charged areas red, and neutral areas white. [Courtesy of H. Ronald
Kaback, UCLA. PDBid 1PV7.]

■ **CHECK YOUR UNDERSTANDING**

Distinguish passive-mediated transport, active
   transport, and secondary active transport.
Explain why the (Na^+-K^+)–ATPase and the
   Ca^{2+}–ATPase carry out transport in one
   direction only.
Explain why a multidrug resistance ABC
   transporter would operate as a flipase.

The X-ray structure of lactose permease in complex with a tight-binding
lactose analog, determined by Kaback and So Iwata, reveals that this
protein consists of two structurally similar and twofold symmetrically
positioned domains containing six transmembrane helices each (Fig. 10-23*a*).
A large internal hydrophilic cavity is open to the cytoplasmic side of the
membrane (Fig. 10-23*b*) so that the structure represents the E-1 state of
the protein. The lactose analog is bound in the cavity at a position that is
approximately equidistant from both sides of the membrane, consistent
with the model that the lactose-binding site is alternately accessible from
each side of the membrane (e.g., Fig. 10-13). Arg, His, and Glu residues
that mutational studies have implicated in proton translocation are located
in the vicinity of the lactose-binding site.

SUMMARY

1. The mediated and nonmediated transport of a substance across
   a membrane is driven by its chemical potential difference.

2. Ionophores facilitate ion diffusion by binding an ion, diffusing through the membrane, and then releasing the ion; or by
   forming a channel.

3. Porins form β barrel structures about a central channel that
   is selective for anions, cations, or certain small molecules.

4. Ion channels mediate changes in membrane potential by allowing the rapid and spontaneous transport of ions. Ion channels
   are highly solute-selective and open and close (gate) in response
   to various stimuli. Nerve impulses involve ion channels.

5. Aquaporins contain channels that allow the rapid transmembrane diffusion of water but not protons.

6. Transport proteins such as GLUT1 alternate between two
   conformational states that expose the ligand-binding site to
   opposite sides of the membrane.

7. Active transport, in most cases, is driven by ATP hydrolysis.
   In the (Na^+-K^+)–ATPase and Ca^{2+}–ATPase, ATP hydrolysis and ion transport are coupled and vectorial.

8. ABC transporters use ATP hydrolysis to trigger conformational changes that move substances, including amphiphilic
   molecules, from one side of the membrane to the other.

9. In secondary active transport, an ion gradient maintained by an ATPase drives the transport of another substance. For example, the transport of lactose into a cell by lactose permease is driven by the cotransport of H^+.

KEY TERMS

chemical potential **296**
$\Delta \Psi$ **296**
electrochemical potentia **296**
nonmediated transport **296**
mediated transport **296**
passive-mediated
  transport **297**

active transport **297**
ionophore **297**
gating **302**
mechanosensitive channel **302**
ligand-gated channel **302**
signal-gated channel **302**
voltage-gated channel **302**

depolarization **302**
repolarization **302**
action potential **302**
aquaporin **306**
gap junction **307**
uniport **310**
symport **310**

antiport **310**
primary active
  transport **313**
secondary active
  transport **313**
ABC transporter **314**

PROBLEMS

1. Indicate whether the following compounds are likely to cross a membrane by nonmediated or mediated transport: (a) ethanol, (b) glycine, (c) cholesterol, (d) ATP.

2. Rank the rate of transmembrane diffusion of the following compounds:

$$CH_3 - \overset{\overset{\displaystyle O}{\|}}{C} - NH_2$$

A. Acetamide

$$CH_3 - CH_2 - CH_2 - \overset{\overset{\displaystyle O}{\|}}{C} - NH_2$$

B. Butyramide

$$H_2N - \overset{\overset{\displaystyle O}{\|}}{C} - NH_2$$

C. Urea

3. Calculate the free energy change for glucose entry into cells when the extracellular concentration is 5 mM and the intracellular concentration is 3 mM.

4. (a) Calculate the chemical potential difference when intracellular $[Na^+] = 10$ mM and extracellular $[Na^+] = 150$ mM at 37°C. (b) What would the electrochemical potential be if the membrane potential were -60 mV (inside negative)?

5. For the problem in Sample Calculation 10-1, calculate ΔG at 37°C when the membrane potential is (a) -50 mV (cytosol negative) and (b) $+150$ mV. In which case is Ca^{2+} movement in the indicated direction thermodynamically favorable?

6. What happens to K^+ transport by valinomycin when the membrane is cooled below its transition temperature?

7. How long would it take 100 molecules of valinomycin to transport enough K^+ to change the concentration inside an erythrocyte of volume 100 μm^3 by 10 mM? (Assume that the valinomycin does not also transport any K^+ out of the cell, which it really does, and that the valinomycin molecules inside the cell are always saturated with K^+.)

8. The rate of movement (flux) of a substance X into cells was measured at different concentrations of X to construct the following graph.

  (a) Does this information suggest that the movement of X into the cells is mediated by a protein transporter? Explain.

(b) What additional experiment could you perform to verify that a transport protein is or is not involved?

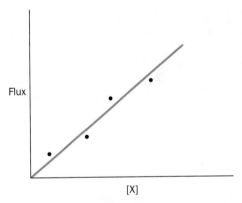

9. If the ATP supply in the cell shown in Fig. 10-21c suddenly vanished, would the intracellular glucose concentration increase, decrease, or remain the same?

10. Endothelial cells and pericytes in the retina of the eye have different mechanisms for glucose uptake. The figure shows the rate of glucose uptake for each type of cell in the presence of increasing amounts of sodium. What do these results reveal about the glucose transporter in each cell type?

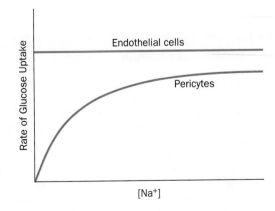

11. The compound shown below is the antiparasitic drug miltefosine.

$$CH_3-(CH_2)_{15}-O-\overset{\overset{O^-}{|}}{\underset{\underset{O}{\|}}{P}}-CH_2-CH_2-N^+(CH_3)_3$$

Miltefosine

(a) Is this compound a glycerophospholipid?

(b) How does miltefosine likely cross the parasite cell membrane?

(c) In what part of the cell would the drug tend to accumulate? Explain.

(d) Miltefosine binds to a protein that also binds some sphingolipids and some glycerophospholipids. What feature common to all these compounds is recognized by the protein? The protein does not bind triacylglycerols.

12. In eukaryotes, ribosomes (approximate mass 4×10^6 D) are assembled inside the nucleus, which is enclosed by a double membrane. Protein synthesis occurs in the cytosol. (a) Could a protein similar to a porin or the glucose transporter be responsible for transporting ribosomes into the cytoplasm? Explain. (b) Would free energy be required to move a ribosome from the nucleus to the cytoplasm? Why or why not?

13. In addition to neurons, muscle cells undergo depolarization, although smaller and slower than in the neuron, as a result of the activity of the acetylcholine receptor.

(a) The acetylcholine receptor is also a gated ion channel. What triggers the gate to open?

(b) The acetylcholine receptor/ion channel is specific for Na^+ ions. Would Na^+ ions flow in or out? Why?

(c) How would the Na^+ flow through the ion channel change the membrane potential?

14. Cells in the wall of the mammalian stomach secrete HCl at a concentration of 0.15 M. The secreted protons, which are derived from the intracellular hydration of CO_2 by carbonic anhydrase, are pumped out by an (H^+-K^+)–ATPase antiport. A K^+-Cl^- cotransporter is also required to complete the overall transport process. (a) Calculate the pH of the secreted HCl. How does this compare to the cytosolic pH (7.4)?

(b) Write the reaction catalyzed by carbonic anhydras
(c) Draw a diagram to show how the action of both transpo
proteins results in the secretion of HCl.

15. Why would overexpression of an MDR transporter in a car cer cell make the cancer more difficult to treat?

CASE STUDIES

Case Study 3 (available at www.wiley.com/college/voet)
Carbonic Anhydrase II Deficiency

Focus concept: Carbonic anhydrase plays a role in normal bor tissue formation.

Prerequisites: Chapters 2, 3, 4, and 10

• Amino acid structure

• The carbonic acid/bicarbonate blood buffering system

• Membrane transport proteins

• Basic genetics

Case Study 14

Shavings from the Carpenter's Bench: The Biological Role of the Insulin C-peptide

Focus concept: Recent experiments indicate that the insulin C peptide, which is removed on conversion of proinsulin to insulin may have biological activity in its own right.

Prerequisites: Chapters 4, 6, and 10

• Amino acid structure

• Principles of protein folding

• Membrane transport proteins

Case Study 17

A Possible Mechanism for Blindness Associated with Diabetes. Na^+-Dependent Glucose Uptake by Retinal Cells

Focus concept: Glucose transport into cells can influence collager synthesis, which causes the basement membrane thickening associated with diabetic retinopathy.

Prerequisite: Chapter 10

• Transport proteins

• (Na^+-K^+)–ATPase and active transport

REFERENCES

Busch, W. and Saier, M.H., Jr., The transporter classification (TC) system, 2002, *Crit. Rev. Biochem. Mol. Biol.* **37,** 287–337 (2002). [Summarizes the classification of the nearly 400 families of transport systems and their distribution among the three domains of life.]

Dutzler, R., Schirmer, T., Karplus, M., and Fischer, S., Translocation mechanism of long sugar chains across the maltoporin membrane channel, *Structure* **10,** 1273–1284 (2002).

Gouaux, E. and MacKinnon, R., Principles of selective ion transport in channels and pumps, *Science* **310,** 1461–1465 (2005). [Compares several transport proteins of known structure and discusses the selectivity of Na^+, K^+, Ca^{2+}, and Cl^- transport.]

Unger, V.M., Kumar, N.M., Gilula, N.B., and Yeager, M., Three-dimensional structure of a recombinant gap junction membrane channel, *Science* **283,** 1176–1180 (1999).

Walmsley, A.R., Barrett, M.P., Bringaud, F., and Gould, G.W., Sugar transporters from bacteria, parasites, and mammals: structure–activity relationships, *Trends Biochem. Sci.* **22,** 476–481 (1998). [Provides structure–function analysis of sugar transporters with 12 transmembrane helices.]

Ion Channels

Dutzler, R., The ClC family of chloride channels and transporters, *Curr. Opin. Struct. Biol.* **16,** 439–446 (2006).

Dutzler, R., Campbell, E.B., Cadene, M., Chait, B.T., and MacKinnon, R., X-Ray structure of a ClC chloride channel at 3.0 Å reveals the molecular basis of anion selectivity, *Nature* **415,** 287–294 (2002).

Jiang, Y., Lee, A., Chen, J., Ruta, V., Cadene, M., Chait, B.T., and MacKinnon, R., X-Ray structure of a voltage-dependent K$^+$ channel, *Nature* **423,** 33–41 (2003).

Long, S.B., Campbell, E.B., and MacKinnon, R., Voltage sensor of Kv1.2: Structural basis of electromechanical coupling, *Science* **30,** 903–908 (2005).

Aquaporins

King, L.S., Kozono, D., and Agre, P., From structure to disease: The evolving tale of aquaporin biology, *Nat. Rev. Mol. Cell Biol.* **5,** 687–698 (2004).

Sui, H., Han, B.-G., Lee, J.K., and Jap, B.K., Structural basis of water-specific transport through the AQP1 water channel, *Nature* **414,** 872–878 (2001).

Active Transporters

Abramson, J., Smirnova, I., Kasho, V., Verner, G., Kaback, H.R., and Iwata, S., Structure and mechanism of the lactose permease of *Escherichia coli, Science* **301,** 610–615 (2003).

Dawson, R.J.P. and Locher, K.P., Structure of a bacterial multidrug ABC transporter, *Nature* **443,** 180–185 (2006). [The structure of Sav1866.]

Hille, B., *Ionic Channels of Excitable Membranes* (3rd ed.), Sinauer Associates (2001).

Kaplan, J.H., Biochemistry of Na,K-ATPase, *Annu. Rev. Biochem.* **71,** 511–535 (2002).

Toyoshima, C. and Nomura, H., Structural changes in the calcium pump accompanying the dissociation of calcium, *Nature* **418,** 605–611 (2002); *and* Toyoshima, C., Nomura, H., and Sugita, Y., Structural basis of ion pumping by Ca^{2+}-ATPase of sarcoplasmic reticulum, *FEBS Lett.* **555,** 106–110 (2003).

11

Enzymatic Catalysis

Like these acrobats, enzymes typically act with great speed and precision, interacting with a substrate to facilitate chemical transformation. [David Madison/Stone/Getty Images.]

■ **CHAPTER CONTENTS**

1 General Properties of Enzymes
  A. Enzymes Are Classified by the Type of Reaction They Catalyze
  B. Enzymes Act on Specific Substrates
  C. Some Enzymes Require Cofactors

2 Activation Energy and the Reaction Coordinate

3 Catalytic Mechanisms
  A. Acid–Base Catalysis Occurs by Proton Transfer
  B. Covalent Catalysis Usually Requires a Nucleophile
  C. Metal Ion Cofactors Act as Catalysts
  D. Catalysis Can Occur through Proximity and Orientation Effects
  E. Enzymes Catalyze Reactions by Preferentially Binding the Transition State

4 Lysozyme
  A. Lysozyme's Catalytic Site Was Identified through Model Building
  B. The Lysozyme Reaction Proceeds via a Covalent Intermediate

5 Serine Proteases
  A. Active Site Residues Were Identified by Chemical Labeling
  B. X-Ray Structures Provide Information about Catalysis, Substrate Specificity, and Evolution
  C. Serine Proteases Use Several Catalytic Mechanisms
  D. Zymogens Are Inactive Enzyme Precursors

■ **MEDIA RESOURCES**

(available at www.wiley.com/college/voet)
Guided Exploration 10. The catalytic mechanism of serine proteases
Interactive Exercise 6. Pancreatic RNase S
Interactive Exercise 7. Carbonic anhydrase
Interactive Exercise 8. Hen egg white lysozyme
Animated Figure 11-15. Effect of preferential transition state binding
Animated Figure 11-18. Chair and half-chair conformations
Kinemage 9. Hen egg white lysozyme—catalytic mechanism
Kinemage 10-1. Structural overview of a trypsin/inhibitor complex
Kinemage 10-2. Evolutionary comparisons of proteases
Kinemage 10-3. A transition state analog bound to chymotrypsin
Case Study 11. Nonenzymatic Deamidization of Asparagine and Glutamine Residues in Proteins

Living systems are shaped by an enormous variety of biochemical reactions, nearly all of which are mediated by a series of remarkable biological catalysts known as enzymes. **Enzymology,** the study of enzymes, has its roots in the early days of biochemistry; both disciplines evolved together from nineteenth century investigations of fermentation and digestion. Initially, the inability to reproduce most biochemical reactions in the laboratory led Louis Pasteur and others to assume that living systems were endowed with a "vital force" that permitted them to evade the laws of nature governing inanimate matter. Some investigators, however, notably Justus von Liebig, argued that biological processes were caused by the action of chemical substances that were then known as "ferments." Indeed, the name "enzyme" (Greek: *en,* in + *zyme,* yeast) was coined in 1878 in an effort to emphasize that there is something *in* yeast, as opposed to the yeast itself, that catalyzes the reactions of fermentation. Eventually, Eduard Buchner showed that a cell-free yeast extract could in fact carry out the synthesis of ethanol from glucose (**alcoholic fermentation;** Section 15-3B):

$$C_6H_{12}O_6 \rightarrow 2\ CH_3CH_2OH + 2\ CO_2$$

This chemical transformation actually proceeds in 12 enzyme-catalyzed steps.

The chemical composition of enzymes was not firmly established until 1926, when James Sumner crystallized jack bean **urease,** which catalyzes the hydrolysis of urea to NH_3 and CO_2, and demonstrated that these crystals consist of protein. Enzymological experience since then has amply demonstrated that most enzymes are proteins.

Certain species of RNA molecules known as **ribozymes** also have enzymatic activity. These include ribosomal RNA, which catalyzes the formation of peptide bonds between amino acids. In fact, laboratory experiments have produced ribozymes that can catalyze reactions similar to those required for replicating DNA, transcribing it to RNA, and attaching amino acids to transfer RNA. These findings are consistent with a precellular world in which RNA molecules enjoyed a more exalted position as the catalytic workhorses of biochemistry. The present-day RNA catalysts are presumably vestiges of this earlier "RNA world." Proteins have largely eclipsed RNA as cellular catalysts, probably because of the greater chemical versatility of proteins. Whereas nucleic acids are polymers of four types of chemically similar monomeric units, proteins have at their disposal 20 types of amino acids with a greater variety of functional groups.

This chapter is concerned with one of the central questions of biochemistry: How do enzymes work? We shall see that enzymes increase the rates of chemical reactions by lowering the free energy barrier that separates the reactants and products. Enzymes accomplish this feat through various mechanisms that depend on the arrangement of functional groups in the enzyme's **active site,** the region of the enzyme where catalysis occurs. In this chapter, we describe these mechanisms, along with examples that illustrate how enzymes combine several mechanisms to catalyze biological reactions. The following chapter includes a discussion of enzyme kinetics, the study of the rates at which such reactions occur.

1 General Properties of Enzymes

Biochemical research since Pasteur's era has shown that, although enzymes are subject to the same laws of nature that govern the behavior of other substances, enzymes differ from ordinary chemical catalysts in several important respects:

1. *Higher reaction rates.* The rates of enzymatically catalyzed reactions are typically 10^6 to 10^{12} times greater than those of the corresponding uncatalyzed reactions (Table 11-1) and are at least several orders of magnitude greater than those of the corresponding chemically catalyzed reactions.

2. *Milder reaction conditions.* Enzymatically catalyzed reactions occur under relatively mild conditions: temperatures below 100°C, atmospheric pressure, and nearly neutral pH. In contrast, efficient chemical

LEARNING OBJECTIVES

- Understand that enzymes differ from ordinary chemical catalysts in reaction rate, reaction conditions, reaction specificity, and control.
- Understand the molecular basis for the stereospecificity and geometric specificity of enzymes.
- Understand the functions and types of enzyme cofactors.

Table 11-1 Catalytic Power of Some Enzymes

Enzyme	Nonenzymatic Reaction Rate (s^{-1})	Enzymatic Reaction Rate (s^{-1})	Rate Enhancement
Carbonic anhydrase	1.3×10^{-1}	1×10^6	7.7×10^6
Chorismate mutase	2.6×10^{-5}	50	1.9×10^6
Triose phosphate isomerase	4.3×10^{-6}	4300	1.0×10^9
Carboxypeptidase A	3.0×10^{-9}	578	1.9×10^{11}
AMP nucleosidase	1.0×10^{-11}	60	6.0×10^{12}
Staphylococcal nuclease	1.7×10^{-13}	95	5.6×10^{14}

Source: Radzicka, A. and Wolfenden, R., *Science* **267,** 91 (1995).

catalysis often requires elevated temperatures and pressures as well as extremes of pH.

3. *Greater reaction specificity.* Enzymes have a vastly greater degree of specificity with respect to the identities of both their **substrates** (reactants) and their products than do chemical catalysts; that is, enzymatic reactions rarely have side products.

4. *Capacity for regulation.* The catalytic activities of many enzymes vary in response to the concentrations of substances other than their substrates. The mechanisms of these regulatory processes include allosteric control, covalent modification of enzymes, and variation of the amounts of enzymes synthesized.

A | Enzymes Are Classified by the Type of Reaction They Catalyze

Before delving further into the specific properties of enzymes, a word on nomenclature is in order. Enzymes are commonly named by appending the suffix -*ase* to the name of the enzyme's substrate or to a phrase describing the enzyme's catalytic action. Thus, urease catalyzes the hydrolysis of urea, and **alcohol dehydrogenase** catalyzes the oxidation of primary and secondary alcohols to their corresponding aldehydes and ketones by removing hydrogen. Since there were at first no systematic rules for naming enzymes, this practice occasionally resulted in two different names being used for the same enzyme or, conversely, in the same name being used for two different enzymes. Moreover, many enzymes, such as **catalase** (which mediates the dismutation of H_2O_2 to H_2O and O_2), were given names that provide no clue to their function. In an effort to eliminate this confusion and to provide rules for rationally naming the rapidly growing number of newly discovered enzymes, a scheme for the systematic functional classification and nomenclature of enzymes was adopted by the International Union of Biochemistry and Molecular Biology (IUBMB).

Enzymes are classified and named according to the nature of the chemical reactions they catalyze. There are six major classes of enzymatic reactions (Table 11-2), as well as subclasses and sub-subclasses. Each enzyme is assigned two names and a four-part classification number. Its **alternative name** is convenient for everyday use and is often an enzyme's previously used trivial name. Its **systematic** or **official name** is used when ambiguity must be minimized; it is the name of its substrate(s) followed by a word ending in -*ase* specifying the type of reaction the enzyme catalyzes according to its major group classification. For example, the enzyme whose alternative name is aconitase (Section 17-3B) has the systematic name aconitate hydratase and the Classification number EC 4.2.1.3 ("EC"

Table 11-2	Enzyme Classification According to Reaction Type
Classification	**Type of Reaction Catalyzed**
1. Oxidoreductases	Oxidation–reduction reactions
2. Transferases	Transfer of functional groups
3. Hydrolases	Hydrolysis reactions
4. Lyases	Group elimination to form double bonds
5. Isomerases	Isomerization
6. Ligases	Bond formation coupled with ATP hydrolysis

tands for Enzyme Commission, and the numbers represent the class, ubclass, sub-subclass, and its arbitrarily assigned serial number in its sub-ubclass). For our purposes, the recommended name of an enzyme is usually adequate. However, EC classification numbers are increasingly used in various Internet-accessible databases (Box 14-2). Systematic names and EC classification numbers can be obtained via the Internet http://expasy.org/enzyme/).

Enzymes Act on Specific Substrates

The noncovalent forces through which substrates and other molecules bind to enzymes are similar in character to the forces that dictate the conformations of the proteins themselves (Section 6-4A). Both involve van der Waals, electrostatic, hydrogen bonding, and hydrophobic interactions. In general, a substrate-binding site consists of an indentation or cleft on the surface of an enzyme molecule that is complementary in shape to the substrate **(geometric complementarity).** Moreover, the amino acid residues that form the binding site are arranged to specifically attract the substrate **(electronic complementarity,** Fig. 11-1). Molecules that differ in shape or functional group distribution from the substrate cannot productively bind to the enzyme. X-Ray studies indicate that the substrate-binding sites of most enzymes are largely preformed but undergo some conformational change on substrate binding (a phenomenon called **induced fit**). The complementarity between enzymes and their substrates is the basis of the "lock-and-key" model of enzyme function first proposed by Emil Fischer in 1894. As we shall see, such specific binding is necessary but not sufficient for efficient catalysis.

Enzymes Are Stereospecific. Enzymes are highly specific both in binding chiral substrates and in catalyzing their reactions. This **stereospecificity** arises because enzymes, by virtue of their inherent chirality (proteins consist of only L-amino acids), form asymmetric active sites. For example, the enzyme **aconitase** catalyzes the interconversion of citrate and isocitrate in the citric acid cycle (Section 17-3B):

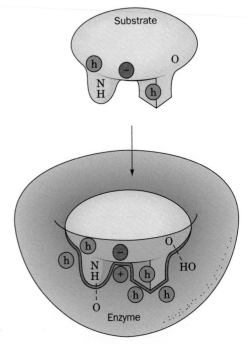

Figure 11-1 | An enzyme–substrate complex. The geometric and the electronic complementarity between the enzyme and substrate depend on noncovalent forces. Hydrophobic groups are represented by an h in a brown circle, and dashed lines represent hydrogen bonds.

$$
\underset{\textbf{Citrate}}{\begin{array}{c} COO^- \\ | \\ CH_2 \\ | \\ HO-C-COO^- \\ | \\ CH_2 \\ | \\ COO^- \end{array}}
\underset{\text{aconitase}}{\rightleftharpoons}
\underset{\textbf{Isocitrate}}{\begin{array}{c} COO^- \\ | \\ CH_2 \\ | \\ H-C-COO^- \\ | \\ HO-C-H \\ | \\ COO^- \end{array}}
$$

Citrate is a **prochiral** molecule; that is, it can become chiral through the substitution of one of its two carboxymethyl ($-CH_2COO^-$) groups (chirality is discussed in Section 4-2). These groups are chemically equivalent but occupy different positions relative to the OH and COO^- groups (likewise, your body is bilaterally symmetric but has distinguishable right and left sides). Aconitase can therefore distinguish between them because citrate interacts asymmetrically with the surface of the enzyme by making a three-point attachment (Fig. 11-2). Because there is only one productive way for citrate to bind to the enzyme, only one of its $-CH_2COO^-$ groups reacts to form isocitrate. The stereospecificity of aconitase is by no means unusual. As we consider biochemical reactions, we shall find that *nearly all enzymes that participate in chiral reactions are absolutely stereospecific.*

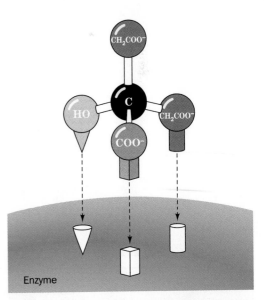

Figure 11-2 | Stereospecificity in substrate binding. The specific binding of a prochiral molecule, such as citrate, in an enzyme active site allows the enzyme to differentiate between prochiral groups.

Enzymes Vary in Geometric Specificity. The stereospecificity of enzymes is not particularly surprising in light of the complementarity of an enzyme's binding site for its substrate. A substance of the wrong chirality will not fit productively into an enzymatic binding site for much the same reason that you cannot fit your right hand into your left glove. In addition to their stereospecificity, however, most enzymes are quite selective about the identities of the chemical groups on their substrates. Indeed, such **geometric specificity** is a more stringent requirement than is stereospecificity.

Enzymes vary considerably in their degree of geometric specificity. A few enzymes are absolutely specific for only one compound. Most enzymes, however, catalyze the reactions of a small range of related compounds although with different efficiencies. For example, alcohol dehydrogenase catalyzes the oxidation of **ethanol** (CH_3CH_2OH) to **acetaldehyde** (CH_3CHO) faster than it oxidizes **methanol** (CH_3OH) to **formaldehyde** (H_2CO) or **isopropanol** [$(CH_3)_2CHOH$] to **acetone** [$(CH_3)_2CO$], even though methanol and isopropanol differ from ethanol by only the deletion or addition of a CH_2 group.

Some enzymes, particularly digestive enzymes, are so permissive in their ranges of acceptable substrates that their geometric specificities are more accurately described as preferences. Some enzymes are not even very specific in the type of reaction they catalyze. For example, chymotrypsin, in addition to its ability to mediate peptide bond hydrolysis, also catalyzes ester bond hydrolysis.

$$\underset{\textbf{Peptide}}{\overset{\overset{\displaystyle O}{\displaystyle \|}}{RC}-NHR'} + H_2O \xrightarrow{\text{chymotrypsin}} \overset{\overset{\displaystyle O}{\displaystyle \|}}{RC}-O^- + H_3\overset{+}{N}R'$$

$$\underset{\textbf{Ester}}{\overset{\overset{\displaystyle O}{\displaystyle \|}}{RC}-OR'} + H_2O \xrightarrow{\text{chymotrypsin}} \overset{\overset{\displaystyle O}{\displaystyle \|}}{RC}-O^- + HOR'$$
$$H^+$$

This property makes it convenient to measure chymotrypsin activity using small synthetic esters as substrates. Such permissiveness is much more the exception than the rule. Indeed, most intracellular enzymes function *in vivo* to catalyze a particular reaction on a particular substrate.

C | Some Enzymes Require Cofactors

The functional groups of proteins, as we shall see, can facilely participate in acid–base reactions, form certain types of transient covalent bonds, and take part in charge–charge interactions. They are, however, less suitable for catalyzing oxidation–reduction reactions and many types of group-transfer processes. Although enzymes catalyze such reactions, they can do so only in association with small **cofactors,** which essentially act as the enzymes' "chemical teeth" (Fig. 11-3).

Cofactors may be metal ions, such as Cu^{2+}, Fe^{3+}, or Zn^{2+}. The essential nature of these cofactors explains why organisms require trace amounts of certain elements in their diets. It also explains, in part, the toxic effects of certain heavy metals. For example, Cd^{2+} and Hg^{2+} can replace Zn^{2+} (all are in the same group of the periodic table) in the active sites of certain enzymes, including RNA polymerase, and thereby render these enzymes inactive.

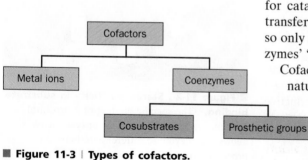

■ **Figure 11-3** | **Types of cofactors.**

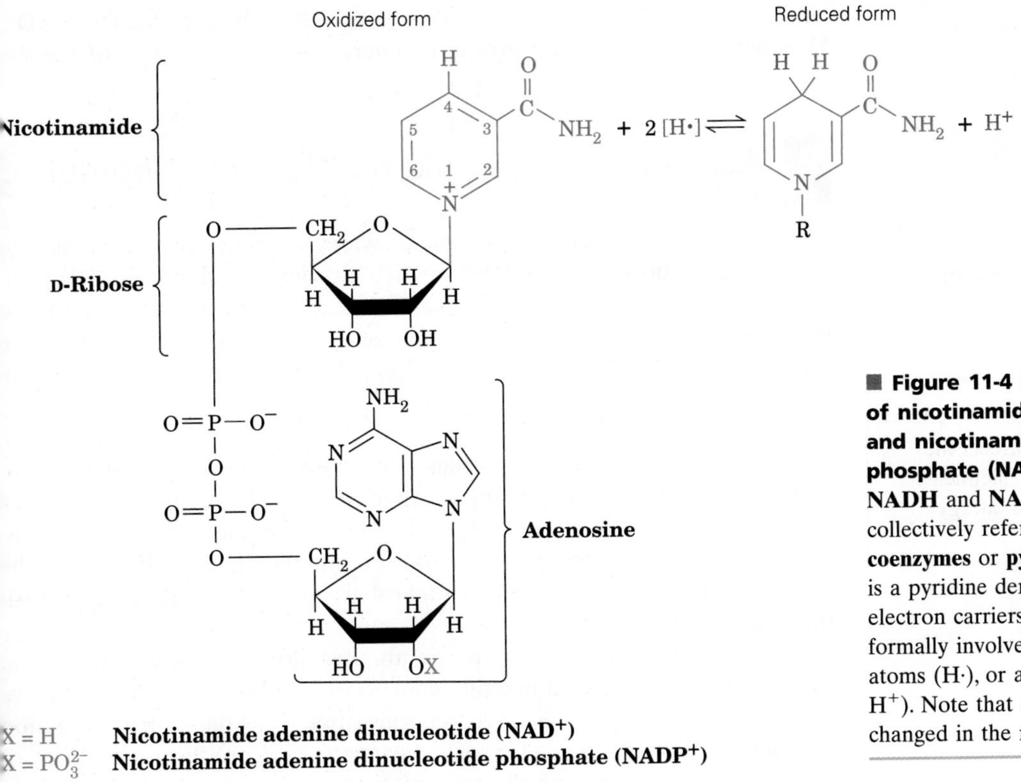

Oxidized form   Reduced form

■ **Figure 11-4** │ **The structures and reaction of nicotinamide adenine dinucleotide (NAD$^+$) and nicotinamide adenine dinucleotide phosphate (NADP$^+$).** Their reduced forms are **NADH** and **NADPH.** These substances, which are collectively referred to as the **nicotinamide coenzymes** or **pyridine nucleotides** (nicotinamide is a pyridine derivative), function as intracellular electron carriers. Reduction (addition of electrons) formally involves the transfer of two hydrogen atoms (H·), or a hydride ion and a proton (H:$^-$ + H$^+$). Note that only the nicotinamide ring is changed in the reaction.

X = H   **Nicotinamide adenine dinucleotide (NAD$^+$)**
X = PO$_3^{2-}$ **Nicotinamide adenine dinucleotide phosphate (NADP$^+$)**

Cofactors may also be organic molecules known as **coenzymes.** Some cofactors are only transiently associated with a given enzyme molecule, so that they function as **cosubstrates. Nicotinamide adenine dinucleotide (NAD$^+$)** and **nicotinamide adenine dinucleotide phosphate (NADP$^+$)** are examples of cosubstrates (Fig. 11-4). For instance, NAD$^+$ is an obligatory oxidizing agent in the alcohol dehydrogenase **(ADH)** reaction:

$$CH_3CH_2OH + NAD^+ \xrightleftharpoons{ADH} CH_3\overset{\overset{\displaystyle O}{\|}}{C}H + NADH + H^+$$

Ethanol   **Acetaldehyde**

The product NADH dissociates from the enzyme for eventual reoxidation to NAD$^+$ in an independent enzymatic reaction.

Other cofactors, known as **prosthetic groups,** are permanently associated with their protein, often by covalent bonds. For example, a heme prosthetic group (Fig. 7-2) is tightly bound to proteins known as **cytochromes** (Fig. 6-32 and Box 18-1) through extensive hydrophobic and hydrogen-bonding interactions together with covalent bonds between the heme and specific protein side chains.

A catalytically active enzyme–cofactor complex is called a **holoenzyme.** The enzymatically inactive protein resulting from the removal of a holoenzyme's cofactor is referred to as an **apoenzyme;** that is,

apoenzyme (*inactive*) + cofactor ⇌ holoenzyme (*active*)

Coenzymes Must Be Regenerated. Coenzymes are chemically changed by the enzymatic reactions in which they participate. *In order to complete the catalytic cycle, the coenzyme must return to its original state.* For a transiently bound coenzyme (cosubstrate), the regeneration reaction may be

■ **CHECK YOUR UNDERSTANDING**

What properties distinguish enzymes from other catalysts?

What factors influence an enzyme's substrate specificity?

Why are cofactors required for some enzymatic reactions?

What is the relationship between cofactors, coenzymes, cosubstrates, and prosthetic groups?

LEARNING OBJECTIVE

■ Understand that an enzyme affects the free energy along the path of a chemical reaction but not the overall free energy change.

---

catalyzed by a different enzyme as we have seen to be the case for NAD$^+$. However, for a prosthetic group, regeneration occurs as part of the enzyme reaction sequence.

2 Activation Energy and the Reaction Coordinate

Much of our understanding of how enzymes catalyze chemical reactions comes from **transition state theory,** which was developed in the 1930s, principally by Henry Eyring. Consider a bimolecular reaction involving three atoms, such as the reaction of a hydrogen atom with diatomic hydrogen (H_2) to yield a new H_2 molecule and a different hydrogen atom:

$$H_A\text{—}H_B + H_C \longrightarrow H_A + H_B\text{—}H_C$$

In this reaction, H_C must approach the diatomic molecule $H_A\text{—}H_B$ so that, at some point in the reaction, there exists a high-energy (unstable) complex represented as $H_A\text{---}H_B\text{---}H_C$. In this complex, the $H_A\text{—}H_B$ covalent bond is in the process of breaking while the $H_B\text{—}H_C$ bond is in the process of forming. The point of highest free energy is called the **transition state** of the system.

Reactants generally approach one another along the path of minimum free energy, their so-called **reaction coordinate.** A plot of free energy versus the reaction coordinate is called a **transition state diagram** or **reaction coordinate diagram** (Fig. 11-5). The reactants and products are states of minimum free energy, and the transition state corresponds to the highest point of the diagram. For the H + H_2 reaction, the reactants and products have the same free energy (Fig. 11-5a). If the atoms in the reacting system are of different types, such as in the reaction

$$A + B \longrightarrow X^{\ddagger} \longrightarrow P + Q$$

where A and B are the reactants, P and Q are the products, and $X^{\ddagger}$ represents the transition state, the transition state diagram is no longer symmetrical because there is a free energy difference between the reactants and products (Fig. 11-5b). In either case, $\mathbf{\Delta G^{\ddagger}}$, the free energy

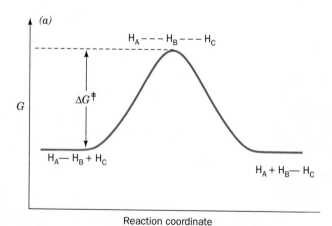

(a)

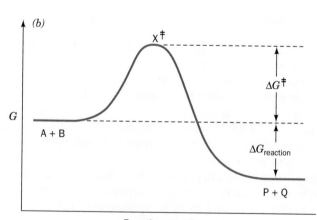

(b)

Reaction coordinate

■ **Figure 11-5 | Transition state diagrams.** (*a*) The H + H_2 reaction. The reactants and products correspond to low free energy structures. The point of highest free energy is the transition state, in which the reactants are partially converted to products. $\Delta G^{\ddagger}$ is the free energy of activation, the difference in free energy between the reactants and the transition state, $X^{\ddagger}$. (*b*) Transition state diagram for the reaction A + B → P + Q. This is a spontaneous reaction; that is, $\Delta G_{\text{reaction}} < 0$ (the free energy of P + Q is less than the free energy of A + B).

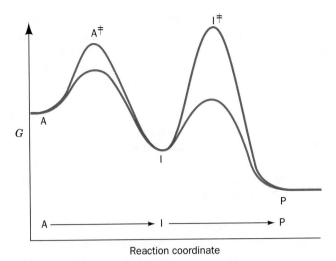

Figure 11-6 | Transition state diagram for a two-step reaction. The blue curve represents a reaction (A → I → P) whose first step is rate determining, and the red curve represents a reaction whose second step is rate determining.

of the transition state less that of the reactants, is known as the **free energy of activation.**

Passage through the transition state requires only 10^{-13} to 10^{-14} s, so the concentration of the transition state in a reacting system is small. Hence, the decomposition of the transition state to products (or back to reactants) is postulated to be the rate-determining process of the overall reaction. Thermodynamic arguments lead to the conclusion that the reaction rate is proportional to $e^{-\Delta G^{\ddagger}/RT}$, where R is the gas constant and T is the absolute temperature. Thus, *the greater the value of* $\Delta G^{\ddagger}$, *the slower the reaction rate.* This is because the larger the $\Delta G^{\ddagger}$, the smaller the number of reactant molecules that have sufficient thermal energy to achieve the transition state free energy.

Chemical reactions commonly consist of several steps. For a two-step reaction such as

$$A \longrightarrow I \longrightarrow P$$

where I is an intermediate of the reaction, there are two transition states and two activation energy barriers. The shape of the transition state diagram for such a reaction reflects the relative rates of the two steps (Fig. 11-6). If the activation energy of the first step is greater than that of the second step, then the first step is slower than the second step, and conversely, if the activation energy of the second step is greater. In a multistep reaction, the step with the highest transition state free energy acts as a "bottleneck" and is therefore said to be the **rate-determining step** of the reaction.

Catalysts Reduce $\Delta G^{\ddagger}$. *Catalysts act by providing a reaction pathway with a transition state whose free energy is lower than that in the uncatalyzed reaction* (Fig. 11-7). The difference between the values of $\Delta G^{\ddagger}$ for the uncatalyzed and catalyzed reactions, $\Delta\Delta G^{\ddagger}_{cat}$, indicates the efficiency of the catalyst. The **rate enhancement** (ratio of the rates of the catalyzed and uncatalyzed reactions) is given by $e^{\Delta\Delta G^{\ddagger}_{cat}/RT}$. Hence, at 25°C (298 K), a 10-fold rate enhancement requires a $\Delta\Delta G^{\ddagger}_{cat}$ of only 5.71 kJ·mol^{-1}, which is less than half the free energy of a typical hydrogen bond. Similarly, a

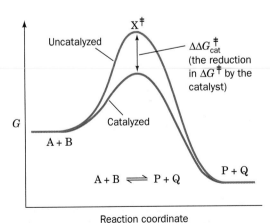

Figure 11-7 | Effect of a catalyst on the transition state diagram of a reaction. Here $\Delta\Delta G^{\ddagger}_{cat} = \Delta G^{\ddagger}(\text{uncat}) - \Delta G^{\ddagger}(\text{cat})$.

millionfold rate acceleration occurs when $\Delta\Delta G^{\ddagger}_{cat} \approx 34 \text{ kJ} \cdot \text{mol}^{-1}$, a small fraction of the free energy of most covalent bonds. Thus, from a theoretical standpoint, tremendous catalytic efficiency seems within reach of the reactive groups that occur in the active sites of enzymes. How these groups actually function at the atomic level is the subject of much of this and other chapters.

Note that a catalyst lowers the free energy barrier by the same amount for both the forward and reverse reactions (Fig. 11-7). Consequently, a catalyst equally accelerates the forward and reverse reactions. Keep in mind also that while a catalyst can accelerate the conversion of reactants to products (or products back to reactants), the likelihood of the net reaction occurring in one direction or the other depends only on the free energy difference between the reactants and the products. If $\Delta G_{reaction} < 0$, the reaction proceeds spontaneously from reactants toward products; if $\Delta G_{reaction} > 0$, the reverse reaction proceeds spontaneously. *An enzyme cannot alter* $\Delta G_{reaction}$; *it can only decrease* $\Delta G^{\ddagger}$ *to allow the reaction to approach equilibrium (where the rates of the forward and reverse reactions are equal) more quickly than it would in the absence of a catalyst.* The actual velocity with which reactants are converted to products is the subject of kinetics (Section 12-1).

3 Catalytic Mechanisms

Enzymes achieve their enormous rate accelerations via the same catalytic mechanisms used by chemical catalysts. Enzymes have simply been better designed through evolution. Enzymes, like other catalysts, reduce the free energy of the transition state ($\Delta G^{\ddagger}$); that is, *they stabilize the transition state of the catalyzed reaction.* What makes enzymes such effective catalysts is their specificity of substrate binding combined with their arrangement of catalytic groups. As we shall see, however, the distinction between substrate-binding groups and catalytic groups is somewhat arbitrary.

Much can be learned about enzymatic reaction mechanisms by examining the corresponding nonenzymatic reactions of model compounds. Both types of reactions can be described using the **curved arrow convention** to trace the electron pair rearrangements that occur in going from reactants to products. The movement of an electron pair (which may be either a lone pair or a pair forming a covalent bond) is symbolized by a curved arrow emanating from the electron pair and pointing to the electron-deficient center attracting the electron pair. For example, imine (**Schiff base**) formation, a biochemically important reaction between an amine and an aldehyde or ketone, is represented as follows:

| Amine | Aldehyde or ketone | Carbinolamine intermediate | Imine (Schiff base) |

In the first reaction step, the amine's unshared electron pair adds to the electron-deficient carbonyl carbon while one electron pair from its C=O double bond transfers to the oxygen atom. In the second step, the unshared electron pair on the nitrogen atom adds to the electron-deficient carbon atom with the elimination of water. *At all times, the rules of chemical*

Sketch and label the various parts of transition state diagrams for a reaction with and without a catalyst.
What is the relationship between ΔG and $\Delta G^{\ddagger}$?

LEARNING OBJECTIVES

■ Understand the chemical basis for acid–base catalysis, covalent catalysis, and metal ion catalysis.
■ Understand how enzymes accelerate reactions through proximity and orientation effects and by preferential binding of the transition state.

eason apply to the system: For example, there are never five bonds to a arbon atom or two bonds to a hydrogen atom.

The types of catalytic mechanisms that enzymes employ have been clas- ified as

1. Acid–base catalysis
2. Covalent catalysis
3. Metal ion catalysis
4. Proximity and orientation effects
5. Preferential binding of the transition state complex

In this section, we consider each of these types of mechanisms in turn.

A | Acid–Base Catalysis Occurs by Proton Transfer

General acid catalysis is a process in which proton transfer from an acid lowers the free energy of a reaction's transition state. For example, an uncatalyzed keto–enol tautomerization reaction occurs quite slowly as a result of the high free energy of its carbanion-like transition state (Fig. 11-8a; the transition state is drawn in square brackets to indicate its instability). Proton donation to the oxygen atom (Fig. 11-8b), however, reduces the carbanion character of the transition state, thereby accelerating the reaction.

A reaction may also be stimulated by *general base catalysis* if its rate is *increased by proton abstraction by a base* (e.g., Fig. 11-8c). Some reactions may be simultaneously subject to both processes; these are **concerted acid–base catalyzed reactions.**

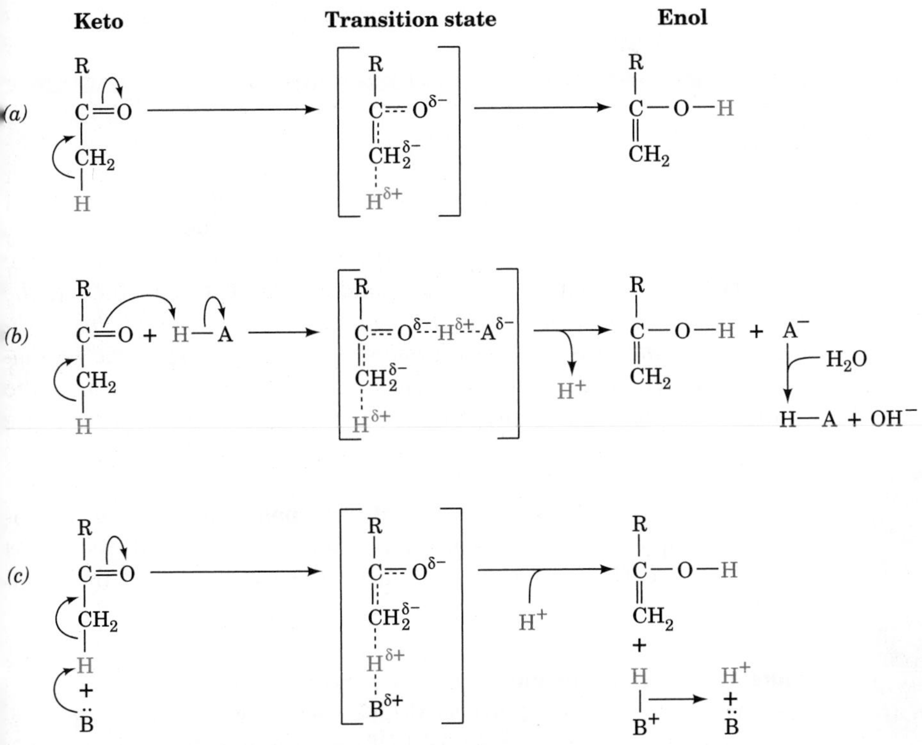

■ **Figure 11-8 | Mechanisms of keto–enol tautomerization.** (a) Uncatalyzed. (b) General acid catalyzed. (c) General base catalyzed. The acid is represented as H—A and the base as B̈.

BOX 11-1 PERSPECTIVES IN BIOCHEMISTRY

Effects of pH on Enzyme Activity

Most enzymes are active within only a narrow pH range, typically 5 to 9. This is a result of the effects of pH on a combination of factors: (1) the binding of substrate to enzyme, (2) the ionization states of the amino acid residues involved in the catalytic activity of the enzyme, (3) the ionization of the substrate, and (4) the variation of protein structure (usually significant only at extremes of pH).

The rates of many enzymatic reactions exhibit bell-shaped curves as a function of pH. For example, the pH dependence of the rate of the reaction catalyzed by **fumarase** (Section 17-3G) produces the following curve:

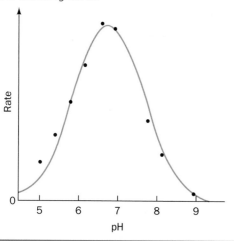

Such curves reflect the ionization of certain amino acid residues that must be in a specific ionization state for enzymatic activity. The observed pK's (the inflection points of the curve) often provide valuable clues to the identities of the amino acid residues essential for enzymatic activity. For example, an observed pK of ~4 suggests that an Asp or Glu residue is essential to the enzyme. Similarly, pK's of ~6 or ~10 suggest the participation of a His or a Lys residue, respectively. However, the pK of a given acid–base group may vary by as much as several pH units from its expected value, depending on its microenvironment (e.g., an Asp residue in a nonpolar environment or in close proximity to another Asp residue would attract protons more strongly than otherwise and hence have a higher pK). Furthermore, pH effects on an enzymatic rate may reflect denaturation of the enzyme rather than protonation or deprotonation of specific catalytic residues. The replacement of a particular residue by site-directed mutagenesis or comparisons of enzyme variants generated by evolution is a more reliable approach to identifying residues that are required for substrate binding or catalysis.

[Figure adapted from Tanford, C., *Physical Chemistry of Macromolecules,* p. 647, Wiley (1961).]

Many types of biochemical reactions are susceptible to acid and/or base catalysis. The side chains of the amino acid residues Asp, Glu, His, Cys, Tyr, and Lys have pK's in or near the physiological pH range (Table 4-1), which permits them to act as acid and/or base catalysts. Indeed, *the ability of enzymes to arrange several catalytic groups around their substrates makes concerted acid–base catalysis a common enzymatic mechanism.* The catalytic activity of these enzymes is sensitive to pH, since the pH influences the state of protonation of side chains at the active site (Box 11-1).

RNase A Is an Acid–Base Catalyst. **Bovine pancreatic RNase A** provides an example of enzymatically mediated acid–base catalysis. This digestive enzyme (Fig. 11-9) is secreted by the pancreas into the small

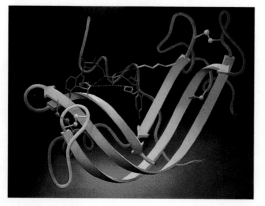

■ **Figure 11-9** | **X-Ray structure of bovine pancreatic RNase S.** A nonhydrolyzable substrate analog, the dinucleotide phosphonate UpcA (*red*), is bound in the active site. RNase S is a catalytically active form of RNase A in which the peptide bond between residues 20 and 21 has been hydrolyzed. [Illustration, Irving Geis/Geis Archives Trust. Copyright Howard Hughes Medical Institute. Reproduced by permission.] 🔍 **See Interactive Exercise 6.**

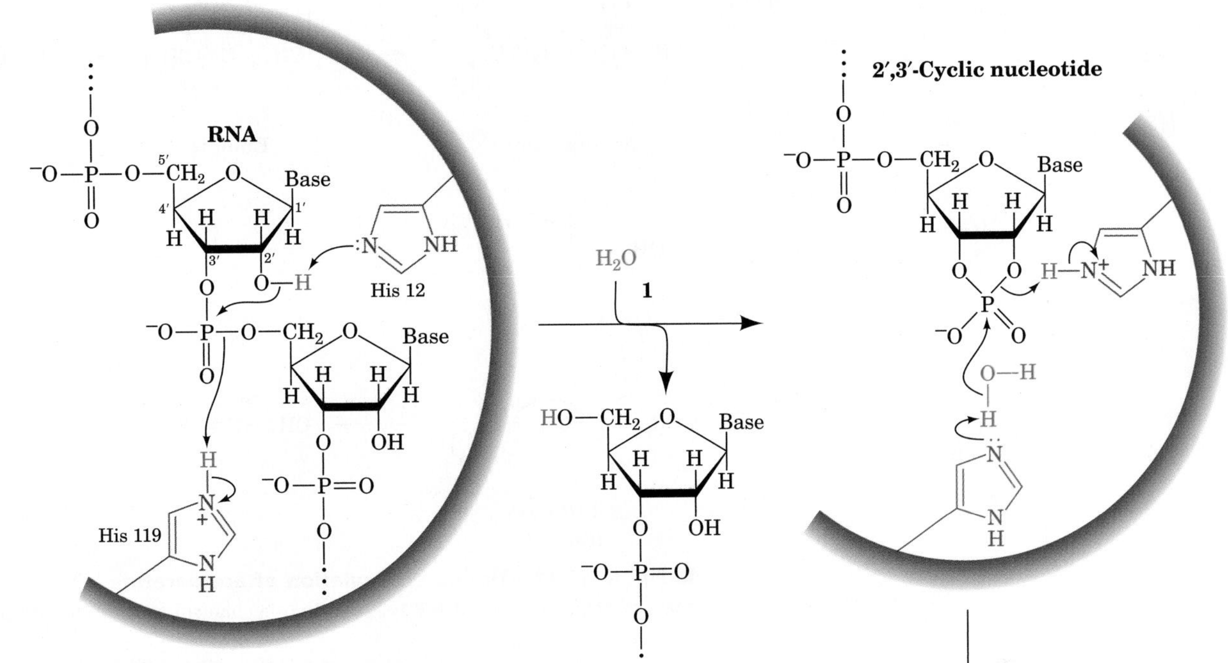

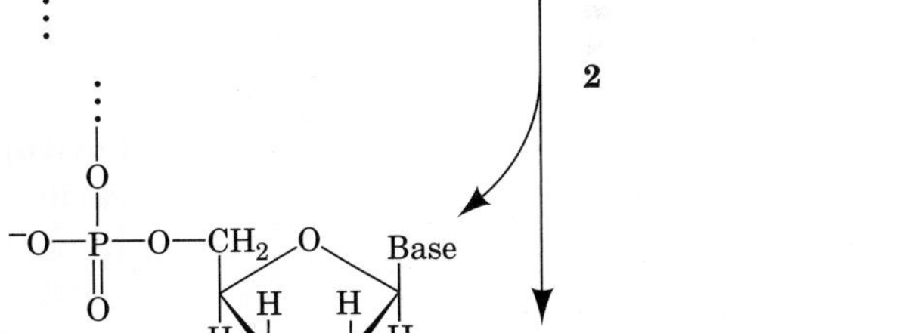

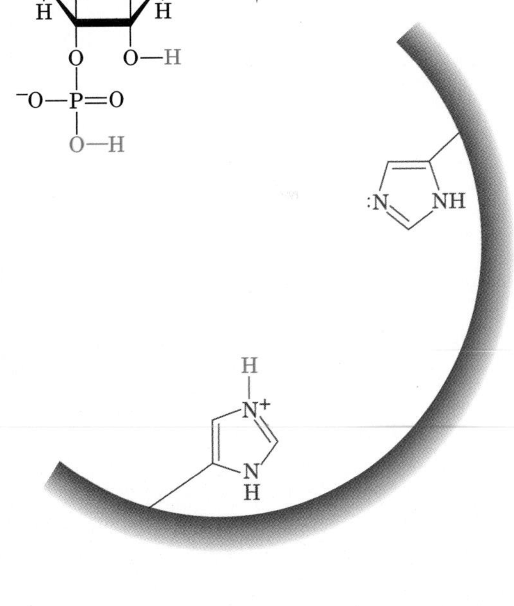

Figure 11-10 | The RNase A mechanism. The bovine pancreatic RNase A–catalyzed hydrolysis of RNA is a two-step process with the intermediate formation of a 2′,3′-cyclic nucleotide.

intestine, where it hydrolyzes RNA to its component nucleotides. The isolation of 2′,3′-cyclic nucleotides from RNase A digests of RNA indicates that 2′,3′-cyclic nucleotides are intermediates in the RNase A reaction (Fig. 11-10). The pH dependence of the rate of the RNase A reaction suggests the involvement of two ionizable residues with pK values of 5.4 and 6.4. This information, together with chemical derivatization and X-ray studies, indicates that RNase A has two essential His residues, His 12 and His 119, that act in a concerted manner as general acid and base catalysts. Evidently, RNase A catalyzes a two-step reaction (Fig. 11-10):

1. His 12, acting as a general base, abstracts a proton from an RNA 2′-OH group, thereby promoting its nucleophilic attack on the adjacent phosphorus atom. His 119, acting as a general acid, promotes bond scission by protonating the leaving group.

2. After the leaving group departs, water enters the active site, and the 2′,3′-cyclic intermediate is hydrolyzed through what is essentially the reverse of the first step. Thus, His 12 now acts as a general acid and His 119 as a general base to yield the hydrolyzed RNA and the enzyme in its original state.

B | Covalent Catalysis Usually Requires a Nucleophile

Covalent catalysis accelerates reaction rates through the transient formation of a catalyst–substrate covalent bond. Usually, this covalent bond is formed by the reaction of a nucleophilic group on the catalyst with an electrophilic group on the substrate, and hence this form of catalysis is often also called

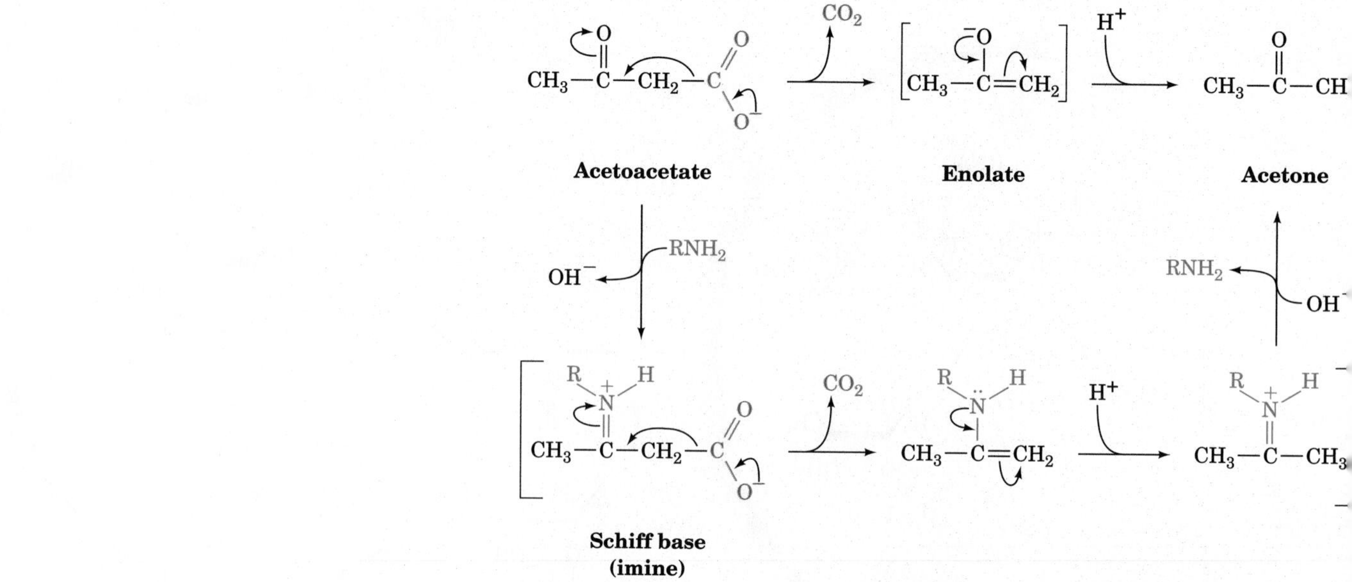

Figure 11-11 | **The decarboxylation of acetoacetate.** The uncatalyzed reaction mechanism is at the top, and the mechanism as catalyzed by primary amines is at the bottom.

nucleophilic catalysis. The decarboxylation of acetoacetate, as chemically catalyzed by primary amines, is an example of such a process (Fig. 11-11). In the first stage of this reaction, the amine, a nucleophile, attacks the carbonyl group of acetoacetate to form a Schiff base (imine bond):

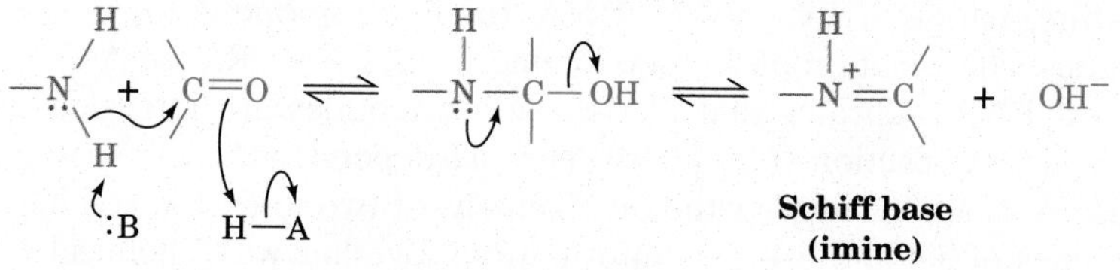

The protonated nitrogen atom of the covalent intermediate then acts as an electron sink (Fig. 11-11, *bottom*) to reduce the high-energy enolate character of the transition state. The formation and decomposition of the Schiff base occurs quite rapidly so that it is not the rate-determining step of this reaction.

Covalent catalysis can be conceptually decomposed into three stages:

1. The nucleophilic reaction between the catalyst and the substrate to form a covalent bond.
2. The withdrawal of electrons from the reaction center by the now electrophilic catalyst.
3. The elimination of the catalyst, a reaction that is essentially the reverse of stage 1.

The nucleophilicity of a substance is closely related to its basicity. Indeed, the mechanism of nucleophilic catalysis resembles that of base catalysis except that, instead of abstracting a proton from the substrate, the catalyst nucleophilically attacks the substrate to form a covalent bond. Biologically important nucleophiles are negatively charged or contain unshared electron pairs that easily form covalent bonds with electron-deficient centers (Fig. 11-12a). Electrophiles, in contrast, include groups that are positively

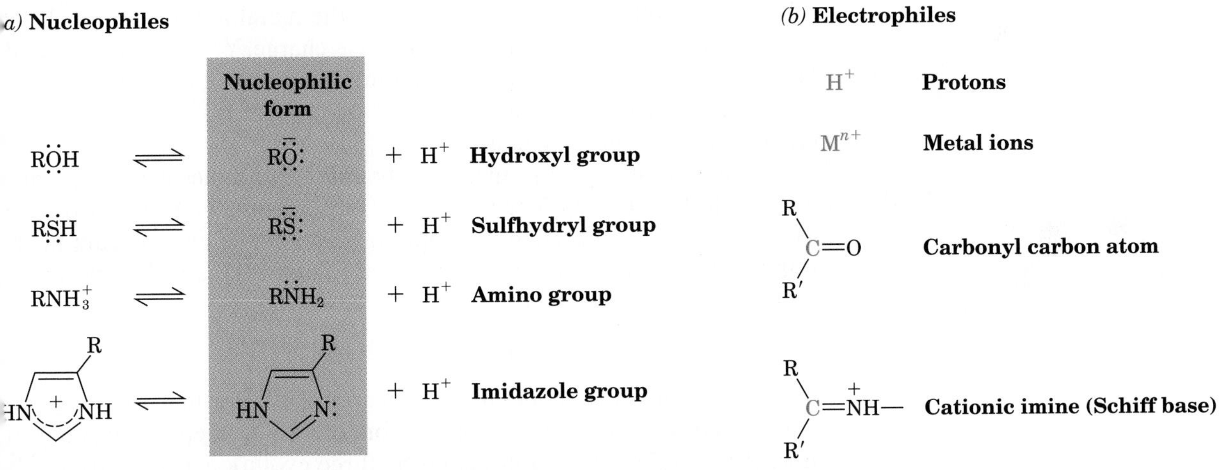

a) **Nucleophiles**

(b) **Electrophiles**

H^+		**Protons**
M^{n+}		**Metal ions**

Nucleophilic form

RÖH ⇌ RÖ: + H⁺ **Hydroxyl group**

RṠH ⇌ RṠ: + H⁺ **Sulfhydryl group**

RNH₃⁺ ⇌ RN̈H₂ + H⁺ **Amino group**

+ H⁺ **Imidazole group**

$$\begin{array}{c} R \\ \diagdown \\ C=O \\ \diagup \\ R' \end{array}$$ **Carbonyl carbon atom**

$$\begin{array}{c} R \\ \diagdown \\ C=\overset{+}{N}H— \\ \diagup \\ R' \end{array}$$ **Cationic imine (Schiff base)**

Figure 11-12 | Biologically important nucleophilic and electrophilic groups. *(a)* Nucleophilic groups such as hydroxyl, sulfhydryl, amino, and imidazole groups are nucleophiles in their basic forms. *(b)* Electrophilic groups contain an electron-deficient atom *(red)*.

charged, contain an unfilled valence electron shell, or contain an electronegative atom (Fig. 11-12*b*).

An important aspect of covalent catalysis is that *the more stable the covalent bond formed, the less easily it can decompose in the final steps of a reaction.* A good covalent catalyst must therefore combine the seemingly contradictory properties of high nucleophilicity and the ability to form a good leaving group, that is, to easily reverse the bond formation step. Groups with high polarizability (highly mobile electrons), such as imidazole and thiol groups, have these properties and hence make good covalent catalysts. Functional groups in proteins that act in this way include the unprotonated amino group of Lys, the imidazole group of His, the thiol group of Cys, the carboxyl group of Asp, and the hydroxyl group of Ser. In addition, several coenzymes, notably **thiamine pyrophosphate** (Section 15-3B) and **pyridoxal phosphate** (Section 21-2A), function in association with their apoenzymes as covalent catalysts. The large variety of covalently linked enzyme–substrate reaction intermediates that have been isolated demonstrates that enzymes commonly employ covalent catalytic mechanisms.

C | Metal Ion Cofactors Act as Catalysts

Nearly one-third of all known enzymes require metal ions for catalytic activity. This group of enzymes includes the **metalloenzymes,** which contain tightly bound metal ion cofactors, most commonly transition metal ions such as Fe^{2+}, Fe^{3+}, Cu^{2+}, Mn^{2+}, or Co^{2+}. These catalytically essential metal ions are distinct from ions such as Na^+, K^+, or Ca^{2+}, which often play a structural rather than a catalytic role in enzymes. Ions such as Mg^{2+} and Zn^{2+} may be either structural or catalytic.

Metal ions participate in the catalytic process in three major ways:

1. By binding to substrates to orient them properly for reaction.
2. By mediating oxidation–reduction reactions through reversible changes in the metal ion's oxidation state.
3. By electrostatically stabilizing or shielding negative charges.

(a)

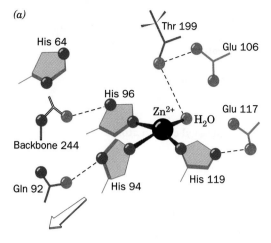

(b)

■ **Figure 11-13** | **The role of Zn²⁺ in carbonic anhydrase.** (a) The active site of the human enzyme. In the X-ray structure, the Zn^{2+} ion is coordinated by three imidazole groups and a water molecule. The arrow points toward the opening of the active site cavity. [After Sheridan, R.P. and Allen, L.C., *J. Am. Chem. Soc.* **103**, 1545 (1981).] ✑ **See Interactive Exercise 7.** (b) The reaction catalyzed by carbonic anhydrase. Im represents the His imidazole group.

In many metal ion–catalyzed reactions, the metal ion acts in much the same way as a proton to neutralize negative charge. Yet metal ions are often much more effective catalysts than protons because metal ions can be present in high concentrations at neutral pH (where $[H^+] = 10^{-7}$ M) and may have charges greater than +1.

A metal ion's charge also makes its bound water molecules more acidic than free H_2O and therefore a source of nucleophilic OH^- ions even below neutral pH. An excellent example of this phenomenon occurs in the catalytic mechanism of carbonic anhydrase (Box 2-1), a widely occurring enzyme that catalyzes the reaction

$$CO_2 + H_2O \rightleftharpoons HCO_3^- + H^+$$

Carbonic anhydrase contains an essential Zn^{2+} ion that the enzyme's X-ray structure indicates lies at the bottom of a 15-Å-deep active site cleft where it is tetrahedrally coordinated by three evolutionarily invariant His side chains and an H_2O molecule (Fig. 11-13a). The Zn^{2+}-polarized H_2O ionizes to form OH^-, which nucleophilically attacks the enzyme-bound CO_2 to yield HCO_3^- (Fig. 11-13b). The proton produced in the reaction is shuttled to the enzyme's surface through base catalysis that is facilitated by a fourth His residue (His 64). The enzyme's catalytic site is then regenerated by the binding of another H_2O to the Zn^{2+} ion.

D | Catalysis Can Occur through Proximity and Orientation Effects

Although enzymes employ catalytic mechanisms that resemble those of organic model reactions, they are far more catalytically efficient than the models. Such efficiency must arise from the specific physical conditions at enzyme catalytic sites that promote the corresponding chemical reactions. The most obvious effects are **proximity** and **orientation**: Reactants must come together with the proper spatial relationship for a reaction to occur. Consider the bimolecular reaction of imidazole with *p*-nitrophenylacetate.

The progress of the reaction is conveniently monitored by the appearance of the intensely yellow *p*-nitrophenolate ion. The related intramolecular reaction

occurs about 24 times faster. Thus, when the imidazole is covalently attached to the reactant, it is 24 times more effective than when it is free ı solution. This rate enhancement results from both proximity and orientation effects.

By simply binding their substrates, enzymes facilitate their catalyzed reactions in four ways:

1. Enzymes bring substrates into contact with their catalytic groups and, in reactions with more than one substrate, with each other. However, calculations based on simple model systems suggest that such proximity effects alone can enhance reaction rates by no more than a factor of ~5.

2. Enzymes bind their substrates in the proper orientations for reaction. Molecules are not equally reactive in all directions. Rather, *they react most readily if they have the proper relative orientation.* For example, in an S_N2 (bimolecular nucleophilic substitution) reaction, the incoming nucleophile optimally attacks its target along the direction opposite to that of the bond to the leaving group (Fig. 11-14). Reacting atoms whose approaches deviate by as little as 10° from this optimum direction are significantly less reactive. It is estimated that properly orienting substrates can increase reaction rates by a factor of up to ~100. Enzymes, as we shall see, align their substrates and catalytic groups so as to optimize reactivity.

3. Charged groups may help stabilize the transition state of the reaction, a phenomenon termed **electrostatic catalysis.** The charge distribution around the active sites of enzymes may also guide polar substrates toward their binding site.

4. Enzymes freeze out the relative translational and rotational motions of their substrates and catalytic groups. This is an important aspect of catalysis because, in the transition state, the reacting groups have

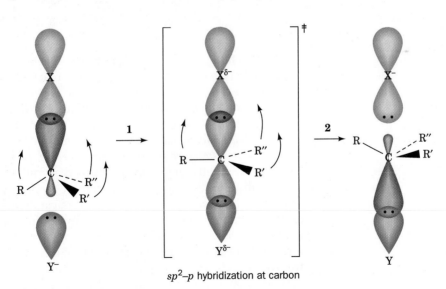

sp^2–p hybridization at carbon

Figure 11-14 | The geometry of an S_N2 reaction. **(1)** The attacking nucleophile, Y^-, must approach the tetrahedrally coordinated and hence sp^3-hybridized C atom along the direction opposite that of its bond to the leaving group, X. In the transition state of the reaction, the C atom becomes trigonal bipyramidally coordinated and hence sp^2–p hybridized, with the p orbital (*blue*) forming partial bonds to X and Y. The three sp^2 orbitals form bonds to the C atom's three other substituents (R, R′, and R″), which have shifted their positions into the plane perpendicular to the X—C—Y axis (*curved arrows*). Any deviation from this optimal geometry would increase the free energy of the transition state, $\Delta G^{\ddagger}$, and hence reduce the rate of the reaction. **(2)** The transition state then decomposes to products in which R, R′, and R″ have inverted their positions about the C atom, which has rehybridized to sp^3, and X^- has been released.

little relative motion. Indeed, experiments with model compound
suggest that *this effect can promote rate enhancements of up to ~10*

Bringing substrates and catalytic groups together in a reactive orientation o
ders them and therefore has a substantial entropic penalty. The free energ
required to overcome this entropy loss is supplied by the binding energy
the substrate(s) to the enzyme and contributes to the decreased $\Delta\Delta G^{\ddagger}$.

E | Enzymes Catalyze Reactions by Preferentially Binding the Transition State

The rate enhancements effected by enzymes are often greater than can b
reasonably accounted for by the catalytic mechanisms discussed so fa
However, we have not yet considered one of the most important mecha
nisms of enzymatic catalysis: *An enzyme may bind the transition state c
the reaction it catalyzes with greater affinity than its substrates or product*
When taken together with the previously described catalytic mechanism
preferential transition state binding explains the observed rates c
enzyme-catalyzed reactions.

The original concept of transition state binding proposed that enzyme
mechanically strained their substrates toward the transition state geome
try through binding sites into which undistorted substrates did not prop
erly fit. Such strain promotes many organic reactions. For example, the rat
of the reaction

is 315 times faster when R is CH_3 rather than H because of the greater steri
repulsion between the CH_3 groups and the reacting groups. The strained re
actant more closely resembles the transition state of the reaction than doe
the corresponding unstrained reactant. Thus, as was first suggested by Linu
Pauling and further amplified by Richard Wolfenden and Gustav Lienhard
*enzymes that preferentially bind the transition state structure increase its con
centration and therefore proportionally increase the reaction rate.*

The more tightly an enzyme binds its reaction's transition state relativ
to the substrate, the greater is the rate of the catalyzed reaction relativ
to that of the uncatalyzed reaction; that is, catalysis results from the pref
erential binding and therefore the stabilization of the transition state
relative to the substrate (Fig. 11-15). In other words, the free energy dif
ference between an enzyme–substrate complex (ES) and an enzyme-
transition state complex (ES‡) is less than the free energy difference
between S and S‡ in an uncatalyzed reaction.

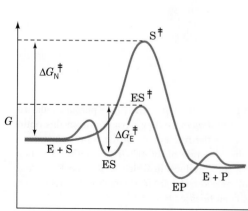

■ **Figure 11-15 | Effect of preferential transition state binding.** The reaction
coordinate diagram for a hypothetical enzyme-catalyzed reaction involving a single
substrate is blue, and the diagram for the corresponding uncatalyzed reaction is red.
$\Delta G_N^{\ddagger}$ is the free energy of activation for the nonenzymatic reaction and $\Delta G_E^{\ddagger}$ is the
free energy of activation for the enzyme-catalyzed reaction. The small dips in the
reaction coordinate diagram for the enzyme-catalyzed reaction arise from the binding
of substrate and product to the enzyme. ✎ **See the Animated Figures.**

Reaction coordinate

As we saw in Section 11-2, the rate enhancement of a catalyzed reaction is given by $e^{\Delta\Delta G^{\ddagger}_{cat}/RT}$, where $\Delta\Delta G^{\ddagger}_{cat}$ is the difference in the values of $\Delta G^{\ddagger}$ for the uncatalyzed (ΔG_N) and the catalyzed (ΔG_E) reactions. Thus, a rate enhancement of 10^6, which requires that an enzyme bind its transition state complex with 10^6-fold higher affinity than its substrate, corresponds to a 34.2 kJ·mol^{-1} stabilization at 25°C, roughly the free energy of two hydrogen bonds. Consequently, the enzymatic binding of a transition state by two hydrogen bonds that cannot form when the substrate first binds to the enzyme should result in a rate enhancement of ~10^6 based on this effect alone.

It is commonly observed that an enzyme binds poor substrates, which have low reaction rates, as well as or even better than good ones, which have high reaction rates. Thus, a good substrate does not necessarily bind to its enzyme with high affinity, but it does so on activation to the transition state.

Transition State Analogs Are Enzyme Inhibitors. *If an enzyme preferentially binds its transition state, then it can be expected that* **transition state analogs,** *stable molecules that geometrically and electronically resemble the transition state, are potent inhibitors of the enzyme.* For example, the reaction catalyzed by **proline racemase** from *Clostridium sticklandii* is thought to occur via a planar transition state:

L-Proline   Planar transition   D-Proline
                        state

Proline racemase is inhibited by the planar analogs of proline, **pyrrole-2-carboxylate** and **Δ-1-pyrroline-2-carboxylate,**

Pyrrole-2-carboxylate   Δ-1-Pyrroline-2-carboxylate

both of which bind to the enzyme with 160-fold greater affinity than does proline. These compounds are therefore thought to be analogs of the transition state in the proline racemase reaction.

Hundreds of transition state analogs for various enzymes have been reported. Some are naturally occurring antibiotics. Others were designed to investigate the mechanism of particular enzymes or to act as specific enzyme inhibitors for therapeutic or agricultural use. Indeed, *the theory that enzymes bind transition states with higher affinity than substrates has led to a rational basis for drug design based on the understanding of specific enzyme reaction mechanisms* (Section 12-4).

4 Lysozyme

In the remainder of this chapter, we investigate the catalytic mechanisms of some well-characterized enzymes. In doing so, we shall see how enzymes apply the catalytic principles described in the preceding section.

■ **CHECK YOUR UNDERSTANDING**

Describe how protein functional groups can act as acid and base catalysts.

Explain how nucleophiles function as covalent catalysts.

List the ways in which metal ions participate in catalysis.

What roles do proximity and orientation play in enzymatic catalysis?

Why is it unlikely that nonenzymatic catalysts operate by preferentially binding the transition state?

LEARNING OBJECTIVES

■ Understand the general features of substrate binding to lysozyme.

■ Understand lysozyme's catalytic mechanisms and how these have been experimentally verified.

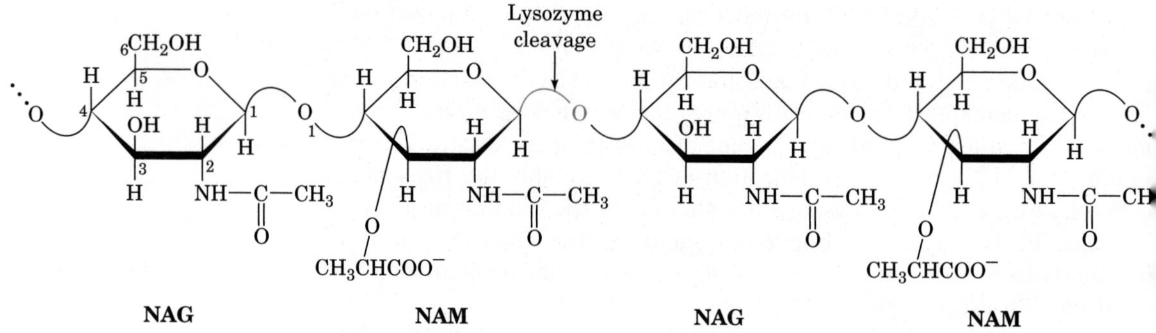

■ **Figure 11-16** | **The lysozyme cleavage site.** The enzyme cleaves after a β(1→4) linkage in the alternating NAG—NAM polysaccharide component of bacterial cell walls.

Lysozyme is an enzyme that destroys bacterial cell walls. It does so by hydrolyzing the β(1→4) glycosidic linkages from **N-acetylmuramic acid** (**NAM** or **MurNAc**) to **N-acetylglucosamine** (**NAG** or **GlcNAc**) in cell wall peptidoglycans (Fig. 11-16 and Section 8-3B). It likewise hydrolyzes β(1→4)-linked poly(NAG) (chitin; Section 8-2B), a cell wall constituent of most fungi as well as the major component of the exoskeletons of insects and crustaceans. Lysozyme occurs widely in the cells and secretions of vertebrates, where it probably functions as a bactericidal agent or helps dispose of bacteria after they have been killed by other means.

Hen egg white (HEW) lysozyme is the most widely studied species of lysozyme and is one of the mechanistically best understood enzymes. It is a rather small protein (14.3 kD) whose single polypeptide chain consists of 129 amino acid residues and is internally cross-linked by four disulfide bonds. Lysozyme catalyzes the hydrolysis of its substrate at a rate that is ~10^8-fold greater than that of the uncatalyzed reaction.

A | Lysozyme's Catalytic Site Was Identified through Model Building

The X-ray structure of HEW lysozyme, which was elucidated by David Phillips in 1965 (and hence was the first enzyme to have its structure determined), shows that the protein molecule is roughly ellipsoidal in shape with dimensions 30 × 30 × 45 Å (Fig. 11-17). *Its most striking feature is a prominent cleft, the substrate-binding site, that traverses one face of the molecule.*

The elucidation of an enzyme's mechanism of action requires a knowledge of the structure of its enzyme–substrate complex. This is because, even if the active site residues have been identified through chemical and physical means, their three-dimensional arrangement relative to the substrate as well as to each other must be known in order to understand how the enzyme works. However, an enzyme binds its good substrates only transiently before it catalyzes a reaction and releases products. Consequently, much of our structural knowledge of enzyme–substrate complexes comes from X-ray studies of enzymes in their complexes with substrate analogs that bind but do not react or react very slowly (but see Box 11-2).

Phillips' X-ray structure of lysozyme includes the trisaccharide (NAG)$_3$ which is only slowly hydrolyzed by lysozyme. However, the enzyme efficiently catalyzes the hydrolysis of substrates containing at least six saccharide units

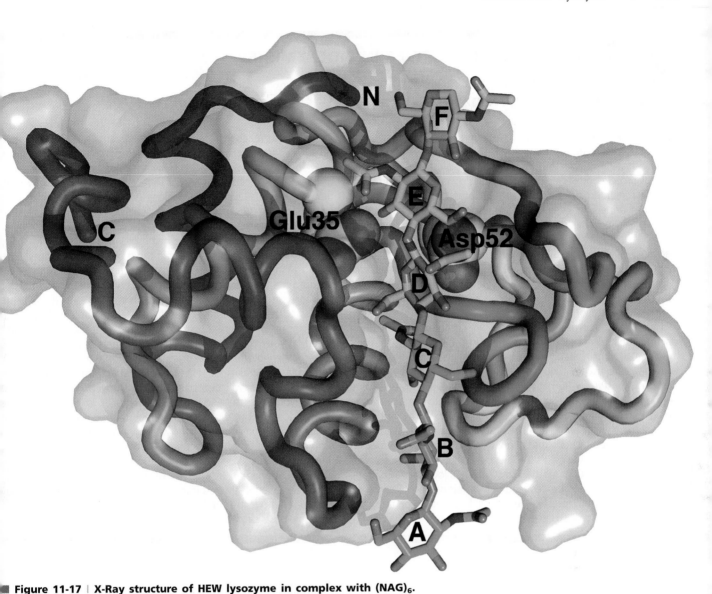

■ Figure 11-17 | X-Ray structure of HEW lysozyme in complex with (NAG)₆.
The protein is represented by its transparent molecular surface with its polypeptide
chain in worm form colored in rainbow order from blue at its N-terminus to red at
its C-terminus. The (NAG)₆, which is drawn in stick form with its sugar rings
designated A, at its nonreducing end, through F, at its reducing end, binds in a deep
cleft in the enzyme surface. Rings A, B, and C (colored according to atom type with
C green, N blue, and O red) are observed in the X-ray structure of the complex of
(NAG)₃ with lysozyme; the positions of rings D, E, and F (C atoms cyan) were
inferred by model building. The side chains of lysozyme's active site residues, Glu 35
and Asp 52, which are drawn in space-filling form (C atoms yellow), catalyze the
hydrolysis of the glycosidic bond between rings D and E. [Based on an X-ray
structure by David Phillips, Oxford University. PDBid 1HEW.] ⌔ **See Interactive
Exercise 8 and Kinemage Exercise 9.**

so Phillips used model building to investigate how a larger substrate
could bind to the enzyme. Lysozyme's active site cleft is long enough to
accommodate an oligosaccharide of six residues (designated A to F in
Fig. 11-17). However, the fourth residue (D) appeared unable to bind to
the enzyme because its C6 and O6 atoms too closely contacted protein

BOX 11-2 PERSPECTIVES IN BIOCHEMISTRY

Observing Enzyme Action by X-Ray Crystallography

The atomic rearrangements that occur during catalysis are to some extent observable during X-ray crystallographic analysis. Because protein crystals are mostly solvent, not only are the native structures of proteins preserved in the crystalline state, but often their catalytic functions are also intact. Substrates can diffuse through solvent channels in the crystal into the enzyme's active site. However, an enzyme rapidly converts its substrates to products. For this reason, the chemical transformations during an enzymatic reaction would be accessible only from "before and after" snapshots, that is, from the structure of the enzyme in the absence of substrate and, in some cases, the structure of the enzyme with its loosely bound products. Several approaches have been used to get around this limitation.

The X-ray structures of enzymes in complexes with slow-reacting substrates may be determined. In this approach, the substrate must remain stably bound to the enzyme for the several hours that are usually required to measure the crystal's X-ray diffraction intensities. Alternatively, an unreactive substrate analog can be used. In this case, the molecule binds much as a substrate would but is not subject to the catalytic reaction. This approach yields somewhat incomplete information, however, since some of the molecular interactions that allow catalysis to occur are missing or distorted. Nevertheless, such data, along with knowledge of nonenzymatic reaction mechanisms, often allow the enzymatic reaction mechanism to be deduced with a fair degree of certainty. Indeed, most of our present structural knowledge of enzyme–substrate interactions is based on this technique.

Enzymatic reactions, like all chemical reactions, are temperature sensitive. Therefore, cooling a crystallized enzyme can significantly slow the rate at which it reacts with a substrate that diffuses to it. For example, cooling a crystal to less than 50 K can slow reaction times from less than a microsecond to hours or days, long enough to measure a set of X-ray diffraction intensities.

Another approach, which has been successfully used to investigate the atomic events at the heme group of myoglobin, solves two problems inherent in analyzing rapid biochemical events. First, taking a "snapshot" of an enzyme in action requires a short exposure time, in analogy to conventional photography. Accordingly, very intense radiation must be used, in this case an X-ray beam generated by a synchrotron (a type of "atom smasher" in which electrons are accelerated around a circular track to near light speed, thereby emitting X-radiation many orders of magnitude more intense than that available from conventional X-ray generators). Second, all the molecules in the crystal must act simultaneously; otherwise, the data will be "blurry." In a study of CO dissociation from myoglobin (the CO binds to myoglobin in much the same way as does O_2 but much more tightly), the molecules were made to dissociate from the heme on cue by a flash of laser light with a duration of a few nanoseconds. Subsequent molecular motions, ultimately leading to the recombination of the CO with myoglobin, were monitored at intervals of microseconds to milliseconds. With refinements, this experimentally complicated technique may eventually prove useful for documenting the operations of enzymes, whose catalytic cycles are complete within nanoseconds.

---

side chains and residue C. This steric interference could be relieved by distorting the glucose ring from its normal chair conformation to that of a half-chair (Fig. 11-18). This distortion moves the C6 group from its norma

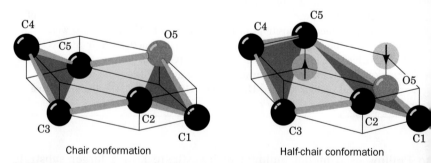

■ **Figure 11-18** | **Chair and half-chair conformations.** Hexose rings normally assume the chair conformation. However, binding to lysozyme distorts the D ring into the half-chair conformation in which atoms C1, C2, C5, and O5 are coplanar.
ℂ **See the Animated Figures.**

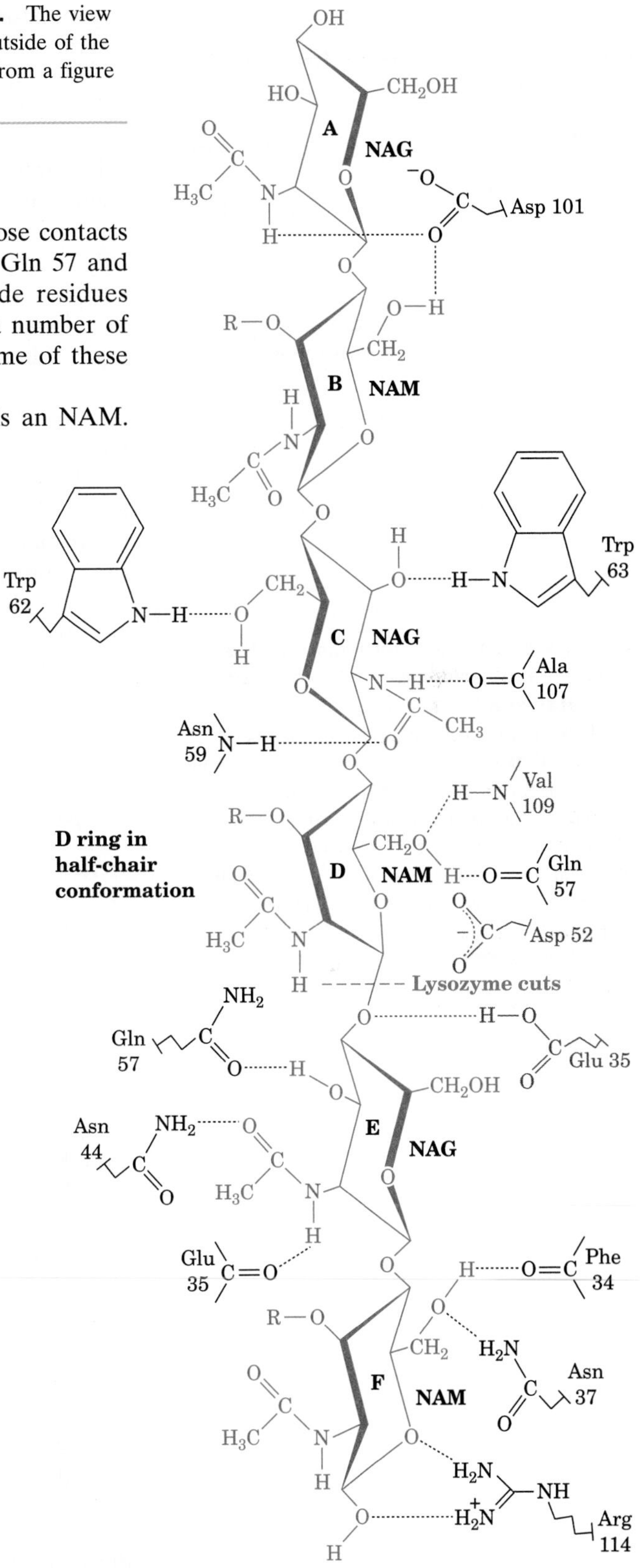

Figure 11-19 | The interactions of lysozyme with its substrate. The view is into the binding cleft with the heavier edges of the rings facing the outside of the enzyme and the lighter ones against the bottom of the cleft. [Modified from a figure by Irving Geis.] See Kinemage Exercise 9.

equatorial position to an axial position, where it makes no close contacts and can hydrogen bond to the backbone carbonyl group of Gln 57 and the backbone amido group of Val 109. The other saccharide residues apparently bind to the enzyme without distortion and with a number of favorable hydrogen-bonding and van der Waals contacts. Some of these hydrogen bonds are diagrammed in Fig. 11-19.

In the enzyme's natural substrate, every second residue is an NAM. Model building, however, indicated that the enzyme could not accommodate a lactyl side chain in subsites C or E. Hence, the NAM residues must bind at positions B, D, and F, as drawn in Fig. 11-19. Moreover, since lysozyme hydrolyzes (NAG)$_6$ between residues D and E, it must cleave the glycosidic bond in its natural substrate between the NAM residue in subsite D and the NAG residue in subsite E.

The bond that lysozyme cleaves was identified by allowing lysozyme to catalyze the hydrolysis of (NAG)$_3$ in H$_2^{18}$O. The bond cleaved could either be between C1 and the bridge oxygen O1 or between O1 and C4 of the next sugar ring. The product of the hydrolysis reaction had ^{18}O bonded to the C1 atom of its newly liberated reducing terminus, thereby demonstrating that bond cleavage occurs between C1 and O1:

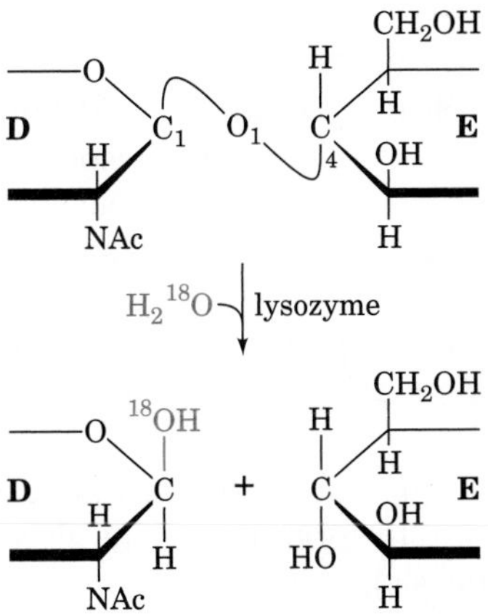

In addition, this reaction occurs with retention of configuration so that the D-ring product remains the β anomer.

B | The Lysozyme Reaction Proceeds via a Covalent Intermediate

The reaction catalyzed by lysozyme, the hydrolysis of a glycoside, is the conversion of an acetal to a hemiacetal. Nonenzymatic acetal hydrolysis is an acid-catalyzed reaction that involves the protonation of a reactant

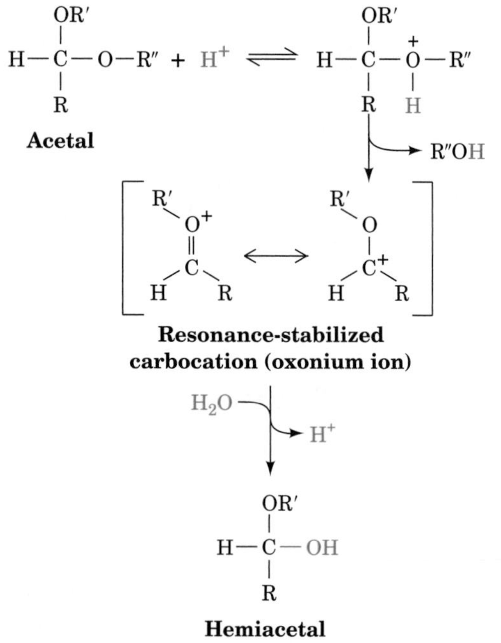

Figure 11-20 | **The mechanism of the nonenzymatic acid-catalyzed hydrolysis of an acetal to a hemiacetal.** The reaction involves the protonation of one of the acetal's oxygen atoms followed by cleavage of its C—O bond to form an alcohol (R″OH) and a resonance-stabilized carbocation (oxonium ion). The addition of water to the oxonium ion forms the hemiacetal and regenerates the H⁺ catalyst. Note that the oxonium ion's C, O, H, R, and R′ atoms all lie in the same plane.

oxygen atom followed by cleavage of its C—O bond (Fig. 11-20). This results in the transient formation of a resonance-stabilized carbocation that is called an **oxonium ion.** To attain resonance stabilization, the oxonium ion's R and R′ groups must be coplanar with its C, O, and H atoms. The oxonium ion then adds water to yield the hemiacetal and regenerate the acid catalyst. An enzyme that mediates acetal hydrolysis should therefore include an acid catalyst and possibly a group that can stabilize an oxonium ion transition state.

Glu 35 and Asp 52 Are Lysozyme's Catalytic Residues. The only functional groups in the immediate vicinity of lysozyme's reactive center that have the required catalytic properties are the side chains of Glu 35 and Asp 52. These side chains, which are disposed to either side of the glycosidic linkage to be cleaved (Fig. 11-17), have markedly different environments. Asp 52 is surrounded by several conserved polar residues with which it forms a complex hydrogen-bonded network. Asp 52 is therefore predicted to have a normal pK; that is, it should be unprotonated and hence negatively charged throughout the 3 to 8 pH range over which lysozyme is catalytically active. Thus, Asp 52 can function to electrostatically stabilize an oxonium ion. In contrast, the carboxyl group of Glu 35 is nestled in a predominantly nonpolar pocket where it is likely to remain protonated at unusually high pH values for carboxyl groups. This residue can therefore act as an acid catalyst. Studies using protein-modifying reagents and site-directed mutagenesis (e.g., changing Asp 52 to Asn and Glu 35 to Gln) have verified that these residues are catalytically important.

Lysozyme's catalytic mechanism occurs as follows (Fig. 11-21):

1. The enzyme attaches to a bacterial cell wall by binding to a hexasaccharide unit. This distorts the D residue toward the half-chair conformation.

2. Glu 35 transfers its proton to the O1 atom bridging the D and E rings, thereby facilitating cleavage of the C1—O1 bond (general acid catalysis). This step converts the D ring to a resonance-stabilized oxonium ion transition state whose formation is facilitated by the strain distorting it to the half-chair conformation (catalysis by the preferential binding of the transition state). The positively charged oxonium ion is stabilized by the presence of the nearby negatively charged Asp 52 carboxylate group (electrostatic catalysis). The E-ring product is released.

3. The Asp 52 carboxylate group nucleophilically attacks the now electron-poor C1 of the D ring to form a covalent glycosyl–enzyme intermediate (covalent catalysis).

4. Water replaces the E-ring product in the active site.

5. Hydrolysis of the covalent bond with the assistance of Glu 35 (general base catalysis), which involves another oxonium ion transition state, regenerates the active site groups. The enzyme then releases the D-ring product, completing the catalytic cycle.

The double-displacement mechanism diagrammed in Fig. 11-21 allows the incoming water molecule to attach to the same face of the D residue as the E residue it replaces. Consequently, the configuration of the D residue is retained. A single-displacement reaction, in which water directly displaces the leaving group, would invert the configuration at C1 of the D ring between the substrate and product, a result that is not observed.

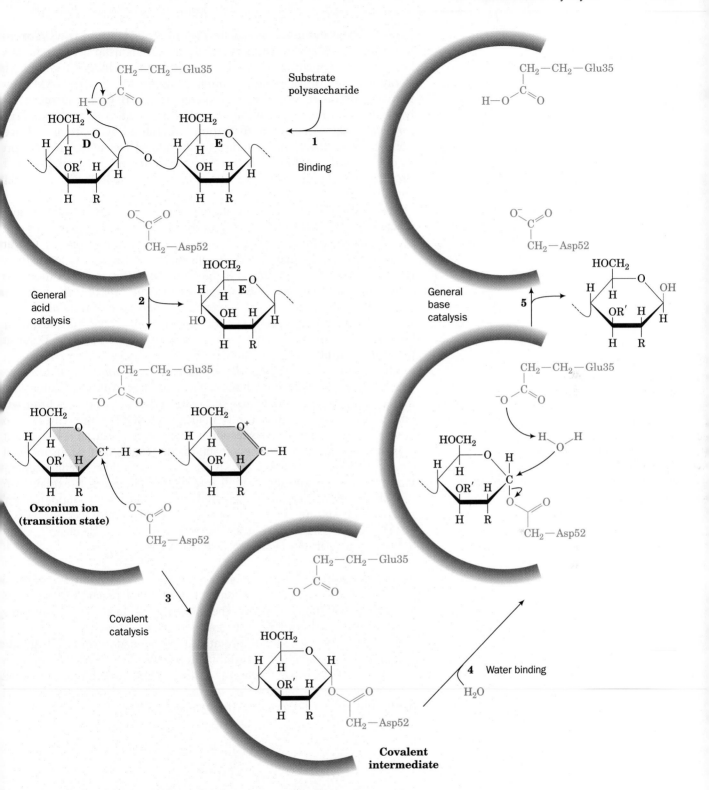

Figure 11-21 | The lysozyme reaction mechanism. Glu 35 acts as an acid catalyst, and Asp 52 acts as a covalent catalyst. Only the substrate D and E rings are shown. R represents the *N*-acetyl group at C2, and R′ represents the CH₃CHCOO⁻ group at C3. The resonance-stabilized oxonium ion transition state requires that C1, C2, C5, and O5 be coplanar (*shading*), creating a half-chair conformation. Step 5 includes the participation of an oxonium ion transition state that is not shown.

See Kinemage Exercise 9.

Experimental Evidence Supports the Role of Strain in the Lysozyme Mechanism. Many of the structural and mechanistic investigations of lysozyme have focused on the catalytic role of strain. For example, the X-ray structure of lysozyme in complex with NAM—NAG—NAM shows that the trisaccharide binds, as predicted, to the B, C, and D subsites of lysozyme, *with the NAM in the D subsite distorted to the half-chair conformation.* This strained conformation is stabilized by a strong hydrogen bond between the D ring O6 and the backbone NH of Val 109 (as predicted by model building; Fig. 11-19). Indeed, the mutation of Val 109 to Pro, which lacks the NH group to make such a hydrogen bond, inactivates the enzyme.

As we have discussed in Section 11-3E, an enzyme that catalyzes a reaction by the preferential binding of its transition state has a greater binding affinity for an inhibitor that has the transition state geometry (a transition state analog) than it does for its substrate. The δ-lactone analog of (NAG)$_4$ (Fig. 11-22), which binds tightly to lysozyme, is a transition state analog of lysozyme since *this compound's lactone ring has the half-chair conformation that geometrically resembles the proposed oxonium ion transition state of the substrate's D ring.* X-Ray studies confirm that this inhibitor binds to lysozyme such that the lactone ring occupies the D subsite in a half-chair-like conformation.

Despite the foregoing, *the role of substrate distortion in lysozyme catalysis has been questioned.* Nathan Sharon and David Chipman determined that the NAG lactone inhibitor (Fig. 11-22) binds to the D subsite with only 9.2 kJ · mol^{-1} greater affinity than does NAG. This quantity, as is explained in Section 11-3E, corresponds to no more than an ~40-fold rate enhancement for the lysozyme reaction, suggesting that strain in the D ring is not a major contributor to lysozyme's ~10^8-fold rate enhancement. However, this unexpectedly small free energy difference is explained by the observation that an undistorted NAG ring can be modeled into lysozyme's D subsite as it occurs in the X-ray structure of its complex with NAM—NAG—NAM. In contrast, NAM's bulky lactyl side chain prevents it from binding to the D subsite in this manner.

Mass Spectrometry and X-Ray Crystallography Provide Support for Covalent Catalysis. The existence of a covalent reaction intermediate has also been difficult to verify. The lifetime of a glucosyl oxonium ion in water is ~10^{-12} s. In order for such a short-lived intermediate to be experimentally observed, its rate of formation must be made significantly greater than its rate of breakdown. To do this, Stephen Withers capitalized on three phenomena. First, if the reaction goes through an oxonium ion transition state, its formation should be slowed by the electron-withdrawing effect of substituting F (the most electronegative element) at C2 of the D ring.

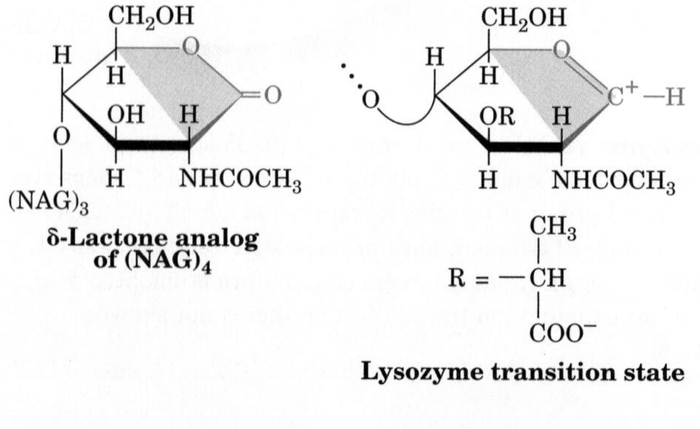

■ **Figure 11-22 | Transition state analog inhibition of lysozyme.** The δ-lactone analog of (NAG)$_4$ (*left*) resembles the transition state of the lysozyme reaction (*right*). Note that atoms C1, C2, C5, and O5 in each structure are coplanar (as indicated by shading), consistent with the half-chair conformation of the hexose ring.

Figure 11-23 | Position of the D ring during catalysis by lysozyme. The position of the substrate's C and D rings and the catalytic Asp 52 are shown in superimposed X-ray structures of the covalent complex between E35Q lysozyme and NAG2FGlcF (C green, N blue, O red, and F magenta) and the noncovalent complex between lysozyme and a NAM—NAG—NAM substrate (C yellow, N blue, and O red). Note that the covalent bond between Asp 52 and C1 of the D ring forms when the D ring in the noncovalent complex relaxes from its distorted half-chair conformation to an undistorted chair conformation and the side chain of Asp 52 undergoes a 45° rotation about its C_α—C_β bond. [Based on X-ray structures by David Vocadlo and Stephen Withers, University of British Columbia, Vancouver, Canada; *and* Michael James, University of Alberta, Edmonton, Canada. PDBid 1H6M.]

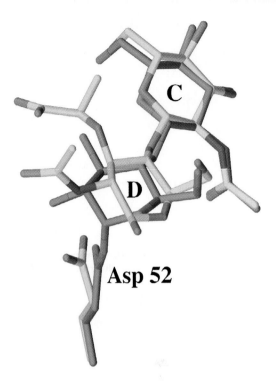

second, mutating Glu 35 to Gln (E35Q) removes the general acid–base catalyst, further slowing all steps involving the oxonium ion transition state. Third, substituting an additional F atom at C1 of the D ring accelerates the formation of the intermediate because this F is a good leaving group without the need of general acid catalysis. Making all three of these changes should increase the rate of formation of the proposed covalent intermediate relative to its breakdown and hence should result in its accumulation. Withers therefore incubated E35Q HEW lysozyme with NAG-β(1→4)-2-deoxy-2-fluoro-β-D-glucopyranosyl fluoride (**NAG2FGlcF**):

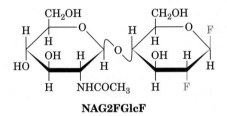

NAG2FGlcF

Electrospray ionization mass spectrometry (ESI-MS; Section 5-3D) of this reaction mixture revealed a sharp peak at 14,683 D, consistent with the formation of the proposed covalent intermediate [lysozyme has a molecular mass of 14,314 D and that of the NAG-β(1→4)-2-deoxy-2-fluoro-β-D-glucopyranosyl group is 369 D].

The X-ray structure of this covalent complex reveals an ~1.4-Å-long covalent bond between C1 of the D ring and a side chain carboxyl O of Asp 52 (Fig. 11-23). This D ring adopts an undistorted chair conformation, thus indicating that it is a reaction intermediate rather than an approximation of the transition state. The superposition of this covalent complex with that of the above-described complex of NAM—NAG—NAM with wild-type HEW lysozyme reveals how this covalent bond forms (Fig. 11-23). The shortening of the 3.2-Å distance between the D ring C1 and the Asp 52 O in the NAM—NAG—NAM complex to ~1.4 Å in the covalent complex occurs as the D ring relaxes from the half-chair to the chair conformation and the Asp 52 side chain rotates ~45° about its C_α—C_β bond.

5 Serine Proteases

Our next example of enzymatic mechanisms is a diverse and widespread group of proteolytic enzymes known as the **serine proteases,** so named because they have a common catalytic mechanism involving a peculiarly reactive Ser residue. The serine proteases include digestive enzymes from

■ **CHECK YOUR UNDERSTANDING**

Explain the importance of conformation in the D ring of a lysozyme substrate.
Describe the catalytic mechanisms employed by lysozyme.

LEARNING OBJECTIVES

■ Understand how chemical labeling and structural analysis can identify an enzyme's catalytic residues and substrate-binding determinants.
■ Understand how serine proteases mediate peptide bond hydrolysis and stabilize the reaction's transition state.
■ Understand that zymogens are the inactive precursors of enzymes.

prokaryotes and eukaryotes, as well as more specialized proteins that pa[r]ticipate in development, blood coagulation (clotting), inflammation, an[d] numerous other processes. In this section, we focus on some of the be[st] studied serine proteases: chymotrypsin, trypsin, and elastase.

A | Active Site Residues Were Identified by Chemical Labelin[g]

Chymotrypsin, trypsin, and elastase are digestive enzymes that are synthe[e]sized by the pancreas and secreted into the duodenum (the sma[ll] intestine's upper loop). All these enzymes catalyze the hydrolysis of pe[p]tide (amide) bonds but with different specificities for the side chains flan[k]ing the scissile (to be cleaved) peptide bond. Chymotrypsin is specific fo[r] a bulky hydrophobic residue preceding the scissile bond, trypsin is specif[ic] for a positively charged residue, and elastase is specific for a small neutr[al] residue (Table 5-3). Together, they form a potent digestive team.

Chymotrypsin's catalytically important groups were identified by chemic[al] labeling studies. A diagnostic test for the presence of the active site Ser [of] serine proteases is its reaction with **diisopropylphosphofluoridate (DIPF** which irreversibly inactivates the enzyme *(at left)*. Other Ser residue[s] including those on the same protein, do not react with DIPF. *DIPF reac[ts] only with Ser 195 of chymotrypsin, thereby demonstrating that this residue [is] the enzyme's active site Ser.* This specificity makes DIPF and related com[m]pounds extremely toxic (Box 11-3).

A second catalytically important residue, His 57, was discovere[d] through **affinity labeling.** In this technique, a substrate analog bearing [a] reactive group specifically binds at the enzyme's active site, where it re[acts] to form a stable covalent bond with a nearby susceptible grou[p] (these reactive substrate analogs have been dubbed the "Trojan horses" of biochemistry). The affinity labeled group(s) can subsequently b[e] isolated and identified.

Chymotrypsin specifically binds **tosyl-L-phenylalanine chloromethylke[e]tone (TPCK)** because of its resemblance to a Phe residue (one of ch[y]motrypsin's preferred substrate residues). Active site–bound TPCK' chloromethylketone group is a strong alkylating agent; it reacts only wit[h] His 57 (Fig. 11-24), thereby inactivating the enzyme. Trypsin, which prefe[rs] basic residues, is similarly inactivated by **tosyl-L-lysine chloromethylketone**

Tosyl-L-lysine chloromethylketone

B | X-Ray Structures Provide Information about Catalysis, Substrate Specificity, and Evolution

Chymotrypsin, trypsin, and elastase are strikingly similar: The primar[y] structures of these ~240-residue enzymes are ~40% identical (for com[parison, the α and β chains of human hemoglobin have 44% sequenc[e

BOX 11-3 BIOCHEMISTRY IN HEALTH AND DISEASE

Nerve Poisons

The use of DIPF as an enzyme-inactivating agent came about through the discovery that organophosphorus compounds such as DIPF are potent nerve poisons. The neurotoxicity of DIPF arises from its ability to inactivate **acetylcholinesterase,** an enzyme that catalyzes the hydrolysis of **acetylcholine:**

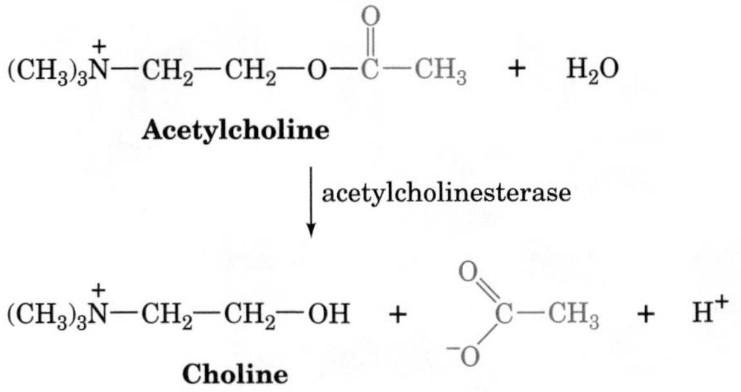

$$(CH_3)_3\overset{+}{N}-CH_2-CH_2-O-\overset{\overset{\displaystyle O}{\|}}{C}-CH_3 \;+\; H_2O$$

Acetylcholine

↓ acetylcholinesterase

$$(CH_3)_3\overset{+}{N}-CH_2-CH_2-OH \;+\; \overset{\overset{\displaystyle O}{\|}}{\underset{-O}{C}}-CH_3 \;+\; H^+$$

Choline

The esterase activity of acetylcholinesterase, like that of chymotrypsin (Section 11-1B), requires a reactive Ser residue.

Acetylcholine is a **neurotransmitter:** It transmits nerve impulses across certain types of **synapses** (junctions between nerve cells). Acetylcholinesterase in the synapse normally degrades acetylcholine so that the nerve impulse has a duration of only a millisecond or so. The inactivation of acetylcholinesterase prevents hydrolysis of the neurotransmitter. As a result, the acetylcholine receptor, which is a Na$^+$–K$^+$ channel, remains open for longer than normal, thereby interfering with the regular sequence of nerve impulses. DIPF is so toxic to humans (death occurs through the inability to breathe) that it has been used militarily as a nerve gas. Related compounds, such as **parathion** and **malathion,** are useful insecticides because they are far more toxic to insects than to mammals.

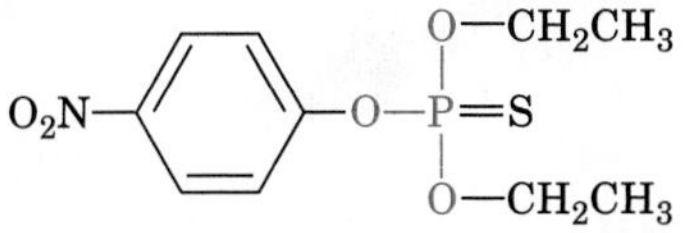

Parathion

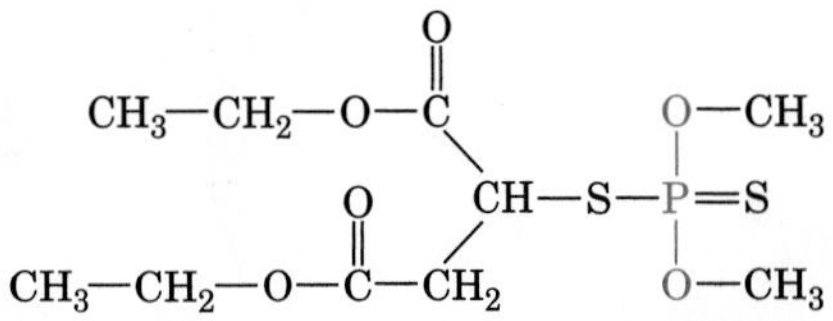

Malathion

Neurotoxins such as DIPF and **sarin** (which gained notoriety after its release by terrorists in a Tokyo subway in 1995)

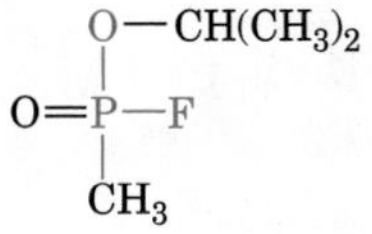

Sarin

are inactivated by the enzyme **paraoxonase.**

This enzyme occurs as two isoforms (one has Arg at position 192 and the other has Gln) with different activities, and individuals express widely differing levels of the enzyme. These factors may account for the large observed differences in individuals' sensitivity to nerve poisons.

---

identity). Furthermore, all these enzymes have a reactive Ser and a catalytically essential His. It therefore came as no surprise when their X-ray structures all proved to be closely related.

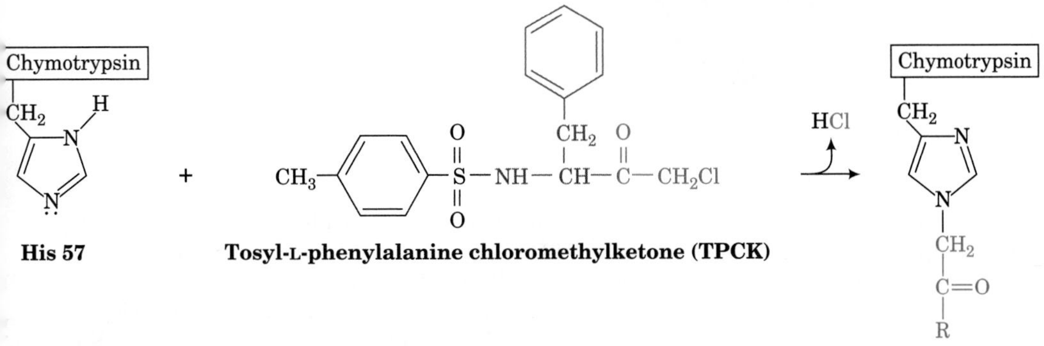

His 57   **Tosyl-L-phenylalanine chloromethylketone (TPCK)**

Figure 11-24 | **Reaction of TPCK with His 57 of chymotrypsin.**

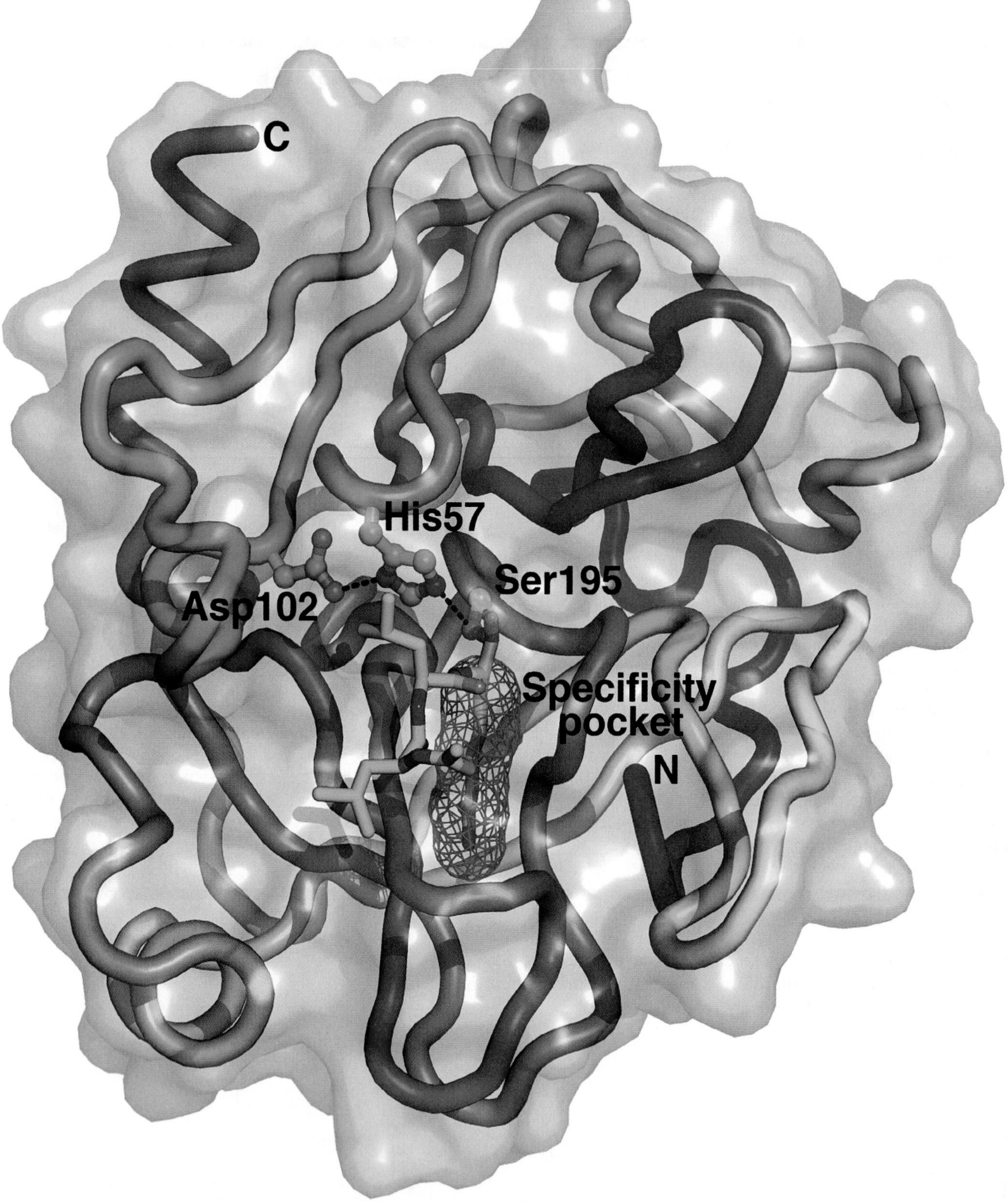

■ **Figure 11-25 | X-Ray structure of bovine trypsin in covalent complex with its inhibitor leupeptin.** The protein is represented by its transparent molecular surface with its polypeptide chain in worm form colored in rainbow order from blue at its N-terminus to red at its C-terminus. The side chains of the catalytic triad, Ser 195, His 57, and Asp 102, are drawn in ball-and-stick form colored according to atom type (C green, N blue, O red) with hydrogen bonds represented by dashed black lines. **Leupeptin** (acetyl-Leu-Leu-Arg in which the terminal carboxyl group is replaced by —CHO) is drawn in stick form (C cyan, N blue, O red) with its Arg side chain occupying the enzyme's specificity pocket (*magenta mesh*). [Based on an X-ray structure by Daniel Koshland, Jr., University of California at Berkeley. PDBid 2AGI.] See **Kinemage Exercise 10-1.**

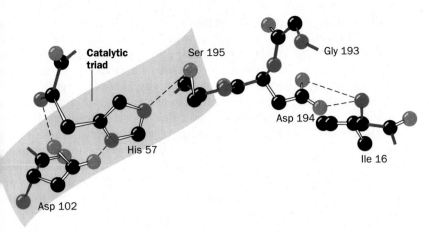

Catalytic triad

Ser 195

Gly 193

Asp 194

Ile 16

His 57

Asp 102

■ **Figure 11-26 | The active site residues of chymotrypsin.** The view is in approximately the same direction as in Fig. 11-25. The catalytic triad consists of Ser 195, His 57, and Asp 102. [After Blow, D.M. and Steitz, T.A., *Annu. Rev. Biochem.* **39**, 86 (1970).]

The structure of bovine chymotrypsin was elucidated in 1967 by David Blow. This was followed by the determination of the structures of bovine trypsin (Fig. 11-25) by Robert Stroud and Richard Dickerson, and porcine elastase by David Shotton and Herman Watson. Each of these proteins is folded into two domains, both of which have extensive regions of antiparallel β sheets in a barrel-like arrangement but contain little helix. For convenience in comparing the structures of these three enzymes, we shall assign them the same residue numbering system—that of bovine **chymotrypsinogen,** the 245-residue precursor of chymotrypsin (Section 11-5D).

In all three structures, the catalytically essential His 57 and Ser 195 residues are located in the enzyme's substrate-binding site (center of Fig. 11-25). The X-ray structures also show that Asp 102, which is present in all serine proteases, is buried in a nearby solvent-inaccessible pocket. *These three invariant residues form a hydrogen-bonded constellation referred to as the* **catalytic triad** (Figs. 11-25 and 11-26).

Substrate Specificities Are Only Partially Rationalized. The X-ray structures of the above three enzymes suggest the basis for their differing substrate specificities (Fig. 11-27):

1. In chymotrypsin, the bulky aromatic side chain of the preferred Phe, Trp, or Tyr residue that contributes the carbonyl group of the scissile peptide fits snugly into a slitlike hydrophobic pocket located near the catalytic groups.

2. In trypsin, the residue corresponding to chymotrypsin Ser 189, which lies at the bottom of the binding pocket, is the anionic residue Asp. The cationic side chains of trypsin's preferred residues, Arg and Lys, can therefore form ion pairs with this Asp residue. The rest of chymotrypsin's specificity pocket is preserved in trypsin so that it can accommodate the bulky side chains of Arg and Lys.

3. Elastase is so named because it rapidly hydrolyzes the otherwise nearly indigestible Ala, Gly, and Val–rich protein **elastin** (a major connective tissue component). Elastase's binding pocket is largely occluded by the side chains of Val and Thr residues that replace the Gly residues lining the specificity pockets in both chymotrypsin and trypsin. Consequently elastase, whose substrate-binding site is better described as merely a depression, specifically cleaves peptide bonds after small neutral residues, particularly Ala. In contrast, chymotrypsin and trypsin hydrolyze such peptide bonds extremely slowly because these small substrates cannot be sufficiently immobilized on the enzyme surface for efficient catalysis to occur.

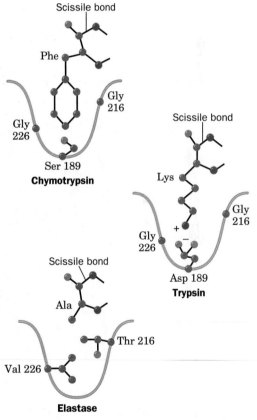

Scissile bond

Phe

Gly 216

Gly 226

Ser 189

Chymotrypsin

Scissile bond

Lys

Gly 216

Gly 226

Asp 189

Trypsin

Scissile bond

Ala

Val 226

Thr 216

Elastase

■ **Figure 11-27 | Specificity pockets of three serine proteases.** The side chains of key residues that determine the size and nature of the specificity pocket are shown along with a representative substrate for each enzyme. Chymotrypsin prefers to cleave peptide bonds following large hydrophobic side chains; trypsin prefers Lys or Arg; and elastase prefers Ala, Gly, or Val. [After a drawing in Branden, C. and Tooze, J., *Introduction to Protein Structure* (2nd ed.), Garland Publishing, p. 213 (1999).]

Despite the foregoing, changing trypsin's Asp 189 to Ser by site-directe[d] mutagenesis (Section 3-5D) does not switch its specificity to that of chy[-] motrypsin but instead yields a poor, nonspecific protease. Replacing addi[-] tional residues in trypsin's specificity pocket with those of chymotrypsi[n] fails to significantly improve this catalytic activity. However, trypsin is con[-] verted to a reasonably active chymotrypsin-like enzyme when two surfac[e] loops that connect the walls of the specificity pocket (residues 185–18[8] and 221–225) are also replaced by those of chymotrypsin. These loop[s,] which are conserved in each enzyme, are apparently necessary not for sub[-] strate binding per se but for properly positioning the scissile bond. Thes[e] results highlight an important caveat for genetic engineers: Enzymes ar[e] so exquisitely tailored to their functions that they often respond to muta[-] genic tinkering in unexpected ways.

Serine Proteases Exhibit Divergent and Convergent Evolution. W[e] have seen that sequence and structural similarities among proteins revea[l] their evolutionary relationships (Sections 5-4 and 6-2D). *The great similar[-] ities among chymotrypsin, trypsin, and elastase indicate that these protein[s] arose through duplications of an ancestral serine protease gene followed b[y] the divergent evolution of the resulting enzymes.* Indeed, the close structura[l] resemblance of these pancreatic enzymes to certain bacterial proteases in[-] dicates that the primordial trypsin gene arose before the diver[-] gence of prokaryotes and eukaryotes.

There are several serine proteases whose primary and ter[-] tiary structures bear no discernible relationship to each other o[r] to chymotrypsin. Nevertheless, these proteins also contain cat[-] alytic triads at their active sites whose structures closely resem[-] ble that of chymotrypsin. These enzymes include **subtilisin,** a[n] endopeptidase that was originally isolated from *Bacillus subtili[s]* and wheat germ **serine carboxypeptidase II,** an exopeptidase[.] Since the orders of the corresponding active site residues in th[e] amino acid sequences of these serine proteases are quite differ[-] ent (Fig. 11-28), it seems highly improbable that they could hav[e] evolved from a common ancestor protein. These enzymes appar[-] ently constitute a remarkable example of **convergent evolution[.]** *Nature seems to have independently discovered the same catalyti[c] mechanism several times.*

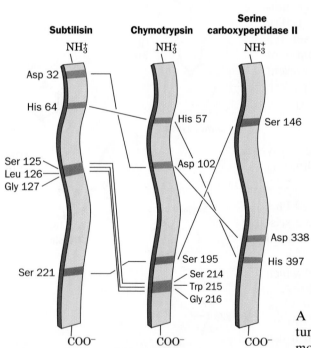

■ **Figure 11-28** | **Diagram indicating the relative positions of the active site residues of three unrelated serine proteases.** The catalytic triads in subtilisin, chymotrypsin, and serine carboxypeptidase II each consist of Ser, His, and Asp residues. The peptide backbones of Ser 214, Trp 215, and Gly 216 in chymotrypsin, and their counterparts in subtilisin, participate in substrate-binding interactions. [After Robertus, J.D., Alden, R.A., Birktoft, J.J., Kraut, J., Powers, J.C., and Wilcox, P.E., *Biochemistry* **11**, 2449 (1972).] ✎ **See Kinemage Exercise 10-2.**

C | Serine Proteases Use Several Catalytic Mechanisms

A catalytic mechanism based on considerable chemical and struc[-] tural data has been formulated and is given here in terms of chy[-] motrypsin (Fig. 11-29), although it applies to all serine proteases an[d] certain other hydrolytic enzymes:

1. After chymotrypsin has bound a substrate, Ser 195 nucleophilically at[-] tacks the scissile peptide's carbonyl group to form the **tetrahedral in[-] termediate,** which resembles the reaction's transition state (covalen[t] catalysis). X-Ray studies indicate that Ser 195 is ideally positioned t[o] carry out this nucleophilic attack (proximity and orientation effects)[.] This nucleophilic attack involves transfer of a proton to the imidazol[e] ring of His 57, thereby forming an imidazolium ion (general base catal[-] ysis). This process is aided by the polarizing effect of the unsolvate[d] carboxylate ion of Asp 102, which is hydrogen bonded to His 57 (elec[-] trostatic catalysis). The tetrahedral intermediate has a well-define[d]

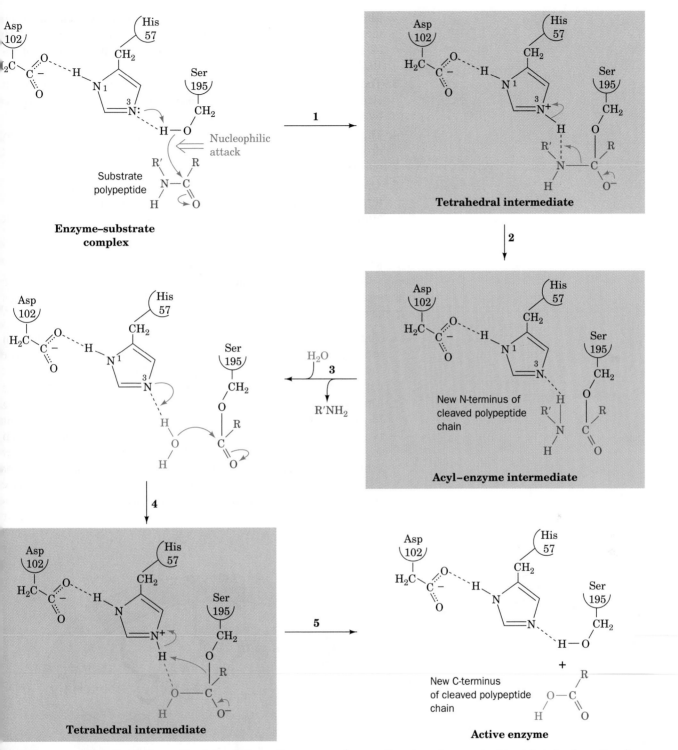

Figure 11-29 | The catalytic mechanism of the serine proteases. The reaction involves (**1**) the nucleophilic attack of the active site Ser on the carbonyl carbon atom of the scissile peptide bond to form the tetrahedral intermediate; (**2**) the decomposition of the tetrahedral intermediate to the acyl–enzyme intermediate through general acid catalysis by the active site Asp-polarized His; (**3**) loss of the amine product and its replacement by a water molecule; (**4**) the reversal of Step 2 to form a second tetrahedral intermediate; and (**5**) the reversal of Step 1 to yield the reaction's carboxyl product and the active enzyme.

although transient, existence. We shall see that *much of chymotrypsin's catalytic power derives from its preferential binding of the transition state leading to this intermediate (transition state binding catalysis).*

See Guided Exploration 10
The catalytic mechanism of serine proteases.

2. The tetrahedral intermediate decomposes to the **acyl–enzyme inte**
mediate under the driving force of proton donation from N3 of H
57 (general acid catalysis) facilitated by the polarizing effect of As
102 on His 57 (electrostatic catalysis).

3. The amine leaving group (R′NH₂, the new N-terminal portion of th
cleaved polypeptide chain) is released from the enzyme and replace
by water from the solvent.

4. The acyl–enzyme intermediate, which is highly susceptible to hy
drolytic cleavage, adds water by the reversal of Step 2, yielding a se
ond tetrahedral intermediate.

5. The reversal of Step 1 yields the carboxylate product (the new C
terminal portion of the cleaved polypeptide chain), thereby regene
ating the active enzyme. In this process, water is the attacking nucl
ophile and Ser 195 is the leaving group.

Serine Proteases Preferentially Bind the Transition State. Detaile
comparisons of the X-ray structures of several serine protease–inhibitc
complexes have revealed a further structural basis for catalysis in thes
enzymes (Fig. 11-30):

1. The conformational distortion that occurs with the formation of th
tetrahedral intermediate causes the now anionic carbonyl oxygen c
the scissile peptide to move deeper into the active site so as to oc
cupy a previously unoccupied position called the **oxanion hole.**

2. There, it forms two hydrogen bonds with the enzyme that cann
form when the carbonyl group is in its normal trigonal conforma
tion. The two enzymatic hydrogen bond donors were first noted t
Joseph Kraut to occupy corresponding positions in chymotrypsin an
subtilisin. He proposed the existence of the oxyanion hole on the ba
sis of the premise that convergent evolution had made the activ
sites of these unrelated enzymes functionally identical.

(a)

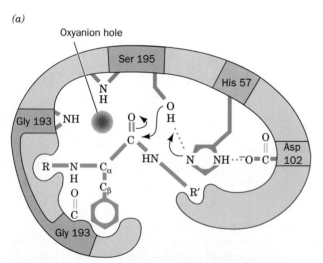

(b)

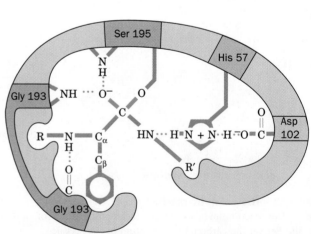

■ **Figure 11-30** | **Transition state stabilization in the serine**
proteases. (*a*) When the substrate binds to the enzyme, the
trigonal carbonyl carbon of the scissile peptide is conformationally
constrained from binding in the oxyanion hole (*upper left*). (*b*) In
the tetrahedral intermediate, the now charged carbonyl oxygen of
the scissile peptide (the oxyanion) enters the oxyanion hole and
hydrogen bonds to the backbone NH groups of Gly 193 and Ser

195. The consequent conformational distortion permits the NH
group of the residue preceding the scissile peptide bond to form a
otherwise unsatisfied hydrogen bond to Gly 193. Serine proteases
therefore preferentially bind the tetrahedral intermediate. [After
Robertus, J.D., Kraut, J., Alden, R.A., and Birktoft, J.J., *Biochemistr*
11, 4302 (1972).] ♻ **See Kinemage Exercise 10-3.**

3. The tetrahedral distortion, moreover, permits the formation of an otherwise unsatisfied hydrogen bond between the enzyme and the backbone NH group of the residue preceding the scissile peptide bond.

This preferential binding of the transition state (or the tetrahedral intermediate) over the enzyme–substrate complex or the acyl–enzyme intermediate is responsible for much of the catalytic efficiency of serine proteases. Thus, mutating any or all of the residues in chymotrypsin's catalytic triad yields enzymes that still enhance proteolysis by ~5 × 10^4-fold over the uncatalyzed reaction (versus a rate enhancement of ~10^{10} for the native enzyme). Similarly, the reason that DIPF is such an effective inhibitor of serine proteases is because its tetrahedral phosphate group makes this compound a transition state analog.

Low-Barrier Hydrogen Bonds May Stabilize the Transition State. The transition state of the chymotrypsin reaction is stabilized not just through the formation of additional hydrogen bonds in the oxyanion hole but possibly also by the formation of an unusually strong hydrogen bond. Proton transfers between hydrogen bonded groups (D—H···A) occur at physiologically reasonable rates only when the pK of the proton donor is no more than 2 or 3 pH units greater than that of the protonated form of the proton acceptor. However, when the pK's of the hydrogen bonding donor (D) and acceptor (A) groups are nearly equal, the distinction between them breaks down: *the hydrogen atom becomes more or less equally shared between them* (D···H···A). Such **low-barrier hydrogen bonds (LBHBs)** are unusually short and strong. Their free energies, as measured in the gas phase, are as high as −40 to −80 kJ · mol^{-1} (versus −12 to −30 kJ · mol^{-1} for normal hydrogen bonds) and they exhibit a D···A bond length of <2.55 Å for O—H···O and <2.65 Å for N—H···O (versus 2.8 to 3.1 Å for normal hydrogen bonds).

LBHBs are unlikely to exist in dilute aqueous solution because water molecules, which are excellent hydrogen bond donors and acceptors, effectively compete with D—H and A for hydrogen bonding sites. However, LBHBs may exist in the nonaqueous active sites of enzymes. In fact, experimental evidence indicates that in the serine protease catalytic triad, the pK's of the protonated His and Asp are nearly equal, and the hydrogen bond between His and Asp has an unusually short N···O distance of 2.62 Å with the H atom nearly centered between the N and O atoms. These findings are consistent with the formation of an LBHB in the transition state. This suggests that the enzyme uses the "strategy" of converting a weak hydrogen bond in the initial enzyme–substrate complex to a strong hydrogen bond in the transition state, thereby facilitating proton transfer while applying the difference in the free energy between the normal and low-barrier hydrogen bonds to preferentially binding the transition state.

Although several studies have revealed the existence of unusually short hydrogen bonds in enzyme active sites, it is far more difficult to demonstrate experimentally that they are unusually strong, as LBHBs are predicted to be. In fact, several studies of the strengths of unusually short hydrogen bonds in organic model compounds in nonaqueous solutions suggest that these hydrogen bonds are not unusually strong. Consequently, a lively debate has ensued as to the catalytic significance of LBHBs. However, if enzymes do not form LBHBs, it remains to be explained how the conjugate base of an acidic group (e.g., Asp 102) partially abstracts a proton from a far more basic group (e.g., His 57), a feature of numerous enzyme mechanisms.

The Tetrahedral Intermediate Resembles the Complex of Trypsin with Trypsin Inhibitor. Perhaps the most convincing structural evidence for the existence of the tetrahedral intermediate was provided by Robert Huber in

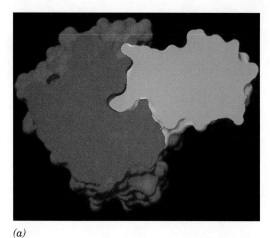

(a)

Ser 195
Lys 15I

(b)

■ **Figure 11-31 | The trypsin–BPTI complex.**
(a) The X-ray structure is shown as a computer-generated cutaway drawing indicating how trypsin (*red*) binds BPTI (*green*). The green protrusion extending into the red cavity near the center of the figure represents the inhibitor's Lys 15 side chain occupying trypsin's specificity pocket. Note the close complementary fit of the two proteins. [Courtesy of Michael Connolly, New York University.] (b) Trypsin Ser 195 is in closer-than-van der Waals contact with the carbonyl carbon of BPTI's scissile peptide, which is pyramidally distorted toward Ser 195. The normal proteolytic reaction is apparently arrested somewhere along the reaction coordinate preceding the tetrahedral intermediate. *See* **Kinemage Exercise 10-1.**

an X-ray study of the complex between **bovine pancreatic trypsin inhibitor (BPTI)** and trypsin. The 58-residue BPTI binds to the active site region of trypsin to form a complex with a tightly packed interface and a network of hydrogen-bonded cross-links. This interaction prevents any trypsin that is prematurely activated in the pancreas from digesting that organ (Section 11-5D). The complex's 10^{13} M^{-1} association constant, among the largest of any known protein–protein interaction, emphasizes BPTI's physiological importance.

The portion of BPTI in contact with the trypsin active site resembles bound substrate. A specific Lys side chain of BPTI occupies the trypsin specificity pocket (Fig. 11-31a), and the inhibitor's Lys-Ala peptide bond is positioned as if it were the scissile peptide bond (Fig. 11-31b). What is most remarkable about the BPTI–trypsin complex is that its conformation is well along the reaction coordinate toward the tetrahedral intermediate: The side chain oxygen of trypsin Ser 195, the active Ser, is in closer-than-van der Waals contact (2.6 Å) with the pyramidally distorted carbonyl carbon of BPTI's "scissile" peptide. However, the proteolytic reaction cannot proceed past this point because of the rigidity of the complex and because it is so tightly sealed that the leaving group cannot leave and water cannot enter the reaction site.

Protease inhibitors are common in nature, where they have protective and regulatory functions. For example, certain plants release protease inhibitors in response to insect bites, thereby causing the offending insect to starve by inactivating its digestive enzymes. Protease inhibitors constitute ~10% of the blood plasma proteins. For instance, **α_1-proteinase inhibitor,** which is secreted by the liver, inhibits **leukocyte elastase** (leukocytes are white blood cells; the action of leukocyte elastase is thought to be part of the inflammatory process). Pathological variants of α_1-proteinase inhibitor with reduced activity are associated with **pulmonary emphysema,** a degenerative disease of the lungs resulting from the hydrolysis of its elastin fibers. Smokers also suffer from reduced activity of their α_1-proteinase inhibitor because smoking oxidizes a required Met residue.

The Tetrahedral Intermediate Has Been Directly Observed. Because the tetrahedral intermediate resembles the transition state of the serine protease reaction, it is thought to be short-lived and unstable. However, a series of X-ray structures of porcine pancreatic elastase with a peptide substrate have shown the progress of the reaction from the acyl–enzyme intermediate stage to the release of product. This second phase of the proteolysis reaction includes a tetrahedral intermediate (Fig. 11-29).

This acyl–enzyme complex, which is stable at pH 5.0, exhibits the expected structure, with the substrate's C-terminal Ile residue covalently linked via an ester bond to Ser 195 (Fig. 11-32a). In this first view of a serine protease acyl–enzyme intermediate, the acyl group is fully planar, with no distortion toward a tetrahedral geometry. A water molecule is located near the intermediate's ester bond, hydrogen-bonded to His 57, where it appears poised to nucleophilically attack the ester linkage. At pH 5.0, His 57 is protonated and acts as a hydrogen bond donor to water (it cannot function as a base catalyst at this pH).

The hydrolytic reaction was triggered by deprotonation of His 57, accomplished by immersing the acyl–enzyme crystal in a solution of pH 9.0. After a period of 1 or 2 minutes, the crystals were frozen in liquid nitrogen to halt the reaction so that the X-ray structure of the enzyme complex could be determined (Box 11-2). In this way, the tetrahedral intermediate was trapped and observed (Fig. 11-32b).

During formation of the tetrahedral intermediate, the oxyanion hole does not undergo any change in its structure, but the peptide substrate

(a)

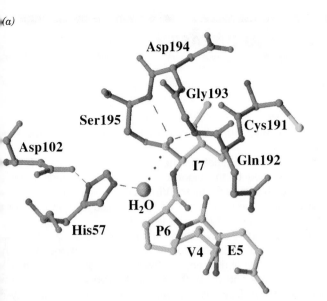

(b)

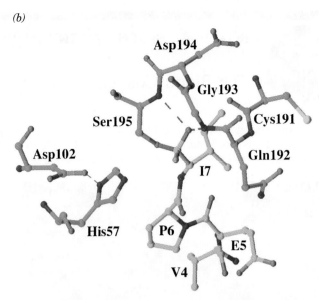

■ Figure 11-32 | Structure of the acyl–enzyme and tetrahedral intermediates. Porcine pancreatic elastase was incubated with a heptapeptide substrate (YPFVEPI, using the one-letter code). Only residues 4–7 are visible. The protease residues are specified by the three-letter code. Atoms are colored according to type with elastase C green, substrate C cyan, N blue, O red, and S yellow. (a) At pH 5.0, a covalent bond (*magenta*) links the Ser 195 O atom to the C-terminal (I7) C atom of the substrate. A water molecule (*orange sphere*) appears poised to nucleophilically attack the acyl–enzyme's carbonyl C atom. The dashed lines represent catalytically important hydrogen bonds, and the dotted line indicates the trajectory that the water molecule presumably follows in nucleophilically attacking the acyl group's carbonyl C atom. (b) When the complex is brought to pH 9.0 and then rapidly frozen, the water molecule becomes a hydroxyl substituent (*orange*) to the carbonyl C atom, thereby yielding the tetrahedral intermediate, which resembles the transition state. [Based on X-ray structures by Christopher Schofield and Janos Hadju, University of Oxford, U.K. PDBids (a) 1HAX and (b) 1HAZ.]

moves within its binding pocket and becomes distorted toward a tetrahedral geometry. The tetrahedral intermediate has the expected shape, similar to known transition state analog inhibitors. However, it does not bind so tightly to the amide group of the oxyanion hole (Fig. 11-30) that it would not be able to subsequently dissociate.

D | Zymogens Are Inactive Enzyme Precursors

Proteolytic enzymes are usually biosynthesized as somewhat larger inactive precursors known as **zymogens** (enzyme precursors, in general, are known as **proenzymes**). In the case of digestive enzymes, the reason for this is clear: If these enzymes were synthesized in their active forms, they would digest the tissues that synthesized them. Indeed, **acute pancreatitis,** a painful and sometimes fatal condition that can be precipitated by pancreatic trauma, is characterized by the premature activation of the digestive enzymes synthesized by that organ.

The activation of **trypsinogen,** the zymogen of trypsin, occurs when trypsinogen enters the duodenum from the pancreas. **Enteropeptidase,** a serine protease whose secretion from the duodenal mucosa is under hormonal control, excises the N-terminal hexapeptide from trypsinogen by specifically cleaving its Lys 15–Ile 16 peptide bond (Fig. 11-33). Since this activating cleavage occurs at a trypsin-sensitive site (recall that trypsin cleaves after Arg and Lys residues), the small amount of trypsin produced by enteropeptidase also catalyzes trypsinogen activation, generating even more trypsin, etc. Thus, trypsinogen activation is said to be **autocatalytic.**

$$\overset{+}{H_3N}\text{—Val}\overset{10}{}\text{—(Asp)}_4\text{—}\overset{15}{Lys}\text{—}\overset{16}{Ile}\text{—Val—}\cdots$$

Trypsinogen

↓ enteropeptidase or trypsin

$$\overset{+}{H_3N}\text{—Val—(Asp)}_4\text{—Lys} \quad + \quad Ile\text{—Val—}\cdots$$

Trypsin

■ Figure 11-33 | The activation of trypsinogen to trypsin. Proteolytic excision of the N-terminal hexapeptide is catalyzed by either enteropeptidase or trypsin. The chymotrypsinogen residue-numbering system is used here; that is, Val 10 is actually trypsinogen's N-terminus and Ile 16 is trypsin's N-terminus.

BOX 11-4 BIOCHEMISTRY IN HEALTH AND DISEASE

The Blood Coagulation Cascade

When a blood vessel is damaged, a clot forms as a result of the aggregation of platelets (small enucleated blood cells) and the formation of an insoluble **fibrin** network that traps additional blood cells.

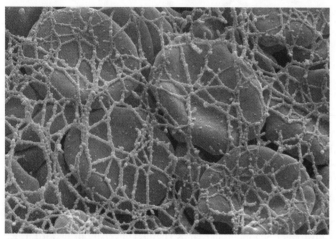

[Andrew Syred/Photo Researchers.]

Fibrin is produced from the soluble circulating protein **fibrinogen** through the action of the serine protease **thrombin.** Thrombin is the last in a series of coagulation enzymes that are sequentially activated by proteolysis of their zymogen forms. The overall process is known as the **coagulation cascade,** although experimental evidence shows that the pathway is not strictly linear, as the waterfall analogy might suggest.

The various components of the coagulation cascade, which include enzymes as well as nonenzymatic protein cofactors, are assigned Roman numerals, largely for historical reasons that do not reflect their order of action *in vivo*. The suffix *a* denotes an active factor. The catalytic domains of the coagulation proteases resemble trypsin in sequence and mechanism but are much more specific for their substrates. Additional domains mediate interactions with cofactors and help anchor the proteins to the platelet membrane, which serves as a stage for many of the coagulatio reactions.

Coagulation is initiated when a membrane protein **(tissu factor)** exposed to the bloodstream by tissue damage forms complex with circulating **factor VII** or VIIa (factor VIIa is generate from factor VII by trace amounts of other coagulation protease including factor VIIa itself). The tissue factor–VIIa complex prote olytically converts the zymogen **factor X** to factor Xa. Factor X then converts **prothrombin** to thrombin, which subsequently gen erates fibrin from fibrinogen. The tissue factor–dependent steps c coagulation are known as the **extrinsic pathway** because th source of tissue factor is extravascular. The extrinsic pathway quickly dampened through the action of a protein that inhibi factor VII once factor Xa has been generated.

Sustained thrombin activation requires the activity of th **intrinsic pathway** (so named because all its components are pres ent in the circulation). The intrinsic pathway is stimulated by th tissue factor–VIIa complex, which converts **factor IX** to its activ form, factor IXa. The ensuing thrombin activates a number of com ponents of the intrinsic pathway, including **factor XI,** a proteas that activates factor IX, to maintain coagulation in the absence c tissue factor or factor VIIa. Thrombin also activates **factors V** an **VIII,** which are cofactors rather than proteases. Factor Va promote prothrombin activation by factor Xa by as much as 20,000-folc and factor VIIIa promotes factor X activation by factor IXa by similar amount. Thus, thrombin promotes its own activatio through a feedback mechanism that amplifies the preceding step of the cascade. **Factor XIII** is also activated by thrombin. Facto XIIIa, which is not a serine protease, chemically cross-links fibri molecules through formation of peptide bonds between glutamat and lysine side chains, which forms a strong fibrin network.

The intrinsic pathway of coagulation can be triggered by expc sure to negatively charged surfaces such as glass. Consequently blood clots when it is collected in a clean glass test tube. In th absence of tissue factor, a fibrin clot may not appear for several min utes, but when tissue factor is present, a clot forms within a few sec onds. This suggests that rapid blood clotting *in vivo* requires tissu

---

Chymotrypsinogen is then activated by trypsin-catalyzed cleavage of it Arg 15–Ile 16 peptide bond.

Proelastase, the zymogen of elastase, is activated by a single trypti cleavage that excises a short N-terminal peptide. Trypsin also activate pancreatic **procarboxypeptidases A** and **B** and **prophospholipase A** (Section 9-1C). The autocatalytic nature of trypsinogen activation and th fact that trypsin activates other hydrolytic enzymes makes it essential tha trypsinogen not be activated in the pancreas. We have seen that the all bu irreversible binding of trypsin inhibitors such as BPTI to trypsin is a de fense against trypsinogen's inappropriate activation.

Sequential proenzyme activation makes it possible to quickly generat large quantities of active enzymes in response to diverse physiologica

actor as well as the proteins of the intrinsic pathway. Additional evidence for the importance of the extrinsic pathway is that individuals who are deficient in factor VII tend to bleed excessively. Abnormal bleeding also results from congenital defects in factor VIII **(hemophilia a)** or factor IX **hemophilia b).**

The sequential activation of zymogens in the coagulation cascade leads to a burst of thrombin activity, since trace amounts of factors VIIa, Xa, and Xa can activate much larger amounts of their respective substrates. The potential for amplification in the coagulation cascade is reflected in the plasma concentrations of the coagulation proteins (see table).

Plasma Concentrations of Some Human Coagulation Factors

Factor	Concentration (μM)[a]
XI	0.06
IX	0.09
VII	0.01
X	0.18
Prothrombin	1.39
Fibrinogen	8.82

[a]Concentrations calculated from data in High, K.A. and Roberts, H.R. (Eds.), *Molecular Basis of Thrombosis and Hemostasis,* Marcel Dekker (1995).

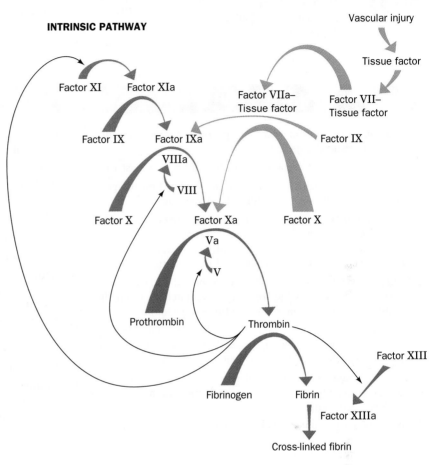

[Figure adapted from Davie, E.W., *Thromb. Haemost.* **74,** 2 (1995).]

Perhaps not surprisingly, thrombin eventually triggers mechanisms that shut down clot formation, thereby limiting the duration of the clotting process and hence the extent of the clot. Such control of clotting is of extreme physiological importance since the formation of even one inappropriate blood clot within an individual's lifetime may have fatal consequences.

signals. For example, the serine proteases that lead to blood clotting are synthesized as zymogens by the liver and circulate until they are activated by injury to a blood vessel (Box 11-4).

Zymogens Have Distorted Active Sites. Since the zymogens of trypsin, chymotrypsin, and elastase have all their catalytic residues, why aren't they enzymatically active? Comparisons of the X-ray structures of trypsinogen with that of trypsin, and of chymotrypsinogen with that of chymotrypsin, show that on activation, the newly liberated N-terminal Ile 16 residue moves from the surface of the protein to an internal position, where its free cationic amino group forms an ion pair with the invariant anionic Asp 194, which is close to the catalytic triad (Fig. 11-26). Without this

■ **CHECK YOUR UNDERSTANDING**

Summarize the roles of the residues that make up the catalytic triad of serine proteases.

What is the function of the oxyanion hole?

What are the advantages of synthesizing proteases as zymogens?

conformational change, the enzyme cannot properly bind its substrate o stabilize the tetrahedral intermediate because its specificity pocket and oxyanion hole are improperly formed. This provides further structural evidence favoring the role of preferential transition state binding in the catalytic mechanism of serine proteases. Nevertheless, because their catalytic triad are structurally intact, the zymogens of serine proteases actually have low levels of enzymatic activity, an observation that was made only after the above structural comparisons suggested that this might be the case.

SUMMARY

1. Enzymes, almost all of which are proteins, are grouped into six mechanistic classes.

2. Enzymes accelerate reactions by factors of up to at least 10^{15}.

3. The substrate specificity of an enzyme depends on the geometric and electronic character of its active site.

4. Some enzymes catalyze reactions with the assistance of metal ion cofactors or organic coenzymes that function as reversibly bound cosubstrates or as permanently associated prosthetic groups. Many coenzymes are derived from vitamins.

5. Enzymes catalyze reactions by decreasing the activation free energy, $\Delta G^{\ddagger}$, which is the free energy required to reach the transition state, the point of highest free energy in the reaction.

6. Enzymes use the same catalytic mechanisms employed by chemical catalysts, including general acid and general base catalysis, covalent catalysis, and metal ion catalysis.

7. The arrangement of functional groups in an enzyme active site allows catalysis by proximity and orientation effects as well as electrostatic catalysis.

8. A particularly important mechanism of enzyme-mediated catalysis is the preferential binding of the transition state o the catalyzed reaction.

9. In the catalytic mechanism of lysozyme, Glu 35 in its protonated form acts as an acid catalyst to cleave the polysaccharide substrate between its D and E rings, and Asp 52 in it anionic state forms a covalent bond to C1 of the D ring The reaction is facilitated by the distortion of residue D to the planar half-chair conformation, which resembles the reaction's oxonium ion transition state.

10. Serine proteases contain a Ser–His–Asp catalytic triad near a binding pocket that helps determine the enzymes' substrate specificity.

11. Catalysis in the serine proteases occurs through acid–base catalysis, covalent catalysis, proximity and orientation effects electrostatic catalysis, and by preferential transition state binding in the oxyanion hole.

12. Synthesis of pancreatic proteases as inactive zymogens protects the pancreas from self-digestion. Zymogens are activated by specific proteolytic cleavages.

KEY TERMS

active site **323**
substrate **324**
EC classification **324**
induced fit **325**
prochirality **325**
cofactor **326**
coenzyme **327**
cosubstrate **327**

prosthetic group **327**
holoenzyme **327**
apoenzyme **327**
transition state **328**
$\Delta G^{\ddagger}$ **328**
rate-determining step **329**
general acid catalysis **331**
general base catalysis **331**

covalent catalysis **333**
metalloenzyme **335**
electrostatic catalysis **337**
transition state analog **339**
oxonium ion **344**
serine protease **347**
affinity labeling **348**
catalytic triad **351**

convergent evolution **352**
tetrahedral intermediate **352**
acyl–enzyme
   intermediate **354**
oxyanion hole **354**
low-barrier hydrogen
   bond **355**
zymogen **357**

PROBLEMS

1. Choose the best description of an enzyme:

   (a) It allows a chemical reaction to proceed extremely fast.

   (b) It increases the rate at which a chemical reaction approaches equilibrium relative to its uncatalyzed rate.

   (c) It makes a reaction thermodynamically favorable.

2. Which type of enzyme (Table 11-2) catalyzes the following reactions?

   (a)

$$H - \underset{\underset{NH_3^+}{|}}{\overset{\overset{COO^-}{|}}{C}} - CH_3 \longrightarrow H_3C - \underset{\underset{NH_3^+}{|}}{\overset{\overset{COO^-}{|}}{C}} - H$$

(b)

$$\begin{array}{c} COO^- \\ | \\ C=O \\ | \\ CH_3 \end{array} \; + \; H^+ \; \longrightarrow \; \begin{array}{c} H \\ | \\ C=O \\ | \\ CH_3 \end{array} \; + \; O=C=O$$

(c)

$$\begin{array}{c} COO^- \\ | \\ C=O \\ | \\ CH_3 \end{array} \; + \; NADH \; + \; H^+ \; \longrightarrow$$

$$\begin{array}{c} COO^- \\ | \\ HO-C-H \\ | \\ CH_3 \end{array} \; + \; NAD^+$$

(d)

$$\begin{array}{c} COO^- \\ | \\ H-C-(CH_2)_2-C{\overset{\displaystyle O}{\underset{\displaystyle O^-}{\diagup}}} \\ | \\ NH_3^+ \end{array} \; + \; ATP \; + \; NH_4^+ \; \longrightarrow$$

$$\begin{array}{c} COO^- \\ | \\ H-C-(CH_2)_2-C{\overset{\displaystyle O}{\underset{\displaystyle NH_2}{\diagup}}} \\ | \\ NH_3^+ \end{array} \; + \; ADP \; + \; P_i$$

3. What is the relationship between the rate of an enzyme-catalyzed reaction and the rate of the corresponding uncatalyzed reaction? Do enzymes enhance the rates of slow uncatalyzed reactions as much as they enhance the rates of fast uncatalyzed reactions?

4. On the free energy diagram shown, label the intermediate(s) and transition state(s). Is the reaction thermodynamically favorable?

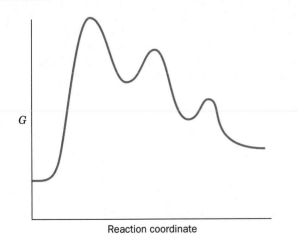

Reaction coordinate

5. Draw a transition state diagram of (a) a nonenzymatic reaction and the corresponding enzyme-catalyzed reaction in which (b) S binds loosely to the enzyme and (c) S binds very tightly to the enzyme. Compare $\Delta G^{\ddagger}$ for each case. Why is tight binding of S not advantageous?

6. Approximately how much does staphylococcal nuclease (Table 11-1) decrease the activation free energy ($\Delta G^{\ddagger}$) of its reaction (the hydrolysis of a phosphodiester bond) at 25°C?

7. Studies at different pH's show that an enzyme has two catalytically important residues whose pK's are ~4 and ~10. Chemical modification experiments indicate that a Glu and a Lys residue are essential for activity. Match the residues to their pK's and explain whether they are likely to act as acid or base catalysts.

8. The covalent catalytic mechanism of an enzyme depends on a single active site Cys whose pK is 8. A mutation in a nearby residue alters the microenvironment so that this pK increases to 10. Would the mutation cause the reaction rate to increase or decrease? Explain.

9. Explain why RNase A cannot catalyze the hydrolysis of DNA.

10. Suggest a transition state analog for proline racemase that differs from those discussed in the text. Justify your suggestion.

11. Wolfenden has stated that it is meaningless to distinguish between the "binding sites" and the "catalytic sites" of enzymes. Explain.

12. Explain why lysozyme cleaves the artificial substrate (NAG)$_4$ ~4000 times more slowly than it cleaves (NAG)$_6$.

13. Lysozyme residues Asp 101 and Arg 114 are required for efficient catalysis, although they are located at some distance from the active site Glu 35 and Asp 52. Substituting Ala for either Asp 101 or Arg 114 does not significantly alter the enzyme's tertiary structure, but it significantly reduces its catalytic activity. Explain.

14. Design a chloromethylketone inhibitor of elastase.

15. Under certain conditions, peptide bond formation rather than peptide bond hydrolysis is thermodynamically favorable. Would you expect chymotrypsin to catalyze peptide bond formation?

16. Diagram the hydrogen-bonding interactions of the catalytic triad His–Lys–Ser during catalysis in a hypothetical hydrolytic enzyme.

17. The comparison of the active site geometries of chymotrypsin and subtilisin under the assumption that their similarities have catalytic significance has led to greater mechanistic understanding of both these enzymes. Discuss the validity of this strategy.

18. Predict the effect of mutating Asp 102 of trypsin to Asn (a) on substrate binding and (b) on catalysis.

19. A genetic defect in coagulation factor IX causes hemophilia b, a disease characterized by a tendency to bleed profusely after very minor trauma. However, a genetic defect in coagulation factor XI has only mild clinical symptoms. Explain this discrepancy in terms of the mechanism for activation of coagulation proteases shown in Box 11-4.

20. Why is the broad substrate specificity of chymotrypsin advantageous *in vivo*? Why would this be a disadvantage for some other proteases?

21. Tofu (bean curd), a high-protein soybean product, is prepared in such a way as to remove the trypsin inhibitor present in soybeans. Explain the reason(s) for this treatment.

CASE STUDIES

Case Study 11 (available at www.wiley.com/college/voet)
Nonenzymatic Deamidation of Asparagine and Glutamine Residues in Proteins

Focus concept: Factors influencing nonenzymatic hydrolytic deamidation of Asn and Gln residues in proteins are examined and possible mechanisms for the reactions are proposed.

Prerequisites: Chapters 5 and 11

• Protein analytical methods, particularly isoelectric focusing

• Enzyme mechanisms, especially proteases such as papain and chymotrypsin

REFERENCES

General

Benkovic, S.J. and Hammes-Schiffer, S., A perspective on enzyme catalysis, *Science* **301,** 1196–1202 (2003). [Includes a history of some of the theories and experiments on catalysis.]

Bruice, T.C. and Benkovic, S.J., Chemical basis for enzyme catalysis, *Biochemistry* **39,** 6267–6274 (2000).

Gerlt, J.A., Protein engineering to study enzyme catalytic mechanisms, *Curr. Opin. Struct. Biol.* **4,** 593–600 (1994). [Describes how information can be gained from mutagenesis and structural analysis of enzymes.]

Hackney, D.D., Binding energy and catalysis, *in* Sigman, D.S. and Boyer, P.D. (Eds.), *The Enzymes* (3rd ed.), Vol. 19, pp. 1–36, Academic Press (1990).

Kraut, J., How do enzymes work? *Science* **242,** 533–540 (1988). [A brief and very readable review of transition state theory and applications.]

Schramm, V.L., Enzymatic transition states and transition state analogues, *Curr. Opin. Struct. Biol.* **15,** 604–613 (2005).

Tipton, K.F., The naming of parts, *Trends Biochem. Sci.* **18,** 113–115 (1993). [A discussion of the advantages of a consistent naming scheme for enzymes and the difficulties of formulating one.]

Lysozyme

Kirby, A.J., The lysozyme mechanism sorted—after 50 years, *Nature Struct. Biol.* **8,** 737–739 (2001). [Briefly summarizes the theoretical and experimental evidence for a covalent intermediate in the lysozyme mechanism.]

McKenzie, H.A. and White, F.H., Jr., Lysozyme and α-lactalbumin: Structure, function and interrelationships, *Adv. Protein Chem.* **41,** 173–315 (1991).

Strynadka, N.C.J. and James, M.N.G., Lysozyme revisited: crystallographic evidence for distortion of an *N*-acetylmuramic acid residue bound in site D, *J. Mol. Biol.* **220,** 401–424 (1991).

Serine Proteases

Cleland, W.W., Frey, P.A., and Gerlt, J.A., The low barrier hydrogen bond in enzymatic catalysis, *J. Biol. Chem.* **273,** 25529–25532 (1998).

Davie, E.W., Biochemical and molecular aspects of the coagulation cascade, *Thromb. Haemost.* **74,** 1–6 (1995). [A brief review by one of the pioneers of the cascade hypothesis.]

Fersht, A., *Structure and Mechanism in Protein Science.* Freeman (1999). [Includes detailed reaction mechanisms for chymotrypsin and other enzymes.]

Perona, J.J. and Craik, C.S., Evolutionary divergence of substrate specificity within the chymotrypsin-like protease fold, *J. Biol. Chem.* **272,** 29987–29990 (1997). [Summarizes research identifying the structural basis of substrate specificity in chymotrypsin and related enzymes.]

Radisky, E.S., Lee, J.M., Lu, C-J.K., and Koshland, D.E., Jr., Insights into the serine protease mechanism from atomic resolution structures of trypsin reaction intermediates, *Proc. Natl. Acad. Sci.* **103,** 6835–6840 (2006). [Superpositions of X-ray structures representing the enzyme–substrate complex, tetrahedral intermediate, and acyl–enzyme intermediate illustrate the progress of the reaction.]

Wilmouth, R.C., Edman, K., Neutze, R., Wright, P.A., Clifton, I.J., Schneider, T.R., Schofield, C.J., and Hajdu, J., X-Ray snapshot of serine protease catalysis reveal a tetrahedral intermediate, *Nature Struct. Biol.* **8,** 689–694 (2001). [Reports the first structural evidence for a tetrahedral intermediate in the hydrolysis reaction catalyzed by a serine protease.]

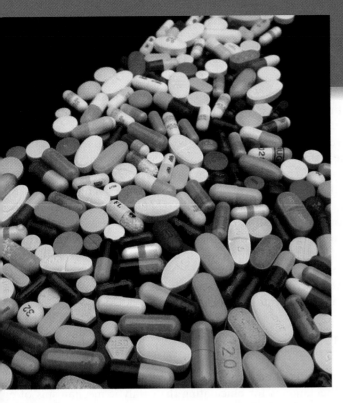

12

Enzyme Kinetics, Inhibition, and Control

Many natural and synthetic substances are known to inhibit the activities of specific enzymes. The study of inhibitor–enzyme interactions, as quantified through enzyme kinetics, is a mainstay of modern drug development. [Larry Kolvoord/The Image Works.]

■ **CHAPTER CONTENTS**

1 Reaction Kinetics

A. Chemical Kinetics Is Described by Rate Equations

B. Enzyme Kinetics Often Follows the Michaelis–Menten Equation

C. Kinetic Data Can Provide Values of V_{max} and K_M

D. Bisubstrate Reactions Follow One of Several Rate Equations

2 Enzyme Inhibition

A. Competitive Inhibition Involves Inhibitor Binding at an Enzyme's Substrate Binding Site

B. Uncompetitive Inhibition Involves Inhibitor Binding to the Enzyme–Substrate Complex

C. Mixed Inhibition Involves Inhibitor Binding to Both the Free Enzyme and the Enzyme–Substrate Complex

3 Control of Enzyme Activity

A. Allosteric Control Involves Binding at a Site Other than the Active Site

B. Control by Covalent Modification Usually Involves Protein Phosphorylation

4 Drug Design

A. Drug Discovery Employs a Variety of Techniques

B. A Drug's Bioavailability Depends on How It Is Absorbed and Transported in the Body

C. Clinical Trials Test for Efficacy and Safety

D. Cytochromes P450 Are Often Implicated in Adverse Drug Reactions

■ **MEDIA RESOURCES**

(available at www.wiley.com/college/voet)

Guided Exploration 11. Michaelis–Menten kinetics, Lineweaver–Burk plots, and enzyme inhibition

Interactive Exercise 9. HIV protease

Animated Figure 12-2. Progress curves for enzyme-catalyzed reaction

Animated Figure 12-3. Plot of initial velocity versus substrate concentration

Animated Figure 12-4. Double-reciprocal (Lineweaver–Burk) plot

Animated Figure 12-7. Lineweaver–Burk plot of competitive inhibition

Animated Figure 12-8. Lineweaver–Burk plot of uncompetitive inhibition

Animated Figure 12-9. Lineweaver–Burk plot of mixed inhibition

Animated Figure 12-10. Plot of v_o versus [aspartate] for ATCase

Kinemage 11-1. Structure of ATCase

Kinemage 11-2. Conformational changes in ATCase

Kinemage 14-1. Glycogen phosphorylase

Kinemage 14-2 and 14-3. Conformational changes in glycogen phosphorylase

Case Study 7. A Storage Protein from Seeds of *Brassica nigra* Is a Serine Protease Inhibitor

Case Study 12. Production of Methanol in Ripening Fruit

Case Study 13. Inhibition of Alcohol Dehydrogenase

Case Study 15. Site-Directed Mutagenesis of Creatine Kinase

Case Study 19. Purification of Rat Kidney Sphingosine Kinase

Bioinformatics Exercise Chapter 12. Enzyme Inhibitors and Rational Drug Design

Early enzymologists, often working with crude preparations of yeast or liver cells, could do little more than observe the conversion of substrates to products catalyzed by as yet unpurified enzymes. Measuring the rates of such reactions therefore came to be a powerful tool for characterizing enzyme activity. The application of simple mathematical models to enzyme activity under varying laboratory conditions, and in the presence of competing substrates or enzyme inhibitors, made it possible to deduce the probable physiological functions and regulatory mechanisms of various enzymes.

The study of enzymatic reaction rates, or **enzyme kinetics,** is no less important now than it was early in the twentieth century. In many cases, the rate of a reaction and how the rate changes in response to different conditions reveal the path followed by the reactants and are therefore indicative of the reaction mechanism. Kinetic data, combined with detailed information about an enzyme's structure and its catalytic mechanisms, provide some of the most powerful clues to the enzyme's biological function and may suggest ways to modify it for therapeutic purposes.

We begin our consideration of enzyme kinetics by reviewing chemical kinetics. Following that, we derive the basic equations of enzyme kinetics and describe the effects of inhibitors on enzymes. We also consider some examples of enzyme control that highlight several aspects of enzyme function. Finally, we describe some practical applications of enzyme inhibition the development of enzyme inhibitors as drugs.

1 Reaction Kinetics

Kinetic measurements of enzymatically catalyzed reactions are among the most powerful techniques for elucidating the catalytic mechanisms of enzymes. Enzyme kinetics is a branch of chemical kinetics, so we begin this section by reviewing the principles of chemical kinetics.

A | Chemical Kinetics Is Described by Rate Equations

A reaction of overall stoichiometry

$$A \longrightarrow P$$

where A represents reactants and P represents products, may actually occur through a sequence of **elementary reactions** (simple molecular processes) such as

$$A \longrightarrow I_1 \longrightarrow I_2 \longrightarrow P$$

Here, I_1 and I_2 symbolize **intermediates** in the reaction. Each elementary reaction can be characterized with respect to the number of reacting species and the rate at which they interact. *Descriptions of each elementary reaction collectively constitute the mechanistic description of the overall reaction process.* Even a complicated enzyme-catalyzed reaction can be analyzed in terms of its component elementary reactions.

Reaction Order Indicates the Number of Molecules Participating in an Elementary Reaction. At constant temperature, *the rate of an elementary reaction is proportional to the frequency with which the reacting molecules come together.* The proportionality constant is known as a **rate constant** and is symbolized $k.$ For the elementary reaction $A \rightarrow P$, the instantaneous rate of appearance of product or disappearance of reactant which is called the **velocity (v)** of the reaction, is

$$v = \frac{d[P]}{dt} = -\frac{d[A]}{dt} = k[A] \qquad [12\text{-}1]$$

In other words, the reaction velocity at any time point is proportional to the concentration of the reactant A. This is an example of a **first-order reaction.** Since the velocity has units of molar per second ($M \cdot s^{-1}$), the

LEARNING OBJECTIVES

■ Understand that rate equations describe the progress of first-order and second-order reactions.

■ Understand how the Michaelis–Menten equation relates the initial velocity of a reaction to the maximal reaction velocity and the Michaelis constant for a particular enzyme and substrate.

■ Understand that a Lineweaver–Burk plot can be used to present kinetic data and to calculate values for K_M and V_{max}.

■ Understand that bisubstrate reactions can occur by an Ordered or Random sequential mechanism or by a Ping Pong mechanism.

first-order rate constant must have units of reciprocal seconds (s^{-1}). *The **reaction order** of an elementary reaction corresponds to the **molecularity** of the reaction, which is the number of molecules that must simultaneously collide to generate a product.* Thus, a first-order elementary reaction is a **unimolecular** reaction.

Consider the elementary reaction $2A \rightarrow P$. This **bimolecular** reaction is a **second-order reaction,** and its instantaneous velocity is described by

$$v = -\frac{d[A]}{dt} = k[A]^2 \qquad [12\text{-}2]$$

In this case, the reaction velocity is proportional to the square of the concentration of A, and the second-order rate constant k has units of $M^{-1} \cdot s^{-1}$.

The bimolecular reaction $A + B \rightarrow P$ is also a second-order reaction with an instantaneous velocity described by

$$v = -\frac{d[A]}{dt} = -\frac{d[B]}{dt} = k[A][B] \qquad [12\text{-}3]$$

Here, the reaction is said to be first order in [A] and first order in [B] (see Sample Calculation 12-1). Unimolecular and bimolecular reactions are common. **Termolecular** reactions are unusual because the simultaneous collision of three molecules is a rare event. Fourth- and higher-order reactions are unknown.

A Rate Equation Indicates the Progress of a Reaction as a Function of Time. A **rate equation** can be derived from the equations that describe the instantaneous reaction velocity. Thus, a first-order rate equation is obtained by rearranging Eq. 12-1

$$\frac{d[A]}{[A]} = d\ln[A] = -k\,dt \qquad [12\text{-}4]$$

and integrating it from $[A]_o$, the initial concentration of A, to [A], the concentration of A at time t:

$$\int_{[A]_o}^{[A]} d\ln[A] = -k\int_0^t dt \qquad [12\text{-}5]$$

This results in

$$\boxed{\ln[A] = \ln[A]_o - kt} \qquad [12\text{-}6]$$

or, taking the antilog of both sides,

$$[A] = [A]_o e^{-kt} \qquad [12\text{-}7]$$

Equation 12-6 is a linear equation of the form $y = mx + b$ and can be plotted as in Fig. 12-1. Therefore, if a reaction is first order, a plot of $\ln[A]$ versus t will yield a straight line whose slope is $-k$ (the negative of the first-order rate constant) and whose intercept on the $\ln[A]$ axis is $\ln[A]_o$.

One of the hallmarks of a first-order reaction is that *the time for half of the reactant initially present to decompose, its **half-time** or **half-life**, $t_{1/2}$, is a constant and hence independent of the initial concentration of the reactant.* This is easily demonstrated by substituting the relationship $[A] = [A]_o/2$ when $t = t_{1/2}$ into Eq. 12-6 and rearranging:

$$\ln\left(\frac{[A]_o/2}{[A]_o}\right) = -kt_{1/2} \qquad [12\text{-}8]$$

SAMPLE CALCULATION 12-1

Determine the velocity of the elementary reaction $X + Y \rightarrow Z$ when the sample contains 3 μM X and 5 μM Y and k for the reaction is 400 $M^{-1} \cdot s^{-1}$.

Use Equation 12-3 and make sure that all units are consistent:

$$\begin{aligned} v &= k[X][Y] \\ &= (400\ M^{-1} \cdot s^{-1})(3\ \mu M)(5\ \mu M) \\ &= (400\ M^{-1} \cdot s^{-1})(3 \times 10^{-6}\ M) \\ &\qquad\qquad (5 \times 10^{-6}\ M) \\ &= 6 \times 10^{-9}\ M \cdot s^{-1} \\ &= 6\ nM \cdot s^{-1} \end{aligned}$$

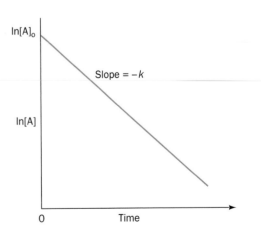

■ **Figure 12-1** | **A plot of a first-order rate equation.** The slope of the line obtained when ln[A] is plotted against time gives the rate constant k.

See Guided Exploration 11
Michaelis–Menten kinetics, Lineweaver–Burk plots, and enzyme inhibition.

SAMPLE CALCULATION 12-2

The decay of a hypothetical radioisotope has a rate constant of 0.01 s^{-1}. How much time is required for half of a 1-g sample of the isotope to decay?

The units of the rate constant indicate a first-order process. Thus, the half-life is independent of concentration. The half-life of the isotope (the half-time for its decay) is given by Eq. 12-9:

$$t_{1/2} = \frac{\ln 2}{k} = \frac{0.693}{0.01 \text{ s}^{-1}} = 69.3 \text{ s}$$

Thus

$$t_{1/2} = \frac{\ln 2}{k} = \frac{0.693}{k} \qquad [12\text{-}9]$$

Substances that are inherently unstable, such as radioactive nuclei, decompose through first-order reactions (Box 12-1 and Sample Calculation 12-2).

In a second-order reaction with one type of reactant, $2A \rightarrow P$, the variation of [A] with time is quite different from that in a first-order reaction. Rearranging Eq. 12-2 and integrating it over the same limits used for the first-order reaction yields

$$\int_{[A]_o}^{[A]} -\frac{d[A]}{[A]^2} = k \int_0^t dt \qquad [12\text{-}10]$$

so that

$$\frac{1}{[A]} = \frac{1}{[A]_o} + kt \qquad [12\text{-}11]$$

Equation 12-11 is a linear equation in terms of the variables $1/[A]$ and t. *The half-time for a second-order reaction is expressed* $t_{1/2} = 1/k[A]_o$ *and therefore, in contrast to a first-order reaction, depends on the initial reactant concentration.* Equations 12-6 and 12-11 may be used to distinguish a first-order from a second-order reaction by plotting $\ln[A]$ versus t and $1/[A]$ versus t and observing which, if any, of these plots is linear.

To experimentally determine the rate constant for the second-order reaction $A + B \rightarrow P$, it is often convenient to increase the concentration of one reactant relative to the other, for example, $[B] \gg [A]$. Under these conditions, [B] does not change significantly over the course of the reaction. The reaction rate therefore depends only on [A], the concentration of the reactant that is present in limited amounts. Hence, the reaction appears to be first order with respect to A and is therefore said to be a **pseudo-first-order reaction.** The reaction is first order with respect to B when $[A] \gg [B]$.

B | Enzyme Kinetics Often Follows the Michaelis–Menten Equation

Enzymes catalyze a tremendous variety of reactions using different combinations of five basic catalytic mechanisms (Section 11-3). Some enzymes act on only a single substrate molecule; others act on two or more different substrate molecules whose order of binding may or may not be obligatory. Some enzymes form covalently bound intermediate complexes with their substrates; others do not. *Yet all enzymes can be analyzed such that their reaction rates as well as their overall efficiency can be quantified.*

The study of enzyme kinetics began in 1902 when Adrian Brown investigated the rate of hydrolysis of sucrose by the yeast enzyme **β-fructofuranosidase:**

$$\text{Sucrose} + H_2O \longrightarrow \text{glucose} + \text{fructose}$$

Brown found that when the sucrose concentration is much higher than that of the enzyme, the reaction rate becomes independent of the sucrose concentration; that is, the rate is **zeroth order** with respect to sucrose. He therefore proposed that the overall reaction is composed of two elementary reactions in which the substrate forms a complex with the enzyme that subsequently decomposes to products, regenerating enzyme:

$$E + S \underset{k_{-1}}{\overset{k_1}{\rightleftharpoons}} ES \overset{k_2}{\longrightarrow} P + E \qquad [12\text{-}12]$$

BOX 12-1 PERSPECTIVES IN BIOCHEMISTRY

Isotopic Labeling

In the laboratory, it is often useful to label large or small molecules so that they can be easily detected after chromatographic or electrophoretic separation or in various binding assays. One of the most common labeling techniques is to attach a radioactive isotope to a molecule or to synthesize the molecule so that it contains a radioactive isotope in place of a normally occurring isotope. Molecules labeled in this way can be detected in solution or in solid form by measuring the radioactivity emitted by the label. This method is more sensitive than spectroscopic measurements, and it is often easier to carry out than more laborious assays based on chemical or biological activities. Metabolites labeled with NMR-active isotopes such as ^{13}C can also be detected in living tissues by NMR techniques.

Some of the most common radioactive isotopes (**radionuclides**) used in biochemistry are listed below, along with their half-lives and the type of radioactivity emitted by the spontaneously disintegrating atomic nuclei.

Radionuclide	Half-life	Type of Radiation[a]
^{3}H	12 years	β
^{14}C	5715 years	β
^{24}Na	15 hours	β
^{32}P	14 days	β
^{35}S	87 days	β
^{40}K	1.25×10^9 years	β
^{45}Ca	163 days	β
^{125}I	59 days	γ
^{131}I	8 days	β, γ

[a] β particles are emitted electrons, and γ rays are emitted photons.

Nucleic acids can be easily labeled by attaching a terminal nucleotide that contains ^{32}P in place of the normal nonradioactive ^{31}P. Proteins can be labeled by chemically or enzymatically linking ^{125}I to a Tyr residue. Assays for cell growth and division often measure the uptake of ^{3}H-labeled **thymidine** (thymidine is incorporated exclusively into DNA). Protein synthesis is similarly monitored by the appearance of ^{35}S-labeled Met in proteins. Of course, the choice of a particular isotopic label also depends on the time course of the experiment and the method for detecting radioactivity.

A **Geiger counter,** which electronically detects the ionization of a gas caused by the passage of radiation, is not sensitive enough to detect low-energy emitters such as ^{3}H and ^{14}C. This limitation is circumvented through **liquid scintillation counting.** In this technique, a β-emitting sample is dissolved in a solvent that contains a fluorescent molecule. The β particles excite this fluor, thereby causing it to emit light that can then be optically detected. Radioactive substances that emit γ rays are detected by **scintillation counters**

when the γ rays dislodge electrons from a crystal of NaI in the counter. These electrons induce fluorescence that is measured. In **autoradiography,** a radioactive substance immobilized in an agarose or polyacrylamide gel is detected by laying X-ray film over the sample followed by incubation and development of the film (dark areas on the developed film correspond to areas exposed to radioactivity). Thin sections of tissue can also be prepared for **microradiography** by covering them with a layer of photographic emulsion and examining the developed emulsion under a microscope (see figure). Instruments that electronically measure radioactivity in solid samples without the use of film **(phosphorimagers)** offer the advantage of digitized results and multiple exposure times (in contrast, film can be developed only once).

The use of radioactive isotopes as molecular labels is not without drawbacks. First and foremost is the danger of working with potentially mutagenic materials (irradiation can cause DNA damage). In addition, radioactive laboratory materials (samples as well as glassware) must be disposed of properly or the resulting contamination can cause errors in subsequent measurements of radioactivity as well as a health hazard. Scintillation fluid presents a particular problem for disposal because of the large volumes required (it also consists largely of organic solvents). The preceding table reveals that while disposal of short-lived radionuclides (such as ^{32}P, ^{35}S, and ^{125}I) can be accomplished mainly by storing the material until the radioactivity has decayed to insignificant levels, the safe disposal of long-lived species (such as ^{3}H and ^{14}C) is a problem that is unlikely to vanish any time soon. This is one reason why molecular labeling techniques that rely on chemical tags or fluorescent compounds have become popular.

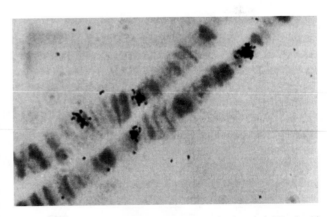

In this autoradiogram, a radioactive RNA probe has hybridized with specific sites in *Drosophila* polytene chromosomes. The black dots reveal the sites where radioactive decay has occurred. [From Loughney, K., Kreber, R., and Ganetzky, B., *Cell* **58,** 1143 (1989), by permission of Cell Press.]

Here E, S, ES, and P symbolize the enzyme, substrate, **enzyme–substrate complex,** and products, respectively. According to this model, when the substrate concentration becomes high enough to entirely convert the enzyme to the ES form, the second step of the reaction becomes rate limiting and the overall reaction rate becomes insensitive to further increase in substrate concentration.

Each of the elementary reactions that make up the above enzymatic reaction is characterized by a rate constant: k_1 and k_{-1} are the forward and reverse rate constants for formation of the ES complex (the first reaction) and k_2 is the rate constant for the decomposition of ES to P (the second reaction). Here we assume, for the sake of mathematical simplicity, that the second reaction is irreversible; that is, no P is converted back to S.

The Michaelis–Menten Equation Assumes that ES Maintains a Steady State. The Michaelis–Menten equation describes the rate of the enzymatic reaction represented by Eq. 12-12 as a function of substrate concentration. In this kinetic scheme, the formation of product from ES is a first-order process. Thus, the rate of formation of product can be expressed as the product of the rate constant of the reaction yielding product and the concentration of its immediately preceding intermediate. The general expression for the velocity (rate) of Reaction 12-12 is therefore

$$v = \frac{d[\mathrm{P}]}{dt} = k_2[\mathrm{ES}] \qquad [12\text{-}13]$$

The overall rate of production of ES is the difference between the rates of the elementary reactions leading to its appearance and those resulting in its disappearance:

$$\frac{d[\mathrm{ES}]}{dt} = k_1[\mathrm{E}][\mathrm{S}] - k_{-1}[\mathrm{ES}] - k_2[\mathrm{ES}] \qquad [12\text{-}14]$$

This equation cannot be explicitly integrated, however, without simplifying assumptions. Two possibilities are

1. **Assumption of equilibrium.** In 1913, Leonor Michaelis and Maud Menten, building on the work of Victor Henri, assumed that $k_{-1} \gg k_2$, so that the first step of the reaction reaches equilibrium:

$$K_{\mathrm{S}} = \frac{k_{-1}}{k_1} = \frac{[\mathrm{E}][\mathrm{S}]}{[\mathrm{ES}]} \qquad [12\text{-}15]$$

Here K_{S} is the dissociation constant of the first step in the enzymatic reaction. With this assumption, Eq. 12-14 can be integrated. Although this assumption is often not correct, in recognition of the importance of this pioneering work, the enzyme–substrate complex, ES, is known as the **Michaelis complex.**

2. **Assumption of steady state.** Figure 12-2 illustrates the progress curves of the various participants in Reaction 12-12 under the physiologically common condition that substrate is in great excess over enzyme ($[\mathrm{S}] \gg [\mathrm{E}]$). With the exception of the initial stage of the reaction, which is usually over within milliseconds of mixing E and S, [ES] remains approximately constant until the substrate is nearly exhausted. Hence, the rate of synthesis of ES must equal its rate of consumption over most of the course of the reaction. In other words, ES maintains a **steady state** and [ES] can be treated as having a constant value:

$$\frac{d[\mathrm{ES}]}{dt} = 0 \qquad [12\text{-}16]$$

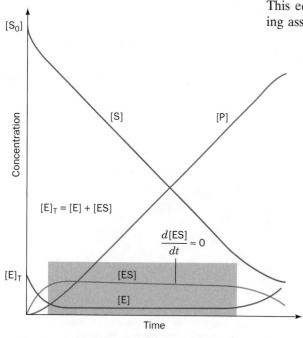

■ **Figure 12-2 | The progress curves for a simple enzyme-catalyzed reaction.** With the exception of the initial phase of the reaction (before the shaded block), the slopes of the progress curves for [E] and [ES] are essentially zero as long as $[\mathrm{S}] \gg [\mathrm{E}]$ (within the shaded block). [After Segel, I.H., *Enzyme Kinetics*, p. 27, Wiley (1993).] ✑ **See the Animated Figures.**

BOX 12-2 PATHWAYS OF DISCOVERY

J.B.S. Haldane and Enzyme Action

J.B.S. Haldane (1892–1964)

John Burdon Sanderson Haldane, the son of a prominent physiologist, was a gifted scientist and writer whose major contributions include the application of mathematics to areas of biology such as genetics and enzyme kinetics. As a scientist as well as a philosopher, he was aware of developments in relativity theory and quantum mechanics and was influenced by a practical philosophy that the natural world obeyed the laws of logic and arithmetic.

When Haldane published his book *Enzymes* in 1930, the idea that enzymes are proteins, rather than small catalysts surrounded by an amorphous protein "colloid," was still controversial. However, even in the absence of structural information, scientists such as Leonor Michaelis and Maud Menten had already applied the principles of thermodynamics to derive some basic equations related to enzyme kinetics. Michaelis and Menten proposed in 1913 that during a reaction, an enzyme and its substrate are in equilibrium with a complex of enzyme and substrate. In 1925, Haldane argued that this was not strictly true, since some enzyme–substrate complex does not dissociate to free enzyme and substrate but instead goes on to form product. When the enzyme and substrate are first mixed together, the concentration of the enzyme–substrate complex increases, but after a time the concentration of the complex levels off because the complex is constantly forming and breaking down to generate product. This principle,

the so-called steady state assumption, underlies modern theories of enzyme activity.

Even without knowing what enzymes were made of, Haldane showed great insight in proposing that an enzyme could catalyze a reaction by bringing its substrates into a strained or out-of-equilibrium arrangement. This idea refined Emil Fischer's earlier lock-and-key simile (and was later elaborated further by Linus Pauling). Haldane's idea of strain was not fully appreciated until around 1970, after the X-ray structures of several enzymes, including lysozyme and chymotrypsin (Chapter 11), had been examined.

In addition to his work in enzymology, Haldane articulated the role of genes in heredity and formulated mathematical estimates of mutation rates—many years before the nature of genes or the structure of DNA were known. However, in addition to being a theorist, Haldane was an experimentalist who frequently performed unpleasant or dangerous experiments on himself. For example, he ingested sodium bicarbonate and ammonium chloride in order to investigate their effect on breathing rate. Beyond the laboratory, Haldane was well-known for his efforts to popularize science. In *Daedalus, or, Science and the Future*, Haldane commented on the status of various branches of science circa 1924 and speculated about future developments. His thoughts and his persona are believed to have inspired various plots and characters in other writers' works of science fiction.

Briggs, G.E. and Haldane, J.B.S., A note on the kinetics of enzyme action, *Biochem. J.* **19**, 339 (1925).

This so-called **steady state assumption,** a more general condition than that of equilibrium, was first proposed in 1925 by George E. Briggs and John B.S. Haldane (Box 12-2).

In order to be useful, kinetic expressions for overall reactions must be formulated in terms of experimentally measurable quantities. The quantities [ES] and [E] are not, in general, directly measurable, but the total enzyme concentration

$$[E]_T = [E] + [ES] \qquad [12\text{-}17]$$

is usually readily determined. The rate equation for the overall enzymatic reaction as a function of [S] and [E] can then be derived. First, Eq. 12-14 is combined with the steady state assumption (Eq. 12-16) to give

$$k_1[E][S] = k_{-1}[ES] + k_2[ES] \qquad [12\text{-}18]$$

Letting $[E] = [E]_T - [ES]$ and rearranging yields

$$\frac{([E]_T - [ES])[S]}{[ES]} = \frac{k_{-1} + k_2}{k_1} \qquad [12\text{-}19]$$

The **Michaelis constant, K_M,** is defined as

$$K_M = \frac{k_{-1} + k_2}{k_1} \qquad [12\text{-}20]$$

so Eq. 12-19 can then be rearranged to give

$$K_M[\text{ES}] = ([\text{E}]_\text{T} - [\text{ES}])[\text{S}] \qquad [12\text{-}21]$$

Solving for [ES],

$$[\text{ES}] = \frac{[\text{E}]_\text{T}[\text{S}]}{K_M + [\text{S}]} \qquad [12\text{-}22]$$

The expression for the **initial velocity** (v_o) of the reaction, the velocity (Eq. 12-13) at $t = 0$, thereby becomes

$$v_\text{o} = \left(\frac{d[\text{P}]}{dt}\right)_{t=0} = k_2[\text{ES}] = \frac{k_2[\text{E}]_\text{T}[\text{S}]}{K_M + [\text{S}]} \qquad [12\text{-}23]$$

Both $[\text{E}]_\text{T}$ and [S] are experimentally measurable quantities. In order to meet the conditions of the steady state assumption, the concentration o the substrate must be much greater than the concentration of the enzyme which allows each enzyme molecule to repeatedly bind a molecule of sub strate and convert it to product, so that [ES] is constant. The use of th initial velocity (operationally taken as the velocity measured be fore more than ~10% of the substrate has been converted to product)—rather than just the velocity—minimizes such compli cating factors as the effects of reversible reactions, inhibition o the enzyme by its product(s), and progressive inactivation o the enzyme. (This is also why the rate of the reverse reaction in Eq. 12-12 can be assumed to be zero.)

The **maximal velocity** of a reaction, V_max, occurs at high sub strate concentrations when the enzyme is **saturated,** that is, when it is entirely in the ES form:

$$V_\text{max} = k_2[\text{E}]_\text{T} \qquad [12\text{-}24]$$

Therefore, combining Eqs. 12-23 and 12-24, we obtain

$$\boxed{v_\text{o} = \frac{V_\text{max}[\text{S}]}{K_M + [\text{S}]}} \qquad [12\text{-}25]$$

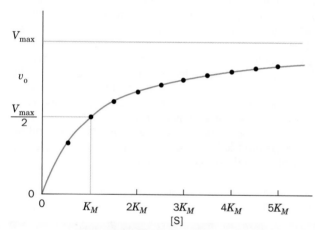

Figure 12-3 | **A plot of the initial velocity v_o of a simple enzymatic reaction versus the substrate concentration [S].** Points are plotted in $0.5K_M$ intervals of substrate concentration between $0.5K_M$ and $5K_M$. 🔊 **See the Animated Figures.**

This expression, the **Michaelis–Menten equation,** *is the basic equation of enzyme kinetics.* It describes a rectangular hyperbola such as that plotted in Fig. 12-3. The saturation function for oxygen binding to myoglobin (Eq. 7-6) has the same algebraic form.

The Michaelis Constant Has a Simple Operational Definition. At the substrate concentration at which [S] = K_M, Eq. 12-25 yields $v_\text{o} = V_\text{max}/2$ so that K_M *is the substrate concentration at which the reaction velocity is half-maximal.* Therefore, if an enzyme has a small value of K_M, it achieves maximal catalytic efficiency at low substrate concentrations.

The K_M is unique for each enzyme–substrate pair: Different substrates that react with a given enzyme do so with different K_M values. Likewise, different enzymes that act on the same substrate have different K_M val ues. The magnitude of K_M varies widely with the identity of the enzyme and the nature of the substrate (Table 12-1). It is also a function of tem perature and pH. The Michaelis constant (Eq. 12-20) can be expressed as

$$K_M = \frac{k_{-1}}{k_1} + \frac{k_2}{k_1} = K_\text{S} + \frac{k_2}{k_1} \qquad [12\text{-}26]$$

Since K_S is the dissociation constant of the Michaelis complex (Eq. 12-15),

Table 12-1	The Values of K_M, k_{cat}, and k_{cat}/K_M for Some Enzymes and Substrates			
Enzyme	**Substrate**	K_M (M)	k_{cat} (s^{-1})	k_{cat}/K_M (M$^{-1} \cdot$ s^{-1})
Acetylcholinesterase	Acetylcholine	9.5×10^{-5}	1.4×10^4	1.5×10^8
Carbonic anhydrase	CO_2	1.2×10^{-2}	1.0×10^6	8.3×10^7
	HCO_3^-	2.6×10^{-2}	4.0×10^5	1.5×10^7
Catalase	H_2O_2	2.5×10^{-2}	1.0×10^7	4.0×10^8
Chymotrypsin	N-Acetylglycine ethyl ester	4.4×10^{-1}	5.1×10^{-2}	1.2×10^{-1}
	N-Acetylvaline ethyl ester	8.8×10^{-2}	1.7×10^{-1}	1.9
	N-Acetyltyrosine ethyl ester	6.6×10^{-4}	1.9×10^2	2.9×10^5
Fumarase	Fumarate	5.0×10^{-6}	8.0×10^2	1.6×10^8
	Malate	2.5×10^{-5}	9.0×10^2	3.6×10^7
Urease	Urea	2.5×10^{-2}	1.0×10^4	4.0×10^5

s K_S decreases, the enzyme's affinity for substrate increases. K_M is therefore also a measure of the affinity of the enzyme for its substrate, provided k_2/k_1 is small compared to K_S, that is, $k_2 < k_{-1}$ so that the ES → P reaction proceeds more slowly than ES reverts to E + S.

k_{cat}/K_M **Is a Measure of Catalytic Efficiency.** We can define the **catalytic constant, k_{cat},** of an enzyme as

$$k_{cat} = \frac{V_{max}}{[E]_T} \qquad [12\text{-}27]$$

This quantity is also known as the **turnover number** of an enzyme because it is the number of reaction processes (turnovers) that each active site catalyzes per unit time. The turnover numbers for a selection of enzymes are given in Table 12-l. Note that these quantities vary by over eight orders of magnitude. Equation 12-24 indicates that for a simple system, such as the Michaelis–Menten model reaction (Eq. 12-12), $k_{cat} = k_2$. For enzymes with more complicated mechanisms (e.g., multiple substrates or multiple reaction intermediates), k_{cat} may be a function of several rate constants. Note that whereas k_{cat} is a constant, V_{max} depends on the concentration of the enzyme present in the experimental system. V_{max} increases as $[E]_T$ increases.

When $[S] \ll K_M$, very little ES is formed. Consequently, $[E] \approx [E]_T$, so Eq. 12-23 reduces to a second-order rate equation:

$$v_o \approx \left(\frac{k_2}{K_M}\right)[E]_T[S] \approx \left(\frac{k_{cat}}{K_M}\right)[E][S] \qquad [12\text{-}28]$$

Here, k_{cat}/K_M is the apparent second-order rate constant of the enzymatic reaction; the rate of the reaction varies directly with how often enzyme and substrate encounter one another in solution. *The quantity k_{cat}/K_M is therefore a measure of an enzyme's catalytic efficiency.*

There is an upper limit to the value of k_{cat}/K_M: It can be no greater than k_1; that is, the decomposition of ES to E + P can occur no more frequently than E and S come together to form ES. The most efficient enzymes have k_{cat}/K_M values near the **diffusion-controlled limit** of 10^8 to 10^9 M$^{-1} \cdot$ s^{-1}. These enzymes catalyze a reaction almost every time they encounter a substrate molecule and hence have achieved a state of virtual catalytic

BOX 12-3 PERSPECTIVES IN BIOCHEMISTRY

Kinetics and Transition State Theory

How is the rate of a reaction related to its activation energy (Section 11-2)? Consider a bimolecular reaction that proceeds along the following pathway:

$$A + B \underset{}{\overset{K^{\ddagger}}{\rightleftharpoons}} X^{\ddagger} \overset{k'}{\longrightarrow} P + Q$$

where $X^{\ddagger}$ represents the transition state. The rate of the reaction can be expressed as

$$\frac{d[P]}{dt} = k[A][B] = k'[X^{\ddagger}] \qquad [12\text{-}A]$$

where k is the ordinary rate constant of the elementary reaction and k' is the rate constant for the decomposition of $X^{\ddagger}$ to products.

Although $X^{\ddagger}$ is unstable, it is assumed to be in rapid equilibrium with the reactants; that is,

$$K^{\ddagger} = \frac{[X^{\ddagger}]}{[A][B]} \qquad [12\text{-}B]$$

where $K^{\ddagger}$ is an equilibrium constant. This central assumption of transition state theory permits the powerful formalism of thermodynamics to be applied to the theory of reaction rates.

Since $K^{\ddagger}$ is an equilibrium constant, it can be expressed as

$$-RT \ln K^{\ddagger} = \Delta G^{\ddagger} \qquad [12\text{-}C]$$

where T is the absolute temperature and R (8.3145 $J \cdot K^{-1} \cdot mol^{-1}$) is the gas constant (this relationship between equilibrium constants and free energy is derived in Section 1-3D). Combining the three preceding equations yields

$$\frac{d[P]}{dt} = k' e^{-\Delta G^{\ddagger}/RT}[A][B] \qquad [12\text{-}D]$$

This equation indicates that the rate of a reaction not only depends on the concentrations of its reactants, but also decreases exponentially with $\Delta G^{\ddagger}$. Thus, *the larger the difference between the free energy of the transition state and that of the reactants (the free energy of activation), that is, the less stable the transition state, the slower the reaction proceeds.*

We must now evaluate k', the rate at which $X^{\ddagger}$ decomposes. The transition state structure is held together by a bond that is assumed to be so weak that it flies apart during its first vibrational excursion. Therefore, k' is expressed

$$k' = \kappa\nu \qquad [12\text{-}E]$$

where ν is the vibrational frequency of the bond that breaks as $X^{\ddagger}$ decomposes to products, and κ, the **transmission coefficient,** is the probability that the breakdown of $X^{\ddagger}$ will be in the direction of product formation rather than back to reactants. For most spontaneous reactions, κ is assumed to be 1.0 (although this number, which must be between 0 and 1, can rarely be calculated with confidence).

Planck's law states that

$$\nu = \varepsilon/h \qquad [12\text{-}F]$$

where, in this case, ε is the average energy of the vibration that leads to the decomposition of $X^{\ddagger}$, and h (6.6261 × 10⁻³⁴ J · s) is **Planck's constant.** Statistical mechanics tells us that at a temperature T, the classical energy of an oscillator is

$$\varepsilon = k_B T \qquad [12\text{-}G]$$

where k_B (1.3807 × 10⁻²³ J · K⁻¹) is the **Boltzmann constant** and $k_B T$ is essentially the available thermal energy. Combining Eqs. 12-E through 12-G gives

$$k' = \frac{k_B T}{h} \qquad [12\text{-}H]$$

Thus, combining Eqs. 12-A, 12-D, and 12-H yields the expression for the rate constant of the elementary reaction:

$$k = \frac{k_B T}{h} e^{-\Delta G^{\ddagger}/RT} \qquad [12\text{-}I]$$

This equation indicates that as the temperature rises, so that there is increased thermal energy available to drive the reacting complex over the activation barrier ($\Delta G^{\ddagger}$), the reaction speeds up.

---

perfection. The relationship between the catalytic rate and the thermodynamics of the transition state can now be appreciated (Box 12-3).

C | Kinetic Data Can Provide Values of V_{max} and K_M

There are several methods for determining the values of the parameters of the Michaelis–Menten equation (i.e., V_{max} and K_M). At very high values of [S], the initial velocity, v_o, asymptotically approaches V_{max} (see Sample Calculation 12-3). In practice, however, it is very difficult to assess V_{max} accurately from direct plots of v_o versus [S] such as Fig. 12-3, because, even at substrate concentrations as high as [S] = 10 K_M, Eq. 12-25

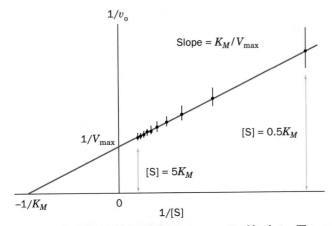

Figure 12-4 | A double-reciprocal (Lineweaver–Burk) plot. The error bars represent $\pm 0.05 V_{max}$. The indicated points are the same as those in Fig. 12-3. Note the large effect of small errors at small [S] (large 1/[S]) and the crowding together of points at large [S]. ⚫ **See the Animated Figures.**

...ndicates that v_o is only 91% of V_{max}, so that the value of V_{max} will almost certainly be underestimated.

A better method for determining the values of V_{max} and K_M, which was formulated by Hans Lineweaver and Dean Burk, uses the reciprocal of the Michaelis–Menten equation (Eq. 12-25):

$$\frac{1}{v_o} = \left(\frac{K_M}{V_{max}}\right)\frac{1}{[S]} + \frac{1}{V_{max}}$$ [12-29]

This is a linear equation in $1/v_o$ and $1/[S]$. If these quantities are plotted to obtain the so-called **Lineweaver–Burk** or **double-reciprocal plot,** the slope of the line is K_M/V_{max}, the $1/v_o$ intercept is $1/V_{max}$, and the extrapolated 1/[S] intercept is $-1/K_M$ (Fig. 12-4 and Sample Calculation 12-4).

SAMPLE CALCULATION 12-3

An enzyme-catalyzed reaction has a K_M of 1 mM and a V_{max} of 5 nM · s^{-1}. What is the reaction velocity when the substrate concentration is (a) 0.25 mM, (b) 1.5 mM, or (c) 10 mM?

Use the Michaelis–Menten equation (Eq. 12-25):

(a) $v_o = \dfrac{(5\text{ nM} \cdot \text{s}^{-1})(0.25\text{ mM})}{(1\text{ mM}) + (0.25\text{ mM})}$

$= \dfrac{1.25}{1.25}\text{ nM} \cdot \text{s}^{-1}$

$= 1\text{ nM} \cdot \text{s}^{-1}$

(b) $v_o = \dfrac{(5\text{ nM} \cdot \text{s}^{-1})(1.5\text{ mM})}{(1\text{ mM}) + (1.5\text{ mM})}$

$= \dfrac{7.5}{2.5}\text{ nM} \cdot \text{s}^{-1}$

$= 3\text{ nM} \cdot \text{s}^{-1}$

(c) $v_o = \dfrac{(5\text{ nM} \cdot \text{s}^{-1})(10\text{ mM})}{(1\text{ mM}) + (10\text{ mM})}$

$= \dfrac{50}{11}\text{ nM} \cdot \text{s}^{-1}$

$= 4.5\text{ nM} \cdot \text{s}^{-1}$

Note: When units in the numerator and denominator cancel it is unnecessary to convert them to standard units before performing the calculation.

SAMPLE CALCULATION 12-4

Determine K_M and V_{max} for an enzyme from the following data using Eq. 12-29:

[S] (mM)	v_o (μM · s^{-1})
1	2.5
2	4.0
5	6.3
10	7.6
20	9.0

First, convert the data to reciprocal form (1/[S] in units of mM^{-1}, and $1/v_o$ in units of μM^{-1} · s). Next, make a plot of $1/v_o$ versus 1/[S]. The x- and y-intercepts can be estimated by extrapolation of the straight line or can be calculated by linear regression. According to Eq. 12-29 and Fig. 12-4, the y-intercept, which has a value of ~0.1 μM^{-1} · s, is equivalent to $1/V_{max}$, so V_{max} (the reciprocal of the y-intercept) is 10 μM · s^{-1}. The x-intercept, -0.33 mM^{-1}, is equivalent to $-1/K_M$, so K_M (the negative reciprocal of the x-intercept) is equal to 3.0 mM.

As can be seen in Fig. 12-3, the best estimates of kinetic parameters are obtained by collecting data over a range of [S] from ~0.5 K_M to ~5 K_M. Thus, a disadvantage of the Lineweaver–Burk plots is that most experimental measurements of [S] are crowded onto the left side of the graph (Fig. 12-4). Moreover, for small values of [S], small errors in v_o lead to large errors in $1/v_o$ and hence to large errors in K_M and V_{max}.

Several other types of plots, each with its advantages and disadvantages, can also be used to determine K_M and V_{max} from kinetic data. However, kinetic data are now commonly analyzed by computer using mathematically sophisticated statistical treatments. Nevertheless, Lineweaver–Burk plots are valuable for the visual presentation of kinetic data.

Steady State Kinetics Cannot Unambiguously Establish a Reaction Mechanism. Although steady state kinetics provides valuable information about the rates of buildup and breakdown of ES, it provides little insight as to the nature of ES. Thus, an enzymatic reaction may, in reality, pass through several more or less stable intermediate states such as

$$E + S \rightleftharpoons ES \rightleftharpoons EX \rightleftharpoons EP \rightleftharpoons E + P$$

or take a more complex path such as

$$
\begin{array}{ccccc}
 & & EX & & \\
 & \nearrow & & \searrow & \\
E + S \rightleftharpoons ES & & & EP & \longrightarrow E + P \\
 & \searrow & & \nearrow & \\
 & & EY & &
\end{array}
$$

Unfortunately, steady state kinetic measurements are incapable of revealing the number of intermediates in an enzyme-catalyzed reaction. Thus, such measurements of a multistep reaction can be likened to a "black box" containing a system of water pipes with one inlet and one drain:

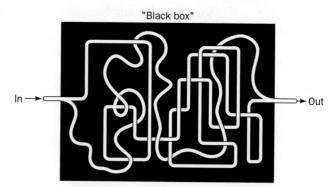

At steady state, that is, after the pipes have filled with water, the relationship between input pressure and output flow can be measured. However, such measurements yield no information concerning the detailed construction of the plumbing connecting the inlet to the drain. This would require additional information, such as opening the box and tracing the pipes. Likewise, steady state kinetic measurements can provide a phenomenological description of enzymatic behavior, but the nature of the intermediates remains indeterminate. The existence of intermediates must be verified independently, for example, by identifying them through the use of spectroscopic techniques.

The foregoing highlights a central principle of enzymology: *The steady state kinetic analysis of a reaction cannot unambiguously establish its mechanism.* This is because no matter how simple, elegant, or rational a postulated mechanism, there are an infinite number of alternative mechanisms that can also account for the kinetic data. Usually, it is the simpler mechanism that turns out to be correct, but this is not always the case. However, *if kinetic data are not compatible with a given mechanism, then that mechanism must be rejected.* Therefore, although kinetics cannot be used to establish a mechanism unambiguously without confirming data, such as the physical demonstration of an intermediate's existence, the steady state kinetic analysis of a reaction is of great value because it can be used to eliminate proposed mechanisms.

Bisubstrate Reactions Follow One of Several Rate Equations

We have heretofore been concerned with simple, single-substrate reactions that obey the Michaelis–Menten model (Reaction 12-12). Yet, enzymatic reactions requiring multiple substrates and yielding multiple products are far more common. Indeed, those involving two substrates and yielding two products

$$A + B \overset{E}{\rightleftharpoons} P + Q$$

account for ~60% of known biochemical reactions. Almost all of these so-called **bisubstrate reactions** are either transfer reactions in which the enzyme catalyzes the transfer of a specific functional group, X, from one of the substrates to the other:

$$P-X + B \overset{E}{\rightleftharpoons} P + B-X$$

or oxidation–reduction reactions in which reducing equivalents are transferred between the two substrates. For example, the hydrolysis of a peptide bond by trypsin (Section 11-5) is the transfer of the peptide carbonyl group from the peptide nitrogen atom to water (Fig. 12-5a), whereas in the alcohol dehydrogenase reaction (Section 11-1B), a hydride ion is formally transferred from ethanol to NAD$^+$ (Fig. 12-5b). Although bisubstrate reactions could, in principle, occur through a vast variety of mechanisms, only a few types are commonly observed.

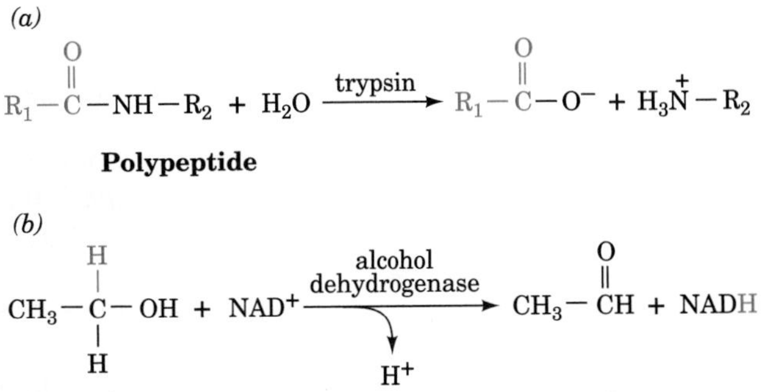

Sequential Reactions Occur via Single Displacements. *Reactions in which all substrates must combine with the enzyme before a reaction can occur and products be released are known as **sequential reactions.*** In such reactions, the group being transferred, X, is directly passed from A ($=P-X$) to B, yielding P and Q ($=B-X$). Hence, such reactions are also called **single-displacement reactions.**

Sequential reactions can be subclassified into those with a compulsory order of substrate addition to the enzyme, which are said to have an **Ordered mechanism,** and those with no preference for the order of substrate addition, which are described as having a **Random mechanism.** In the Ordered mechanism, the binding of the first substrate is apparently required for the enzyme to form the binding site for the second substrate, whereas in the Random mechanism, both binding sites are present on the free enzyme.

In a notation developed by W.W. Cleland, substrates are designated by the letters A and B in the order that they add to the enzyme, products are designated by P and Q in the order that they leave the enzyme, the enzyme is represented by a horizontal line, and successive additions of substrates and releases of products are denoted by vertical arrows. An

(a)

$$R_1-\overset{\overset{\displaystyle O}{\|}}{C}-NH-R_2 + H_2O \xrightarrow{\text{trypsin}} R_1-\overset{\overset{\displaystyle O}{\|}}{C}-O^- + H_3\overset{+}{N}-R_2$$

Polypeptide

(b)

$$CH_3-\overset{\overset{\displaystyle H}{|}}{\underset{\underset{\displaystyle H}{|}}{C}}-OH + NAD^+ \xrightarrow[\text{H}^+]{\substack{\text{alcohol}\\\text{dehydrogenase}}} CH_3-\overset{\overset{\displaystyle O}{\|}}{C}H + NADH$$

■ **Figure 12-5** | **Some bisubstrate reactions.** (*a*) In the peptide hydrolysis reaction catalyzed by trypsin, the peptide carbonyl group, with its pendent polypeptide chain, R$_1$, is transferred from the peptide nitrogen atom to a water molecule. (*b*) In the alcohol dehydrogenase reaction, a hydride ion is formally transferred from ethanol to NAD$^+$.

Ordered bisubstrate reaction is thereby diagrammed:

where A and B are said to be the **leading** and **following** substrates, re
spectively. Many NAD$^+$- and NADP$^+$-requiring dehydrogenases follow
an Ordered bisubstrate mechanism in which the coenzyme is the leading
substrate.

A Random bisubstrate reaction is diagrammed:

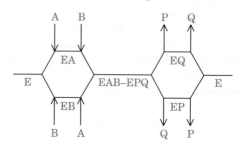

Some dehydrogenases and **kinases** operate through Random bisubstrate
mechanisms (kinases are enzymes that transfer phosphoryl groups from
ATP to other compounds or vice versa).

Ping Pong Reactions Occur via Double Displacements. *Group-transfer
reactions in which one or more products are released before all substrates
have been added are known as* **Ping Pong reactions.** The Ping Pong bisubstrate reaction is represented by

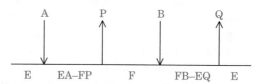

Here, a functional group X of the first substrate A (= P—X) is displaced
from the substrate by the enzyme E to yield the first product P and a stable enzyme form F (= E—X) in which X is tightly (often covalently) bound
to the enzyme (Ping). In the second stage of the reaction, X is displaced
from the enzyme by the second substrate B to yield the second product Q
(= B—X), thereby regenerating the original form of the enzyme, E (Pong).
Such reactions are therefore also known as **double-displacement reactions.**
*Note that in Ping Pong reactions, the substrates A and B do not encounter
one another on the surface of the enzyme.* Many enzymes, including trypsin
(in which F is the acyl–enzyme intermediate; Section 11-5), transaminases,
and some flavoenzymes, react with Ping Pong mechanisms.

**Bisubstrate Mechanisms Can Be Distinguished by Kinetic Measure-
ments.** The rate equations that describe the foregoing bisubstrate
mechanisms are considerably more complicated than the equation for a
single-substrate reaction. In fact, the equations for bisubstrate mechanisms
(which are beyond the scope of this text) contain as many as four kinetic
constants versus two (V_{max} and K_M) for the Michaelis–Menten equation.
Nevertheless, steady state kinetic measurements can be used to distinguish
among the various bisubstrate mechanisms.

■ **CHECK YOUR UNDERSTANDING**

Write the rate equations for a first-order and
    a second-order reaction.
What are the differences between
    instantaneous velocity, initial velocity, and
    maximal velocity for an enzymatic reaction?
Derive the Michaelis–Menten equation.
What do the values of K_M and k_{cat}/K_M reveal
    about an enzyme?
Write the Lineweaver–Burk (double-reciprocal)
    equation and describe the features of a
    Lineweaver–Burk plot.
Use Cleland notation to describe Ordered
    and Random sequential reactions and a
    Ping Pong reaction.

2 Enzyme Inhibition

Many substances alter the activity of an enzyme by combining with it in a way that influences the binding of substrate and/or its turnover number. *Substances that reduce an enzyme's activity in this way are known as inhibitors.* A large part of the modern pharmaceutical arsenal consists of enzyme inhibitors. For example, AIDS is treated almost exclusively with drugs that inhibit the activities of certain viral enzymes.

Inhibitors act through a variety of mechanisms. Irreversible enzyme inhibitors, or **inactivators,** bind to the enzyme so tightly that they permanently block the enzyme's activity. Reagents that chemically modify specific amino acid residues can act as inactivators. For example, the compounds used to identify the catalytic Ser and His residues of serine proteases (Section 11-5A) are inactivators of these enzymes.

Reversible enzyme inhibitors diminish an enzyme's activity by interacting reversibly with it. Some enzyme inhibitors are substances that structurally resemble their enzyme's substrates but either do not react or react very slowly. These substances are commonly used to probe the chemical and conformational nature of an enzyme's active site in an effort to elucidate the enzyme's catalytic mechanism. Other inhibitors affect catalytic activity without interfering with substrate binding. Many do both. In this section, we discuss several of the simplest mechanisms for reversible inhibition and their effects on the kinetic behavior of enzymes that follow the Michaelis–Menten model. As in the preceding discussion, we will base our analysis on a simple one-substrate reaction model.

LEARNING OBJECTIVE

■ Understand that competitive, uncompetitive, and mixed enzyme inhibitors interact with the enzyme and/or the enzyme–substrate complex to alter its K_M and/or V_{max} values.

A | Competitive Inhibition Involves Inhibitor Binding at an Enzyme's Substrate Binding Site

A substance that competes directly with a normal substrate for an enzyme's substrate-binding site is known as a **competitive inhibitor.** Such an inhibitor usually resembles the substrate so that it specifically binds to the active site but differs from the substrate so that it cannot react as the substrate does. For example, **succinate dehydrogenase,** a citric acid cycle enzyme that converts **succinate** to **fumarate** (Section 17-3F), is competitively inhibited by **malonate,** which structurally resembles succinate but cannot be dehydrogenated:

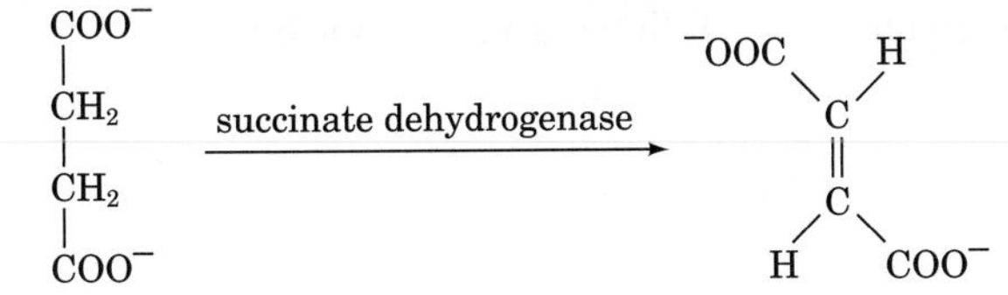

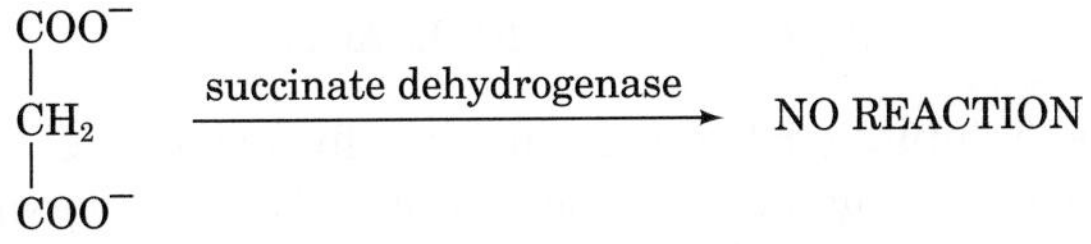

The effectiveness of malonate as a competitive inhibitor of succinate dehydrogenase strongly suggests that the enzyme's substrate-binding site is designed to bind both of the substrate's carboxylate groups, presumabl[y] through the influence of appropriately placed positively charge[d] residues.

Similar principles are responsible for **product inhibition.** In this phenom[en]on, a product of the reaction, which necessarily is able to bind to th[e] enzyme's active site, may accumulate and compete with substrate for bind[ing] to the enzyme in subsequent catalytic cycles. Product inhibition is on[e] way in which the cell controls the activities of its enzymes (Section 12-3)[.]

Transition state analogs are particularly effective inhibitors. This is be[-]cause effective catalysis depends on the enzyme's ability to bind to an[d] stabilize the reaction's transition state (Section 11-3E). A compound tha[t] mimics the transition state exploits these binding interactions in ways tha[t] a substrate analog cannot. For example, **adenosine deaminase** converts th[e] nucleoside adenosine to inosine as follows:

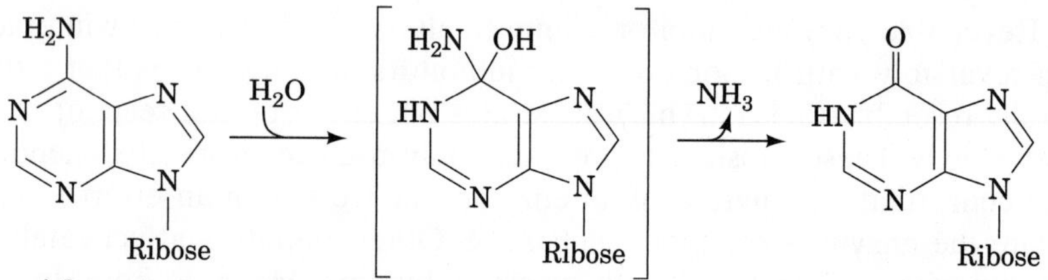

Adenosine   **Inosine**

The K_M of the enzyme for the substrate adenosine is 3×10^{-5} M. Th[e] product inosine acts as an inhibitor of the reaction, with an **inhibition con**[-]**stant** (K_I, the dissociation constant for enzyme–inhibitor binding; see be[-]low) of 3×10^{-4} M. However, a transition state analog,

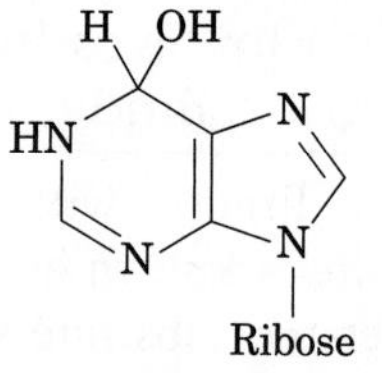

1,6-Dihydroinosine

inhibits the reaction with a K_I of 1.5×10^{-13} M.

The Degree of Competitive Inhibition Varies with the Fraction o[f] **Enzyme That Has Bound Inhibitor.** The general model for competitive inhibition is given by the following reaction scheme:

Here, I is the inhibitor, EI is the catalytically inactive enzyme–inhibitor complex, and it is assumed that the inhibitor binds reversibly to the enzyme and is in rapid equilibrium with it so that

$$K_I = \frac{[E][I]}{[EI]} \qquad [12\text{-}30]$$

A competitive inhibitor therefore reduces the concentration of free enzyme available for substrate binding.

The Michaelis–Menten equation for a competitively inhibited reaction is derived as before (Section 12-1B), but with an additional term to account for the fraction of $[E]_T$ that binds to I to form EI ($[E]_T = [E] + [ES] + [EI]$). The resulting equation,

$$v_o = \frac{V_{max}[S]}{\alpha K_M + [S]} \qquad [12\text{-}31]$$

is the Michaelis–Menten equation that has been modified by a factor, α, which is defined as

$$\alpha = 1 + \frac{[I]}{K_I} \qquad [12\text{-}32]$$

Note that α, a function of the inhibitor's concentration and its affinity for the enzyme, cannot be less than 1. Comparison of Eqs. 12-25 and 12-31 indicates that $K_M^{app} = \alpha K_M$, where K_M^{app} is the apparent K_M, that is, the K_M value that would be measured in the absence of the knowledge that inhibitor is present. Figure 12-6 shows the hyperbolic plots of Eq. 12-31 for increasing values of α. The presence of I makes [S] appear to be less than it really is (makes K_M appear to be larger than it really is), a consequence of the binding of I and S to E being mutually exclusive. However, increasing [S] can overwhelm a competitive inhibitor. In fact, α *is the factor by which [S] must be increased in order to overcome the effect of the presence of inhibitor.* As [S] approaches infinity, v_o approaches V_{max} for any value of α (that is, for any concentration of inhibitor). Thus, the inhibitor does not affect the enzyme's turnover number.

Competitive inhibition is the principle behind the use of ethanol to treat methanol poisoning. Methanol itself is only mildly toxic. However, the liver enzyme alcohol dehydrogenase converts methanol to the highly toxic formaldehyde, only small amounts of which cause blindness and death. Ethanol competes with methanol for binding to the active site of liver alcohol dehydrogenase, thereby slowing the production of formaldehyde from methanol (the ethanol is converted to the readily metabolized acetaldehyde):

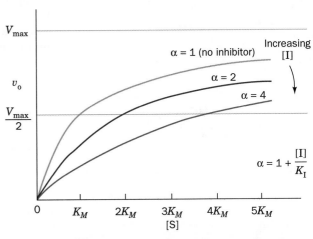

■ **Figure 12-6** | **A plot of v_o versus [S] for a Michaelis–Menten reaction in the presence of different concentrations of a competitive inhibitor.**

$$\underset{\textbf{Methanol}}{\overset{\displaystyle H}{\underset{\displaystyle H}{H-C-OH}}} \longrightarrow \underset{\textbf{Formaldehyde}}{\overset{\displaystyle O}{H-C-H}}$$

$$\underset{\textbf{Ethanol}}{\overset{\displaystyle H}{\underset{\displaystyle H}{H_3C-C-OH}}} \longrightarrow \underset{\textbf{Acetaldehyde}}{\overset{\displaystyle O}{H_3C-C-H}}$$

Thus, through the administration of ethanol, a large portion of the methanol will be harmlessly excreted from the body in the urine before it can be converted to formaldehyde. The same principle underlies the use of ethanol to treat antifreeze (ethylene glycol, $HOCH_2CH_2OH$) poisoning, which, due to its sweet taste, often afflicts cats and dogs.

SAMPLE CALCULATION 12-5

An enzyme has a K_M of 8 μM in the absence of a competitive inhibitor and a K_M^{app} of 12 μM in the presence of 3 μM of the inhibitor. Calculate K_I.

First calculate the value of α when K_M = 8 μM and K_M^{app} = 12 μM:

$$K_M^{app} = \alpha K_M$$

$$\alpha = \frac{K_M^{app}}{K_M}$$

$$\alpha = \frac{12\ \mu M}{8\ \mu M} = 1.5$$

Next, calculate K_I from Eq. 12-32:

$$\alpha = 1 + \frac{[I]}{K_I}$$

$$K_I = \frac{[I]}{\alpha - 1}$$

$$K_I = \frac{3\ \mu M}{1.5 - 1} = 6\ \mu M$$

K_I Can Be Measured. Recasting Eq. 12-31 in the double-reciprocal form yields

$$\frac{1}{v_o} = \left(\frac{\alpha K_M}{V_{max}}\right)\frac{1}{[S]} + \frac{1}{V_{max}} \qquad [12\text{-}33]$$

A plot of this equation is linear and has a slope of $\alpha K_M/V_{max}$, a 1/[S] intercept of $-1/\alpha K_M$, and a $1/v_o$ intercept of $1/V_{max}$ (Fig. 12-7). The double-reciprocal plots for a competitive inhibitor at various concentrations of I intersect at $1/V_{max}$ on the $1/v_o$ axis, a property that is diagnostic of competitive inhibition.

The value of K_I for a competitive inhibitor can be determined from the plot of $K_M^{app} = (1 + [I]/K_I)K_M$ versus [I]; its intercept on the [I] axis is $-K_I$. K_I can also be calculated from Eq. 12-32 if $K_M^{app} = \alpha K_M$ is determined at a known [I] for an enzyme of known K_M (see Sample Calculation 12-5). Comparing the K_I values of competitive inhibitors with different structures can provide information about the binding properties of an enzyme's active site and hence its catalytic mechanism. For example, to ascertain the importance of the various segments of an ATP molecule

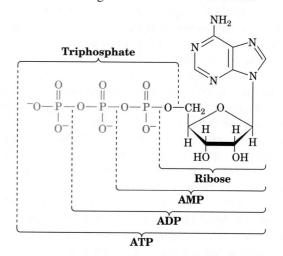

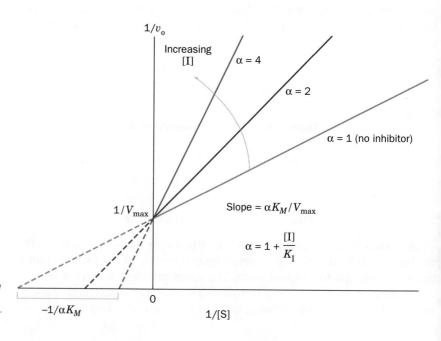

■ Figure 12-7 | A Lineweaver–Burk plot of the competitively inhibited Michaelis–Menten enzyme described by Fig. 12-6. Note that all lines intersect on the $1/v_o$ axis at $1/V_{max}$. The varying slopes indicate the effect of the inhibitor on $\alpha K_M = K_M^{app}$. 🔊 **See the Animated Figures.**

or binding to the active site of an ATP-requiring enzyme, one might determine the K_I, say, for ADP, AMP, ribose, triphosphate, etc. Since many of these ATP components are unreactive, inhibition studies are the most convenient method of monitoring their binding to the enzyme.

Competitive inhibition studies are also used to determine the affinities of transition state analogs for an enzyme's active site (Section 11-3E). For example, the HIV protease inhibitors (Box 12-4) have been designed to mimic the enzyme's transition state and thus bind to the enzyme with high affinity. Inhibitor studies are the mainstays of such drug development, as is described in Section 12-4.

Uncompetitive Inhibition Involves Inhibitor Binding to the Enzyme–Substrate Complex

In **uncompetitive inhibition,** the inhibitor binds directly to the enzyme–substrate complex but not to the free enzyme:

$$\text{E} + \text{S} \underset{k_{-1}}{\overset{k_1}{\rightleftharpoons}} \text{ES} \xrightarrow{k_2} \text{P} + \text{E}$$

$$+$$

$$\text{I}$$

$$K_I' \Big\Updownarrow$$

$$\text{ESI} \longrightarrow \text{NO REACTION}$$

In this case, the inhibitor binding step has the dissociation constant

$$K_I' = \frac{[\text{ES}][\text{I}]}{[\text{ESI}]} \qquad [12\text{-}34]$$

The binding of uncompetitive inhibitor, which need not resemble substrate, presumably *distorts the active site, thereby rendering the enzyme catalytically inactive.*

The Michaelis–Menten equation for uncompetitive inhibition and the equation for its double-reciprocal plot are given in Table 12-2. The double-

---

Table 12-2 Effects of Inhibitors on Michaelis–Menten Reactions[a]

Type of Inhibition	Michaelis–Menten Equation	Lineweaver–Burk Equation	Effect of Inhibitor
None	$v_0 = \dfrac{V_{max}[\text{S}]}{K_M + [\text{S}]}$	$\dfrac{1}{v_0} = \dfrac{K_M}{V_{max}} \dfrac{1}{[\text{S}]} + \dfrac{1}{V_{max}}$	None
Competitive	$v_0 = \dfrac{V_{max}[\text{S}]}{\alpha K_M + [\text{S}]}$	$\dfrac{1}{v_0} = \dfrac{\alpha K_M}{V_{max}} \dfrac{1}{[\text{S}]} + \dfrac{1}{V_{max}}$	Increases K_M^{app}
Uncompetitive	$v_0 = \dfrac{V_{max}[\text{S}]}{K_M + \alpha'[\text{S}]} = \dfrac{(V_{max}/\alpha')[\text{S}]}{K_M/\alpha' + [\text{S}]}$	$\dfrac{1}{v_0} = \dfrac{K_M}{V_{max}} \dfrac{1}{[\text{S}]} + \dfrac{\alpha'}{V_{max}}$	Decreases K_M^{app} and V_{max}^{app}
Mixed (noncompetitive)	$v_0 = \dfrac{V_{max}[\text{S}]}{\alpha K_M + \alpha'[\text{S}]} = \dfrac{(V_{max}/\alpha')[\text{S}]}{(\alpha/\alpha')K_M + [\text{S}]}$	$\dfrac{1}{v_0} = \dfrac{\alpha K_M}{V_{max}} \dfrac{1}{[\text{S}]} + \dfrac{\alpha'}{V_{max}}$	Decreases V_{max}^{app}; may increase or decrease K_M^{app}

[a]$\alpha = 1 + \dfrac{[\text{I}]}{K_I}$ and $\alpha' = 1 + \dfrac{[\text{I}]}{K_I'}$

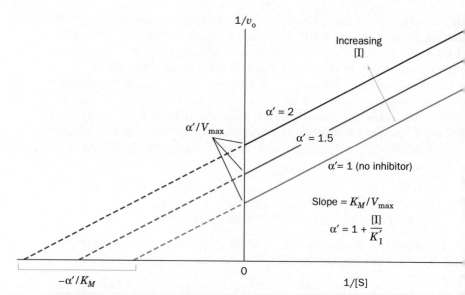

■ **Figure 12-8** | **A Lineweaver–Burk plot of a Michaelis–Menten enzyme in the presence of an uncompetitive inhibitor.** Note that all lines have identical slopes of K_M/V_{max}. ✆ **See the Animated Figures.**

reciprocal plot consists of a family of parallel lines (Fig. 12-8) with slope K_M/V_{max}, $1/v_o$ intercepts of α'/V_{max}, and $1/[S]$ intercepts of $-\alpha'/K_M$. Note that in uncompetitive inhibition, both $K_M^{app} = K_M/\alpha'$ and $V_{max}^{app} = V_{max}/\alpha'$ are decreased, but that $K_M^{app}/V_{max}^{app} = K_M/V_{max}$. In contrast to the case for competitive inhibition, adding substrate does not reverse the effect of an uncompetitive inhibitor because the binding of substrate does not interfere with the binding of uncompetitive inhibitor.

Uncompetitive inhibition requires that the inhibitor affect the catalytic function of the enzyme but not its substrate binding. This is difficult to envision for single-substrate enzymes. In actuality, uncompetitive inhibition is significant only for multisubstrate enzymes.

C | Mixed Inhibition Involves Inhibitor Binding to Both the Free Enzyme and the Enzyme–Substrate Complex

Many reversible inhibitors interact with the enzyme in a way that affects substrate binding as well as catalytic activity. In other words, both the enzyme and the enzyme–substrate complex bind inhibitor, resulting in the following model:

$$
\begin{array}{ccccc}
E + S & \underset{k_{-1}}{\overset{k_1}{\rightleftharpoons}} & ES & \xrightarrow{k_2} & P + E \\
+ & & + & & \\
I & & I & & \\
K_I \big\Updownarrow & & K_I' \big\Updownarrow & & \\
EI & & ESI & \longrightarrow & \text{NO REACTION}
\end{array}
$$

This phenomenon is known as **mixed inhibition** (alternatively, **noncompetitive inhibition**). Presumably, *a mixed inhibitor binds to enzyme sites that participate in both substrate binding and catalysis.* For example, metal ions, which do not compete directly with substrates for binding to an enzyme

ctive site, as do competitive inhibitors, may act as mixed inhibitors. The
wo dissociation constants for inhibitor binding

$$K_I = \frac{[E][I]}{[EI]} \quad \text{and} \quad K_I' = \frac{[ES][I]}{[ESI]} \qquad [12\text{-}35]$$

re not necessarily equivalent.

The Michaelis–Menten equation and the corresponding double-reciprocal
quation for mixed inhibition are given in Table 12-2. As in uncompetitive
1hibition, the apparent values of K_M and V_{max} are modulated by the pres-
nce of inhibitor. The name *mixed inhibition* arises from the fact that the
enominator of the Michaelis–Menten equation has the factor α multiply-
1g K_M as in competitive inhibition and the factor α' multiplying [S] as in
ncompetitive inhibition. Thus $K_M^{app} = (\alpha/\alpha')K_M$ and $V_{max}^{app} = V_{max}/\alpha'$.

Depending on the relative values of α and α' (and hence K_I and K_I'),
$_M^{app}$ may increase (as in competitive inhibition) or decrease. If the enzyme
nd enzyme–substrate complex bind I with equal affinity, then $\alpha = \alpha'$ and
1e K_M^{app} value is unchanged from the K_M for the reaction in the absence
f inhibitor. In this case, only V_{max} is affected, a phenomenon that is
amed **pure noncompetitive inhibition.**

Double-reciprocal plots for mixed inhibition consist of lines that have
he slope $\alpha K_M/V_{max}$, a $1/v_o$ intercept of α'/V_{max}, and a $1/[S]$ intercept of
$-\alpha'/\alpha K_M$ (Fig. 12-9). The lines for increasing values of [I] (representing
1creasing saturation of E and ES with I) intersect to the left of the $1/v_o$
xis. For pure noncompetitive inhibition, the lines intersect on the $1/[S]$
xis at $-1/K_M$. As with uncompetitive inhibition, substrate binding does
ot reverse the effects of mixed inhibition.

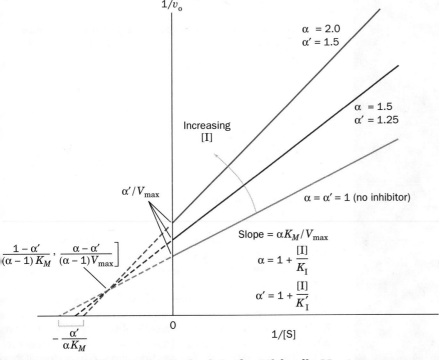

Figure 12-9 | **A Lineweaver–Burk plot of a Michaelis–Menten enzyme
n the presence of a mixed inhibitor.** Note that the lines all intersect to
he left of the $1/v_o$ axis. The coordinates of the intersection point are given in
prackets. When $K_I = K_I'$ ($\alpha = \alpha'$), the lines intersect on the $1/[S]$ axis at $-1/K_M$.
See the Animated Figures.

BOX 12-4 BIOCHEMISTRY IN HEALTH AND DISEASE

HIV Enzyme Inhibitors

The **human immunodeficiency virus (HIV)** causes **acquired immunodeficiency syndrome (AIDS)** by infecting and destroying the host's immune system. In the first steps of infection, HIV attaches to a target cell and injects its genetic material (which is RNA rather than DNA) into the host cell. The viral RNA is transcribed into DNA by a viral enzyme called **reverse transcriptase** (Box 25-2). After this DNA is integrated into the host's genome, the cell can produce more viral RNA and proteins for packaging it into new viral particles.

Most of the viral proteins are synthesized as parts of larger polypeptide precursors known as **polyproteins.** Consequently, proteolytic processing by the virally encoded **HIV protease** to release these viral proteins is necessary for viral reproduction. In the absence of an effective vaccine for HIV, efforts to prevent and treat AIDS have led to the development of compounds that inhibit HIV reverse transcriptase and HIV protease.

Several inhibitors of reverse transcriptase have been developed. The archetype is **AZT (3′-azido-3′-deoxythymidine Zidovudine),** which is taken up by cells, phosphorylated, and incorporated into the DNA chains synthesized from the HIV template by reverse transcriptase. Because AZT lacks a 3′-OH group, it cannot support further polynucleotide chain elongation and therefore terminates DNA synthesis (Section 3-4C). Most cellular DNA polymerases have a low affinity for phosphorylated AZT, but reverse transcriptase has a high affinity for this drug, which makes AZT effective against viral replication. Other nucleoside analogs that are used to treat HIV infection are **2′,3′-dideoxycytidine (ddC Zalcitabine)** and **2′,3′-dideoxyinosine (ddI, Didanosine;** inosine nucleotides are metabolically converted to adenosine and guanosine nucleotides), which also act as chain terminators. Nonnucleoside compounds such as **nevirapine** do not bind to the reverse transcriptase active site but instead bind to a hydrophobic pocket elsewhere on the enzyme.

3′-Azido-3′-deoxythymidine (AZT; Zidovudine)

2′,3′-Dideoxycytidine (ddC, Zalcitabine)

2′,3′-Dideoxyinosine (ddI, Didanosine)

Nevirapine

HIV protease is a homodimer of 99-residue subunits. Mechanistically, it is a so-called **aspartic protease,** a family of proteases that includes **pepsin** (the gastric protease that operates at low pH). Comparisons among the active sites of the aspartic proteases were instrumental in designing HIV protease inhibitors. HIV protease cleaves a number of specific peptide bonds, including Phe–Pro and Tyr–Pro peptide bonds in its physiological substrates, the HIV proteins. Inhibitors based on these sequences should therefore selectively inhibit the viral protease. The **peptidomimetic** (peptide-imitating) drugs ritonavir and saquinavir contain phenyl and other bulky groups that bind in the HIV protease active site. Of perhaps even greater importance, these drugs have the geometry of the catalyzed

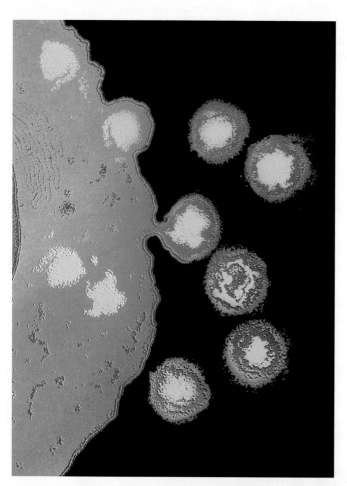

HIV particles budding from a lymphocyte. [© Chris Bjomberg/Photo Researchers.]

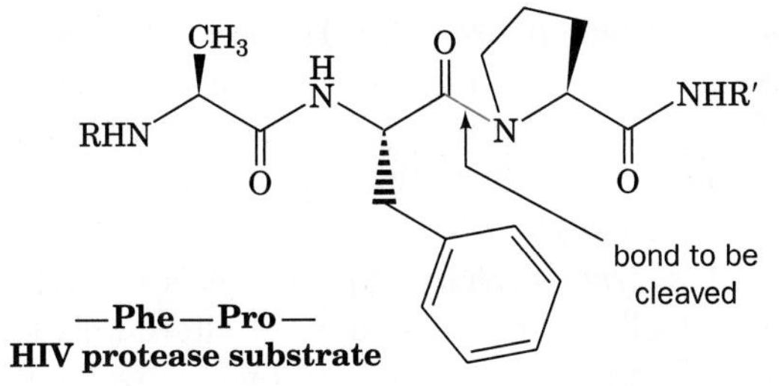

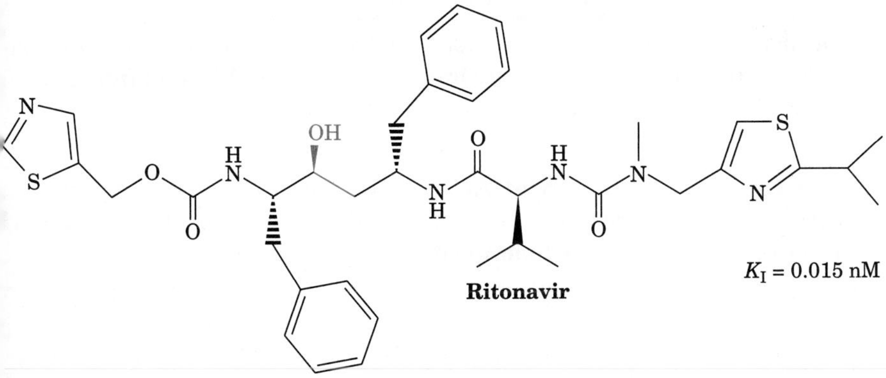

—Phe—Pro—
HIV protease substrate

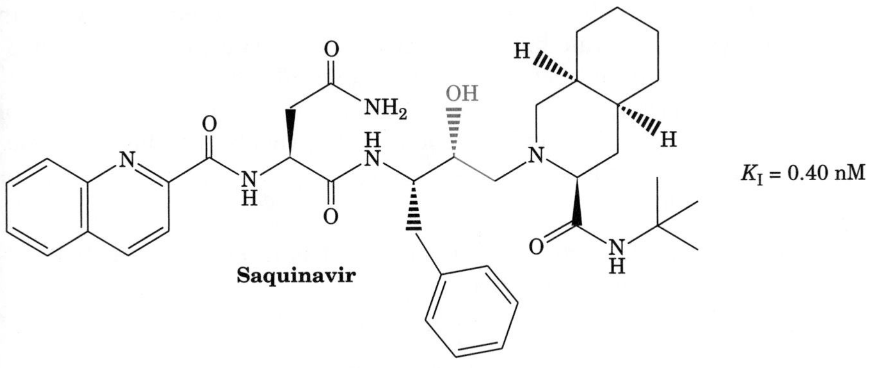

Saquinavir

$K_I = 0.40$ nM

Ritonavir

$K_I = 0.015$ nM

reaction's tetrahedral transition state (*red*). The enzyme's peptide substrate is shown for comparison. 🔁 **See Interactive Exercise 9.**

The efficacy of anti-HIV agents, like that of many drugs, is limited by their side effects. Despite their preference for viral enzymes, anti-HIV drugs also interfere with normal cellular processes. For example, the inhibition of DNA synthesis by reverse transcriptase inhibitors in rapidly dividing cells, such as the bone marrow cells that give rise to erythrocytes, can lead to severe anemia. Other side effects include nausea, kidney stones, and rashes. Side effects are particularly problematic in HIV infection, because drugs must be taken several times daily for many years, if not for a lifetime.

Acquired resistance also limits the effectiveness of antiviral drugs. This is a significant problem in HIV infection because the error-prone reverse transcriptase allows HIV to mutate rapidly. Numerous mutations in HIV are known to be associated with drug resistance.

In the case of HIV infection, it seems unlikely that a single drug will prove to be a "magic bullet," in part because HIV infects many cell types, but mostly because of its ability to rapidly evolve resistance against any one drug. The outstanding success of anti-HIV therapy rests on combination therapy, in which several different drugs are administered simultaneously. This successfully keeps AIDS at bay by reducing levels of HIV, in some cases to undetectable levels, thereby reducing the probability that HIV will evolve a drug-resistant variant. The advantages of using an inhibitor "cocktail" containing inhibitors of reverse transcriptase and HIV protease include (1) decreasing the likelihood that a viral strain will simultaneously develop resistance to every compound in the mix and (2) decreasing the doses and hence the side effects of the individual compounds.

The kinetics of an enzyme inactivator (an irreversible inhibitor) resembles that of a pure noncompetitive inhibitor because the inactivator reduces the concentration of functional enzyme at all substrate concentrations. Consequently, V_{max} decreases and K_M is unchanged. The double-reciprocal plots for irreversible inactivation therefore resemble those for pure noncompetitive inhibition (the lines intersect on the 1/[S] axis).

■ **CHECK YOUR UNDERSTANDING**

What distinguishes an inhibitor from an inactivator?

Describe the effects of competitive, uncompetitive, and mixed inhibitors on K_M and V_{max}.

3 Control of Enzyme Activity

LEARNING OBJECTIVES

■ Understand that allosteric effectors bind to multisubunit enzymes such as aspartate transcarbamoylase, thereby inducing cooperative conformational changes that alter the enzyme's catalytic activity.
■ Understand that phosphorylation and dephosphorylation of an enzyme such as glycogen phosphorylase can control its activity by shifting the equilibrium between more active and less active conformations.

An organism must be able to control the catalytic activities of its component enzymes so that it can coordinate its numerous metabolic processes, respond to changes in its environment, and grow and differentiate, all in an orderly manner. There are two ways that this may occur:

1. **Control of enzyme availability.** The amount of a given enzyme in a cell depends on both its rate of synthesis and its rate of degradation. Each of these rates is directly controlled by the cell and is subject to dramatic changes over time spans of minutes (in bacteria) to hours (in higher organisms).

2. **Control of enzyme activity.** An enzyme's catalytic activity can be directly controlled through structural alterations that influence the enzyme's substrate-binding affinity or turnover number. Just as hemoglobin's oxygen affinity is allosterically regulated by the binding of ligands such as O_2, CO_2, H^+, and BPG (Section 7-1D), an enzyme's substrate-binding affinity may likewise vary with the binding of small molecules, called **allosteric effectors**. *Allosteric mechanisms can cause large changes in enzymatic activity.* The activities of many enzymes are similarly controlled by **covalent modification,** usually phosphorylation and dephosphorylation of specific Ser, Thr, or Tyr residues.

In the following sections we discuss the control of enzyme activity by allosteric interactions and covalent modification.

A | Allosteric Control Involves Binding at a Site Other than the Active Site

In this section we examine allosteric control of enzymatic activity by considering one example—**aspartate transcarbamoylase (ATCase)** from *E. coli.* Other allosteric enzymes are discussed in later chapters.

The Feedback Inhibition of ATCase Regulates Pyrimidine Synthesis. Aspartate transcarbamoylase catalyzes the formation of **N-carbamoyl aspartate** from **carbamoyl phosphate** and aspartate:

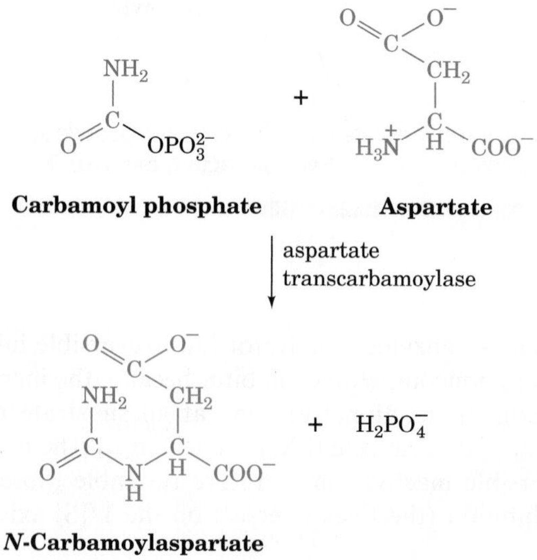

Carbamoyl phosphate   **Aspartate**

aspartate transcarbamoylase

N-Carbamoylaspartate $+$ $H_2PO_4^-$

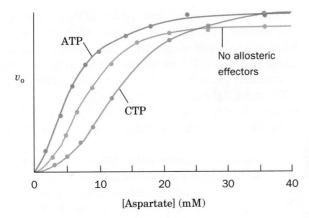

■ **Figure 12-10 | Plot of v_o versus [aspartate] for the ATCase reaction.** Reaction velocity was measured in the absence of allosteric effectors, in the presence of 0.4 mM CTP (an inhibitor), and in the presence of 2.0 mM ATP (an activator). [After Kantrowitz, E.R., Pastra-Landis, S.C., and Lipscomb, W.N., *Trends Biochem. Sci.* **5**, 125 (1980).] 🖙 **See the Animated Figures.**

This reaction is the first step unique to the biosynthesis of pyrimidines (Section 23-2A). The allosteric behavior of *E. coli* ATCase has been investigated by John Gerhart and Howard Schachman, who demonstrated that both of its substrates bind cooperatively to the enzyme. Moreover, ATCase is allosterically inhibited by **cytidine triphosphate (CTP),** a pyrimidine nucleotide, and is allosterically activated by adenosine triphosphate (ATP), a purine nucleotide.

The v_o versus [S] curve for ATCase (Fig. 12-10) is sigmoidal, rather than hyperbolic as it is in enzymes that follow the Michaelis–Menten model. This is consistent with cooperative substrate binding (recall that hemoglobin's O_2-binding curve is also sigmoidal; Fig. 7-6). ATCase's allosteric effectors shift the entire curve to the right or the left: At a given substrate concentration, CTP decreases the enzyme's catalytic rate, whereas ATP increases it.

CTP, which is a product of the pyrimidine biosynthetic pathway, is an example of a **feedback inhibitor,** since *it inhibits an earlier step in its own biosynthesis* (Fig. 12-11). Thus, when CTP levels are high, CTP binds to ATCase, thereby reducing the rate of CTP synthesis. Conversely, when cellular [CTP] decreases, CTP dissociates from ATCase and CTP synthesis accelerates.

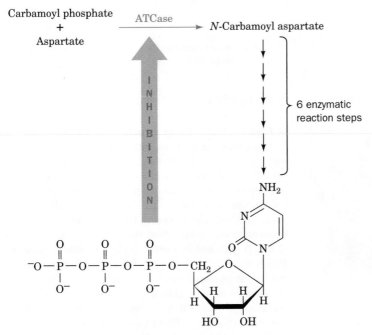

■ **Figure 12-11 | A schematic representation of the pyrimidine biosynthesis pathway.** CTP, the end product of the pathway, inhibits ATCase, which catalyzes the pathway's first step.

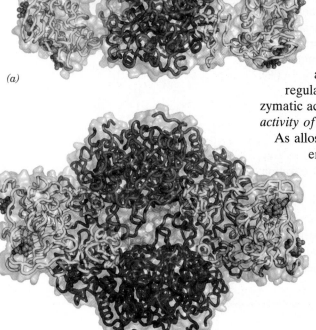

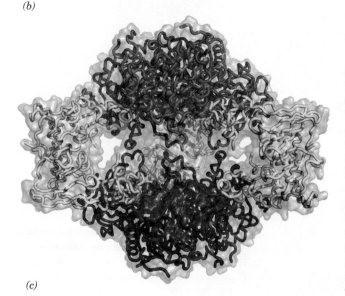

The metabolic significance of the ATP activation of ATCase is that it tend to coordinate the rates of synthesis of purine and pyrimidine nucleotides which are required in roughly equal amounts in nucleic acid biosynthesis. For instance, if the ATP concentration is much greater than that of CTP, ATCase is activated to synthesize pyrimidine nucleotides until the concentrations of ATP and CTP become balanced. Conversely, if the CTP concentration is greater than that of ATP, CTP inhibition of ATCase permits purine nucleotide biosynthesis to balance the ATP and CTP concentrations.

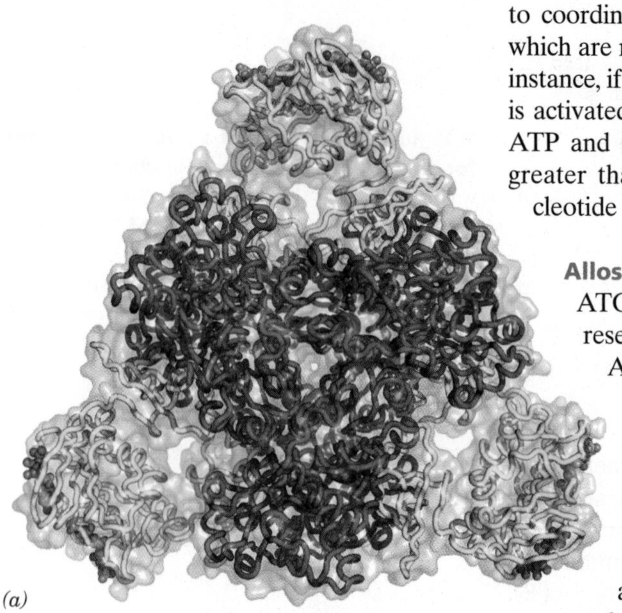

Allosteric Changes Alter ATCase's Substrate-Binding Sites. *E. coli* ATCase (300 kD) has the subunit composition c_6r_6, where c and r represent its catalytic and regulatory subunits. The X-ray structure of ATCase (Fig. 12-12), determined by William Lipscomb, reveals that the catalytic subunits are arranged as two sets of trimers (c_3) in complex with three sets of regulatory dimers (r_2). Each regulatory dimer joins two catalytic subunits in different c_3 trimers.

The isolated catalytic trimers are catalytically active, have a maximum catalytic rate greater than that of intact ATCase, exhibit a noncooperative (hyperbolic) substrate saturation curve, and are unaffected by the presence of ATP or CTP. The isolated regulatory dimers bind the allosteric effectors but are devoid of enzymatic activity. Evidently, *the regulatory subunits allosterically reduce the activity of the catalytic subunits in the intact enzyme.*

As allosteric theory predicts (Section 7-1D), the activator ATP preferentially binds to ATCase's active (R or high substrate affinity) state, whereas the inhibitor CTP preferentially binds to the enzyme's inactive (T or low substrate affinity) state. Similarly, the unreactive bisubstrate analog *N*-(phosphonacetyl)-L-aspartate (PALA)

$$\begin{array}{cc}
\begin{array}{c}
\overset{\displaystyle O}{\overset{\displaystyle \|}{C}}-CH_2-PO_3^{2-} \\
| \\
NH \\
| \\
{}^-OOC-CH_2-CH-COO^-
\end{array}
&
\begin{array}{c}
H_2N-\overset{\displaystyle O}{\overset{\displaystyle \|}{C}}-O-PO_3^{2-} \\
\\
NH_3^+ \\
| \\
{}^-OOC-CH_2-CH-COO^-
\end{array}
\end{array}$$

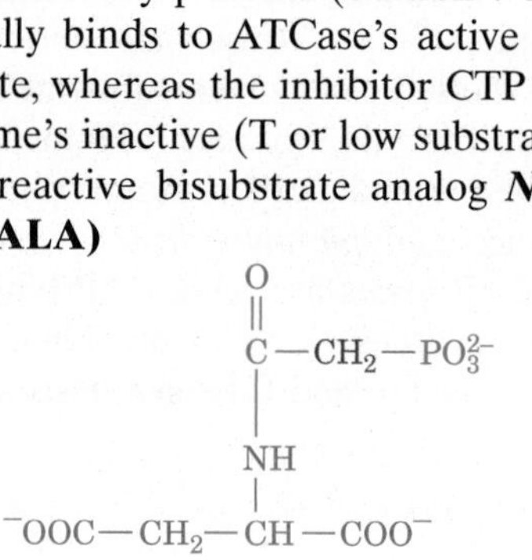

N-(Phosphonacetyl)-L-aspartate (PALA) 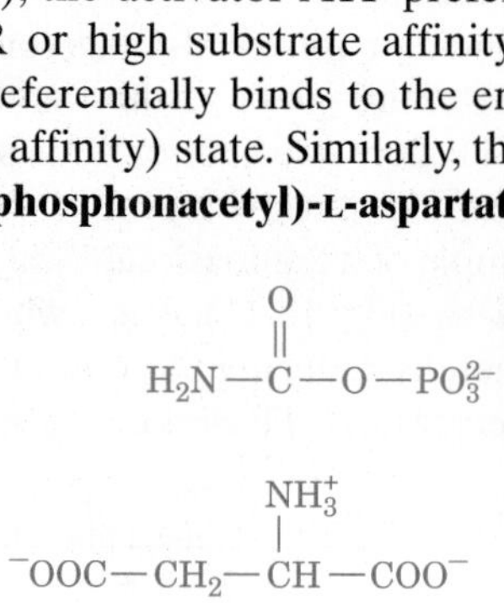   **Carbamoyl phosphate**
+
Aspartate

binds tightly to R-state but not to T-state ATCase.

■ **Figure 12-12 | X-Ray structure of ATCase from *E. coli*.** The T-state enzyme in complex with CTP is viewed (*a*) along the protein's molecular threefold axis of symmetry and (*b*) along a molecular twofold axis of symmetry perpendicular to the view in Part *a*. The polypeptide chains are drawn in worm form embedded in their transparent molecular surface. The regulatory dimers (*yellow*) join the upper catalytic trimer (*red*) to the lower catalytic trimer (*blue*). CTP is drawn in space-filling form colored according to atom type (C green, O red, N blue, and P orange). (*c*) The R-state enzyme in complex with PALA viewed as in Part *b*. PALA (which is bound to the *c* subunits but largely obscured here) is drawn in space-filling form. Note how the rotation of the regulatory dimers in the T → R transition causes the catalytic trimers to move apart along the threefold axis. [Based on X-ray structures by William Lipscomb, Harvard University. PDBids 5AT1 and 8ATC.] *See Kinemage Exercise 11-1.*

(a)

(b)

(c)

X-Ray structures have been determined for the T-state ATCase–CTP complex and the R-state ATCase–PALA complex (as a rule, unreactive substrate analogs, such as PALA, form complexes with an enzyme that are more amenable to structural analysis than complexes of the enzyme with rapidly reacting substrates; Box 11-2). Structural studies reveal that in the $T \rightarrow R$ transition, the enzyme's catalytic trimers separate along the molecular threefold axis by ~11 Å and reorient around this axis relative to each other by 12° (Fig. 12-12b,c). In addition, the regulatory dimers rotate clockwise by 15° around their twofold axes and separate by ~4 Å along the threefold axis. Such large quaternary shifts are reminiscent of those in hemoglobin (Section 7-3A).

Each catalytic subunit of ATCase consists of a carbamoyl phosphate–binding domain and an aspartate-binding domain. The binding of PALA to the enzyme, which presumably mimics the binding of both substrates, induces a conformational change that swings the two domains together such that their two bound substrates can react to form product (Fig. 12-13). The conformational changes—movements of up to 8 Å for some residues—in a single catalytic subunit trigger ATCase's $T \rightarrow R$ quaternary shift. ATCase's tertiary and quaternary shifts are tightly coupled (i.e., ATCase closely follows the symmetry model of allosterism; Section 7-1D). *The*

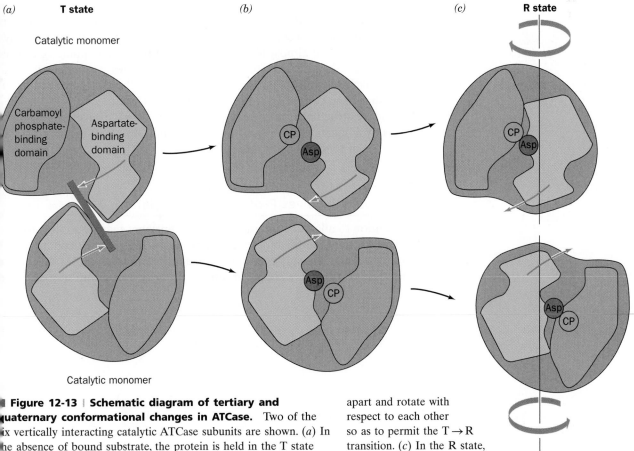

(a) **T state**

Catalytic monomer

Carbamoyl phosphate-binding domain

Aspartate-binding domain

(b)

CP

Asp

Asp

CP

(c) **R state**

CP

Asp

Asp

CP

Catalytic monomer

Figure 12-13 | Schematic diagram of tertiary and quaternary conformational changes in ATCase. Two of the six vertically interacting catalytic ATCase subunits are shown. (*a*) In the absence of bound substrate, the protein is held in the T state because the motions that bring together the two domains of each subunit (*green arrows*) are prevented by steric interference (*purple bar*) between the contacting aspartic acid–binding domains. (*b*) The binding of carbamoyl phosphate (CP) followed by aspartic acid (Asp) to their respective binding sites causes the subunits to move apart and rotate with respect to each other so as to permit the $T \rightarrow R$ transition. (*c*) In the R state, the two domains of each subunit come together to promote the reaction of their bound substrates to form products. [Illustration, Irving Geis/Geis Archives Trust. Copyright Howard Hughes Medical Institute. Reproduced with permission.] *&2* **See Kinemage Exercises 11-1 and 11-2.**

binding of substrate to one catalytic subunit therefore increases the substrate binding affinity and catalytic activity of the other five catalytic subunits and hence accounts for the enzyme's cooperative substrate binding.

The Binding of Allosteric Modifiers Causes Structural Changes in ATCase. The structural basis for the effects of CTP and ATP on ATCase activity has been partially unveiled. Both the inhibitor CTP and the activator ATP bind to the same site on the outer edge of the regulatory subunit about 60 Å away from the nearest catalytic site. CTP binds preferentially to the T state, increasing its stability, whereas ATP binds preferentially to the R state, increasing its stability.

The binding of CTP and ATP to their less favored enzyme states also has structural consequences. When CTP binds to R-state ATCase, it induces a contraction in the regulatory dimer that causes the catalytic trimers to come together by 0.5 Å (become more T-like, that is, less active). This, in turn, reorients key residues in the enzyme's active sites, thereby decreasing the enzyme's catalytic activity. ATP has essentially opposite effects when binding to the T-state enzyme: It causes the catalytic trimers to move apart by 0.4 Å (become more R-like, that is, more active), thereby reorienting key residues in the enzyme's active sites so as to increase the enzyme's catalytic activity.

Allosteric Transitions in Other Enzymes Often Resemble Those of Hemoglobin and ATCase. Allosteric enzymes are widely distributed in nature and tend to occupy key regulatory positions in metabolic pathways. Such enzymes are almost always symmetrical proteins containing at least two subunits, in which quaternary structural changes communicate binding and catalytic effects among all active sites in the enzyme. The quaternary shifts are primarily rotations of subunits relative to one another. Secondary structures are largely preserved in T → R transitions, which is probably important for mechanically transmitting allosteric effects over distances of tens of angstroms.

B | Control by Covalent Modification Usually Involves Protein Phosphorylation

In addition to allosteric interactions, many enzymes may be subject to control by covalent modification. In eukaryotes, by far the most common such modification is phosphorylation and dephosphorylation (the attachment and removal of a phosphoryl group) of the hydroxyl group of a Ser, Thr, or Tyr residue.

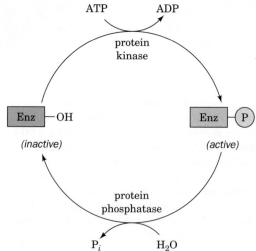

uch enzymatic modification/demodification processes, which are catalyzed by enzymes known as **protein kinases** and **protein phosphatases,** alter the activities of the modified proteins. Indeed, ~30% of human proteins, which collectively participate in nearly all biological processes, are subject to control by reversible phosphorylation.

As an example of an enzyme whose activity is controlled by covalent modification, let us consider **glycogen phosphorylase** (or simply **phosphorylase**), which catalyzes the **phosphorolysis** (bond cleavage by the substitution of a phosphate group) of glycogen [the starchlike polysaccharide that consists mainly of $\alpha(1\rightarrow4)$-linked glucose residues; Section 8-2C] to yield **glucose-1-phosphate (G1P):**

$$\text{Glycogen} + P_i \rightleftharpoons \text{glycogen} + \text{G1P}$$
$$(n\text{ residues}) \qquad (n-1\text{ residues})$$

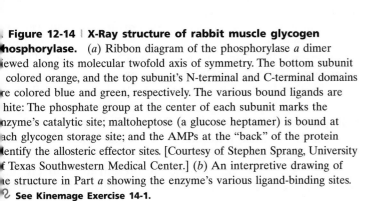

Glucose-1-
phosphate
(G1P)

This is the rate-controlling step in the metabolic pathway of glycogen breakdown, an important supplier of fuel for metabolic activities (Section 16-1).

Mammals express three **isozymes** (catalytically and structurally similar but genetically distinct enzymes from the same organism; also called **isoforms**) of glycogen phosphorylase, those from muscle, brain, and liver. Muscle glycogen phosphorylase, which we discuss here, is a dimer of identical 842-residue subunits. It is regulated both by allosteric interactions and by phosphorylation/dephosphorylation. The phosphorylated form of the enzyme, **phosphorylase** *a,* has a phosphoryl group esterified to its Ser 14. The dephospho form is called **phosphorylase** *b.*

The X-ray structures of phosphorylase *a* and phosphorylase *b,* which were respectively determined by Robert Fletterick and Louise Johnson, are similar. Both have a large N-terminal domain (484 residues; the largest known domain) and a smaller C-terminal domain (Fig. 12-14). The N-terminal domain contains the phosphorylation site (Ser 14), an allosteric effector site, a glycogen-binding site (called the glycogen storage site), and all the intersubunit contacts in the dimer. The enzyme's active site is located at the center of the subunit.

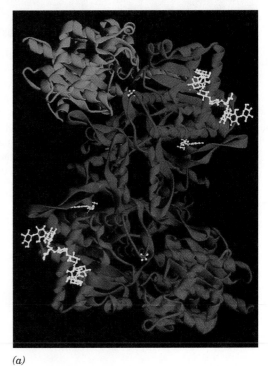

(a)

(b)

Figure 12-14 | X-Ray structure of rabbit muscle glycogen phosphorylase. (*a*) Ribbon diagram of the phosphorylase *a* dimer viewed along its molecular twofold axis of symmetry. The bottom subunit is colored orange, and the top subunit's N-terminal and C-terminal domains are colored blue and green, respectively. The various bound ligands are white: The phosphate group at the center of each subunit marks the enzyme's catalytic site; maltoheptose (a glucose heptamer) is bound at each glycogen storage site; and the AMPs at the "back" of the protein identify the allosteric effector sites. [Courtesy of Stephen Sprang, University of Texas Southwestern Medical Center.] (*b*) An interpretive drawing of the structure in Part *a* showing the enzyme's various ligand-binding sites.
See Kinemage Exercise 14-1.

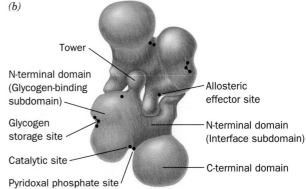

Tower

N-terminal domain
(Glycogen-binding
subdomain)

Glycogen
storage site

Catalytic site

Pyridoxal phosphate site

Allosteric
effector site

N-terminal domain
(Interface subdomain)

C-terminal domain

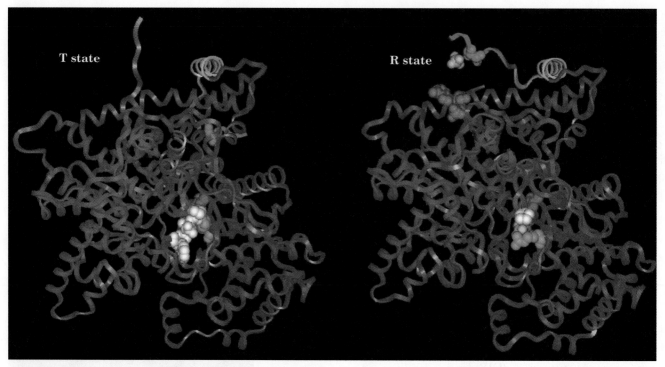

■ **Figure 12-15** | **Conformational changes in glycogen phosphorylase.** One subunit of the dimeric phosphorylase *b* is shown (*left*) in the T state in the absence of allosteric effectors and (*right*) in the R state with bound AMP. The view is of the lower (*orange*) subunit in Fig. 12-14 as seen from the top of the page. The tower helix is blue, the N-terminal helix is cyan, and the N-terminal residues that change conformation on AMP binding are green. Of the groups that are shown in space-filling representation, Ser 14, the phosphorylation site, is light green; AMP is orange; the active site

PLP (a prosthetic group) is red; the Arg 569 side chain, which reorients in the T → R transition so as to interact with the substrate phosphate, is cyan; loop residues 282 to 284, which in the R state are mostly disordered and hence not seen, are white; and the phosphates, both at the active site and at the R state Ser 14 phosphorylation site (not present in phosphorylase *b* but shown for position), are yellow. [X-Ray structure coordinates courtesy of Stephan Sprang, University of Texas Southwest Medical Center.] 🔗 **See Kinemage Exercises 14-2 and 14-3.**

Phosphorylation and Dephosphorylation Can Alter Enzymatic Activity in a Manner That Resembles Allosteric Control. Glycogen phosphorylase has two conformational states, the enzymatically active R state and the enzymatically inactive T state (Fig. 12-15). The T-state enzyme is inactive because it has a malformed active site and a surface loop (residues 282–284) that blocks substrate access to its binding site. In contrast, in the R-state enzyme, the side chain of Arg 569 has reoriented so as to bind the substrate phosphate ion and the 282–284 loop no longer blocks the active site, thereby permitting the enzyme to bind substrate and efficiently catalyze the phosphorolysis of glycogen.

The phosphorylation of Ser 14 promotes phosphorylase's T (inactive) → R (active) conformational change. Moreover, these different enzymatic forms respond to different allosteric effectors (Fig. 12-16). Thus ATP and **glucose-6-phosphate [G6P;** to which the G1P product of the glycogen phosphorylase reaction is converted (Section 16-1C)] preferentially bind to the T state of phosphorylase *b* and, in doing so, inactivate the enzyme, whereas AMP preferentially binds to the R state of phosphorylase *b* and hence activates it. In contrast, phosphorylase *a*'s only allosteric effector is glucose, which binds to the enzyme's T state and inactivates the enzyme. Note that ATP, G6P, and glucose are present in relatively high concentrations in muscle under conditions of low exertion, a state when

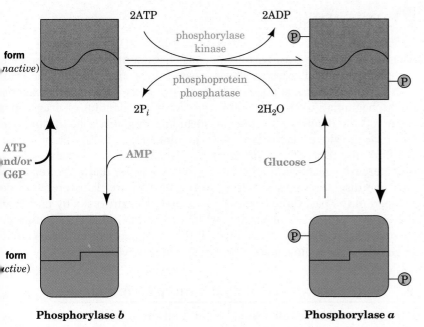

form
(nactive)

2ATP   2ADP

phosphorylase
kinase

phosphoprotein
phosphatase

2P$_i$ 2H$_2$O

ATP
and/or   AMP
G6P

Glucose

form
(ctive)

Phosphorylase *b*   Phosphorylase *a*

■ **Figure 12-16** │ **The control of glycogen phosphorylase activity.** The enzyme may assume the enzymatically inactive T conformation (*above*) or the catalytically active R form (*below*). The conformation of phosphorylase *b* is allosterically controlled by the effectors AMP, ATP, and G6P and is mostly in the T state under physiological conditions. In contrast, the phosphorylated form of the enzyme, phosphorylase *a*, is unresponsive to these effectors and is mostly in the R state unless there is a high level of glucose. Thus, under usual physiological conditions, the enzymatic activity of glycogen phosphorylase is largely determined by its rates of phosphorylation and dephosphorylation.

lycogen breakdown would be superfluous, whereas AMP is present in elatively high concentration in muscles under conditions of high exeron, a state when the G1P product of the phosphorylase reaction helps uel muscle contraction.

The phosphate group, with its double negative charge (a property not hared with naturally occurring amino acid residues) and its covalent atachment to a protein, can induce dramatic conformational changes. In hosphorylase *a*, the Ser 14 phosphate group forms ion pairs with two ationic Arg side chains, thereby linking the active site, the subunit interace, and the N-terminal region, the latter having undergone a large conormational shift from its position in the T-state enzyme (Fig. 12-15). These inding interactions cause glycogen phosphorylase's tower helices (Figs. 2-14 and 12-15) to tilt and pull apart so as to pack more favorably, which i turn triggers a quaternary T → R transition, which largely consists of n ~10° relative rotation of the two subunits. *Thus the Ser 14–phosphate roup functions as a sort of internal allosteric effector that shifts the nzyme's T ⇌ R equilibrium in favor of the R state.*

Cascades of Protein Kinases Enable Sensitive Responses to Metabolic Needs. The enzymes that catalyze the phosphorylation and dephosphoryation of glycogen phosphorylase are named **phosphorylase kinase** and **hosphoprotein phosphatase** (Fig. 12-16). The activities of these latter enymes are themselves controlled, both allosterically and by phosphorylaion/dephosphorylation. Thus, as we shall see in Section 13-2, sequences of rotein kinases and protein phosphatases, both linked in cascade fashion i.e., protein kinase X phosphorylates protein kinase Y, which phosphorylates protein kinase Z), have far greater capacities for signal amplification a small fractional change in effector concentration causing a larger fracional change in enzyme activity) and flexibility in response to a greater umber of allosteric effectors (the activity of each protein in the cascade nay be influenced by different sets of effectors) than does a simple alosteric enzyme. Indeed, just such cascades permit glycogen phosphorylase o respond with great sensitivity to the metabolic needs of the organism.

■ **CHECK YOUR UNDERSTANDING**

Explain the structural basis for cooperative substrate binding and allosteric control in ATCase.

Describe how phosphorylation and dephosphorylation control the activity of glycogen phosphorylase.

LEARNING OBJECTIVES

- Understand that structure-based design and combinatorial chemistry approaches are used to discover new drugs.
- Understand that a drug's interactions with the body determine its bioavailability.
- Understand that a drug's effectiveness and safety are tested in clinical trials.
- Understand that cytochrome P450 may modify a drug to alter its bioavailability or toxicity.

4 Drug Design

The use of drugs to treat various maladies has a long history, but the modern pharmaceutical industry, which is based on science (rather than tradition or superstition), is a product of the twentieth century. For example, at the beginning of the twentieth century, only a handful of drugs, apart from folk medicines, were known, including **digitalis,** a heart stimulant from the foxglove plant (Box 10-3); **quinine** (Fig. 12-17), obtained from the bark and roots of the *Cinchona* tree, which was used to treat malaria; and mercury, which was used to treat syphilis—a cure that was often worse than the disease. Almost all drugs in use today were discovered and developed in the past three decades. The majority of drugs act by modifying the activity of a receptor protein, with enzyme inhibitors constituting the second largest class of drugs. Indeed, the techniques of enzyme kinetics have proved to be invaluable for evaluating drug candidates.

A | Drug Discovery Employs a Variety of Techniques

How are new drugs discovered? Nearly all drugs that have been in use for over a decade were discovered by screening large numbers of compounds—either synthetic compounds or those derived from natural products (often plants used in folk remedies). Initial screening involves *in vitro* assessment of, for example, the degree of binding of a drug candidate to an enzyme that is implicated in a disease of interest, that is, determining its K_I value. Later, as the number of drug candidates is winnowed down, more sensitive screens such as testing in animals are employed.

A drug candidate that exhibits a desired effect is called a **lead compound.** A good lead compound binds to its target protein with a dissociation constant (for an enzyme, an inhibition constant) of less than 1 μM. Such a high affinity is necessary to minimize a drug's less specific binding to other macromolecules in the body and to ensure that only low doses of the drug need be taken.

A lead compound is used as a point of departure to design more efficacious compounds. Even minor modifications to a drug candidate can result in major changes in its pharmacological properties. Thus, substitution of methyl, chloro, hydroxyl, or benzyl groups at various places on a lead

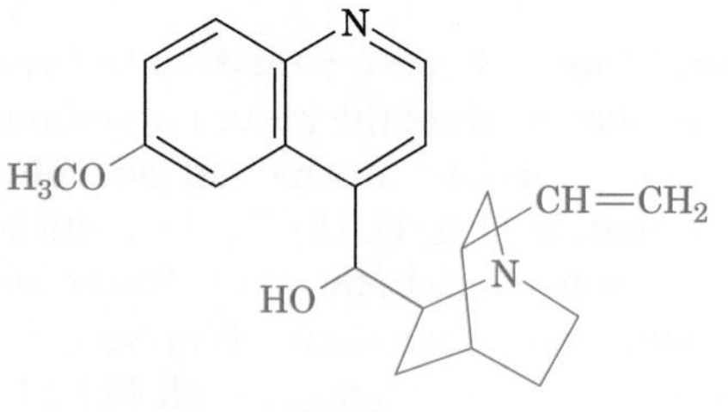

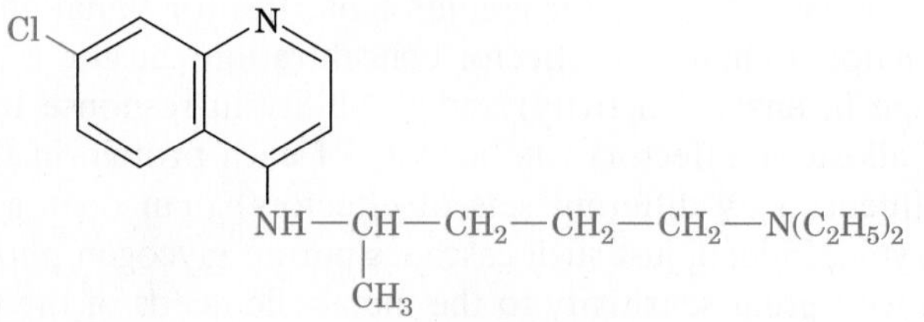

Figure 12-17 | Quinine and chloroquine.
These two compounds, which share a quinoline ring system, are effective antimalarial agents. The *Plasmodium* parasite multiplies within red blood cells, where it proteolyzes hemoglobin to meet its nutritional needs. This process releases heme, which in its soluble form is toxic to the parasite. The parasite sequesters the heme in a crystalline (nontoxic) form. Quinine and chloroquine pass through cell membranes and inhibit heme crystallization in the parasite.

compound may improve its action. For most drugs in use today, 5000 to 10,000 related compounds were typically synthesized and tested. Drug development is a systematic and iterative process in which the most promising derivatives of the lead compound serve as the starting points for the next round of derivatization and testing.

Structure-Based Drug Design Accelerates Drug Discovery. Since the mid 1980s, dramatic advances in the speed and precision with which a macromolecular structure can be determined by X-ray crystallography and NMR (Section 6-2A) have enabled **structure-based drug design,** a process that greatly reduces the number of compounds that need be synthesized in a drug discovery program. As its name implies, structure-based drug design (also called **rational drug design**) uses the structure of a receptor or enzyme in complex with a drug candidate to guide the development of more efficacious compounds. Such a structure will reveal, for example, the positions of the hydrogen bonding donors and acceptors in the binding site as well as cavities in the binding site into which substituents might be placed on a drug candidate to increase its binding affinity. These direct visualization techniques are usually supplemented with molecular modeling tools such as the computation of the minimum energy conformation of a proposed derivative, quantum mechanical calculations that determine its charge distribution and hence how it would interact electrostatically with the protein, and docking simulations in which an inhibitor candidate is computationally modeled into the binding site on the receptor to assess potential interactions. A structure-based approach was used to develop the analgesics (pain relievers) Celebrex and Vioxx (Section 20-6C) and to develop drugs to treat HIV infection (Box 12-4).

Combinatorial Chemistry and High-Throughput Screening Are Useful Drug Discovery Tools. As structure-based methods were developed, it appeared that they would become the dominant mode of drug discovery. However, the recent advent of **combinatorial chemistry** techniques to rapidly and inexpensively synthesize large numbers of related compounds combined with the development of robotic **high-throughput screening** techniques has caused the drug discovery "pendulum" to again swing toward the "make-many-compounds-and-see-what-they-do" approach. If a lead compound can be synthesized in a stepwise manner from several smaller modules, then the substituents on each of these modules can be varied in parallel to produce a library of related compounds (Fig. 12-18).

A variety of synthetic techniques have been developed that permit the combinatorial synthesis of thousands of related compounds in a single procedure. Thus, whereas investigations into the importance of a hydrophobic group at a particular position in a lead compound might previously have prompted the individual syntheses of only the ethyl, propyl, and benzyl derivatives of the compound, the use of combinatorial synthesis would

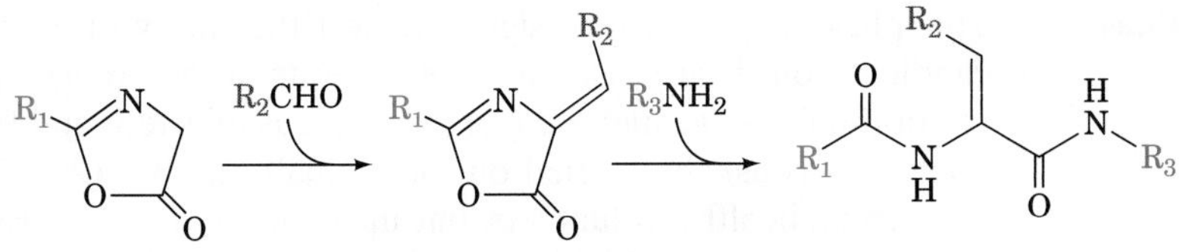

Figure 12-18 | The combinatorial synthesis of arylidene diamides. If ten different variants of each R group are used in the synthesis, then 1000 different derivatives will be synthesized.

permit the generation of perhaps 100 different groups at that position. This would far more effectively map out the potential range of the substituents and possibly identify an unexpectedly active analog.

B | A Drug's Bioavailability Depends on How It Is Absorbed and Transported in the Body

The *in vitro* development of an effective drug candidate is only the first step in the drug development process. *Besides causing the desired response in its isolated target protein, a useful drug must be delivered in sufficiently high concentration to this protein where it resides in the human body.* For example, a drug that is administered orally (the most convenient route) must surmount a series of formidable barriers: (1) The drug must be chemically stable in the highly acidic environment of the stomach and must not be degraded by digestive enzymes; (2) it must be absorbed from the gastrointestinal tract into the bloodstream, that is, it must pass through several cell membranes; (3) it must not bind too tightly to other substances in the body (e.g., lipophilic substances tend to be absorbed by certain plasma proteins and by fat tissue); (4) it must survive derivatization by the battery of enzymes, mainly in the liver, that detoxify **xenobiotics** (foreign compounds; note that the intestinal blood flow drains directly into the liver via the portal vein so that the liver processes all orally ingested substances before they reach the rest of the body); (5) it must avoid rapid excretion by the kidneys; (6) it must pass from the capillaries to its target tissue; (7) if it is targeted to the brain, it must cross the **blood–brain barrier,** which blocks the passage of most polar substances; and (8) if it is targeted to an intracellular protein, it must pass through the plasma membrane and possibly one or more intracellular membranes.

The ways in which a drug interacts with the barriers listed above is known as its **pharmacokinetics.** Thus, the **bioavailability** of a drug (the extent to which it reaches its site of action, which is usually taken to be the systemic circulation) depends on both the dose given and its pharmacokinetics. *The most effective drugs are usually a compromise; they are neither too lipophilic nor too hydrophilic.* In addition, their pK values are usually in the range 6 to 8 so that they can readily assume both their ionized and unionized forms at physiological pH's. This permits them to cross cell membranes in their unionized form and to bind to their target protein in their ionized form.

C | Clinical Trials Test for Efficacy and Safety

Above all else, a successful drug candidate must be safe and efficacious in humans. Tests for these properties are initially carried out in animals, but since humans and animals often react quite differently to a drug, it must ultimately be tested in humans through **clinical trials.** In the United States, clinical trials are monitored by the Food and Drug Administration (FDA) and have three increasingly detailed (and expensive) phases:

Phase I. This phase is primarily designed to test the safety of a drug candidate but is also used to determine its dosage range and the optimal dosage method (e.g., oral versus injected) and frequency. It is usually carried out on a small number (20–100) of normal, healthy volunteers, but in the case of a drug candidate known to be highly toxic (e.g., a cancer chemotherapeutic agent), it is carried out on volunteer patients with the target disease.

Phase II. This phase mainly tests the efficacy of the drug against the target disease in 100 to 500 volunteer patients but also refines the dosage range and checks for side effects. The effects of the drug candidate are usually assessed via **single blind tests,** procedures in which the patient is unaware of whether he or she has received the drug or a control substance. Usually the control substance is a **placebo** (an inert substance with the same physical appearance, taste, etc., as the drug being tested) but, in the case of a life-threatening disease, it is an ethical necessity that the control substance be the best available treatment against the disease.

Phase III. This phase monitors adverse reactions from long-term use as well as confirming efficacy in 1000 to 5000 patients. It pits the drug candidate against control substances through the statistical analysis of carefully designed **double blind tests,** procedures in which neither the patients nor the clinical investigators know whether a given patient has received the drug or a control substance. This is done to minimize bias in the subjective judgments the investigators must make.

Currently, only about 5 drug candidates in 5000 that enter preclinical trials reach clinical trials. Of these, only one, on average, is ultimately approved for clinical use, with the majority failing in Phase II trials. In recent years, the preclinical portion of a drug discovery process has averaged ~3 years to complete, whereas successful clinical trials have usually required an additional 7 to 10 years. These successive stages of the drug discovery process are increasingly expensive so that successfully bringing a drug to market costs, on average, around $300 million.

The most time-consuming and expensive aspect of a drug development program is identifying a drug candidate's rare adverse reactions. Nevertheless, it is not an uncommon experience for a drug to be brought to market only to be withdrawn some months or years later when it is found to have caused unanticipated life-threatening side effects in as few as 1 in 10,000 individuals (the post-marketing surveillance of a drug is known as its Phase IV clinical trial). For example, in 1997, the FDA withdrew its approval of the drug **fenfluramine (fen),**

Fenfluramine   **Phentermine**

which it had approved in 1973 for use as an appetite suppressant in short-term (a few weeks) weight-loss programs. Fenfluramine had become widely prescribed, often for extended periods, together with another appetite suppressant, **phentermine (phen;** approved in 1959), a combination known as **fen-phen** (although the FDA had not approved of the use of the two drugs in combination, once it approves a drug for some purpose, a physician may prescribe it for any other purpose). The withdrawal of fenfluramine was prompted by over 100 reports of heart valve damage in individuals (mostly women) who had taken fen-phen for an average of 12 months (phentermine was not withdrawn because the evidence indicated that fenfluramine was the responsible agent). This rare side effect had not been observed in the clinical trials of fenfluramine, in part because is such an unusual type of drug reaction that it had not been screened fo

More recently (2004), the widely prescribed analgesic Vioxx was witl drawn from use due to its previously undetected cardiac side effects, althoug the closely related analgesic Celebrex remains available (Section 20-6C).

D | Cytochromes P450 Are Often Implicated in Adverse Drug Reactions

Why is it that a drug that is well tolerated by the majority of patients ca pose a danger to others? *Differences in reactions to drugs arise from ge netic differences among individuals as well as differences in their diseas states, other drugs they are taking, age, sex, and environmental factors.* Th **cytochromes P450,** which function in large part to detoxify xenobiotics an which participate in the metabolic clearance of the majority of drugs i use, provide instructive examples of these phenomena.

The cytochromes P450 constitute a superfamily of heme-containing er zymes that occur in nearly all living organisms, from bacteria to mamma [their name arises from the characteristic 450-nm peak in their absorptio spectra when reacted in their Fe(II) state with CO]. The human genom encodes 57 isozymes of cytochrome P450, around one-third of which oc cur in the liver (P450 isozymes are named by the letters "CYP" followe by a number designating its family, an uppercase letter designating its sut family, and often another number; e.g., CYP2D6). These **monooxygenase** (Fig. 12-19), which in animals are embedded in the endoplasmic reticulur membrane, catalyze reactions of the sort

$$RH + O_2 + 2\,H^+ + 2\,e^- \rightarrow ROH + H_2O$$

The electrons (e^-) are supplied by NADPH, which passes them to cy tochrome P450's heme prosthetic group via the intermediacy of th enzyme **NADPH-P450 reductase.** Here RH represents a wide variety c usually lipophilic compounds for which the different cytochromes P450 ar specific. They include polycyclic aromatic hydrocarbons [PAHs; frequentl carcinogenic (cancer-causing) compounds that are present in tobacc smoke, broiled meats, and other pyrolysis products], polycyclic biphenyl (PCBs; which were widely used in electrical insulators and as plasticizer and are also carcinogenic), steroids (in whose syntheses cytochromes P45 participate), and many different types of drugs. The xenobiotics ar thereby converted to a more water-soluble form, which aids in their ex cretion by the kidneys. Moreover, the newly generated hydroxyl group are often enzymatically conjugated (covalently linked) to polar substance such as glucuronic acid (Section 8-1C), glycine, sulfate, and acetate, whic further enhances aqueous solubility. The many types of cytochromes P45 in animals, which have different substrate specificities (although thes specificities tend to be broad and hence often overlap), are thought t have arisen in response to the numerous toxins that plants produce, pre sumably to discourage animals from eating them (other P450s function t catalyze specific biosynthetic reactions).

Drug–drug interactions are often mediated by cytochromes P450. Fo example, if drug A is metabolized by or otherwise inhibits a cytochrom P450 isozyme that metabolizes drug B, then coadministering drugs A an B will cause the bioavailability of drug B to increase above the value : would have had if it alone had been administered. This phenomenon is c particular concern if drug B has a low **therapeutic index** (the ratio of th dose of the drug that produces toxicity to that which produces the desire

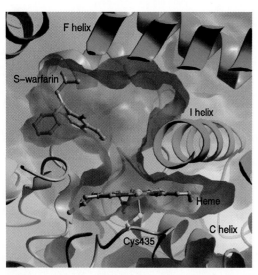

■ **Figure 12-19 | X-Ray structure of the human cytochrome P450 CYP2C9 in complex with the blood clotting inhibitor warfarin (Coumadin).** A cutaway diagram of the enzyme's active site region drawn with its surface purple and with its polypeptide backbone in ribbon form colored in rainbow order from N-terminus (*blue*) to C-terminus (*red*). The heme (seen edgewise), the Cys side chain that axially ligands the heme Fe atom, and the warfarin are shown in ball-and-stick form with C gray, N blue, O red, S yellow, and Fe orange. [Image courtesy of Astex Therapeutics Limited. PDBid 1OG5.]

ffect). Conversely, if, as is often the case, drug A induces the increased xpression of the cytochrome P450 isozyme that metabolizes it and drug , then coadministering drugs A and B will reduce drug B's bioavailabil-y, a phenomenon that was first noted when certain antibiotics caused oral ontraceptives to lose their efficacy. Moreover, if drug B is metabolized to toxic product, its increased rate of reaction may result in an adverse re-ction. Environmental pollutants such as PAHs and PCBs are also known) induce the expression of specific cytochrome P450 isozymes and ereby alter the rates at which certain drugs are metabolized. Finally,)me of these same effects may occur in patients with liver disease, as well s arising from age-based, gender-based, and individual differences in ver physiology.

Although many cytochromes P450 presumably evolved to detoxify nd/or help eliminate harmful substances, in several cases they have been nown to participate in converting relatively innocuous compounds to)xic agents. For example, **acetaminophen** (Fig. 12-20), a widely used anal-esic and antipyretic (fever reducer) is quite safe when taken in therapeu-c doses (1.2 g/day for an adult) but, in large doses (>10 g), is highly toxic. his is because, in therapeutic amounts, 95% of the acetaminophen pres-nt is enzymatically glucuronidated or sulfated at its —OH group to the

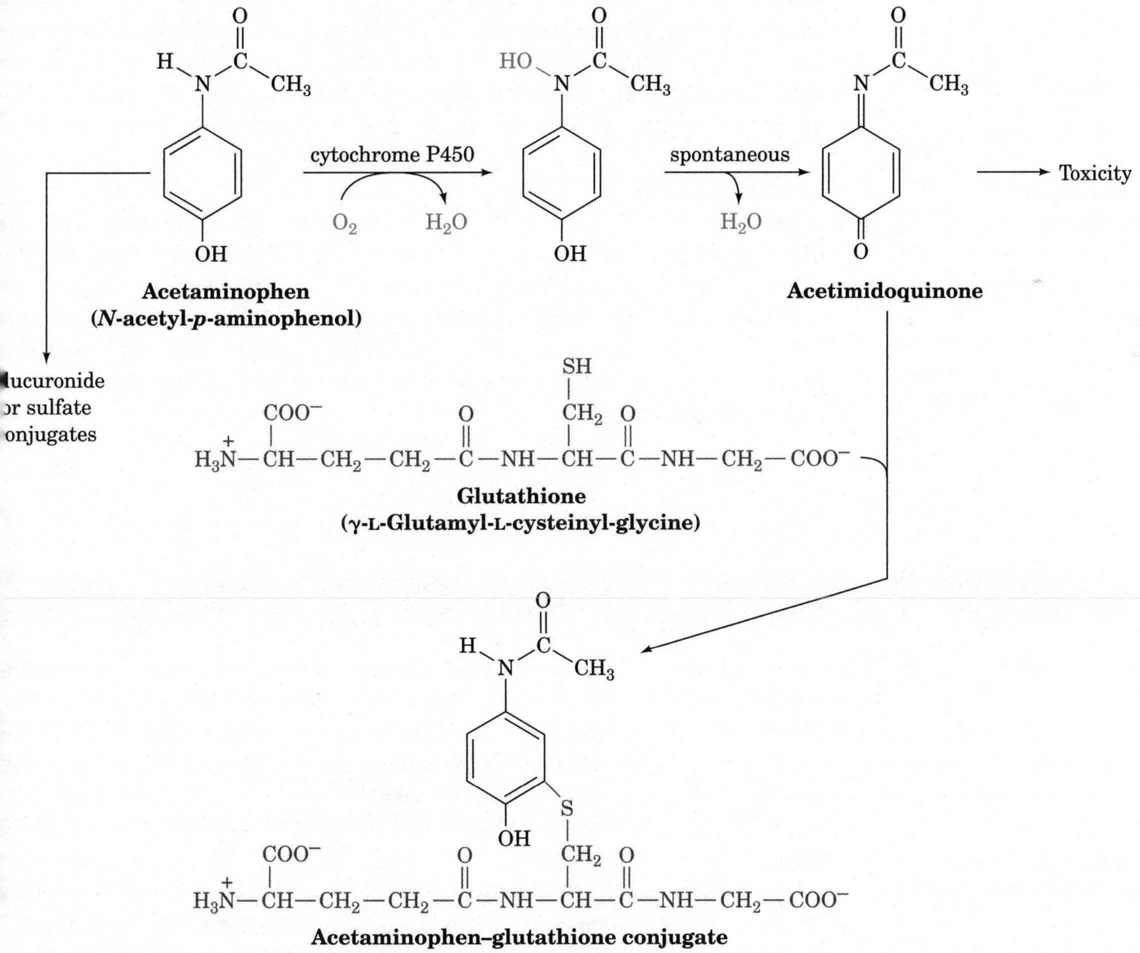

Figure 12-20 | **The metabolic reactions of acetaminophen.** An overdose of :etaminophen leads to the buildup of acetimidoquinone, which is toxic.

corresponding conjugates, which are readily excreted. The remaining 5% is converted, through the action of a cytochrome P450 (CYP2E1), to **acet imidoquinone** (Fig. 12-20), which is then conjugated with glutathion (Section 4-3B). However, when acetaminophen is taken in large amount the glucuronidation and sulfation pathways become saturated and henc the cytochrome P450-mediated pathway becomes increasingly importan If hepatic (liver) glutathione is depleted faster than it can be replaced, acet imidoquinone, a reactive compound, instead conjugates with the sulfhydry groups of cellular proteins resulting in often fatal hepatotoxicity.

Many of the cytochromes P450 in humans are unusually **polymorphi** that is, there are several common alleles (variants) of the genes encodin each of these enzymes in the human population. Alleles that cause dimir ished, enhanced, and qualitatively altered rates of drug metabolism hav been characterized for many of the cytochromes P450. The distributions these various alleles differs markedly among ethnic groups and hence prob ably arose to permit each group to cope with the toxins in its particular die

Polymorphism in a given cytochrome P450 results in differences be tween individuals in the rates at which they metabolize certain drugs. Fo instance, in cases in which a cytochrome P450 variant has absent or dimir ished activity, otherwise standard doses of a drug that the enzyme nor mally metabolizes may cause the bioavailability of the drug to reach toxi levels. Conversely, if a particular P450 enzyme has enhanced activity (usu ally because the gene encoding it has been duplicated one or more times higher than normal doses of a drug that the enzyme metabolizes woul have to be administered to obtain the required therapeutic effec However, if the drug is metabolized to a toxic product, this may result i an adverse reaction. Several known P450 variants have altered substrat specificities and hence produce unusual metabolites, which also may caus harmful side effects.

Experience has amply demonstrated that *there is no such thing as a dru that is entirely free of adverse reactions.* However, as the enzymes and the variants that participate in drug metabolism are characterized and as rapi and inexpensive genotyping methods are developed, it is becoming poss ble to tailor drug treatment to an individual's genetic makeup rather tha to the population as a whole. This rapidly developing area of study is calle **pharmacogenomics.**

■ **CHECK YOUR UNDERSTANDING**

Compare structure-based drug design and combinatorial chemistry as tools for developing drug candidates.

List the factors that influence a drug's bioavailability.

Summarize the purpose of phases I through III of a clinical trial.

Indicate how drugs that are well tolerated by the majority of the population cause adverse reactions in certain individuals.

SUMMARY

1. Elementary chemical reactions may be first order, second order, or, rarely, third order. In each case, a rate equation describes the progress of the reaction as a function of time.

2. The Michaelis–Menten equation describes the relationship between initial reaction velocity and substrate concentration under steady state conditions.

3. K_M is the substrate concentration at which the reaction velocity is half-maximal. The value of k_{cat}/K_M indicates an enzyme's catalytic efficiency.

4. Kinetic data can be plotted in double-reciprocal form to determine K_M and V_{max}.

5. Bisubstrate reactions are classified as sequential (single dis-

placement) or Ping Pong (double displacement). A sequentia reaction may proceed by an Ordered or Random mechanism

6. Reversible inhibitors reduce an enzyme's activity by bindin to the substrate-binding site (competitive inhibition), to th enzyme–substrate complex (uncompetitive inhibition), or both the enzyme and the enzyme–substrate complex (mixe inhibition).

7. Enzyme activity may be controlled by allosteric effectors.

8. The activity of ATCase is increased by ATP and decreased b CTP, which alter the conformation of the catalytic sites by sta bilizing the R and the T states of the enzyme, respectively.

9. Enzyme activity may be controlled by covalent modificatio

0. The enzymatic activity of glycogen phosphorylase is controlled by its phosphorylation/dephosphorylation as well as by the influence of allosteric effectors.

11. An enzyme inhibitor can be developed for use as a drug through structure-based and/or combinatorial methods. It must then be tested for safety and efficacy in clinical trials. Adverse reactions to drugs and drug–drug interactions are often mediated by a cytochrome P450.

KEY TERMS

elementary reaction **364**
k **364**
v **364**
first-order reaction **364**
reaction order **365**
molecularity **365**
second-order reaction **365**
rate equation **365**
$t_{1/2}$ **365**
pseudo-first-order
  reaction **366**
zero-order reaction **366**
radionuclide **367**
autoradiography **367**
ES complex **368**
k_{-1} **368**
k_2 **368**
Michaelis complex **368**

steady state **368**
steady state assumption **369**
K_M **369**
v_o **370**
V_{max} **370**
enzyme saturation **370**
Michaelis–Menten
  equation **370**
k_{cat} **371**
turnover number **371**
k_{cat}/K_M **371**
diffusion-controlled limit **371**
Lineweaver–Burk (double-
  reciprocal) plot **373**
sequential reaction **375**
single-displacement
  reaction **375**

Ordered mechanism **375**
Random mechanism **375**
Ping Pong reaction **376**
double-displacement
  reaction **376**
inhibitor **377**
inactivator **377**
competitive inhibition **377**
product inhibition **378**
transition state analog **378**
K_I **378**
K_M^{app} **379**
uncompetitive inhibition **381**
V_{max}^{app} **381**
mixed (noncompetitive)
  inhibition **382**
allosteric effector **386**

covalent modification **386**
feedback inhibitor **387**
protein kinase **391**
protein phosphatase **391**
isozyme (isoform) **391**
lead compound **394**
structure-based (rational)
  drug design **395**
combinatorial chemistry **395**
xenobiotic **396**
pharmacokinetics **396**
bioavailability **396**
clinical trial **396**
cytochrome P450 **398**
drug–drug interaction **398**
therapeutic index **398**
pharmacogenomics **400**

PROBLEMS

1. Consider the nonenzymatic elementary reaction A → B. When the concentration of A is 20 mM, the reaction velocity is measured as 5 μM B produced per minute. (a) Calculate the rate constant for this reaction. (b) What is the molecularity of the reaction?

2. If there are 10 μmol of the radioactive isotope ^{32}P (half-life 14 days) at $t = 0$, how much ^{32}P will remain at (a) 7 days, (b) 14 days, (c) 21 days, and (d) 70 days?

3. The hypothetical elementary reaction $2A \rightarrow B + C$ has a rate constant of $10^{-6} \, M^{-1} \cdot s^{-1}$. What is the reaction velocity when the concentration of A is 10 mM?

4. For each reaction below, determine whether the reaction is first order or second order and calculate the rate constant.

Time (s)	Reaction A reactant (mM)	Reaction B reactant (mM)
0	6.2	5.4
1	3.1	4.6
2	2.1	3.9
3	1.6	3.2
4	1.3	2.7
5	1.1	2.3

5. For an enzymatic reaction, draw curves that show the appropriate relationships between the variables in each plot below.

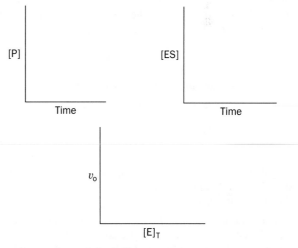

6. Explain why it is usually easier to calculate an enzyme's reaction velocity from the rate of appearance of product rather than the rate of disappearance of a substrate.

7. At what concentration of S (expressed as a multiple of K_M) will $v_o = 0.95 V_{max}$?

8. Identify the enzymes in Table 12-1 whose catalytic efficiencies are near the diffusion-controlled limit.

9. Explain why each of the following data sets from a Lineweaver–Burk plot are not individually ideal for determining K_M for an enzyme-catalyzed reaction that follows Michaelis–Menten kinetics.

Set A	1/[S] (mM^{-1})	1/v_o (μM$^{-1} \cdot$ s)
	0.5	2.4
	1.0	2.6
	1.5	2.9
	2.0	3.1

Set B	1/[S] (mM^{-1})	1/v_o (μM$^{-1} \cdot$ s)
	8	5.9
	10	6.8
	12	7.8
	14	8.7

10. Calculate K_M and V_{max} from the following data:

[S] (μM)	v_o (mM $\cdot$ s^{-1})
0.1	0.34
0.2	0.53
0.4	0.74
0.8	0.91
1.6	1.04

11. You are trying to determine the K_M for an enzyme. Due to a lab mishap, you have only two usable data points:

Substrate concentration (μM)	Reaction velocity (μM $\cdot$ s^{-1})
1	5
100	50

Use these data to calculate an approximate value for K_M. Is this value likely to be an overestimate or an underestimate of the true value? Explain.

12. You are attempting to determine K_M by measuring the reaction velocity at different substrate concentrations, but you do not realize that the substrate tends to precipitate under the experimental conditions you have chosen. How would this affect your measurement of K_M?

13. You are constructing a velocity versus [substrate] curve for an enzyme whose K_M is believed to be about 2 μM. The enzyme concentration is 200 nM and the substrate concentrations range from 0.1 μM to 10 μM. What is wrong with this experimental setup and how could you fix it?

14. Is it necessary for measurements of reaction velocity to be expressed in units of concentration per time (M $\cdot$ s^{-1}, for example) in order to calculate an enzyme's K_M?

15. Is it necessary to know [E]$_T$ in order to determine (a) K_M (b) V_{max}, or (c) k_{cat}?

16. The K_M for the reaction of chymotrypsin with N-acetylvaline ethyl ester is 8.8×10^{-2} M, and the K_M for the reaction of chymotrypsin with N-acetyltyrosine ethyl ester is 6.6×10^{-4} M (a) Which substrate has the higher apparent affinity for the enzyme? (b) Which substrate is likely to give a higher value for V_{max}?

17. Enzyme A catalyzes the reaction S$\rightarrow$P and has a K_M of 50 μM and a V_{max} of 100 nM $\cdot$ s^{-1}. Enzyme B catalyzes the reaction S$\rightarrow$Q and has a K_M of 5 mM and a V_{max} of 120 nM $\cdot$ s^{-1}. When 100 μM of S is added to a mixture containing equivalent amounts of enzymes A and B, after one minute which reaction product will be more abundant P or Q?

18. In a bisubstrate reaction, a small amount of the first product P is isotopically labeled (P*) and added to the enzyme and the first substrate A. No B or Q is present. Will A (= P—X) become isotopically labeled (A*) if the reaction follows (a) a Ping Pong mechanism or (b) a Sequential mechanism?

19. Determine the type of inhibition of an enzymatic reaction from the following data collected in the presence and absence of the inhibitor.

[S] (mM)	v_o (mM $\cdot$ min^{-1})	v_o with I present (mM $\cdot$ min^{-1})
1	1.3	0.8
2	2.0	1.2
4	2.8	1.7
8	3.6	2.2
12	4.0	2.4

20. Estimate K_I for a competitive inhibitor when [I] = 5 mM gives an apparent value of K_M that is three times the K_M for the uninhibited reaction.

21. For an enzyme-catalyzed reaction, the presence of 5 nM of a reversible inhibitor yields a V_{max} value that is 80% of the value in the absence of the inhibitor. The K_M value is unchanged. (a) What type of inhibition is likely occurring? (b) What proportion of the enzyme molecules have bound inhibitor? (c) Calculate the inhibition constant.

22. How would diisopropylphosphofluoridate (DIPF; Section 11-5A) affect the apparent K_M and V_{max} of a sample of chymotrypsin?

23. Based on some preliminary measurements, you suspect that a sample of enzyme contains an irreversible enzyme inhibitor. You decide to dilute the sample 100-fold and remeasure the enzyme's activity. What would your results show if the inhibitor in the sample is (a) irreversible or (b) reversible?

4. Enzyme X and enzyme Y catalyze the same reaction and exhibit the v_o versus [S] curves shown below. Which enzyme is more efficient at low [S]? Which is more efficient at high [S]?

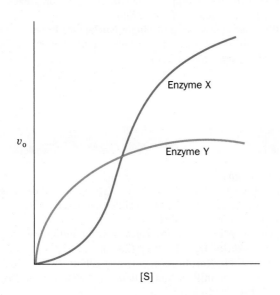

5. Sphingosine-1-phosphate (SPP) is important for cell survival. The synthesis of SPP from sphingosine and ATP is catalyzed by the enzyme sphingosine kinase. An understanding of the kinetics of the sphingosine kinase reaction may be important in the development of drugs to treat cancer. The velocity of the sphingosine kinase reaction was measured in the presence and absence of *threo*-sphingosine, a stereoisomer of sphingosine that inhibits the enzyme. The results are shown below.

[Sphingosine] (μM)	v_o (mg · min^{-1}) (no inhibitor)	v_o (mg · min^{-1}) (with *threo*-sphingosine)
2.5	32.3	8.5
3.5	40	11.5
5	50.8	14.6
10	72	25.4
20	87.7	43.9
50	115.4	70.8

Construct a Lineweaver–Burk plot to answer the following questions:

(a) What are the apparent K_M and V_{max} values in the presence and absence of the inhibitor?

(b) What kind of an inhibitor is *threo*-sphingosine? Explain.

CASE STUDIES

Case 7
A Storage Protein from Seeds of **Brassica nigra** *Is a Serine Protease Inhibitor*

Focus concept: Purification of a novel seed storage protein allows sequence analysis and determination of the protein's secondary and tertiary structure.

Prerequisites: Chapters 5, 11, and 12

- Protein purification techniques, particularly gel filtration and dialysis
- Protein sequencing using Edman degradation and overlapping peptides
- Structure and mechanism of serine proteases
- Reversible inhibition of enzymes

Case 12
Production of Methanol in Ripening Fruit

Focus concept: The link between the production of methanol in ripening fruit and the activity of pectin methylesterase, the enzyme responsible for methanol production, is examined in wild-type and transgenic tomato fruit.

Prerequisite: Chapter 12

- Enzyme kinetics and inhibition

Case 13
Inhibition of Alcohol Dehydrogenase

Focus concept: The inhibition of the alcohol dehydrogenase by a formamide compound is examined.

Prerequisite: Chapter 12

- Principles of enzyme kinetics
- Identification of inhibition via Lineweaver–Burk plots

Case 15
Site-Directed Mutagenesis of Creatine Kinase

Focus concept: Site-directed mutagenesis is used to create mutant creatine kinase enzymes so that the role of a single reactive cysteine in binding and catalysis can be assessed.

Prerequisites: Chapters 4, 6, 11, and 12

- Amino acid structure
- Protein architecture
- Enzyme kinetics and inhibition
- Basic enzyme mechanisms

Case 19
Purification of Rat Kidney Sphingosine Kinase

Focus concept: The purification and kinetic analysis of an enzyme that produces a product important in cell survival is the focus of this study.

Prerequisites: Chapters 5 and 12

- Protein purification techniques and protein analytical methods
- Basic enzyme kinetics

BIOINFORMATICS EXERCISES

Bioinformatics Exercises are available at www.wiley.com/college/voet.

Chapter 12
Enzyme Inhibitors and Rational Drug Design
1. **Dihydrofolate Reductase.** Examine the structure of an enzyme with an inhibitor bound to it.

2. **HIV Protease.** Compare the structures of complexes containing HIV protease and an inhibitor.
3. **Pharmacogenomics and Single Nucleotide Polymorphisms.** Use online databases to find information on cytochrome P450 polymorphisms.

REFERENCES

Kinetics

Cornish-Bowden, A., *Fundamentals of Enzyme Kinetics* (revised ed.), Portland Press (1995). [A lucid and detailed account of enzyme kinetics.]

Fersht, A., *Structure and Mechanism in Protein Science: A Guide to Enzyme Catalysis and Protein Folding,* W.H. Freeman (1999).

Gutfreund, H., *Kinetics for the Life Sciences: Receptors, Transmitters, and Catalysts,* Cambridge University Press (1995).

Segel, I.H., *Enzyme Kinetics,* Wiley-Interscience (1993). [A detailed and understandable treatise providing full explanations of many aspects of enzyme kinetics.]

Allosteric Control and Control by Covalent Modification

Jin, L., Stec, B., Lipscomb, W.N., and Kantrowitz, E.R., Insights into the mechanisms of catalysis and heterotropic regulation of *Escherichia coli* aspartate transcarbamoylase based upon a structure of the enzyme complexed with the bisubstrate analogue *N*-phosphonacetyl-L-aspartate at 2.1Å, *Proteins* **37,** 729–742 (1999).

Johnson, L.N. and Lewis, R.J., Structural basis for control by phosphorylation, *Chem. Rev.* **101,** 2209–2242 (2001).

Lipscomb, W.N., Structure and function of allosteric enzymes, *Chemtracts—Biochem. Mol. Biol.* **2,** 1–15 (1991).

Perutz, M., *Mechanisms of Cooperativity and Allosteric Regulation in Proteins,* Cambridge University Press (1990).

Drug Design

Furge, L.L. and Guengerich, F.P., Cytochrome P450 enzymes in drug metabolism and chemical toxicology, *Biochem. Mol. Biol. Educ.* **34,** 66–74 (2006).

Jorgenson, W.L., The many roles of computation in drug discovery, *Science* **303,** 1813–1818 (2004).

Ohlstein, E.H., Ruffolo, R.R., Jr., and Elliott, J.D., Drug discovery in the next millennium, *Annu. Rev. Pharmacol. Toxicol.* **40,** 177–191 (2000).

Smith, D.A. and van der Waterbeemd, H., Pharmacokinetics and metabolism in early drug design, *Curr. Opin. Chem. Biol.* **3,** 373–378 (1999).

Williams, P.A., Cosme, J., Ward, A., Angove, H.C., Vinkovic, D.M., and Jhoti, H., Crystal structure of human cytochrome P450 2C9 with bound warfarin, *Nature* **424,** 464–468 (2003).

White, R.E., High-throughput screening in drug metabolism and pharmokinetic support of drug discovery, *Annu. Rev. Pharmacol. Toxicol.* **40,** 133–157 (2000).

Wlodawer, A. and Vondrasek, J., Inhibitors of HIV-1 protease: A major success of structure-assisted drug design, *Annu. Rev. Biophys. Biomol. Struct.* **27,** 249–284 (1998). [Reviews the development of some HIV-1 protease inhibitors.]

Biochemical Signaling

A cell must have an appropriate receptor to recognize and respond to a chemical signal produced by another cell. [Grant V. Faint/Digital Vision/Getty Images]

■ **MEDIA RESOURCES**

available at www.wiley.com/college/voet)

Guided Exploration 12. Hormone signaling by the receptor tyrosine kinase system
Guided Exploration 13. Hormone signaling by the adenylate cyclase system
Interactive Exercise 10. X-Ray structure of human growth hormone (hGH)
Interactive Exercise 11. Tyrosine kinase domain of insulin receptor
Interactive Exercise 12. A heterotrimeric G protein
Interactive Exercise 13. C subunit of protein kinase A
Animated Figure 13-7. The Ras signaling cascade
Animated Figure 13-24. The phosphoinositide signaling system
Kinemage 15. cAMP-dependent protein kinase (PKA)
Kinemage 16-1. The structure of calmodulin
Kinemage 16-2. Calmodulin complex with target polypeptide

L iving things coordinate their activities at every level of their organization through complex biochemical signaling systems. Intercellular signals are mediated by chemical messengers known as **hormones** and, in higher animals, by neuronally transmitted electrochemical impulses. Intracellular communications are maintained by the synthesis or alteration of a great variety of different substances that are often integral components of the processes they control. For example, metabolic pathways, as we have seen (Section 12-3), are regulated by the feedback control of allosteric enzymes by metabolites in those pathways or by the covalent modification of the enzymes. In this chapter we consider the nature of chemical signals and how the signals are transmitted.

*In general, every signaling pathway consists of a **receptor protein** that specifically binds a hormone or other ligand, a mechanism for transmitting the ligand-binding event to the cell interior, and a series of intracellular responses that may involve the synthesis of a **second messenger** and/or*

■ **CHAPTER CONTENTS**

1 Hormones
   A. Pancreatic Islet Hormones Control Fuel Metabolism
   B. Epinephrine and Norepinephrine Prepare the Body for Action
   C. Steroid Hormones Regulate a Wide Variety of Metabolic and Sexual Processes
   D. Growth Hormone Binds to Receptors in Muscle, Bone, and Cartilage

2 Receptor Tyrosine Kinases
   A. Receptor Tyrosine Kinases Transmit Signals across the Cell Membrane
   B. Kinase Cascades Relay Signals to the Nucleus
   C. Some Receptors Are Associated with Nonreceptor Tyrosine Kinases
   D. Protein Phosphatases Are Signaling Proteins in Their Own Right

3 Heterotrimeric G Proteins
   A. G Protein–Coupled Receptors Contain Seven Transmembrane Helices
   B. Heterotrimeric G Proteins Dissociate on Activation
   C. Adenylate Cyclase Synthesizes cAMP to Activate Protein Kinase A
   D. Phosphodiesterases Limit Second Messenger Activity

4 The Phosphoinositide Pathway
   A. Ligand Binding Results in the Cytoplasmic Release of the Second Messengers IP_3 and Ca^{2+}
   B. Calmodulin Is a Ca^{2+}-Activated Switch
   C. DAG Is a Lipid-Soluble Second Messenger That Activates Protein Kinase C
   D. Epilog: Complex Systems Have Emergent Properties

chemical changes catalyzed by **kinases** *and* **phosphatases.** *These pathway
often involve* **enzyme cascades,** *in which a succession of events that eac
depend on the previous one amplifies the signal.*

We begin by discussing the functions of some representative huma
hormone systems. We then discuss the three major pathways whereb
intercellular signals are converted (transduced) to intracellular signal
those that (1) involve receptor tyrosine kinases, (2) utilize heterotrimer
G proteins, and (3) employ phosphoinositide cascades. Neurotransmissio
is discussed in Section 10-2C.

LEARNING OBJECTIVES

■ Understand the general functions of
hormones produced by the pancreas, adrenal
cortex, and adrenal medulla.

■ Understand that a hormone's effects
depend on the presence of a specific cellular
receptor, the tissue distribution of the
receptor, and the receptor's sensitivity to
agonists and antagonists.

■ Understand that hormone binding induces
changes in the receptor, such as dimerization.

1 Hormones

In higher animals, specialized ductless **endocrine glands** (Fig. 13-1) synthe
size **endocrine hormones** that they release into the bloodstream in respons
to external stimuli. These hormones are thereby carried to their target cel

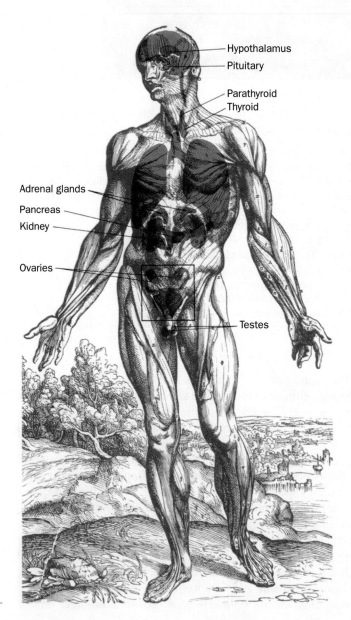

Hypothalamus
Pituitary
Parathyroid
Thyroid
Adrenal glands
Pancreas
Kidney
Ovaries
Testes

■ **Figure 13-1** | **The major glands of the
human endocrine system.** Other tissues, such
as the intestines, also secrete endocrine hormones.

Fig. 13-2) in which they elicit a response. The human endocrine system secretes a wide variety of hormones that enable the body to:

1. Maintain **homeostasis** (a steady state; e.g., insulin and glucagon maintain the blood glucose level within rigid limits during feast or famine).

2. Respond to a wide variety of external stimuli (such as the preparation for "fight or flight" by epinephrine and norepinephrine).

3. Follow various cyclic and developmental programs (for instance, sex hormones regulate sexual differentiation, maturation, the menstrual cycle, and pregnancy).

Most hormones are either polypeptides, amino acid derivatives, or steroids, although there are important exceptions to this generalization. In any case, *only those cells with a specific receptor for a given hormone will respond to its presence even though nearly all cells in the body may be exposed to the hormone.* Hormonal messages are therefore quite specifically addressed.

Although we discuss specific hormones and their function in many other chapters, in this section we outline the activities of hormones produced by some representative endocrine glands. These glands are not just a collection of independent secretory organs but form a complex and highly interdependent control network. Indeed, the secretion of many hormones is under feedback control through the secretion of other hormones to which the original hormone-secreting gland responds. The concentrations of circulating hormones are typically measured using the radioimmunoassay developed by Rosalyn Yalow (Box 13-1).

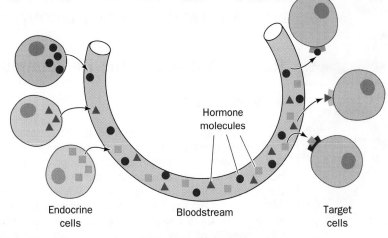

■ **Figure 13-2** | **Endocrine signaling.** Hormones produced by endocrine cells reach their target cells via the bloodstream. Only cells that display the appropriate receptors can respond to the hormones.

Pancreatic Islet Hormones Control Fuel Metabolism

The pancreas is a large glandular organ, the bulk of which is an **exocrine gland** dedicated to producing digestive enzymes—such as trypsin, chymotrypsin, RNase A, α-amylase, and phospholipase A_2—that are secreted via the pancreatic duct into the small intestine. However, ~1 to 2% of pancreatic tissue consists of scattered clumps of cells known as **islets of Langerhans,** which comprise an endocrine gland that functions to maintain energy homeostasis. Pancreatic islets contain three types of cells, each of which secretes a characteristic polypeptide hormone:

1. The α cells secrete **glucagon** (29 residues).
2. The β cells secrete insulin (51 residues; Fig. 5-1).
3. The δ cells secrete **somatostatin** (14 residues).

Insulin, which is secreted in response to high blood glucose levels, primarily functions to stimulate muscle, liver, and adipose cells to store glucose for later use by synthesizing glycogen, protein, and fat (Section 22-2). Glucagon, which is secreted in response to low blood glucose, has essentially the opposite effects: It stimulates the liver to release glucose through the breakdown of glycogen (**glycogenolysis;** Section 16-1) and the synthesis of glucose from noncarbohydrate precursors (**gluconeogenesis,** Section 16-4). It also stimulates adipose tissue to release fatty acids through lipolysis. Somatostatin, which is also secreted by the hypothalamus, inhibits the release of insulin and glucagon from their islet cells.

BOX 13-1 PATHWAYS OF DISCOVERY

Rosalyn Yalow and the Radioimmunoassay (RIA)

Rosalyn Yalow (1921–)

Rosalyn Sussman Yalow was born on July 19, 1921, in New York City. Neither of her parents had the advantage of a high school education but there was never a doubt that their two children would make it through college. While Rosalyn was at Hunter, the college for women in New York City's college system (now the City University of New York), Eve Curie had just published the biography of her mother, Madame Marie Curie, a "must-read" for every aspiring female scientist. Rosalyn's goal at that time was achieving a career in physics. Despite suggestions from her family that becoming an elementary school teacher would be more practical, she persisted.

In 1941, after graduating from college, Yalow received an offer of a teaching assistantship in physics at the University of Illinois in Champaign–Urbana. At the first meeting of the faculty of the College of Engineering, she discovered that she was the only woman among its 400 members. The dean of the faculty congratulated her on her achievement and told her she was the first woman there since 1917. The draft of young men into the armed forces, even before America entered World War II, had made possible her entrance into graduate school. On the first day of graduate school she met Aaron Yalow, who was also beginning graduate study in physics at Illinois and who in 1943 was to become her husband.

In January 1945, Yalow received a Ph.D. in nuclear physics and returned to New York as assistant engineer at the Federal Telecommunications Laboratory—its only woman engineer. In 1946, she returned to Hunter College to teach physics, not to women but to returning veterans in a preengineering program. During that time she became interested in the medical aspects of radioisotopes. She joined the Bronx Veterans Administration (VA) as a part-time consultant in December 1947. Even while teaching full-time at Hunter, she equipped and developed the Radioisotope Service at the VA hospital and initiated a variety of research projects with several physicians. In January 1950, Yalow chose to leave teaching and join the VA full time. That spring, Dr. Solomon A Berson joined the Service and began a 22-year partnership tha lasted until his death in 1972.

In their joint studies, Yalow and Berson concentrated on th application of isotopes to clinical problems such as hormone analy sis. At the time, insulin was the hormone most readily available i a highly purified form. In studying the reaction of insulin with an tibodies, Yalow and Berson recognized that they had a tool wit the potential for measuring the concentration of insulin in complex mixture such as blood. By 1959, they had developed practical method for quantifying insulin in human plasma, th **radioimmunoassay (RIA).** RIA is now used to measure hundred of substances of biological interest.

The serum concentrations of insulin and other hormones ar extremely low, generally between 10^{-12} and 10^{-7} M, so they usu ally must be measured by indirect means. In RIAs, the unknow concentration of a hormone, H, is determined by measuring ho much of a known amount of the radioactively labeled hormone H*, binds to a fixed quantity of anti-H antibody in the presenc of H. This competition reaction is easily calibrated by constructin a standard curve indicating how much H* binds to the antibod as a function of [H]. The high binding affinity and specificity of an tibodies for their ligands gives RIAs the advantages of great sen sitivity and specificity.

By 1977, Yalow's hospital was affiliated with the Mount Sina School of Medicine, and Yalow held the title of Distinguishe Service Professor. She is a member of the National Academy c Sciences and has received numerous awards and honors, incluc ing the 1977 Nobel Prize in Physiology or Medicine (Berson die before this Nobel prize was awarded and so could not share th prize) and the 1988 National Medal of Science. "The excitemer of learning separates youth from old age," Rosalyn Yalow has saic "As long as you're learning, you're not old."*

Mostly abridged from Rosalyn Yalow's autobiography, *Les Prix Nobel. Th Nobel Prizes 1977*, Wilhelm Odelberg (Ed.), Nobel Foundation, 1978.

*From *O, The Oprah Magazine*, January 1, 2005.

Polypeptide hormones, like other proteins destined for secretion, are ri bosomally synthesized as prohormones, processed in the rough endoplas mic reticulum and Golgi apparatus to form the mature hormone, and thei packaged in secretory granules to await the signal for their release by ex ocytosis (Sections 9-4D–F). The most potent physiological stimuli for th release of insulin and glucagon are, respectively, high and low blood glu cose concentrations so that islet cells act as the body's primary glucos sensors. However, the release of the hormones is also influenced by th autonomic (involuntary) nervous system and by hormones secreted by th gastrointestinal tract.

Epinephrine and Norepinephrine Prepare the Body for Action

The **adrenal glands** consist of two distinct types of tissue: the **medulla** (core), which is really an extension of the sympathetic nervous system (a part of the autonomic nervous system), and the more typically glandular **cortex** (outer layer). Here we consider the hormones of the adrenal medulla; those of the cortex are discussed in the following section.

*The adrenal medulla synthesizes two hormonally active **catecholamines** (amine-containing derivatives of **catechol**, 1,2-dihydroxybenzene): **norepinephrine (noradrenalin)** and its methyl derivative **epinephrine (adrenalin;** at right).* These hormones are synthesized from tyrosine as is described in Section 21-6B and stored in granules to await their exocytotic release under the control of the sympathetic nervous system.

The biological effects of catecholamines are mediated by two classes of plasma membrane receptors, the α- and β-**adrenoreceptors** (also known as **adrenergic receptors**). These transmembrane glycoproteins were originally identified on the basis of their varying responses to certain **agonists** (substances that bind to a receptor so as to evoke a response) and **antagonists** (substances that bind to a receptor but fail to elicit a response, thereby blocking agonist action). The β- but not the α-adrenoreceptors, for example, are stimulated by **isoproterenol** but blocked by **propranolol**, whereas α- but not β-adrenoreceptors are blocked by **phentolamine.**

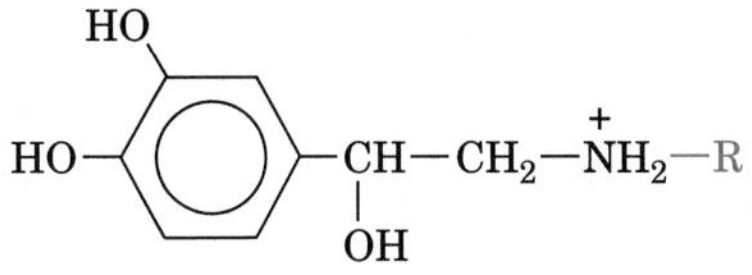

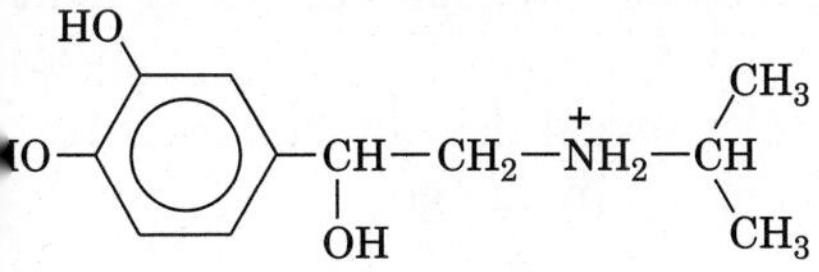

R = H   **Norepinephrine (noradrenalin)**
R = CH$_3$ **Epinephrine (adrenalin)**

Isoproterenol

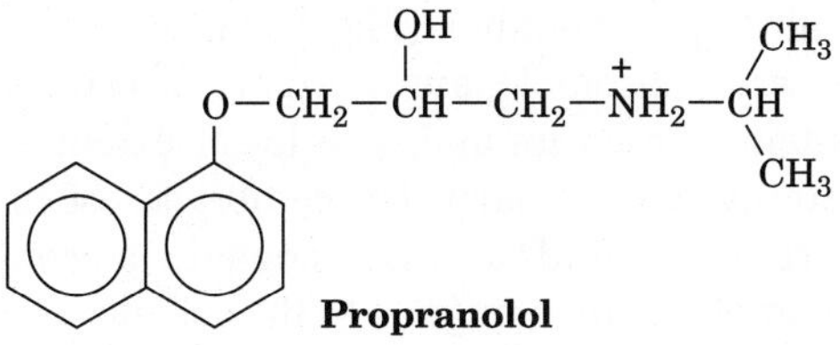

Propranolol

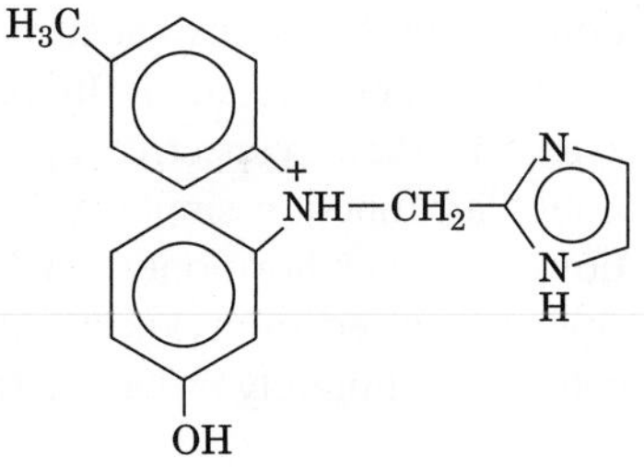

Phentolamine

The α- and β-adrenoreceptors, which occur on separate tissues in mammals, generally respond differently and often oppositely to catecholamines. For instance, β-adrenoreceptors stimulate glycogenolysis and gluconeogenesis in liver (Sections 16-1 and 16-4), glycogenolysis in skeletal muscle, lipolysis in adipose tissue, the relaxation of smooth (involuntary) muscle in the bronchi and in the blood vessels supplying the skeletal (voluntary) muscles, and increased heart action. In contrast, α-adrenoreceptors stimulate smooth muscle contraction in blood vessels supplying peripheral organs such as skin and kidney, smooth muscle relaxation in the gastrointestinal tract, and blood platelet aggregation. *Most*

*of these diverse effects are directed toward a common end: the mobiliza-
tion of energy resources and their shunting to where they are most needed
to prepare the body for action.*

The tissue distributions of the α- and β-adrenoreceptors and their varying responses to different agonists and antagonists have important therapeutic consequences. For example, propranolol is used to treat high blood
pressure and protects against heart attacks, whereas epinephrine's bron-
chodilator effects make it clinically useful in the treatment of **asthma,** a
breathing disorder caused by the inappropriate contraction of bronchial
smooth muscle.

C | Steroid Hormones Regulate a Wide Variety of Metabolic and Sexual Processes

The adrenal cortex produces at least 50 different **adrenocortical steroids***.*
These have been classified according to the physiological responses they
evoke (Section 9-1E):

1. The **glucocorticoids** affect carbohydrate, protein, and lipid metabolism in a manner nearly opposite to that of insulin and influence a
   wide variety of other vital functions, including inflammatory reactions and the capacity to cope with stress.
2. The **mineralocorticoids** largely function to regulate the excretion of
   salt and water by the kidneys.
3. The **androgens** and **estrogens** affect sexual development and function. They are made in larger quantities by the gonads.

Glucocorticoids, the most common of which is **cortisol** (also known as **hydrocortisone**), and the mineralocorticoids, the most common of which is
aldosterone, are all C_{21} compounds (Fig. 9-11).

Steroids, being water insoluble, are transported in the blood in complex
with the glycoprotein **transcortin** and, to a lesser extent, with albumin. The
steroids spontaneously pass through the membranes of their target cells to
the cytosol, where they bind to their cognate **steroid receptors.** The
steroid–receptor complexes then migrate to the cell nucleus, where they function as transcription factors to induce, or in some cases repress, the transcription of specific genes (Section 28-3B). In this way, the glucocorticoids and
the mineralocorticoids influence the expression of numerous metabolic enzymes in their respective target tissues. Thyroid hormones, which are also
nonpolar, function similarly. However, as we shall see in the following sections, all other hormones act less directly in that they bind to their cognate
cell-surface receptors and thereby trigger complex cascades of events within
cells that ultimately influence transcription as well as other cellular processes.

Gonadal Steroids Mediate Sexual Development and Function. *The*
gonads (testes in males, ovaries in females), in addition to producing sperm
or ova, secrete steroid hormones (androgens and estrogens) that regulate
sexual differentiation, the expression of secondary sex characteristics, and
sexual behavior patterns. Although testes and ovaries both synthesize androgens and estrogens, the testes predominantly secrete androgens, which
are therefore known as **male sex hormones,** whereas ovaries produce
mostly estrogens, which are consequently termed **female sex hormones.**

Androgens, of which **testosterone** (Fig. 9-11) is prototypic, lack the C
substituent at C17 that occurs in glucocorticoids and are therefore C_{19}
compounds. Estrogens, such as **β-estradiol** (Fig. 9-11), resemble androgen

ut lack a C10 methyl group because they have an aromatic A ring and re therefore C_{18} compounds. Interestingly, testosterone is an intermedi- e in estrogen biosynthesis. Another class of ovarian steroids, C_{21} com- ounds called **progestins,** help mediate the menstrual cycle and pregnancy.

Androgens that promote muscle growth are known as **anabolic steroids.** any individuals have taken anabolic steroids, both natural and synthetic, an effort to enhance their athletic performance or for cosmetic reasons. owever, because these substances and their metabolic products interact ith the various steroid receptors, their use may cause adverse side effects cluding cardiovascular disease, the development of breast tissue in males, asculinization in females, temporary infertility in both sexes, and, in ado- scents, stunted growth due to accelerated bone maturation and preco- ous and/or exaggerated sexual development. Consequently, anabolic eroids have been classified as controlled substances and, to prevent an nfair advantage over those not taking them, their use by competitive ath- tes has been banned.

exual Differentiation Is Both Hormonally and Genetically ontrolled. What factors control sexual differentiation? If the gonads of a embryonic male mammal are surgically removed, that individual will ecome a phenotypic female. Evidently, *mammals are programmed to evelop as females unless embryonically subjected to the influence of sticular hormones.* Indeed, genetic males with absent or nonfunctional ytosolic androgen receptors are phenotypic females, a condition named **sticular feminization.** Curiously, estrogens appear to play no part in mbryonic female sexual development, although they are essential for male sexual maturation and function.

Normal individuals have either the XY (male) or the XX (female) geno- ypes. However, those with the abnormal genotypes XXY **(Klinefelter's yndrome)** and X0 (only one sex chromosome; **Turner's syndrome)** are, espectively, phenotypic males and phenotypic females, although both are erile. Apparently, *the normal Y chromosome confers the male phenotype, hereas its absence results in the female phenotype.*

Growth Hormone Binds to Receptors in Muscle, Bone, and Cartilage

rowth hormone (GH), a 19-residue polypeptide, is produced by the an- erior lobe of the pituitary gland. Its binding to receptors directly stimu- tes growth and metabolism in muscle, bone, and cartilage cells. GH also cts indirectly by stimulating the liver to produce additional growth factors.

Overproduction of GH, usually a consequence of a pituitary tumor, esults in excessive growth. If this condition commences while the skeleton still growing, that is, before its growth plates have ossified, then this xcessive growth is of normal proportions over the entire body, resulting in **igantism.** Moreover, since excessive GH inhibits the testosterone produc- on necessary for growth plate ossification, such "giants" continue grow- g throughout their abnormally short lives. If, however, the skeleton has lready matured, GH stimulates only the growth of soft tissues, resulting enlarged hands and feet and thickened facial features, a condition named **cromegaly.** The opposite problem, GH deficiency, which results in insuffi- ient growth **(dwarfism),** can be treated before skeletal maturity by regu- ar injections of human GH **(hGH;** animal GH is ineffective in humans).

Since hGH was, at first, available only from the pituitaries of cadavers, was in very short supply. Now, however, hGH can be synthesized in

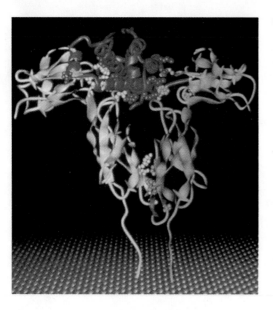

■ **Figure 13-3** | **X-Ray structure of human growth hormone (hGH) in comple**
with two molecules of its receptor's extracellular domain (hGHbp). The
proteins are shown in ribbon form, with the two hGHbp molecules, which together
bind one molecule of hGH, green and blue and with the hGH red. The side chains
involved in intersubunit interactions are shown in space-filling form. The orange
pebbled surface represents the cell membrane through which the C-terminal ends of
the hGHbp molecules are shown penetrating as they do in the intact hGH receptor.
[Courtesy of Abraham de Vos and Anthony Kossiakoff Genentech Inc., South San
Francisco, California.] ☞ **See Interactive Exercise 10.**

virtually unlimited amounts via recombinant DNA techniques (Section 3-5D
Indeed, hGH has been taken by individuals to increase their athleti
prowess, although there is no clear evidence that it does so. Howeve
because of its adverse side effects, which include high blood pressure, joir
and muscle pain, and acromegaly, as well as to eliminate any unfair com
petitive advantages in athletes, its nonmedical use is prohibited.

The GH Receptor Dimerizes on Hormone Binding. The 620-residue GI
receptor is a member of a large family of structurally related proteins. Thes
receptors consist of an N-terminal extracellular ligand-binding domain,
single transmembrane segment that is almost certainly helical, and a C
terminal cytoplasmic domain that is not homologous within the superfam
ily but in many cases contains a tyrosine kinase function (Section 13-2A).

The X-ray structure of hGH in complex with the extracellular domai
of its binding protein **(hGHbp)** reveals that the complex consists of tw
molecules of hGHbp bound to a single hGH molecule (Fig. 13-3). hGH
like many other protein growth factors, consists largely of a four-helix bun
dle. Each hGHbp molecule consists of two structurally homologou
domains, each of which forms a topologically identical sandwich of a three
and a four-stranded antiparallel β sheet that resembles the immunoglob
ulin fold (Section 7-3B).

The two hGHbp molecules bind to hGH with near twofold symmetr
about an axis that is roughly perpendicular to the helical axes of the hGH
four-helix bundle and, presumably, to the plane of the cell membrane t
which the intact hGH receptor is anchored (Fig. 13-3). The C-terminal dc
mains of the two hGHbp molecules are almost parallel and in contact wit
one another. Intriguingly, the two hGHbp molecules use essentially th
same residues to bind to sites that are on opposite sides of hGH's fou
helix bundle and which have no structural similarity.

*The ligand-induced dimerization of hGHbp has important implication
for the mechanism of* **signal transduction.** The dimerization, which does nc
occur in the absence of hGH, apparently brings together the intact recep
tors' intracellular domains in a way that activates an effector protein suc
as a tyrosine kinase. Indeed, hGH mutants that cannot induce recepto
dimerization are biologically inactive. Numerous other protein growth fac
tors also induce the dimerization of their receptors.

2 Receptor Tyrosine Kinases

We have seen (Section 12-3B) that the activities of many enzymes are con
trolled by their covalent modification, mainly the phosphorylation of Se
and Thr residues. A similar process forms the basis of one of the majo

---

■ **CHECK YOUR UNDERSTANDING**

List some of the physiological effects of
insulin, glucagon, norepinephrine,
glucocorticoids, mineralocorticoids,
gonadal steroids, and growth hormone.
What are some dangers of nonmedical use
of steroids and growth hormone?
Describe the general properties of hormone
receptors.
What is the significance of dimerization of
the GH receptor?

LEARNING OBJECTIVES

■ Understand that dimerization and
autophosphorylation allow receptor tyrosine
kinases to become active as protein tyrosine
kinases.
■ Understand that adaptor proteins
containing SH2 and SH3 domains can link
an RTK with G proteins and additional
kinases that operate as a cascade.
■ Understand that some receptors act via
associated nonreceptor tyrosine kinases.
■ Understand that protein phosphorylation
participates in signaling pathways by
removing phosphoryl groups from receptors
and target proteins.

intracellular signaling systems, the ATP-dependent phosphorylation of Tyr side chains by **protein tyrosine kinases (PTKs)**:

Phospho-Tyr residues mediate protein–protein interactions that are involved in numerous cell functions. Consequently, the PTKs play a central role in signal transduction, regulation of central metabolic pathways, cell cycle control, and cell growth and differentiation. In this section, we discuss the proteins that participate in this signaling system and how their activities are orchestrated to transmit signals within the cell.

Receptor Tyrosine Kinases Transmit Signals across the Cell Membrane

*The first step in all biochemical signaling pathways is the binding of a **ligand** to its receptor protein.* Box 13-2 discusses how receptor–ligand interactions are quantitated. Insulin and many other polypeptide growth factors bind to receptors whose C-terminal domains have tyrosine kinase activity. Such **receptor tyrosine kinases (RTKs)** typically contain only a single transmembrane segment and are monomers in the unliganded state. These structural features make it unlikely that ligand binding to an extracellular domain manifests itself as a conformational change in an intracellular domain (such a conformational shift seems more likely to occur in receptors with multiple transmembrane segments). Indeed, the most common mechanism for activating RTKs appears to be ligand-induced dimerization of receptor proteins as is the case with the growth hormone receptor (Section 13-1D; although it lacks tyrosine kinase activity). The insulin receptor is unusual in that it is a dimer in the unliganded state. In this case, ligand binding apparently induces a conformational change in the receptor.

Autophosphorylation Activates Receptor Tyrosine Kinases. When an RTK dimerizes (or its conformation changes on ligand binding, in the case of the insulin receptor), its cytoplasmic protein tyrosine kinase (PTK) domains are brought close together so that they cross-phosphorylate each other on specific Tyr residues. *This **autophosphorylation** activates the PTK so that it can phosphorylate other protein substrates.*

How does autophosphorylation activate the PTK activity of the insulin receptor? The human protein is synthesized as a single 1382-residue precursor peptide that is proteolytically processed to yield the disulfide-linked α and β subunits of the mature receptor (Fig. 13-4). Insulin binds to the receptor's α subunits, which are entirely extracellular, whereas the β subunit contains a PTK domain on its intracellular side.

Figure 13-4 | Schematic diagram of the insulin receptor. The subunits of the α₂β₂ heterotetramer are linked by disulfide bonds (short horizontal bars). The extracellular 731-residue α subunits form the insulin-binding site. The cytoplasmic portions of the 620-residue β subunits are tyrosine kinases that are activated by insulin binding.

See Guided Exploration 12
Mechanisms of hormone signaling involving the receptor tyrosine kinase system.

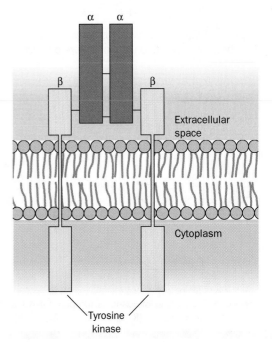

BOX 13-2 PERSPECTIVES IN BIOCHEMISTRY

Receptor–Ligand Binding Can Be Quantitated

Receptors, like other proteins, bind their corresponding ligands according to the laws of mass action:

$$R + L \rightleftharpoons R \cdot L$$

Here R and L represent receptor and ligand, and the reaction's dissociation constant is expressed:

$$K_L = \frac{[R][L]}{[R \cdot L]} = \frac{([R]_T - [R \cdot L])[L]}{[R \cdot L]} \qquad [13\text{-}1]$$

where the total receptor concentration, $[R]_T$, is equal to $[R] + [R \cdot L]$. Equation 13-1 may be rearranged to a form analogous to the Michaelis–Menten equation of enzyme kinetics (Section 12-1B):

$$Y = \frac{[R \cdot L]}{[R]_T} = \frac{[L]}{K_L + [L]} \qquad [13\text{-}2]$$

where Y is the fractional occupation of the ligand-binding sites. Equation 13-2 represents a hyperbolic curve (Fig. 1a) in which K_L may be operationally defined as the ligand concentration at which the receptor is half-maximally occupied by ligand.

Although K_L and $[R]_T$ may, in principle, be determined from an analysis of a hyperbolic plot such as Fig. 1a, the analysis of a linear form of the equation is a more common procedure. Equation 13-1 may be rearranged to

$$\frac{[R \cdot L]}{[L]} = \frac{([R]_T - [R \cdot L])}{K_L} \qquad [13\text{-}3]$$

Now, in keeping with customary receptor-binding nomenclature, let us redefine $[R \cdot L]$ as B (for bound ligand), $[L]$ as F (for free ligand), and $[R]_T$ as B_{max}. Then Eq. 13-3 becomes

$$\frac{B}{F} = \frac{(B_{max} - B)}{K_L} \qquad [13\text{-}4]$$

A plot of B/F versus B, which is known as a **Scatchard plot** (after George Scatchard, its originator), therefore yields a straight line of slope $-1/K_L$ whose intercept on the B axis is B_{max} (Fig. 1b). Here both B and F may be determined by filter-binding assays as follow. Most receptors are insoluble membrane-bound proteins and ma therefore be separated from soluble free ligand by filtration (receptors that have been solubilized may be separated from free ligan by filtration, for example, through nitrocellulose since proteins nor specifically bind to nitrocellulose). Hence, by using radioactive labeled ligand, the values of B and F ($[R \cdot L]$ and $[L]$) may be determined, respectively, from the radioactivity on the filter and tha remaining in solution. The rate of $R \cdot L$ dissociation is generally s slow (half-times of minutes to hours) as to cause insignificant error when the filter is washed to remove residual free ligand.

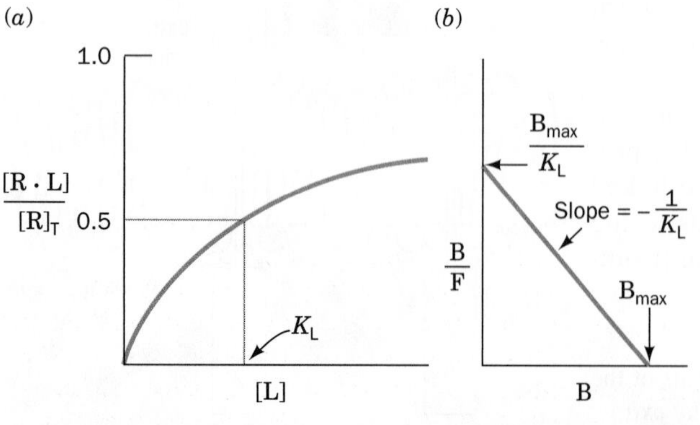

Once the receptor-binding parameters for one ligand have bee determined, the dissociation constant of other ligands for the sam ligand-binding site may be determined through competitive binding studies. The model describing this competitive binding analogous to the competitive inhibition of a Michaelis–Mente enzyme (Section 12-2A):

$$
\begin{array}{ccc}
 & K_L & \\
R + L & \rightleftharpoons & R \cdot L \\
+ & & \\
I & & \\
K_I \big\Updownarrow & & \\
R \cdot I + L & \longrightarrow & \text{No binding}
\end{array}
$$

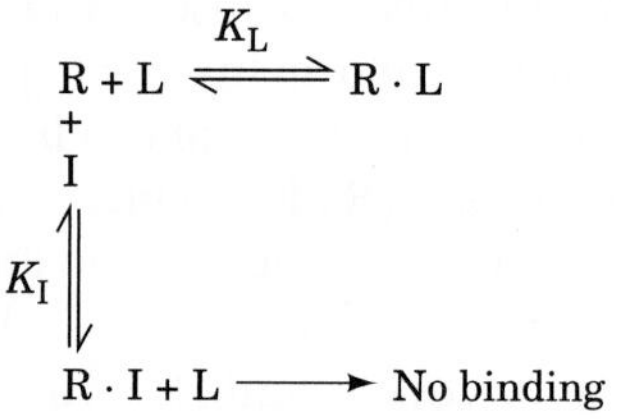

where I is the competing ligand whose dissociation constant wit the receptor is expressed:

$$K_I = \frac{[R][I]}{[R \cdot I]} \qquad [13\text{-}5]$$

Thus, in direct analogy with the derivation of the equation describ ing competitive inhibition:

$$[R \cdot L] = \frac{[R]_T[L]}{K_L\left(1 + \dfrac{[I]}{K_I}\right) + [L]} \qquad [13\text{-}6]$$

The relative affinities of a ligand and an inhibitor may therefor be determined by dividing Eq. 13-6 in the presence of inhibito with that in the absence of inhibitor:

$$\frac{[R \cdot L]_I}{[R \cdot L]_0} = \frac{K_L + [L]}{K_L\left(1 + \dfrac{[I]}{K_I}\right) + [L]} \qquad [13\text{-}7]$$

When this ratio is 0.5 (50% inhibition), the competitor concentra tion is referred to as $[I_{50}]$. Thus, solving Eq. 13-7 for K_I at 50% in hibition:

$$K_I = \frac{[I_{50}]}{1 + \dfrac{[L]}{K_L}} \qquad [13\text{-}8]$$

Figure 1 The binding of ligand to receptor. (a) A hyperbolic plot. (b) A Scatchard plot. Here, $B = [R \cdot L]$, $F = [L]$, and $B_{max} = [R]_T$.

The X-ray structure of the β subunit's 306-residue PTK domain (Fig. 13-5a) reveals a deeply clefted bilobal protein whose N-terminal domain consists of a five-stranded β sheet and an α helix and whose larger C-terminal domain is mainly α helical. This structure, as we shall repeatedly see, is typical of the large family of protein kinases, enzymes that phosphorylate the OH groups of Tyr residues and/or Ser and Thr residues. Indeed, the human genome encodes 90 PTKs and 388 protein Ser/Thr kinases (representing >2% of human genes) that collectively phosphorylate an estimated one-third of the proteins in human cells. In doing so, they play key roles in the signaling pathways by which many hormones, growth factors, neurotransmitters, and toxins affect the functions of their target cells.

In the X-ray structure of the insulin receptor PTK domain (Fig. 13-5a), the nonhydrolyzable ATP analog **adenosine-5′-(β,γ-imido)triphosphate** (**AMPPNP;** alternatively **ADPNP;** *at right*) is bound in the cleft between the protein domains. There, its γ-phosphate group is in close juxtaposition to the OH group of the target Tyr residue in the 18-residue substrate peptide that is also bound to the protein. Three of the PTK's Tyr residues, all of which are located on its C-terminal domain, are phosphorylated.

Comparison of this X-ray structure with that of the unphosphorylated and uncomplexed protein indicates that on ligand binding and

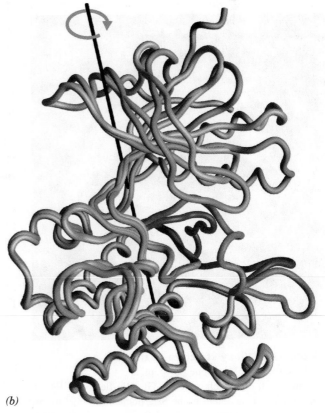

Adenosine-5′-(β,γ-imido)triphosphate (AMPPNP)

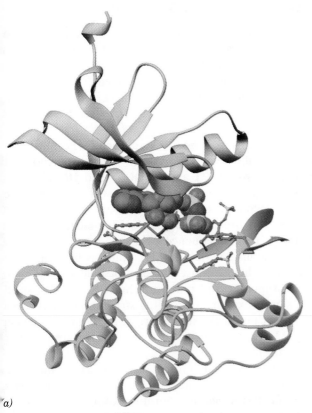

(a)

■ Figure 13-5 | X-Ray structure of the tyrosine kinase domain of the insulin receptor. (*a*) The tyrosine kinase domain is shown in the "standard" protein kinase orientation with its N-terminal domain lavender, its C-terminal domain cyan, and its activation loop light blue. Its three phosphorylated Tyr side chains are shown in ball-and-stick form with C green, N blue, O red, and P yellow. The ATP analog AMPPNP is shown in space-filling form. The substrate polypeptide is orange (only six of its residues are visible) and its phosphorylatable Tyr residue is shown with C magenta and O red.

(*b*) The polypeptide backbones of the phosphorylated and unphosphorylated forms of the insulin receptor tyrosine kinase domain are shown superimposed on their C-terminal lobes. The phosphorylated protein is green with its activation loop blue, and the unphosphorylated protein is yellow with its activation loop red. The blue arrow and black axis indicate the rotation required to align the two N-terminal lobes. [Part *a* based on an X-ray structure by and Part *b* courtesy of Stevan Hubbard, New York University Medical School. PDBids 1IR3 and 1IRK.] **⌘2 See Interactive Exercise 11.**

phosphorylation, the PTK's N-terminal lobe undergoes a nearly rigid 21° rotation relative to the C-terminal lobe (Fig. 13-5b). This dramatic conformational change closes the active site cleft, presumably positioning critical residues for substrate binding and catalysis. The three phospho-Tyr residues are all located on the protein's so-called activation loop. The unphosphorylated activation loop threads through the PTK active site so as to prevent the binding of both ATP and protein substrates. On phosphorylation, however, the activation loop changes its conformation such that it does not occlude the active site (Fig. 13-5b) but instead forms part of the substrate recognition site. In fact, the PTK activity of the insulin receptor increases with the degree of phosphorylation of its three autophosphorylatable Tyr residues.

Nearly all known PTKs have between one and three autophosphorylatable Tyr residues in their activation loops, which assume similar conformations in all phosphorylated PTKs of known structure. Moreover, many activated PTKs also phosphorylate the opposing RTK at cytoplasmic Tyr residues outside of its PTK domain. The specificity of PTKs for phosphorylating Tyr rather than Ser or Thr is explained by the observation that the side chain of Tyr, but not those of Ser or Thr, is long enough to reach the active site.

B | Kinase Cascades Relay Signals to the Nucleus

Although certain autophosphorylated RTKs directly phosphorylate their ultimate target proteins, many do not do so. How then, are these target proteins activated? The answer, as we shall see, is through a highly diverse and complicated set of interconnected signaling pathways involving cascades of associating proteins.

SH2 Domains Bind Phospho-Tyr Residues. The main substrates of the insulin receptor tyrosine kinase are known as **insulin receptor substrates 1** and **2 (IRS-1** and **IRS-2).** When phosphorylated, these proteins can interact with yet another set of proteins that contain one or two conserved ~100-residue modules known as **Src homology 2 (SH2) domains** [because they are similar to the sequence of a domain in the protein named **Src** (pronounced "sarc")]. SH2 domains bind phospho-Tyr residues with high affinity but do not bind the far more abundant phospho-Ser and phospho-Thr residues. This specificity has a simple explanation. X-Ray structural studies reveal that phospho-Tyr interacts with an Arg at the bottom of a deep pocket (Fig. 13-6). The side chains of Ser and Thr are too short to interact with this residue.

The SH2-containing proteins that interact with the IRSs and other substrates have varied functions: Some are kinases, some are phosphatases, and some are GTPases that are therefore known as **G proteins** (Section 13-3B). To further complicate matters, IRS-1 is subject to serine phosphorylation, which attenuates the effects of insulin-stimulated tyrosine phosphorylation.

Activated RTKs Indirectly Activate the G Protein Ras. Molecular genetic analysis of signaling in a variety of distantly related organisms revealed a remarkably conserved pathway that regulates such essential functions as cell growth and differentiation. Briefly, growth factor binding to

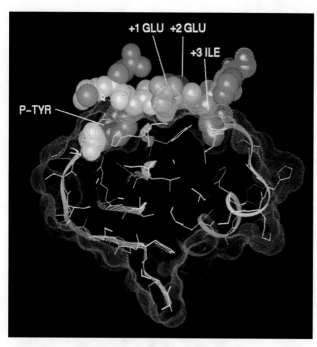

■ **Figure 13-6** | **X-Ray structure of the Src SH2 domain.** An 11-residue polypeptide containing the protein's phospho-Tyr-Glu-Glu-Ile target tetrapeptide is bound to the SH2 domain. In this cutaway view, the protein surface is represented by red dots, the protein backbone (*pink*) is shown in ribbon form with its side chains in stick form, and the bound polypeptide's N-terminal 8-residue segment is shown in space-filling form with its backbone yellow, its side chains green, and its phosphate group white. [Courtesy of John Kuriyan, The Rockefeller University.]

s cognate RTK activates a monomeric G protein (GTPase) named **Ras** hat is anchored to the inner surface of the plasma membrane by prenyl- tion (Section 9-3B). Activated Ras, as we shall see below, then activates **kinase cascade** that relays the signal to the transcriptional apparatus in he nucleus.

H3 Domains Bind Pro-Rich Sequences. The binding of a growth actor to its RTK leads to autophosphorylation of the RTK, which then nteracts with an SH2-containing protein (Fig. 13-7, *left*). Many proteins that ontain SH2 domains also have one or more unrelated 50- to 75-residue **H3 domains.** SH3 domains, which bind Pro-rich sequences of 9 or 10

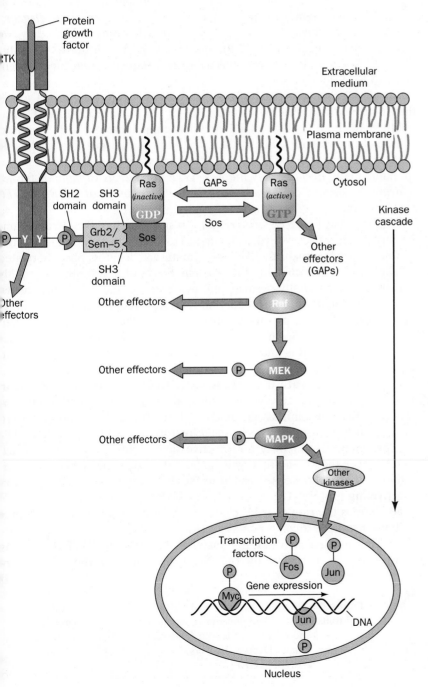

■ **Figure 13-7 | The Ras signaling cascade.** RTK binding to its cognate growth factor induces the autophosphorylation of the RTK's cytosolic domain. Grb2/Sem-5 binds to the resulting phospho-Tyr–containing peptide segment via its SH2 domain and simultaneously binds to Pro-rich segments on Sos via its two SH3 domains. This activates Sos to exchange Ras's bound GDP for GTP, which activates Ras to bind to Raf. Then, in a so-called kinase cascade, Raf, a Ser/Thr kinase, phosphorylates MEK, which in turn phosphorylates MAPK, which then migrates to the nucleus, where it phosphorylates transcription factors such as Fos, Jun, and Myc, thereby modulating gene expression. Ras is inactivated by GTP hydrolysis, a process that is accelerated by GTPase-activating proteins (GAPs). The kinase cascade eventually returns to its resting state through the action of protein phosphatases (Section 13-2D). [After Egan, S.E. and Weinberg, R.A., *Nature* **365,** 782 (1993).] ᥒ **See the Animated Figures.**

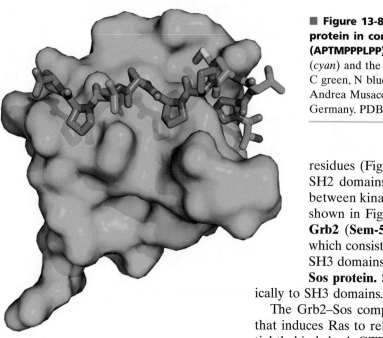

■ **Figure 13-8** | **X-Ray structure of the SH3 domain from Ab1 protein in complex with its 10-residue target Pro-rich polypeptide (APTMPPPLPP).** The protein is represented by its surface diagram (*cyan*) and the peptide is drawn in stick form with Pro C magenta, other C green, N blue, O red, and S yellow. [Based on an X-ray structure by Andrea Musacchio, European Molecular Biology Laboratory, Heidelberg, Germany. PDBid 1ABO.]

residues (Fig. 13-8), are also present in some proteins that lack SH2 domains. Both types of domains mediate the interactions between kinases and regulatory proteins. In the signaling cascade shown in Fig. 13-7, a 217-residue mammalian protein known as **Grb2** (**Sem-5** in the nematode worm *Caenorhabditis elegans*), which consists almost entirely of an SH2 domain flanked by two SH3 domains (Fig. 13-9), forms a complex with the 1596-residue **Sos protein.** Sos contains a Pro-rich sequence that binds specifically to SH3 domains.

The Grb2–Sos complex bridges the activated RTK and Ras in a way that induces Ras to release its bound GDP and replace it with GTP. Ras tightly binds both GTP and GDP and hence must interact with Sos to exchange the nucleotides. Sos is therefore known as a **guanine nucleotide exchange factor (GEF).** Most G proteins, as we shall see, have a corresponding GEF. *Because only the Ras·GTP complex is capable of further relaying the signal from an activated RTK, the exchange of GDP for GTP activates Ras.*

The X-ray structure of Grb2 (Fig. 13-9) suggests that its SH2 domain is flexibly linked to its two SH3 domains. How does the binding of such a pliable **adaptor** (a linker that lacks enzymatic activity) to a phosphorylated RTK cause Sos to activate Ras? Grb2 and Sos bind one another so tightly that they are essentially permanently associated in the cell. Hence, when Grb2 binds to a phosphorylated RTK, it recruits Sos to the inner surface of the plasma membrane, where the increased local concentration of Sos causes it to more readily bind to the membrane-anchored Ras and thus act as a GEF.

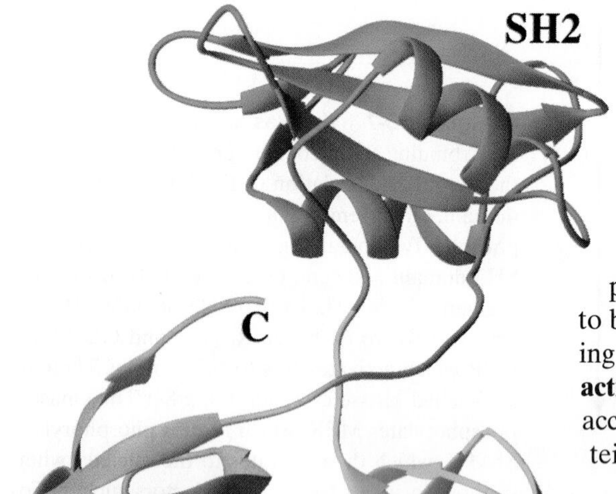

GAPs Accelerate the GTPase Activities of G Proteins. Ras is an enzyme that catalyzes the hydrolysis of its bound GTP to GDP + P_i, thereby limiting the magnitude of the cell's response to the growth factor. Yet, Ras by itself hydrolyzes only two to three GTPs per minute, too slowly for effective signal transduction (for a signal to be more than a one-time switch, there must be a mechanism for turning it off as well as on). This led to the discovery of a 120-kD **GTPase activating protein (GAP)** named **RasGAP** that, on binding Ras·GTP, accelerates the rate of GTP hydrolysis by a factor of 10^5. Most G proteins also have a corresponding GAP.

The mechanism whereby RasGAP activates the GTPase activity of Ras was revealed by the X-ray structure of the 334-residue

SH2

C

N

SH3-N

SH3-C

■ **Figure 13-9** | **X-Ray structure of Grb2.** Its SH2 domain (*green*) is linked to its flanking SH3 domains (*cyan and orange*) via apparently unstructured and hence flexible four-residue linkers. [Based on an X-ray structure by Arnaud Ducruix, Université de Paris-Sud, Gif sur Yvette Cedex, France. PDBid 1GRI.]

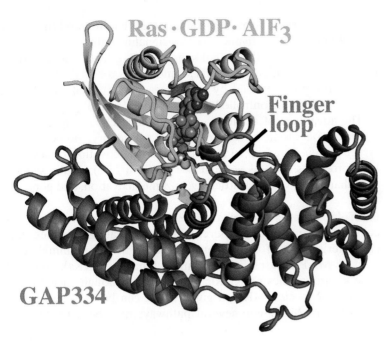

Ras·GDP·AlF₃

Finger loop

GAP334

■ **Figure 13-10** | **X-Ray structure of the GAP334·Ras·GDP·AlF₃ complex.** Ras and GAP334 are cyan and magenta with the finger loop of GAP334 red. The GDP and AlF₃ are drawn in space-filling form with C green, N blue, O red, F light green, and Al light blue. The side chain of Arg 789, which is drawn in stick form, extends from the finger loop. Note how it interacts with both the AlF₃ and the β phosphate group of the GDP. [Based on an X-ray structure by Alfred Wittinghofer, Max-Planck-Institut für Molekulare Physiologie, Dortmund, Germany. PDBid 1WQ1.]

GTPase-activating domain of RasGAP (GAP334) bound to Ras in its complex with GDP and AlF₃ (Fig. 13-10). GAP334 interacts with Ras over an extensive surface. The AlF₃, which has trigonal planar geometry, binds to Ras at the expected position of GTP's γ phosphate group with the Al atom opposite a bound water molecule that presumably would be the attacking nucleophile in the GTPase reaction. Since Al—F and P—O bonds have similar lengths, the GDP–AlF₃–H_2O assembly resembles the GTPase reaction's expected transition state with the AlF₃ mimicking the planar PO_3 group.

GAP334 binds to Ras with GAP334's so-called finger loop inserted into the Ras active site such that the finger loop's Arg 789 side chain interacts with both the Ras-bound GDP's β phosphate and the AlF₃ (Fig. 13-10). In Ras · GTP, this Arg side chain would be in an excellent position to stabilize the developing negative charge in the GTPase reaction's transition state. Indeed, catalytically more efficient G proteins contain an Arg residue that occupies a nearly identical position.

A Kinase Cascade Completes the Signaling Pathway. The signaling pathway downstream of Ras consists of a linear cascade of protein kinases (Fig. 13-7, *right*). The Ser/Thr kinase **Raf,** which is activated by direct interaction with Ras · GTP, phosphorylates a protein alternatively known as **MEK** or **MAP kinase kinase,** thereby activating it as a kinase. Activated MEK phosphorylates a family of proteins variously termed **mitogen-activated protein kinases (MAPKs)** or **extracellular-signal-regulated kinases (ERKs).** A MAPK must be phosphorylated at both its Thr and Tyr residues in the sequence Thr-Glu-Tyr for full activity. MEK (which stands for *M*AP kinase/*E*RK kinase-activating *k*inase) catalyzes both phosphorylations; it is therefore a protein Ser/Thr kinase as well as a protein Tyr kinase.

The activated MAP kinases migrate from the cytosol to the nucleus, where they phosphorylate a variety of proteins, including **Fos, Jun,** and **Myc.** These proteins are **transcription factors** (proteins that induce the transcription of their target genes; Section 28-3B): In their activated forms they stimulate various genes to produce the effects commissioned by the extracellular presence of the growth factor that initiated the signaling cascade. When insulin activates the Ras signaling pathway, the result is an increase in protein synthesis that supports cell growth and differentiation, a response consistent with insulin's function as a signal of fuel abundance. Variant proteins encoded by **oncogenes** subvert such signaling pathways so as to induce uncontrolled cell growth (Box 13-3).

The advantage of a kinase cascade is that *a small signal can be amplified manyfold inside the cell.* In addition, phosphorylation of more than one target protein can lead to the simultaneous activation of several intracellular processes. Thus as we shall see (Section 22-2), insulin signaling mediates changes in vesicle trafficking, enzyme activation, and gene expression.

Scaffold Proteins Organize and Position Protein Kinases. Eukaryotic cells contain numerous different MAPK signaling cascades, each with a characteristic set of component kinases, which in mammals comprise at least 12 MAP kinases, 7 MAP kinase kinases (MKKs), and 14 MAP kinase kinase kinases (MKKKs; Fig. 13-11). Although each MAPK is activated by a specific MKK, a given MKK can be activated by more than one MKKK. Moreover, several pathways may be activated by a single

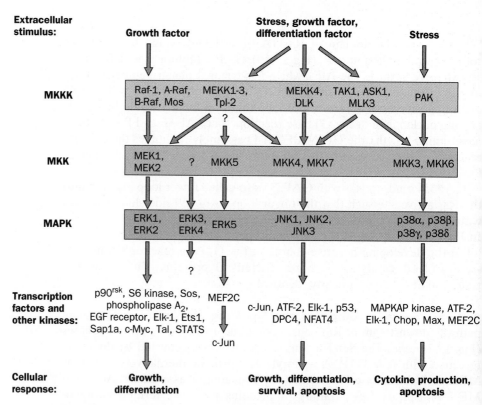

■ **Figure 13-11 | MAP kinase cascades in mammalian cells.** Each MAP kinase cascade consists of an MKKK, an MKK, and a MAPK. Various external stimuli may each activate one or more MKKKs, which in turn may activate one or more MKKs. However, the MKKs are relatively specific for their target MAPKs. The activated MAPKs phosphorylate specific transcription factors (e.g., **Elk-1, Ets-1, p53, NFAT4,** and **Max**), which are then translocated to the nucleus, as well as specific kinases (e.g., **p90**rsk, **S6 kinase,** and **MAPKAP kinase**). The resulting activated transcription factors and kinases then induce cellular responses such as growth, differentiation, and **apoptosis** (programmed cell death; Section 28-4C). [After Garrington, T.P. and Johnson, G.L., *Curr. Opin. Cell Biol.* **11,** 212 (1999).]

BOX 13-3 BIOCHEMISTRY IN HEALTH AND DISEASE

Oncogenes and Cancer

The growth and differentiation of cells in the body are normally strictly controlled. Thus, with few exceptions (e.g., blood-forming cells and hair follicles), cells in the adult body are largely quiescent. However, for a variety of reasons, a cell may be made to proliferate uncontrollably to form a tumor.

Malignant tumors (cancers) grow in an invasive manner and are almost invariably life threatening. They are responsible for 20% of the mortalities in the United States.

Among the many causes of cancer are viruses that carry **oncogenes** (Greek: *onkos,* mass or tumor). For example, the **Rous sarcoma virus (RSV),** which induces the formation of **sarcomas** (cancers arising from connective tissues) in chickens, contains four genes. Three of the genes are essential for viral replication, whereas the fourth, **v-*src*** (v for viral, *src* for sarcoma), an oncogene, induces tumor formation. What is the origin of v-*src,* and how does it function? Hybridization studies by Michael Bishop and Harold Varmus in 1976 led to the remarkable discovery that uninfected chicken cells contain a gene, **c-*src*** (c for cellular), that is homologous to v-*src* and that is highly conserved in a wide variety of eukaryotes, suggesting that it is an essential cellular gene. Apparently, v-*src* was originally acquired from a cellular source by a non-tumor-forming ancestor of RSV. Both v-*src* and c-*src* encode a 60-kD tyrosine kinase. However, whereas the activity of c-*src* is strictly regulated, that of v-*src* is under no such control and hence its presence maintains the host cell in a proliferative state. Since cells are not killed by an RSV infection, this presumably enhances the viral replication rate.

Other oncogenes have been similarly linked to processes that regulate cell growth. For example, the **v-*erbB*** oncogene specifies a truncated version of the **epidermal growth factor (EGF) receptor,** which lacks the EGF-binding domain but retains its transmembrane segment and its tyrosine kinase domain. This kinase phosphorylates its target proteins in the absence of an extracellular signal, thereby driving uncontrolled cell proliferation.

The **v-*ras*** oncogene encodes a 21-kD protein, **v-Ras,** that resembles cellular Ras but hydrolyzes GTP much more slowly. The reduced braking effect of GTP hydrolysis on the rate of protein phosphorylation leads to increased activation of the kinases downstream of Ras (Fig. 13-7).

The transcription factors that respond to Ras-mediated signaling (e.g., Fos and Jun) are also encoded by **proto-oncogenes,** the normal cellular analogs of oncogenes. The viral genes **v-*fos*** and **v-*jun*** encode proteins that are nearly identical to their cellular counterparts and mimic their effects on host cells but in an uncontrolled fashion.

Oncogenes are not necessarily of viral origin. Indeed, few human cancers are caused by viruses. Rather, they are caused by proto-oncogenes that have mutated to form oncogenes. For example, a mutation in the **c-*ras*** gene, which converts Gly 12 of Ras to Val, reduces Ras's GTPase activity without affecting its ability to stimulate protein phosphorylation. This prolongs the time that Ras is in the "on" state, thereby inducing uncontrolled cell proliferation. In fact, oncogenic versions of c-*ras* are among the most commonly implicated oncogenes in human cancers.

To date, over 50 oncogenes have been identified. The subversive effects of oncogene products arise through their differences from the corresponding normal cellular proteins: They may have different rates of synthesis and/or degradation; they may have altered cellular functions; or they may resist control by cellular regulatory mechanisms. However, in order for a normal cell to undergo a **malignant transformation** (become a cancer cell), it must undergo several (an average of five) independent oncogenic events. This is a reflection of the complexity of cellular signaling networks (cells respond to a variety of hormones, growth factors, and transcription factors in partially overlapping ways) and explains why the incidence of cancer increases with age.

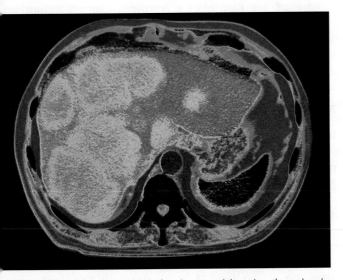

An X-ray–based false-color image showing an axial section through a human abdomen that has cancer of the liver. The liver is the large red mass occupying much of the abdomen; the light patches on the liver are cancerous tumors. A vertebra (*dark green*) can be seen at the lower center of the image. [Salisbury/Photo Researchers.]

type of receptor. How then does a cell prevent inappropriate **cross talk** between closely related signaling pathways? One way that this occurs is through the use of **scaffold proteins** that bind some or all of the component protein kinases of a particular signaling cascade so as to ensure that the protein kinases of a given pathway interact only with one another. In addition, a scaffold protein can control the subcellular location of its associated kinases.

The first known scaffold protein was discovered through the genetic analysis of a MAP kinase cascade in yeast, which demonstrated that this protein, **Ste5p,** binds the MKKK, MKK, and MAPK components of the pathway and that, *in vivo,* the scaffold's absence inactivates the pathway. Evidently, the interactions between successive kinase components of this MAP kinase cascade are, by themselves, insufficient for signal transmission.

C | Some Receptors Are Associated with Nonreceptor Tyrosine Kinases

Many cell-surface receptors are not members of the receptor families that we have discussed so far and do not respond to ligand binding by autophosphorylation. These include the receptors for growth hormone (Fig. 13-3), the **cytokines** (protein growth factors that regulate the differentiation, proliferation, and activities of numerous types of cells, most conspicuously blood cells), the **interferons** (protein growth factors that stimulate antiviral defenses), and **T cell receptors** [which control the proliferation of immune system cells known as T lymphocytes (T cells); Section 7-3]. *Ligand binding induces these tyrosine kinase–associated receptors to dimerize (and, in some cases, to trimerize), often with different types of subunits, in a way that activates associated* **nonreceptor tyrosine kinases (NRTKs).**

The Structure of Src Reveals Its Autoinhibitory Mechanism.
Many of the NRTKs that are activated by tyrosine kinase–associated receptors belong to the **Src family,** which contains at least nine members including Src, **Fyn,** and **Lck.** Most of these ~530-residue membrane-anchored (by myristoylation) proteins have both an SH2 and an SH3 domain and all have a PTK domain. Hence, a Src-related kinase may also be activated by association with an autophosphorylated RTK. Although Src-related kinases are each associated with different receptors, they phosphorylate overlapping sets of target proteins. This complex web of interactions explains why different ligands often activate some of the same signaling pathways.

Src consists of, from N- to C-terminus, a myristoylated N-terminal "unique" domain that differs among Src family members, an SH3 domain, an SH2 domain, a PTK domain, and a short C-terminal tail. Phosphorylation of Tyr 416 in the PTK's activation loop activates Src, whereas phosphorylation of Tyr 527 in its C-terminal tail deactivates it. *In vivo,* Src is phosphorylated at either Tyr 416 or Tyr 527, but not at both. The dephosphorylation of Tyr 527 or the binding of external ligands to the SH2 or the SH3 domain activates Src, a state that is then maintained by the autophosphorylation of Tyr 416. When Tyr 527 is phosphorylated and no activating phosphopeptides are available, Src's SH2 and SH3 domains function to deactivate its PTK domain; that is, Src is then autoinhibited.

The X-ray structure of Src·AMPPNP lacking its N-terminal domain and with Tyr 527 phosphorylated reveals the structural basis of Src autoinhibition (Fig. 13-12). As biochemical studies had previously shown, the SH2 domain binds phospho-Tyr 527, which occurs in the sequence pYNPG rather than the pYEEI sequence characteristic of high-affinity Src SH2

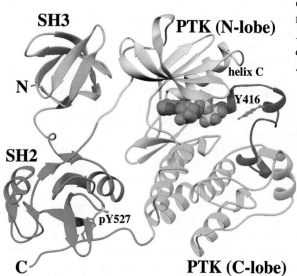

■ **Figure 13-12 | X-Ray structure of Src·AMPPNP lacking its N-terminal domain and with Tyr 527 phosphorylated.** The protein is oriented such that its PTK domain is seen in "standard" view (compare it with Fig. 13-5*a*). The SH3 domain is orange, the SH2 domain is magenta, the linker joining the SH2 domain to the PTK domain is green with residues 249 to 253, which interact with the SH3 domain, yellow, the N-terminal lobe of the PTK domain is lavender, its C-terminal lobe is cyan with its activation loop light blue, and its C-terminal tail is red. The AMPPNP is shown in space-filling form and Y416 and pY527 are shown in ball-and-stick form, all with C green, N blue, O red, and P yellow. [Based on an X-ray structure by Stephen Harrison and Michael Eck, Harvard Medical School. PDBid 2SRC.]

rget peptides. Although the pYNP segment binds to SH2 as does the YEE segment in Fig. 13-6, the succeeding residues are poorly ordered in e X-ray structure and, moreover, the SH2 pocket in which the Ile side ain of pYEEI binds is unoccupied. Apparently, the phospho-Tyr 27–containing peptide segment binds to the Src SH2 domain with reuced affinity relative to its target peptides.

The SH3 domain binds to the linker connecting the SH3 domain to the -terminal lobe of the PTK domain. Residues 249 to 253 of the linker ind to the SH3 domain in much the same way as do SH3's Pro-rich tar-et peptides (Fig. 13-8). However, the only Pro in this segment is residue 50. The polar side chain of Gln 253, which occupies the position of the econd Pro in SH3's normal Pro-X-X-Pro target sequence, does not enter e hydrophobic binding pocket that this second Pro would occupy Fig. 13-8) and hence the path of the peptide deviates from that of Pro-rich arget peptides at this point. Apparently, this interaction is also weaker an those with Src's SH3 target peptides.

Src's SH2 and SH3 domains bind the PTK domain on the side oppo-te its active site. How, then, does the conformation shown in Fig. 13-12 hibit the PTK's activity? The two lobes of Src's PTK domain are, for the ost part, closely superimposable on their counterparts in the PTK domains f phosphorylated and hence activated protein kinases (e.g., Fig. 13-5a). owever, Src helix C (the only helix in the PTK's N-terminal lobe) is splaced from the interface between the N- and C-terminal lobes relative its position in other activated protein kinases. Helix C contains the

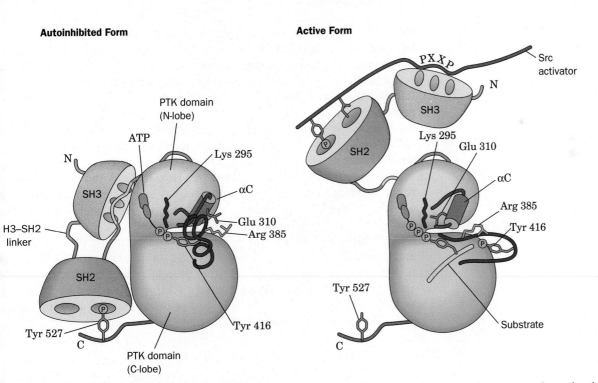

Figure 13-13 | Schematic model of Src activation. In the utoinhibited form (*left*), the SH2 domain (*magenta*) binds to hospho-Tyr 527, and the SH3 domain (*orange*) binds to an internal ro-containing segment (*yellow*). Glu 310 forms a salt bridge to rg 385, the partially helical activation loop (*blue*) blocks the active ite, and Tyr 416 is buried. In the active form (*right*), the SH2 and H3 domains bind to a Src activator, Tyr 527 is dephosphorylated,

the activation loop has undergone a conformational change to expose Tyr 416 to phosphorylation, Glu 310 forms a salt bridge with Lys 295, and phospho-Tyr 416 forms a salt bridge with Arg 385. The coloring scheme and viewpoint largely match those in Fig. 13-12. [After Young, M.A., Gonfloni, F., Superti-Furga, G., Roux, B., and Kuriyan, J., *Cell* **105,** 116 (2001).]

conserved residue Glu 310 (using Src numbering), which in other activate
protein kinases projects into the catalytic cleft where it forms a salt bridg
with Lys 295, an important ligand of the substrate ATP's α and
phosphates. In inactive Src, Glu 310 forms an alternative salt bridge wit
Arg 385, and Lys 295 instead interacts with Asp 404. In activated Lck, Ar
385 forms a salt bridge with phospho-Tyr 416.

The foregoing structural observations suggest the following scenario fo
Src activation (Fig 13-13):

1. The dephosphorylation of Tyr 527 and/or the binding of the SH
and/or SH3 domains to their target peptides (for which SH2 and SH
have greater affinity than their internal Src-binding sites) release
these domains from their PTK-bound positions shown in Fig. 13-12
thus relaxing conformational constraints on the PTK domain. Thi
allows the PTK's active site cleft to open, thereby disrupting the
structure of its partially helical activation loop (which occupies
blocking position in the active site cleft; Fig. 13-12) so as to expos
Tyr 416 to autophosphorylation.

2. The resulting phospho-Tyr 416 forms a salt bridge with Arg 385
which sterically requires the structural reorganization of the activa
tion loop to its active, nonblocking conformation. The consequen
rupture of the Glu 310—Arg 385 salt bridge frees helix C to assum
its active orientation which, in turn, allows Glu 310 to form its cat
alytically important salt bridge to Lys 295, thereby activating the Sr
PTK activity.

PTKs Are Targets of Anticancer Drugs. The hallmark of **chronic mye
logenous leukemia (CML)** is a specific chromosomal translocation forming
the so-called **Philadelphia chromosome** in which the *Abl* gene (which en
codes the NRTK **Abl**) is fused with the *Bcr* gene (which encodes the pro
tein Ser/Thr kinase **Bcr**). The Abl portion of the resulting Bcr–Abl fusion
protein is constitutively activated (that is, continuously, without regula
tion), probably because its Bcr portion oligomerizes. Hematopoietic stem
cells (from which all blood cells are descended) bearing the Philadelphia
chromosome are therefore primed to develop CML (malignancy requires
several independent genetic alterations; Box 13-3). Without a bone mar
row transplant (a high-risk procedure that is unavailable to most individ
uals due to the lack of a suitable donor), CML is invariably fatal with an
average survival time of ~6 years.

An inhibitor of Abl would be expected to prevent the proliferation of
and even kill, CML cells. However, to be an effective anti-CML agent
such a substance must not inhibit other protein kinases because this would
almost certainly cause serious side effects. Derivatives of 2-phenyl
aminopyrimidine bind to Abl with exceptionally high affinity and speci
ficity. One such derivative, **imatinib** (trade name **Gleevec**),

Gleevec (imatinib)

which was developed by Brian Druker and Nicholas Lydon, has caused the remission of symptoms in >90% of CML patients with almost no serious side effects. This unprecedented performance occurs, in part, because Gleevec does not bind to other protein kinases.

Abl resembles Src but lacks Src's C-terminal regulatory phosphorylation site (Figs. 13-12 and 13). The X-ray structure of Abl's PTK domain in complex with a truncated form of Gleevec, determined by John Kuriyan (Fig. 13-14), reveals, as expected, that the drug binds in Abl's ATP-binding site. Abl thereby adopts an inactive conformation in which its activation loop, which is not phosphorylated, assumes an autoinhibitory conformation.

Gleevec was the first of several 2-phenylaminopyrimidine derivatives, which inhibit specific protein kinases, to be approved by the FDA for clinical use against certain cancers. In addition, several monoclonal antibodies (Box 7-5) that bind to specific PTKs or their ligands are in clinical use as anticancer agents [e.g., **trastuzumab** (trade name **Herceptin**), which is effective against breast cancers that overexpress the RTK named **HER2;** Box 7-5]. Such receptor-targeted therapies hold enormous promise for controlling, if not curing, cancers by specifically targeting the aberrant proteins that cause the cancers. In contrast, most chemotherapeutic agents that are presently in use indiscriminately kill fast-growing cells and hence tend to have debilitating side effects.

D | Protein Phosphatases Are Signaling Proteins in Their Own Right

Intracellular signals must be "turned off" after the system has delivered its message so that the system can transmit future messages. In the case of protein kinases, their activities are balanced by the activities of **protein phosphatases** that hydrolyze the phosphoryl groups attached to Ser, Thr, or Tyr side chains and thereby limit the effects of the signal that activated the kinase. Although protein kinases have traditionally garnered more attention, mammalian cells express a large number of protein phosphatases with substrate specificities comparable to those of kinases.

Protein Tyrosine Phosphatases Are Multidomain Proteins. The enzymes that dephosphorylate Tyr residues, the **protein tyrosine phosphatases (PTPs),** are not just simple housekeeping enzymes but are important signal transducers. These enzymes, 107 of which are encoded by the human genome, are members of four families. Each tyrosine phosphatase contains at least one conserved ~240-residue phosphatase domain that has the 11-residue signature sequence [(I/V)HCXAGXGR(S/T)G], the so-called CX_5R motif, which contains the enzyme's catalytically essential Cys and Arg residues. During the hydrolysis reaction, the phosphoryl group is transferred from the tyrosyl residue of the substrate protein to the essential Cys on the enzyme, forming a covalent Cys–phosphate intermediate that is subsequently hydrolyzed.

Some tyrosine phosphatases are constructed much like the receptor tyrosine kinases; that is, they have an extracellular domain, a single transmembrane helix, and a cytoplasmic domain consisting of a catalytically active PTP domain that, in most cases, is followed by a second PTP domain with little or no catalytic activity. These inactive PTP domains are, nevertheless, highly conserved, which suggests that they have an important although as yet unknown function. Biochemical and structural analyses indicate that ligand-induced dimerization of a receptor-like PTP reduces its catalytic activity, probably by blocking their active sites.

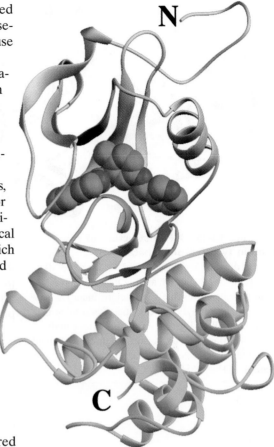

■ **Figure 13-14** | **X-Ray structure of the Abl PTK domain in complex with a truncated derivative of Gleevec.** The protein is viewed from the right of the "standard" view of protein kinases (e.g., Figs. 13-5*a* and 13-12), with its N-terminal lobe lavender, its C-terminal lobe cyan, and its activation loop light blue. The truncated Gleevec, which occupies the PTK's ATP-binding site, is shown in space-filling form with C green, N blue, and O red. [Based on an X-ray structure by John Kuriyan, The Rockefeller University. PDBid 1FPU.]

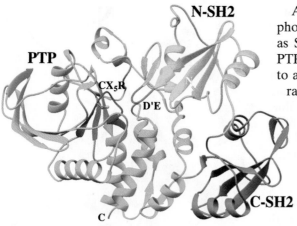

■ Figure 13-15 | X-Ray structure of the protein tyrosine phosphatase SHP-2. Its N-SH2 domain is gold with its D′E loop red, its C-SH2 domain is green, and its PTP domain is cyan with its 11-residue CX₅R motif blue. The side chain of the catalytically essential Cys residue is shown in ball-and-stick form with C green and S yellow. [Based on an X-ray structure by Michael Eck and Steven Shoelson, Harvard Medical School. PDBid 2SHP.]

A second group of PTPs, intracellular PTPs, contain only one tyrosine phosphatase domain, which is flanked by regions containing motifs, such as SH2 domains, that participate in protein–protein interactions. The PTP known as **SHP-2,** which is expressed in all mammalian cells, binds to a variety of phosphorylated (that is, ligand-activated) RTKs. The X-ray structure of SHP-2 lacking its C-terminal tail reveals two SH2 domains, followed by a tyrosine phosphatase domain (Fig. 13-15). The N-terminal SH2 domain (N-SH2) functions as an autoinhibitor by inserting a protein loop (labeled D′E in Fig. 13-15) into the PTP's 9-Å-deep catalytic cleft. When N-SH2 recognizes and binds a phospho-Tyr group on a substrate protein, its conformation changes, unmasking the PTP catalytic site so that the phosphatase can hydrolyze another phospho-Tyr group on the target protein (activated RTKs typically bear multiple phosphorylated Tyr residues).

The active site cleft of intracellular tyrosine phosphatases such as SHP-2 is too deep to cleave phospho-Ser/Thr side chains. However, the active site pockets of a third group of PTPs, the so-called **dual-specificity tyrosine phosphatases,** are sufficiently shallow to bind both phospho-Tyr and phospho-Ser/Thr residues.

Bubonic Plague Virulence Requires a PTP. Bacteria lack PTKs and hence do not synthesize phospho-Tyr residues. Nevertheless, PTPs are expressed by bacteria of the genus *Yersinia,* most notably *Yersinia pestis,* the pathogen that causes **bubonic plague** (the flea-transmitted "Black Death," which, since the sixth century, has been responsible for an estimated 200 million human deaths including about one-third of the European population in the years 1347–1350). The *Y. pestis* PTP, **YopH,** which is required for bacterial virulence, is far more catalytically active than other known PTPs. Hence, when *Yersinia* injects YopH into a cell, the cell's phospho-Tyr-containing proteins are catastrophically dephosphorylated. Although YopH and mammalian PTPs are only ~15% identical in sequence, they share a set of invariant residues and have similar X-ray structures. This suggests that an ancestral *Yersinia* acquired a PTP gene from a eukaryote.

Protein Ser/Thr Phosphatases Participate in Numerous Regulatory Processes. The **protein Ser/Thr phosphatases** in mammalian cells belong to two protein families: the **PPP family** and the **PPM family.** The PPP and PPM families are unrelated to each other or to the PTPs. X-Ray structures have shown that PPP catalytic centers each contain an Fe^{2+} (or possibly an Fe^{3+}) ion and a Zn^{2+} (or possibly an Mn^{2+}) ion, whereas PPM catalytic centers each contain two Mn^{2+} ions. These binuclear metal ion centers nucleophilically activate water molecules to dephosphorylate substrates in a single reaction step.

The PPP family member named **phosphoprotein phosphatase-1 (PP1),** as we shall see, plays an important role in regulating glycogen metabolism (Section 16-3B). The PPP member known as **PP2A** participates in a wide variety of regulatory processes including those governing metabolism, DNA replication, transcription, and development. PP2A is a heterotrimer that consists of a scaffold (A) subunit that binds both a catalytic (C) subunit and a regulatory (B) subunit. The A subunit, which consists of 15 imperfect tandem repeats of a 39-residue sequence termed HEAT (because it occurs in proteins named *H*untingtin, *E*F3, *A* subunit of PP2A, and *T*OR1), has a remarkable structure in which its HEAT repeats are joined in a horseshoe-shaped solenoidal arrangement (Fig. 13-16a).

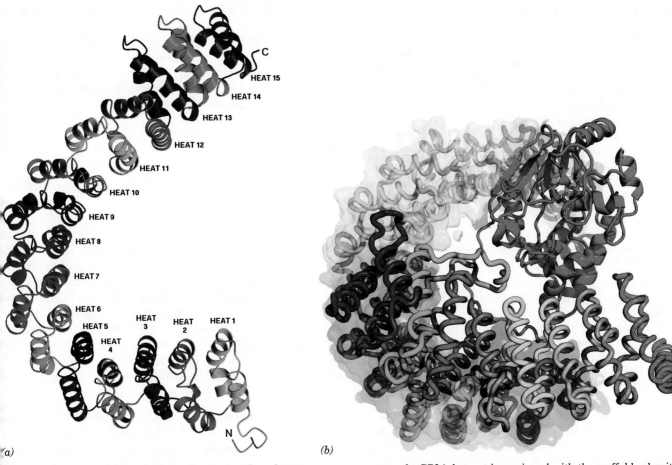

(a)

(b)

■ **Figure 13-16** | **X-Ray structure of protein phosphatase PP2A.** (*a*) The structure of an isolated scaffold (A) subunit. HEAT repeats, which are drawn here in different colors, each consist of two antiparallel helices joined by a short linker. These stack on one another with their corresponding helices nearly parallel to form an ~100-Å-long right-handed superhelix (helix of helices) with a hooklike shape. [Courtesy of Bostjan Kobe, St. Vincent's Institute of Medical Research, Fitzroy, Victoria, Australia. X-Ray structure by David Barford, University of Oxford, U.K. PDBid 1B3U.] (*b*) The structure of a PP2A heterotrimer viewed with the scaffold subunit oriented approximately as in Part *a*. Here the scaffold (A; 589 residues) and regulatory (B; 449 residues) subunits are drawn in worm form, each colored in rainbow order from its N-terminus (*blue*) to its C-terminus (*red*). In addition, the A subunit is embedded in its transparent molecular surface. The catalytic (C; 309 residues) subunit (*magenta*) is drawn in ribbon form. Note the close structural resemblance of the A and B subunits. [Based on an X-ray structure by Yigong Shi, Princeton University. PDBid 2NPP.]

The X-ray structure of a PP2A **holoenzyme** (complete enzyme; Fig 13-16*b*) reveals, unexpectedly, that its regulatory subunit consists of 8 tandem HEAT-like repeats arranged like those of the A subunit, despite their lack of sequence similarity. The C subunit binds to the A subunit's concave surface along a ridge of conserved hydrophobic side chains spanning HEAT repeats 11 to 15. The regulatory subunit similarly interacts with the A subunit's HEAT repeats 2 to 8 and also binds to the C subunit via a ridge spanning its own HEAT-like repeats 6 to 8. The highly acidic, convex side of the regulatory subunit (lower part of Fig. 13-16*b*) is thereby left unoccupied, which suggests that it interacts with substrate proteins.

PP2A's catalytic and scaffold subunits both have two isoforms, and there are 16 isoforms of the regulatory subunit. This results in an enormous panoply of enzymes that are targeted to different phosphoproteins in distinct subcellular sites during different developmental stages. This complexity is a major cause of our limited understanding of how PP2A

■ **CHECK YOUR UNDERSTANDING**

Describe how an RTK becomes an active PTK.

Summarize the roles of SH2 and SH3 domains, Ras, GTP, and protein kinases in transmitting a signal from an RTK to a transcription factor.

What is the advantage of a pathway involving sequential kinase activation?

Describe how SH2 and SH3 domains and Tyr phosphorylation influence PTK activity.

Explain what protein phosphatases do and why they exist as multidomain or multisubunit proteins.

LEARNING OBJECTIVES

■ Understand that G protein–coupled receptors contain seven membrane-spanning helices.

■ Understand that ligand binding to a GPCR induces the α subunit of the associated G protein to exchange GDP for GTP and dissociate from the β and γ subunits.

■ Understand that adenylate cyclase is activated to produce cAMP, which in turn activates protein kinase A.

■ Understand that signaling activity is limited through the action of phosphodiesterases that act on cAMP and cGMP.

carries out its diverse cellular functions, even though it comprises between 0.3 and 1% of cellular proteins.

The PPP family also includes **calcineurin** (also called **PP2B**), a Ser/Thr phosphatase that is activated by Ca^{2+}. Calcineurin plays an essential role in T cell proliferation. It is inhibited by the action of drugs such as **cyclosporin A,** which is used clinically to suppress immune system function following organ transplantation.

3 Heterotrimeric G Proteins

The second major class of signal transduction pathways that we shall discuss involves **heterotrimeric G proteins.** These proteins are members of the superfamily of regulatory GTPases that are collectively known as G proteins, which, as we have seen, are named for their ability to bind the guanine nucleotides GTP and GDP and hydrolyze GTP to GDP and P_i. The monomeric G proteins are essential for a wide variety of processes, including signal transduction (e.g., Ras; Section 13-2B), vesicle trafficking (Section 9-4E), the growth of actin microfilaments (Section 7-2C), translation (as ribosomal accessory factors; Section 27-4), and protein targeting [as components of the signal recognition particle (SRP) and the SRP receptor; Section 9-4D]. The many G proteins share common structural motifs that bind guanine nucleotides and catalyze the hydrolysis of GTP.

Many heterotrimeric G proteins participate in signal transduction systems that consist of three major components:

1. **G protein–coupled receptors (GPCRs),** transmembrane proteins that bind their corresponding ligand (e.g., a hormone) on their extracellular side, which induces a conformational change on their cytoplasmic side.

2. Heterotrimeric G proteins, which are anchored to the cytoplasmic side of the plasma membrane and which are activated by a GPCR when it binds its corresponding ligand.

3. **Adenylate cyclase (AC),** a transmembrane enzyme that is activated (or in some cases inhibited) by activated heterotrimeric G proteins.

Activated AC catalyzes the synthesis of **adenosine-3′,5′-cyclic monophosphate (3′,5′-cyclic AMP** or **cAMP)** from ATP.

ATP → **3′,5′-Cyclic AMP (cAMP)**

The cAMP, in turn, binds to a variety of proteins so as to activate numerous cellular processes. Thus, as Earl Sutherland first showed, *cAMP is a second messenger,* that is, it intracellularly transmits the signal originated by the extracellular ligand.

What are the mechanisms through which the binding of ligand to an extracellular receptor induces AC to synthesize cAMP in the cytosol? In answering this question we shall see that the signaling system outlined above has a surprising complexity that endows it with immense capacity for both signal amplification and regulatory flexibility.

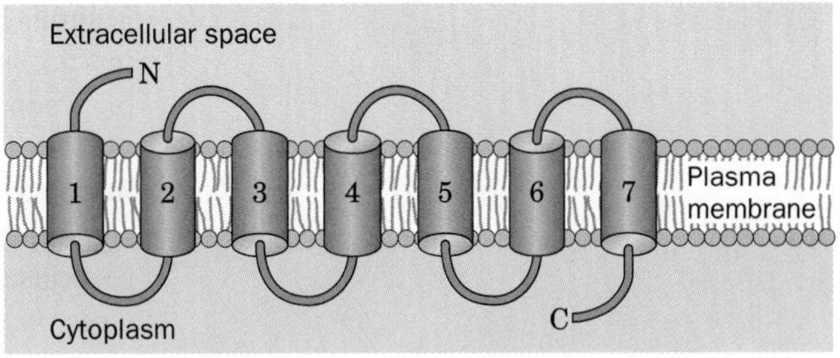

A | G Protein–Coupled Receptors Contain Seven Transmembrane Helices

The G protein–coupled receptors include the glucagon receptor, the β-adrenoreceptor (to which epinephrine binds; Section 13-1B), and a host of other proteins that bind peptide hormones, odorant (having an odor) and tastant (having a taste) molecules, eicosanoids (Section 9-1F), and other compounds. All of these receptors are integral membrane proteins with seven transmembrane α helices (Fig. 13-17). The mammalian genome is estimated to contain over 1000 different GPCRs (>4% of its ~23,000 genes). The importance of these receptors is also evident in the fact that some 60% of the therapeutic drugs presently in use target specific GPCRs.

The first and, as yet, the only GPCR to be structurally characterized at the atomic level is **rhodopsin,** a light-sensing protein in the retina. Rhodopsin consists of the 348-residue protein **opsin** and the covalently linked chromophore retinal (Fig. 13-18), which is similarly linked to the homologous protein bacteriorhodopsin (Section 9-3A). The absorption of a photon causes the rhodopsin-bound retinal to isomerize from its ground-state 11-cis form to its all-trans form. The isomerization causes opsin to undergo a transient conformational change that activates its associated heterotrimeric G protein.

The transmembrane helices of GPCRs are generally uniform in size: 20 to 27 residues, which is sufficient to span a lipid bilayer. However, their N- and C-terminal segments and the loops connecting their transmembrane helices vary widely in length. These are the portions of the protein that bind ligands (on the extracellular side) and heterotrimeric G proteins (on the cytoplasmic side). Rhodopsin is posttranslationally modified by *N*-linked oligosaccharides, two of which are positioned on extracellular loops, and palmitoyl groups, at least one of which interacts with membrane lipids.

GPCRs function much like allosteric proteins such as hemoglobin (Section 7-1). *By alternating between two discrete conformations, one with ligand bound and one without, the receptor can transmit an extracellular signal to the cell interior.* This model of receptor action

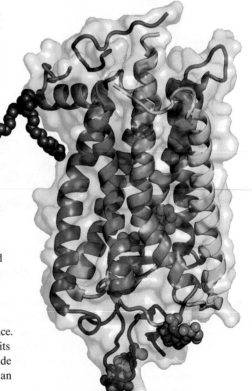

■ **Figure 13-17** | **General structure of a G protein–coupled receptor (GPCR).**

■ **Figure 13-18** | **X-Ray structure of bovine rhodopsin.** The structure is viewed parallel to the plane of the membrane with the cytoplasm above. The protein is represented by its transparent molecular surface with its polypeptide chain in ribbon form colored in rainbow order from blue at its N-terminus to red at its C-terminus. Note its bundle of seven nearly parallel transmembrane helices. Two of the protein's cytoplasmic loops are partially disordered, which results in their fragmented appearance. The protein's retinal prosthetic group (*magenta*) is drawn in space-filling form as are its two covalently linked palmitoyl groups (*dark green*) and its two *N*-linked oligosaccharide groups (colored according to atom type with C green, N blue, and O red). [Based on an X-ray structure by Ronald Stenkamp, University of Washington. PDBid 1HZX.]

is similar to the operation of membrane transport proteins (e.g., Fig. 10-13); in fact, some membrane-bound receptors are ion channels that switch between the open and closed conformations in response to ligand binding.

Receptors Are Subject to Desensitization. A hallmark of biological signaling systems is that they adapt to long-term stimuli by reducing their response to them, a process named **desensitization.** *These signaling systems therefore respond to changes in stimulation levels rather than to their absolute values.* In the case of the β-adrenoreceptor, continuous exposure to epinephrine leads to the phosphorylation of one or more of the receptor's Ser residues. This phosphorylation, which is catalyzed by a specific kinase that acts on the hormone–receptor complex but not on the receptor alone, reduces the receptor's affinity for epinephrine. If the epinephrine level is reduced, the receptor is slowly dephosphorylated, eventually restoring the cell's initial epinephrine sensitivity.

B | Heterotrimeric G Proteins Dissociate on Activation

Heterotrimeric G proteins, as their name implies, are G proteins that consist of an α, β, and γ subunit (45, 37, and 9 kD, respectively). The X-ray structures of entire heterotrimeric G proteins were independently determined by Alfred Gilman and Stephan Sprang (Fig. 13-19) and by Heidi Hamm and Paul Sigler. The large α subunit, designated G_α, consists of two domains connected by two polypeptide linkers (Fig. 13-19a): (1) a highly conserved GTPase domain that is structurally similar to those in monomeric G proteins such as Ras and hence is known as a Ras-like domain, and (2) a

(a)

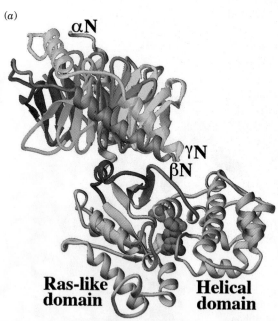

(b)

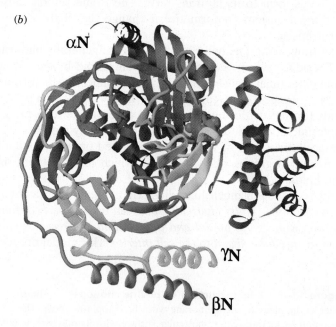

■ **Figure 13-19 | X-Ray structure of a heterotrimeric G protein.** (*a*) The G_α subunit is violet with the segments known as Switch I, II, and III green, blue, and red, respectively. A bound GDP is shown in space-filling form with C green, N blue, O red, and P yellow. The G_β subunit's N-terminal segment is light blue and each blade of its β-propeller has a different color. The G_γ subunit is gold. The plasma membrane is probably at the top of the drawing, as inferred from the positions of the N terminus of G_α and the neighboring C terminus of G_γ, which are lipid-linked *in vivo,* although the orientation of the protein relative to the membrane is unknown. (*b*) View related to that in Part *a* by a 90° rotation about the horizontal axis, that is, looking from the general direction of the plasma membrane. The protein is colored as in Part *a* except that the G_α subunit is mainly gray. [Based on an X-ray structure by Alfred Gilman and Stephan Sprang, University of Texas Southwestern Medical Center. PDBid 1GP2.] ✑ **See Interactive Exercise 12.**

helical domain that is unique to heterotrimeric G proteins. The Ras-like domain contains the guanine nucleotide–binding site in a deep cleft and is anchored to the membrane by a myristoyl or palmitoyl group, or both, covalently attached near the protein's N-terminus. The G_β subunit, which is anchored to the membrane via prenylation of its C-terminus, consists of an N-terminal helical domain followed by a C-terminal domain comprising seven 4-stranded antiparallel β sheets arranged like the blades of a propeller—a so-called **β propeller** (Fig. 13-19b). The G_γ subunit consists mainly of two helical segments joined by a polypeptide link (Fig. 13-19b). It is closely associated with G_β along its entire extended length through mainly hydrophobic interactions. G_γ binds to G_β with such high affinity that they dissociate only under denaturing conditions. Consequently, we shall henceforth refer to their complex as $G_{\beta\gamma}$.

In its unactivated state, a heterotrimeric G protein maintains its heterotrimeric state and its G_α subunit binds GDP. However, *the binding of such a $G_\alpha \cdot GDP$–$G_{\beta\gamma}$ complex to its cognate GPCR in complex with its ligand induces the G_α subunit to exchange its bound GDP for GTP.* Thus, the ligand–GPCR complex functions as the G_α subunit's guanine nucleotide exchange factor (GEF).

When GTP is bound to G_α, its γ phosphate group promotes conformational changes in three of G_α's so-called **switch regions** (Fig. 13-19a), causing G_α to dissociate from $G_{\beta\gamma}$. This occurs because the binding of GTP's γ phosphoryl group and the binding of $G_{\beta\gamma}$ to G_α are mutually exclusive; the γ phosphoryl group hydrogen-bonds with side chains in Switches I and II so as to prevent the segments from interacting with the loops and turns at the bottom of G_β's β-propeller. Switches I and II have counterparts in other G proteins of known structure. Comparison of the X-ray structures of the $G_\alpha \cdot GDP$–$G_{\beta\gamma}$ complex and $G_{\beta\gamma}$ alone indicates that the structure of $G_{\beta\gamma}$ is unchanged by its association with $G_\alpha \cdot GDP$. Nevertheless, both G_α and $G_{\beta\gamma}$ are active in signal transduction; they interact with additional cellular components, as we discuss below.

The effect of G protein activation is short-lived, because G_α is also a GTPase that catalyzes the hydrolysis of its bound GTP to GDP + P_i, although at the relatively sluggish rate of 2 to 3 min^{-1}. GTP hydrolysis causes the heterotrimeric G protein to reassemble as the inactive $G_\alpha \cdot GDP$–$G_{\beta\gamma}$ complex. This prevents a runaway response to ligand binding to a GPCR.

Heterotrimeric G Proteins Activate Other Proteins. A mammalian cell can contain numerous different kinds of heterotrimeric G proteins, since there are 20 different α subunits, 6 different β subunits, and 12 different γ subunits. This heterozygosity presumably permits various cell types to respond in different ways to a variety of stimuli.

One of the major targets of the heterotrimeric G protein system is the enzyme adenylate cyclase (described more fully in the next section). For example, when a $G_\alpha \cdot GTP$ complex dissociates from $G_{\beta\gamma}$, it may bind with high affinity to AC, thereby activating the enzyme. Such a G_α protein is known as a stimulatory G protein, $G_{s\alpha}$. Other G_α proteins, known as inhibitory G proteins, $G_{i\alpha}$, inhibit AC activity. The heterotrimeric G_s and G_i proteins, which differ in their α subunits, may actually contain the same β and γ subunits. Other types of heterotrimeric G proteins—acting through their G_α or $G_{\beta\gamma}$ units—stimulate the opening of ion channels, participate in the phosphoinositide signaling system (Section 13-4), activate phosphodiesterases, and activate protein kinases.

Because a single ligand–receptor interaction can activate more than one G protein, this step of the signal transduction pathway serves to amplify the original extracellular signal. In addition, several types of ligand–receptor complexes may activate the same G protein so that different extracellular signals elicit the same cellular response.

C | Adenylate Cyclase Synthesizes cAMP to Activate Protein Kinase A

See Guided Exploration 13
Mechanisms of hormone signaling involving the adenylate cyclase system.

Mammals have 10 different isoforms of adenylate cyclase, which are each expressed in a tissue-specific manner and differ in their regulatory properties. These ~120-kD transmembrane glycoproteins each consist of a small N-terminal domain (N), followed by two repeats of a unit consisting of a transmembrane domain (M) followed by two consecutive cytoplasmic domains (C), thus forming the sequence $NM_1C_{1a}C_{1b}M_2C_{2a}C_{2b}$ (Fig. 13-20). The 40% identical C_{1a} and C_{2a} domains associate to form the enzyme's catalytic core, whereas C_{1b}, as well as C_{1a} and C_{2a}, bind regulatory molecules. For example, $G_{s\alpha}$ binds to C_{2a} to activate AC, and $G_{i\alpha}$ binds to C_{1a} to inhibit the enzyme. Other regulators of AC activity include Ca^{2+} and certain Ser/Thr protein kinases. Clearly, *cells can adjust their cAMP levels in response to a great variety of stimuli.*

The structure of intact adenylate cyclase is not known, but X-ray structural studies of the catalytic domains indicate that $G_{s\alpha} \cdot GTP$ binds to the $C_{1a} \cdot C_{2a}$ complex via its Switch II region. This binding alters the orientation of the C_{1a} and C_{2a} domains so as to position their catalytic residues for the efficient conversion of ATP to cAMP. When $G_{s\alpha}$ hydrolyzes its bound GTP, its Switch II region reorients so that it can no longer bind to C_{2a}, and the adenylate cyclase reverts to its inactive conformation.

Protein Kinase A Is Activated by Binding Four cAMP. cAMP is a polar, freely diffusing second messenger. In eukaryotic cells, its main target is **protein kinase A (PKA;** also known as **cAMP-dependent protein kinase** or **cAPK),** an enzyme that phosphorylates specific Ser or Thr residues of numerous cellular proteins. These proteins all contain a consensus kinase-recognition sequence, Arg-Arg-X-Ser/Thr-Y, where Ser/Thr is the phospho-

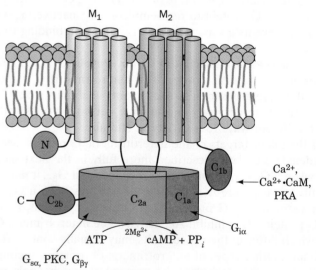

■ **Figure 13-20** | **Schematic diagram of a typical mammalian adenylate cyclase.** The M_1 and M_2 domains are each predicted to contain six transmembrane helices. C_{1a} and C_{2a} form the enzyme's pseudosymmetric catalytic core. The domains with which various regulatory proteins are known to interact are indicated. [After Tesmer, J.J.G. and Sprang, S.R., *Curr. Opin. Struct. Biol.* **8,** 713 (1998).]

Figure 13-21 | X-Ray structure of the catalytic (C) subunit of mouse protein kinase A (PKA). The protein, which is shown in its "standard" view, is in complex with ATP and a 20-residue peptide segment of a naturally occurring protein kinase inhibitor. The N-terminal domain is pink, the C-terminal domain is cyan, and the activation loop containing Thr 197 is light blue. The polypeptide inhibitor is orange and its pseudo-target sequence, Arg-Arg-Asn-Ala-Ile, is magenta (the Ala, which replaces the Ser or Thr of a true substrate, is white). The substrate ATP and the phosphoryl group of phospho-Thr 197 are shown in space-filling form and the side chains of the catalytically essential Arg 165, Asp 166, and Thr 197 are shown in stick form, all colored according to atom type (C green, N blue, O red, and P yellow). Note that the inhibitor's pseudo-target sequence is close to ATP's γ phosphate group, the group that the enzyme transfers to the Ser or Thr of the target sequence. [Based on an X-ray structure by Susan Taylor and Janusz Sowadski, University of California at San Diego. PDBid 1ATP.] 🖇 **See Interactive Exercise 13 and Kinemage Exercise 15.**

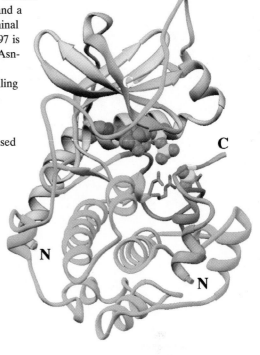

ylation site, X is any small residue, and Y is a large hydrophobic residue.

In the absence of cAMP, PKA is an inactive heterotetramer of two regulatory and two catalytic subunits, R_2C_2. The cAMP binds to the regulatory subunits to cause the dissociation of active catalytic monomers:

$$R_2C_2 + 4\text{ cAMP} \rightleftharpoons 2C + R_2(\text{cAMP})_4$$
(inactive)   *(active)*

The intracellular concentration of cAMP therefore determines the fraction of PKA in its active form and thus the rate at which it phosphorylates its substrates.

The X-ray structure of the 350-residue C subunit of mouse PKA in complex with ATP and a 20-residue inhibitor peptide, which was determined by Susan Taylor and Janusz Sowadski, is shown in Fig. 13-21. The C subunit closely resembles other protein kinases of known structure (e.g., Figs. 13-5a and 13-12). In the PKA structure, the deep cleft between the lobes is occupied by ATP and a segment of the inhibitor peptide that resembles the 5-residue consensus sequence for phosphorylation except that the phosphorylated Ser/Thr is replaced by Ala. Thr 197, which is part of the activation loop, must be phosphorylated for maximal activity. The phosphoryl group at Thr 197 interacts with Arg 165, a conserved catalytic residue that is adjacent to Asp 166, the catalytic base that activates the substrate protein's target Ser/Thr hydroxyl group for phosphorylation. Thus, the phosphoryl group at PKA's Thr 197 functions to properly orient its active site residues.

The R subunit of protein kinase A competitively inhibits its C subunit. The R subunit has a well-defined structure containing two homologous cAMP-binding domains, A and B, and a so-called **autoinhibitor segment** (Fig. 13-22). In the inactive R_2C_2 complex, the autoinhibitor segment, which resembles the C subunit's substrate, binds in the C subunit's active site (as does the inhibitory peptide in Fig. 13-21) so as to block substrate binding. Each R subunit cooperatively binds two cAMPs. When the B domain lacks bound cAMP, it masks the A domain so as to prevent it from binding cAMP. However, the binding of cAMP to the B domain triggers

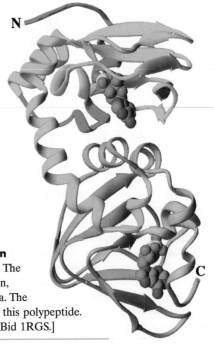

Figure 13-22 | X-Ray structure of the regulatory (R) subunit of bovine protein kinase A (PKA) in complex with cAMP. Domain A is cyan and domain B is orange. The cAMP molecules are shown in space-filling form colored according to atom type (C green, N blue, O red, and P yellow). The region containing the autoinhibitor segment is magenta. The N-terminal 91 residues of the R subunit, which mediate its dimerization, are absent from this polypeptide. [Based on an X-ray structure by Susan Taylor, University of California at San Diego. PDBid 1RGS.]

a conformational change that permits the A domain to bind cAMP, which in turn releases the now-active C subunits from the complex.

The targets of PKA include enzymes involved in glycogen metabolism. For example, when epinephrine binds to the β-adrenoreceptor of a muscle cell, the sequential activation of a heterotrimeric G protein, adenylate cyclase, and PKA leads to the activation of glycogen phosphorylase, thereby making glucose-6-phosphate available for glycolysis in a "fight-or-flight" response (Section 16-3).

Each step of a signal transduction pathway can potentially be regulated, so *the nature and magnitude of the cellular response ultimately reflect the presence and degree of activation or inhibition of all the preceding components of the pathway.* For example, the adenylate cyclase signaling pathway can be limited or reversed through ligand activation of a receptor coupled to an inhibitory G protein. The activity of the cAMP second messenger can be attenuated by the action of phosphodiesterases that hydrolyze cAMP to AMP (see below). In addition, reactions catalyzed by PKA are reversed by protein Ser/Thr phosphatases (Section 13-2D). Some of these features of the adenylate cyclase signaling pathway are illustrated in Fig. 13-23. Many drugs and toxins exert their effects by modifying components of the adenylate cyclase system (Box 13-4).

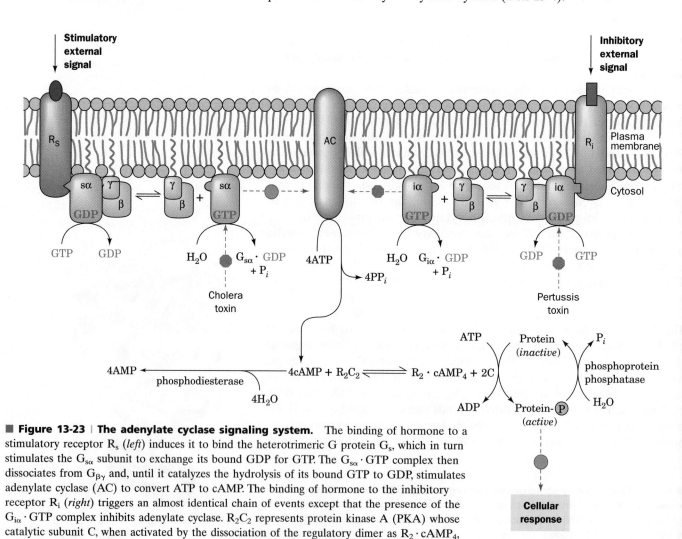

■ **Figure 13-23** | **The adenylate cyclase signaling system.** The binding of hormone to a stimulatory receptor R_s (*left*) induces it to bind the heterotrimeric G protein G_s, which in turn stimulates the $G_{s\alpha}$ subunit to exchange its bound GDP for GTP. The $G_{s\alpha} \cdot$ GTP complex then dissociates from $G_{\beta\gamma}$ and, until it catalyzes the hydrolysis of its bound GTP to GDP, stimulates adenylate cyclase (AC) to convert ATP to cAMP. The binding of hormone to the inhibitory receptor R_i (*right*) triggers an almost identical chain of events except that the presence of the $G_{i\alpha} \cdot$ GTP complex inhibits adenylate cyclase. R_2C_2 represents protein kinase A (PKA) whose catalytic subunit C, when activated by the dissociation of the regulatory dimer as $R_2 \cdot cAMP_4$, activates various cellular proteins by catalyzing their phosphorylation. The sites of action of certain toxins are indicated.

| Phosphodiesterases Limit Second Messenger Activity

In any chemically based signaling system, the signal molecule must eventually be eliminated in order to control the amplitude and duration of the signal and to prevent interference with the reception of subsequent signals. In

BOX 13-4 BIOCHEMISTRY IN HEALTH AND DISEASE

Drugs and Toxins That Affect Cell Signaling

Complex processes such as the adenylate cyclase signaling system can be sabotaged by a variety of agents. For example, the methylated purine derivatives **caffeine** (an ingredient of coffee and tea), **theophylline** (an asthma treatment), and **theobromine** (found in chocolate)

R = CH₃   X = CH₃   **Caffeine (1,3,7-trimethylxanthine)**
R = H   X = CH₃   **Theophylline (1,3-dimethylxanthine)**
R = CH₃   X = H   **Theobromine (1,7-dimethylxanthine)**

are stimulants because they antagonize adenosine receptors that act through inhibitory G proteins. This antagonism results in an increase in cAMP concentration.

Deadlier effects result from certain bacterial toxins that interfere with heterotrimeric G protein function. The toxin released by *Vibrio cholerae* (the bacterium causing cholera) triggers massive fluid loss of over a liter per hour from diarrhea. Victims die from dehydration unless their lost water and salts are replaced. **Cholera**

toxin, an 87-kD protein of subunit composition AB₅, binds to ganglioside G_{M1} (Fig. 9-9) on the surface of intestinal cells via its B subunits. This permits the toxin to enter the cell, probably via receptor-mediated endocytosis, where an ~195-residue proteolytic fragment of its A subunit is released. This fragment catalyzes the transfer of the ADP–ribose unit from NAD^+ to a specific Arg side chain of $G_{s\alpha}$ (*below*).

ADP-ribosylated $G_{s\alpha} \cdot$ GTP can activate adenylate cyclase but cannot hydrolyze its bound GTP (Fig. 13-23). As a consequence, the adenylate cyclase is locked in its active state and cellular cAMP levels increase ~100-fold. Intestinal cells, which normally respond to small increases in cAMP by secreting digestive fluid (an HCO_3^--rich salt solution), pour out enormous quantities of this fluid in response to the elevated cAMP concentrations.

Other bacterial toxins act similarly. Certain strains of *E. coli* cause a diarrheal disease similar to but less serious than cholera through their production of **heat-labile enterotoxin,** a protein that is closely similar to cholera toxin (their A and B subunits are >80% identical) and has the same mechanism of action. **Pertussis toxin** [secreted by *Bordetella pertussis,* the bacterium that causes **pertussis** (whooping cough), which is responsible for ~400,000 infant deaths per year worldwide] is an AB₅ protein homologous to cholera toxin that ADP-ribosylates a specific Cys residue of $G_{i\alpha}$. The modified $G_{i\alpha}$ cannot exchange its bound GDP for GTP and therefore cannot inhibit adenylate cyclase (Fig. 13-23).

Nicotinamide

NAD⁺   →[cholera toxin]→   **ADP-ribosylated $G_{s\alpha}$**

the case of cAMP, this second messenger is hydrolyzed to AMP by enzymes known as **cAMP-phosphodiesterases (cAMP-PDEs).**

The PDE superfamily, which includes both cAMP-PDEs and **cGMP-PDEs** (**cGMP** is the guanine analog of cAMP), is encoded in mammals by at least 20 different genes grouped into 11 families (PDE1 through PDE11). These are functionally distinguished by their substrate specificities (for cAMP, cGMP, or both) and kinetic properties, their responses (or lack of them) to various activators and inhibitors (see below), and their tissue, cellular, and subcellular distributions. The PDEs have characteristic modular architectures with a conserved ~270-residue catalytic domain near their C-termini and widely divergent regulatory domains or motifs, usually in their N-terminal portions. Some PDEs are membrane-anchored, whereas others are cytosolic.

PDE activity, as might be expected, is elaborately controlled. Depending on its isoform, a PDE may be activated by one or more of a variety of agents, including Ca^{2+} ion and phosphorylation by PKA and **insulin-stimulated protein kinase.** Phosphorylated PDEs are dephosphorylated by a variety of protein phosphatases. Thus, the PDEs provide a means for cross talk between cAMP-based signaling systems and those using other types of signals.

PDEs are inhibited by a variety of drugs that influence such widely divergent disorders as asthma, congestive heart failure, depression, erectile dysfunction, inflammation, and retinal degeneration. **Sildenafil** (trade name **Viagra**),

Sildenafil (Viagra)

a compound used to treat erectile dysfunction, specifically inhibits PDE5, which hydrolyzes only cGMP. Sexual stimulation in males causes penile nerves to release nitric oxide (NO), which activates **guanylate cyclase** to produce cGMP from GTP. The cGMP induces vascular smooth muscle relaxation in the penis, thereby increasing the inflow of blood, which results in an erection. This cGMP is eventually hydrolyzed by PDE5. Sildenafil is therefore an effective treatment in men who produce insufficient NO and hence cGMP to otherwise generate a satisfactory erection.

4 The Phosphoinositide Pathway

A discussion of signal transduction pathways would not be complete without the **phosphoinositide pathway,** which mediates the effects of a variety of hormones. This signaling pathway requires a receptor with seven transmembrane segments, a heterotrimeric G protein, a specific kinase, and a

---

■ CHECK YOUR UNDERSTANDING

Summarize the steps of signal transduction from a GPCR to phosphorylation of target proteins by PKA.

Describe how G proteins are activated and inactivated.

What is the purpose of a second messenger such as cAMP?

Why does the adenylate cyclase signaling system include phosphodiesterases?

LEARNING OBJECTIVES

■ Understand that signal transduction via the phosphoinositide pathway generates the second messenger inositol trisphosphate, which triggers Ca^{2+} release, and diacylglycerol, which activates protein kinase C.

■ Understand that in the presence of Ca^{2+}, calmodulin binds and activates its target proteins.

■ Understand that a hormone can activate multiple signal transduction pathways to elicit a variety of intracellular responses.

phosphorylated glycerophospholipid that is a minor component of the plasma membrane's inner leaflet. It involves the production of three second messengers, **inositol-1,4,5-trisphosphate** (IP$_3$), Ca^{2+}, and **1,2-diacylglycerol (DAG).**

A | Ligand Binding Results in the Cytoplasmic Release of the Second Messengers IP$_3$ and Ca^{2+}

Ligand binding to its receptor, such as epinephrine binding to the α_1-adrenoreceptor, activates a heterotrimeric G protein, G$_q$, whose membrane-anchored α subunit in complex with GTP diffuses laterally along the plasma membrane to activate the membrane-bound enzyme **phospholipase C (PLC;** Fig. 13-24, *upper left*). Activated PLC catalyzes the hydrolysis of **phosphatidylinositol-4,5-bisphosphate (PIP$_2$)** at its glycero-phospho bond (Section 9-1C), yielding inositol-1,4,5-trisphosphate (IP$_3$) and 1,2-

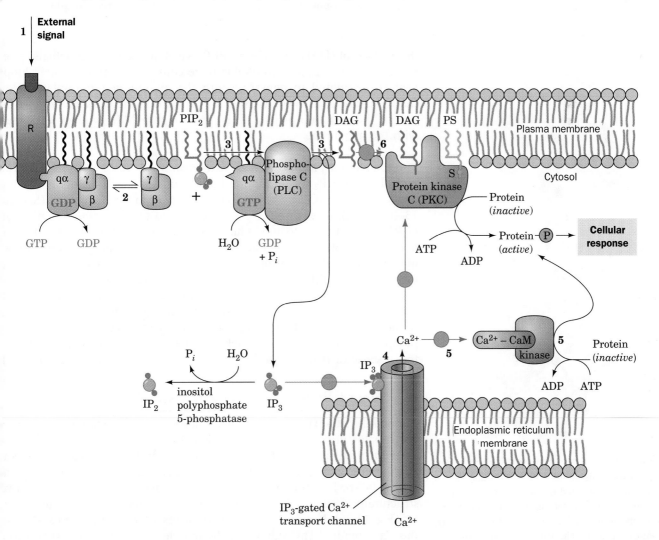

◾ Figure 13-24 | The phosphoinositide signaling system.
Ligand binding to a cell-surface receptor R (**1**) activates phospholipase C through the heterotrimeric G protein G$_q$ (**2**). Phospholipase C catalyzes the hydrolysis of PIP$_2$ to IP$_3$ and DAG (**3**). The water-soluble IP$_3$ stimulates the release of Ca^{2+} sequestered in the endoplasmic reticulum (**4**), which in turn activates numerous cellular processes through the intermediacy of calmodulin (CaM; **5**). The nonpolar DAG remains associated with the membrane, where it activates protein kinase C (PKC) to phosphorylate and thereby modulate the activities of a number of cellular proteins (**6**). PKC activation also requires the presence of the membrane lipid phosphatidylserine (PS) and Ca^{2+}. **See the Animated Figures.**

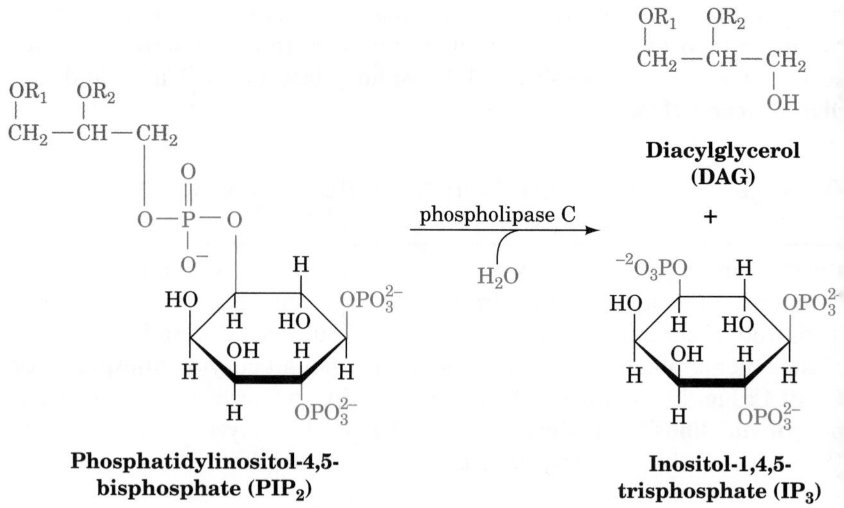

■ **Figure 13-25** | **Phosphatidylinositol-4,5-bisphosphate (PIP$_2$) and its hydrolysis products.** PIP$_2$ is cleaved by phospholipase C to produce diacylglycerol (DAG) and inositol-1,4,5-trisphosphate (IP$_3$), both of which are second messengers. (The *bis* and *tris* prefixes denote, respectively, two and three phosphoryl groups that are linked separately to the inositol; in di- and triphosphates, the phosphoryl groups are linked sequentially.)

Phosphatidylinositol-4,5-bisphosphate (PIP$_2$)

phospholipase C

H_2O

Diacylglycerol (DAG)

+

Inositol-1,4,5-trisphosphate (IP$_3$)

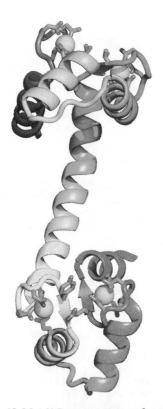

■ **Figure 13-26** | **X-Ray structure of rat testis calmodulin.** This monomeric 148-residue protein, which is colored in rainbow order from N-terminus (*blue*) to C-terminus (*red*), contains two remarkably similar globular domains separated by a seven-turn α helix. The two Ca^{2+} ions bound to each domain are represented by cyan spheres. The side chains liganding the Ca^{2+} ions are drawn in stick form colored according to atom type (C green, N blue, and O red). [Based on an X-ray structure by Charles Bugg, University of Alabama at Birmingham. PDBid 3CLN.] *See* Kinemage Exercise 16-1.

diacylglycerol (DAG; Fig. 13-25). PLC, which in mammals is actually a set of 11 isozymes, has a hydrophobic ridge consisting of three protein loops that is postulated to penetrate into the membrane's nonpolar region during catalysis. This would explain how the enzyme can catalyze hydrolysis of the membrane-bound PIP$_2$, leaving the DAG product associated with the membrane.

The Charged IP$_3$ Molecule Is a Water-Soluble Second Messenger. The hydrolysis of PIP$_2$ sets in motion both cytoplasmic and membrane-bound events. While DAG acts as a second messenger in the membrane (Section 13-4C), IP$_3$ diffuses through the cytoplasm to the endoplasmic reticulum (ER). There, it binds to and induces the opening of a Ca^{2+} transport channel (an example of a receptor that is also an ion channel), thereby allowing the efflux of Ca^{2+} from the ER. This causes the cytosolic [Ca^{2+}] to increase from ~0.1 μM to as much as 10 mM, which triggers such diverse cellular processes as glucose mobilization and muscle contraction through the intermediacy of the Ca^{2+}-binding protein **calmodulin** (see below) and its homologs. The ER contains embedded Ca^{2+}–ATPases that actively pump Ca^{2+} from the cytosol back into the ER (Section 10-3B) so that in the absence of IP$_3$, the cytosolic [Ca^{2+}] rapidly returns to its resting level.

B | Calmodulin Is a Ca^{2+}-Activated Switch

Calmodulin **(CaM)** is a ubiquitous, eukaryotic Ca^{2+}-binding protein that participates in numerous cellular regulatory processes. In some of these, CaM functions as a free-floating monomeric protein, whereas in others it is a subunit of a larger protein. The X-ray structure of this highly conserved 148-residue protein has a curious dumbbell-like shape in which two structurally similar globular domains are connected by a seven-turn α helix (Fig. 13-26). Note the close structural resemblance between CaM and the Ca^{2+}-binding TnC subunit of the muscle protein troponin (Fig. 7-31).

CaM's two globular domains each contain two high-affinity Ca^{2+}-binding sites. The Ca^{2+} ion in each of these sites is octahedrally coordinated by oxygen atoms from the backbone and side chains as well as from a protein-associated water molecule. Each of the Ca^{2+}-binding sites is formed by nearly superimposable helix–loop–helix motifs known as **EF hands** (Fig. 13-27) that form the Ca^{2+}-binding sites in numerous other Ca^{2+}-binding proteins of known structure.

Figure 13-27 | The EF hand. The Ca^{2+}-binding sites in many proteins that sense the level of Ca^{2+} are formed by helix–loop–helix motifs named EF hands. [After Kretsinger, R.H., *Annu. Rev. Biochem.* **45**, 241 (1976).] 🔗 **See Kinemage Exercise 16-1.**

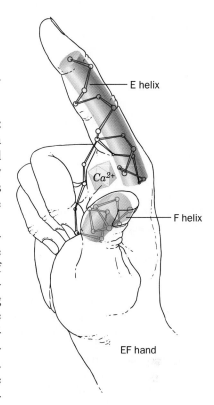

E helix

F helix

Ca^{2+}

EF hand

Ca^{2+}–CaM Activates Its Target Proteins via an Intrasteric Mechanism. The binding of Ca^{2+} to either domain of CaM induces a conformational change in that domain, which exposes an otherwise buried Met-rich hydrophobic patch. This patch, in turn, binds with high affinity to the CaM-binding domains of numerous Ca^{2+}-regulated protein kinases (see below). These CaM-binding domains have little mutual sequence homology but are all basic amphiphilic α helices.

Despite uncomplexed CaM's extended appearance (Fig. 13-26), a variety of studies indicate that both of its globular domains bind to a single target helix. This was confirmed by the NMR structure (Fig. 13-28) of $(Ca^{2+})_4$–CaM in complex with its 26-residue CaM-binding target polypeptide from skeletal muscle **myosin light chain kinase (MLCK;** a homolog of the PKA C subunit, which phosphorylates and thereby activates the light chains of the muscle protein myosin; Section 7-2A). Thus, CaM's central α helix serves as a flexible tether rather than a rigid spacer, a property that probably extends the range of sequences to which CaM can bind. Indeed, both of CaM's globular domains are required for CaM to activate its targets: CaM domains that have been separated by proteolytic cleavage bind to their target peptides but do not cause enzyme activation.

(b)

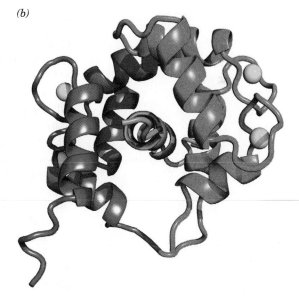

(a)

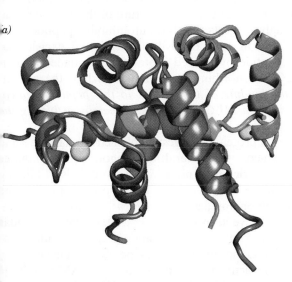

Figure 13-28 | NMR structure of calmodulin in complex with a target polypeptide. The N-terminal domain of CaM (from the fruit fly *Drosophila melanogaster*) is blue, its C-terminal domain is red, the 26-residue target polypeptide, which is from rabbit skeletal muscle myosin light chain kinase (MLCK), is green, and the Ca^{2+} ions are represented by cyan spheres. (*a*) A view of the complex in which the N-terminus of the target polypeptide is on the right. (*b*) The perpendicular view as seen from the right side of the structure shown in Part *a*. In both views, the pseudo-twofold axis relating the N- and C-terminal domains of CaM is approximately vertical. Note how the segment that joins the two domains is unwound and bent (bottom loop in Part *b*) so that CaM forms a globular protein that largely encloses the helical target polypeptide within a hydrophobic tunnel in a manner resembling two hands holding a rope. [Based on an NMR structure by Marius Clore, Angela Gronenborn, and Ad Bax, NIH. PDBid 2BBM.] 🔗 **See Kinemage Exercise 16-2.**

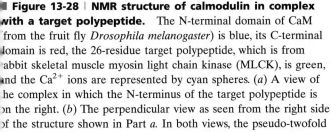

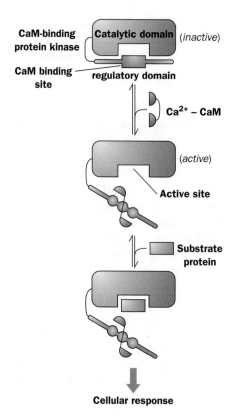

■ **Figure 13-29** | **A schematic diagram of the Ca²⁺–CaM-dependent activation of protein kinases.** Autoinhibited kinases have an N- or C-terminal "pseudosubstrate" sequence (*red*) that binds at or near the enzyme's active site (*brown*) so as to inhibit its function. The autoinhibitory segment is in close proximity with or overlaps a Ca²⁺–CaM binding sequence. Consequently, Ca²⁺–CaM (*green*) binds to the sequence so as to extract it from the enzyme's active site, thereby activating the enzyme to phosphorylate other proteins (*purple*). [After Crivici, A. and Ikura, M., *Annu. Rev. Biophys. Biomol. Struct.* **24,** 88 (1995).]

How does Ca²⁺–CaM activate its target protein kinases? MLCK contains a C-terminal segment whose sequence resembles that of MLCK's target polypeptide on the light chain of myosin but lacks a phosphorylation site. A model of MLCK, based on the X-ray structure of the 30% identical C subunit of PKA, strongly suggests that this autoinhibitor peptide inactivates MLCK by binding in its active site. Indeed, the excision of MLCK's autoinhibitor peptide by limited proteolysis permanently activates the enzyme. MLCK's CaM-binding segment overlaps the autoinhibitor peptide. Thus, *the binding of Ca²⁺–CaM to this peptide segment extracts the autoinhibitor from MLCK's active site, thereby activating the enzyme* (Fig. 13-29).

Ca²⁺–CaM's other target proteins are presumably activated in the same way. In fact, the X-ray structures of several homologous protein kinases support this so-called **intrasteric mechanism.** While the details of binding of the autoinhibitory sequence differ for each of the protein kinases, the general mode of autoinhibition and activation by Ca²⁺–CaM is the same.

PKA's R subunit, as we have seen (Section 13-3C), contains a similar autoinhibitory sequence adjacent to its two tandem cAMP-binding domains. In this case, however, the autoinhibitory peptide is allosterically ejected from the C subunit's active site by the binding of cAMP to the R subunit (which lacks a Ca²⁺–CaM-binding site).

C | DAG Is a Lipid-Soluble Second Messenger That Activates Protein Kinase C

The second product of the phospholipase C reaction, diacylglycerol (DAG), is a lipid-soluble second messenger. It therefore remains embedded in the plasma membrane, where it activates the membrane-bound **protein kinase C (PKC)** to phosphorylate and thereby modulate the

ctivities of several different cellular proteins (Fig. 13-24, *right*). Multiple
PKC enzymes are known; they differ in tissue expression, intracellular lo-
ation, and their requirement for the DAG that activates them. PKC is a
phosphorylated, cytosolic protein in its resting state. DAG increases the
membrane affinity of PKC and also helps stabilize its active conformation.
The catalytic activities of PKC and PKA are similar: Both kinases phosphorylate Ser and Thr residues.

The X-ray structure of a DAG-bound segment of PKC shows that the
0-residue motif is largely knit together by two Zn^{2+} ions, each of which
s tetrahedrally liganded by one His and three Cys side chains (Fig. 13-30).
A DAG analog, **phorbol-13-acetate,**

Phorbol-13-acetate

binds in a narrow groove between two long nonpolar loops. Very few soluble proteins have such a large continuous nonpolar region, suggesting
that this portion of PKC inserts into the membrane. Full activation of PKC
requires phosphatidylserine (which is present only in the cytoplasmic
leaflet of the plasma membrane) and, in some cases, Ca^{2+} ion (presumably made available through the action of the IP_3 second messenger). Like
other signaling systems, the phosphoinositide system is limited by the
destruction of its second messengers, for example, through the action of
inositol polyphosphate 5-phosphatase (Fig. 13-24, *lower left*).

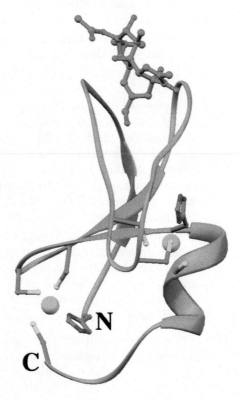

■ **Figure 13-30** | **X-Ray structure of a portion
of protein kinase C in complex with
phorbol-13-acetate.** The protein tetrahedrally
ligands two Zn^{2+} ions (*cyan spheres*), each via His
and Cys side chains (shown in ball-and-stick
form). Phorbol-13-acetate (*top*), which mimics the
natural diacylglycerol ligand, binds between two
nonpolar protein loops. Atoms are colored
according to type with C green, N blue, O red,
and S yellow. [Based on an X-ray structure by
James Hurley, NIH. PDBid 1PTR.]

PLC Acts on Several Phospholipids to Release Different Second Messengers. Choline-containing phospholipids hydrolyzed by phospholipase C yield DAGs that differ from those released from PIP$_2$ and exert different effects on PKC. Another lipid second messenger, sphingosine released from sphingolipids, inhibits PKC.

The phosphoinositide signaling pathway in some cells yields a DAG that is predominantly l-stearoyl-2-arachidonoyl-glycerol. This molecule is further degraded to yield arachidonate, the precursor of the bioactive eicosanoids (prostaglandins and thromboxanes; Section 20-6C), and hence the phosphoinositide pathway yields up to four different second messengers. In other cells, IP$_3$ and diacylglycerol are rapidly recycled to re-form PIP$_2$ in the inner leaflet of the membrane. Some receptor tyrosine kinases activate an isoform of phospholipase C that contains two SH2 domains. This is another example of cross talk, the interactions of different signal transduction pathways.

D | Epilog: Complex Systems Have Emergent Properties

Complex systems are, by definition, difficult to understand and substantiate. Familiar examples include the earth's weather system, the economies of large countries, the ecologies of even small areas, and the human brain. Biological signal transduction systems, as is amply evident from a reading of this chapter, are complex systems. Thus, a hormonal signal is typically transduced through several intracellular signaling pathways, each of which consists of numerous components, many of which interact with components of other signaling pathways. For example, the **insulin signaling system** (Fig. 13-31), although not yet fully elucidated, is clearly highly complex. Upon binding insulin, the insulin receptor autophosphorylates itself at several Tyr residues (Section 13-2A) and then Tyr-phosphorylates its target proteins, thereby activating several signaling pathways that control a diverse array of effects:

1. Phosphorylation of the adaptor protein **Shc,** which generates a binding site for Grb2's SH2 domain, results in stimulation of a MAP kinase cascade (Section 13-2B), ultimately affecting growth and differentiation.

2. Phosphorylation of **Gab-1 (Grb2-associated binder-1)** similarly activates the MAP kinase cascade.

3. Phosphorylation of insulin receptor substrate (IRS) proteins (Section 13-2A) activates enzymes known as a **phosphoinositide 3-kinases (PI3Ks).** These enzymes add a phosphoryl group to the 3'-OH group of a phosphatidylinositol, often the 4,5-bisphosphate shown in Fig. 13-25. The 3-phosphorylated lipid activates **phosphoinositide-dependent protein kinase-1 (PDK1)** that in turn initiates cascades leading to glycogen synthesis (Section 16-3C) and the translocation of the glucose transporter GLUT4 to the surface of insulin-responsive cells (Section 22-2), as well as affecting cell growth and differentiation.

4. Phosphorylation of the **APS/Cbl** complex (APS for *A*daptor protein containing *p*lekstrin homology and *S*rc homology-2 domains; Cbl is an SH2/SH3-binding docking protein that is a proto-oncogene product) leads to the stimulation of **TC10** (a monomeric G protein) and to the PI3K-independent regulation of glucose transport involving the participation of lipid rafts and caveolae (Section 9-4C).

Thus, by activating multiple pathways, a hormone such as insulin can trigger a variety of physiological effects that would not be possible in a one hormone–one target regulatory system.

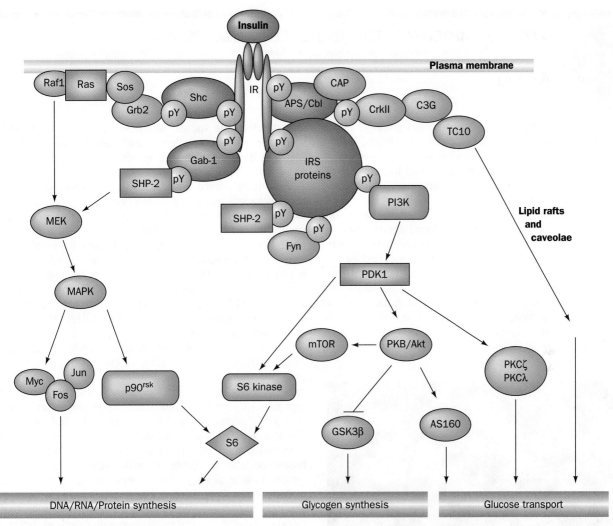

Figure 13-31 | Insulin signal transduction. The binding of insulin to the insulin receptor **(IR)** induces tyrosine phosphorylations (pY) that lead to the activation of the MAPK and PI3K phosphorylation cascades as well as a lipid raft and caveolae-associated regulation process. The MAPK cascade regulates the expression of genes involved in cellular growth and differentiation. The PI3K cascade leads to changes in the phosphorylation states of several enzymes, so as to stimulate glycogen synthesis as well as other metabolic pathways. The PI3K cascade also participates in the control of vesicle trafficking, leading to the translocation of the GLUT4 glucose transporter to the cell surface and thus increasing the rate of glucose transport into the cell. Glucose transport control is also exerted by the APS/Cbl system in a PI3K-independent manner involving lipid rafts and caveolae (Section 9-4C). Other symbols: Myc, Fos, and Jun (transcription factors), SHP-2 (an SH2-containing PTP), **CAP** (Cbl-associated protein), **C3G** [a guanine nucleotide exchange factor (GEF)], **CrkII** (an SH2/SH3-containing adaptor protein), PDK1 (phosphoinositide-dependent protein kinase-1), **PKB (protein kinase B,** also named **Akt), GSK3β (glycogen synthase-3β,** which is inhibited by phosphorylation by PKB), **mTOR** (for *m*ammalian *t*arget *o*f *r*apamycin, a PI3K-related protein kinase; **rapamycin** is an immunosuppressant), **S6** (a protein subunit of the eukaryotic ribosome's small subunit whose phosphorylation stimulates translation), and PKCζ and PKCλ (atypical isoforms of protein kinase C). [After Zick, Y., *Trends Cell Biol.* **11,** 437 (2001).]

Understanding a Complex System Requires an Integrative Approach.

The predominant approach in science is reductionist: the effort to understand a system in terms of its component parts. Thus chemists and biochemists explain the properties of molecules in terms of the properties of their component atoms, cell biologists explain the nature of cells in terms of the properties of their component macromolecules, and biologists explain the characteristics of multicellular organisms in terms of the

BOX 13-5 **BIOCHEMISTRY IN HEALTH AND DISEASE**

Anthrax

Anthrax is a bacterial disease that is widespread among herbivorous animals. It is rare in humans but potentially deadly, leading to its exploitation as an agent of biological warfare. The effectiveness of anthrax as a weapon was first confirmed through the accidental release of anthrax spores from a laboratory in the Soviet Union in 1979, when 68 people died.

Bacillus anthracis is a nonmotile aerobic bacterium that quickly dies outside of host tissues. However, it forms spores, particles about 1 μm in diameter, that can survive for decades. Such spores are naturally present in soils worldwide and are ingested by herbivores. The mechanism whereby the spores germinate to form full-sized bacterial cells is not well understood. If released into the air, the odorless and invisible spores can travel long distances and easily find their way indoors. The spores can cause inhalation anthrax in humans, although it is an extremely rare disease. Consequently, a cluster of inhalation anthrax cases almost certainly

indicates that the spores have been specifically targeted to humans, for example, in letters or packages. As events in the United States in 2001 have shown, spores from one piece of mail can easily infect many individuals.

Historically, anthrax infections in humans have been of the cutaneous variety and are easily recognized by the black skin lesion that result (the word anthrax is derived from the Greek *anthraki* coal). Cutaneous anthrax, which is fatal in ~20% of cases, was understood to be an occupational hazard for woolsorters and others who worked with animal hides. However, inhalation anthrax is nearly always fatal. This is because the early symptoms of inhalation anthrax are nonspecific and resemble the flu, whereas the later stages of the disease, even with antibiotic treatment, are rapidly fatal, with an average interval of only 3 days between the onset of symptoms and death.

Like many deadly microbes, *B. anthracis* synthesizes a toxin (see below) that is particularly lethal to cells of the immune system. Thus, the toxin prevents the immune system from destroying the bacteria. Early identification of anthrax infection—or even just exposure—is essential to prevent death. Most naturally occurring strains of *B. anthracis* are sensitive to penicillin, but it is feared that "weaponized" anthrax may have been engineered for resistance to common antibiotics. The drug of choice is therefore the newer broad-spectrum antibiotic **ciprofloxacin** (which inhibits DNA gyrase, a bacterial enzyme that helps maintain the proper degree of DNA supercoiling; Section 24-1D and Box 24-2). Treatment for about 60 days is required to prevent infection by spores that have delayed germination. The good news is that anthrax, unlike smallpox and bubonic plague, for example, is not highly contagious.

The Anthrax Toxin Includes Edema Factor and Lethal Factor. Even if *B. anthracis* cells can be eliminated, the toxins they have already synthesized continue to damage the host, which is why antibiotic treatment beginning in the later stages of anthrax infection does not prevent a fatal outcome. Anthrax toxin consists of three proteins that act in concert: **protective antigen (PA)**, **edema factor (EF)**, and **lethal factor (LF)**. PA, which is named for its use in vaccines, is a 735-residue protein that binds to a host cell-surface protein. The receptor is a 368-residue membrane

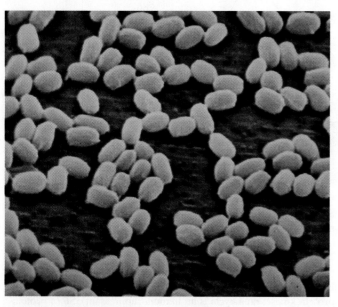

Anthrax spores. [© A. Dowsett/Photo Researchers.]

properties of their component cells. However, complex systems have **emergent properties** that are not readily predicted from an understanding of their component parts (i.e., the whole is greater than the sum of its parts). Indeed, life itself is an emergent property that arises from the numerous chemical reactions that occur in a cell.

In order to elucidate the emergent properties of a complex system, an integrative approach is required. For signal transduction systems, such an approach would entail determining how each of the components of each signaling pathway in a cell interacts with all of the other such components under the conditions that each of these components experiences within it

protein with a single bilayer-spanning α helix. Its normal cellular function is not known. After PA has bound, a cell-surface protease cleaves it, and its N-terminal fragment diffuses away. The remaining membrane-bound portions of PA form a heptameric complex that can bind the other two toxin proteins, EF and LF. The resulting toxin complex is then internalized by receptor-mediated endocytosis (Section 20-1B), following which EF and LF enter the cytosol.

EF is an adenylate cyclase that interferes with normal intracellular signaling, especially in cells such as macrophages, whose functions include the engulfment and destruction of pathogenic bacteria. *The toxic effects of EF may reflect the ability of the resulting increased concentrations of cAMP to inhibit a cellular signaling pathway necessary to maintain an effective immune response.* EF also upsets water homeostasis and hence is responsible for the massive edema (abnormal buildup of intercellular fluid) seen in cutaneous anthrax infection.

The mechanism of EF action is notable because it requires the host protein calmodulin (bacteria lack calmodulin, so this feature may protect *B. anthracis* from its own toxin). Calmodulin (Figs. 13-26 and 13-28) binds to EF by wrapping around it. This induces a conformational change that stabilizes the substrate-binding site of its adenylate cyclase function, thereby activating it. In addition, the bound calmodulin can no longer carry out its normal cellular duties, which include activating certain cAMP-phosphodiesterases (Section 13-3D). Thus, by "soaking up" calmodulin, EF enhances its ability to produce cAMP.

The other component of the anthrax toxin, LF, is a relatively large (776-residue) protease. Its X-ray structure reveals that it consists of four domains (*right*). Domain I binds to the protective antigen. Domain II resembles another bacterial toxin but has a mutated and nonfunctional active site. Domain III appears to be a duplicated version of Domain II. Domains II and III function to hold the substrate for Domain IV, which is a protease with an active site Zn^{2+} ion. The sequence of Domain IV exhibits no homology to known zinc proteases; its activity was identified on the basis of its three-dimensional structure and the position of its catalytic Zn^{2+} ion.

The substrates for lethal factor are the members of the mitogen-activated protein kinase kinase (MAPKK) family (e.g., MEK; Fig. 13-11). LF is an extremely specific protease because it

interacts extensively with its substrates: The substrate-binding groove extends for about 40 Å and accommodates a 16-residue sequence of a MAPKK. Cleavage of the kinase by LF excises its docking sequence for downstream MAPKs and thereby blocks its signaling activity. Low levels of LF, which occur early in *B. anthracis* infection, inhibit the ability of macrophages to release inflammatory mediators such as cytokines and nitric oxide (Section 21-6C). This has the effect of reducing or delaying an immune response to the bacteria. Later in infection, when concentrations of the toxin are high, LF triggers macrophage lysis, causing the sudden release of inflammatory mediators. This results in massive **septic shock** (an immune system overreaction to bacterial infection resulting in a catastrophic reduction in blood pressure), the direct cause of death.

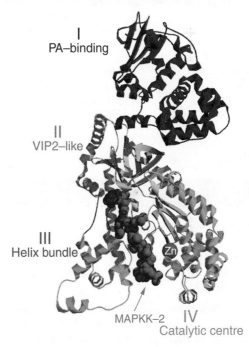

X-Ray structure of anthrax lethal factor. [Courtesy of Robert Liddington, The Burnham Institute, La Jolla, California. PDBid 1J7N.]

local environment. Yet, existing techniques for doing so are crude at best. Moreover, these systems are by no means static but vary, over multiple time scales, in response to cellular and organismal programs. Consequently, the means for understanding the holistic performance of cellular signal transduction systems are only in their earliest stages of development. Such an understanding is likely to have important biomedical consequences since many diseases, including cancer, diabetes, and a variety of neurological disorders, are caused by malfunctions of signal transduction systems. Similarly, during *Bacillus anthracis* infection, the anthrax toxin interferes with more than one signaling pathway (Box 13-5).

■ CHECK YOUR UNDERSTANDING

Describe how ligand binding to a receptor leads to the production of IP₃ and DAG and the release of Ca^{2+}.

How does calmodulin activate target proteins?

How is protein kinase C activated?

SUMMARY

1. Hormones produced by endocrine glands and other tissues regulate such diverse physiological processes as fuel metabolism (insulin and glucagon), fight-or-flight responses (epinephrine), sexual development (steroids), and growth (growth hormone).

2. Hormone signals interact with target tissues by binding to receptors that transduce the signal to the interior of the cell.

3. On ligand binding, receptor tyrosine kinases such as the insulin receptor undergo autophosphorylation. This activates them to phosphorylate their target proteins, in some cases triggering a kinase cascade.

4. The effects of protein kinases are reversed by the activity of protein phosphatases.

5. The G protein–coupled receptors (GPCRs) have seven transmembrane helices and, on ligand binding, activate an associated heterotrimeric G protein. The G_α and $G_{\beta\gamma}$ units may activate or inhibit targets such as adenylate cyclase, which produces the cAMP activator of protein kinase A (PKA).

6. In the phosphoinositide pathway, hormone binding leads to the hydrolysis of phosphatidylinositol-4,5-bisphosphate (PIP_2) to yield inositol-1,4,5-trisphosphate (IP_3), which open Ca^{2+} channels, and diacylglycerol (DAG), which activate protein kinase C (PKC).

KEY TERMS

hormone **405**
receptor **405**
homeostasis **407**
adrenoreceptor **409**
agonist **409**
antagonist **409**
signal transduction **412**

ligand **413**
receptor tyrosine
  kinase **413**
autophosphorylation **413**
G protein **416**
kinase cascade **417**
GEF **418**

GAP **418**
oncogene **420**
cross talk **421**
nonreceptor tyrosine
  kinase **422**
protein phosphatase **425**
GPCR **428**

second messenger **429**
desensitization **430**
heterotrimeric G protein **430**
phosphoinositide
  pathway **436**
calmodulin **438**
emergent properties **444**

PROBLEMS

1. Would the following alterations to Src be oncogenic? Explain. (a) The deletion or inactivation of the SH3 domain. (b) The mutation of Tyr 416 to Phe. (c) The mutation of Tyr 527 to Phe. (d) The replacement of Src residues 249 to 253 with the sequence APTMP.

2. A growth factor that acts through a receptor tyrosine kinase stimulates cell division. Predict the effect of a viral protein that inhibits the corresponding protein tyrosine phosphatase.

3. Retroviruses bearing oncogenes will infect cells from their corresponding host animal but will usually not transform them. Yet, these retroviruses will readily transform immortalized cells derived from the same organism. Explain.

4. How does the presence of the poorly hydrolyzable GTP analog **GTPγS** (in which an O atom on the terminal phosphate is replaced by an S atom) affect cAMP production by adenylate cyclase?

5. Explain why mutations of the Arg residue in $G_{s\alpha}$ that is ADP-ribosylated by cholera toxin are oncogenic mutations. Why doesn't cholera toxin cause cancer?

6. Phosphatidylethanolamine and PIP_2 containing identical fatty acyl residues can be hydrolyzed with the same efficiency by a certain phospholipase C. Will the hydrolysis products of the two lipids have the same effect on protein kinase C? Explain.

7. Why does pertussis toxin appear to inhibit certain isozyme of PLC? Identify those isozymes.

8. PKC's autoinhibitory pseudosubstrate occurs at its N-terminus whereas that of MLCK occurs at its C-terminus (Fig. 13-29). To further investigate this phenomenon, a colleague proposes to construct a PKC with its pseudosubstrate attached to the protein's C-terminus with a sufficiently long linker so that the pseudosubstrate could bind in the enzyme's active site. Would you expect this variant PKC to be activatable? Explain.

9. Diacylglycerol is a substrate for the enzyme diacylglycerol kinase.

  (a) What is the product of this reaction?

  (b) Explain why activation of diacylglycerol kinase would limit signaling by the phosphoinositide pathway.

10. Lithium ion, which is used to treat bipolar disorder, interfere with the phosphoinositide signaling pathway by inhibiting enzymes such as inositol monophosphatase and inositol polyphosphate 1-phosphatase. Predict the effect of Li^+ on the supply of cellular inositol, a precursor of phosphatidylinositol and PIP_2.

REFERENCES

Alonso, A., et al., Protein tyrosine phosphatases in the human genome, *Cell* **117,** 699–711 (2004).

Baselga, J., Targeting tyrosine kinases in cancer: The second wave, *Science* **312,** 1175–1178 (2006).

Carrasco, S. and Mérida, I., Diacylglycerol, when simplicity becomes complex, *Trends Biochem. Sci.* **32,** 27–36 (2007). [Reviews diacylglycerol-based signaling.]

Chang, L. and Karin, M., Mammalian MAP kinase signaling cascades, *Nature* **410,** 37–40 (2001).

Cho, U.S. and Xu, W., Crystal structure of a protein phosphatase 2A heterotrimeric holoenzyme, *Nature* **445,** 53–57 (2007); *and* Xu, Y., Xing, Y., Chen, Y., Chao, Y., Lin, Z., Fan, E., Yu, J., Stack, S., Jeffrey, P., and Shi, Y., Structure of the protein phosphatase 2A holoenzyme, *Cell* **127,** 1239–1251 (2006).

Di Paolo, G. and De Camilli, P., Phosphoinositides in cell regulation and membrane dynamics, *Nature* **443,** 651–657 (2006).

Murphy, L.O. and Blenis, J., MAPK signal specificity: the right place at the right time, *Trends Biochem. Sci.* **31,** 268–275 (2006).

Neves, S.R., Ram, P.T., and Iyengar, R., G protein pathways, *Science* **296,** 1636–1639 (2002). [A brief introduction to the four families of G proteins.]

Pawson, T. and Scott, J.D., Protein phosphorylation in signaling—50 years and counting, *Trends Biochem. Sci.* **30,** 286–290 (2005).

Science's Signal Transduction Knowledge Environment (STKE). http://stke.sciencemag.org/. [A database on signaling molecules and their relationships to each other. Full access to the database requires an individual or institutional subscription.]

Yaffe, M.B., Phosphotyrosine-binding domains in signal transduction, *Nature Rev. Mol. Cell Biol.* **3,** 177–186 (2002).

14

Introduction to Metabolism

The processes by which biological molecules are broken down and resynthesized form a complex, yet highly regulated, network of interdependent enzymatic reactions that are collectively known as life. [Designed by Donald E. Nicholson, Department of Biochemistry and Molecular Biology, The University of Leeds, England, and Sigma.]

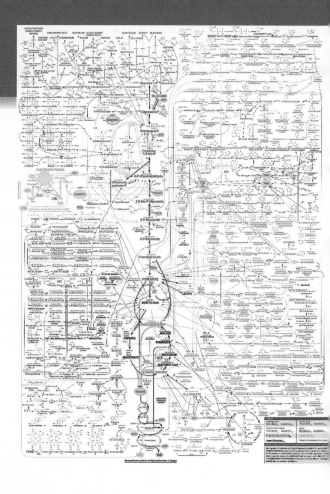

■ CHAPTER CONTENTS

1 Overview of Metabolism
- **A.** Nutrition Involves Food Intake and Use
- **B.** Vitamins and Minerals Assist Metabolic Reactions
- **C.** Metabolic Pathways Consist of Series of Enzymatic Reactions
- **D.** Thermodynamics Dictates the Direction and Regulatory Capacity of Metabolic Pathways
- **E.** Metabolic Flux Must Be Controlled

2 "High-Energy" Compounds
- **A.** ATP Has a High Phosphoryl Group-Transfer Potential
- **B.** Coupled Reactions Drive Endergonic Processes
- **C.** Some Other Phosphorylated Compounds Have High Phosphoryl Group-Transfer Potentials
- **D.** Thioesters Are Energy-Rich Compounds

3 Oxidation–Reduction Reactions
- **A.** NAD^+ and FAD Are Electron Carriers
- **B.** The Nernst Equation Describes Oxidation–Reduction Reactions
- **C.** Spontaneity Can Be Determined by Measuring Reduction Potential Differences

4 Experimental Approaches to the Study of Metabolism
- **A.** Labeled Metabolites Can Be Traced
- **B.** Studying Metabolic Pathways Often Involves Perturbing the System
- **C.** Systems Biology Has Entered the Study of Metabolism

■ MEDIA RESOURCES

(available at www.wiley.com/college/voet)
Interactive Exercise 14. Conformational changes in *E. coli* adenylate kinase
Case Study 16. Allosteric Regulation of ATCase
Bioinformatics Exercises Chapter 14: Metabolic Enzymes, Microarrays, and Proteomics

Understanding the chemical compositions and three-dimensional structures of biological molecules is not sufficient to understand how they are assembled into organisms or how they function to sustain life. We must therefore examine the reactions in which biological molecules are built and broken down. We must also consider how free energy is consumed in building cellular materials and carrying out cellular work and how free energy is generated from organic or other sources. **Metabolism,** the overall process through which living systems acquire and use free energy to carry out their various functions, is traditionally divided into two parts:

1. **Catabolism,** or degradation, in which nutrients and cell constituents are broken down to salvage their components and/or to generate energy.

2. **Anabolism,** or biosynthesis, in which biomolecules are synthesized from simpler components.

In general, catabolic reactions carry out the exergonic oxidation of nutrient molecules. The free energy thereby released is used to drive such endergonic processes as anabolic reactions, the performance of mechanical ork, and the active transport of molecules against concentration gradients. Exergonic and endergonic processes are often coupled through the intermediate synthesis of a "high-energy" compound such as ATP. This simple principle underlies many of the chemical reactions presented in the following chapters. In this chapter, we introduce the general features of metabolic reactions and the roles of ATP and other compounds as energy carriers. Because many metabolic reactions are also oxidation–reduction reactions, we review the thermodynamics of these processes. Finally, we examine some approaches to studying metabolic reactions.

1 Overview of Metabolism

A bewildering array of chemical reactions occur in any living cell. Yet the principles that govern metabolism are the same in all organisms, a result of their common evolutionary origin and the constraints of the laws of thermodynamics. In fact, many of the specific reactions of metabolism are common to all organisms, with variations due primarily to differences in the source of the free energy that supports them.

A | Nutrition Involves Food Intake and Use

Nutrition, the intake and utilization of food, affects health, development, and performance. Food supplies the energy that powers life processes and provides the raw materials to build and repair body tissues. The nutritional requirements of an organism reflect its source of metabolic energy. For example, some prokaryotes are **autotrophs** (Greek: *autos,* self + *trophos,* feeder), which can synthesize all their cellular constituents from simple molecules such as H_2O, CO_2, NH_3, and H_2S. There are two possible free energy sources for this process. **Chemolithotrophs** (Greek: *lithos,* stone) obtain their energy through the oxidation of inorganic compounds such as NH_3, H_2S, or even Fe^{2+}:

$$2\,NH_3 + 4\,O_2 \rightarrow 2\,HNO_3 + 2\,H_2O$$
$$H_2S + 2\,O_2 \rightarrow H_2SO_4$$
$$4\,FeCO_3 + O_2 + 6\,H_2O \rightarrow 4\,Fe(OH)_3 + 4\,CO_2$$

Photoautotrophs do so via photosynthesis, a process in which light energy powers the transfer of electrons from inorganic donors to CO_2 to produce carbohydrates, $(CH_2O)_n$, which are later oxidized to release free energy. **Heterotrophs** (Greek: *hetero,* other) obtain free energy through the oxidation of organic compounds (carbohydrates, lipids, and proteins) and hence ultimately depend on autotrophs and/or phototrophs for those substances.

Organisms can be further classified by the identity of the oxidizing agent for nutrient breakdown. **Obligate aerobes** (which include animals) must use O_2, whereas **anaerobes** employ oxidizing agents such as sulfate or nitrate. **Facultative anaerobes,** such as *E. coli,* can grow in either the presence or the absence of O_2. **Obligate anaerobes,** in contrast, are poisoned by the presence of O_2. Their metabolisms are thought to resemble those of the earliest life-forms, which arose over 3.5 billion years ago when the earth's atmosphere lacked O_2. Most of our discussion of metabolism will focus on aerobic processes.

Animals are obligate **aerobic** heterotrophs, whose nutrition depends on a balanced intake of the **macronutrients** proteins, carbohydrates, and lipids. These are broken down by the digestive system to their component amino

LEARNING OBJECTIVES

■ Understand that different organisms use different strategies for capturing free energy from their environment and can be classified by their requirement for oxygen.

■ Understand that mammalian nutrition involves the intake of proteins, carbohydrates, lipids, vitamins, minerals, and water.

■ Appreciate the importance of thermodynamics in determining the direction and regulatory capabilities of metabolic pathways.

■ Understand the mechanisms by which metabolic flux is controlled.

Table 14-1	Characteristics of Common Vitamins		
Vitamin	**Coenzyme Product**	**Reaction Mediated**	**Human Deficiency Disease**
Water-Soluble			
Biotin	Biocytin	Carboxylation	*a*
Pantothenic acid	Coenzyme A	Acyl transfer	*a*
Cobalamin (B$_{12}$)	Cobalamin coenzymes	Alkylation	Pernicious anemia
Riboflavin (B$_2$)	Flavin coenzymes	Oxidation–reduction	*a*
—	Lipoic acid	Acyl transfer	*a*
Nicotinamide (niacin)	Nicotinamide coenzymes	Oxidation–reduction	Pellagra
Pyridoxine (B$_6$)	Pyridoxal phosphate	Amino group transfer	*a*
Folic acid	Tetrahydrofolate	One-carbon group transfer	Megaloblastic anemia
Thiamine (B$_1$)	Thiamine pyrophosphate	Aldehyde transfer	Beriberi
Ascorbic acid (C)	Ascorbate	Hydroxylation	Scurvy
Fat-Soluble			
Vitamin A		Vision	Night blindness
Vitamin D		Ca^{2+} absorption	Rickets
Vitamin E		Antioxidant	*a*
Vitamin K		Blood clotting	Hemorrhage

*a*No specific name; deficiency in humans is rare or unobserved.

Table 14-2	Major Essential Minerals and Trace Elements
Major Minerals	**Trace Elements**
Sodium	Iron
Potassium	Copper
Chlorine	Zinc
Calcium	Selenium
Phosphorus	Iodine
Magnesium	Chromium
Sulfur	Fluorine

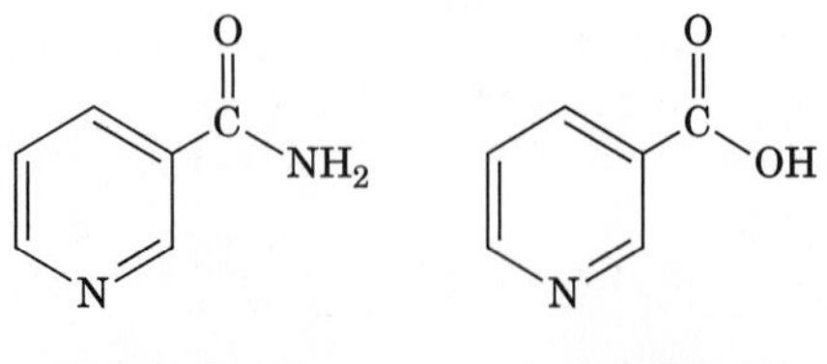

■ **Figure 14-1 | The structures of nicotinamide and nicotinic acid.** These vitamins form the redox-active components of the nicotinamide coenzymes NAD$^+$ and NADP$^+$ (compare with Fig. 11-4).

acids, monosaccharides, fatty acids, and glycerol, the major nutrients involved in cellular metabolism, which are then transported by the circulatory system to the tissues. The metabolic utilization of the latter substances also requires the intake of O$_2$ and water, as well as **micronutrients** composed of **vitamins** and **minerals.**

B | Vitamins and Minerals Assist Metabolic Reactions

Vitamins are organic molecules that an animal is unable to synthesize and must therefore obtain from its diet. Vitamins can be divided into two groups, **water-soluble vitamins** and **fat-soluble vitamins.** Table 14-1 lists many common vitamins and the types of reactions or processes in which they participate (we shall consider the structures of these substances and their reaction mechanisms in the appropriate sections of the text).

Table 14-2 lists the essential minerals and trace elements necessary for metabolism. They participate in metabolic processes in many ways. Mg^{2+}, for example, is involved in nearly all reactions that involve ATP and other nucleotides, including the synthesis of DNA, RNA, and proteins. Zn^{2+} is a cofactor in a variety of enzymatic reactions including that catalyzed by carbonic anhydrase (Section 11-3C). Ca^{2+}, in addition to being the major mineral component of bones and teeth, is a vital participant in signal transduction processes (Section 13-4).

Most Water-Soluble Vitamins Are Converted to Coenzymes. Many coenzymes (Section 11-1C) were discovered as growth factors for microorganisms or as substances that cure nutritional deficiency diseases in humans and/or animals. For example, the NAD$^+$ component **nicotinamide** or its carboxylic acid analog **nicotinic acid** (**niacin**; Fig. 14-1), relieves the ultimately fatal dietary deficiency disease in humans known as **pellagra.** The symptoms of pellagra include diarrhea, dermatitis, and dementia.

The water-soluble vitamins in the human diet are all coenzyme precursors. In contrast, the fat-soluble vitamins, with the exception of vitamin
. (Section 9-1F), are not components of coenzymes, although they are also
required in small amounts in the diets of many higher animals. The distant ancestors of humans probably had the ability to synthesize the various vitamins, as do many modern plants and microorganisms. Yet since vitamins are normally available in the diets of animals, which all eat other
organisms, or are synthesized by the bacteria that normally inhabit their
digestive systems, it seems likely that the superfluous cellular machinery
to synthesize them was lost through evolution. For example, vitamin C
(ascorbic acid) is required in the diets of only humans, apes, and guinea
pigs (Section 6-1C and Box 6-2) because, in what is apparently a recent
evolutionary loss, they lack a key enzyme for ascorbic acid biosynthesis.

Metabolic Pathways Consist of
Series of Enzymatic Reactions

*Metabolic pathways are series of connected enzymatic reactions that pro-
duce specific products.* Their reactants, intermediates, and products are referred to as **metabolites.** There are around 4000 known metabolic reactions, each catalyzed by a distinct enzyme. The types of enzymes and
metabolites in a given cell vary with the identity of the organism, the cell
type, its nutritional status, and its developmental stage. Many metabolic
pathways are branched and interconnected, so delineating a pathway from
a network of thousands of reactions is somewhat arbitrary and is driven
by tradition as much as by chemical logic.

In general, degradative and biosynthetic pathways are related as follows (Fig. 14-2): In degradative pathways, the major nutrients, referred to
as complex metabolites, are exergonically broken down into simpler products. The free energy released in the degradative process is conserved by
the synthesis of ATP from ADP + P_i or by the reduction of the coenzyme
NADP$^+$ (Fig. 11-4) to NADPH. ATP and NADPH are the major free
energy sources for biosynthetic reactions. We shall consider the thermodynamic properties of ATP and NADPH later in this chapter.

A striking characteristic of degradative metabolism is that *the pathways
for the catabolism of a large number of diverse substances (carbohydrates,
lipids, and proteins) converge on a few common intermediates,* in many cases,
a two-carbon acetyl unit linked to **coenzyme A** to form **acetyl-coenzyme A**

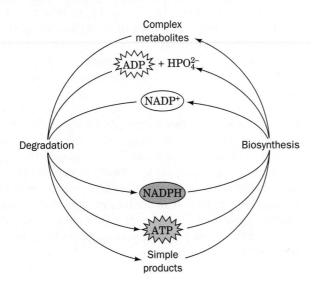

■ **Figure 14-2** | **Roles of ATP and NADP$^+$ in
metabolism.** ATP and NADPH, generated
through the degradation of complex metabolites
such as carbohydrates, lipids, and proteins, are
sources of free energy for biosynthetic and other
reactions.

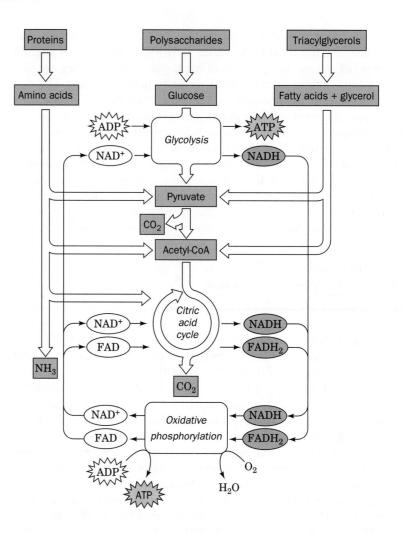

■ Figure 14-3 | Overview of catabolism.
Complex metabolites such as carbohydrates,
proteins, and lipids are degraded first to their
monomeric units, chiefly glucose, amino acids,
fatty acids, and glycerol, and then to the common
intermediate, acetyl-CoA. The acetyl group is
oxidized to CO_2 via the citric acid cycle with
concomitant reduction of NAD^+ and FAD.
Reoxidation of NADH and $FADH_2$ by O_2 during
electron transport and oxidative phosphorylation
yields H_2O and ATP.

(**acetyl-CoA;** Section 14-2D). These intermediates are then further metab
olized in a central oxidative pathway. Figure 14-3 outlines the breakdow
of various foodstuffs to their monomeric units and then to acetyl-CoA. Thi
is followed by the oxidation of the acetyl carbons to CO_2 by the **citric aci
cycle** (Chapter 17). When one substance is **oxidized** (loses electrons), an
other must be **reduced** (gain electrons; Box 14-1). The citric acid cycle thu
produces the reduced coenzymes **NADH** and **$FADH_2$** (Section 14-3A
which then pass their electrons to O_2 to produce H_2O in the processes c
electron transport and **oxidative phosphorylation** (Chapter 18).

Biosynthetic pathways carry out the opposite process. *Relatively fe
metabolites serve as starting materials for a host of varied products.* In th
next several chapters, we discuss many catabolic and anabolic pathway
in detail.

Enzymes Catalyze the Reactions of Metabolic Pathways. With a fe
exceptions, the interconversions of metabolites in degradative and biosyr
thetic pathways are catalyzed by enzymes. In the absence of enzymes, th
reactions would occur far too slowly to support life. In addition, the speci
ficity of enzymes guarantees the efficiency of metabolic reactions by pre
venting the formation of useless or toxic by-products. Most importantl
enzymes provide a mechanism for coupling an endergonic chemical reac
tion (which would not occur on its own) with an energetically favorabl
reaction, as discussed below.

BOX 14-1 PERSPECTIVES IN BIOCHEMISTRY

Oxidation States of Carbon

The carbon atoms in biological molecules can assume different oxidation states depending on the atom to which they are bonded. For example, a carbon atom bonded to less electronegative hydrogen atoms is more reduced than a carbon atom bonded to highly electronegative oxygen atoms.

The simplest way to determine the oxidation number (and hence the oxidation state) of a particular carbon atom is to examine each of its bonds and assign the electrons to the more electronegative atom. In a C—O bond, both electrons "belong" to O; in a C—H bond, both electrons "belong" to C; and in a C—C bond, each carbon "owns" one electron. An atom's oxidation number is the number of valence electrons on the free atom (4 for carbon) minus the number of its lone pair and assigned electrons. For example, the oxidation number of carbon in CO_2 is $4 - (0 + 0) = +4$, and the oxidation number of carbon in CH_4 is $4 - (0 + 8) = -4$, Keep in mind, however, that oxidation numbers are only accounting devices; actual atomic charges are much closer to neutrality.

The following compounds are listed according to the oxidation state of the highlighted carbon atom. In general, the more oxidized compounds have fewer electrons per C atom and are richer in oxygen, and the more reduced compounds have more electrons per C atom and are richer in hydrogen. But note that not all reduction events (gain of electrons) or oxidation events (loss of electrons) are associated with bonding to oxygen. For example, when an alkane is converted to an alkene, the formation of a carbon–carbon double bond involves the loss of electrons and therefore is an oxidation reaction although no oxygen is involved. Knowing the oxidation number of a carbon atom is seldom required. However, it is useful to be able to determine whether the oxidation state of a given atom increases or decreases during a chemical reaction.

Compound	Formula	Oxidation Number
Carbon dioxide	O=C=O	4 (most oxidized)
Acetic acid	$H_3C-C\overset{O}{\underset{OH}{}}$	3
Carbon monoxide	:C≡O:	2
Formic acid	$H-C\overset{O}{\underset{OH}{}}$	2
Acetone	$H_3C-\overset{O}{\overset{\|}{C}}-CH_3$	2
Acetaldehyde	$H_3C-\overset{O}{\overset{\|}{C}}-H$	1
Formaldehyde	$H-\overset{O}{\overset{\|}{C}}-H$	0
Acetylene	HC≡CH	−1
Ethanol	$H_3C-\overset{H}{\underset{H}{\overset{\|}{C}}}-OH$	−1
Ethene	$H_2C=C\overset{H}{\underset{H}{}}$	−2
Ethane	$H_3C-\overset{H}{\underset{H}{\overset{\|}{C}}}-H$	−3
Methane	$H-\overset{H}{\underset{H}{\overset{\|}{C}}}-H$	−4 (least oxidized)

We will see examples of reactions catalyzed by all six classes of enzymes introduced in Section 11-1A. These reactions fall into four major types: **oxidations and reductions** (catalyzed by oxidoreductases), **group-transfer reactions** (catalyzed by transferases and hydrolases), **eliminations, isomerizations, and rearrangements** (catalyzed by isomerases and mutases), and **reactions that make or break carbon–carbon bonds** (catalyzed by hydrolases, lyases, and ligases). Details about the enzymes that catalyze individual steps of metabolic pathways are available from Internet-accessible databases (Box 14-2).

Metabolic Pathways Occur in Specific Cellular Locations. The compartmentation of the eukaryotic cytoplasm allows different metabolic pathways to operate in different locations. For example, electron transport and oxidative phosphorylation occur in the mitochondria, whereas **glycolysis** (a carbohydrate degradation pathway) and fatty acid biosynthesis occur in

BOX 14-2 PERSPECTIVES IN BIOCHEMISTRY

Mapping Metabolic Pathways

The task of cataloging all the enzymatic reactions that occur in a given organism is formidable and, in many cases, far from complete. However, the metabolic reactions that constitute the major catabolic and anabolic pathways can be organized in a diagram. Typically, the structures or names of the intermediates are shown, and details about the enzymes that catalyze their interconversions can be called up. The following figure, which diagrams a portion of the photosynthetic pathway in plants, shows the interconver-

sions of several three- and four-carbon compounds. The boxes represent enzymes, identified by their EC number (Section 11-1A).

Various Internet-accessible databases contain "universal" maps of all possible metabolic reactions or more specialized maps devoted to a single species or focused on a specific pathway. Such databases may link individual enzymes in a pathway to gene sequences and to the three-dimensional structures of the proteins if known. Information about an enzyme's activators and inhibitors may also be included. Two examples of such databases are the Kyoto Encyclopedia of Genes and Genomes (KEGG) Metabolic Pathways: www.genome.jp/kegg/metabolism.html; and BRENDA (BRaunschweig ENzyme DAtabase: www.brenda.uni-koeln.de/.

Understanding the chemical logic of metabolic pathways requires more than listing the substrates and products of each step. The ability to recognize the types of reactions that occur in a pathway provides insights into the overall metabolic capabilities of an organism and makes it easier to see the similarities and differences between pathways. At a deeper level, understanding the mechanisms and regulation of metabolic enzymes may lead to advances in treating metabolic and other diseases.

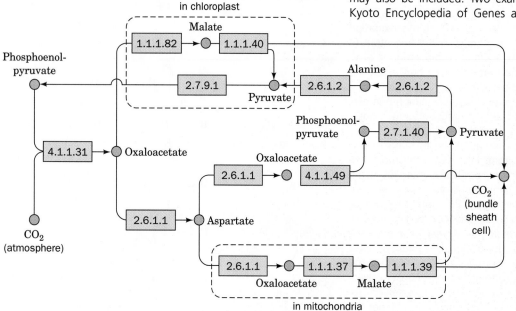

[Redrawn from the Kyoto Encyclopedia of Genes and Genomes (KEGG) Metabolic Pathways: http://www.genome.jp/kegg/metabolism.html.]

the cytosol. Table 14-3 lists the major metabolic features of eukaryotic organelles. Metabolic processes in prokaryotes, which lack organelles, may be localized to particular areas of the cytosol.

The synthesis of metabolites in specific membrane-bounded compartments in eukaryotic cells requires mechanisms to transport these substances between compartments. Accordingly, transport proteins (Chapter 10) are essential components of many metabolic processes. For example, a transport protein is required to move ATP, which is generated in the mitochondria, to the cytosol, where most of it is consumed (Section 18-1).

In multicellular organisms, compartmentation is carried a step further, to the level of tissues and organs. The mammalian liver, for example, is largely responsible for the synthesis of glucose from noncarbohydrate precursors (**gluconeogenesis;** Section 16-4) so as to maintain a relatively constant level of glucose in the circulation, whereas adipose tissue is specialized for storage of triacylglycerols. The interdependence of the metabolic functions of the various organs is the subject of Chapter 22.

Table 14-3	Metabolic Functions of Eukaryotic Organelles
Organelle	**Major functions**
Mitochondrion	Citric acid cycle, electron transport and oxidative phosphorylation, fatty acid oxidation, amino acid breakdown
Cytosol	Glycolysis, pentose phosphate pathway, fatty acid biosynthesis, many reactions of gluconeogenesis
Lysosome	Enzymatic digestion of cell components and ingested matter
Nucleus	DNA replication and transcription, RNA processing
Golgi apparatus	Posttranslational processing of membrane and secretory proteins; formation of plasma membrane and secretory vesicles
Rough endoplasmic reticulum	Synthesis of membrane-bound and secretory proteins
Smooth endoplasmic reticulum	Lipid and steroid biosynthesis
Peroxisome (glyoxysome in plants)	Oxidative reactions catalyzed by amino acid oxidases and catalase; glyoxylate cycle reactions in plants

An intriguing manifestation of specialization of tissues and subcellular compartments is the existence of **isozymes,** enzymes that catalyze the same reaction but are encoded by different genes and have different kinetic or regulatory properties. For example, we have seen that mammals have three isozymes of glycogen phosphorylase, those expressed in muscle, brain, and liver (Section 12-3B). Similarly, vertebrates possess two homologs of the enzyme **lactate dehydrogenase:** the M type, which predominates in tissues subject to anaerobic conditions such as skeletal muscle and liver, and the H type, which predominates in aerobic tissues such as heart muscle. Lactate dehydrogenase catalyzes the interconversion of **pyruvate,** a product of glycolysis, and **lactate** (Section 15-3A). The M-type isozyme appears mainly to function in the reduction by NADH of pyruvate to lactate, whereas the H-type enzyme appears to be better adapted to catalyze the reverse reaction. The existence of isozymes allows for the testing of various illnesses. For example, heart attacks cause the death of heart muscle cells, which consequently rupture and release H-type LDH into the blood. A blood test indicating the presence of H-type LDH is therefore diagnostic of a heart attack.

D | Thermodynamics Dictates the Direction and Regulatory Capacity of Metabolic Pathways

Knowing the location of a metabolic pathway and enumerating its substrates and products does not necessarily reveal how that pathway functions as part of a larger network of interrelated biochemical processes. It is also necessary to appreciate how fast end product can be generated by the pathway as well as how pathway activity is regulated as the cell's needs change. Conclusions about a pathway's output and its potential for regulation can be gleaned from information about the thermodynamics of each enzyme-catalyzed step.

SAMPLE CALCULATION 14-1

Calculate the equilibrium constant for the hydrolysis of glucose-1-phosphate at 37°C. $\Delta G^{\circ\prime}$ for the reaction

Glucose-1-phosphate + $H_2O \rightarrow$ glucose + P_i

is -20.9 kJ $\cdot$ mol^{-1} (Table 14-4). At equilibrium, $\Delta G = 0$ and Eq. 14-1 becomes

$$\Delta G^{\circ\prime} = -RT \ln K \quad \text{(Eq. 14-2)}$$

Therefore,

$K = e^{-\Delta G^{\circ\prime}/RT}$
$K = e^{-(-20,900 \text{ J} \cdot \text{mol}^{-1})/(8.3145 \text{ J} \cdot \text{K}^{-1} \cdot \text{mol}^{-1})(310 \text{ K})}$
$K = 3.3 \times 10^3$

Recall from Section 1-3D that the free energy change (ΔG) of a biochemical process, such as the reaction

$$A + B \rightleftharpoons C + D$$

is related to the standard free energy change ($\Delta G^{\circ\prime}$) and the concentrations of the reactants and products (Eq. 1-15):

$$\Delta G = \Delta G^{\circ\prime} + RT \ln\left(\frac{[C][D]}{[A][B]}\right) \quad \text{[14-1}$$

At equilibrium $\Delta G = 0$, and the equation becomes

$$\Delta G^{\circ\prime} = -RT \ln K_{eq} \quad \text{[14-2}$$

Thus, the value of $\Delta G^{\circ\prime}$ can be calculated from the equilibrium constant and vice versa (see Sample Calculation 14-1).

When the reactants are present at values close to their equilibrium values, $[C]_{eq}[D]_{eq}/[A]_{eq}[B]_{eq} \approx K_{eq}$, and $\Delta G \approx 0$. This is the case for many metabolic reactions, which are said to be **near-equilibrium reactions**. Because their ΔG values are close to zero, they can be relatively easily reversed by changing the ratio of products to reactants. When the reactants are in excess of their equilibrium concentrations, the net reaction proceeds in the forward direction until the excess reactants have been converted to products and equilibrium is attained. Conversely, when products are in excess, the net reaction proceeds in the reverse direction so as to convert products to reactants until the equilibrium concentration ratio is again achieved. *Enzymes that catalyze near-equilibrium reactions tend to act quickly to restore equilibrium concentrations, and the net rates of such reactions are effectively controlled by the relative concentrations of substrates and products.*

Other metabolic reactions function far from equilibrium; that is, they are irreversible. This is because an enzyme catalyzing such a reaction has insufficient catalytic activity (the rate of the reaction it catalyzes is too slow) to allow the reaction to come to equilibrium under physiological conditions. Reactants therefore accumulate in large excess of their equilibrium amounts, making $\Delta G \ll 0$. Changes in substrate concentrations therefore have relatively little effect on the rate of an irreversible reaction; the enzyme is essentially saturated. Only changes in the activity of the enzyme through allosteric interactions, for example, can significantly alter the rate. The enzyme is therefore analogous to a dam on a river: *It controls the flow of substrate through the reaction by varying its activity, much as a dam controls the flow of a river by varying the opening of its floodgates.*

Understanding the **flux** (rate of flow) of metabolites through a metabolic pathway requires knowledge of which reactions are functioning near equilibrium and which are far from it. Most enzymes in a metabolic pathway operate near equilibrium and therefore have net rates that vary with their substrate concentrations. However, certain enzymes that operate far from equilibrium are strategically located in metabolic pathways. This has several important implications:

1. **Metabolic pathways are irreversible.** A highly exergonic reaction (one with $\Delta G \ll 0$) is irreversible; that is, it goes to completion. If such a reaction is part of a multistep pathway, it confers directionality on the pathway; that is, it makes the entire pathway irreversible.

2. **Every metabolic pathway has a first committed step.** Although most reactions in a metabolic pathway function close to equilibrium, there is generally an irreversible (exergonic) reaction early in the pathway

that "commits" its product to continue down the pathway (likewise, water that has gone over a dam cannot spontaneously return).

3. **Catabolic and anabolic pathways differ.** If a metabolite is converted to another metabolite by an exergonic process, free energy must be supplied to convert the second metabolite back to the first. This energetically "uphill" process requires a different pathway for at least one of the reaction steps.

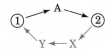

The existence of independent interconversion routes, as we shall see, is an important property of metabolic pathways because it allows independent control of the two processes. If metabolite 2 is required by the cell, it is necessary to "turn off" the pathway from 2 to 1 while "turning on" the pathway from 1 to 2. Such independent control would be impossible without different pathways.

Metabolic Flux Must Be Controlled

Living organisms are thermodynamically open systems that tend to maintain a steady state rather than reaching equilibrium (Section 1-3E). This is strikingly demonstrated by the observation that, over a 40-year time span, a normal human adult consumes literally tons of nutrients and imbibes over 20,000 L of water but does so without major weight change. *The flux of intermediates through a metabolic pathway in a steady state is more or less constant; that is, the rates of synthesis and breakdown of each pathway intermediate maintain it at a constant concentration.* A steady state far from equilibrium is thermodynamically efficient, because only a non-equilibrium process ($\Delta G \neq 0$) can perform useful work. Indeed, living systems that have reached equilibrium are dead.

Since a metabolic pathway is a series of enzyme-catalyzed reactions, it is easiest to describe the flux of metabolites through the pathway by considering its reaction steps individually. The flux of metabolites, J, through each reaction step is the rate of the forward reaction, v_f, less that of the reverse reaction, v_r:

$$J = v_f - v_r \qquad [14\text{-}3]$$

At equilibrium, by definition, there is no flux ($J = 0$), although v_f and v_r may be quite large. In reactions that are far from equilibrium, $v_f \gg v_r$, the flux is essentially equal to the rate of the forward reaction ($J \approx v_f$).

For the pathway as a whole, flux is set by the rate-determining step of the pathway. By definition, this step is the pathway's slowest step, which is often the first committed step of the pathway. In some pathways, flux control is distributed over several enzymes, all of which help determine the overall rate of flow of metabolites through the pathway. Because a rate-determining step is slow relative to other steps in the pathway, its product is removed by succeeding steps in the pathway before it can equilibrate with reactant. Thus, *the rate-determining step functions far from equilibrium and has a large negative free energy change.* In an analogous manner, a dam creates a difference in water levels between its upstream and downstream sides, and a large negative free energy change results from the hydrostatic pressure difference. The dam can release water to generate electricity, varying the water flow according to the need for electrical power.

Reactions that function near equilibrium respond rapidly to changes in substrate concentration. For example, upon a sudden increase in the concentration of a reactant for a near-equilibrium reaction, the enzyme catalyzing it would increase the net reaction rate so as to rapidly achieve the new equilibrium level. Thus, a series of near-equilibrium reactions downstream from the rate-determining step all have the same flux. Likewise, the flux of water in a river is the same at all points downstream from a dam.

In practice, it is often possible to identify flux control points for a pathway by identifying reactions that have large negative free energy changes. The relative insensitivity of the rates of these nonequilibrium reactions to variations in the concentrations of their substrates permits the establishment of a steady state flux of metabolites through the pathway. Of course, flux through a pathway must vary in response to the organism's requirements so as to reach a new steady state. Altering the rates of the rate-determining steps can alter the flux of material through the entire pathway, often by an order of magnitude or more.

Cells use several mechanisms to control flux through the rate-determining steps of metabolic pathways:

1. *Allosteric control.* Many enzymes are allosterically regulated (Section 12-3A) by effectors that are often substrates, products, or coenzymes of the pathway but not necessarily of the enzyme in question. For example, in negative feedback regulation, the product of a pathway inhibits an earlier step in the pathway:

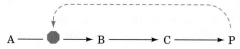

Thus, as we have seen, CTP, a product of pyrimidine biosynthesis, inhibits ATCase, which catalyzes the rate-determining step in the pathway (Fig. 12-11).

2. *Covalent modification.* Many enzymes that control pathway fluxes have specific sites that may be enzymatically phosphorylated and dephosphorylated (Section 12-3B) or covalently modified in some other way. Such enzymatic modification processes, which are themselves subject to control by external signals such as hormones (Section 13-1), greatly alter the activities of the modified enzymes. The signaling methods involved in such flux control mechanisms are discussed in Chapter 13.

3. *Substrate cycles.* If v_f and v_r represent the rates of two opposing nonequilibrium reactions that are catalyzed by different enzymes, v_f and v_r may be independently varied.

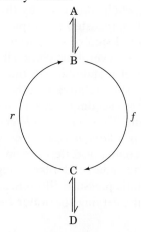

For example, flux ($v_f - v_r$) can be increased not just by accelerating the forward reaction but by slowing the reverse reaction. The flux through such a **substrate cycle,** as we shall see in Section 15-4, is more sensitive to the concentrations of allosteric effectors than is the flux through a single unopposed nonequilibrium reaction.

4. *Genetic control.* Enzyme concentrations, and hence enzyme activities, may be altered by protein synthesis in response to metabolic needs. With the sequencing of entire genomes, the genetic response of an organism to environmental changes has become a major field of study. **Transcriptomics** (the study of the entire collection of RNA transcribed by a cell) and **proteomics** (the study of the complete set of proteins synthesized by a cell in response to changing conditions) are part of the emerging field of **systems biology** (Section 14-4C). Mechanisms of genetic control of enzyme concentrations are a major concern of Part V of this text.

Mechanisms 1 to 3 can respond rapidly (within seconds or minutes) to external stimuli and are therefore classified as "short-term" control mechanisms. Mechanism 4 responds more slowly to changing conditions (within hours or days in higher organisms) and is therefore regarded as a "long-term" control mechanism.

Control of most metabolic pathways involves several nonequilibrium steps. Hence, the flux of material through a pathway that supplies intermediates for use by an organism may depend on multiple effectors whose relative importance reflects the overall metabolic demands of the organism at a given time. Thus, a metabolic pathway is part of a **supply–demand process.**

■ **CHECK YOUR UNDERSTANDING**

Describe the differences between autotrophs and heterotrophs.

List the categories of macronutrients and micronutrients required for mammalian metabolism.

Describe the roles of vitamins and minerals in nutrition.

Explain the metabolic significance of reactions that function near equilibrium and reactions that function far from equilibrium.

Discuss the mechanisms by which the flux through a metabolic pathway can be controlled.

2 "High-Energy" Compounds

The complete oxidation of a metabolic fuel such as glucose

$$C_6H_{12}O_6 + 6\,O_2 \longrightarrow 6\,CO_2 + 6\,H_2O$$

releases considerable energy ($\Delta G^{\circ\prime} = -2850\ \text{kJ} \cdot \text{mol}^{-1}$). The complete oxidation of palmitate, a typical fatty acid,

$$C_{16}H_{32}O_2 + 23\,O_2 \longrightarrow 16\,CO_2 + 16\,H_2O$$

is even more exergonic ($\Delta G^{\circ\prime} = -9781\ \text{kJ} \cdot \text{mol}^{-1}$). Oxidative metabolism proceeds in a stepwise fashion, so the released free energy can be recovered in a manageable form at each exergonic step of the overall process. *These "packets" of energy are conserved by the synthesis of a few types of "high-energy" intermediates whose subsequent exergonic breakdown drives endergonic processes.* These intermediates therefore form a sort of free energy "currency" through which free energy–producing reactions such as glucose oxidation or fatty acid oxidation "pay for" the free energy–consuming processes in biological systems (Box 14-3).

The cell uses several forms of energy currency, including phosphorylated compounds such as the nucleotide ATP (the cell's primary energy currency), compounds that contain thioester bonds, and reduced coenzymes such as NADH. Each of these represents a source of free energy that the cell can use in various ways, including the synthesis of ATP. We will first examine ATP and then discuss the properties of other forms of energy currency.

LEARNING OBJECTIVES

■ Understand that organisms capture the free energy released on degradation of nutrients as "high-energy" compounds such as ATP, whose subsequent breakdown is used to power otherwise endergonic reactions.

■ Understand that "high-energy" usually means high free energy of hydrolysis or oxidation.

■ Understand that phosphoryl groups are transferred from compounds with high phosphoryl group-transfer potentials to those with low phosphoryl group-transfer potentials.

■ Understand that the thioester bond in acetyl-CoA is a "high-energy" bond.

BOX 14-3 **PATHWAYS OF DISCOVERY**

Fritz Lipmann and "High-Energy" Compounds

Fritz Albert Lipmann (1899–1986)

Among the many scientists who fled Europe for the United States in the 1930s was Fritz Lipmann, a German-born physician-turned-biochemist. During the first part of the twentieth century, scientists were primarily interested in the structures and compositions of biological molecules, and not much was known about their biosynthesis. Lipmann's contribution to this field centers on his understanding of "energy-rich" phosphates and other "active" compounds.

Lipmann began his research career by studying creatine phosphate, a compound that could provide energy for muscle contraction. He, like many of his contemporaries, was puzzled by the absence of an obvious link between this phosphorylated compound and the known metabolic activity of a contracting muscle, namely, converting glucose to lactate. One link was discovered by Otto Warburg (Box 15-1), who showed that one of the steps of glycolysis was accompanied by the incorporation of inorganic phosphate. The resulting acyl phosphate (1,3-bisphosphoglycerate) could then react with ADP to form ATP.

Lipmann wondered whether other phosphorylated compounds might behave in a similar manner. Because the purification of such labile (prone to degradation) compounds from whole cells was impractical, Lipmann synthesized them himself. He was able to show that cell extracts used synthetic acetyl phosphate to produce ATP. Lipmann went on to propose that cells contain two classes of phosphorylated compounds, which he termed "energy-poor" and "energy-rich," by which he meant compounds with low and high negative free energies of hydrolysis (the "squiggle," ~, which is still used, was his symbol for an "energy-rich" bond). Lipmann described

a sort of "phosphate current" in which photosynthesis or breakdown of food molecules generates "energy-rich" phosphates that lead to the synthesis of ATP. The ATP, in turn, can power mechanical work such as muscle contraction or drive biosynthetic reactions.

Until this point (1941), biochemists studying biosynthetic processes were largely limited to working with whole animals or relatively intact tissue slices. Lipmann's insight regarding the role of ATP freed researchers from their cumbersome and poorly reproducible experimental systems. Biochemists could simply add ATP to their cell-free preparations to reconstitute the biosynthetic process.

Lipmann was intrigued by the discovery that a two-carbon group, an "active acetate," served as a precursor for the synthesis of fatty acids and steroids. Was acetyl phosphate also the "active acetate"? This proved not to be the case, although Lipmann was able to show that the addition of a two-carbon unit to another molecule (acetylation) required acetate, ATP, and a heat-stable factor present in pigeon liver extracts. He isolated and determined the structure of this factor, which he named coenzyme A. For this seminal discovery, Lipmann was awarded the 1953 Nobel Prize for Physiology or Medicine.

Even after "high-energy" thioesters (as in acetyl-CoA) came on the scene, Lipmann remained a staunch advocate of "high-energy" phosphates. For example, he realized that carbamoyl phosphate (H_2N—COO—PO_3^{2-}) could function as an "active" carbamoyl group donor in biosynthetic reactions. He also helped identify more obscure compounds, mixed anhydrides between phosphate and sulfate, as "active" sulfates that function as sulfate group donors.

Kleinkauf, H., von Döhren, H., and Jaenicke, L. (Eds.), *The Roots of Modern Biochemistry. Fritz Lipmann's Squiggle and Its Consequences,* Walter de Gruyter (1988).

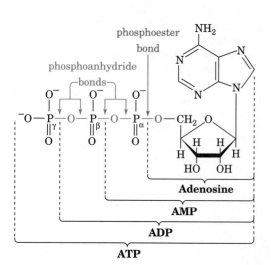

Adenosine
AMP
ADP
ATP

A | ATP Has a High Phosphoryl Group-Transfer Potential

The "high-energy" intermediate adenosine triphosphate (ATP; Fig. 14-4) occurs in all known life-forms. ATP consists of an **adenosine** moiety (adenine + ribose) to which three phosphoryl (—PO_3^{2-}) groups are sequentially linked via a **phosphoester** bond followed by two **phosphoanhydride** bonds.

The biological importance of ATP rests in the large free energy change that accompanies cleavage of its phosphoanhydride bonds. This occurs when either a phosphoryl group is transferred to another compound

■ **Figure 14-4** | **The structure of ATP indicating its relationship to ADP, AMP, and adenosine.** The phosphoryl groups, starting from AMP, are referred to as the α-, β-, and γ-phosphates. Note the differences between phosphoester and phosphoanhydride bonds.

eaving ADP, or a nucleotidyl (AMP) group is transferred, leaving **pyrophosphate** ($P_2O_7^{4-}$; **PP$_i$**). When the acceptor is water, the process is known as hydrolysis:

$$ATP + H_2O \rightleftharpoons ADP + P_i$$
$$ATP + H_2O \rightleftharpoons AMP + PP_i$$

Most biological group-transfer reactions involve acceptors other than water. However, knowing the free energy of hydrolysis of various phosphoryl compounds allows us to calculate the free energy of transfer of phosphoryl groups to other acceptors by determining the difference in free energy of hydrolysis of the phosphoryl donor and acceptor.

The $\Delta G^{\circ\prime}$ values for hydrolysis of several phosphorylated compounds of biochemical importance are tabulated in Table 14-4. The negatives of these values are often referred to as **phosphoryl group-transfer potentials;** they are a measure of the tendency of phosphorylated compounds to transfer their phosphoryl groups to water. Note that ATP has an intermediate phosphate group-transfer potential. Under standard conditions, the compounds above ATP in Table 14-4 can spontaneously transfer a phosphoryl group to ADP to form ATP, which can, in turn, spontaneously transfer a phosphoryl group to the appropriate groups to form the compounds listed below it. Note that a favorable free energy change for a reaction does not indicate how quickly the reaction occurs. Despite their high group-transfer potentials, ATP and related phosphoryl compounds are **kinetically stable** and do not react at a significant rate unless acted upon by an appropriate enzyme.

What Is the Nature of the "Energy" in "High-Energy" Compounds?

Bonds whose hydrolysis proceeds with large negative values of $\Delta G^{\circ\prime}$ (customarily more than -25 kJ $\cdot$ mol^{-1}) are often referred to as **"high-energy" bonds** or **"energy-rich" bonds** and are frequently symbolized by the squiggle (~). Thus, ATP can be represented as AR—P~P~P, where A, R, and P symbolize adenyl, ribosyl, and phosphoryl groups, respectively. Yet the phosphoester bond joining the adenosyl group of ATP to its α-phosphoryl group appears to be not greatly different in electronic character from the "high-energy" bonds bridging its α- and β- and its β- and γ-phosphoryl groups. In fact, none of these bonds has any unusual properties, so the term "high-energy" bond is somewhat of a misnomer (in any case, it should not be confused with the term "bond energy," which is defined as the energy required to break, not hydrolyze, a covalent bond). Why, then, are the phosphoryl group-transfer reactions of ATP so exergonic? Several factors appear to be responsible for the "high-energy" character of phosphoanhydride bonds such as those in ATP (Fig. 14-5):

1. The resonance stabilization of a phosphoanhydride bond is less than that of its hydrolysis products. This is because a phosphoanhydride's two strongly electron-withdrawing groups must compete for the lone pairs of electrons of its bridging oxygen atom, whereas this competition is absent in the hydrolysis products. In other words, the electronic requirements of the phosphoryl groups are less satisfied in a phosphoanhydride than in its hydrolysis products.

2. Of perhaps greater importance is the destabilizing effect of the electrostatic repulsions between the charged groups of a phosphoanhydride compared to those of its hydrolysis products. In the physiological pH range, ATP has three to four negative charges whose mutual electrostatic repulsions are partially relieved by ATP hydrolysis.

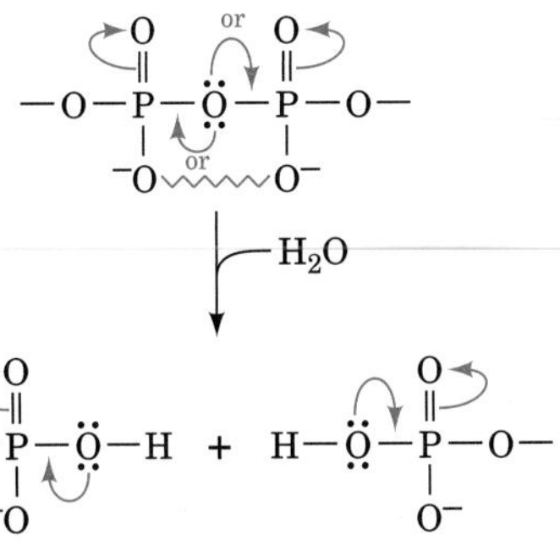

Table 14-4	Standard Free Energies of Phosphate Hydrolysis of Some Compounds of Biological Interest
Compound	$\Delta G^{\circ\prime}$ (kJ $\cdot$ mol^{-1})
Phosphoenolpyruvate	-61.9
1,3-Bisphosphoglycerate	-49.4
ATP ($\rightarrow$ AMP + PP$_i$)	-45.6
Acetyl phosphate	-43.1
Phosphocreatine	-43.1
ATP ($\rightarrow$ ADP + P$_i$)	-30.5
Glucose-1-phosphate	-20.9
PP$_i$	-19.2
Fructose-6-phosphate	-13.8
Glucose-6-phosphate	-13.8
Glycerol-3-phosphate	-9.2

Source: Mostly from Jencks, W.P., *in* Fasman, G.D. (Ed.), *Handbook of Biochemistry and Molecular Biology* (3rd ed.), Physical and Chemical Data, Vol. I, pp. 296–304, CRC Press (1976).

■ **Figure 14-5 | Resonance and electrostatic stabilization in a phosphoanhydride and its hydrolytic products.** The competing resonances (*curved arrows* from the central O) and charge–charge repulsions (*zigzag lines*) between phosphoryl groups decrease the stability of a phosphoanhydride relative to its hydrolysis products.

BOX 14-4 PERSPECTIVES IN BIOCHEMISTRY

ATP and ΔG

The standard conditions reflected in $\Delta G^{\circ\prime}$ values never occur in living organisms. Furthermore, other compounds that are present at high concentrations and that can potentially interact with the substrates and products of a metabolic reaction may dramatically affect ΔG values. For example, Mg^{2+} ions in cells partially neutralize the negative charges on the phosphate groups in ATP and its hydrolysis products, thereby diminishing the electrostatic repulsions that make ATP hydrolysis so exergonic. Similarly, changes in pH alter the ionic character of phosphorylated compounds and therefore alter their free energies.

In a given cell, the concentrations of many ions, coenzymes, and metabolites vary with both location and time, often by several orders of magnitude. Intracellular ATP concentrations are maintained within a relatively narrow range, usually 2–10 mM, but the concentrations of ADP and P_i are more variable. Consider a typical cell with [ATP] = 3.0 mM, [ADP] = 0.8 mM, and [P_i] = 4.0 mM. Using Eq. 14-1, the actual free energy of ATP hydrolysis at 37°C is calculated as follows.

$$\Delta G = \Delta G^{\circ\prime} + RT \ln\left(\frac{[ADP][P_i]}{[ATP]}\right)$$

$$= -30.5 \text{ kJ} \cdot \text{mol}^{-1} + (8.3145 \text{ J} \cdot \text{K}^{-1} \cdot \text{mol}^{-1})(310 \text{ K})$$

$$\ln\left(\frac{(0.8 \times 10^{-3} \text{ M})(4.0 \times 10^{-3} \text{ M})}{(3.0 \times 10^{-3} \text{ M})}\right)$$

$$= -30.5 \text{ kJ} \cdot \text{mol}^{-1} - 17.6 \text{ kJ} \cdot \text{mol}^{-1}$$

$$= -48.1 \text{ kJ} \cdot \text{mol}^{-1}$$

This value is even greater than the standard free energy of ATP hydrolysis. However, because of the difficulty in accurately measuring the concentrations of particular chemical species in a cell or organelle, the ΔG's for most *in vivo* reactions are little more than estimates. For the sake of consistency, we shall, for the most part, use $\Delta G^{\circ\prime}$ values in this textbook.

---

3. Another destabilizing influence, which is difficult to assess, is the smaller solvation energy of a phosphoanhydride compared to that of its hydrolysis products. Some estimates suggest that this factor provides the dominant thermodynamic driving force for the hydrolysis of phosphoanhydrides.

Of course, the free energy change for any reaction, including phosphoryl group transfer from a "high-energy" compound, depends in part on the concentrations of the reactants and products (Eq. 14-1). Furthermore, because ATP and its hydrolysis products are ions, ΔG also depends on pH and ionic strength (Box 14-4).

B | Coupled Reactions Drive Endergonic Processes

The exergonic reactions of "high-energy" compounds can be coupled to endergonic processes to drive them to completion. The thermodynamic explanation for the coupling of an exergonic and an endergonic process is based on the additivity of free energy. Consider the following two-step reaction pathway:

$$(1) \quad A + B \rightleftharpoons C + D \qquad \Delta G_1$$
$$(2) \quad D + E \rightleftharpoons F + G \qquad \Delta G_2$$

If $\Delta G_1 \geq 0$, Reaction 1 will not occur spontaneously. However, if ΔG_2 is sufficiently exergonic so that $\Delta G_1 + \Delta G_2 < 0$, then although the equilibrium concentration of D in Reaction 1 will be relatively small, it will be larger than that in Reaction 2. As Reaction 2 converts D to products, Reaction 1 will operate in the forward direction to replenish the equilibrium concentration of D. The highly exergonic Reaction 2 therefore "drives" or "pulls" the endergonic Reaction 1, and the two reactions are said to be coupled through their common intermediate, D. That these

$\Delta G^{\circ\prime}$ (kJ·mol^{-1})

(a)

Endergonic half-reaction 1	P_i + glucose	$\rightleftharpoons$ glucose-6-P + H_2O	+13.8
Exergonic half-reaction 2	ATP + H_2O	$\rightleftharpoons$ ADP + P_i	−30.5
Overall coupled reaction	ATP + glucose	$\rightleftharpoons$ ADP + glucose-6-P	−16.7

$\Delta G^{\circ\prime}$ (kJ·mol^{-1})

(b)

Exergonic half-reaction 1

$$\underset{\textbf{Phosphoenolpyruvate}}{\text{CH}_2\!\!=\!\!\underset{\text{OPO}_3^{2-}}{\overset{\text{COO}^-}{\text{C}}}} + H_2O \rightleftharpoons \underset{\textbf{Pyruvate}}{\text{CH}_3\!-\!\overset{\overset{\text{O}}{\|}}{\text{C}}\!-\!\text{COO}^-} + P_i \qquad -61.9$$

Endergonic half-reaction 2 $\qquad$ ADP + P_i $\rightleftharpoons$ ATP + H_2O $\qquad$ +30.5

Overall coupled reaction

$$\text{CH}_2\!\!=\!\!\underset{\text{OPO}_3^{2-}}{\overset{\text{COO}^-}{\text{C}}} + \text{ADP} \rightleftharpoons \text{CH}_3\!-\!\overset{\overset{\text{O}}{\|}}{\text{C}}\!-\!\text{COO}^- + \text{ATP} \qquad -31.4$$

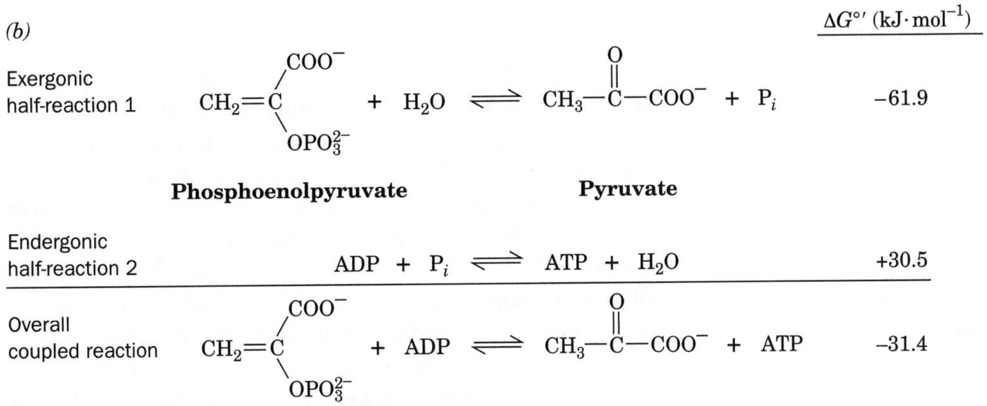

■ **Figure 14-6** | **Some coupled reactions involving ATP.**
(a) The phosphorylation of glucose to form glucose-6-phosphate and ADP. (b) The phosphorylation of ADP by phosphoenolpyruvate to form ATP and pyruvate. Each reaction has been conceptually decomposed into a direct phosphorylation step (half-reaction 1) and a step in which ATP is hydrolyzed (half-reaction 2). Both half-reactions proceed in the direction that makes the overall reaction exergonic ($\Delta G < 0$).

coupled reactions proceed spontaneously can also be seen by summing Reactions 1 and 2 to yield the overall reaction

$$(1 + 2) \quad A + B + E \rightleftharpoons C + F + G \qquad \Delta G_3$$

where $\Delta G_3 = \Delta G_1 + \Delta G_2 < 0$. *As long as the overall pathway is exergonic, it will operate in the forward direction.*

To illustrate this concept, let us consider two examples of phosphoryl group-transfer reactions. The initial step in the metabolism of glucose is its conversion to **glucose-6-phosphate** (Section 15-2A). Yet the direct reaction of glucose and P_i is thermodynamically unfavorable ($\Delta G^{\circ\prime} = +13.8$ kJ·mol^{-1}; Fig. 14-6a). In cells, however, this reaction is coupled to the exergonic cleavage of ATP (for ATP hydrolysis, $\Delta G^{\circ\prime} = -30.5$ kJ·mol^{-1}), so the overall reaction is thermodynamically favorable ($\Delta G^{\circ\prime} = +13.8 - 30.5 = -16.7$ kJ·mol^{-1}). ATP can be similarly regenerated ($\Delta G^{\circ\prime} = +30.5$ kJ·mol^{-1}) by coupling its synthesis from ADP and P_i to the even more exergonic cleavage of **phosphoenolpyruvate** ($\Delta G^{\circ\prime} = -61.9$ kJ·mol^{-1}; Fig. 14-6b and Section 15-2J).

Note that the half-reactions shown in Fig. 14-6 do not actually occur as written in an enzyme active site. **Hexokinase,** the enzyme that catalyzes the formation of glucose-6-phosphate (Fig. 14-6a), does not catalyze ATP hydrolysis but instead catalyzes the transfer of a phosphoryl group from ATP directly to glucose. Likewise, **pyruvate kinase,** the enzyme that catalyzes the reaction shown in Fig. 14-6b, does not add a free phosphoryl group to ADP but transfers a phosphoryl group from phosphoenolpyruvate to ADP to form ATP.

Phosphoanhydride Hydrolysis Drives Some Biochemical Processes
The free energy of the phosphoanhydride bonds of "high-energy" compounds such as ATP can be used to drive reactions even when the phosphoryl groups are not transferred to another organic compound. For example, ATP hydrolysis (i.e., phosphoryl group transfer directly to H_2O) provides the free energy for the operation of molecular chaperones (Section 6-5B), muscle contraction (Section 7-2B), and transmembrane active transport (Section 10-3). In these processes, proteins undergo conformational changes in response to binding ATP. *The exergonic hydrolysis of ATP and release of ADP and P_i renders these changes irreversible and thereby drives the processes forward.* GTP hydrolysis functions similarly to drive some of the reactions of signal transduction (Section 13-3B) and protein synthesis (Section 27-4).

In the absence of an appropriate enzyme, phosphoanhydride bonds are stable; that is, they hydrolyze quite slowly, despite the large amount of free energy released by these reactions. This is because these hydrolysis reactions have unusually high free energies of activation ($\Delta G^{\ddagger}$; Section 11-2). Consequently, *ATP hydrolysis is thermodynamically favored but kinetically disfavored.* For example, consider the reaction of glucose with ATP that yields glucose-6-phosphate (Fig. 14-6a). $\Delta G^{\ddagger}$ for the nonenzymatic transfer of a phosphoryl group from ATP to glucose is greater than that for ATP hydrolysis, so the hydrolysis reaction predominates (although neither reaction occurs at a biologically significant rate). However, in the presence of the appropriate enzyme, **hexokinase** (Section 15-2A), glucose-6-phosphate is formed far more rapidly than ATP is hydrolyzed. This is because the catalytic influence of the enzyme reduces the activation energy for phosphoryl group transfer from ATP to glucose to less than the activation energy for ATP hydrolysis. This example underscores the point that even a thermodynamically favored reaction ($\Delta G < 0$) may not occur in a living system in the absence of a specific enzyme that catalyzes the reaction (i.e., lowers $\Delta G^{\ddagger}$ to increase the rate of product formation; Box 12-3).

Inorganic Pyrophosphatase Catalyzes Additional Phosphoanhydride Bond Cleavage. Although many reactions involving ATP yield ADP and P_i **(orthophosphate cleavage)**, others yield AMP and PP_i **(pyrophosphate cleavage)**. In these latter cases, the PP_i is rapidly hydrolyzed to 2 P_i by **inorganic pyrophosphatase** ($\Delta G^{\circ\prime} = -19.2 \text{ kJ} \cdot \text{mol}^{-1}$) so that *the pyrophosphate cleavage of ATP ultimately consumes two "high-energy" phosphoanhydride bonds.* The attachment of amino acids to tRNA molecules for protein synthesis is an example of this phenomenon (Fig. 14-7 and Section 27-2B). The two steps of the reaction are readily reversible because the free energies of hydrolysis of the bonds formed are comparable to that of ATP hydrolysis. The overall reaction is driven to completion by the irreversible hydrolysis of PP_i. Nucleic acid biosynthesis from nucleoside triphosphates also releases PP_i (Sections 25-1 and 26-1). The standard free energy changes of these reactions are around 0, so the subsequent hydrolysis of PP_i is also essential for the synthesis of nucleic acids.

C | Some Other Phosphorylated Compounds Have High Phosphoryl Group-Transfer Potentials

"High-energy" compounds other than ATP are essential for energy metabolism, in part because they help maintain a relatively constant level of cellular ATP. *ATP is continually being hydrolyzed and regenerated.* Indeed, experimental evidence indicates that the metabolic half-life of an ATP

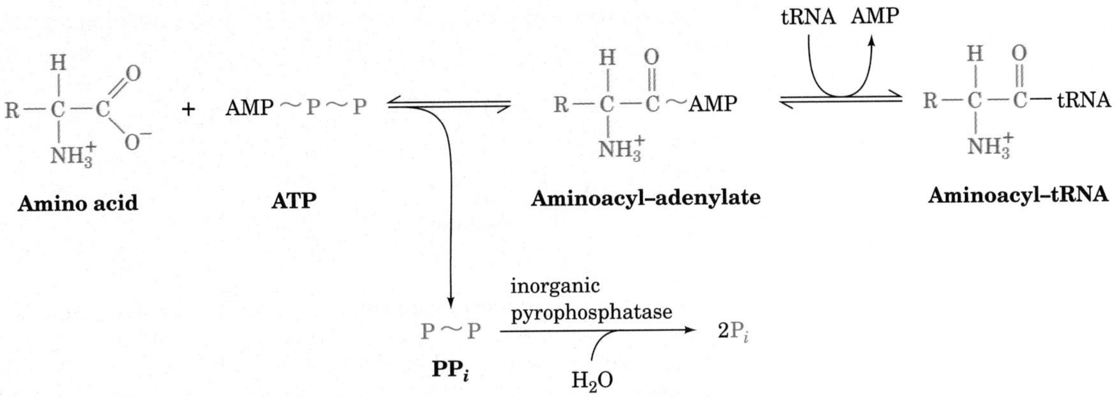

The chemical reaction scheme at the top of the page:

$$R-\underset{\underset{NH_3^+}{|}}{\overset{\overset{H}{|}}{C}}-C\overset{O}{\underset{O^-}{\diagdown}} + AMP\sim P\sim P \rightleftharpoons R-\underset{\underset{NH_3^+}{|}}{\overset{\overset{H}{|}}{C}}-\overset{\overset{O}{\|}}{C}\sim AMP \rightleftharpoons R-\underset{\underset{NH_3^+}{|}}{\overset{\overset{H}{|}}{C}}-\overset{\overset{O}{\|}}{C}-tRNA$$

Amino acid   **ATP**   **Aminoacyl–adenylate**   **Aminoacyl–tRNA**

tRNA AMP

$$P\sim P \xrightarrow[\text{H}_2\text{O}]{\text{inorganic}\atop\text{pyrophosphatase}} 2P_i$$

PP$_i$

Figure 14-7 ╎ **Pyrophosphate cleavage in the synthesis of an aminoacyl–tRNA.** In the first reaction step, the amino acid is adenylylated by ATP. In the second step, a tRNA molecule displaces the AMP moiety to form an aminoacyl–tRNA. The exergonic hydrolysis of pyrophosphate ($\Delta G^{\circ\prime} = -19.2\,\text{kJ}\cdot\text{mol}^{-1}$) drives the reaction forward.

molecule varies from seconds to minutes depending on the cell type and its metabolic activity. For instance, brain cells have only a few seconds supply of ATP (which partly accounts for the rapid deterioration of brain tissue by oxygen deprivation). An average person at rest consumes and regenerates ATP at a rate of ~3 mol (1.5 kg) per hour and as much as an order of magnitude faster during strenuous activity.

Just as ATP drives endergonic reactions through the exergonic process of phosphoryl group transfer and phosphoanhydride hydrolysis, *ATP itself can be regenerated by coupling its formation to a more highly exergonic metabolic process.* As Table 14-4 indicates, in the thermodynamic hierarchy of phosphoryl-transfer agents, ATP occupies the middle rank. ATP can therefore be formed from ADP by direct transfer of a phosphoryl group from a "high-energy" compound (e.g., phosphoenolpyruvate; Fig. 14-6*b* and Section 15-2J). Such a reaction is referred to as a **substrate-level phosphorylation.** Other mechanisms generate ATP indirectly, using the energy supplied by transmembrane proton concentration gradients. In oxidative metabolism, this process is called **oxidative phosphorylation** (Section 18-3), whereas in photosynthesis, it is termed **photophosphorylation** (Section 19-2D).

The flow of energy from "high-energy" phosphate compounds to ATP and from ATP to "low-energy" phosphate compounds is diagrammed in Fig. 14-8. These reactions are catalyzed by enzymes known as **kinases,** which transfer phosphoryl groups from ATP to other compounds or from phosphorylated compounds to ADP. We shall revisit these processes in our discussions of carbohydrate metabolism in Chapters 15 and 16.

The compounds whose phosphoryl group-transfer potentials are greater than that of ATP have additional stabilizing effects. For example, the hydrolysis of **acyl phosphates** (mixed phosphoric–carboxylic anhydrides), such as **acetyl phosphate** and **1,3-bisphosphoglycerate,**

$$CH_3-\overset{\overset{O}{\|}}{C}\sim OPO_3^{2-} \qquad {}^{-2}O_3POCH_2-\overset{\overset{OH}{|}}{C}H-\overset{\overset{O}{\|}}{C}\sim OPO_3^{2-}$$

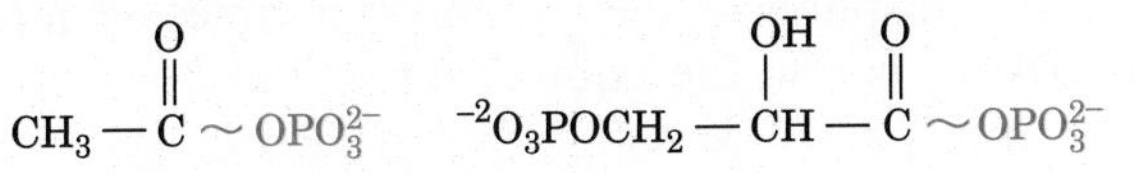

Acetyl phosphate   **1,3-Bisphosphoglycerate**

is driven by the same competing resonance and differential solvation effects that influence the hydrolysis of phosphoanhydrides (Fig. 14-5). Apparently, these effects are more pronounced for acyl phosphates than for phosphoanhydrides, as the rankings in Table 14-4 indicate.

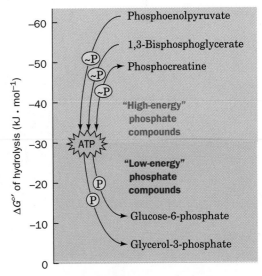

Figure 14-8 ╎ **Position of ATP relative to "high-energy" and "low-energy" phosphate compounds.** Phosphoryl groups flow from the "high-energy" donors, via the ATP–ADP system, to "low-energy" acceptors.

In contrast, compounds such as glucose-6-phosphate and **glycerol-3 phosphate,**

α-D-Glucose-6-phosphate   **L-Glycerol-3-phosphate**

which are below ATP in Table 14-4, have no significantly different reso nance stabilization or charge separation compared to their hydrolysis products. Their free energies of hydrolysis are therefore much less than those of the preceding "high-energy" compounds.

The high phosphoryl group-transfer potentials of **phosphoguanidines** such as **phosphocreatine** and **phosphoarginine,** largely result from the competing resonances in the **guanidino** group, which are even more pro nounced than they are in the phosphate group of phosphoanhydrides:

$R = CH_2-CO_2^-$; $X = CH_3$ **Phosphocreatine**

$R = CH_2-CH_2-CH_2-\overset{\overset{\displaystyle NH_3^+}{|}}{CH}-CO_2^-$; $X = H$ **Phosphoarginine**

Consequently, phosphocreatine can transfer its phosphoryl group to ADP to form ATP.

Phosphocreatine Provides a "High-Energy" Reservoir for ATP Formation. Muscle and nerve cells, which have a high ATP turnover, rely on phosphoguanidines to regenerate ATP rapidly. In vertebrates, phosphocreatine is synthesized by the reversible phosphorylation of crea tine by ATP catalyzed by **creatine kinase:**

$$ATP + creatine \rightleftharpoons phosphocreatine + ADP$$

$$\Delta G^{\circ\prime} = +12.6 \, kJ \cdot mol^{-1}$$

Note that this reaction is endergonic under standard conditions; however, *the intracellular concentrations of its reactants and products are such that it operates close to equilibrium* ($\Delta G \approx 0$). Accordingly, when the cell is in a resting state, so that [ATP] is relatively high, the reaction proceeds with net synthesis of phosphocreatine, whereas at times of high metabolic activity, when [ATP] is low, the equilibrium shifts so as to yield net syn thesis of ATP from phosphocreatine and ADP. *Phosphocreatine thereby acts as an ATP "buffer" in cells that contain creatine kinase.* A resting ver tebrate skeletal muscle normally has sufficient phosphocreatine to supply its free energy needs for several minutes (but for only a few seconds at maximum exertion). In the muscles of some invertebrates, such as lobsters, phosphoarginine performs the same function. These phosphoguanidines are collectively named **phosphagens.**

Nucleoside Triphosphates Are Freely Interconverted.   Many biosynthetic processes, such as the synthesis of proteins and nucleic acids, require nucleoside triphosphates other than ATP. For example, RNA synthesis requires the ribonucleotides CTP, GTP, and UTP, along with ATP, and DNA synthesis requires dCTP, dGTP, dTTP, and dATP (Section 3-1). All these nucleoside triphosphates (**NTPs**) are synthesized from ATP and the corresponding nucleoside diphosphate (**NDP**) in a reaction catalyzed by the nonspecific enzyme **nucleoside diphosphate kinase:**

$$ATP + NDP \rightleftharpoons ADP + NTP$$

The $\Delta G°'$ values for these reactions are nearly 0, as might be expected from the structural similarities among the NTPs. These reactions are driven by the depletion of the NTPs through their exergonic utilization in subsequent reactions.

Other kinases reversibly convert nucleoside monophosphates to their diphosphate forms at the expense of ATP. One of these phosphoryl group-transfer reactions is catalyzed by **adenylate kinase:**

$$AMP + ATP \rightleftharpoons 2\ ADP$$

This enzyme is present in all tissues, where it functions to maintain equilibrium concentrations of the three nucleotides. When AMP accumulates, it is converted to ADP, which can be used to synthesize ATP through substrate-level phosphorylation, oxidative phosphorylation, or photophosphorylation. The reverse reaction helps restore cellular ATP as rapid consumption of ATP increases the level of ADP.

The X-ray structure of adenylate kinase, determined by Georg Schulz, reveals that, in the reaction catalyzed by the enzyme, two ~30-residue domains of the enzyme close over the substrates (Fig. 14-9), thereby tightly binding them and preventing water from entering the active site (which would lead to hydrolysis rather than phosphoryl group transfer). The movement of one of the domains depends on the presence of four invariant charged residues. Interactions between those groups and the bound substrates apparently trigger the rearrangements around the substrate-binding site (Fig. 14-9*b*).

Once the adenylate kinase reaction is complete, the tightly bound products must be rapidly released to maintain the enzyme's catalytic efficiency. Yet since the reaction is energetically neutral (the net number of phosphoanhydride bonds is unchanged), another source of free energy is required for rapid product release. Comparison of the X-ray structures of unliganded adenylate kinase and adenylate kinase in complex with the bisubstrate model compound **Ap₅A** (AMP and ATP connected by a fifth phosphate) show how the enzyme avoids the kinetic trap of tight-binding substrates and products: On binding substrate, a portion of the protein

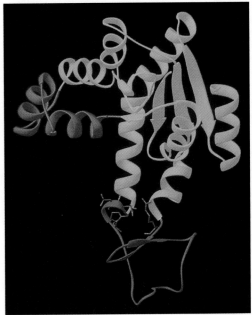

(*a*)

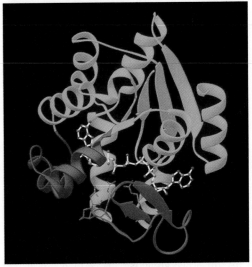

(*b*)

■ **Figure 14-9** | **Conformational changes in *E. coli* adenylate kinase on binding substrate.**   (*a*) The unliganded enzyme. (*b*) The enzyme with the bound bisubstrate analog Ap₅A. The Ap₅A is shown in ball-and-stick form (C green, N blue, O red, and P yellow). Several of the protein's side chains that have been implicated in substrate binding are shown in stick form. The protein's magenta and blue domains undergo extensive conformational changes on ligand binding, whereas the remainder of the protein (*gold*), whose orientation is the same in *a* and *b*, largely maintains its conformation. [Based on X-ray structures by Georg Schulz, Institut für Organische Chemie und Biochemie, Freiburg, Germany. PDBids (*a*) 4AKE and (*b*) 1AKE.] ✌ **See Interactive Exercises 14.**

remote from the active site increases its chain mobility and thereby con
sumes some of the free energy of substrate binding. The regior
"resolidifies" when the binding site is opened and the products are re
leased. This mechanism is thought to act as an "energetic counterweight"
to help adenylate kinase maintain a high reaction rate.

D | Thioesters Are Energy-Rich Compounds

The ubiquity of phosphorylated compounds in metabolism is consisten
with their early evolutionary appearance. Yet phosphate is (and was
scarce in the abiotic world, which suggests that other kinds of molecule:
might have served as energy-rich compounds even before metabolic path
ways became specialized for phosphorylated compounds. One candidate
for a primitive "high-energy" compound is the **thioester,** which offers as
its main recommendation its occurrence in the central metabolic pathway:
of all known organisms. Notably, the thioester bond is involved in
substrate-level phosphorylation, an ATP-generating process that is inde
pendent of—and presumably arose before—oxidative phosphorylation.

The thioester bond appears in modern metabolic pathways as a reac
tion intermediate (involving a Cys residue in an enzyme active site) and
in the form of acetyl-CoA (Fig. 14-10), the common product of carbohy
drate, fatty acid, and amino acid catabolism. **Coenzyme A (CoASH or
CoA)** consists of a β-mercaptoethylamine group bonded through an amide
linkage to the vitamin **pantothenic acid,** which, in turn, is attached to a
3′-phosphoadenosine moiety via a pyrophosphate bridge. The acetyl group
of acetyl-CoA is bonded as a thioester to the sulfhydryl portion of the

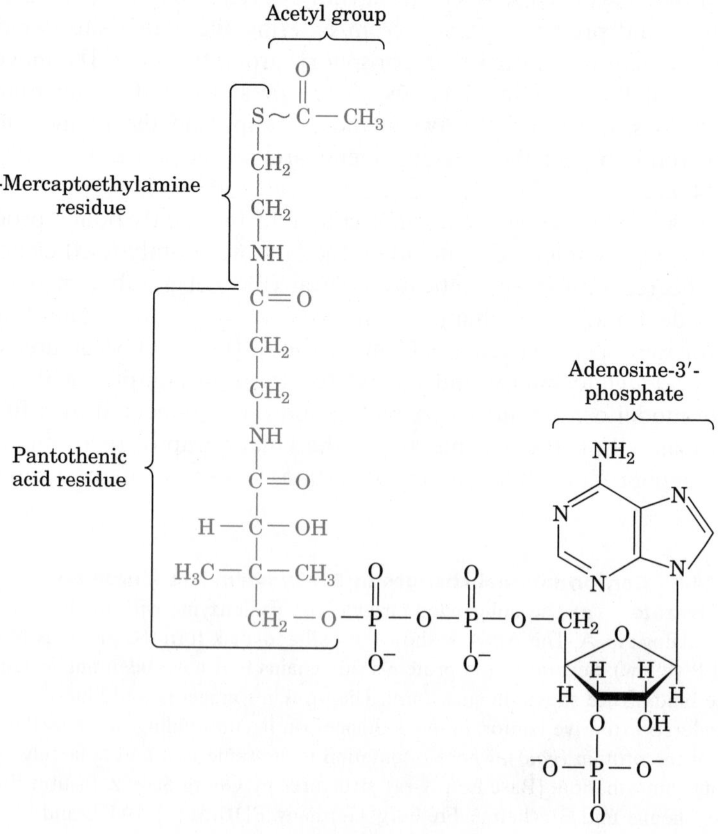

■ **Figure 14-10 | The chemical structure of
acetyl-CoA.** The thioester bond is drawn with a
$\sim$ to indicate that it is a "high-energy" bond (has
a high negative free energy of hydrolysis). In
CoA, the acetyl group is replaced by hydrogen.

Acetyl-coenzyme A (acetyl-CoA)

3-mercaptoethylamine group. *CoA thereby functions as a carrier of acetyl and other acyl groups (the A of CoA stands for "Acetylation").* Thioesters also take the form of acyl chains bonded to a phosphopantetheine residue that is linked to a Ser OH group in a protein (Section 20-4C) rather than to 3′-phospho-AMP, as in CoA.

Acetyl-CoA is a "high-energy" compound. The $\Delta G°'$ for the hydrolysis of its thioester bond is -31.5 kJ · mol^{-1}, which makes this reaction slightly (1 kJ · mol^{-1}) more exergonic than ATP hydrolysis. The hydrolysis of thioesters is more exergonic than that of ordinary esters because the thioester is less stabilized by resonance. This destabilization is a result of the large atomic radius of S, which reduces the electronic overlap between C and S compared to that between C and O.

The formation of a thioester bond in a metabolic intermediate conserves a portion of the free energy of oxidation of a metabolic fuel. That free energy can then be used to drive an exergonic process. In the citric acid cycle, for example, cleavage of a thioester (**succinyl-CoA**) releases sufficient free energy to synthesize GTP from GDP and P$_i$ (Section 17-3E).

■ **CHECK YOUR UNDERSTANDING**

Why is ATP a "high-energy" compound?
Describe the ways an exergonic process can drive an endergonic process.
Explain how cellular ATP is replenished.
Why is a thioester bond a "high-energy" bond?

3 | Oxidation–Reduction Reactions

As metabolic fuels are oxidized to CO_2, electrons are transferred to molecular carriers that, in aerobic organisms, ultimately transfer the electrons to molecular oxygen. The process of electron transport results in a transmembrane proton concentration gradient that drives ATP synthesis (oxidative phosphorylation; Section 18-3). Even obligate anaerobes, which do not carry out oxidative phosphorylation, rely on the oxidation of substrates to drive ATP synthesis. In fact, oxidation–reduction reactions (also known as **redox reactions**) supply living things with most of their free energy. In this section, we examine the thermodynamic basis for the conservation of free energy during substrate oxidation.

A | NAD$^+$ and FAD Are Electron Carriers

Two of the most widely occurring electron carriers are the nucleotide coenzymes nicotinamide adenine dinucleotide (NAD$^+$) and **flavin adenine dinucleotide (FAD)**. The nicotinamide portion of NAD$^+$ (and its phosphorylated counterpart NADP$^+$; Fig. 11-4) is the site of reversible reduction, which formally occurs as the transfer of a hydride ion (H$^-$; a proton with two electrons) as indicated in Fig. 14-11. The terminal electron acceptor in

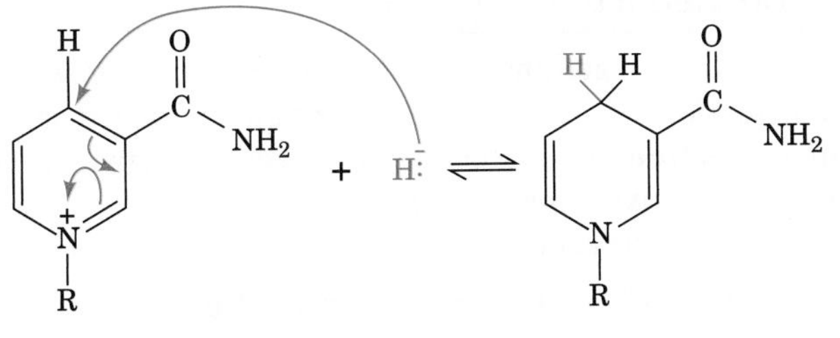

LEARNING OBJECTIVES

■ Understand the role of NAD$^+$ and FAD in metabolism.
■ Understand that the Nernst equation describes the thermodynamics of oxidation–reduction reactions.
■ Understand that the reduction potential describes the tendency for an oxidized compound to gain electrons (become reduced); the change in reduction potential for a reaction describes the tendency for a given oxidized compound to accept electrons from a given reduced compound.
■ Appreciate that free energy and reduction potential are negatively related: the greater the reduction potential, the more negative the free energy and the more spontaneous the reaction.

■ **Figure 14-11** | **Reduction of NAD$^+$ to NADH.** R represents the ribose–pyrophosphoryl–adenosine portion of the coenzyme. Only the nicotinamide ring is affected by reduction, which is formally represented here as occurring by hydride transfer.

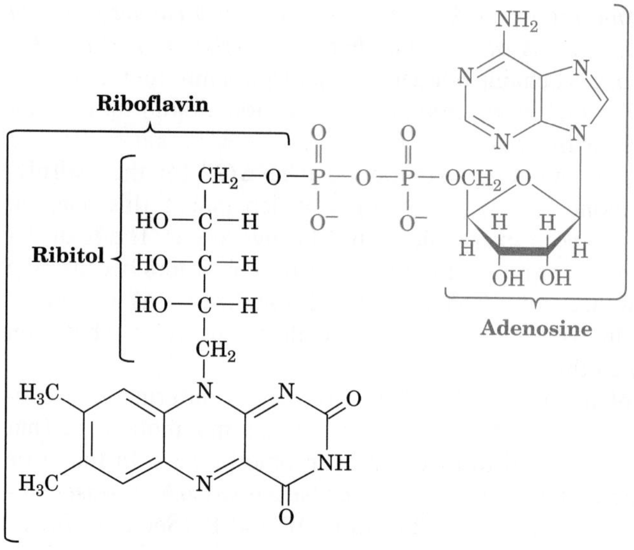

Figure 14-12 | Flavin adenine dinucleotide (FAD). Adenosine (*red*) is linked to **riboflavin** (*black*) by a pyrophosphoryl group (*green*). The riboflavin portion of FAD is also known as **vitamin B$_2$.**

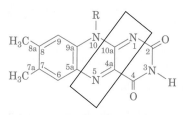

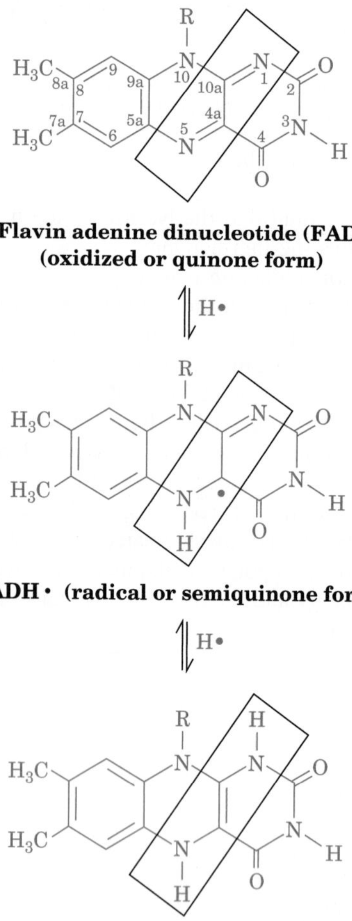

Flavin adenine dinucleotide (FAD)
(oxidized or quinone form)

H•

FADH• (radical or semiquinone form)

H•

FADH$_2$ (reduced or hydroquinone form)

Figure 14-13 | Reduction of FAD to FADH$_2$.
R represents the ribitol–pyrophosphoryl–adenosine portion of the coenzyme. The conjugated ring system of FAD undergoes two sequential one-electron reductions or a two-electron transfer that bypasses the **semiquinone** state.

aerobic organisms, O$_2$, can accept only unpaired electrons; that is, electrons must be transferred to O$_2$ one at a time. Electrons that are removed from metabolites as pairs (e.g., with the two-electron reduction of NAD$^+$) must be transferred to other carriers that can undergo both two-electron and one-electron redox reactions. FAD (Fig. 14-12) is such a coenzyme.

The conjugated ring system of FAD can accept one or two electrons to produce the stable radical (semiquinone) FADH· or the fully reduced (hydroquinone) FADH$_2$ (Fig. 14-13). The change in the electronic state of the ring system on reduction is reflected in a color change from brilliant yellow (in FAD) to pale yellow (in FADH$_2$). The metabolic functions of NAD$^+$ and FAD demand that they undergo reversible reduction so that they can accept electrons, pass them on to other electron carriers, and thereby be regenerated to participate in additional cycles of oxidation and reduction.

Humans cannot synthesize the flavin moiety of FAD but, rather, must obtain it from their diets, for example, in the form of riboflavin (vitamin B$_2$; Fig. 14-12). Nevertheless, riboflavin deficiency is quite rare in humans, in part because of the tight binding of flavin prosthetic groups to their apoenzymes. The symptoms of riboflavin deficiency, which are associated with general malnutrition or bizarre diets, include an inflamed tongue, lesions in the corner of the mouth, and dermatitis.

B | The Nernst Equation Describes Oxidation–Reduction Reactions

Oxidation–reduction reactions resemble other types of group-transfer reactions except that the "groups" transferred are electrons, which are passed from an **electron donor (reductant** or **reducing agent)** to an **electron acceptor (oxidant** or **oxidizing agent).**

For example, in the reaction

$$Fe^{3+} + Cu^+ \rightleftharpoons Fe^{2+} + Cu^{2+}$$

Cu$^+$, the reductant, is oxidized to Cu^{2+} while Fe^{3+}, the oxidant, is reduced to Fe^{2+}.

Redox reactions can be divided into two **half-reactions,** such as

$$Fe^{3+} + e^- \rightleftharpoons Fe^{2+} \quad \text{(reduction)}$$
$$Cu^+ \rightleftharpoons Cu^{2+} + e^- \quad \text{(oxidation)}$$

whose sum is the whole reaction above. These particular half-reactions occur during the oxidation of cytochrome *c* oxidase in the mitochondrion (Section 18-2F). Note that for electrons to be transferred, both half-reactions must occur simultaneously. In fact, the electrons are the two half-reactions' common intermediate.

A half-reaction consists of an electron donor and its conjugate electron acceptor; in the oxidative half-reaction shown above, Cu^+ is the electron donor and Cu^{2+} is its conjugate electron acceptor. Together these constitute a **redox couple** or **conjugate redox pair** analogous to a conjugate acid–base pair (HA and A^-; Section 2-2B). An important difference between redox pairs and acid–base pairs, however, is that *the two half-reactions of a redox reaction, each consisting of a conjugate redox pair, can be physically separated to form an **electrochemical cell*** (Fig. 14-14). In such a device, each half-reaction takes place in its separate **half-cell,** and electrons are passed between half-cells as an electric current in the wire connecting their two electrodes. A salt bridge is necessary to complete the electrical circuit by providing a conduit for ions to migrate and thereby maintain electrical neutrality.

The free energy of an oxidation–reduction reaction is particularly easy to determine by simply measuring the voltage difference between its two half-cells. Consider the general reaction

$$A_{ox}^{n+} + B_{red} \rightleftharpoons A_{red} + B_{ox}^{n+}$$

in which *n* electrons per mole of reactants are transferred from reductant (B_{red}) to oxidant (A_{ox}^{n+}). The free energy of this reaction is expressed as

$$\Delta G = \Delta G^{o\prime} + RT \ln\left(\frac{[A_{red}][B_{ox}^{n+}]}{[A_{ox}^{n+}][B_{red}]}\right) \qquad [14\text{-}4]$$

Under reversible conditions,

$$\Delta G = -w' = -w_{el} \qquad [14\text{-}5]$$

where *w'* is non-pressure–volume work. In this case, *w'* is equivalent to w_{el}, the electrical work required to transfer the *n* moles of electrons through the **electrical potential difference, $\Delta\mathscr{E}$** [where the units of $\mathscr{E}$ are volts (V), the number of joules (J) of work required to transfer 1 coulomb (C) of charge]. This, according to the laws of electrostatics, is

$$w_{el} = n\mathscr{F}\Delta\mathscr{E} \qquad [14\text{-}6]$$

where $\mathscr{F}$, the **faraday,** is the electrical charge of 1 mol of electrons (1 $\mathscr{F}$ = 96,485 $C \cdot mol^{-1}$ = 96,485 $J \cdot V^{-1} \cdot mol^{-1}$), and *n* is the number of moles of electrons transferred per mole of reactant converted. Thus, substituting Eq. 14-6 into Eq. 14-5,

$$\Delta G = -n\mathscr{F}\Delta\mathscr{E} \qquad [14\text{-}7]$$

Combining Eqs. 14-4 and 14-7, and making the analogous substitution for $\Delta G^{o\prime}$, yields the **Nernst equation:**

$$\Delta\mathscr{E} = \Delta\mathscr{E}^{o\prime} - \frac{RT}{n\mathscr{F}}\ln\left(\frac{[A_{red}][B_{ox}^{n+}]}{[A_{ox}^{n+}][B_{red}]}\right) \qquad [14\text{-}8]$$

which was originally formulated in 1881 by Walther Nernst. Here $\mathscr{E}$ is the

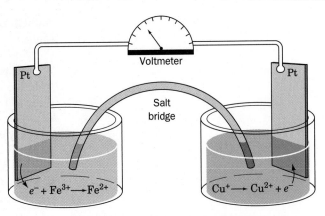

■ Figure 14-14 | **An electrochemical cell.** The half-cell undergoing oxidation (here $Cu^+ \rightarrow Cu^{2+} + e^-$) passes the liberated electrons through the wire to the half-cell undergoing reduction (here $e^- + Fe^{3+} \rightarrow Fe^{2+}$). Electroneutrality in the two half-cells is maintained by the transfer of ions through the electrolyte-containing salt bridge.

reduction potential, the tendency for a substance to undergo reduction (gain electrons). $\Delta\mathscr{E}$, the **electromotive force (emf),** can be described as the "electron pressure" that the electrochemical cell exerts. The quantity $\mathscr{E}°$, the reduction potential when all components are in their standard states, is called the **standard reduction potential.** If these standard states refer to biochemical standard states (Section 1-3D), then $\mathscr{E}°$ is replaced by $\mathscr{E}°'$. Note that a positive $\Delta\mathscr{E}$ in Eq. 14-7 results in a negative ΔG; in other words, *a positive $\Delta\mathscr{E}$ indicates a spontaneous reaction, one that can do work.*

C | Spontaneity Can Be Determined by Measuring Reduction Potential Differences

Equation 14-7 shows that the free energy change of a redox reaction can be determined by directly measuring its change in reduction potential with a voltmeter (Fig. 14-14). Such measurements make it possible to determine the order of spontaneous electron transfers among a set of electron carriers such as those of the electron-transport pathway that mediates oxidative phosphorylation in cells.

Any redox reaction can be divided into its component half-reactions:

$$A_{ox}^{n+} + n\,e^- \rightleftharpoons A_{red}$$
$$B_{ox}^{n+} + n\,e^- \rightleftharpoons B_{red}$$

where, by convention, both half-reactions are written as reductions. These half-reactions can be assigned reduction potentials, $\mathscr{E}_A$ and $\mathscr{E}_B$, in accordance with the Nernst equation:

$$\mathscr{E}_A = \mathscr{E}_A^{°'} - \frac{RT}{n\mathscr{F}}\ln\left(\frac{[A_{red}]}{[A_{ox}^{n+}]}\right) \qquad [14\text{-}9]$$

$$\mathscr{E}_B = \mathscr{E}_B^{°'} - \frac{RT}{n\mathscr{F}}\ln\left(\frac{[B_{red}]}{[B_{ox}^{n+}]}\right) \qquad [14\text{-}10]$$

For the overall redox reaction involving the two half-reactions, the difference in reduction potential, $\Delta\mathscr{E}°'$, is defined as

$$\Delta\mathscr{E}°' = \mathscr{E}_{(e^-\text{ acceptor})}^{°'} - \mathscr{E}_{(e^-\text{ donor})}^{°'} \qquad [14\text{-}11]$$

Thus, when the reaction proceeds with A as the electron acceptor and B as the electron donor, $\Delta\mathscr{E}°' = \mathscr{E}_A^{°'} - \mathscr{E}_B^{°'}$, and $\Delta\mathscr{E} = \mathscr{E}_A - \mathscr{E}_B$.

Standard Reduction Potentials Are Used to Compare Electron Affinities. Reduction potentials, like free energies, must be defined with respect to some arbitrary standard, in this case, the hydrogen half-reaction

$$2H^+ + 2\,e^- \rightleftharpoons H_2(g)$$

in which H^+ is in equilibrium with $H_2(g)$ that is in contact with a Pt electrode. This half-cell is arbitrarily assigned a standard reduction potential $\mathscr{E}°$ of 0 V ($1V = 1\,J\cdot C^{-1}$) at pH 0, 25°C, and 1 atm. Under the biochemical convention, where the standard state is pH 7.0, the hydrogen half-reaction has a standard reduction potential $\mathscr{E}°'$ of -0.421 V.

When $\Delta\mathscr{E}$ is positive, ΔG is negative (Eq. 14-7), indicating a spontaneous process. In combining two half-reactions under standard conditions, the direction of spontaneity therefore involves the reduction of the redox couple with the more positive standard reduction potential. In other words, *the more positive the standard reduction potential, the higher the*

ffinity of the redox couple's oxidized form for electrons, that is, the greater
e tendency for the redox couple's oxidized form to accept electrons and
us become reduced.

iochemical Half-Reactions Are Physiologically Significant. The bio-
hemical standard reduction potentials ($\mathscr{E}°'$) of some biochemically
mportant half-reactions are listed in Table 14-5. The oxidized form of a
edox couple with a large positive standard reduction potential has a high
ffinity for electrons and is a strong electron acceptor (oxidizing agent),
hereas its conjugate reductant is a weak electron donor (reducing agent).
or example, O_2 is the strongest oxidizing agent in Table 14-5, whereas
$_2O$, which tightly holds its electrons, is the table's weakest reducing
gent. The converse is true of half-reactions with large negative standard
eduction potentials.

Since electrons spontaneously flow from low to high reduction poten-
ials, they are transferred, under standard conditions, from the reduced

Table 14-5	Standard Reduction Potentials of Some Biochemically Important Half-Reactions

Half-Reaction	$\mathscr{E}°'$ (V)
$\frac{1}{2}O_2 + 2H^+ + 2e^- \rightleftharpoons H_2O$	0.815
$NO_3^- + 2H^+ + 2e^- \rightleftharpoons NO_2^- + H_2O$	0.42
Cytochrome a_3 (Fe^{3+}) $+ e^- \rightleftharpoons$ cytochrome a_3 (Fe^{2+})	0.385
$O_2(g) + 2H^+ + 2e^- \rightleftharpoons H_2O_2$	0.295
Cytochrome a (Fe^{3+}) $+ e^- \rightleftharpoons$ cytochrome a (Fe^{2+})	0.29
Cytochrome c (Fe^{3+}) $+ e^- \rightleftharpoons$ cytochrome c (Fe^{2+})	0.235
Cytochrome c_1 (Fe^{3+}) $+ e^- \rightleftharpoons$ cytochrome c_1 (Fe^{2+})	0.22
Cytochrome b (Fe^{3+}) $+ e^- \rightleftharpoons$ cytochrome b (Fe^{2+}) (*mitochondrial*)	0.077
Ubiquinone $+ 2H^+ + 2e^- \rightleftharpoons$ ubiquinol	0.045
Fumarate$^-$ $+ 2H^+ + 2e^- \rightleftharpoons$ succinate$^-$	0.031
FAD $+ 2H^+ + 2e^- \rightleftharpoons$ FADH$_2$ (*in flavoproteins*)	~0.
Oxaloacetate$^-$ $+ 2H^+ + 2e^- \rightleftharpoons$ malate$^-$	−0.166
Pyruvate$^-$ $+ 2H^+ + 2e^- \rightleftharpoons$ lactate$^-$	−0.185
Acetaldehyde $+ 2H^+ + 2e^- \rightleftharpoons$ ethanol	−0.197
FAD $+ 2H^+ + 2e^- \rightleftharpoons$ FADH$_2$ (*free coenzyme*)	−0.219
$S + 2H^+ + 2e^- \rightleftharpoons H_2S$	−0.23
Lipoic acid $+ 2H^+ + 2e^- \rightleftharpoons$ dihydrolipoic acid	−0.29
$NAD^+ + H^+ + 2e^- \rightleftharpoons$ NADH	−0.315
$NADP^+ + H^+ + 2e^- \rightleftharpoons$ NADPH	−0.320
Cysteine disulfide $+ 2H^+ + 2e^- \rightleftharpoons$ 2 cysteine	−0.340
Acetoacetate$^-$ $+ 2H^+ + 2e^- \rightleftharpoons$ β-hydroxybutyrate$^-$	−0.346
$H^+ + e^- \rightleftharpoons \frac{1}{2}H_2$	−0.421
$SO_4^{2-} + 2H^+ + 2e^- \rightleftharpoons SO_3^{2-} + H_2O$	−0.515
Acetate$^-$ $+ 3H^+ + 2e^- \rightleftharpoons$ acetaldehyde $+ H_2O$	−0.581

Source: Mostly from Loach, P.A., *In* Fasman, G.D. (Ed.), *Handbook of Biochemistry and Molecular Biology* (3rd ed.), Physical and Chemical Data, Vol. I, pp. 123–130, CRC Press (1976).

SAMPLE CALCULATION 14-2

Calculate $\Delta G^{\circ\prime}$ for the oxidation of NADH by FAD.

Combining the relevant half-reactions gives

$$\text{NADH} + \text{FAD} + \text{H}^+ \rightarrow \text{NAD}^+ + \text{FADH}_2$$

Next, calculate the electromotive force ($\Delta\mathscr{E}^{\circ\prime}$) from the standard reduction potentials given in Table 14-5, using one of the following methods.

Method 1
According to Eq. 14-11,

$$\Delta\mathscr{E}^{\circ\prime} = \mathscr{E}^{\circ\prime}_{(e^- \text{ acceptor})} - \mathscr{E}^{\circ\prime}_{(e^- \text{ donor})}$$

Since FAD ($\mathscr{E}^{\circ\prime} = -0.219$ V) is the electron acceptor, and NADH ($\mathscr{E}^{\circ\prime} = -0.315$ V) is the electron donor,

$$\Delta\mathscr{E}^{\circ\prime} = (-0.219 \text{ V}) - (-0.315 \text{ V}) = +0.096 \text{ V}$$

Method 2
Write the net reaction as a sum of the two relevant half-reactions. For FAD, the half-reaction is the same as the reductive half-reaction given in Table 14-5, and its $\mathscr{E}^{\circ\prime}$ value is -0.219 V. For NADH, which undergoes oxidation rather than reduction, the half-reaction is the reverse of the one given in Table 14-5, and its $\mathscr{E}^{\circ\prime}$ value is $+0.315$ V, the reverse of the reduction potential given in the table. The two half-reactions are added to give the net oxidation–reduction reaction, and the $\mathscr{E}^{\circ\prime}$ values are also added:

$\text{FAD} + 2\,\text{H}^+ + 2\,e^- \rightarrow \text{FADH}_2$	$\mathscr{E}^{\circ\prime} = -0.219$ V
$\text{NADH} \rightarrow \text{NAD}^+ + \text{H}^+ + 2\,e^-$	$\mathscr{E}^{\circ\prime} = +0.315$ V
$\text{NADH} + \text{FAD} + \text{H}^+ \rightarrow \text{NAD}^+ + \text{FADH}_2$	$\Delta\mathscr{E}^{\circ\prime} = +0.096$ V

Next, use Eq. 14-7 to calculate $\Delta G^{\circ\prime}$. Because two moles of electrons are transferred for every mole of NADH oxidized to NAD^+, $n = 2$.

$$\Delta G^{\circ\prime} = -n\mathscr{F}\Delta\mathscr{E}^{\circ\prime}$$
$$\Delta G^{\circ\prime} = -(2)(96{,}485 \text{ J}\cdot\text{V}^{-1}\cdot\text{mol}^{-1})(0.096 \text{ V}) = -18.5 \text{ bJ}$$

products in any half-reaction in Table 14-5 to the oxidized reactants of any half-reaction above it (see Sample Calculation 14-2). However, such a reaction may not occur at a measurable rate in the absence of a suitable enzyme. Note that Fe^{3+} ions of the various cytochromes listed in Table 14-5 have significantly different reduction potentials. This indicates that *the protein components of redox enzymes play active roles in electron-transfer reactions by modulating the reduction potentials of their bound redox-active centers.*

Electron-transfer reactions are of great biological importance. For example, in the mitochondrial electron-transport chain (Section 18-2), electrons are passed from NADH along a series of electron acceptors of increasing reduction potential (including FAD and others listed in Table 14-5) to O_2. ATP is generated from ADP and P_i by coupling its synthesis to this free energy cascade. *NADH thereby functions as an energy-rich electron-transfer coenzyme.* In fact, the oxidation by O_2 of one NADH to NAD^+ supplies sufficient free energy to generate almost three ATPs. NAD^+ is an electron acceptor in many exergonic metabolite oxidations. In serving as the electron donor in ATP synthesis, it fulfills its cyclic role as a free energy conduit in a manner analogous to ATP (Fig. 14-8).

■ **CHECK YOUR UNDERSTANDING**

What is the metabolic role of reduced coenzymes?
Explain the terms of the Nernst equation.
How is $\Delta\mathscr{E}$ related to ΔG?

4 Experimental Approaches to the Study of Metabolism

A metabolic pathway can be understood at several levels:

1. In terms of the sequence of reactions by which a specific nutrient is converted to end products, and the energetics of the conversions.
2. In terms of the mechanisms by which each intermediate is converted to its successor. Such an analysis requires the isolation and characterization of the specific enzymes that catalyze each reaction.
3. In terms of the control mechanisms that regulate the flow of metabolites through the pathway. These mechanisms include the interorgan relationships that adjust metabolic activity to the needs of the entire organism.

Elucidating a metabolic pathway on all these levels is a complex process, often requiring contributions from a variety of disciplines.

The outlines of the major metabolic pathways have been known for decades, although in many cases, the enzymology behind various steps of the pathways remains unclear. Likewise, the mechanisms that regulate pathway activity under different physiological conditions are not entirely understood. These areas are of great interest because of their potential to yield information that could be useful in improving human health and curing metabolic diseases. In addition, the unexplored metabolisms of unusual organisms, including recently discovered "extremophiles," hold the promise of novel biological materials and enzymatic processes that can be exploited for the environmentally sensitive production of industrial materials, foods, and therapeutic drugs.

Early metabolic studies used whole organisms, often yeast, but also mammals. For example, Frederick Banting and Charles Best established the role of the pancreas in diabetes in 1921; they surgically removed that organ from dogs and observed that the animals then developed the disease (Box 22-1). Techniques for studying metabolic processes have since become more refined, progressing from whole-organ preparations and thin tissue slices to cultured cells and isolated organelles. The most recent approaches include identifying active genes and cataloguing their protein products.

LEARNING OBJECTIVES
■ Understand that metabolic pathways are often studied by tracing labeled metabolites and perturbing the system so that intermediates accumulate.
■ Understand how DNA microarrays and proteomics techniques are used to determine the genetic expression of metabolic enzymes.

A | Labeled Metabolites Can Be Traced

A metabolic pathway in which one compound is converted to another can be followed by tracing a specifically labeled metabolite. Franz Knoop formulated this technique in 1904 to study fatty acid oxidation. He fed dogs fatty acids chemically labeled with phenyl groups and isolated the phenyl-substituted end products from the dogs' urine. From the differences in these products, depending on whether the phenyl-substituted starting material contained odd or even numbers of carbon atoms, Knoop deduced that fatty acids are degraded in two-carbon units (Section 20-2).

Chemical labeling has the disadvantage that the chemical properties of labeled metabolites differ from those of normal metabolites. This problem is largely eliminated by labeling molecules with isotopes. *The fate of an isotopically labeled atom in a metabolite can therefore be elucidated by following its progress through the metabolic pathway of interest.* The advent of isotopic labeling and tracing techniques in the 1940s revolutionized the study of metabolism.

One of the early advances in metabolic understanding resulting from the use of isotopic tracers was the demonstration, by David Shemin and David Rittenberg in 1945, that the nitrogen atoms of heme (Fig. 7-2) are derived from glycine rather than from ammonia, glutamic acid, proline, or leucine (Section 21-6A). They showed this by feeding rats the ^{15}N-labeled nutrients, isolating the heme in their blood, and analyzing it by mass spectrometry for ^{15}N content. Only when the rats were fed [^{15}N]glycine did the heme contain ^{15}N. This technique was also used with the radioactive isotope ^{14}C to demonstrate that all of cholesterol's carbon atoms are derived from acetyl-CoA (Section 20-7A). Radioactive isotopes (Box 12-1) have become virtually indispensable for establishing the metabolic origins of complex metabolites.

Another method for tracing the fates of labeled metabolites is nuclear magnetic resonance (NMR), which detects specific isotopes, including ^{1}H, ^{13}C, ^{15}N, and ^{31}P, by their characteristic nuclear spins. Since the NMR spectrum of a particular nucleus varies with its immediate environment, it is possible to identify the peaks corresponding to specific atoms even in relatively complex mixtures. The development of magnets large enough to accommodate animals and humans, and to localize spectra to specific organs, has made it possible to study metabolic pathways noninvasively by NMR techniques. For example, ^{31}P NMR can be used to study energy metabolism in muscle by monitoring the levels of phosphorylated compounds such as ATP, ADP, and phosphocreatine.

Isotopically labeling specific atoms of metabolites with ^{13}C (which is only 1.10% naturally abundant) permits the metabolic progress of the labeled atoms to be followed by ^{13}C NMR. Figure 14-15 shows *in vivo* ^{13}C NMR spectra of a rat liver before and after an injection of D-[1-^{13}C]

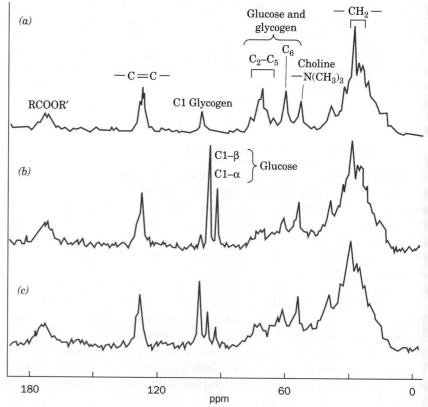

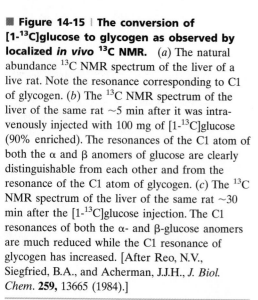

Figure 14-15 | The conversion of [1-^{13}C]glucose to glycogen as observed by localized *in vivo* ^{13}C NMR. (*a*) The natural abundance ^{13}C NMR spectrum of the liver of a live rat. Note the resonance corresponding to C1 of glycogen. (*b*) The ^{13}C NMR spectrum of the liver of the same rat ~5 min after it was intravenously injected with 100 mg of [1-^{13}C]glucose (90% enriched). The resonances of the C1 atom of both the α and β anomers of glucose are clearly distinguishable from each other and from the resonance of the C1 atom of glycogen. (*c*) The ^{13}C NMR spectrum of the liver of the same rat ~30 min after the [1-^{13}C]glucose injection. The C1 resonances of both the α- and β-glucose anomers are much reduced while the C1 resonance of glycogen has increased. [After Reo, N.V., Siegfried, B.A., and Acherman, J.J.H., *J. Biol. Chem.* **259**, 13665 (1984).]

glucose. The ^{13}C can be seen entering the liver and then being incorporated into glycogen (the storage form of glucose; Section 16-2).

B | Studying Metabolic Pathways Often Involves Perturbing the System

Many of the techniques used to elucidate the intermediates and enzymes of metabolic pathways involve perturbing the system in some way and observing how this affects the activity of the pathway. One way to perturb a pathway is to add certain substances, called **metabolic inhibitors,** that block the pathway at specific points, thereby causing the preceding intermediates to build up. This approach was used in elucidating the conversion of glucose to ethanol in yeast by glycolysis (Section 15-2). Similarly, the addition of substances that block electron transfer at different sites was used to deduce the sequence of electron carriers in the mitochondrial electron-transport chain (Section 18-2B).

Genetic Defects Also Cause Metabolic Intermediates to Accumulate. Archibald Garrod's realization, in the early 1900s, that human genetic diseases are the consequence of deficiencies in specific enzymes also contributed to the elucidation of metabolic pathways. For example, upon the ingestion of either phenylalanine or tyrosine, individuals with the largely harmless inherited condition known as **alcaptonuria,** but not normal subjects, excrete **homogentisic acid** in their urine (Box 21-2). This is because the liver of alcaptonurics lacks an enzyme that catalyzes the breakdown of homogentisic acid (Fig. 14-16).

Genetic Manipulation Alters Metabolic Processes. Early studies of metabolism led to the astounding discovery that *the basic metabolic pathways in most organisms are essentially identical.* This metabolic uniformity has greatly facilitated the study of metabolic reactions. Thus, although a mutation that inactivates or deletes an enzyme in a pathway of interest may be unknown in higher organisms, it can be readily generated in a rapidly reproducing microorganism through the use of **mutagens** (chemical agents that induce genetic changes; Section 25-4A), X-rays, or, more recently, through genetic engineering techniques (Section 3-5). The desired mutants, which cannot synthesize the pathway's end product, can be identified by their requirement for that product in their culture medium.

Higher organisms that have been engineered to lack particular genes (i.e., gene "knockouts"; Section 3-5D) are useful, particularly in cases in which the absence of a single gene product results in a metabolic defect but is not lethal. Genetic engineering techniques have advanced to the point that it is possible to selectively "knock out" a gene only in a particular tissue. This approach is necessary in cases in which a gene product is required for development and therefore cannot be entirely deleted. In the opposite approach, techniques for constructing transgenic animals make it possible to express genes in tissues in which they were not originally present.

C | Systems Biology Has Entered the Study of Metabolism

Metabolism has traditionally been studied by hypothesis-driven research: isolating individual enzymes and metabolites and assembling them into metabolic pathways as guided by experimentally testable hypotheses. A new approach, **systems biology,** has emerged with the advent of complete

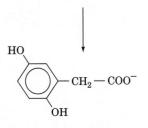

■ **Figure 14-16 | Pathway for phenylalanine degradation.** Alcaptonurics lack the enzyme that breaks down homogentisate; therefore, this intermediate accumulates and is excreted in the urine.

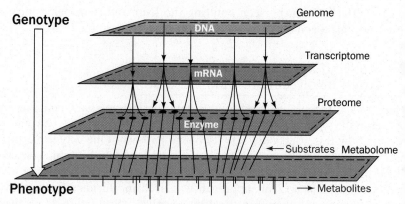

■ **Figure 14-17** | **The relationship between genotype and phenotype.** The path from genetic information (genotype) to metabolic function (phenotype) has several steps. Portions of the genome are transcribed to produce the transcriptome, which directs the synthesis of the proteome, whose various activities are responsible for synthesizing and degrading the components of the metabolome.

genome sequences, the development of rapid and sensitive techniques for analyzing large numbers of gene transcripts, proteins, and metabolites all at once, and the development of new computational and mathematical tools. Systems biology is discovery-based: collecting and integrating enormous amounts of data in searchable databases so that the properties and dynamics of entire biological networks can be analyzed. As a result, our understanding of the path from genotype to phenotype has expanded. In addition to the central dogma (Section 3-3B) that a single gene composed of DNA is transcribed to mRNA which is translated to a single protein that influences metabolism, we are increasingly taking into account the **genome, transcriptome, proteome,** and **metabolome** and their interrelationships (Fig. 14-17). The term **bibliome** (Greek: *biblion,* book) has even been coined to denote the systematic incorporation of pre-existing information about reaction mechanisms and metabolic pathways (such as the one shown in Box 14-2). In the following paragraphs we discuss some of these emerging technologies and new fields of study.

Genomics Examines the Entire Complement of an Organism's DNA Sequences. The overall metabolic capabilities of an organism are encoded by its genome (its entire complement of genes). In theory, it should be possible to reconstruct a cell's metabolic activities from its DNA sequences. At present, this can be done only in a general sense. For example, the sequenced genome of *Vibrio cholerae,* the bacterium that causes cholera, reveals a large repertoire of genes encoding transport proteins and enzymes for catabolizing a wide range of nutrients. This is consistent with the complicated lifestyle of *V. cholerae,* which can live on its own, in association with zooplankton, or in the human gastrointestinal tract (where it causes cholera). Of course, a simple catalog of an organism's genes does not reveal how the genes function. Thus, some genes are expressed continuously at high levels, whereas others are expressed rarely, for example, only when the organism encounters a particular metabolite.

The Transcriptome Includes All the RNAs Transcribed by a Cell. Creating an accurate picture of gene expression is the goal of **transcriptomics,** the study of a cell's transcriptome (which, in analogy with the word genome," is the entire collection of RNAs that the cell transcribes). Identifying and quantifying all the transcripts from a single cell type reveals which genes are active. Cells transcribe thousands of genes at once so this study requires the use of new techniques, including DNA microarray technology.

DNA Microarrays Help Create an Accurate Picture of Gene Expression. DNA microarrays or DNA chips are made by depositing numerous (up to several hundred thousand) different DNA segments of known gene sequences in a precise array on a solid support such as a coated glass surface. These DNAs are often PCR-amplified cDNA clones derived from mRNAs (PCR is discussed in Section 3-5C) or their robotically synthesized counterparts. The mRNAs extracted from cells, tissues, or other biological sources grown under differing conditions are then reverse-transcribed to cDNA, labeled with a fluorescent dye (a different color for each growth condition), and allowed to hybridize with the DNAs on the DNA microarray. After the unhybridized cDNA is washed away, the resulting fluorescence intensity and color at each site on the DNA microarray indicates how much cDNA (and therefore how much mRNA) has bound to a particular complementary DNA sequence for each growth condition. Figure 14-18 shows a DNA chip that demonstrates the change in yeast gene expression when yeast grown on glucose have depleted their glucose supply.

(a)

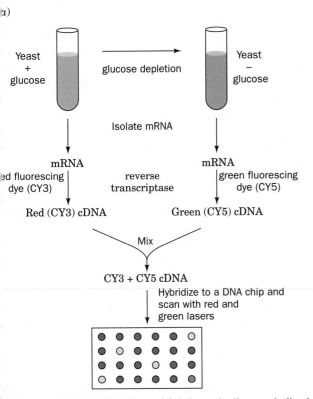

(b)

■ **Figure 14-18 | DNA chips.** (*a*) Schematic diagram indicating how DNA chips are used. (*b*) This ~6000-gene array contains most of the genes from baker's yeast, one per spot. The chip had been hybridized to the cDNAs derived from mRNAs extracted from yeast. The cDNAs derived from cells that were grown in glucose were labeled with a red-fluorescing dye, whereas the cDNAs derived from cells harvested after glucose depletion were labeled with a green-fluorescing dye. The cDNAs were mixed before hybridization. The red and green spots, respectively, reveal those genes that are transcriptionally activated by the presence or absence of glucose, whereas the yellow spots (*red plus green*) indicate genes whose expression is unaffected by the level of glucose. [Courtesy of Patrick Brown, Stanford University School of Medicine.]

HCC   Non-tumor Liver

0.25   0.5   1   2   4

■ **Figure 14-19 | The relative transcriptional activities of the genes in hepatocellular carcinoma (HCC) tumors as determined using DNA microarrays.** The data are presented in matrix form with each column representing one of 156 tissue samples [82 HCC tumors (the most common human liver cancer and among the five leading causes of cancer deaths in the world) and 74 nontumor liver tissues] and each row representing one of 3180 genes (those of the ~17,400 genes on the DNA microarray with the greatest variation in transcriptional activity among the various tissue samples). The data are arranged so as to group the genes as well as the tissue samples on the basis of similarities of their expression patterns. The color of each cell indicates the expression level of the corresponding gene in the corresponding tissue relative to its mean expression level in all the tissue samples with bright red, black, and bright green indicating expression levels of 4, 1, and 1/4 times that of the mean for that gene (as indicated on the scale below). The dendrogram at the top of the matrix indicates the similarities in expression patterns among the various tissue samples. [Courtesy of David Botstein and Patrick Brown, Stanford University School of Medicine.]

Differences in the expression of particular genes have been correlated with many developmental processes or growth patterns. For example, DNA microarrays have been used to profile the patterns of gene expression in tumor cells because different types of tumors synthesize different types and amounts of proteins (Fig. 14-19). This information is useful in choosing how best to treat a cancer.

Proteomics Studies All the Cell's Proteins. Unfortunately, the correlation between the amount of a particular mRNA and the amount of its protein product is imperfect. This is because the various mRNAs and their corresponding proteins are synthesized and degraded at different rates. Furthermore, many proteins are posttranslationally modified, sometimes in several different ways (e.g., by phosphorylation or glycosylation). Consequently, the number of unique proteins in a cell exceeds the number of unique mRNAs.

A more reliable way than transcriptomics to assess gene expression is to examine a cell's proteome, the complete set of proteins that the cell synthesizes. This **proteomics** approach requires that the proteins first be separated, usually by two-dimensional (2D) gel electrophoresis (a technique that separates proteins by isoelectric point in one direction and by mass in the perpendicular direction; Section 5-2D). Individual proteins are then identified by using tandem mass spectrometry to obtain amino acid sequence information (Section 5-3D) and correlating it with protein sequence databases. Because many peptides are generated from a single protein, the technique enables the redundant and unambiguous identification of that protein from the database. In this way we can catalogue all the proteins that are contained in a cell or tissue under a given set of conditions.

Can we compare all the proteins synthesized by a cell under two different sets of conditions as is done for mRNA? The answer is yes, by using different isotopically labeled reagents that are either contained in the growth medium (e.g., deuterated amino acids) or that are reacted with the cell extract. One technique for labeling cellular proteins uses **isotope-coded affinity tags (ICAT),** which are analogous to the different fluorescent dyes that label cDNA.

An ICAT contains three functional elements: an iodoacetyl group to react with cysteine residues, a linker that contains either 8 hydrogen (light) or 8 deuterium (heavy) atoms, and **biotin,** a coenzyme (Section 16-4A).

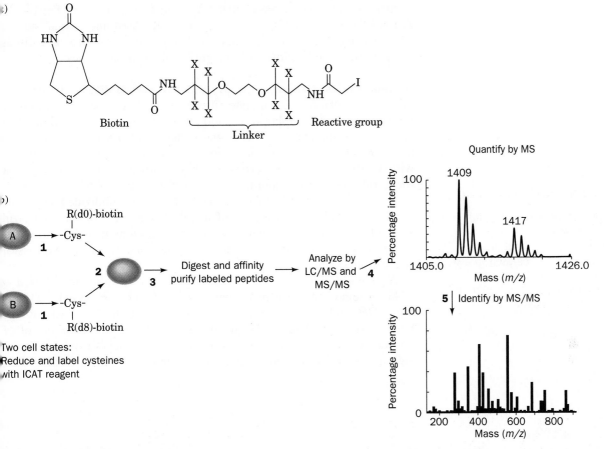

Figure 14-20 | The isotope-coded affinity tag (ICAT) method for quantitative proteome analysis. (*a*) An example of an ICAT reagent that contains an iodoacetyl reactive group, a linker, and a biotin residue. X denotes the position of hydrogen (d0) or deuterium (d8). (*b*) The ICAT strategy for differential labeling of proteins expressed by cells under two different sets of conditions. (**1**) Proteins from States A and B are treated with light (d0) or heavy (d8) versions of the ICAT reagent. (**2**) The labeled protein mixtures are combined. (**3**) The labeled proteins are digested with trypsin to form Cys-containing labeled peptides. These peptides are then purified by biotin/avidin affinity chromatography. The purified peptides are analyzed by mass spectrometry in two ways: (**4**) Liquid chromatography followed by mass spectrometry (LC/MS) is used to quantitate the peptides. The ratio of the signal intensities from the corresponding light and heavy peptides indicates the relative peptide abundance in the two mixtures. (**5**) Tandem mass spectrometry (MS/MS) is used to determine the amino acid sequence of each peptide and identify the protein from which it is derived by comparing the peptide's sequence to those in a database of all known proteins.

that is also used as a biotechnology tool because of its extremely tight binding to the protein **avidin** ($K = 10^{-15}$ M; Fig. 14-20*a*). Avidin is immobilized on a chromatographic resin so that the ICAT-labeled peptides can be isolated by biotin/avidin affinity chromatography (Section 5-2C).

The ICAT procedure is illustrated in Fig. 14-20*b*. Two protein mixtures representing two different growth conditions are treated with light (d0) or heavy (d8) versions of the ICAT reagent. The labeled protein mixtures are then combined and digested with trypsin to form Cys-containing labeled peptides, which are then purified by biotin/avidin affinity chromatography. Individual peptides are separated by liquid chromatography and detected by mass spectrometry (LC/MS). The ratio of the intensities of the light and heavy peptide signals indicates the relative peptide abundance in the two samples. Tandem mass spectrometry (MS/MS) is then used to sequence each peptide and determine its identity. This method was used to identify many of the yeast proteins whose mRNA concentrations increased or decreased when glucose was depleted from the growth medium (Fig. 14-18b). A hope for the future is that samples from diseased and normal subject can be compared in this manner to find previously undetected diseas markers that would allow early diagnosis of various diseases.

Metabolomics Analyzes All of a Cell's Metabolites. In order to describe a cell's functional state (its phenotype) we need, in addition to the cell's genome, transcriptome, and proteome, a quantitative description of all of the metabolites it contains under a given set of conditions, it metabolome. However, a cell or tissue contains thousands of metabolites with vastly different properties, so that identifying and quantifying al these substances is a daunting task, requiring many different analytica tools. Consequently, this huge undertaking is often subdivided. For exam ple, **lipidomics** is the subsection of **metabolomics** aimed at characterizing all lipids in a cell under a particular set of conditions, including how these lipids influence membrane structure, cell signaling, gene expression cell–cell interactions, and so on.

A recently constructed model of the human metabolome—based on 1496 protein-encoding genes (open reading frames or ORFs), 2004 proteins, 2766 metabolites, and 3311 metabolic and transport reactions—has been used to simulate 288 known metabolic functions in a variety of cell and tissue types. This *in silico* (computerized) model is expected to provide a framework for future advances in human systems biology.

■ CHECK YOUR UNDERSTANDING

How are isotopically labeled compounds used to study metabolism?

Describe how information about an organism's genome can be used to assess and manipulate its metabolic activities.

What is the difference between hypothesis-driven research and discovery-based research?

Describe the "central dogma" in the "-omics" era.

SUMMARY

1. The free energy released from catabolic oxidation reactions is used to drive endergonic anabolic reactions.

2. Nutrition is the intake and utilization of food to supply free energy and raw materials.

3. Heterotrophic organisms obtain their free energy from compounds synthesized by chemolithotrophic or photoautotrophic organisms.

4. Food contains proteins, carbohydrates, fats, water, vitamins, and minerals.

5. Metabolic pathways are sequences of enzyme-catalyzed reactions that occur in different cellular locations.

6. Near-equilibrium reactions are freely reversible, whereas reactions that function far from equilibrium serve as regulatory points and render metabolic pathways irreversible.

7. Flux through a metabolic pathway is controlled by regulating the activities of the enzymes that catalyze its rate-determining steps.

8. The free energy of the "high-energy" compound ATP is made available through cleavage of one or both of its phosphoanhydride bonds.

9. An exergonic reaction such as ATP or PP_i hydrolysis can be coupled to an endergonic reaction to make it more favorable.

10. Substrate-level phosphorylation is the synthesis of ATP from ADP by phosphoryl group transfer from another compound.

11. The common product of carbohydrate, lipid, and protein catabolism, acetyl-CoA, is a "high-energy" thioester.

12. The coenzymes NAD^+ and FAD are reversibly reduced during the oxidation of metabolites.

13. The Nernst equation relates the electromotive force of a redox reaction to the standard reduction potentials and concentrations of the electron donors and acceptors.

14. Electrons flow spontaneously from the reduced member of a redox couple with the more negative reduction potential to the oxidized member of a redox couple with the more positive reduction potential.

15. Studies of metabolic pathways determine the order of metabolic transformations, their enzymatic mechanisms, their regulation, and their relationships to metabolic processes in other tissues.

16. Metabolic pathways are studied using isotopic tracers, enzyme inhibitors, natural and engineered mutations, DNA microarrays, and proteomics techniques.

17. Systems biology endeavors to quantitatively describe the properties and dynamics of biological networks as a whole through the integration of genomic, transcriptomic, proteomic, and metabolomic information.

KEY TERMS

metabolism **448**
catabolism **448**
anabolism **448**
nutrition **449**
autotroph **449**
chemolithotroph **449**
photoautotroph **449**
heterotroph **449**
aerobic **449**
anaerobic **449**
macronutrient **449**
micronutrient **450**

vitamin **450**
mineral **450**
metabolite **451**
oxidation **453**
reduction **453**
isozyme **455**
near-equilibrium reaction **456**
flux **456**
substrate cycle **459**
"high-energy"
    intermediate **461**
orthophosphate cleavage **464**

pyrophosphate cleavage **464**
substrate-level
    phosphorylation **465**
oxidative phosphorylation **465**
photophosphorylation **465**
kinase **465**
phosphagen **466**
reducing agent **470**
oxidizing agent **470**
half-reaction **470**
redox couple **471**
conjugate redox pair **471**

electrochemical cell **471**
$\Delta \mathscr{E}$ **471**
$\mathscr{F}$ **471**
Nernst equation **471**
$\mathscr{E}^{\circ\prime}$ **472**
systems biology **477**
genomics **478**
transcriptomics **478**
DNA microarray **479**
proteomics **480**
metabolomics **482**
in silico **482**

PROBLEMS

1. Rank the following compounds in order of increasing oxidation state.

$$H_3C-\underset{\underset{\displaystyle OH}{|}}{CH}-CH_2OH \qquad {}^-OOC-CH_2-COO^-$$

$$\qquad\qquad \textbf{A} \qquad\qquad\qquad\qquad \textbf{B}$$

$$H_3C-CH_2-CH_3 \qquad H_3C-CH=CH_2 \qquad H_3C-\underset{\underset{\displaystyle}{\overset{\displaystyle O}{\overset{\displaystyle \|}{}}}}{C}-COO^-$$

$$\qquad \textbf{C} \qquad\qquad\quad \textbf{D} \qquad\qquad\quad \textbf{E}$$

2. A certain metabolic reaction takes the form A → B. Its standard free energy change is 7.5 kJ·mol^{-1}. (a) Calculate the equilibrium constant for the reaction at 25°C. (b) Calculate ΔG at 37°C when the concentration of A is 0.5 mM and the concentration of B is 0.1 mM. Is the reaction spontaneous under these conditions? (c) How might the reaction proceed in the cell?

3. Choose the best definition for a near-equilibrium reaction:

   (a) always operates with a favorable free energy change.

   (b) has a free energy change near zero.

   (c) is usually a control point in a metabolic pathway.

   (d) operates very slowly *in vivo*.

4. Assuming 100% efficiency of energy conservation, how many moles of ATP can be synthesized under standard conditions by the complete oxidation of (a) 1 mol of glucose and (b) 1 mol of palmitate?

5. Does the magnitude of the free energy change for ATP hydrolysis increase or decrease as the pH increases from 5 to 6?

6. The reaction for "activation" of a fatty acid ($RCOO^-$),

   $$ATP + CoA + RCOO^- \rightleftharpoons RCO-CoA + AMP + PP_i$$

   has $\Delta G^{\circ\prime} = +4.6$ kJ · mol^{-1}. What is the thermodynamic driving force for this reaction?

7. Predict whether creatine kinase will operate in the direction of ATP synthesis or phosphocreatine synthesis at 25°C when [ATP] = 4 mM, [ADP] = 0.15 mM, [phosphocreatine] = 2.5 mM, and [creatine] = 1 mM.

8. If intracellular [ATP] = 5 mM, [ADP] = 0.5 mM, and [P_i] = 1.0 mM, calculate the concentration of AMP at pH 7 and 25°C under the condition that the adenylate kinase reaction is at equilibrium.

9. List the following substances in order of their increasing oxidizing power: (a) acetoacetate, (b) cytochrome b (Fe^{3+}), (c) NAD^+, (d) SO_4^{2-}, and (e) pyruvate.

10. Write a balanced equation for the oxidation of ubiquinol by cytochrome c. Calculate $\Delta G^{\circ\prime}$ and $\Delta \mathscr{E}^{\circ\prime}$ for the reaction.

11. Under standard conditions, will the following reactions proceed spontaneously as written?

    (a) Fumarate + NADH + H$^+$ $\rightleftharpoons$ succinate + NAD$^+$

    (b) Cyto a (Fe^{2+}) + cyto b (Fe^{3+}) $\rightleftharpoons$
    cyto a (Fe^{3+}) + cyto b (Fe^{2+})

12. Under standard conditions, is the oxidation of free FADH$_2$ by ubiquinone sufficiently exergonic to drive the synthesis of ATP?

13. A hypothetical three-step metabolic pathway consists of intermediates W, X, Y, and Z and enzymes A, B, and C. Deduce the order of the enzymatic steps in the pathway from the following information:

    1. Compound Q, a metabolic inhibitor of enzyme B, causes Z to build up.

    2. A mutant in enzyme C requires Y for growth.

    3. An inhibitor of enzyme A causes W, Y, and Z to accumulate.

    4. Compound P, a metabolic inhibitor of enzyme C, causes W and Z to build up.

14. A certain metabolic pathway can be diagrammed as

$$A \xrightarrow{\ X\ } B \xrightarrow{\ Y\ } C \xrightarrow{\ Z\ } D$$

where A, B, C, and D are the intermediates, and X, Y, and Z are the enzymes that catalyze the reactions. The physiological free energy changes for the reactions are

$$
\begin{array}{ll}
X & -0.2 \text{ kJ} \cdot \text{mol}^{-1} \\
Y & -12.3 \text{ kJ} \cdot \text{mol}^{-1} \\
Z & -1.2 \text{ kJ} \cdot \text{mol}^{-1}
\end{array}
$$

(a) Which reaction is likely to be a major regulatory point for the pathway? (b) If your answer in Part a was in fact the case, in the presence of an inhibitor that blocks the activity of enzyme Z, would the concentrations of A, B, C, and D increase, decrease, or not be affected?

CASE STUDY

Case 16
Allosteric Regulation of ATCase

Focus concept: An enzyme involved in nucleotide synthesis is subject to regulation by a variety of combinations of nucleotides.

Prerequisites: Chapters 7, 12, and 14

- Properties of allosteric enzymes
- Basic mechanisms involving regulation of metabolic pathways

BIOINFORMATICS EXERCISES

Bioinformatics Exercises are available at www.wiley.com/college/voet.

Chapter 14
Metabolic Enzymes, Microarrays, and Proteomics
1. **Metabolic Enzymes.** Use the KEGG and Enzyme Structure databases to obtain information about dihydrofolate reductase.

2. **Microarrays.** Learn about microarray technology and its use in studying disease.
3. **Proteomics.** Review some methods and their limitations.
4. **Two-Dimensional Gel Electrophoresis.** Obtain data about dihydrofolate reductase from the Swiss-2DPAGE resource.

REFERENCES

Aebersold, R., Quantitative proteome analysis: Methods and applications, *J. Infectious Diseases*, **182** (supplement 2), S315–S320 (2003).

Alberty, R.A., Calculating apparent equilibrium constants of enzyme-catalyzed reactions at pH 7, *Biochem. Ed.* **28**, 12–17 (2000).

Campbell, A.M. and Heyer, L.J., *Discovering Genomics, Proteomics and Bioinformatics*. 2nd Ed., Pearson Benjamin Cummings, New York (2007). [An interactive introduction to these subjects.]

Duarte, N.C., Becker, S.A., Jamshidi, N., Thiele, I., Mo, M.L., Vo, T.D., Srivas, R., and Palsson, B. Ø., Global reconstruction of the human metabolic network based on genomic and bibliomic data, *Proc. Natl. Acad. Sci*, **104**, 1777–1782 (2007).

Go, V.L.W., Nguyen, C.T.H., Harris, D.M., and Lee, W.-N.P., Nutrient–gene interaction: Metabolic genotype–phenotype relationship, *J. Nutrition*, **135**, 2016s–3020s (2005).

Hanson, R.W., The role of ATP in metabolism, *Biochem. Ed.* **17**, 86–92 (1989). [Provides an excellent explanation of why ATP is an energy transducer rather than an energy store.]

Schena, M., *Microarray Analysis,* Wiley-Liss (2003).

Schulman, R.G. and Rothman, D.L., ^{13}C NMR of intermediary metabolism: Implications for systematic physiology, *Annu. Rev. Physiol.* **63**, 15–48 (2001).

Scriver, C.R., Beaudet, A.L., Sly, W.S., and Valle, D., (Eds.), *The Metabolic and Molecular Bases of Inherited Disease* (8th ed.). McGraw-Hill (2001). [Most chapters in this encyclopedic work include a review of a normal metabolic process that is disrupted by disease.]

Smolin, L.A. and Grosvenor, M.B, *Nutrition: Science and Applications,* Wiley (2008). [A good text for those interested in pursuing nutritional aspects of metabolism].

Westheimer, F.H., Why nature chose phosphates, *Science* **235** 1173–1178 (1987).

Young, R., Biomedical discovery with DNA arrays, *Cell* **102**, 9–15 (2000).

Xia, Y., Yu, H., Jansen, R., Seringhaus, M., Baxter, S., Greenbaum, D., Zhao, H., and Gerstein, M., Analyzing cellular biochemistry in terms of molecular networks, *Annu. Rev. Biochem.* **73**, 1051–1087 (2004).

During a short race, for example, of 100 to 200 m, a major source of power for a runner's muscles is the free energy produced through anaerobic glycolysis, a catabolic pathway that breaks down carbohydrates and produces ATP but does not depend on the presence of oxygen. Even under aerobic conditions, glycolysis is the major starting point for carbohydrate metabolism. [AFLO Foto/Alamy Images.]

Glucose Catabolism

■ CHAPTER CONTENTS

1 Overview of Glycolysis

2 The Reactions of Glycolysis
- **A.** Hexokinase Uses the First ATP
- **B.** Phosphoglucose Isomerase Converts Glucose-6-Phosphate to Fructose-6-Phosphate
- **C.** Phosphofructokinase Uses the Second ATP
- **D.** Aldolase Converts a 6-Carbon Compound to Two 3-Carbon Compounds
- **E.** Triose Phosphate Isomerase Interconverts Dihydroxyacetone Phosphate and Glyceraldehyde-3-Phosphate
- **F.** Glyceraldehyde-3-Phosphate Dehydrogenase Forms the First "High-Energy" Intermediate
- **G.** Phosphoglycerate Kinase Generates the First ATP
- **H.** Phosphoglycerate Mutase Interconverts 3-Phosphoglycerate and 2-Phosphoglycerate
- **I.** Enolase Forms the Second "High-Energy" Intermediate
- **J.** Pyruvate Kinase Generates the Second ATP

3 Fermentation: The Anaerobic Fate of Pyruvate
- **A.** Homolactic Fermentation Converts Pyruvate to Lactate
- **B.** Alcoholic Fermentation Converts Pyruvate to Ethanol and CO_2
- **C.** Fermentation Is Energetically Favorable

4 Regulation of Glycolysis
- **A.** Phosphofructokinase Is the Major Flux-Controlling Enzyme of Glycolysis in Muscle
- **B.** Substrate Cycling Fine-Tunes Flux Control

5 Metabolism of Hexoses Other than Glucose
- **A.** Fructose Is Converted to Fructose-6-Phosphate or Glyceraldehyde-3-Phosphate
- **B.** Galactose Is Converted to Glucose-6-Phosphate
- **C.** Mannose Is Converted to Fructose-6-Phosphate

6 The Pentose Phosphate Pathway
- **A.** Oxidative Reactions Produce NADPH in Stage 1
- **B.** Isomerization and Epimerization of Ribulose-5-Phosphate Occur in Stage 2
- **C.** Stage 3 Involves Carbon–Carbon Bond Cleavage and Formation
- **D.** The Pentose Phosphate Pathway Must Be Regulated

■ MEDIA RESOURCES

(available at www.wiley.com/college/voet)

Guided Exploration 14. Glycolysis overview

Interactive Exercise 15. Conformational changes in yeast hexokinase

Interactive Exercise 16. Yeast TIM in complex with 2-phosphoglycolate

Interactive Exercise 17. TPP binding to pyruvate decarboxylase

Animated Figure 15-1. Overview of glycolysis

Animated Figure 15-5. Mechanism of aldolase

Animated Figure 15-9. Mechanism of GAPDH

Animated Figure 15-23. PFK activity versus F6P concentration

Kinemages 12-1, 12-2. Triose phosphate isomerase

Kinemage 13-1. Phosphofructokinase

Kinemage 13-2. Allosteric changes in phosphofructokinase

Case Study 18. Purification of Phosphofructokinase 1-C

Case Study 20. NAD⁺-Dependent Glyceraldehyde-3-Phosphate Dehydrogenase from *Thermoproteus tenax*

Glucose is a major source of metabolic energy in many cells. The fermentation (anaerobic breakdown) of glucose to ethanol and CO_2 by yeast has been exploited for many centuries in baking and winemaking. However, scientific investigation of the chemistry of this catabolic pathway began only in the mid-nineteenth century, with the experiments of Louis Pasteur and others. Nearly a century would pass before the complete pathway was elucidated. During that interval, several important features of the pathway came to light:

1. In 1905, Arthur Harden and William Young discovered that phosphate is required for glucose fermentation.

2. Certain reagents, such as iodoacetic acid and fluoride ion, inhibit the formation of pathway products, thereby causing pathway intermediates to accumulate. Different substances caused the buildup of different intermediates and thereby revealed the sequence of molecular interconversions.

3. Studies of how different organisms break down glucose indicate that, with few exceptions, all of them do so the same way.

The efforts of many investigators came to fruition in 1940, when the complete pathway of glucose breakdown was described. This pathway, which is named **glycolysis** (Greek: *glykus,* sweet + *lysis,* loosening), is alternately known as the **Embden–Meyerhof–Parnas pathway** to commemorate the work of Gustav Embden, Otto Meyerhof, and Jacob Parnas in its elucidation. The discovery of glycolysis came at a time when other significant inroads were being made in the area of metabolism (Box 15-1).

Glycolysis, which is probably the most completely understood biochemical pathway, is a sequence of 10 enzymatic reactions in which one molecule of glucose is converted to two molecules of the three-carbon compound pyruvate with the concomitant generation of 2 ATP. It plays a key role in energy metabolism by providing a significant portion of the free energy used by most organisms and by preparing glucose and other compounds for further oxidative degradation. Thus, it is fitting that we begin our discussion of specific metabolic pathways by considering glycolysis. We shall examine the sequence of reactions by which glucose is degraded along with some of the relevant enzyme mechanisms. We will then examine the features that influence glycolytic flux and the ultimate fate of its products. Finally, we will discuss the catabolism of other hexoses and the **pentose phosphate pathway,** an alternative pathway for glucose catabolism that functions to provide biosynthetic precursors.

1 Overview of Glycolysis

Before beginning our detailed discussion of glycolysis, let us first take a moment to survey the overall pathway as it fits in with animal metabolism as a whole. Glucose usually appears in the blood as a result of the breakdown of polysaccharides (e.g., liver glycogen or dietary starch and glycogen) or from its synthesis from noncarbohydrate precursors (**gluconeogenesis;** Section 16-4). Glucose enters most cells by a specific carrier that transports it from the exterior of the cell into the cytosol (Section 10-2E). The enzymes of glycolysis are located in the cytosol, where they are only loosely associated, if at all, with each other or with other cell structures.

Glycolysis converts glucose to two C_3 units (pyruvate). The free energy released in the process is harvested to synthesize ATP from ADP and P_i. Thus glycolysis is a pathway of chemically coupled phosphorylation reactions (Section 14-2B). The 10 reactions of glycolysis are diagrammed in Fig. 15-1. Note that ATP is used early in the pathway to synthesize phosphorylated compounds (Reactions 1 and 3) but is later resynthesized twice over (Reactions 7 and 10). Glycolysis can therefore be divided into two stages:

Stage I Energy investment (Reactions 1–5). In this preparatory stage, the hexose glucose is phosphorylated and cleaved to yield two molecules of the triose **glyceraldehyde-3-phosphate.** This process consumes 2 ATP.

LEARNING OBJECTIVES

■ Understand that glycolysis involves the breakdown of glucose to pyruvate while using the free energy released in the process to synthesize ATP from ADP and P_i.

■ Understand that the 10-reaction sequence of glycolysis is divided into two stages: energy investment and energy recovery.

■ **Figure 15-1** | (*opposite*) **Glycolysis.** In its first stage (Reactions 1–5), one molecule of glucose is converted to two glyceraldehyde-3-phosphate molecules in a series of reactions that consumes 2 ATP. In the second stage of glycolysis (Reactions 6–10), the two glyceraldehyde-3-phosphate molecules are converted to two pyruvate molecules, generating 4 ATP and 2 NADH. ♻ **See the Animated Figures.**

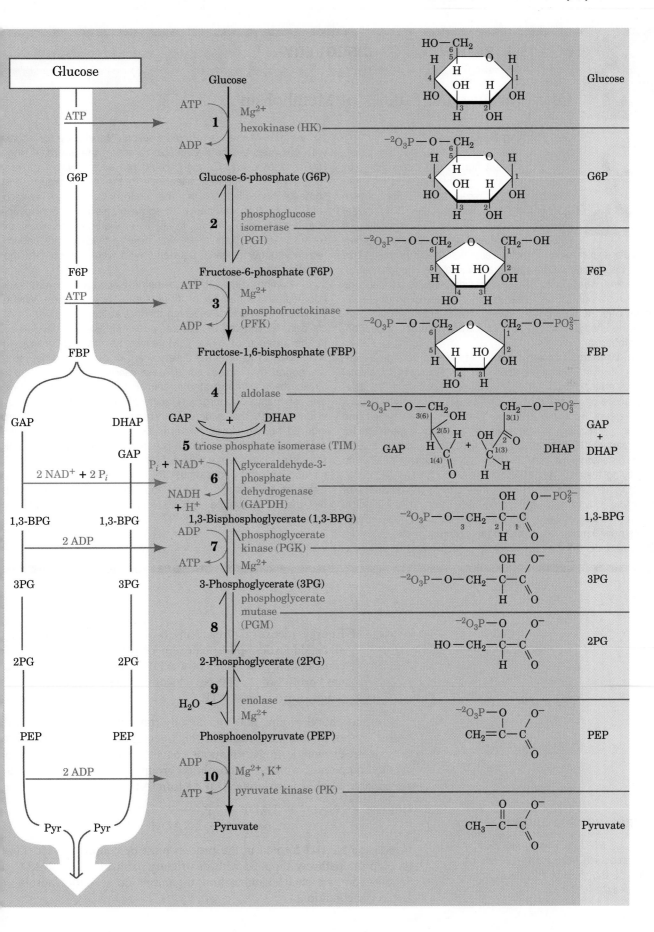

BOX 15-1 PATHWAYS OF DISCOVERY

Otto Warburg and Studies of Metabolism

Otto Warburg (1883–1970)

One of the great figures in biochemistry—by virtue of his own contributions and his influence on younger researchers—is the German biochemist Otto Warburg. His long career spanned a period during which studies of whole organisms and crude extracts gave way to molecular explanations of biological structure and function. Like others of his generation, he earned a doctorate in chemistry at an early age and went on to obtain a medical degree, although he spent the remainder of his career in scientific research rather than in patient care. He became interested primarily in three subjects related to the chemistry of oxygen and carbon dioxide: respiration, photosynthesis, and cancer.

One of Warburg's first accomplishments was to develop a technique for studying metabolic reactions in thin slices of animal tissue. This method produced more reliable results than the alternative practice of chopping or mincing tissues (such manipulations tend to release lysosomal enzymes that degrade enzymes and other macromolecules). Warburg was also largely responsible for refining manometry, the measurement of gas pressure, as a technique for analyzing the consumption and production of O_2 and CO_2 by living tissues.

Warburg received a Nobel prize in 1931 for his discovery of the catalytic role of iron porphyrins (heme groups) in biological oxidation (the subject was the reaction carried out by the enzyme complex now known as cytochrome oxidase; Section 18-2F). Warburg also identified nicotinamide as an active part of some en-

zymes. In 1944, he was offered a second Nobel prize for his wor with enzymes, but he was unable to accept the award, owing t Hitler's decree that Germans could not accept Nobel prizes. I fact, Warburg's apparent allegiance to the Nazi regime incense some of his colleagues in other countries and may have con tributed to their resistance to some of his more controversi; scientific pronouncements. In any case, Warburg was not know for his warm personality. He was never a teacher and tended t recruit younger research assistants who were expected to mov on after a few years.

In addition to the techniques he developed, which were wide adopted, and a number of insights into enzyme action, Warbur formulated some wide-reaching theories about the growth of can cer cells. He showed that cancer cells could live and develop eve in the absence of oxygen. Moreover, he came to believe tha anaerobiosis triggered the development of cancer, and he rejecte the notion that viruses could cause cancer, a principle that ha already been demonstrated in animals but not in humans. In th eyes of many, Warburg was guilty of equating the absence o evidence with the evidence of absence in the matter of virus induced human cancer. Nevertheless, Warburg's observations o cancer cell metabolism, which is generally characterized by a hig rate of glycolysis, were sound. Even today, the oddities of tumo metabolism offer opportunities for chemotherapy. Warburg's ded ication to his research in cancer and other areas is revealed by th fact that he continued working in his laboratory until just a fe days before his death at age 87.

Warburg, O., On the origin of cancer cells, *Science* **123**, 309–314 (1956

Stage II Energy recovery (Reactions 6–10). The two molecules o glyceraldehyde-3-phosphate are converted to pyruvate, wit] concomitant generation of 4 ATP. Glycolysis therefore has net "profit" of 2 ATP per glucose: Stage I consumes 2 ATF Stage II produces 4 ATP.

The phosphoryl groups that are initially transferred from ATP to th hexose do not immediately result in "high-energy" compounds. Howevei subsequent enzymatic transformations convert these "low-energy" prod ucts to compounds with high phosphoryl group-transfer potentials, whicl are capable of phosphorylating ADP to form ATP. The overall reaction i

$$\text{Glucose} + 2\,\text{NAD}^+ + 2\,\text{ADP} + 2\,\text{P}_i \longrightarrow$$
$$2\,\text{pyruvate} + 2\,\text{NADH} + 2\,\text{ATP} + 2\,\text{H}_2\text{O} + 4\,\text{H}^+$$

Hence, the NADH formed in the process must be continually reoxidize(to keep the pathway supplied with its primary oxidizing agent, NAD^+. I; Section 15-3, we shall examine how organisms do so under aerobic o anaerobic conditions.

■ **CHECK YOUR UNDERSTANDING**

How many ATP are invested and how many are recovered from each molecule of glucose that follows the glycolytic pathway?

See Guided Exploration 14
Glycolysis overview

2 The Reactions of Glycolysis

In this section, we examine the reactions of glycolysis more closely, describing the properties of the individual enzymes and their mechanisms. As we study the individual glycolytic enzymes, we shall encounter many of the catalytic mechanisms described in Section 11-3.

A | Hexokinase Uses the First ATP

Reaction 1 of glycolysis is the transfer of a phosphoryl group from ATP to glucose to form **glucose-6-phosphate (G6P)** in a reaction catalyzed by **hexokinase.**

LEARNING OBJECTIVES

- Understand the chemical logic and the types of reactions that act in sequence to convert glucose to pyruvate.
- Understand the catalytic mechanisms of the enzymes involved, and how amino acid side chains, coenzymes, and cofactors participate.
- Understand how chemical coupling of endergonic and exergonic reactions is used to generate ATP during glycolysis.

A kinase is an enzyme that transfers phosphoryl groups between ATP and a metabolite (Section 14-2C). The metabolite that serves as the phosphoryl group acceptor is indicated in the prefix of the kinase name. Hexokinase is a ubiquitous, relatively nonspecific enzyme that catalyzes the phosphorylation of hexoses such as D-glucose, D-mannose, and D-fructose. Liver cells also contain the isozyme **glucokinase,** which catalyzes the same reaction but which is primarily involved in maintaining blood glucose levels (Section 22-1D).

The second substrate for hexokinase, as for other kinases, is an Mg^{2+}–ATP complex. In fact, uncomplexed ATP is a potent competitive inhibitor of hexokinase. Although we do not always explicitly mention the participation of Mg^{2+}, it is essential for kinase activity. The Mg^{2+} shields the negative charges of the ATP's α- and β- or β- and γ-phosphate oxygen atoms, making the γ-phosphorus atom more accessible for nucleophilic attack by the C6-OH group of glucose:

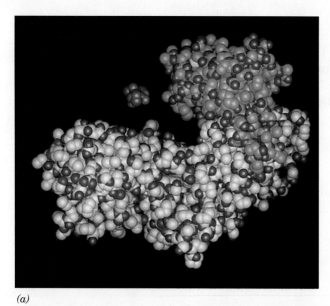

(a)

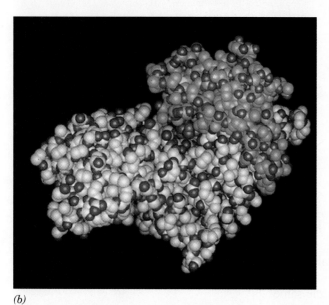

(b)

■ Figure 15-2 | Substrate-induced conformational changes in yeast hexokinase.
(a) Space-filling model of a hexokinase subunit showing the prominent bilobal appearance of the free enzyme (the C atoms in the small lobe are shaded green, and those in the large lobe are light gray; the N and O atoms are blue and red).
(b) Model of the hexokinase complex with glucose (*purple*). The lobes have swung together to engulf the substrate. [Based on X-ray structures by Thomas Steitz, Yale University. PDBids (a) 2YHX and (b) 1HKG.] **See Interactive Exercise 15.**

Comparison of the X-ray structures of yeast hexokinase an the glucose–hexokinase complex indicates that *glucose induces large conformational change in hexokinase* (Fig. 15-2). The tw lobes that form its active site cleft swing together by up to 8 Å s as to engulf the glucose in a manner that suggests the closing o jaws. *This movement places the ATP close to the —C6H2OH grou of glucose and excludes water from the active site (catalysis by prox imity effects;* Section 11-3D). If the catalytic and reacting group were in the proper position for reaction while the enzyme was i the open position (Fig. 15-2a), ATP hydrolysis (i.e., phosphory group transfer to water, which is thermodynamically favorec Fig. 14-6a) would almost certainly be the dominant reaction.

Clearly, the substrate-induced conformational change i hexokinase is responsible for the enzyme's specificity. I addition, the active site polarity is reduced by exclusion o water, thereby expediting the nucleophilic reaction proces Other kinases have the same deeply clefted structure a hexokinase and undergo conformational changes on bindin their substrates (e.g., adenylate kinase; Fig. 14-9).

B | Phosphoglucose Isomerase Converts Glucose-6-Phosphate to Fructose-6-Phosphate

Reaction 2 of glycolysis is the conversion of G6P to **fructose-6 phosphate (F6P)** by **phosphoglucose isomerase (PGI).**

$$^{-2}O_3POCH_2$$

Glucose-6-phosphate (G6P)

phosphoglucose isomerase (PGI)

$$^{-2}O_3POCH_2 \quad CH_2OH$$

Fructose-6-phosphate (F6P)

This is the isomerization of an aldose to a ketose.

Since G6P and F6P both exist predominantly in their cyclic forms, th reaction requires ring opening followed by isomerization and subsequen ring closure (the interconversions of cyclic and linear forms of hexoses ar shown in Fig. 8-3).

A proposed reaction mechanism for the PGI reaction involves genera acid–base catalysis by the enzyme (Fig. 15-3):

Step 1 The substrate binds.

Step 2 An enzymatic acid, probably the ε-amino group of a conserve Lys residue, catalyzes ring opening.

Step 3 A base, thought to be a conserved His residue, abstracts the

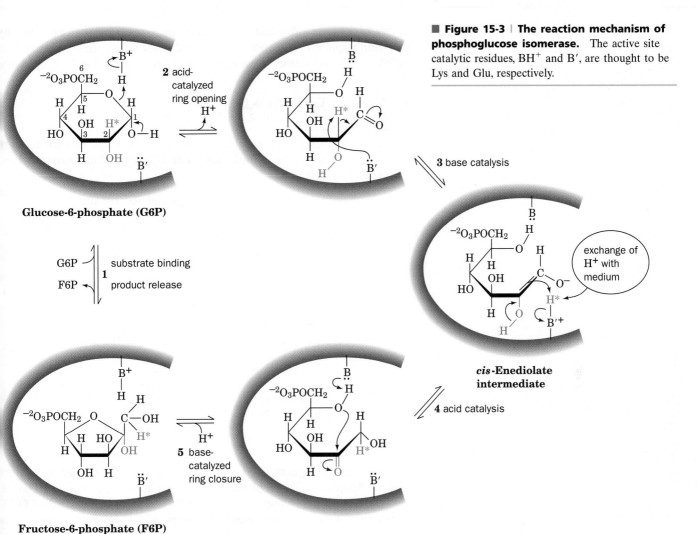

Glucose-6-phosphate (G6P)

G6P, F6P — substrate binding, product release **1**

Fructose-6-phosphate (F6P)

3 base catalysis

exchange of H^+ with medium

cis-**Enediolate intermediate**

4 acid catalysis

acidic proton from C2 to form a *cis*-enediolate intermediate (the proton is acidic because it is α to a carbonyl group).

Step 4 The proton is replaced on C1 in an overall proton transfer. Protons abstracted by bases rapidly exchange with solvent protons. Nevertheless, Irwin Rose confirmed this step by demonstrating that 2-[^{3}H]G6P is occasionally converted to 1-[^{3}H]F6P by intramolecular proton transfer before the ^{3}H has had a chance to exchange with the medium.

Step 5 The ring closes to form the product, which is subsequently released to yield free enzyme, thereby completing the catalytic cycle.

☐ | Phosphofructokinase Uses the Second ATP

n Reaction 3 of glycolysis, **phosphofructokinase (PFK)** phosphorylates ʹ6P to yield **fructose-1,6-bisphosphate (FBP** or **F1,6P;** *at right*). (The product is a *bis*phosphate rather than a *di*phosphate because its two phosphate ;roups are not attached directly to each other.)

The PFK reaction is similar to the hexokinase reaction. The enzyme cat-lyzes the nucleophilic attack by the C1-OH group of F6P on the electrophilic γ-phosphorus atom of the Mg^{2+}-ATP complex.

Phosphofructokinase plays a central role in control of glycolysis because it cat-lyzes one of the pathway's rate-determining reactions. In many organisms, the

Fructose-6-phosphate (F6P)

+ ATP

phosphofructokinase (PFK) Mg^{2+}

+ ADP + H^+

Fructose-1,6-bisphosphate (FBP)

activity of PFK is enhanced allosterically by several substances, includin
AMP, and inhibited allosterically by several other substances, including ATI
and citrate. The regulatory properties of PFK are examined in Section 15-4A

D | Aldolase Converts a 6-Carbon Compound to Two 3-Carbon Compounds

Aldolase catalyzes Reaction 4 of glycolysis, the cleavage of FBP to forr
the two trioses **glyceraldehyde-3-phosphate (GAP)** and **dihydroxyaceton**
phosphate (DHAP):

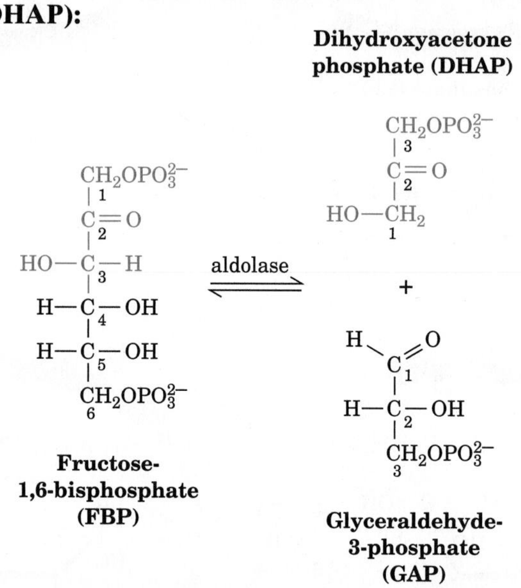

**Fructose-
1,6-bisphosphate
(FBP)**

**Dihydroxyacetone
phosphate (DHAP)**

**Glyceraldehyde-
3-phosphate
(GAP)**

Note that at this point in the pathway, the atom numbering systen
changes. Atoms 1, 2, and 3 of glucose become atoms 3, 2, and 1 of DHAI
thus reversing order. Atoms 4, 5, and 6 become atoms 1, 2, and 3 of GAF

Reaction 4 is an **aldol cleavage (retro aldol condensation)** whose
nonenzymatic base-catalyzed mechanism is shown in Fig. 15-4. The **enolat**
intermediate is stabilized by resonance, as a result of the electron-withdrawin
character of the carbonyl oxygen atom. Note that aldol cleavage between C:
and C4 of FBP requires a carbonyl at C2 and a hydroxyl at C4. Hence, th
"logic" of Reaction 2 in the glycolytic pathway, the isomerization of G6P t
F6P, is clear. Aldol cleavage of G6P would yield products of unequal carbo
chain length, while *aldol cleavage of FBP results in two interconvertible C*
compounds that can therefore enter a common degradative pathway.

Aldol cleavage is catalyzed by stabilizing its enolate intermediat
through increased electron delocalization. In animals and plants, the reac
tion occurs as follows (Fig. 15-5):

Step 1 Substrate binding.

Step 2 Reaction of the FBP carbonyl group with the ε-amino group o

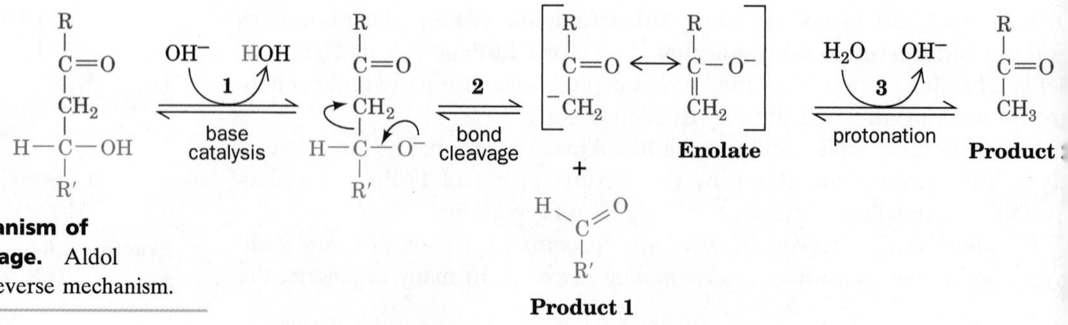

■ **Figure 15-4 | The mechanism of
base-catalyzed aldol cleavage.** Aldol
condensation occurs by the reverse mechanism.

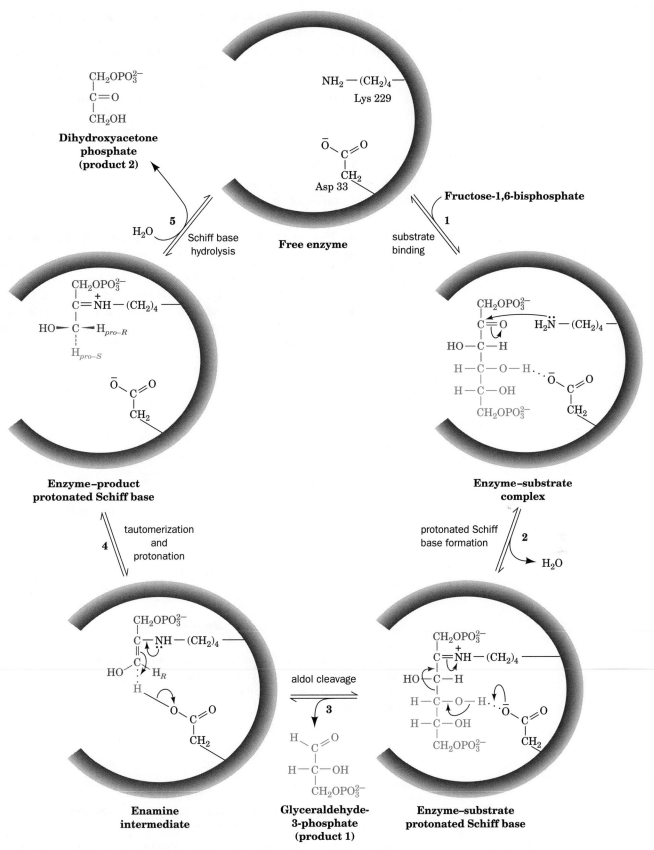

Figure 15-5 | The enzymatic mechanism of aldolase. The reaction involves (**1**) substrate binding; (**2**) Schiff base (imine) formation between the enzyme's active site Lys residue and the open-chain form of FBP; (**3**) aldol cleavage to form an enamine intermediate of the enzyme and DHAP, with release of GAP; (**4**) tautomerization and protonation to the iminium form of the Schiff base; and (**5**) hydrolysis of the Schiff base with release of DHAP. 🔊 **See the Animated Figures.**

the active site Lys to form an iminium cation, that is, a proton ated Schiff base.

Step 3 C3—C4 bond cleavage resulting in enamine formation an the release of GAP. The iminium ion is a better electror withdrawing group than the oxygen atom of the precurso carbonyl group. Thus, catalysis occurs because the enamin intermediate (Fig. 15-5, Step 3) is more stable than the corre sponding enolate intermediate of the base-catalyzed aldol cleav age reaction (Fig. 15-4, Step 2).

Step 4 Protonation of the enamine to an iminium cation.

Step 5 Hydrolysis of the iminium cation to release DHAP, with reger eration of the free enzyme.

E | Triose Phosphate Isomerase Interconverts Dihydroxyacetone Phosphate and Glyceraldehyde-3-Phosphate

Only one of the products of the aldol cleavage reaction, GAP, continue along the glycolytic pathway (Fig. 15-1). However, DHAP and GAP ar ketose–aldose isomers (like F6P and G6P). They are interconverted by a isomerization reaction with an **enediol** (or **enediolate**) **intermediate. Trios phosphate isomerase (TIM)** catalyzes this process in Reaction 5 of glyco ysis, the final reaction of Stage I:

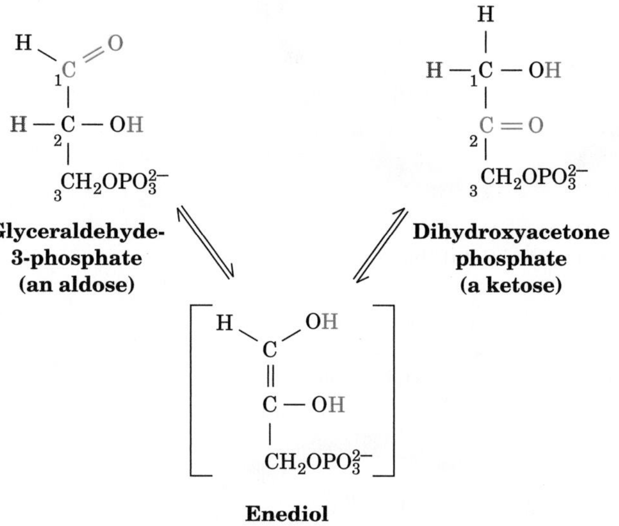

Glyceraldehyde-3-phosphate (an aldose)

Dihydroxyacetone phosphate (a ketose)

Enediol intermediate

Support for this reaction scheme comes from the use of the transitio state analogs **phosphoglycohydroxamate** and **2-phosphoglycolate,** stabl compounds whose geometry resembles that of the proposed enediol c enediolate intermediate:

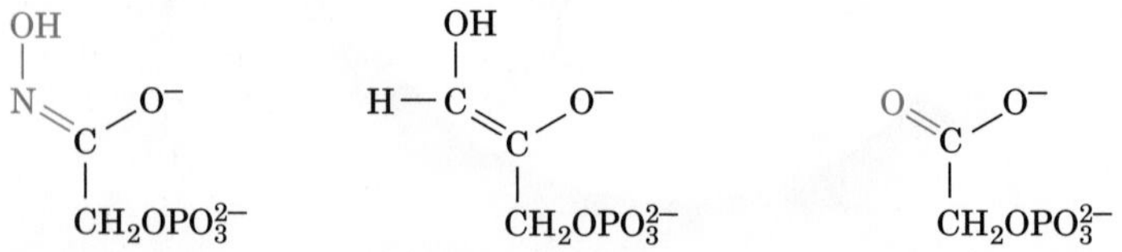

Phosphoglyco-hydroxamate

Proposed enediolate intermediate

2-Phosphoglycolate

Enzymes catalyze reactions by binding the transition state complex mor tightly than the substrate (Section 11-3E), and, in fact, phosphoglycohy droxamate and 2-phosphoglycolate bind 155- and 100-fold more tightly t TIM than does either GAP or DHAP.

Glu 165 and His 95 Act as General Acids and Bases. Mechanistic considerations suggest that the conversion of GAP to the enediol intermediate is catalyzed by a general base, which abstracts a proton from C2 of GAP, and by a general acid, which protonates its carbonyl oxygen atom. X-Ray studies reveal that the Glu 165 side chain of TIM is ideally situated to abstract the C2 proton from GAP (Fig. 15-6). In fact, the mutagenic replacement of Glu 165 by Asp, which X-ray studies show withdraws the carboxylate group only ~1 Å farther away from the substrate than its position in the wild-type enzyme, reduces TIM's catalytic activity 1000-fold. X-Ray studies similarly indicate that His 95 is hydrogen bonded to and hence is properly positioned to protonate GAP's carbonyl oxygen. The positively charged side chain of Lys 12 is thought to electrostatically stabilize the negatively charged transition state in the reaction. In the conversion of the enediol intermediate to DHAP, Glu 165 acts as a general acid to protonate C1 and His 95 acts as a general base to abstract the proton from the OH group, thereby restoring the catalytic groups to their initial protonation states.

Flexible Loop Closes over the Active Site. The comparison of the X-ray structure of TIM (Fig. 6-30c) with that of the enzyme–2-phosphoglycolate complex reveals that when substrate binds to TIM, a conserved 10-residue loop closes over the active site like a hinged lid, in a movement that involves main chain shifts of >7 Å (Fig. 15-6). A four-residue segment of the loop makes a hydrogen bond with the phosphate group of the substrate. Mutagenic excision of these four residues does not significantly distort the protein, so substrate binding is not greatly impaired. However, the catalytic power of the mutant enzyme is reduced 10^5-fold, and it only weakly binds phosphoglycohydroxamate. Evidently, loop closure preferentially stabilizes the enzymatic reaction's enediol-like transition state.

Loop closure in the TIM reaction also supplies a striking example of the so-called **stereoelectronic control** that enzymes can exert on a reaction. In solution, the enediol intermediate readily breaks down with the elimination of the phosphate at C3 to form the toxic compound **methylglyoxal**:

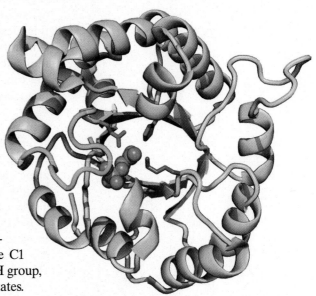

■ **Figure 15-6** | **Ribbon diagram of yeast TIM in complex with its transition state analog 2-phosphoglycolate.** A single subunit of this homodimeric enzyme is viewed roughly along the axis of its α/β barrel. The enzyme's flexible loop is cyan, and the side chains of the catalytic Lys, His, and Glu residues are purple, magenta, and red, respectively. The 2-phosphoglycolate is represented by a space-filling model colored according to atom type (C, green; O, red; P, orange). [Based on an X-ray structure by Gregory Petsko, Brandeis University. PDBid 2YPI.] *See* **Interactive Exercise 16 and Kinemage Exercises 12-1 and 12-2.**

$$
\begin{array}{c}
\mathrm{O} \\
\parallel \\
\mathrm{H-C} \\
\backslash \\
\mathrm{C=O} \\
/ \\
\mathrm{H_3C}
\end{array}
$$

Methylglyoxal

On the enzyme's surface, however, that reaction is prevented because the phosphate group is held by the flexible loop in a position that disfavors phosphate elimination. In the mutant enzyme lacking the flexible loop, the enediol is able to escape: ~85% of the enediol intermediate is released into solution where it rapidly decomposes to methylglyoxal and P_i. Thus, the flexible loop closure assures that substrate is efficiently transformed to product.

α/β Barrel Enzymes May Have Evolved by Divergent Evolution. TIM was the first protein found to contain an α/β barrel (also known as a TIM barrel), a cylinder of eight parallel β strands surrounded by eight parallel α helices (Fig. 6-30c). This striking structural motif has since been found in numerous different proteins, essentially all of which are enzymes (including the glycolytic enzymes aldolase, enolase, and pyruvate kinase). Intriguingly, the active sites of nearly all known α/β barrel enzymes are located in the mouth of the barrel at the end that contains the C-terminal ends of the β strands, although there is no obvious structural rationale fo this. Despite the fact that few of these proteins exhibit significant sequenc similarity, it has been postulated that all of them have evolved from a com mon ancestor (divergent evolution). However, it has also been argued tha the α/β barrel is a particularly stable arrangement that nature has inde pendently discovered on several occasions (convergent evolution).

Triose Phosphate Isomerase Is a Catalytically Perfect Enzyme Jeremy Knowles has demonstrated that TIM has achieved **catalytic per fection.** This means that the rate of the bimolecular reaction between en zyme and substrate is diffusion controlled, so product formation occurs a rapidly as enzyme and substrate can collide in solution. Any increase i TIM's catalytic efficiency therefore would not increase its reaction rate.

GAP and DHAP are interconverted so efficiently that the concentra tions of the two metabolites are maintained at their equilibrium value $K = [GAP]/[DHAP] = 4.73 \times 10^{-2}$. At equilibrium, $[DHAP] \gg [GAP]$ However, under the steady state conditions in a cell, GAP is consumed i the succeeding reactions of the glycolytic pathway. *As GAP is siphone off in this manner, more DHAP is converted to GAP to maintain the equ librium ratio.* In effect, DHAP follows GAP into the second stage of gly colysis, so a single pathway accounts for the metabolism of both product of the aldolase reaction.

Taking Stock of Glycolysis So Far. At this point in the glycolytic path way, one molecule of glucose has been transformed into two molecules c GAP. This completes the first stage of glycolysis (Fig. 15-7). Note that ATP have been consumed in generating the phosphorylated intermediate This energy investment has not yet paid off, but with a little chemica artistry, the "low-energy" GAP can be converted to "high-energy" com pounds whose free energies of hydrolysis can be coupled to ATP synthe sis in the second stage of glycolysis.

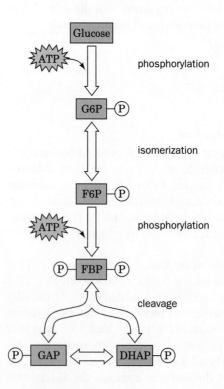

■ **Figure 15-7** | **Schematic diagram of the first stage of glycolysis.** In this series of five reactions, a hexose is phosphorylated, isomerized, phosphorylated again, and then cleaved to two interconvertible triose phosphates. Two ATP are consumed in the process.

Glyceraldehyde-3-Phosphate Dehydrogenase Forms the First "High-Energy" Intermediate

Reaction 6 of glycolysis is the oxidation and phosphorylation of GAP by NAD$^+$ and P$_i$ as catalyzed by **glyceraldehyde-3-phosphate dehydrogenase (GAPDH;** *at right*; Fig. 6-31). This is the first instance of the chemical artistry alluded to above. *In this reaction, aldehyde oxidation, an exergonic reaction, drives the synthesis of the "high-energy" acyl phosphate 1, 3-bisphosphoglycerate (1,3-BPG).* Recall that acyl phosphates are compounds with high phosphoryl group-transfer potential (Section 14-2C).

Several key enzymological experiments have contributed to the elucidation of the GAPDH reaction mechanism:

1. GAPDH is inactivated by alkylation with stoichiometric amounts of iodoacetate. The presence of **carboxymethylcysteine** in the hydrolysate of the resulting alkylated enzyme (Fig. 15-8*a*) suggests that GAPDH has an active site Cys sulfhydryl group.

2. GAPDH quantitatively transfers ^{3}H from C1 of GAP to NAD$^+$ (Fig. 15-8*b*), thereby establishing that this reaction occurs via direct hydride transfer.

3. GAPDH catalyzes exchange of ^{32}P between P$_i$ and the product analog **acetyl phosphate** (Fig. 15-8*c*). Such isotope exchange reactions are indicative of an acyl–enzyme intermediate; that is, the acetyl group forms

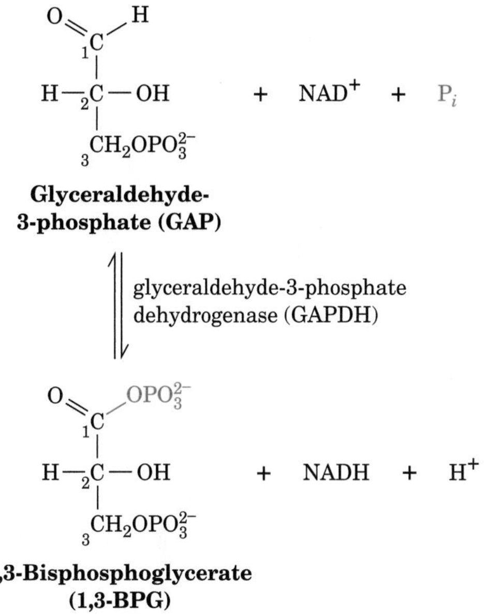

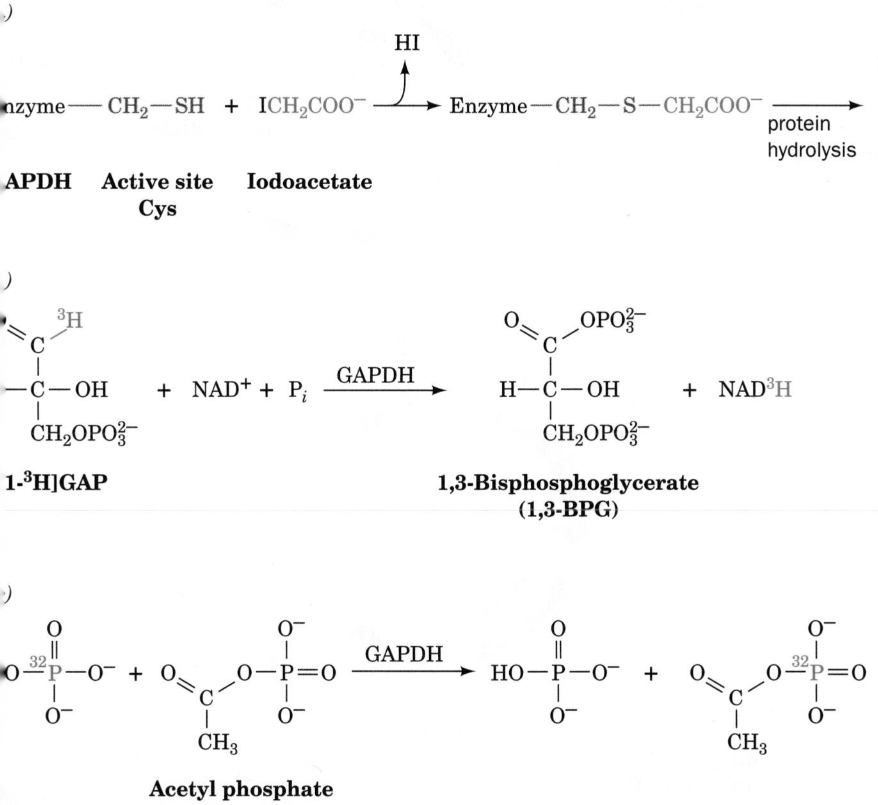

Glyceraldehyde-3-phosphate (GAP)

glyceraldehyde-3-phosphate dehydrogenase (GAPDH)

1,3-Bisphosphoglycerate (1,3-BPG)

GAPDH   Active site   Iodoacetate
           Cys

Carboxy-methylcysteine

[1-^{3}H]GAP

1,3-Bisphosphoglycerate (1,3-BPG)

Acetyl phosphate

Figure 15-8 | Reactions that were used to elucidate the enzymatic mechanism of GAPDH. (*a*) The reaction of iodoacetate with an active site Cys residue. (*b*) Quantitative tritium transfer from substrate to NAD$^+$. (*c*) The enzyme-catalyzed exchange of ^{32}P from phosphate to acetyl phosphate.

a covalent complex with the enzyme, similar to the acyl–enzyme inter-mediate in the serine protease reaction mechanism (Section 11-5C).

David Trentham has proposed a mechanism for GAPDH based on this information and the results of kinetic studies (Fig. 15-9):

Step 1 GAP binds to the enzyme.

Step 2 The essential sulfhydryl group, acting as a nucleophile, attacks the aldehyde to form a **thiohemiacetal.**

Step 3 The thiohemiacetal undergoes oxidation to an **acyl thioester** by direct hydride transfer to NAD⁺. This intermediate, which has been isolated, has a large free energy of hydrolysis. Thus, *the energy of aldehyde oxidation has not been dissipated but has been conserved through the synthesis of the thioester and the reduction of NAD⁺ to NADH.*

Step 4 P$_i$ binds to the enzyme–thioester–NADH complex.

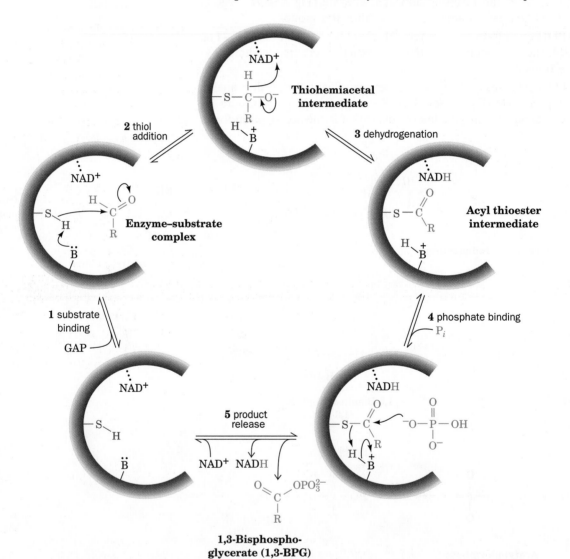

■ **Figure 15-9 | The enzymatic mechanism of GAPDH.**
(**1**) GAP binds to the enzyme; (**2**) the active site sulfhydryl group forms a thiohemiacetal with the substrate; (**3**) NAD⁺ oxidizes the thiohemiacetal to a thioester; (**4**) P$_i$ binds to the enzyme; and (**5**) P$_i$ attacks the thioester, forming the acyl phosphate product, 1,3-BPG, which dissociates from the enzyme followed by the replacement of the newly formed NADH by NAD⁺, thereby regenerating the active enzyme. *See the Animated Figures.*

Step 5 The thioester intermediate undergoes nucleophilic attack by P_i to form the "high-energy" mixed anhydride 1,3-BPG, which then dissociates from the enzyme followed by replacement of NADH by another molecule of NAD^+ to regenerate the active enzyme.

G | Phosphoglycerate Kinase Generates the First ATP

Reaction 7 of the glycolytic pathway yields ATP together with **3-phosphoglycerate (3PG)** in a reaction catalyzed by **phosphoglycerate kinase (PGK;** *at right*). (Note that this enzyme is called a "kinase" because the reverse reaction is phosphoryl group transfer from ATP to 3PG.)

PGK (Fig. 15-10) is conspicuously bilobal in appearance. The Mg^{2+}–ADP-binding site is located on one domain, ~10 Å from the 1,3-BPG-binding site, which is on the other domain. Physical measurements suggest that, on substrate binding, the two domains of PGK swing together to permit the substrates to react in a water-free environment, as occurs in hexokinase (Section 15-2A). Indeed, the appearance of PGK is remarkably similar to that of hexokinase (Fig. 15-2), although the structures of the proteins are otherwise unrelated.

The GAPDH and PGK Reactions Are Coupled. As described in Section 14-2B, a slightly unfavorable reaction can be coupled to a highly favorable reaction so that both reactions proceed in the forward direction. In the case of the sixth and seventh reactions of glycolysis, *1,3-BPG is the common intermediate whose consumption in the PGK reaction "pulls" the GAPDH reaction forward.* The energetics of the overall reaction pair are

$$GAP + P_i + NAD^+ \longrightarrow 1{,}3\text{-BPG} + NADH \qquad \Delta G^{\circ\prime} = +6.7 \text{ kJ} \cdot \text{mol}^{-1}$$

$$1{,}3\text{-BPG} + ADP \longrightarrow 3PG + ATP \qquad \Delta G^{\circ\prime} = -18.8 \text{ kJ} \cdot \text{mol}^{-1}$$

$$GAP + P_i + NAD^+ + ADP \longrightarrow 3PG + NADH + ATP$$
$$\Delta G^{\circ\prime} = -12.1 \text{ kJ} \cdot \text{mol}^{-1}$$

Although the GAPDH reaction is endergonic, the strongly exergonic nature of the transfer of a phosphoryl group from 1,3-BPG to ADP makes the overall synthesis of NADH and ATP from GAP, P_i, NAD^+, and ADP favorable. *This production of ATP, which does not involve O_2, is an example of substrate-level phosphorylation.* The subsequent oxidation of the NADH produced in this reaction by O_2 generates additional ATP by oxidative phosphorylation, as we shall see in Section 18-3.

H | Phosphoglycerate Mutase Interconverts 3-Phosphoglycerate and 2-Phosphoglycerate

In Reaction 8 of glycolysis, 3PG is converted to **2-phosphoglycerate (2PG)** by **phosphoglycerate mutase (PGM):**

3-Phosphoglycerate (3PG) → (phosphoglycerate mutase (PGM)) → **2-Phosphoglycerate (2PG)**

1,3-Bisphosphoglycerate (1,3-BPG)

Mg^{2+} | phosphoglycerate kinase (PGK)

3-Phosphoglycerate (3PG)

■ **Figure 15-10 | A space-filling model of yeast phosphoglycerate kinase.** The substrate-binding site is at the bottom of a deep cleft between the two lobes of the protein. This site is marked by the P atom (*magenta*) of 3PG. Compare this structure with that of hexokinase (Fig. 15-2a). [Based on an X-ray structure by Herman Watson, University of Bristol, U.K. PDBid 3PGK.]

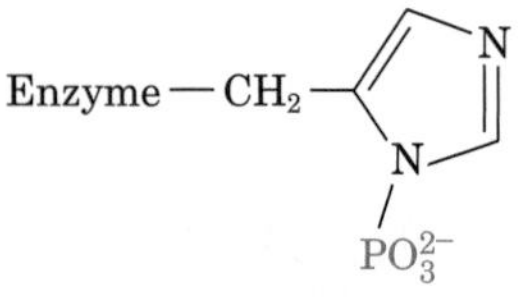

Phospho-His residue

A **mutase** catalyzes the transfer of a functional group from one position to another on a molecule. This more or less energetically neutral reaction is necessary preparation for the next reaction in glycolysis, which generates a "high-energy" phosphoryl compound.

At first sight, the reaction catalyzed by phosphoglycerate appears to be a simple intramolecular phosphoryl group transfer. This is not the case however. The active enzyme has a phosphoryl group at its active site, attached to His 8 (*at left*). The phosphoryl group is transferred to the substrate to form a bisphospho intermediate. This intermediate then rephosphorylates the enzyme to form the product and regenerate the active phosphoenzyme. The enzyme's X-ray structure shows the proximity of His 8 to the substrate (Fig. 15-11).

Catalysis by phosphoglycerate mutase occurs as follows (Fig. 15-12):

Step 1 3PG binds to the phosphoenzyme in which His 8 is phosphorylated.

Step 2 The enzyme's phosphoryl group is transferred to the substrate, resulting in an intermediate 2,3-bisphosphoglycerate–enzyme complex.

Steps 3 and 4 The complex decomposes to form the product 2PG and regenerate the phosphoenzyme.

The phosphoryl group of 3PG therefore ends up on C2 of the next 3PG to undergo reaction.

Occasionally, 2,3-bisphosphoglycerate (2,3-BPG) formed in Step 2 of the reaction dissociates from the dephosphoenzyme, leaving it in an inactive form. Trace amounts of 2,3-BPG must therefore always be available to regenerate the active phosphoenzyme by the reverse reaction. 2,3-BPG also specifically binds to deoxyhemoglobin, thereby decreasing its oxygen affinity (Section 7-1D). Consequently, erythrocytes require much more 2,3-BPG (5 mM) than the trace amounts that are used to prime phosphoglycerate mutase (Box 15-2).

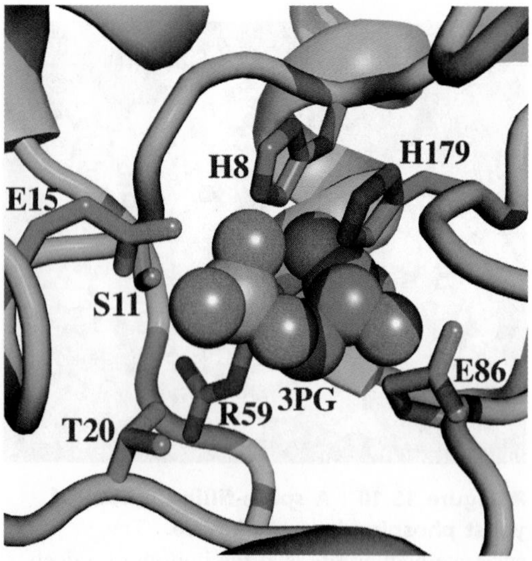

Enolase Forms the Second "High-Energy" Intermediate

In Reaction 9 of glycolysis, 2PG is dehydrated to **phosphoenolpyruvate (PEP)** in a reaction catalyzed by **enolase:**

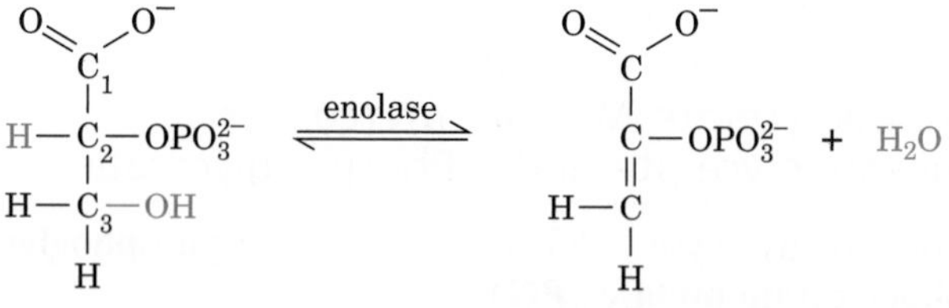

2-Phosphoglycerate (2PG)   **Phosphoenolpyruvate (PEP)**

The enzyme forms a complex with a divalent cation such as Mg^{2+} before the substrate binds. Fluoride ion inhibits glycolysis by blocking enolase activity (F^- was one of the metabolic inhibitors used in elucidating the glycolytic pathway). In the presence of P_i, F^- blocks substrate binding to enolase by forming a bound complex with Mg^{2+} at the enzyme's active site. Enolase's substrate, 2PG, therefore builds up, and, through the action of PGM, 3PG also builds up.

■ **Figure 15-11** | **The active site region of yeast phosphoglycerate mutase (dephospho form).** The substrate, 3PG, binds to an ionic pocket. His 8 is phosphorylated in the active enzyme. [Based on an X-ray structure by Herman Watson, University of Bristol, U.K. PDBid 3PGM.]

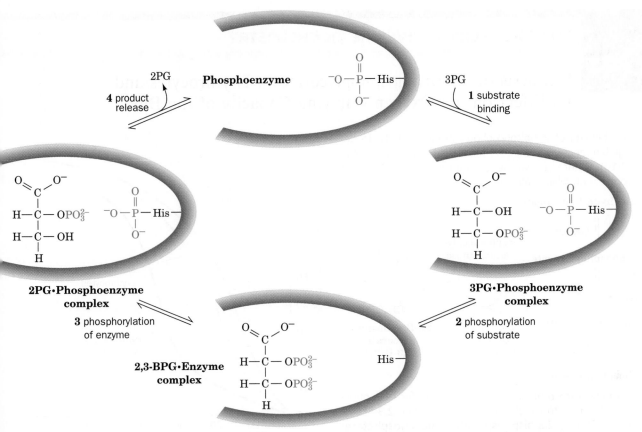

Figure 15-12 | A proposed reaction mechanism for phosphoglycerate mutase. The active form of the enzyme contains a phospho-His residue at the active site. (**1**) Formation of an enzyme–substrate complex; (**2**) transfer of the enzyme-bound phosphoryl group to the substrate; (**3**) rephosphorylation of the enzyme by the other phosphoryl group of the substrate; and (**4**) release of product, regenerating the active phosphoenzyme.

Pyruvate Kinase Generates the Second ATP

In Reaction 10 of glycolysis, its final reaction, **pyruvate kinase (PK)** couples the free energy of PEP cleavage to the synthesis of ATP during the formation of pyruvate:

$$
\begin{array}{c}
\text{O} \diagup \text{C} \diagdown \text{O}^- \\
| \\
\text{C}-\text{OPO}_3^{2-} \quad + \quad \text{ADP} \quad + \quad \text{H}^+ \\
|| \\
\text{CH}_2
\end{array}
$$

Phosphoenolpyruvate
(PEP)

pyruvate
kinase (PK) ↓

$$
\begin{array}{c}
\text{O} \diagup \text{C} \diagdown \text{O}^- \\
| \\
\text{C}=\text{O} \quad + \quad \text{ATP} \\
| \\
\text{CH}_3
\end{array}
$$

Pyruvate

BOX 15-2 PERSPECTIVES IN BIOCHEMISTRY

Synthesis of 2,3-Bisphosphoglycerate in Erythrocytes and Its Effect on the Oxygen Carrying Capacity of the Blood

The specific binding of 2,3-bisphosphoglycerate (2,3-BPG) to deoxyhemoglobin decreases the oxygen affinity of hemoglobin (Section 7-1D). Erythrocytes synthesize and degrade 2,3-BPG by a detour from the glycolytic pathway.

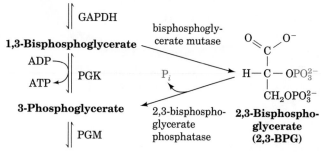

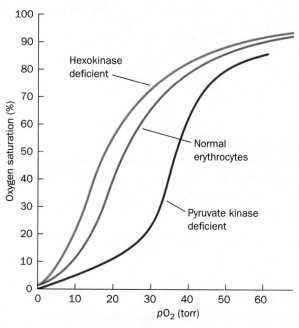

Bisphosphoglycerate mutase catalyzes the transfer of a phosphoryl group from C1 to C2 of 1,3-BPG. The resulting 2,3-BPG is hydrolyzed to 3PG by **2,3-bisphosphoglycerate phosphatase.** The 3PG then continues through the glycolytic pathway.

The level of available 2,3-BPG regulates hemoglobin's oxygen affinity. Consequently, inherited defects of glycolysis in erythrocytes alter the ability of the blood to carry oxygen as is indicated by the oxygen-saturation curve of its hemoglobin.

For example, in hexokinase-deficient erythrocytes, the concentrations of all the glycolytic intermediates are low (since hexokinase catalyzes the first step of glycolysis), thereby resulting in a diminished 2,3-BPG concentration and an increased hemoglobin oxygen affinity (*green curve*). Conversely, a deficiency in pyruvate

kinase (which catalyzes the final reaction of glycolysis; Fig. 15-decreases hemoglobin's oxygen affinity (*purple curve*) through a increase in 2,3-BPG concentration resulting from this blockad Thus, although erythrocytes, which lack nuclei and other organelle have only a minimal metabolism, this metabolism is physiological significant.

[Oxygen-saturation curves after Delivoria-Papadopoulos, M., Oski, F.A., a Gottlieb, A.J., *Science* **165,** 601 (1969).]

The PK reaction, which requires both monovalent (K^+) and divalen (Mg^{2+}) cations, occurs as follows (Fig. 15-13):

Step 1 A β-phosphoryl oxygen of ADP nucleophilically attacks th PEP phosphorus atom, thereby displacing **enolpyruvate** an forming ATP.

Step 2 Enolpyruvate tautomerizes to pyruvate.

The PK reaction is highly exergonic, supplying more than enough fre energy to drive ATP synthesis (another example of substrate-level phos phorylation). At this point, the "logic" of the enolase reaction become clear. The standard free energy of hydrolysis of 2PG is only -16 kJ·mol$^-$ which is insufficient to drive ATP synthesis from ADP ($\Delta G^{\circ\prime} = 30.5$ kJ·mol^{-1}). However, the dehydration of 2PG results in the forma tion of a "high-energy" compound capable of such synthesis. *The hig*

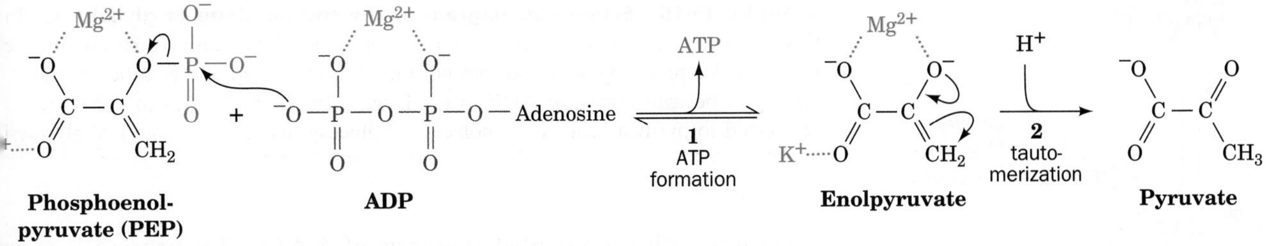

Figure 15-13 | **Figure 15-13 The mechanism of the reaction catalyzed by pyruvate kinase.** (1) Nucleophilic attack of an ADP β-phosphoryl oxygen atom on the phosphorus atom of PEP to form ATP and enolpyruvate; and (2) tautomerization of enolpyruvate to pyruvate.

phosphoryl group-transfer potential of PEP reflects the large release of free energy on converting the product enolpyruvate to its keto tautomer. Consider the hydrolysis of PEP as a two-step reaction (Fig. 15-14). The tautomerization step supplies considerably more free energy than the phosphoryl group transfer step.

Assessing Stage II of Glycolysis. The energy investment of the first stage of glycolysis (2 ATP consumed) is doubly repaid in the second stage of glycolysis because two phosphorylated C_3 units are transformed to two

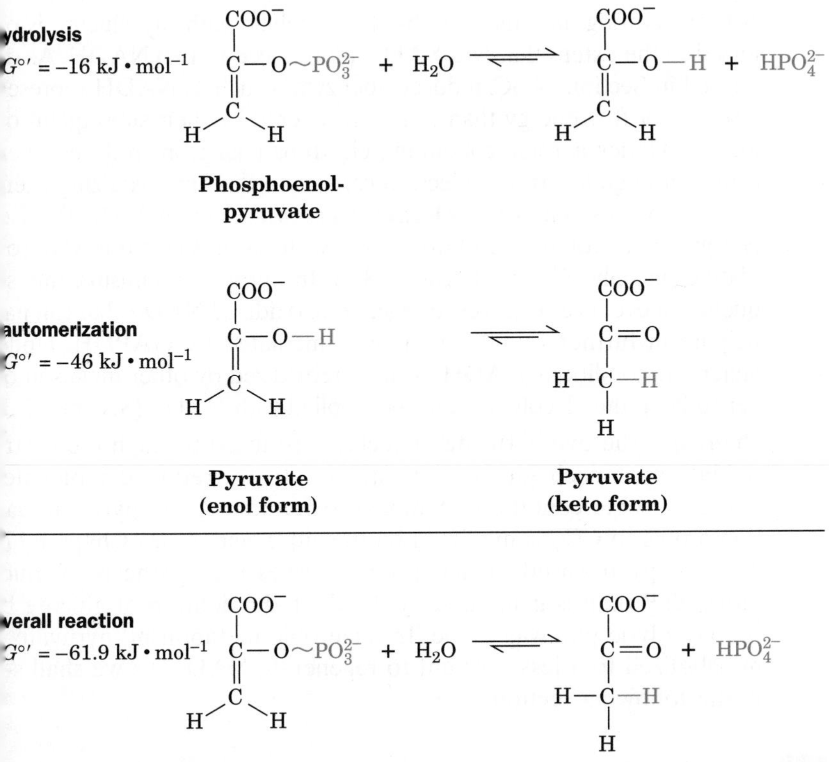

Figure 15-14 | **The hydrolysis of PEP.** The reaction is broken down into two steps, hydrolysis and tautomerization. The overall $\Delta G^{\circ\prime}$ value is much more negative than that required to provide the $\Delta G^{\circ\prime}$ for ATP synthesis from ADP and P_i.

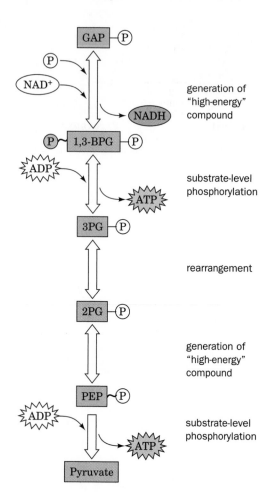

generation of "high-energy" compound

substrate-level phosphorylation

rearrangement

generation of "high-energy" compound

substrate-level phosphorylation

■ **Figure 15-15** | **Schematic diagram of the second stage of glycolysis.** In this series of five reactions, GAP undergoes phosphorylation and oxidation, followe by molecular rearrangements so that both phosphoryl groups have sufficient free energy to be transferred to ADP to produce ATP. Two molecules of GAP are converted to pyruvate for every molecule of glucose that enters Stage I of glycolys

pyruvates with the coupled synthesis of 4 ATP. This process is show schematically in Fig. 15-15.

The overall reaction of glycolysis, as we have seen, is

$$\text{Glucose} + 2\,\text{NAD}^+ + 2\,\text{ADP} + 2\,\text{P}_i \longrightarrow$$
$$2\,\text{pyruvate} + 2\,\text{NADH} + 2\,\text{ATP} + 2\,\text{H}_2\text{O} + 4\,\text{F}$$

Let us consider each of the three products of glycolysis:

1. *ATP.* The initial investment of 2 ATP per glucose in Stage I and t subsequent generation of 4 ATP by substrate-level phosphorylatic (two for each GAP that proceeds through Stage II) gives a net yie of 2 ATP per glucose. In some tissues and organisms for which gl cose is the primary metabolic fuel, ATP produced by glycolys satisfies most of the cell's energy needs. For example, the parasi protozoans *Trypanosoma* and *Leishmania* (which are the causes several human diseases, including **African sleeping sickness** a **leishmaniasis**) rely almost entirely on glycolysis. Some of the gl colytic enzymes in these organisms differ structurally from the mammalian counterparts, which makes them attractive targets for r tional drug design (Section 12-4).

2. *NADH.* During its catabolism by the glycolytic pathway, glucose is o idized to the extent that two NAD^+ are reduced to two NADH. As d scribed in Section 14-3C, reduced coenzymes such as NADH represe a source of free energy than can be recovered by their subsequent o idation. Under aerobic conditions, electrons pass from reduced coe zymes through a series of electron carriers to the final oxidizing ager O_2, in a process known as **electron transport** (Section 18-2). The fr energy of electron transport drives the synthesis of ATP from ADP (o idative phosphorylation; Section 18-3). In aerobic organisms, this s quence of events also serves to regenerate oxidized NAD^+ that can pa ticipate in further rounds of catalysis mediated by GAPDH. Und anaerobic conditions, NADH must be reoxidized by other means in o der to keep the glycolytic pathway supplied with NAD^+ (Section 15-3

3. *Pyruvate.* The two pyruvate molecules produced through the parti oxidation of each glucose are still relatively reduced molecule Under aerobic conditions, complete oxidation of the pyruvate ca bon atoms to CO_2 is mediated by the citric acid cycle (Chapter 17 The energy released in that process drives the synthesis of muc more ATP than is generated by the limited oxidation of glucose b the glycolytic pathway alone. In anaerobic metabolism, pyruvate metabolized to a lesser extent to regenerate NAD^+, as we shall se in the following section.

3 Fermentation: The Anaerobic Fate of Pyruvate

The three common metabolic fates of pyruvate produced by glycolysis ar outlined in Fig. 15-16.

■ **CHECK YOUR UNDERSTANDING**

Write the reactions of glycolysis, showing the structural formulas of the intermediates and the names of the enzymes that catalyze the reactions.

What compounds with high phosphate group-transfer potential are synthesized during glycolysis?

What is the fate of the electrons obtained from the partial oxidation of glucose during glycolysis?

LEARNING OBJECTIVES

■ Understand that NADH must be reoxidized for glycolysis to continue.
■ Understand that the anaerobic reoxidation of NADH occurs by different paths in different organisms.
■ Understand how various coenzymes and cofactors participate in the different types of fermentation.

1. *Under aerobic conditions, the pyruvate is completely oxidized via the citric acid cycle to CO_2 and H_2O.*

2. *Under anaerobic conditions, pyruvate must be converted to a reduced end product in order to reoxidize the NADH produced by the GAPDH reaction.* This occurs in two ways:

   (a) Under anaerobic conditions in muscle, pyruvate is reduced to **lactate** to regenerate NAD^+ in a process known as **homolactic fermentation** (a fermentation is an anaerobic biological reaction process).

   (b) In yeast, pyruvate is decarboxylated to yield CO_2 and **acetaldehyde,** which is then reduced by NADH to yield NAD^+ and ethanol. This process is known as **alcoholic fermentation.**

Thus, in aerobic glycolysis, NADH acts as a "high-energy" compound, whereas in anaerobic glycolysis, its free energy of oxidation is dissipated as heat.

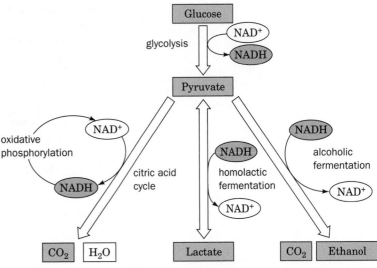

■ **Figure 15-16** | **Metabolic fate of pyruvate.**
Under aerobic conditions (*left*), the pyruvate carbons are oxidized to CO_2 by the citric acid cycle and the electrons are eventually transferred to O_2 to yield H_2O in oxidative phosphorylation. Under anaerobic conditions in muscle, pyruvate is reversibly converted to lactate (*middle*), whereas in yeast, it is converted to CO_2 and ethanol (*right*).

A | Homolactic Fermentation Converts Pyruvate to Lactate

In muscle, during vigorous activity, when the demand for ATP is high and oxygen is in short supply, ATP is largely synthesized via anaerobic glycolysis, which rapidly generates ATP, rather than through the slower process of oxidative phosphorylation. Under these conditions, **lactate dehydrogenase (LDH)** catalyzes the oxidation of NADH by pyruvate to yield NAD^+ and lactate:

Pyruvate + **NADH** + H^+

↑↓ lactate dehydrogenase (LDH)

L-Lactate + **NAD$^+$**

This reaction is often classified as Reaction 11 of glycolysis. The lactate dehydrogenase reaction is freely reversible, so *pyruvate and lactate concentrations are readily equilibrated.*

In the proposed mechanism for pyruvate reduction by LDH, a hydride ion is stereospecifically transferred from C4 of NADH to C2 of pyruvate with concomitant transfer of a proton from the imidazolium moiety of His 195:

L-Lactate

Both His 195 and Arg 171 interact electrostatically with the substrate to orient pyruvate (or lactate, in the reverse reaction) in the enzyme active site.

The overall process of anaerobic glycolysis in muscle can be represented as

$$\text{Glucose} + 2\,\text{ADP} + 2\,\text{P}_i \rightarrow 2\,\text{lactate} + 2\,\text{ATP} + 2\,\text{H}_2\text{O} + 2\,\text{H}^+$$

Lactate represents a sort of dead end for anaerobic glucose metabolism. The lactate can either be exported from the cell or converted back to pyruvate. Much of the lactate produced in skeletal muscle cells is carried by the blood to the liver, where it is used to synthesize glucose (Section 22-1F).

Contrary to widely held belief, it is not lactate buildup in the muscle per se that causes muscle fatigue and soreness but the accumulation of glycolytically generated acid (muscles can maintain their workload in the presence of high lactate concentrations if the pH is kept constant).

B | Alcoholic Fermentation Converts Pyruvate to Ethanol and CO_2

Under anaerobic conditions in yeast, NAD^+ for glycolysis is regenerated in a process that has been valued for thousands of years: the conversion of pyruvate to ethanol and CO_2. Ethanol is, of course, the active ingredient of wine and spirits; CO_2 so produced leavens bread.

Yeast (Fig. 15-17) produces ethanol and CO_2 via two consecutive reactions (Fig. 15-18):

1. The decarboxylation of pyruvate to form acetaldehyde and CO_2 as catalyzed by **pyruvate decarboxylase** (an enzyme not present in animals).

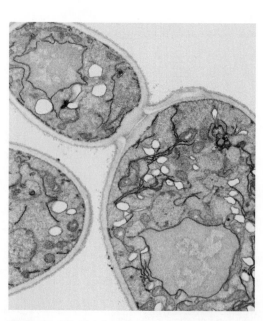

■ **Figure 15-17** | **An electron micrograph of yeast cells.** [Biophoto Associates Photo Researchers.]

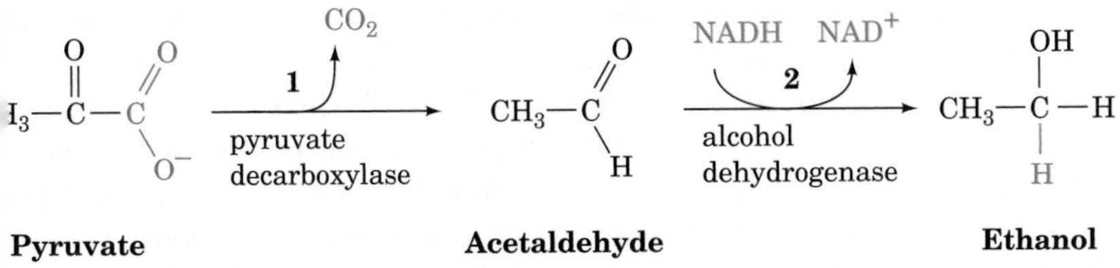

$$\underset{\textbf{Pyruvate}}{\text{H}_3\text{—C—C} \underset{\text{O}^-}{\overset{\text{O \quad O}}{\parallel \quad \parallel}}} \xrightarrow[\substack{\text{pyruvate} \\ \text{decarboxylase}}]{\overset{\text{CO}_2}{\overset{1}{\curvearrowright}}} \underset{\textbf{Acetaldehyde}}{\text{CH}_3\text{—C} \overset{\text{O}}{\underset{\text{H}}{\parallel}}} \xrightarrow[\substack{\text{alcohol} \\ \text{dehydrogenase}}]{\overset{\text{NADH \quad NAD}^+}{\overset{2}{\curvearrowright}}} \underset{\textbf{Ethanol}}{\text{CH}_3\text{—} \underset{\text{H}}{\overset{\text{OH}}{\text{C}}}\text{—H}}$$

■ **Figure 15-18 | The two reactions of alcoholic fermentation.** (**1**) Decarboxylation of pyruvate to form acetaldehyde; and (**2**) reduction of acetaldehyde to ethanol by NADH.

2. The reduction of acetaldehyde to ethanol by NADH as catalyzed by alcohol dehydrogenase (Section 11-1C), thereby regenerating NAD$^+$ for use in the GAPDH reaction of glycolysis.

PP Is an Essential Cofactor of Pyruvate Decarboxylase. Pyruvate derboxylase contains the coenzyme **thiamine pyrophosphate (TPP; also lled thiamin diphosphate, ThDP):**

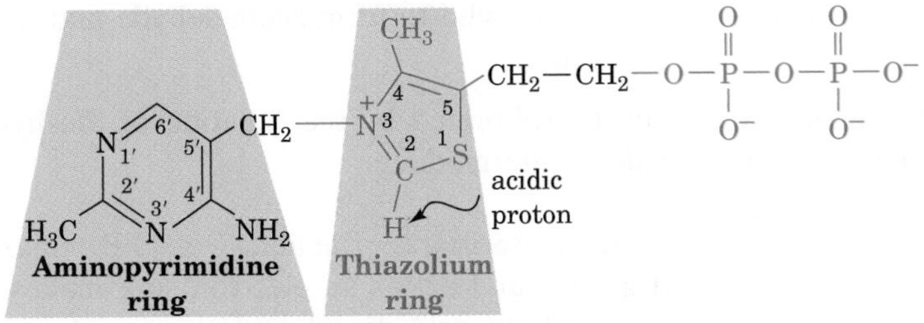

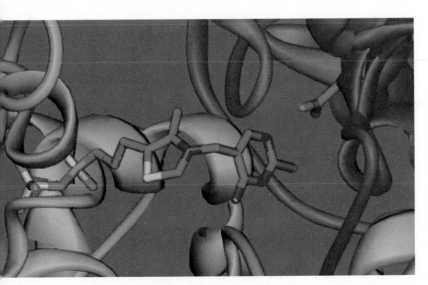

Thiamine pyrophosphate (TPP)

PP, which is synthesized from thiamine **(vitamin B$_1$)**, binds tightly but oncovalently to pyruvate decarboxylase (Fig. 15-19).

The enzyme uses TPP because uncatalyzed decarboxylation of an α-keto id such as pyruvate requires the buildup of negative charge on the caronyl carbon atom in the transition state, an unstable situation:

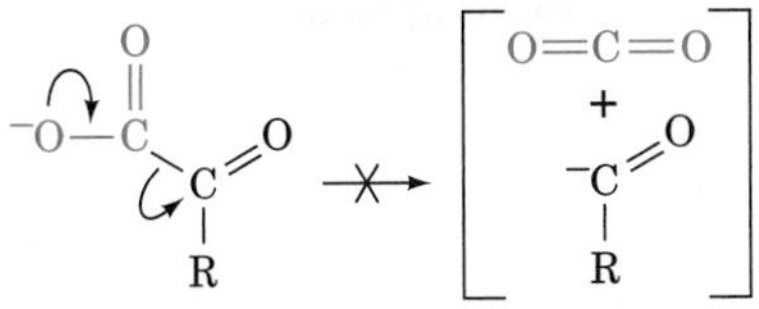

■ **Figure 15-19 | TPP binding to pyruvate decarboxylase from *Saccharomyces uvarum* (brewer's yeast).** The TPP and the side chain of Glu 51 are shown in stick form with C green, N blue, O red, S yellow, and P orange. The TPP binds in a cavity situated between the dimer's two subunits (*cyan and magenta*) where it hydrogen bonds to Glu 51. [Based on an X-ray structure by William Furey and Martin Sax, Veterans Administration Medical Center and University of Pittsburgh. PDBid 1PYD.] *See* **Interactive Exercise 17.**

This transition state can be stabilized by delocalizing the developing ne[g]ative charge into a suitable "electron sink." The amino acid residues [of] proteins function poorly in this capacity but TPP does so easily.

*TPP's catalytically active functional group is the **thiazolium ring**. T[he]* C2-H atom of this group is relatively acidic because of the adjacent pos[i]tively charged quaternary nitrogen atom, which electrostatically stabiliz[es] the carbanion formed when the proton dissociates. This dipolar carbani[on] (or **ylid**) is the active form of the coenzyme. Pyruvate decarboxylase o[p]erates as follows (Fig. 15-20):

Step 1 Nucleophilic attack by the ylid form of TPP on the carbonyl ca[r]bon of pyruvate.

Step 2 Departure of CO_2 to generate a resonance-stabilized carbani[on] adduct in which the thiazolium ring of the coenzyme acts as a[n] electron sink.

Step 3 Protonation of the carbanion.

Step 4 Elimination of the TPP ylid to form acetaldehyde and regene[r]ate the active enzyme.

This mechanism has been corroborated by the isolation of the **hydrox**[y]**ethylthiamine pyrophosphate** intermediate.

Vitamin B₁ Deficiency Causes Beriberi. The ability of TPP's thiazoliu[m] ring to add to carbonyl groups and act as an electron sink makes it th[e] coenzyme most utilized in α-keto acid decarboxylation reactions. Suc[h]

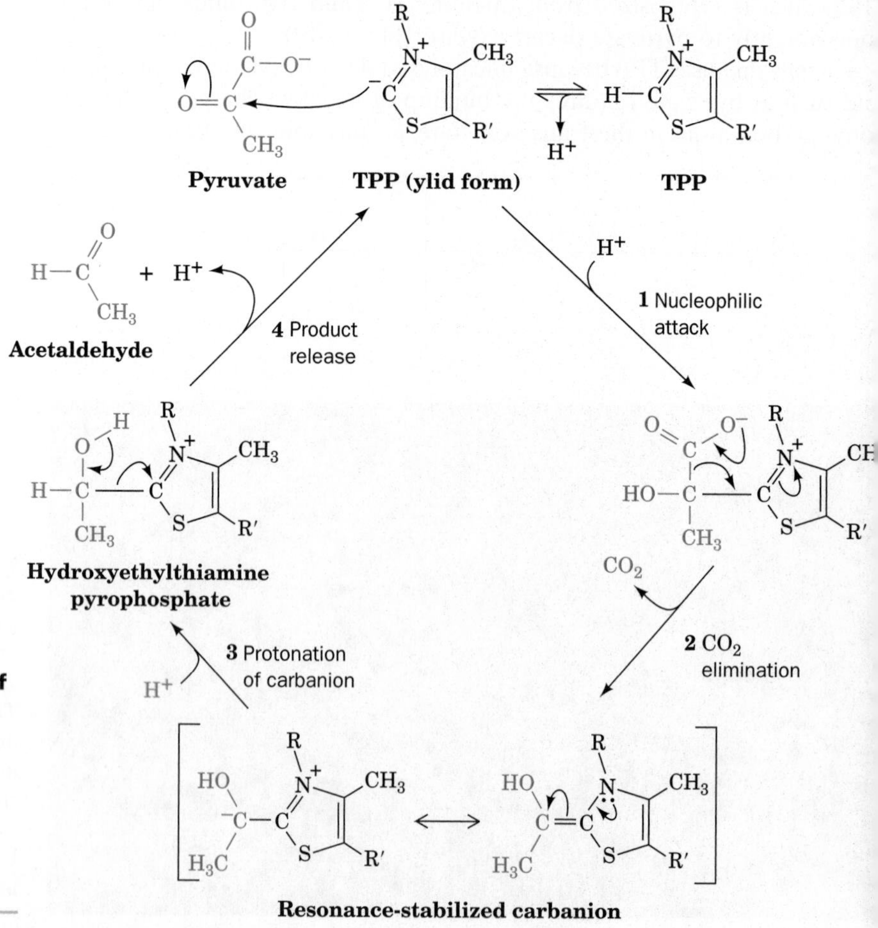

■ **Figure 15-20 | The reaction mechanism of pyruvate decarboxylase.** (**1**) Nucleophilic attack by the ylid form of TPP on the carbonyl carbon of pyruvate; (**2**) departure of CO_2 to generate a resonance-stabilized carbanion; (**3**) protonation of the carbanion; and (**4**) elimination of the TPP ylid and release of product.

actions occur in all organisms, not just yeast. Consequently, thiamine
(vitamin B_1), which is neither synthesized nor stored in significant quantities by the tissues of most vertebrates, is required in their diets. Thiamine
deficiency in humans results in an ultimately fatal condition known as
beriberi (Singhalese for weakness) that is characterized by neurological
disturbances causing pain, paralysis, and atrophy (wasting) of the limbs
and/or edema (accumulation of fluid in tissues and body cavities). Beriberi
was particularly prevalent in the late eighteenth and early nineteenth
centuries in the rice-consuming areas of Asia after the introduction of
steam-powered milling machines that polished the rice grains to remove
their coarse but thiamine-containing outer layers (the previously used
milling procedures were less efficient and hence left sufficient thiamine on
the grains). Parboiling rice before milling, a process common in India,
causes the rice kernels to absorb nutrients from their outer layers, thereby
decreasing the incidence of beriberi. Once thiamine deficiency was recognized as the cause of beriberi, enrichment procedures were instituted so
that today it has ceased to be a problem except in areas undergoing
famine. However, beriberi occasionally develops in alcoholics due to their
penchant for drinking but not eating.

Reduction of Acetaldehyde and Regeneration of NAD^+. Yeast alcohol
dehydrogenase **(YADH)**, the enzyme that converts acetaldehyde to ethanol,
is a tetramer, each subunit of which binds one Zn^{2+} ion. The Zn^{2+} polarizes the carbonyl group of acetaldehyde to stabilize the developing negative
charge in the transition state of the reaction *(at right)*. This facilitates the
stereospecific transfer of a hydrogen from NADH to acetaldehyde.

Mammalian liver alcohol dehydrogenase **(LADH)** metabolizes the
alcohols anaerobically produced by the intestinal flora as well as those
from external sources (the direction of the alcohol dehydrogenase reaction varies with the relative concentrations of ethanol and acetaldehyde).
Mammalian LADH is a dimer with significant amino acid sequence similarity to YADH, although LADH subunits each contain a second Zn^{2+}
ion that presumably has a structural role.

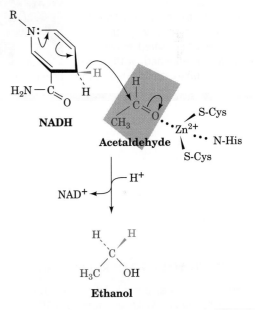

Fermentation Is Energetically Favorable

Thermodynamics permits us to dissect the process of fermentation into its
component parts and to account for the free energy changes that occur. This
enables us to calculate the efficiency with which the free energy of glucose
metabolism is used in the synthesis of ATP. For homolactic fermentation,

$$\text{Glucose} \longrightarrow 2 \text{ lactate} + 2 \text{ H}^+ \qquad \Delta G^{\circ\prime} = -196 \text{ kJ} \cdot \text{mol}^{-1}$$

For alcoholic fermentation,

$$\text{Glucose} \longrightarrow 2 \text{ CO}_2 + 2 \text{ ethanol} \qquad \Delta G^{\circ\prime} = -235 \text{ kJ} \cdot \text{mol}^{-1}$$

Each of these processes is coupled to the net formation of 2 ATP, which
requires $\Delta G^{\circ\prime} = +61 \text{ kJ} \cdot \text{mol}^{-1}$ of glucose consumed. Dividing $\Delta G^{\circ\prime}$ of
ATP formation by that of lactate formation indicates that homolactic fer-
mentation is 31% "efficient"; that is, 31% of the free energy released by
the process under standard biochemical conditions is sequestered in the
form of ATP. The rest is dissipated as heat, thereby making the process
irreversible. Likewise, alcoholic fermentation is 26% efficient under
biochemical standard state conditions. *Under physiological conditions,
where the concentrations of reactants and products differ from those of the
standard state, these reactions have thermodynamic efficiencies of >50%.*

BOX 15-3 PERSPECTIVES IN BIOCHEMISTRY

Glycolytic ATP Production in Muscle

Skeletal muscle consists of both **slow-twitch** (Type I) and **fast-twitch** (Type II) **fibers.** Fast-twitch fibers, so called because they predominate in muscles capable of short bursts of rapid activity, are nearly devoid of mitochondria (where oxidative phosphorylation occurs). Consequently, they must obtain nearly all of their ATP through anaerobic glycolysis, for which they have a particularly large capacity. Muscles designed to contract slowly and steadily, in contrast, are enriched in slow-twitch fibers that are rich in mitochondria and obtain most of their ATP through oxidative phosphorylation.

Fast- and slow-twitch fibers were originally known as white and red fibers, respectively, because otherwise pale-colored muscle tissue, when enriched with mitochondria, takes on the red color

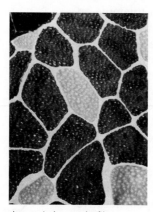

slow-twitch muscle fiber

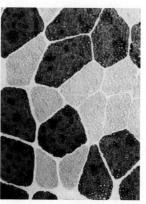

fast-twitch muscle fiber

characteristic of their heme-containing cytochromes. Howev[...] fiber color is an imperfect indictor of muscle physiology.

In a familiar example, the flight muscles of migratory birds su[...] as ducks and geese, which need a continuous energy supply, are ri[...] in slow-twitch fibers. Therefore, the[...] birds have dark breast meat. In co[...] trast, the flight muscles of less am[...] tious fliers, such as chickens a[...] turkeys, which are used only for sh[...] bursts (often to escape danger), co[...] sist mainly of fast-twitch fibers th[...] form white meat. In humans, t[...] muscles of sprinters are relatively ri[...] in fast-twitch fibers, whereas distar[...] runners have a greater proportion [...] slow-twitch fibers (although th[...] muscles have the same color).

[Photo of muscle courtesy of J. MacDougall, McMaster Universi[...] Canada.]

Anaerobic fermentation uses glucose in a profligate manner compare[...] to oxidative phosphorylation: Fermentation results in the production [...] 2 ATP per glucose, whereas oxidative phosphorylation yields up to 32 AT[...] per glucose (Section 18-3C). This accounts for Pasteur's observation th[...] yeast consume far more sugar when growing anaerobically than whe[...] growing aerobically (the **Pasteur effect**). However, *the rate of ATP pr[...] duction by anaerobic glycolysis can be up to 100 times faster than that [...] oxidative phosphorylation. Consequently, when tissues such as muscle a[...] rapidly consuming ATP, they regenerate it almost entirely by anaerob[...] glycolysis.* (Homolactic fermentation does not really "waste" glucose sin[...] the lactate can be aerobically reconverted to glucose by the liver; Sectio[...] 22-1F.) Certain muscles are specialized for the rapid production of AT[...] by glycolysis (Box 15-3).

■ **CHECK YOUR UNDERSTANDING**

Describe the three possible fates of pyruvate.
Compare the ATP yields and rates of ATP production for anaerobic and aerobic degradation of glucose.

LEARNING OBJECTIVES

■ Understand that enzymes that function with large negative free energy changes are candidates for flux-control points.
■ Understand that phosphofructokinase, the major regulatory point for glycolysis in muscle, is controlled by allosteric interactions.
■ Understand that substrate cycling allows the rate of glycolysis to respond rapidly to changing needs.

4 Regulation of Glycolysis

Under steady state conditions, glycolysis operates continuously in mo[...] tissues, although the glycolytic flux must vary to meet the needs of th[...] organism. Elucidation of the flux control mechanisms of a given pathwa[...] such as glycolysis, commonly involves three steps:

1. Identification of the rate-determining step(s) of the pathway b[...] measuring the *in vivo* ΔG for each reaction. Enzymes that opera[...] far from equilibrium are potential control points (Section 14-1D).

2. *In vitro* identification of allosteric modifiers of the enzymes cataly[...] ing the rate-determining reactions. The mechanisms by which thes[...]

Table 15-1	$\Delta G^{\circ\prime}$ and ΔG for the Reactions of Glycolysis in Heart Muscle[a]		
Reaction	Enzyme	$\Delta G^{\circ\prime}$ $(kJ \cdot mol^{-1})$	ΔG $(kJ \cdot mol^{-1})$
	Hexokinase	−20.9	−27.2
	PGI	+2.2	−1.4
	PFK	−17.2	−25.9
	Aldolase	+22.8	−5.9
	TIM	+7.9	~0
+ 7	GAPDH + PGK	−16.7	−1.1
	PGM	+4.7	−0.6
	Enolase	−3.2	−2.4
0	PK	−23.0	−13.9

Calculated from data in Newsholme, E.A. and Start, C., *Regulation in Metabolism,* p. 97, Wiley (1973).

compounds act are determined from their effects on the enzymes' kinetics.

3. Measurement of the *in vivo* levels of the proposed regulators under various conditions to establish whether the concentration changes are consistent with the proposed control mechanism.

Let us examine the thermodynamics of glycolysis in muscle tissue with an eye toward understanding its control mechanisms (keep in mind that different tissues control glycolysis in different ways). Table 15-1 lists the standard free energy changes ($\Delta G^{\circ\prime}$) and the actual physiological free energy change (ΔG) associated with each reaction in the pathway. It is important to realize that the free energy changes associated with the reactions under standard conditions may differ dramatically from the actual values *in vivo*.

Only three reactions of glycolysis, those catalyzed by hexokinase, phosphofructokinase, and pyruvate kinase, function with large negative free energy changes in heart muscle under physiological conditions (Fig. 15-21). These nonequilibrium reactions of glycolysis are candidates for flux-control points. The other glycolytic reactions function near equilibrium: Their forward and reverse rates are much faster than the actual flux through the pathway. Consequently, these equilibrium reactions are very sensitive to changes in the concentration of pathway intermediates and readily accommodate changes in flux generated at the rate-determining step(s) of the pathway.

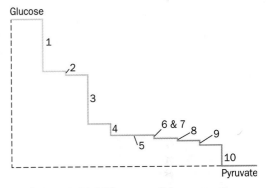

■ **Figure 15-21** | **Diagram of free energy changes in glycolysis.** This "waterfall" diagram illustrates the actual free energy changes for the glycolytic reactions in heart muscle (Table 15-1). Reactions 1, 3, and 10 are irreversible. The other reactions operate near equilibrium and can mediate flux in either direction.

A | Phosphofructokinase Is the Major Flux-Controlling Enzyme of Glycolysis in Muscle

In vitro studies of hexokinase, phosphofructokinase, and pyruvate kinase indicate that each is controlled by a variety of compounds. Yet when the G6P source for glycolysis is glycogen, rather than glucose, as is often the case in skeletal muscle, the hexokinase reaction is not required (Section 16-1). Pyruvate kinase catalyzes the last reaction of glycolysis and is therefore unlikely to be the primary point for regulating flux through the entire pathway. Evidently, PFK, an elaborately regulated enzyme functioning far from equilibrium, is the major control point for glycolysis in muscle under most conditions.

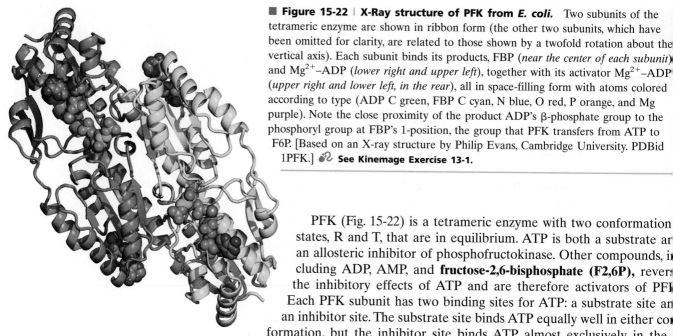

■ **Figure 15-22** I **X-Ray structure of PFK from *E. coli*.** Two subunits of the tetrameric enzyme are shown in ribbon form (the other two subunits, which have been omitted for clarity, are related to those shown by a twofold rotation about the vertical axis). Each subunit binds its products, FBP (*near the center of each subunit*) and Mg^{2+}–ADP (*lower right and upper left*), together with its activator Mg^{2+}–ADP (*upper right and lower left, in the rear*), all in space-filling form with atoms colored according to type (ADP C green, FBP C cyan, N blue, O red, P orange, and Mg purple). Note the close proximity of the product ADP's β-phosphate group to the phosphoryl group at FBP's 1-position, the group that PFK transfers from ATP to F6P. [Based on an X-ray structure by Philip Evans, Cambridge University. PDBid 1PFK.] *See Kinemage Exercise 13-1.*

PFK (Fig. 15-22) is a tetrameric enzyme with two conformation states, R and T, that are in equilibrium. ATP is both a substrate and an allosteric inhibitor of phosphofructokinase. Other compounds, including ADP, AMP, and **fructose-2,6-bisphosphate (F2,6P),** revers the inhibitory effects of ATP and are therefore activators of PFK Each PFK subunit has two binding sites for ATP: a substrate site and an inhibitor site. The substrate site binds ATP equally well in either conformation, but the inhibitor site binds ATP almost exclusively in the state. The other substrate of PFK, F6P, preferentially binds to the R stat Consequently, at high concentrations, ATP acts as an allosteric inhibitor of PFK by binding to the T state, thereby shifting the T $\rightleftharpoons$ R equilibrium in favor of the T state and thus decreasing PFK's affinity for F6P (this similar to the action of 2,3-BPG in decreasing the affinity of hemoglobin for O_2; Section 7-1D).

In graphical terms, high concentrations of ATP shift the curve of PFK activity versus [F6P] to the right and make it even more sigmoidal (cooperative) (Fig. 15-23). For example, when [F6P] = 0.5 mM (the dashed line in Fig. 15-23), the enzyme is nearly maximally active, but in the presence of 1 mM ATP, the activity drops to 15% of its original level, a nearly sever fold decrease. An activator such as AMP or ADP counters the effect of ATP by binding to R-state PFK, thereby shifting the T $\rightleftharpoons$ R equilibrium toward the R state. (Actually, the most potent allosteric effector of PFK is F2,6P, which we discuss in Section 16-4C.)

Allosterism in Phosphofructokinase Involves Arg and Glu Side Chains. The X-ray structures of PFK from several organisms have been determined in both the R and the T states by Philip Evans. The R stat of PFK is stabilized by the binding of its substrate F6P. In the R state of *Bacillus stearothermophilus* PFK, the side chain of Arg 162 forms an io pair with the phosphoryl group of an F6P bound in the active site of another subunit (Fig. 15-24). However, Arg 162 is located at the end of helical turn that unwinds on transition to the T state. The positively charged side chain of Arg 162 thereby swings away and is replaced by th negatively charged side chain of Glu 161. As a consequence, the doubly negative phosphoryl group of F6P has a greatly diminished affinity for the T-state enzyme. The unwinding of this helical turn, which is obligatory for the R → T transition, is prevented by the binding of the activator ADP to its effector site on the enzyme. Presumably, ATP can bind to this site only when the helical turn is in its unwound conformation (the T state).

AMP Overcomes the ATP Inhibition of PFK. Direct allosteric regulation of PFK by ATP may at first appear to be the means by which

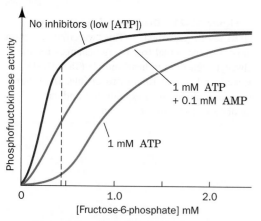

■ **Figure 15-23** I **PFK activity versus F6P concentration.** The various conditions are as follows: purple, no inhibitors or activators; green, 1 mM ATP; and red, 1 mM ATP + 0.1 mM AMP. [After data from Mansour, T.E. and Ahlfors, C.E., *J. Biol. Chem.* **243**, 2523–2533 (1968).] *See the Animated Figures.*

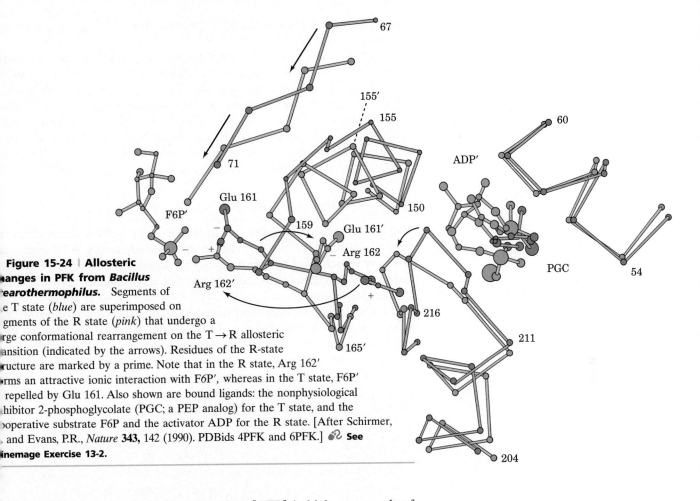

Figure 15-24 | Allosteric changes in PFK from *Bacillus stearothermophilus.* Segments of the T state (*blue*) are superimposed on segments of the R state (*pink*) that undergo a large conformational rearrangement on the T → R allosteric transition (indicated by the arrows). Residues of the R-state structure are marked by a prime. Note that in the R state, Arg 162′ forms an attractive ionic interaction with F6P′, whereas in the T state, F6P′ is repelled by Glu 161. Also shown are bound ligands: the nonphysiological inhibitor 2-phosphoglycolate (PGC; a PEP analog) for the T state, and the cooperative substrate F6P and the activator ADP for the R state. [After Schirmer, T. and Evans, P.R., *Nature* **343**, 142 (1990). PDBids 4PFK and 6PFK.] ⟲ **See Kinemage Exercise 13-2.**

glycolytic flux is controlled. After all, when [ATP] is high as a result of low metabolic demand, PFK is inhibited and flux through glycolysis is low; conversely when [ATP] is low, flux through the pathway is high and ATP is synthesized to replenish the pool. Consideration of the physiological variation in ATP concentration, however, indicates that the situation must be more complex. The metabolic flux through glycolysis may vary by 100-fold or more, depending on the metabolic demand for ATP. However, *measurements of [ATP] in vivo at various levels of metabolic activity indicate that [ATP] varies <10% between rest and vigorous exertion.* Yet there is no known allosteric mechanism that can account for a 100-fold change in flux of a nonequilibrium reaction with only a 10% change in effector concentration. Thus, some other mechanism(s) must be responsible for controlling glycolytic flux.

The inhibition of PFK by ATP is relieved by AMP as well as ADP. This results from AMP's preferential binding to the R state of PFK. If a PFK solution containing 1 mM ATP and 0.5 mM F6P is brought to 0.1 mM in AMP, the activity of PFK rises from 15 to 50% of its maximal activity, a threefold increase (Fig. 15-23).

The [ATP] decreases by only 10% in going from a resting state to one of vigorous activity because it is buffered by the action of two enzymes: creatine kinase and adenylate kinase (Section 14-2C). Adenylate kinase catalyzes the reaction

$$2\,ADP \rightleftharpoons ATP + AMP \qquad K = \frac{[ATP][AMP]}{[ADP]^2} = 0.44$$

which rapidly equilibrates the ADP resulting from ATP hydrolysis in mu
cle contraction with ATP and AMP.

In muscle, [ATP] is ~50 times greater than [AMP] and ~10 time
greater than [ADP]. Consequently, *a change in [ATP] from, for example
1 to 0.9 mM, a 10% decrease, can result in a 100% increase in [ADP] (from
0.1 to 0.2 mM) as a result of the adenylate kinase reaction, and a >400%
increase in [AMP] (from 0.02 to ~0.1 mM)*. Therefore, a metabolic signal
consisting of a decrease in [ATP] too small to relieve PFK inhibition
amplified significantly by the adenylate kinase reaction, which increase
[AMP] by an amount that produces a much larger increase in PFK activity

B | Substrate Cycling Fine-Tunes Flux Control

Even a finely tuned allosteric mechanism like that of PFK can account fo
only a fraction of the 100-fold alterations in glycolytic flux. Additional con
trol may be achieved by substrate cycling. Recall from Section 14-1D tha
only a near-equilibrium reaction can undergo large changes in flux becaus
in a near-equilibrium reaction, $v_f - v_r \approx 0$ (where v_f and v_r are the forwar
and reverse reaction rates) and hence a small change in v_f will result in
large fractional change in $v_f - v_r$. However, this is not the case for the PF
reaction because, for such nonequilibrium reactions, v_r is negligible.

Nevertheless, *such equilibrium-like conditions may be imposed on
nonequilibrium reaction if a second enzyme (or series of enzymes) catalyze
the regeneration of its substrate from its product in a thermodynamicall
favorable manner.* This can be diagrammed as

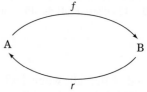

Since two different enzymes catalyze the forward (f) and reverse (r
reactions, v_f and v_r may be independently varied and v_r is no longer neg
ligible compared to v_f. Note that the forward process (e.g., formation c
FBP from F6P) and the reverse process (e.g., breakdown of FBP to F6P
must be carried out by different enzymes since the laws of thermodynam
ics would otherwise be violated (i.e., for a single reaction, the forward an
reverse reactions cannot simultaneously be favorable).

Under physiological conditions, the reaction catalyzed by PFK:

$$\text{F6P} + \text{ATP} \longrightarrow \text{FBP} + \text{ADP}$$

is highly exergonic ($\Delta G = -25.9 \text{ kJ} \cdot \text{mol}^{-1}$). Consequently, the back reac
tion has a negligible rate compared to the forward reaction. **Fructose-1,6
bisphosphatase (FBPase),** however, which is present in many mammalia
tissues (and which is an essential enzyme in gluconeogenesis; Section 16-4B
catalyzes the exergonic hydrolysis of FBP ($\Delta G = -8.6 \text{ kJ} \cdot \text{mol}^{-1}$).

$$\text{FBP} + \text{H}_2\text{O} \longrightarrow \text{F6P} + \text{P}_i$$

Note that the combined reactions catalyzed by PFK and FBPase result in
net ATP hydrolysis:

$$\text{ATP} + \text{H}_2\text{O} \rightleftharpoons \text{ADP} + \text{P}_i$$

Such a set of opposing reactions (Section 14-1E) is known as a **substrate
cycle** because it cycles a substrate to an intermediate and back again
When this set of reactions was discovered, it was referred to as a **futile
cycle** since its net result seemed to be the useless consumption of ATP.

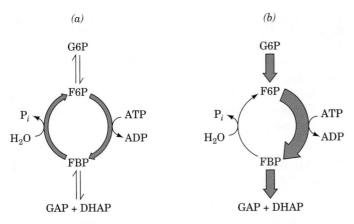

(a)   (b)

■ **Figure 15-25** | **Substrate cycling in the regulation of PFK.** (*a*) In resting muscle, both enzymes in the F6P/FBP substrate cycle are active, and glycolytic flux is low. (*b*) In active muscle, PFK activity increases while FBPase activity decreases. This dramatically increases the flux through PFK and therefore results in high glycolytic flux.

Eric Newsholme has proposed that substrate cycles are not at all "futile" but, rather, have a regulatory function. *The combined effects of allosteric effectors on the opposing reactions of a substrate cycle can produce a much greater fractional effect on pathway flux* ($v_f - v_r$) *than is possible through allosteric regulation of a single enzyme.* For example, the allosteric effector F2,6P activates the PFK reaction while inhibiting the FBPase reaction (this regulatory mechanism is important for balancing glycolysis and gluconeogenesis in liver cells; Section 16-4C).

Substrate cycling does not increase the maximum flux through a pathway. On the contrary, it functions to decrease the minimum flux. In a sense, the substrate is put into a "holding pattern." In the PFK/FBPase example (Fig. 15-25), the cycling of substrate appears to be the energetic "price" that a muscle must pay to be able to change rapidly from a resting state (where $v_f - v_r$ is small), in which substrate cycling is maximal, to one of sustained high activity (where $v_f - v_r$ is large). The rate of substrate cycling itself may be under hormonal or neuronal control so as to increase the sensitivity of the metabolic system under conditions when high activity (fight or flight) is anticipated.

Substrate cycling and other mechanisms that control PFK activity *in vivo* are part of larger systems that regulate all the cell's metabolic activities. At one time, it was believed that because PFK is the controlling enzyme of glycolysis, increasing its level of expression via genetic engineering would increase flux through glycolysis. However, this is not the case, because the *activity* of PFK, whatever its concentration, is ultimately controlled by factors that reflect the cell's demand for the products supplied by glycolysis and all other metabolic pathways.

Substrate Cycling Is Related to Thermogenesis and Obesity. Many animals, including adult humans, are thought to generate much of their body heat, particularly when it is cold, through substrate cycling in muscle and liver, a process known as **nonshivering thermogenesis** (the muscle contractions of shivering or any other movement also produce heat). Substrate cycling is stimulated by thyroid hormones (which stimulate metabolism in most tissues) as is indicated, for example, by the observation that rats lacking a functional thyroid gland do not survive at 5°C. Chronically obese individuals tend to have lower than normal metabolic rates, which is probably due, in part, to a reduced rate of nonshivering thermogenesis. Such individuals therefore tend to be cold sensitive. Indeed, whereas normal individuals increase their rate of thyroid hormone activation on exposure to cold, genetically obese animals and obese humans fail to do so.

■ **CHECK YOUR UNDERSTANDING**

Which glycolytic enzymes are potential control points?

Describe the mechanisms that control phosphofructokinase activity.

What is the metabolic advantage of a substrate cycle?

5 Metabolism of Hexoses Other than Glucose

LEARNING OBJECTIVE

■ Understand that the commonly available hexoses are converted to glycolytic intermediates for further metabolism.

Together with glucose, the hexoses fructose, galactose, and mannose are prominent metabolic fuels. After digestion, these monosaccharides enter the bloodstream, which carries them to various tissues. Fructose, galactose, and mannose are converted to glycolytic intermediates that are then metabolized by the glycolytic pathway (Fig. 15-26).

A | Fructose Is Converted to Fructose-6-Phosphate or Glyceraldehyde-3-Phosphate

Fructose is a major fuel source in diets that contain large amounts of fruit or sucrose (a disaccharide of fructose and glucose; Section 8-2A). There are two pathways for the metabolism of fructose; one occurs in muscle and the other occurs in liver. This dichotomy results from the different enzymes present in these tissues.

Fructose metabolism in muscle differs little from that of glucose. Hexokinase (Section 15-2A), which converts glucose to G6P, also phosphorylates fructose, yielding F6P (Fig. 15-27, *left*). The entry of fructose into glycolysis therefore involves only one reaction step.

Liver contains a hexokinase known as **glucokinase,** which has a low affinity for hexoses, including fructose (Section 22-1D). Fructose metabolism in liver must therefore differ from that in muscle. In fact, liver converts fructose to glycolytic intermediates through a pathway that involves seven enzymes (Fig. 15-27, *right*):

1. **Fructokinase** catalyzes the phosphorylation of fructose by ATP at C1 to form **fructose-1-phosphate.** Neither hexokinase nor PFK can phosphorylate fructose-1-phosphate at C6 to form the glycolytic intermediate FBP.

2. Aldolase (Section 15-2D) has several isozymic forms. Muscle contains Type A aldolase, which is specific for FBP. Liver, however, contains Type B aldolase, for which fructose-1-phosphate is also a substrate (Type B aldolase is sometimes called **fructose-1-phosphate aldolase**). In liver, fructose-1-phosphate therefore undergoes an aldol cleavage:

   Fructose-1-phosphate $\rightleftharpoons$
   $$\text{dihydroxyacetone phosphate + glyceraldehyde}$$

3. Direct phosphorylation of **glyceraldehyde** by ATP through the action of **glyceraldehyde kinase** forms the glycolytic intermediate GAP.

4–7. Alternatively, glyceraldehyde is converted to the glycolytic intermediate DHAP by its NADH-dependent reduction to glycerol as catalyzed by alcohol dehydrogenase (Reaction 4), phosphorylation to **glycerol-3-phosphate** through the action of **glycerol kinase** (Reaction 5), and NAD$^+$-dependent reoxidation to DHAP catalyzed by **glycerol phosphate dehydrogenase** (Reaction 6). The DHAP is then converted to GAP by triose phosphate isomerase (Reaction 7).

The two pathways leading from glyceraldehyde to GAP have the same net cost: Both consume ATP, and although NADH is oxidized in Reaction 4, it is reduced again in Reaction 6. The longer pathway, however, produces glycerol-3-phosphate, which (along with DHAP) can become the glycerol backbone of glycerophospholipids and triacylglycerols (Section 20-6A).

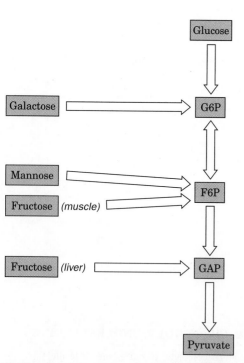

■ **Figure 15-26** | **Entry of other hexoses into glycolysis.** Fructose (in muscle) and mannose are converted to F6P; liver fructose is converted to GAP; and galactose is converted to G6P.

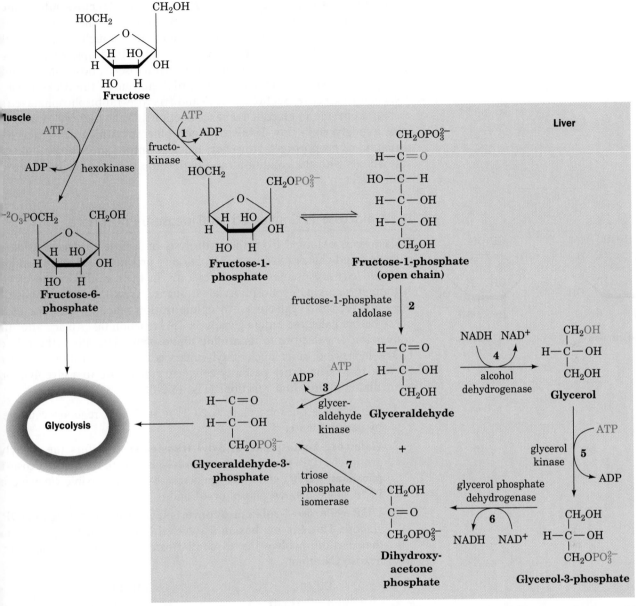

Figure 15-27 | The metabolism of fructose. In muscle (left), the conversion of fructose to the glycolytic intermediate F6P involves only one enzyme, hexokinase. In liver (right), seven enzymes participate in the conversion of fructose to glycolytic intermediates: (**1**) fructokinase, (**2**) fructose-1-phosphate aldolase, (**3**) glyceraldehyde kinase, (**4**) alcohol dehydrogenase, (**5**) glycerol kinase, (**6**) glycerol phosphate dehydrogenase, and (**7**) triose phosphate isomerase.

Is Excess Fructose Harmful? The consumption of fructose in the United States has increased at least 10-fold in the last quarter century, in large part due to the use of high-fructose corn syrup as a sweetener in soft drinks and other foods. Fructose has a sweeter taste than sucrose (Box 8-2) and is inexpensive to produce. One possible hazard of excessive fructose intake is that fructose catabolism in liver bypasses the PFK-catalyzed step of glycolysis and thereby avoids a major metabolic control point. This could potentially disrupt fuel metabolism so that glycolytic flux is directed toward lipid synthesis in the absence of a need for ATP production. This hypothesis suggests a link between the increase in both fructose consumption and the recently increasing incidence of obesity in the United States.

At the opposite extreme are individuals with **fructose intolerance**, which results from a deficiency in Type B aldolase. In the absence of this aldolase, fructose-1-phosphate may accumulate enough to deplete the liver's store of P_i. Under these conditions, [ATP] drops, which causes liver damage. In addition, the increased [fructose-1-phosphate] inhibits both **glycogen phosphorylase** (an essential enzyme in the breakdown of glycogen to glucose; Section 16-1A) and fructose-1,6-bisphosphatase (an essential enzyme in gluconeogenesis; Section 16-4B), thereby causing severe **hypoglycemia** (low levels of blood glucose), which can reach life threatening proportions. However, fructose intolerance is self-limiting. Individuals with the condition rapidly develop a strong distaste for anything sweet.

B | Galactose Is Converted to Glucose-6-Phosphate

Galactose is obtained from the hydrolysis of lactose (a disaccharide of galactose and glucose; Section 8-2A) in dairy products. Galactose and glucose (*at left*) are epimers that differ only in their configuration at C4. Although hexokinase phosphorylates glucose, fructose, and mannose, it does not recognize galactose. An epimerization reaction must therefore occur before galactose enters glycolysis. This reaction takes place after the conversion of galactose to its **uridine diphosphate** derivative (the role of UDP–sugars and other nucleotidyl–sugars is discussed in more detail in Section 16-5). The entire pathway converting galactose to a glycolytic intermediate requires four reactions (Fig. 15-28):

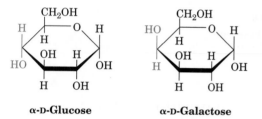

α-D-Glucose   α-D-Galactose

1. Galactose is phosphorylated at C1 by ATP in a reaction catalyzed by **galactokinase.**

2. **Galactose-1-phosphate uridylyl transferase** transfers the uridylyl group of UDP–glucose to **galactose-1-phosphate** to yield **glucose-1-phosphate (G1P)** and **UDP–galactose** by the reversible cleavage of UDP–glucose's pyrophosphoryl bond.

3. **UDP–galactose-4-epimerase** converts UDP–galactose back to UDP–glucose. This enzyme has an associated NAD^+, which suggests that the reaction involves the sequential oxidation and reduction of the hexose C4 atom:

UDP–Galactose   **UDP–Glucose**

NAD^+ NAD^+

NADH   NADH

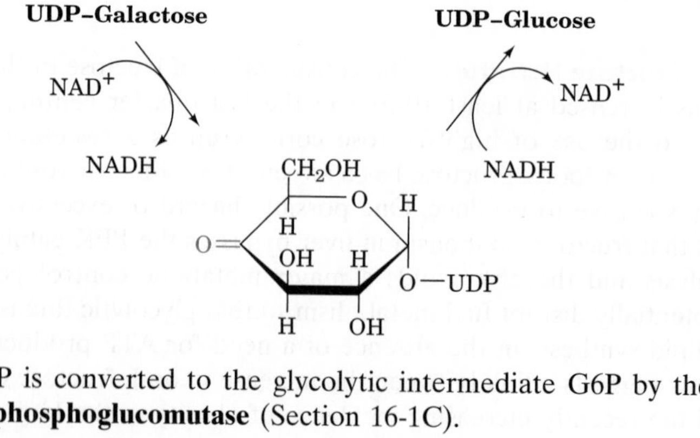

4. G1P is converted to the glycolytic intermediate G6P by the action of **phosphoglucomutase** (Section 16-1C).

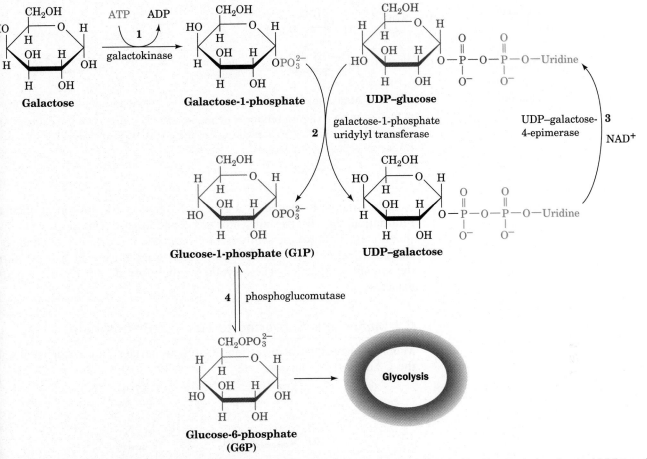

■ **Figure 15-28** | **The metabolism of galactose.** Four enzymes participate in the conversion of galactose to the glycolytic intermediate G6P: (**1**) galactokinase, (**2**) galactose-1-phosphate uridylyl transferase, (**3**) UDP–galactose-4-epimerase, and (**4**) phosphoglucomutase.

Individuals with Galactosemia Cannot Metabolize Galactose.

Galactosemia is a genetic disease characterized by the inability to convert galactose to glucose. Its symptoms include failure to thrive, mental retardation, and, in some instances, death from liver damage. Most cases of galactosemia involve a deficiency in the enzyme catalyzing Reaction 2 of the interconversion, galactose-1-phosphate uridylyl transferase. Formation of UDP–galactose from galactose-1-phosphate is thus prevented, leading to a buildup of toxic metabolic by-products. For example, the increased galactose concentration in the blood results in a higher galactose concentration in the lens of the eye, where the sugar is reduced to **galactitol:**

$$
\begin{array}{c}
CH_2OH \\
| \\
H-C-OH \\
| \\
HO-C-H \\
| \\
HO-C-H \\
| \\
H-C-OH \\
| \\
CH_2OH
\end{array}
$$

Galactitol

The presence of this sugar alcohol in the lens eventually causes cataract formation (clouding of the lens).

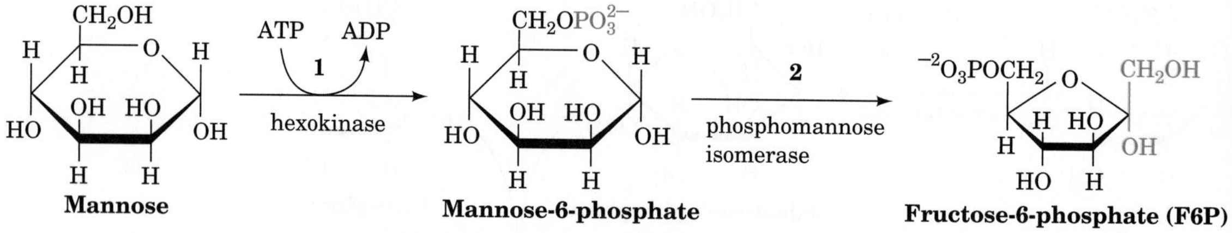

Figure 15-29 | The metabolism of mannose. Two enzymes are required to convert mannose to the glycolytic intermediate F6P: (**1**) hexokinase and (**2**) phosphomannose isomerase.

Galactosemia is treated by a galactose-free diet. Except for the mental retardation, this reverses all symptoms of the disease. The galactosyl units that are essential for the synthesis of glycoproteins (Section 8-3C) and glycolipids (Section 9-1D) can be synthesized from glucose by a reversal of the epimerase reaction. These syntheses therefore do not require dietary galactose.

C | Mannose Is Converted to Fructose-6-Phosphate

Mannose, a product of digestion of polysaccharides and glycoproteins, is the C2 epimer of glucose:

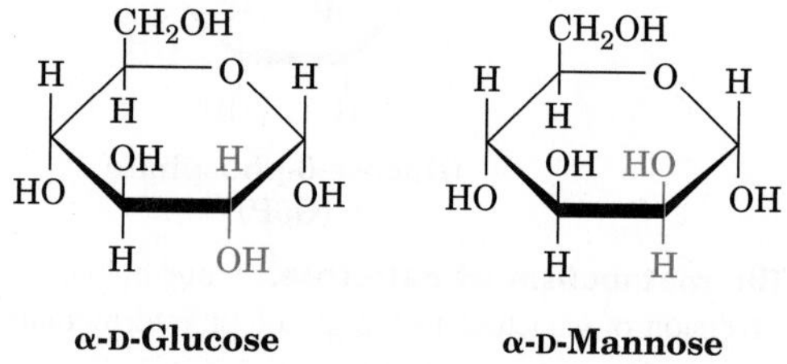

Mannose enters the glycolytic pathway after its conversion to F6P via a two-reaction pathway (Fig. 15-29):

1. Hexokinase recognizes mannose and converts it to **mannose-6-phosphate.**
2. **Phosphomannose isomerase** then converts this aldose to the glycolytic intermediate F6P in a reaction whose mechanism resembles that of phosphoglucose isomerase (Section 15-2B).

■ **CHECK YOUR UNDERSTANDING**

Describe how fructose, galactose, and mannose enter the glycolytic pathway.

6 The Pentose Phosphate Pathway

LEARNING OBJECTIVES

■ Understand that the pentose phosphate pathway consists of three stages, in which NADPH is produced, pentoses undergo isomerization, and glycolytic intermediates are recovered.
■ Understand that the pathway provides NADPH for reductive biosynthesis and ribose-5-phosphate for nucleotide biosynthesis in the quantities that the cell requires.

ATP is the cell's "energy currency"; its exergonic cleavage is coupled to many otherwise endergonic cell functions. *Cells also have a second currency, reducing power.* Many endergonic reactions, notably the reductive biosynthesis of fatty acids (Section 20-4) and cholesterol (Section 20-7A), require NADPH in addition to ATP. Despite their close chemical resemblance, *NADPH and NADH are not metabolically interchangeable.* Whereas NADH uses the free energy of metabolite oxidation to synthesize ATP (oxidative phosphorylation), NADPH uses the free energy of metabolite oxidation for reductive biosynthesis. This differentiation is possible because the dehydrogenases involved in oxidative and reductive metabolism are highly specific for their respective coenzymes. Indeed, cells normally maintain their [NAD$^+$]/[NADH] ratio near 1000, which favors metabolite oxidation, while keeping their $[NADP^+]/[NADPH]$ ratio near 0.01, which favors reductive biosynthesis.

NADPH is generated by the oxidation of glucose-6-phosphate via an alternative pathway to glycolysis, the pentose phosphate pathway (also called the **hexose monophosphate shunt;** Fig. 15-30). Tissues most heavily involved in lipid biosynthesis (liver, mammary gland, adipose tissue, and

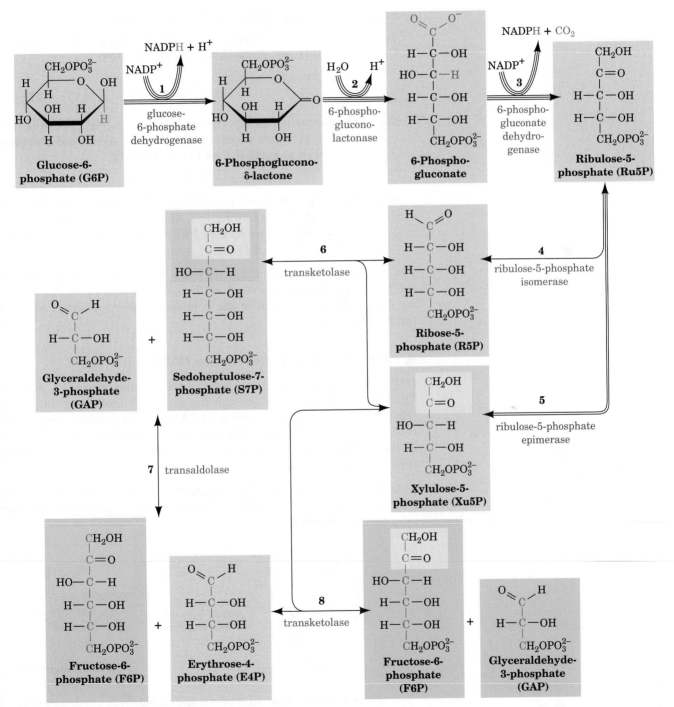

■ **Figure 15-30 | The pentose phosphate pathway.** The number of lines in an arrow represents the number of molecules reacting in one turn of the pathway so as to convert 3 G6P to 3 CO_2, 2 F6P, and 1 GAP. For the sake of clarity, sugars from Reaction 3 onward are shown in their linear forms. The carbon skeleton of R5P and the atoms derived from it are drawn in red, and those from Xu5P are drawn in green. The C_2 units transferred by transketolase are shaded in green, and the C_3 units transferred by transaldolase are shaded in blue. Double-headed arrows indicate reversible reactions.

adrenal cortex) are rich in pentose phosphate pathway enzymes. Indeed some 30% of the glucose oxidation in liver occurs via the pentose phosphate pathway rather than glycolysis.

The overall reaction of the pentose phosphate pathway is

$$3\ G6P + 6\ NADP^+ + 3\ H_2O \rightleftharpoons$$
$$6\ NADPH + 6\ H^+ + 3\ CO_2 + 2\ F6P + GAP$$

However, the pathway can be considered to have three stages:

Stage 1 Oxidative reactions (Fig. 15-30, Reactions 1–3), which yield NADPH and **ribulose-5-phosphate (Ru5P):**

$$3\ G6P + 6\ NADP^+ + 3\ H_2O \longrightarrow$$
$$6\ NADPH + 6\ H^+ + 3\ CO_2 + 3\ Ru5P$$

Stage 2 Isomerization and epimerization reactions (Fig. 15-30, Reactions 4 and 5), which transform Ru5P either to **ribose-5-phosphate (R5P)** or to **xylulose-5-phosphate (Xu5P):**

$$3\ Ru5P \rightleftharpoons R5P + 2\ Xu5P$$

Stage 3 A series of C—C bond cleavage and formation reactions (Fig. 15-30, Reactions 6–8) that convert two molecules of Xu5P and one molecule of R5P to two molecules of F6P and one molecule of GAP.

The reactions of Stages 2 and 3 are freely reversible, so the products of the pathway vary with the needs of the cell (see below). In this section, we discuss the three stages of the pentose phosphate pathway and how the pathway is controlled.

A | Oxidative Reactions Produce NADPH in Stage 1

G6P is considered the starting point of the pentose phosphate pathway. This metabolite may arise through the action of hexokinase on glucose (Reaction 1 of glycolysis; Section 15-2A) or from glycogen breakdown (which produces G6P directly; Section 16-1). Only the first three reactions of the pentose phosphate pathway are involved in NADPH production (Fig. 15-30):

1. **Glucose-6-phosphate dehydrogenase (G6PD)** catalyzes net transfer of a hydride ion to $NADP^+$ from C1 of G6P to form **6-phospho-glucono-δ-lactone:**

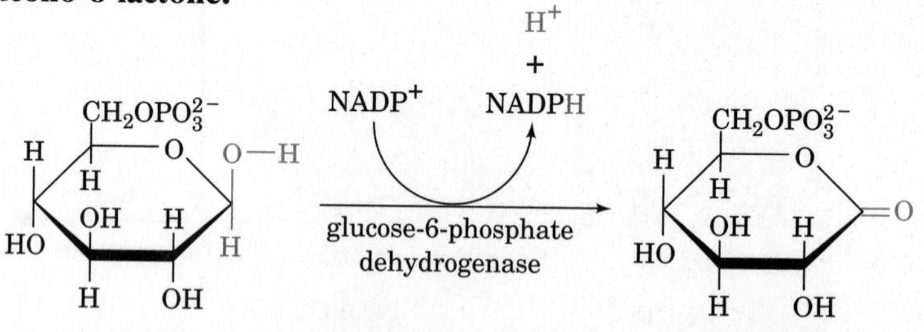

G6P   glucose-6-phosphate dehydrogenase   **6-Phosphoglucono-δ-lactone**

G6P, a cyclic hemiacetal with C1 in the aldehyde oxidation state, is thereby oxidized to a cyclic ester (lactone). The enzyme is specific for $NADP^+$ and is strongly inhibited by NADPH.

2. **6-Phosphogluconolactonase** increases the rate of hydrolysis of 6-phosphoglucono-δ-lactone to **6-phosphogluconate** (the nonenzymatic reaction occurs at a significant rate).

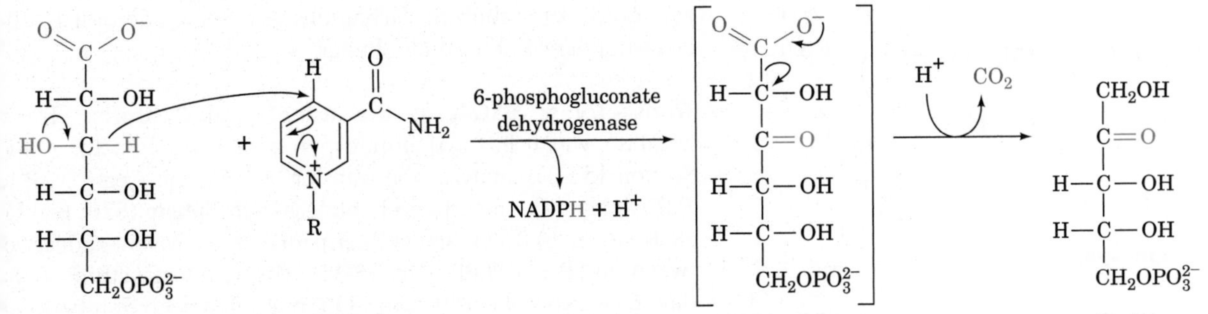

Figure 15-31 | The 6-phosphogluconate dehydrogenase reaction. Oxidation of the OH group forms an easily decarboxylated β-keto acid (although the proposed intermediate has not been isolated).

3. **6-Phosphogluconate dehydrogenase** catalyzes the oxidative decarboxylation of 6-phosphogluconate, a β-hydroxy acid, to Ru5P and CO_2 (Fig. 15-31). This reaction is thought to proceed via the formation of a β-keto acid intermediate. The keto group presumably facilitates decarboxylation by acting as an electron sink.

Formation of Ru5P completes the oxidative portion of the pentose phosphate pathway. *It generates two molecules of NADPH for each molecule of G6P that enters the pathway.*

B | Isomerization and Epimerization of Ribulose-5-Phosphate Occur in Stage 2

Ru5P is converted to R5P by **ribulose-5-phosphate isomerase** (Fig. 15-30, Reaction 4) or to Xu5P by **ribulose-5-phosphate epimerase** (Fig. 15-30, Reaction 5). These isomerization and epimerization reactions, like the reaction catalyzed by triose phosphate isomerase (Section 15-2E), are thought to occur via enediolate intermediates.

The relative amounts of R5P and Xu5P produced from Ru5P depend on the needs of the cell. For example, R5P is an essential precursor in the biosynthesis of nucleotides (Chapter 23). Accordingly, R5P production is relatively high (in fact, the entire pentose phosphate pathway activity may be elevated) in rapidly dividing cells, in which the rate of DNA synthesis is increased. If the pathway is being used solely for NADPH production, Xu5P and R5P are produced in a 2:1 ratio for conversion to glycolytic intermediates in the third stage of the pentose phosphate pathway as is discussed below.

C | Stage 3 Involves Carbon–Carbon Bond Cleavage and Formation

How is a five-carbon sugar transformed to a six-carbon sugar such as F6P? The rearrangements of carbon atoms in the third stage of the pentose phosphate pathway are easier to follow by considering the stoichiometry of the pathway. Every three G6P molecules that enter the pathway yield three Ru5P molecules in Stage 1. These three pentoses are then converted to one R5P and two Xu5P (Fig. 15-30, Reactions 4 and 5). The conversion of these three C_5 sugars to two C_6 sugars and one C_3 sugar involves a remarkable "juggling act" catalyzed by two enzymes, **transaldolase** and **transketolase**. These enzymes have mechanisms that involve the

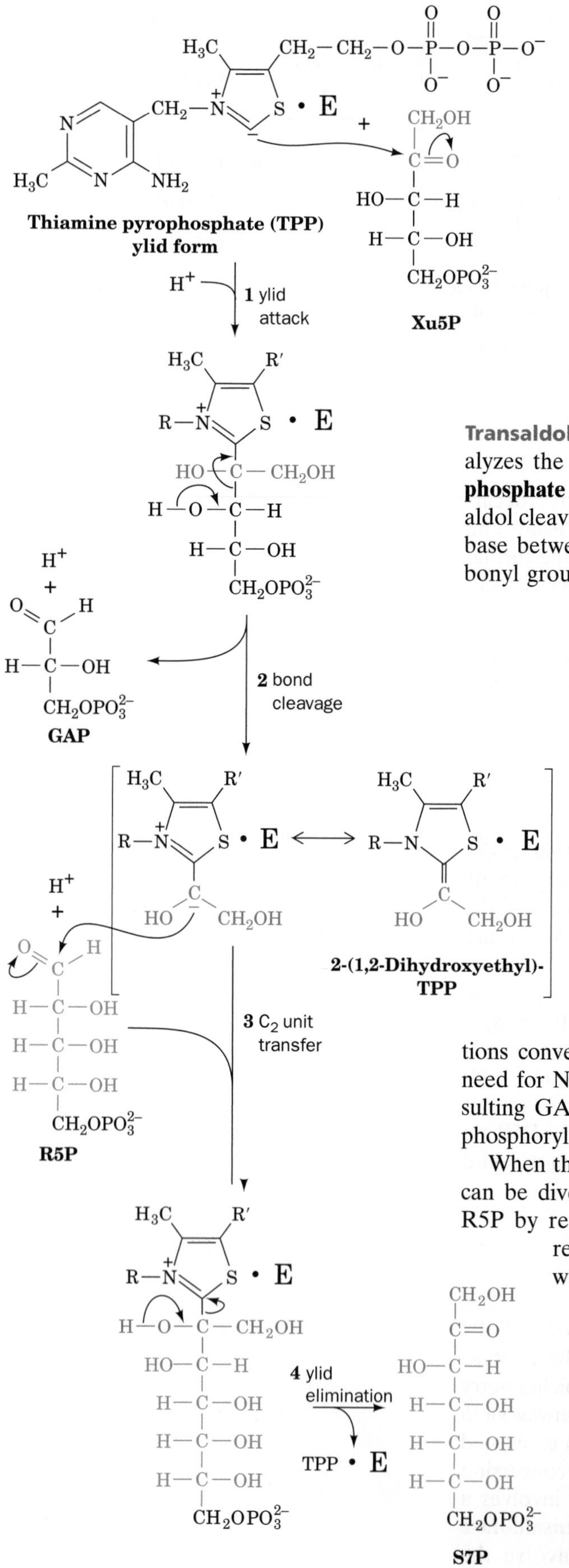

Thiamine pyrophosphate (TPP) ylid form

H_3C ... $CH_2-CH_2-O-P-O-P-O^-$

Thiamine pyrophosphate (TPP) ylid form

CH_2OH
$C=O$
$HO-C-H$
$H-C-OH$
$CH_2OPO_3^{2-}$

Xu5P

H^+ **1** ylid attack

H_3C ... R'
$R-N ... S \cdot E$
$HO-C-CH_2OH$
$H-O-C-H$
$H-C-OH$
$CH_2OPO_3^{2-}$

H^+
$O=C-H$
$H-C-OH$
$CH_2OPO_3^{2-}$

GAP

2 bond cleavage

H_3C ... R' H_3C ... R'
$R-N ... S \cdot E \longleftrightarrow R-N ... S \cdot E$
$HO ... C ... CH_2OH$ $HO ... C ... CH_2OH$

2-(1,2-Dihydroxyethyl)-TPP

H^+
$O ... C ... H$
$H-C-OH$
$H-C-OH$
$H-C-OH$
$CH_2OPO_3^{2-}$

R5P

3 C_2 unit transfer

H_3C ... R'
$R-N ... S \cdot E$
$H-O-C-CH_2OH$
$HO-C-H$
$H-C-OH$
$H-C-OH$
$H-C-OH$
$CH_2OPO_3^{2-}$

4 ylid elimination

$TPP \cdot E$

CH_2OH
$C=O$
$HO-C-H$
$H-C-OH$
$H-C-OH$
$H-C-OH$
$CH_2OPO_3^{2-}$

S7P

generation of stabilized carbanions and their addition to the electrophilic centers of aldehydes.

Transketolase Catalyzes the Transfer of C_2 Units. Transketolase, which has a thiamine pyrophosphate cofactor (TPP; Section 15-3B), catalyzes the transfer of a C_2 unit from Xu5P to R5P, yielding GAP and **sedoheptulose-7-phosphate** (**S7P**; Fig. 15-30, Reaction 6). The reaction intermediate is a covalent adduct between Xu5P and TPP (Fig. 15-32). The X-ray structure of the dimeric enzyme shows that the TPP binds in a deep cleft between the subunits so that residues from both subunits participate in its binding, just as in pyruvate decarboxylase (another TPP-requiring enzyme; Fig. 15-19). In fact, the structures are so similar that the enzymes likely diverged from a common ancestor.

Transaldolase Catalyzes the Transfer of C_3 Units. Transaldolase catalyzes the transfer of a C_3 unit from S7P to GAP yielding **erythrose-4-phosphate** (**E4P**) and F6P (Fig. 15-30, Reaction 7). The reaction occurs by aldol cleavage (Section 15-2D), which begins with the formation of a Schiff base between an ε-amino group of an essential Lys residue and the carbonyl group of S7P (Fig. 15-33).

A Second Transketolase Reaction Yields Glyceraldehyde-3-Phosphate and a Second Fructose-6-Phosphate Molecule. In a second transketolase reaction, a C_2 unit is transferred from a second molecule of Xu5P to E4P to form GAP and another molecule of F6P (Fig. 15-30, Reaction 8). The third stage of the pentose phosphate pathway thus transforms two molecules of Xu5P and one of R5P to two molecules of F6P and one molecule of GAP. These carbon skeleton transformations (Fig. 15-30, Reactions 6–8) are summarized in Fig. 15-34.

D | The Pentose Phosphate Pathway Must Be Regulated

The principal products of the pentose phosphate pathway are R5P and NADPH. The transaldolase and transketolase reactions convert excess R5P to glycolytic intermediates when the metabolic need for NADPH exceeds that of R5P in nucleotide biosynthesis. The resulting GAP and F6P can be consumed through glycolysis and oxidative phosphorylation or recycled by gluconeogenesis (Section 16-4) to form G6P.

When the need for R5P outstrips the need for NADPH, F6P and GAP can be diverted from the glycolytic pathway for use in the synthesis of R5P by reversal of the transaldolase and transketolase reactions. The relationship between glycolysis and the pentose phosphate pathway is diagrammed in Fig. 15-35.

■ **Figure 15-32 | Mechanism of transketolase.** Transketolase (represented by E) uses the coenzyme TPP to stabilize the carbanion formed on cleavage of the C2—C3 bond of Xu5P. The reaction occurs as follows: (**1**) The TPP ylid attacks the carbonyl group of the Xu5P; (**2**) C2—C3 bond cleavage yields GAP and enzyme-bound 2-(1,2-dihydroxyethyl)-TPP, a resonance-stabilized carbanion; (**3**) the C2 carbanion attacks the aldehyde carbon of R5P to form an S7P–TPP adduct; (**4**) TPP is eliminated, yielding S7P and the regenerated TPP–enzyme.

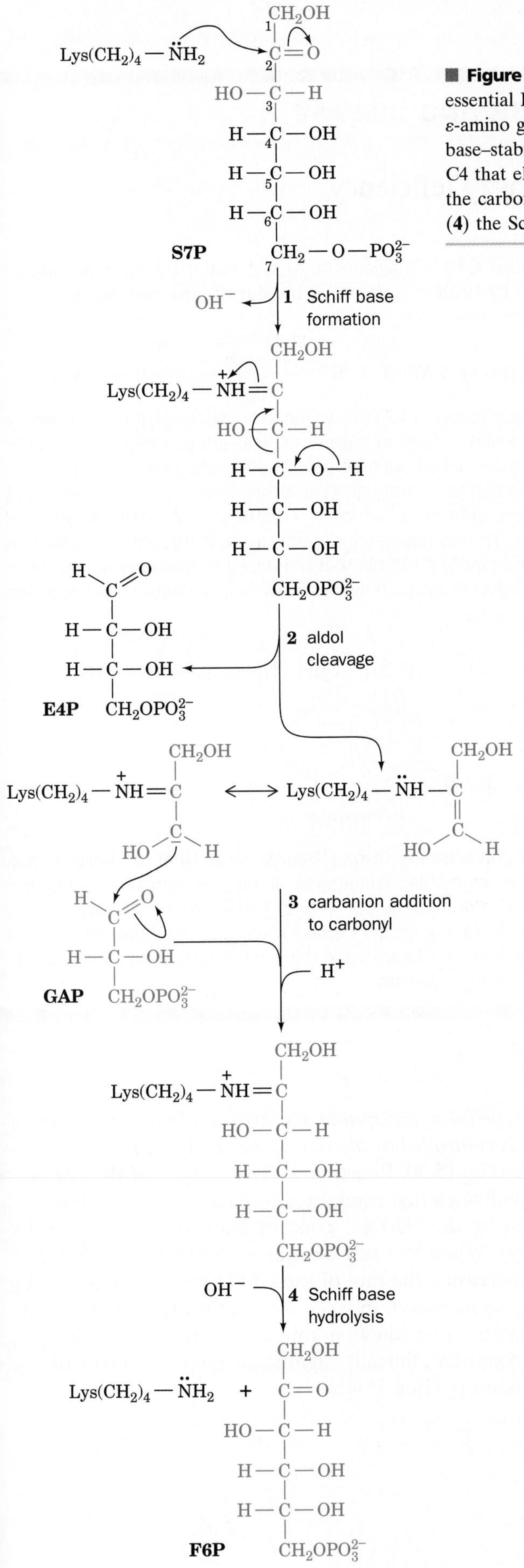

Figure 15-33 | Mechanism of transaldolase. Transaldolase contains an essential Lys residue that facilitates an aldol cleavage reaction as follows: (**1**) The ε-amino group of Lys forms a Schiff base with the carbonyl group of S7P; (**2**) a Schiff base–stabilized C3 carbanion is formed in an aldol cleavage reaction between C3 and C4 that eliminates E4P; (**3**) the enzyme-bound resonance-stabilized carbanion adds to the carbonyl C atom of GAP, forming F6P linked to the enzyme via a Schiff base; (**4**) the Schiff base hydrolyzes, regenerating active enzyme and releasing F6P.

$$(6) \quad C_5 + C_5 \rightleftharpoons C_7 + C_3$$

$$(7) \quad C_7 + C_3 \rightleftharpoons C_6 + C_4$$

$$(8) \quad \underline{C_5 + C_4 \rightleftharpoons C_6 + C_3}$$

$$(\text{Sum}) \quad 3\,C_5 \rightleftharpoons 2\,C_6 + C_3$$

Figure 15-34 | Summary of carbon skeleton rearrangements in the pentose phosphate pathway. A series of carbon–carbon bond formations and cleavages convert three C_5 sugars to two C_6 and one C_3 sugar. The number to the left of each reaction is keyed to the corresponding reaction in Fig. 15-30.

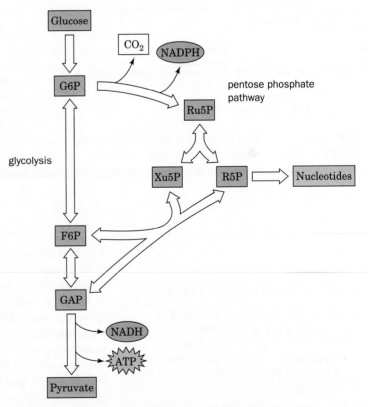

Figure 15-35 | Relationship between glycolysis and the pentose phosphate pathway. The pentose phosphate pathway, which begins with G6P produced in Step 1 of glycolysis, generates NADPH for use in reductive reactions and R5P for nucleotide synthesis. Excess R5P is converted to glycolytic intermediates by a sequence of reactions that can operate in reverse to generate additional R5P, if needed.

BOX 15-4 BIOCHEMISTRY IN HEALTH AND DISEASE

Glucose-6-Phosphate Dehydrogenase Deficiency

NADPH is required for several reductive processes in addition to biosynthesis. For example, erythrocytes require a plentiful supply of reduced **glutathione (GSH)**, a Cys-containing tripeptide (Section 4-3B).

$$
\underset{\underset{\text{COO}^-}{|}}{\overset{+}{\text{H}_3\text{N}}}-\text{CH}-\text{CH}_2-\text{CH}_2-\overset{\overset{\text{O}}{\|}}{\text{C}}-\text{NH}-\underset{\underset{\underset{\underset{\text{SH}}{|}}{\text{CH}_2}}{|}}{\text{CH}}-\overset{\overset{\text{O}}{\|}}{\text{C}}-\text{NH}-\text{CH}_2-\text{COO}^-
$$

Glutathione (GSH)
(γ-L-glutamyl-L-cysteinylglycine)

A major function of GSH in the erythrocyte is to reductively eliminate H_2O_2 and organic hydroperoxides, which are reactive oxygen metabolites that can irreversibly damage hemoglobin and cleave the C—C bonds in the phospholipid tails of cell membranes. The unchecked buildup of peroxides results in premature cell lysis. Peroxides are eliminated by reaction with glutathione, catalyzed by **glutathione peroxidase:**

$$2\,\text{GSH} + \text{R}-\text{O}-\text{O}-\text{H} \xrightarrow{\overset{\text{glutathione}}{\text{peroxidase}}} \text{GSSG} + \text{ROH} + \text{H}_2\text{O}$$

Organic
hydroperoxide

GSSG represents oxidized glutathione (two GSH molecules linked through a disulfide bond between their sulfhydryl groups).

Reduced GSH is subsequently regenerated by the reduction of GSSG by NADPH as catalyzed by **glutathione reductase:**

$$\text{GSSG} + \text{NADPH} + \text{H}^+ \xrightarrow{\overset{\text{glutathione}}{\text{reductase}}} 2\,\text{GSH} + \text{NADP}^+$$

A steady supply of NADPH is therefore vital for erythrocyte integrity.

The erythrocytes in individuals who are deficient in glucose-6-phosphate dehydrogenase (G6PD) are particularly sensitive to oxidative damage, although clinical symptoms may be absent. This enzyme deficiency, which is common in African, Asian, and Mediterranean populations, came to light through investigations of the hemolytic anemia that is induced in these individuals when they ingest drugs such as the antimalarial compound **primaquine**

$$
\text{NH}-\underset{\underset{\text{CH}_3}{|}}{\text{CH}}-\text{CH}_2-\text{CH}_2-\text{CH}_2-\text{NH}_2
$$

Primaquine

or eat **fava beans (broad beans,** *Vicia faba*), a staple Middle Eastern vegetable. Primaquine stimulates peroxide formation, thereby increasing the demand for NADPH to a level that the mutant cells cannot meet. Certain toxic glycosides present in small amounts in fava beans have the same effect, producing a condition known as **favism.**

■ CHECK YOUR UNDERSTANDING

Summarize the reactions of each stage of the pentose phosphate pathway.
How does flux through the pentose phosphate pathway change in response to the need for NADPH or ribose-5-phosphate?

Flux through the pentose phosphate pathway and thus the rate of NADPH production is controlled by the rate of the glucose-6-phosphate dehydrogenase reaction (Fig. 15-30, Reaction 1). The activity of the enzyme, which catalyzes the pathway's first committed step ($\Delta G = -17.6$ kJ·mol^{-1} in liver), is regulated by the NADP$^+$ concentration (i.e., regulation by substrate availability). When the cell consumes NADPH, the NADP$^+$ concentration rises, increasing the rate of the G6PD reaction and thereby stimulating NADPH regeneration. In some tissues, the amount of enzyme synthesized also appears to be under hormonal control. A deficiency in G6PD is the most common clinically significant enzyme defect of the pentose phosphate pathway (Box 15-4).

The major reason for low enzymatic activity in affected cells appears to be an accelerated rate of breakdown of the mutant enzyme. This explains why patients with relatively mild forms of G6PD deficiency react to primaquine with hemolytic anemia but recover within a week despite continued primaquine treatment. Mature erythrocytes lack a nucleus and protein synthesizing machinery and therefore cannot synthesize new enzyme molecules to replace degraded ones (they likewise cannot synthesize new membrane components, which is why they are so sensitive to membrane damage in the first place). The initial primaquine treatments result in the lysis of old red blood cells whose defective G6PD has been largely degraded. Lysis products stimulate the release of young cells that contain more enzyme and are therefore better able to cope with primaquine stress.

It is estimated that ~400 million people are deficient in G6PD, which makes this condition the most common human enzyme deficiency. Indeed, ~400 G6PD variants have been reported and at least 125 of them have been characterized at the molecular level. G6PD is active in a dimer–tetramer equilibrium. Many of the mutation sites in individuals with the most severe G6PD deficiency are at the dimer interface, shifting the equilibrium toward the inactive and unstable monomer.

The high prevalence of defective G6PD in malarial areas of the world suggests that such mutations confer resistance to the malarial parasite, *Plasmodium falciparum*. Indeed, erythrocytes with G6PD deficiency appear to be less suitable hosts for plasmodia than normal cells. Thus, like the sickle-cell trait (Section 7-1E), *a defective G6PD confers a selective advantage on individuals living where malaria is endemic.*

The G6PD deficiency primarily affects erythrocytes, in which the lack of a nucleus prevents replacement of the unstable mutant enzyme. However, the importance of NADPH in cells other than erythrocytes has been demonstrated through the development of mice in which the G6PD gene has been knocked out. All the cells in these animals are extremely sensitive to oxidative stress, even though they contain other mechanisms for eliminating reactive oxygen species.

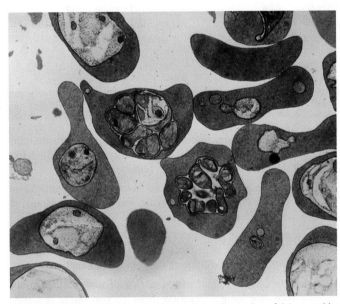

Photo of red blood cells showing intracellular *Plasmodium falciparum* (the malaria parasite). [© Dr. Gopal Murti/Photo Researchers, Inc.]

SUMMARY

1. Glycolysis is a sequence of 10 enzyme-catalyzed reactions by which one molecule of glucose is converted to two molecules of pyruvate, with the net production of 2 ATP and the reduction of 2 NAD$^+$ to 2 NADH.

2. In the first stage of glycolysis, glucose is phosphorylated by hexokinase, isomerized by phosphoglucose isomerase (PGI), phosphorylated by phosphofructokinase (PFK), and cleaved by aldolase to yield the trioses glyceraldehyde-3-phosphate (GAP) and dihydroxyacetone phosphate (DHAP), which are interconverted by triose phosphate isomerase (TIM). These reactions consume 2 ATP per glucose.

3. In the second stage of glycolysis, GAP is oxidatively phosphorylated by glyceraldehyde-3-phosphate dehydrogenase (GAPDH), dephosphorylated by phosphoglycerate kinase (PGK) to produce ATP, isomerized by phosphoglycerate mutase (PGM), dehydrated by enolase, and dephosphorylated by pyruvate kinase to produce a second ATP and pyruvate. This stage produces 4 ATP per glucose for a net yield of 2 ATP per glucose.

4. Under anaerobic conditions, pyruvate is reduced to regenerate NAD$^+$ for glycolysis. In homolactic fermentation, pyruvate is reversibly reduced to lactate.

5. In alcoholic fermentation, pyruvate is decarboxylated by a thiamine pyrophosphate (TPP)-dependent mechanism, and the resulting acetaldehyde is reduced to ethanol.

6. The glycolytic reactions catalyzed by hexokinase, phosphofructokinase, and pyruvate kinase are metabolically irreversible.

7. Phosphofructokinase is the primary flux control point for glycolysis. ATP inhibition of this allosteric enzyme is relieved by AMP and ADP, whose concentrations change more dramatically than those of ATP.

8. The opposing reactions of the fructose-6-phosphate (F6P)/fructose-1,6-bisphosphate (FBP) substrate cycle allow large changes in glycolytic flux.

9. Fructose, galactose, and mannose are enzymatically converted to glycolytic intermediates for catabolism.

10. In the pentose phosphate pathway, glucose-6-phosphate (G6P) is oxidized and decarboxylated to produce two NADPH, CO_2, and ribulose-5-phosphate (Ru5P).

11. Depending on the cell's needs, ribulose-5-phosphate may be isomerized to ribose-5-phosphate (R5P) for nucleotide synthesis or converted, via ribose-5-phosphate and xylulose-5-phosphate (Xu5P), to fructose-6-phosphate and glyceraldehyde-3-phosphate, which can re-enter the glycolytic pathway.

KEY TERMS

glycolysis **486**
pentose phosphate
   pathway **486**
aldol cleavage **492**
enediol intermediate **495**
catalytic perfection **496**
mutase **500**
homolactic fermentation **505**
alcoholic fermentation **505**
TPP **507**
Pasteur effect **510**
substrate cycle **514**

PROBLEMS

1. Which of the 10 reactions of glycolysis are (a) phosphorylations, (b) isomerizations, (c) oxidation–reductions, (d) dehydrations, and (e) carbon–carbon bond cleavages?

2. The aldolase reaction can proceed in reverse as an enzymatic aldol condensation. If the enzyme were not stereospecific, how many different products would be obtained?

3. Bacterial aldolase does not form a Schiff base with the substrate. Instead, it has a divalent Zn^{2+} ion in the active site. How does the ion facilitate the aldolase reaction?

4. Arsenate (AsO_4^{3-}), a structural analog of phosphate, can act as a substrate for any reaction in which phosphate is a substrate. Arsenate esters, unlike phosphate esters, are kinetically as well as thermodynamically unstable and hydrolyze almost instantaneously. Write a balanced overall equation for the conversion of glucose to pyruvate in the presence of ATP, ADP, NAD^+, and either (a) phosphate or (b) arsenate. (c) Why is arsenate a poison?

5. Draw the enediolate intermediates of the ribulose-5-phosphate isomerase reaction (Ru5P → R5P) and the ribulose-5-phosphate epimerase reaction (Ru5P → Xu5P).

6. (a) Why is it possible for the ΔG values in Table 15-1 to differ from the $\Delta G^{\circ\prime}$ values? (b) If a reaction has a $\Delta G^{\circ\prime}$ value of at least -30.5 kJ $\cdot$ mol^{-1}, sufficient to drive the synthesis of ATP ($\Delta G^{\circ\prime} = 30.5$ kJ $\cdot$ mol^{-1}), can it still drive the synthesis of ATP *in vivo* when its ΔG is only -10 kJ $\cdot$ mol^{-1}? Explain.

7. $\Delta G^{\circ\prime}$ for the aldolase reaction is 22.8 kJ $\cdot$ mol^{-1}. In the cell at 37°C, [DHAP]/[GAP] = 5.5. Calculate the equilibrium ratio of [FBP]/[GAP] when [GAP] = 10^{-4} M.

8. The half-reactions involved in the lactate dehydrogenase (LDH) reaction and their standard reduction potentials are

$$\text{Pyruvate} + 2\,H^+ + 2\,e^- \longrightarrow \text{lactate} \qquad \mathscr{E}^{\circ\prime} = -0.185 \text{ V}$$

$$NAD^+ + 2\,H^+ + 2\,e^- \longrightarrow NADH + H^+ \qquad \mathscr{E}^{\circ\prime} = -0.315 \text{ V}$$

Calculate ΔG at pH 7.0 for the LDH-catalyzed reduction of pyruvate under the following conditions:

  (a) [lactate]/[pyruvate] = 1 and [NAD^+]/[NADH] = 1

  (b) [lactate]/[pyruvate] = 160 and [NAD^+]/[NADH] = 160

  (c) [lactate]/[pyruvate] = 1000 and [NAD^+]/[NADH] = 1000

  (d) Discuss the effect of the concentration ratios in parts a–c on the direction of the reaction.

9. Although it is not the primary flux-control point for glycolysis, pyruvate kinase is subject to allosteric regulation. (a) What is the metabolic importance of regulating flux through the pyruvate kinase reaction? (b) What is the advantage of activating pyruvate kinase with fructose-1,6-bisphosphate?

10. Compare the ATP yield of three glucose molecules that enter glycolysis and are converted to pyruvate with that of three glucose molecules that proceed through the pentose phosphate pathway such that their carbon skeletons (as two F6P and one GAP) re-enter glycolysis and are metabolized to pyruvate.

11. If G6P is labeled at its C2 position, where will the label appear in the products of the pentose phosphate pathway?

12. (a) Describe the lengths of the products of the transketolase reaction when the two substrates are both five-carbon sugars. (b) Describe the products of the reaction when the substrates are a five-carbon aldose and a six-carbon ketose. Does it matter which of the substrates binds to the enzyme first?

13. Explain why some tissues continue to produce CO_2 in the presence of high concentrations of fluoride ion, which inhibits glycolysis.

14. The catalytic behavior of liver and brain phosphofructokinase-1 (PFK-1) was observed in the presence of AMP, phosphate, and fructose-2,6-bisphosphate. The following table lists the concentrations of each effector required to achieve 50% of the maximal velocity. Compare the response of the two isozymes to the

three effectors and discuss the possible implications of their different responses.

PFK-1 isozyme	[Phosphate]	[AMP]	[F2,6P]
Liver	200 μM	10 μM	0.05 μM
Brain	350 μM	75 μM	4.5 μM

5. Some bacteria catabolize glucose by the Entner–Doudoroff pathway, a variant of glycolysis in which glucose-6-phosphate is converted to 6-phosphogluconate (as in the pentose phosphate pathway) and then to **2-keto-3-deoxy-6-phosphogluconate (KDPG)**.

$$
\begin{array}{c}
\text{COO}^- \\
| \\
\text{C}=\text{O} \\
| \\
\text{H}-\text{C}-\text{H} \\
| \\
\text{H}-\text{C}-\text{OH} \\
| \\
\text{H}-\text{C}-\text{OH} \\
| \\
\text{CH}_2\text{OPO}_3^{2-}
\end{array}
$$

KDPG

Next, an aldolase acts on KDPG. (a) Draw the structures of the products of the KDPG aldolase reaction. (b) Describe how these reaction products are further metabolized by glycolytic enzymes. (c) What is the ATP yield when glucose is metabolized to pyruvate by the Entner–Doudoroff pathway? How does this compare to the ATP yield of glycolysis?

CASE STUDIES

Case 18 (available at www.wiley.com/college/voet)
Purification of Phosphofructokinase 1-C

Focus concept: The purification of the C isozyme of PFK-1 is presented and the kinetic properties of the purified enzyme are examined.

Prerequisites: Chapters 5, 12, and 15

- Protein purification techniques
- Enzyme kinetics and inhibition
- The glycolytic pathway

Case 20

NAD$^+$-Dependent Glyceraldehyde-3-Phosphate Dehydrogenase from *Thermoproteus tenax*

Focus concept: Glycolytic enzymes from *T. tenax* are regulated in an unusual manner.

Prerequisites: Chapters 7, 12, and 15

- The glycolytic pathway
- Enzyme kinetics and inhibition
- The cooperative nature of regulated enzymes

REFERENCES

…erstein, B.E., Michels, P.A.M., and Hol, W.G.J., Synergistic effects of substrate-induced conformational changes in phosphoglycerate activation, *Nature* **385**, 275–278 (1997).

…alby, A., Dauter, Z., and Littlechild, J.A., Crystal structure of human muscle aldolase complexed with fructose 1,6-bisphosphate: Mechanistic implications, *Protein Science* **8**, 291–297 (1999).

…epre, C., Rider, M.H., and Hue, L., Mechanisms of control of heart glycolysis, *Eur. J. Biochem.* **258**, 277–290 (1998). [Discusses how the control of glycolysis in heart muscle is distributed among several enzymes, transporters, and other pathways.]

…rey, P.A., The Leloir pathway: a mechanistic imperative for three enzymes to change the stereochemical configuration of a single carbon in galactose, *FASEB J.* **10**, 461–470 (1996).

…efflaut, T., Blonski, C., Perie, J., and Wilson, M., Class I aldolases: substrate specificity, mechanism, inhibitors and structural aspects, *Prog. Biophys. Molec. Biol.* **63**, 301–340 (1995).

Hofmeyr, J.-H.S. and Cornish-Bowden, A., Regulating the cellular economy of supply and demand, *FEBS Lett.* **476**, 47–51 (2000).

Lindqvist, Y. and Schneider, G., Thiamin diphosphate dependent enzymes: transketolase, pyruvate oxidase and pyruvate decarboxylase, *Curr. Opin. Struct. Biol.* **3**, 896–901 (1993).

Muirhead, H. and Watson, H., Glycolytic enzymes; from hexose to pyruvate, *Curr. Opin. Struct. Biol.* **2**, 870–876 (1992). [A brief summary of the structures of glycolytic enzymes.]

Schirmer, T. and Evans, P.R., Structural basis of the allosteric behaviour of phosphofructokinase, *Nature* **343**, 140–145 (1990).

Scriver, C.R., Beaudet, A., Sly, W.S., and Valle, D. (Eds.), *The Metabolic and Molecular Bases of Inherited Disease* (8th ed.), pp. 4517–4553, McGraw-Hill (2001). [Chapters 70 and 72 discuss fructose and galactose metabolism and their genetic disorders. Chapter 179 discusses glucose-6-phosphate dehydrogenase deficiency.]

16

Glycogen Metabolism and Gluconeogenesis

The muscles of animals contain glycogen, a storage form of the metabolic fuel glucose. In living animals, the balance between glycogen synthesis and utilization is carefully regulated. Measurement of glycogen levels in lobster has been used to determine environmental conditions, since animals that have been undernourished or stressed have depleted glycogen stores. [Andrew J. Martinez/Photo Researchers]

■ CHAPTER CONTENTS

1 Glycogen Breakdown

A. Glycogen Phosphorylase Degrades Glycogen to Glucose-1-Phosphate

B. Glycogen Debranching Enzyme Acts as a Glucosyltransferase

C. Phosphoglucomutase Interconverts Glucose-1-Phosphate and Glucose-6-Phosphate

2 Glycogen Synthesis

A. UDP–Glucose Pyrophosphorylase Activates Glucosyl Units

B. Glycogen Synthase Extends Glycogen Chains

C. Glycogen Branching Enzyme Transfers Seven-Residue Glycogen Segments

3 Control of Glycogen Metabolism

A. Glycogen Phosphorylase and Glycogen Synthase Are under Allosteric Control

B. Glycogen Phosphorylase and Glycogen Synthase Undergo Control by Covalent Modification

C. Glycogen Metabolism Is Subject to Hormonal Control

4 Gluconeogenesis

A. Pyruvate Is Converted to Phosphoenolpyruvate in Two Steps

B. Hydrolysis Reactions Bypass Irreversible Glycolytic Reactions

C. Gluconeogenesis and Glycolysis Are Independently Regulated

5 Other Carbohydrate Biosynthetic Pathways

■ MEDIA RESOURCES

(available at www.wiley.com/college/voet)

Guided Exploration 15. Control of glycogen metabolism

Animated Figure 16-1. Overview of glucose metabolism

Animated Figure 16-13. Major phosphorylation and dephosphorylation systems in glycogen metabolism

Animated Figure 16-15. Comparison of gluconeogenesis and glycolysis

Animated Figure 16-20. Transport of PEP and oxaloacetate from mitochondrion to cytosol

Animated Figure 16-27. Pathway for dolichol-PP-oligosaccharide synthesis

Case Study 22. Carrier-Mediated Uptake of Lactate in Rat Hepatocytes

Case Study 26. The Role of Specific Amino Acids in the Peptide Hormone Glucagon in Receptor Binding and Signal Transduction

Glycogen (in animals, fungi, and bacteria) and starch (in plants) can function to stockpile glucose for later metabolic use. In animals, a constant supply of glucose is essential for tissues such as the brain and red blood cells, which depend almost entirely on glucose as an energy source (other tissues can also oxidize fatty acids for energy; Section 20-2). The mobilization of glucose from glycogen stores, primarily in the liver, provides a constant supply of glucose (~5 mM in blood) to all tissues. When glucose is plentiful, such as immediately after a meal, glycogen synthesis accelerates. Yet the liver's capacity to store glycogen is sufficient to supply the brain with glucose for about half a day. Under fasting conditions, most of the body's glucose needs are met by **gluconeogenesis** (literally, new glucose synthesis) from noncarbohydrate precursors such as amino acids. Not surprisingly, the regulation of glucose synthesis, storage, mobilization, and catabolism by glycolysis (Section 15-2) or the pentose

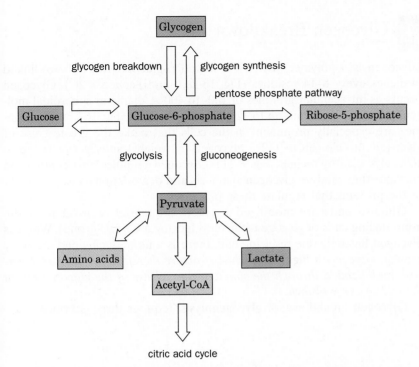

■ **Figure 16-1** | **Overview of glucose metabolism.** Glucose-6-phosphate (G6P) is produced by the phosphorylation of free glucose, by glycogen degradation, and by gluconeogenesis. It is also a precursor for glycogen synthesis and the pentose phosphate pathway. The liver can hydrolyze G6P to glucose. Glucose is metabolized by glycolysis to pyruvate, which can be further broken down to acetyl-CoA for oxidation by the citric acid cycle. Lactate and amino acids, which are reversibly converted to pyruvate, are precursors for gluconeogenesis. 🖧 **See the Animated Figures.**

phosphate pathway (Section 15-6) is elaborate and is sensitive to the immediate and long-term energy needs of the organism.

The importance of glycogen for glucose storage is plainly illustrated by the effects of deficiencies of the enzymes that release stored glucose. **McArdle's disease,** for example, is an inherited condition whose major symptom is painful muscle cramps on exertion. The muscles in afflicted individuals lack the enzyme required for glycogen breakdown to yield glucose. Although glycogen is synthesized normally, it cannot supply fuel for glycolysis to keep up with the demand for ATP.

Figure 16-1 summarizes the metabolic uses of glucose. Glucose-6-phosphate (G6P), a key branch point, is derived from free glucose through the action of hexokinase (Section 15-2A) or is the product of glycogen breakdown or gluconeogenesis. G6P has several possible fates: It can be used to synthesize glycogen; it can be catabolized via glycolysis to yield ATP and carbon atoms (as acetyl-CoA) that are further oxidized by the citric acid cycle; and it can be shunted through the pentose phosphate pathway to generate NADPH and/or ribose-5-phosphate. In the liver and kidney, G6P can be converted to glucose for export to other tissues via the bloodstream.

The opposing processes of glycogen synthesis and degradation, and of glycolysis and gluconeogenesis, are reciprocally regulated; that is, one is largely turned on while the other is largely turned off. In this chapter, we examine the enzymatic steps of glycogen metabolism and gluconeogenesis, paying particular attention to the regulatory mechanisms that ensure efficient operation of opposing metabolic pathways.

1 Glycogen Breakdown

LEARNING OBJECTIVES

■ Understand that glycogen, the storage form of glucose, is a branched polymer.

■ Understand that glucose mobilization in the liver involves a series of conversions from glycogen to glucose-1-phosphate to glucose-6-phosphate and finally to glucose.

Glycogen is a polymer of $\alpha(1\rightarrow4)$-linked D-glucose with $\alpha(1\rightarrow6)$-linked branches every 8–14 residues (Fig. 16-2a,b and Section 8-2C). Glycogen occurs as intracellular granules of 100- to 400-Å-diameter spheroidal molecules that each contain up to 120,000 glucose units (Fig. 16-2c). The granules are especially prominent in the cells that make the greatest use of glycogen: muscle (up to 1–2% glycogen by weight) and liver cells (up to 10% glycogen by weight; Fig. 8-11). Glycogen granules also contain the enzymes that catalyze glycogen synthesis and degradation as well as many of the proteins that regulate these processes.

Glucose units are mobilized by their sequential removal from the nonreducing ends of glycogen (the ends lacking a C1-OH group). Whereas glycogen has only one reducing end, there is a nonreducing end on every branch. *Glycogen's highly branched structure therefore permits rapid glucose mobilization through the simultaneous release of the glucose units at the end of every branch.*

Glycogen breakdown, or **glycogenolysis,** requires three enzymes:

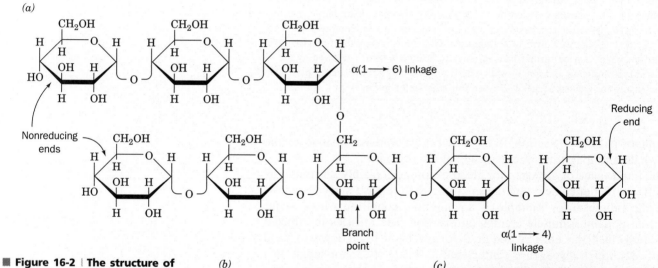

(a)

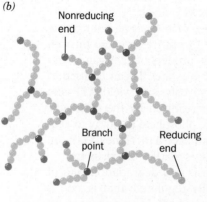

(b)

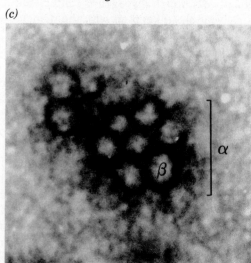

(c)

■ **Figure 16-2** | **The structure of glycogen.** (*a*) Molecular formula. In the actual molecule, there are ~12 residues per chain. (*b*) Schematic diagram of glycogen's branched structure. Note that the molecule has many nonreducing ends but only one reducing end. (*c*) Electron micrograph of a glycogen granule from rat skeletal muscle. Each granule (labeled α) consists of several spherical glycogen molecules (β) and associated proteins. [From Calder, P.C., *Int. J. Biochem.* **23,** 1339 (1991). Copyright Elsevier Science. Used with permission.]

BOX 16-1 PATHWAYS OF DISCOVERY

Carl and Gerty Cori and Glucose Metabolism

Carl F. Cori (1896–1984)
Gerty T. Cori (1896–1957)

A lifelong collaboration commenced with the marriage of Carl and Gerty Cori in 1920. Although the Coris began their professional work in Austria, they fled the economic and social hardships of Europe in 1922 and moved to Buffalo, New York. They later made their way to Washington University School of Medicine in St. Louis, where Carl served as chair of the Pharmacology Department and, later, chair of the Biochemistry Department. Despite her role as an equal partner in their research work, Gerty officially remained a research associate.

The Coris' research focused primarily on the metabolism of glucose. One of their first discoveries was the connection between glucose metabolism in muscle and glycogen metabolism in the liver. The "Cori cycle" (Section 22-1F) describes how lactate produced by glycolysis in active muscle is transported to the liver, where it is used to synthesize glucose that is stored as glycogen until needed.

After describing the interorgan movement of glucose in intact animals, the Coris turned their attention to the metabolic fate of glucose, specifically, the intermediates and enzymes of glucose metabolism. In 1936, using a preparation of minced frog muscle, the Coris found glucose in the form of a phosphate ester (called the Cori ester, now known as glucose-1-phosphate). They traced the presence of the Cori ester to the activity of a phosphorylase (glycogen phosphorylase). This was a notable discovery, because the enzyme used phosphate, rather than water, to split glucose residues from the ends of glycogen chains. Even more

remarkably, the enzyme could be made to work in reverse to elongate a glycogen polymer by adding glucose residues (from glucose-1-phosphate). For the first time, a large biological molecule could be synthesized *in vitro*.

During the 1940s, the Coris unraveled many of the secrets of glycogen phosphorylase. For example, they found that the enzyme exists in two forms, one that requires the activator AMP and one that is active in the absence of an allosteric activator. Although it was not immediately appreciated that the differences between the two forms resulted from the presence of covalently bound phosphate, this work laid the foundation for subsequent research on enzyme regulation through phosphorylation and dephosphorylation.

Carl and Gerty Cori also described phosphoglucomutase, the enzyme that converts glucose-1-phosphate to glucose-6-phosphate so that it can participate in other pathways of glucose metabolism. Over time, the Cori lab became a magnet for scientists interested in purifying and characterizing other enzymes of glucose metabolism.

Perhaps because of their experience with discrimination and—especially for Gerty—the lack of equal opportunity, the Cori lab welcomed a more diverse group of scientists than was typical of labs of that era. The Coris received the 1947 Nobel Prize in Physiology or Medicine. Several of their junior colleagues, Arthur Kornberg (see Box 25-1), Severo Ochoa, Luis Leloir, Earl Sutherland, Christian de Duve, and Edwin G. Krebs, later earned Nobel prizes of their own, quite possibly reflecting the work ethic, broad view of science and medicine, and meticulous work habits instilled by Carl and Gerty Cori.

Cori, G.T., Colowick, S.P., and Cori, C.F., The activity of the phosphorylating enzyme in muscle extracts, *J. Biol. Chem.* **127,** 771–782 (1939).

Kornberg, A., Remembering our teachers, *J. Biol. Chem. Reflections,* www.jbc.org.

1. **Glycogen phosphorylase** (or simply **phosphorylase**) catalyzes glycogen **phosphorolysis** (bond cleavage by the substitution of a phosphate group) to yield **glucose-1-phosphate (G1P):**

   $$\text{Glycogen} + P_i \rightleftharpoons \text{Glycogen} + \text{G1P}$$
   $$(n \text{ residues}) \qquad\qquad (n-1 \text{ residues})$$

   The enzyme releases a glucose unit only if it is at least five units away from a branch point.

2. **Glycogen debranching enzyme** removes glycogen's branches, thereby making additional glucose residues accessible to glycogen phosphorylase.

3. **Phosphoglucomutase** converts G1P to G6P, which has several metabolic fates (Fig. 16-1).

Several key features of glycogen metabolism were discovered by the team of Carl and Gerty Cori (Box 16-1).

A | Glycogen Phosphorylase Degrades Glycogen to Glucose-1-Phosphate

Glycogen phosphorylase is a dimer of identical 842-residue (97-kD) subunits that catalyzes the rate-controlling step in glycogen breakdown. It is regulated both by allosteric interactions and by covalent modification (phosphorylation and dephosphorylation). Phosphorylase's allosteric inhibitors (ATP, G6P, and glucose) and its allosteric activator (AMP) interact differently with the phospho- and dephosphoenzymes, resulting in an extremely sensitive regulation process. The structure of glycogen phosphorylase as well as its regulation by phosphorylation are discussed in Section 12-3B.

An ~30-Å-long crevice on the surface of the phosphorylase monomer connects the glycogen storage site to the active site. *Since this crevice can accommodate four or five sugar residues in a chain but is too narrow to admit branched oligosaccharides, it provides a clear physical rationale for the inability of phosphorylase to cleave glycosyl residues closer than five units from a branch point.* Presumably, the glycogen storage site increases the catalytic efficiency of phosphorylase by permitting it to phosphorylyze many glucose residues on the same glycogen particle without having to dissociate and reassociate completely between catalytic cycles.

Phosphorylase binds the cofactor **pyridoxal-5′-phosphate** (**PLP;** *at left*), which it requires for activity. This prosthetic group, a **vitamin B$_6$** derivative, is covalently linked to the enzyme via a Schiff base (imine) formed between its aldehyde group and the ε-amino group of Lys 680. PLP also occurs in a variety of enzymes involved in amino acid metabolism, where PLP's conjugated ring system functions catalytically to delocalize electrons (Sections 21-2A and 21-4A). In phosphorylase, however, only the phosphate group participates in catalysis, where it acts as a general acid–base catalyst. Phosphorolysis of glycogen proceeds by a Random mechanism (Section 12-1D) involving an enzyme · P$_i$ · glycogen ternary complex. An oxonium ion intermediate forms during C1—O1 bond cleavage, similar to the transition state that forms in the reaction catalyzed by lysozyme (Section 11-4B). The phosphorylase reaction mechanism is diagrammed in Fig. 16-3, which shows how PLP's phosphate group functions as a general acid–base catalyst.

Pyridoxal-5′-phosphate (PLP)

Glycogen Phosphorylase Undergoes Conformational Changes. The structural differences between the active (R) and inactive (T) conformations of phosphorylase (Fig. 12-15) are fairly well understood in terms of the symmetry model of allosterism (Section 7-1D). The T-state enzyme has a buried active site and hence a low affinity for its substrates, whereas the R-state enzyme has an accessible catalytic site and a high-affinity phosphate-binding site.

AMP promotes phosphorylase's T (*inactive*) → R (*active*) conformational shift by binding to the R state of the enzyme at its allosteric effector site. This conformational change results in increased access of the substrate to the active site by disordering a loop of residues (282–284) that otherwise block the active site. The conformational change also causes the Arg 569 side chain, which is located in the active site near the PLP and the P$_i$-binding site, to rotate in a way that increases the enzyme's binding affinity for its anionic P$_i$ substrate (Fig. 12-15).

ATP also binds to the allosteric effector site, but in the T state, so that it inhibits rather than promotes the T → R conformational shift. This is because the β- and γ-phosphate groups of ATP prevent the alignment of

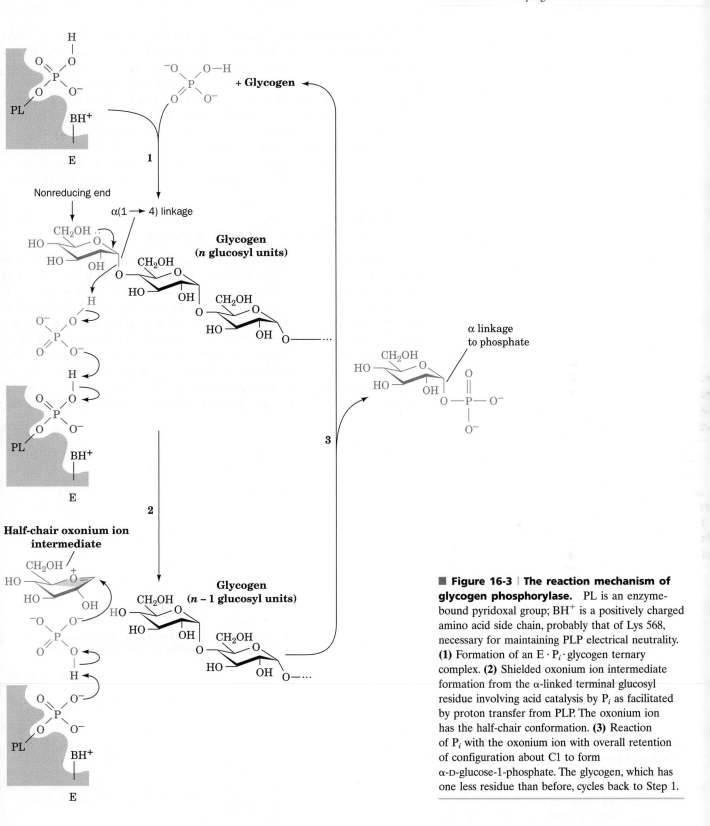

■ **Figure 16-3 | The reaction mechanism of glycogen phosphorylase.** PL is an enzyme-bound pyridoxal group; BH$^+$ is a positively charged amino acid side chain, probably that of Lys 568, necessary for maintaining PLP electrical neutrality. **(1)** Formation of an E · P$_i$ · glycogen ternary complex. **(2)** Shielded oxonium ion intermediate formation from the α-linked terminal glucosyl residue involving acid catalysis by P$_i$ as facilitated by proton transfer from PLP. The oxonium ion has the half-chair conformation. **(3)** Reaction of P$_i$ with the oxonium ion with overall retention of configuration about C1 to form α-D-glucose-1-phosphate. The glycogen, which has one less residue than before, cycles back to Step 1.

its ribose and α-phosphate groups that are required for the conformational changes elicited by AMP.

Phosphorylation and dephosphorylation alter the enzymatic activity in a manner reminiscent of allosteric regulation. The phosphate group has a double negative charge (a property not shared by naturally occurring amino acid residues) and its covalent attachment to Ser 14 causes dramatic tertiary and quaternary changes as the N-terminal segment moves to allow the phospho-Ser to ion pair with two cationic Arg residues. *The presence of the Ser 14–phosphoryl group causes conformational changes similar to those triggered by AMP binding, thereby shifting the enzyme's $T \rightleftharpoons R$ equilibrium in favor of the R state.* This accounts for the observation that phosphorylase b requires AMP for activity and that the a form is active without AMP. We shall return to the regulation of phosphorylase activity when we discuss the mechanisms that balance glycogen synthesis against glycogen degradation (Section 16-3).

B | Glycogen Debranching Enzyme Acts as a Glucosyltransferase

Phosphorolysis proceeds along a glycogen branch until it approaches to within four or five residues of an $\alpha(1\rightarrow6)$ branch point, leaving a "limit branch." Glycogen debranching enzyme acts as an **$\alpha(1\rightarrow4)$ transglycosylase** (glycosyltransferase) by transferring an $\alpha(1\rightarrow4)$-linked trisaccharide unit from a limit branch of glycogen to the nonreducing end of another branch (Fig. 16-4). This reaction forms a new $\alpha(1\rightarrow4)$ linkage with three more units available for phosphorylase-catalyzed phosphorolysis. The $\alpha(1\rightarrow6)$ bond linking the remaining glycosyl residue in the branch to the main chain is hydrolyzed (not phosphorylyzed) by the same debranching enzyme to yield glucose and debranched glycogen. About 10% of the

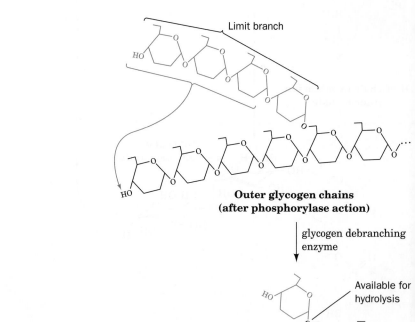

Limit branch

Outer glycogen chains (after phosphorylase action)

glycogen debranching enzyme

Available for hydrolysis

Available for further phosphorolysis

■ **Figure 16-4 | The reactions catalyzed by debranching enzyme.** The enzyme transfers the terminal three $\alpha(1 \rightarrow 4)$-linked glucose residues from a "limit branch" of glycogen to the nonreducing end of another branch. The $\alpha(1 \rightarrow 6)$ bond of the residue remaining at the branch point is hydrolyzed by further action of debranching enzyme to yield free glucose. The newly elongated branch is subject to degradation by glycogen phosphorylase.

residues in glycogen (those at the branch points) are therefore converted to glucose rather than G1P. *Debranching enzyme has separate active sites for the transferase and the α(1→6)-glucosidase reactions.* The presence of two independent catalytic activities on the same enzyme no doubt improves the efficiency of the debranching process.

The maximal rate of the glycogen phosphorylase reaction is much greater than that of the glycogen debranching reaction. Consequently, the outermost branches of glycogen, which constitute nearly half of its residues, are degraded in muscle in a few seconds under conditions of high metabolic demand. Glycogen degradation beyond this point requires debranching and hence occurs more slowly. This, in part, accounts for the fact that a muscle can sustain its maximum exertion for only a few seconds.

C | Phosphoglucomutase Interconverts Glucose-1-Phosphate and Glucose-6-Phosphate

Phosphorylase converts the glucosyl units of glycogen to G1P, which, in turn, is converted by phosphoglucomutase to G6P. The phosphoglucomutase reaction is similar to that catalyzed by phosphoglycerate mutase (Section 15-2H). A phosphoryl group is transferred from the active phosphoenzyme to G1P, forming **glucose-1,6-bisphosphate (G1,6P),** which then rephosphorylates the enzyme to yield G6P (Fig. 16-5; this near-equilibrium reaction also functions in reverse). An important difference between this enzyme and phosphoglycerate mutase is that the phosphoryl group in phosphoglucomutase is covalently bound to a Ser hydroxyl group rather than to a His imidazole nitrogen.

Glucose-6-Phosphatase Generates Glucose in the Liver. The G6P produced by glycogen breakdown can continue along the glycolytic pathway or the pentose phosphate pathway (note that the glucose is already phosphorylated, so that the ATP-consuming hexokinase-catalyzed phosphory-

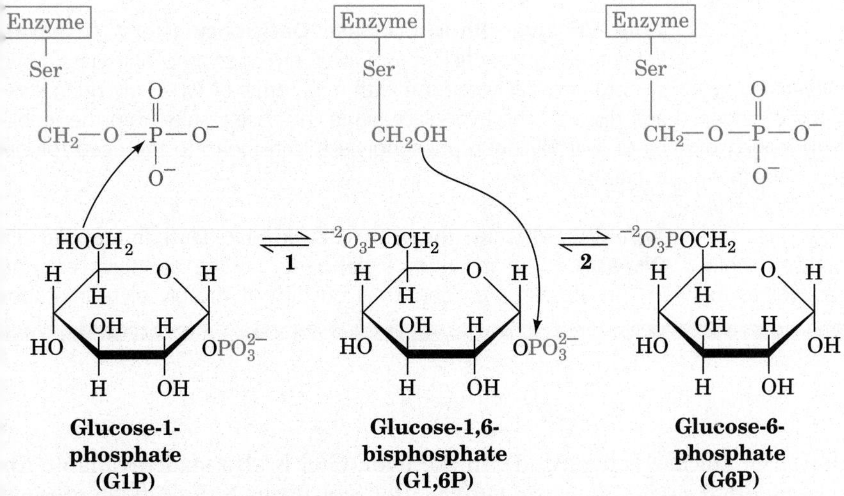

Figure 16-5 | The mechanism of phosphoglucomutase. (1) The OH group at C6 of G1P attacks the phosphoenzyme to form a dephosphoenzyme–G1,6P intermediate. (2) The Ser OH group on the dephosphoenzyme attacks the phosphoryl group at C1 to regenerate the phosphoenzyme with the formation of G6P.

BOX 16-2 BIOCHEMISTRY IN HEALTH AND DISEASE

Glycogen Storage Diseases

Glycogen storage diseases are inherited disorders that affect glycogen metabolism, producing glycogen that is abnormal in either quantity or quality. Studies of the genetic defects that underlie these diseases have helped elucidate the complexities of glycogen metabolism (e.g., McArdle's disease). Conversely, the biochemical characterization of the pathways affected by a genetic disease often leads to useful strategies for its treatment. The table on p. 539 lists the enzyme deficiencies associated with each type of glycogen storage disease.

Glycogen storage diseases that mainly affect the liver generally produce **hepatomegaly** (enlarged liver) and **hypoglycemia** (low blood sugar), whereas glycogen storage diseases that affect the muscles cause muscle cramps and weakness. Both types of disease may also cause cardiovascular and renal disturbances.

Type I: Glucose-6-Phosphatase Deficiency (von Gierke's Disease). Glucose-6-phosphatase catalyzes the final step leading to the release of glucose into the bloodstream by the liver. Deficiency of the enzyme results in an increase of intracellular [G6P], which leads to a large accumulation of glycogen in the liver and kidney (recall that G6P activates glycogen synthase) and an inability to increase blood glucose concentration in response to the hormones glucagon or epinephrine. The symptoms of Type I glycogen storage disease include severe hepatomegaly and hypoglycemia and a general failure to thrive. Treatment of the disease has included drug-induced inhibition of glucose uptake by the liver (to increase blood [glucose]), continuous intragastric feeding overnight (again to increase blood [glucose]), surgical transposition of the portal vein, which ordinarily feeds the liver directly from the intestines (to allow this glucose-rich blood to reach peripheral tissues before it reaches the liver), and liver transplantation.

Type II: α-1,4-Glucosidase Deficiency (Pompe's Disease). α-1,4-Glucosidase deficiency is the most devastating of the glycogen storage diseases. It results in a large accumulation of glycogen of normal structure in the lysosomes of all cells and causes death by cardiorespiratory failure, usually before the age of 1 year. α-1,4-Glucosidase is not involved in the main pathways of glycogen metabolism. It occurs in lysosomes, where it hydrolyzes maltose (a glucose disaccharide) and other linear oligosaccharides, as well as the

outer branches of glycogen, thereby yielding free glucose. Normally, this alternative pathway of glycogen metabolism is not quantitatively important, and its physiological significance is not known.

Type III: Amylo-1,6-Glucosidase (Debranching Enzyme) Deficiency (Cori's Disease). In Cori's disease, glycogen of abnormal structure containing very short outer chains accumulates in both liver and muscle since, in the absence of debranching enzyme, the glycogen cannot be further degraded. The resulting hypoglycemia is not as severe as in von Gierke's disease (Type I) and can be treated with frequent feedings and a high-protein diet (to offset the loss of amino acids used for gluconeogenesis). For unknown reasons, the symptoms of Cori's disease often disappear at puberty.

Type IV: Amylo-(1,4→1,6)-Transglycosylase (Branching Enzyme) Deficiency (Andersen's Disease). Andersen's disease is one of the most severe glycogen storage diseases; victims rarely survive past the age of 4 years because of liver dysfunction. Liver glycogen is present in normal concentrations, but it contains long unbranched chains that greatly reduce its solubility. The liver dysfunction may be caused by a "foreign body" immune reaction to the abnormal glycogen.

Type V: Muscle Phosphorylase Deficiency (McArdle's Disease). The symptoms of McArdle's disease, painful muscle cramps on exertion, typically do not appear until early adulthood and can be prevented by avoiding strenuous exercise. This condition affects glycogen metabolism in muscle but not in liver, which contains normal amounts of a different phosphorylase isozyme.

Type VI: Liver Phosphorylase Deficiency (Hers' Disease). Patients with a deficiency of liver glycogen phosphorylase have symptoms similar to those with mild forms of Type I glycogen storage disease. The hypoglycemia in this case results from the inability of liver glycogen phosphorylase to respond to the need for circulating glucose.

Type VII: Muscle Phosphofructokinase Deficiency (Tarui's Disease). The result of a deficiency of the glycolytic enzyme PFK in muscle is an abnormal buildup of the glycolytic metabo-

lation of glucose is bypassed). In the liver, G6P is also made available for use by other tissues. Because G6P cannot pass through the cell membrane, it is first hydrolyzed by **glucose-6-phosphatase (G6Pase):**

$$G6P + H_2O \rightarrow glucose + P_i$$

Although G6P is produced in the cytosol, G6Pase resides in the endoplasmic reticulum (ER) membrane. Consequently G6P must be imported into

es G6P and F6P. High concentrations of G6P increase the activities of glycogen synthase and UDP–glucose pyrophosphorylase ($G6P is in equilibrium with G1P, a substrate for UDP–glucose pyrophosphorylase) so that glycogen accumulates in muscle. Other symptoms are similar to those of muscle phosphorylase deficiency, since PFK deficiency prevents glycolysis from keeping up with the ATP demand in contracting muscle.

Type VIII: X-Linked Phosphorylase Kinase Deficiency. Some individuals with symptoms of Type VI glycogen storage disease have normal phosphorylase enzymes but a defective phosphorylase kinase, which results in their inability to convert phosphorylase b to phosphorylase a. The α subunit of phosphorylase kinase is encoded by a gene on the X chromosome, so Type VIII disease is X-linked rather than autosomal recessive, as are the other glycogen storage diseases.

Type IX: Phosphorylase Kinase Deficiency. Phosphorylase kinase deficiency, an autosomal recessive disease, results from a mutation in one of the genes that encode the β, γ, and δ subunits of phosphorylase kinase. Because different tissues contain different phosphorylase kinase isozymes, the symptoms and severity of the disease vary according to the affected organs. Techniques for identifying genetic lesions are therefore more reliable than clinical symptoms for diagnosing a particular glycogen storage disease.

Type 0: Liver Glycogen Synthase Deficiency. Liver glycogen synthase deficiency is the only disease of glycogen metabolism in which there is a deficiency rather than an overabundance of glycogen. The activity of liver glycogen synthase is extremely low in individuals with Type 0 disease, who exhibit hyperglycemia after meals and hypoglycemia at other times. Some individuals, however, are asymptomatic, which suggests that there may be multiple forms of this autosomal recessive disorder.

Hereditary Glycogen Storage Diseases

Type	Enzyme Deficiency	Tissue	Common Name	Glycogen Structure
	Glucose-6-phosphatase	Liver	von Gierke's disease	Normal
I	α-1,4-Glucosidase	All lysosomes	Pompe's disease	Normal
II	Amylo-1,6-glucosidase (debranching enzyme)	All organs	Cori's disease	Outer chains missing or very short
V	Amylo-(1,4→1,6)-transglycosylase (branching enzyme)	Liver, probably all organs	Andersen's disease	Very long unbranched chains
V	Glycogen phosphorylase	Muscle	McArdle's disease	Normal
VI	Glycogen phosphorylase	Liver	Hers' disease	Normal
VII	Phosphofructokinase	Muscle	Tarui's disease	Normal
VIII	Phosphorylase kinase	Liver	X-Linked phosphorylase kinase deficiency	Normal
IX	Phosphorylase kinase	All organs		Normal
0	Glycogen synthase	Liver		Normal, deficient in quantity

the ER by a **G6P translocase** before it can be hydrolyzed. The resulting glucose and P_i are then returned to the cytosol via specific transport proteins. A defect in any of the components of this G6P hydrolysis system results in **type I glycogen storage disease** (Box 16-2). Glucose leaves the liver cell via a specific glucose transporter named **GLUT2** and is carried by the blood to other tissues. Muscle and other tissues lack G6Pase and therefore retain their G6P.

■ CHECK YOUR UNDERSTANDING

List the metabolic sources and products of G6P.
How does the structure of glycogen relate to its metabolic function?
Describe the enzymatic degradation of glycogen.

LEARNING OBJECTIVES

- Understand that liver glycogen synthesis involves a series of conversions from glucose to glucose-6-phosphate, to UDP–glucose, and finally to glycogen.
- Understand that UPD–glucose is an activated molecule.
- Appreciate that glycogen is extended from a primer built on and by the protein glycogenin.

2 Glycogen Synthesis

The $\Delta G^{\circ\prime}$ for the glycogen phosphorylase reaction is $+3.1$ kJ $\cdot$ mol^{-1}, but under physiological conditions, glycogen breakdown is exergonic ($\Delta G^{\circ\prime}$ = -5 to -8 kJ $\cdot$ mol^{-1}). The synthesis of glycogen from G1P under physiological conditions is therefore thermodynamically unfavorable without free energy input. Consequently, *glycogen synthesis and breakdown must occur by separate pathways.* This recurrent metabolic strategy—that biosynthetic and degradative pathways of metabolism are different—is particularly important when both pathways must operate under similar physiological conditions. This situation is thermodynamically impossible if one pathway is just the reverse of the other.

It was not thermodynamics, however, that led to recognition of the separation of synthetic and degradative pathways for glycogen, but McArdle's disease. Individuals with the disease lack muscle glycogen phosphorylase activity and therefore cannot break down glycogen. Yet their muscles contain moderately high quantities of normal glycogen. Clearly, glycogen synthesis does not require glycogen phosphorylase. In this section, we describe the three enzymes that participate in glycogen synthesis: **UDP–glucose pyrophosphorylase, glycogen synthase,** and **glycogen branching enzyme**. The opposing reactions of glycogen synthesis and degradation are diagrammed in Fig. 16-6.

A | UDP–Glucose Pyrophosphorylase Activates Glucosyl Units

Since the direct conversion of G1P to glycogen and P$_i$ is thermodynamically unfavorable (positive ΔG) under physiological conditions, glycogen biosynthesis requires an exergonic step. This is accomplished, as Luis Leloir discovered in 1957, by combining G1P with uridine triphosphate (UTP) in a reaction catalyzed by UDP–glucose pyrophosphorylase (Fig. 16-7). The product of this reaction, **uridine diphosphate glucose (UDP–glucose** or **UDPG),** is an "activated" compound that can donate a glucosyl unit to the growing glycogen chain. The formation of UDPG itself has $\Delta G^{\circ\prime} \approx 0$ (it is a phosphoanhydride exchange reaction), but the subsequent exergonic hydrolysis of PP$_i$ by the omnipresent enzyme inorganic pyrophosphatase makes the overall reaction exergonic.

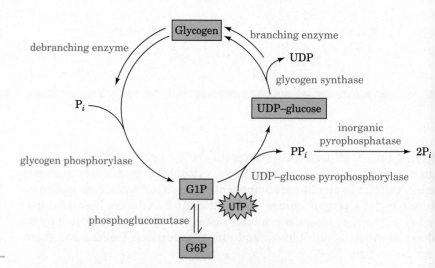

■ **Figure 16-6** | **Opposing pathways of glycogen synthesis and degradation.** The exergonic process of glycogen breakdown is reversed by a process that uses UTP to generate a UDP–glucose intermediate.

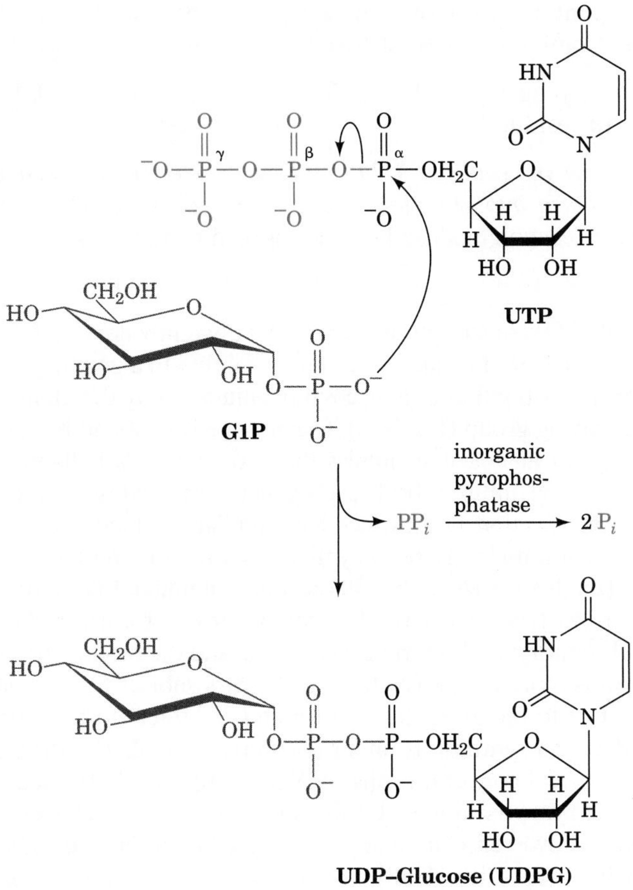

Figure 16-7 | The reaction catalyzed by UDP–glucose pyrophosphorylase. In this phosphoanhydride exchange reaction, the phosphoryl oxygen of G1P attacks the α-phosphorus atom of UTP to form UDP–glucose and PP$_i$. The PP$_i$ is rapidly hydrolyzed by inorganic pyrophosphatase.

	$\Delta G^{\circ\prime}$ (kJ · mol^{-1})
G1P + UTP $\rightleftharpoons$ UDPG + PP$_i$	~0
H$_2$O + PP$_i$ $\rightarrow$ 2P$_i$	−19.2
Overall G1P + UTP $\rightarrow$ UDPG + 2 P$_i$	−19.2

This is an example of the common biosynthetic strategy of cleaving a nucleoside triphosphate to form PP$_i$. The free energy of PP$_i$ hydrolysis can then be used to drive an otherwise unfavorable reaction to completion (Section 14-2B); the near total elimination of the PP$_i$ by the highly exergonic (irreversible) pyrophosphatase reaction prevents the reverse of the PP$_i$-producing reaction from occurring.

B | Glycogen Synthase Extends Glycogen Chains

In the next step of glycogen synthesis, the glycogen synthase reaction, the glucosyl unit of UDPG is transferred to the C4-OH group on one of glycogen's nonreducing ends to form an α(1→4) glycosidic bond. The $\Delta G^{\circ\prime}$ for the glycogen synthase reaction

$$\begin{array}{ccccc} \text{UDPG} & + & \text{glycogen} & \rightarrow & \text{UDP} & + & \text{glycogen} \\ & & (n \text{ residues}) & & & & (n + 1 \text{ residues}) \end{array}$$

is −13.4 kJ · mol^{-1}, making the overall reaction spontaneous under the same conditions that glycogen breakdown by glycogen phosphorylase is also spontaneous. However, glycogen synthesis does have an energetic price. Combining the first two reactions of glycogen synthesis gives

$$\text{Glycogen} + \text{G1P} + \text{UTP} \rightarrow \underset{(n + 1 \text{ residues})}{\text{glycogen}} + \text{UDP} + 2\,\text{P}_i$$
$$(n \text{ residues})$$

Thus, *one molecule of UTP is cleaved to UDP for each glucose residue incorporated into glycogen.* The UTP is replenished through a phosphoryl-transfer reaction mediated by nucleoside diphosphate kinase (Section 14-2C):

$$\text{UDP} + \text{ATP} \rightleftharpoons \text{UTP} + \text{ADP}$$

so that UTP consumption is energetically equivalent to ATP consumption.

The transfer of a glucosyl unit from UDPG to a growing glycogen chain involves the formation of a glycosyl oxonium ion by the elimination of UDP, a good leaving group (Fig. 16-8). The enzyme is inhibited by **1,5-gluconolactone** *(at left)*, an analog that mimics the oxonium ion's half-chair geometry. The same analog inhibits both glycogen phosphorylase (Section 16-1A) and lysozyme (Section 11-4), which have similar mechanisms.

Human muscle glycogen synthase is a homotetramer of 737-residue subunits (the liver isozyme has 703-residue subunits). Like glycogen phosphorylase, it has two enzymatically interconvertible forms; in this case, however, the phosphorylated *b* form is less active, and the original (dephosphorylated) *a* form is more active. (Note: For enzymes subject to covalent modification, "*a*" refers to the more active form and "*b*" refers to the less active form.)

Glycogen synthase is under allosteric control; it is strongly inhibited by physiological concentrations of ATP, ADP, and P_i. In fact, the phosphorylated enzyme is almost totally inactive *in vivo*. The dephosphorylated enzyme, however, can be activated by G6P, so the cell's glycogen synthase activity varies with [G6P] and the fraction of the enzyme in its dephosphorylated form. The mechanistic details of the interconversion of

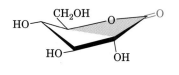

1,5-Gluconolactone

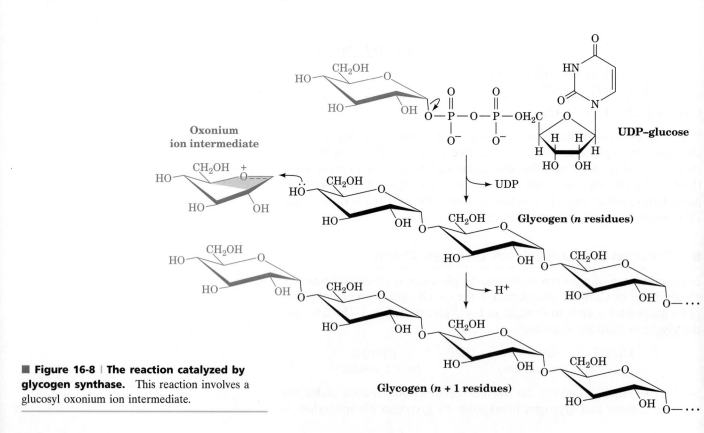

■ **Figure 16-8 | The reaction catalyzed by glycogen synthase.** This reaction involves a glucosyl oxonium ion intermediate.

phosphorylated and dephosphorylated forms of glycogen synthase are complex and are not as well understood as those of glycogen phosphorylase (for one thing, glycogen synthase has multiple phosphorylation sites). We shall discuss the regulation of glycogen synthase further in Section 16-3B.

Glycogenin Primes Glycogen Synthesis. Glycogen synthase cannot simply link together two glucose residues; it can only extend an already existing α(1→4)-linked glucan chain. How, then, is glycogen synthesis initiated? In the first step of this process, a 349-residue protein named **glycogenin,** acting as a glycosyltransferase, attaches a glucose residue donated by UDPG to the OH group of its Tyr 194. Glycogenin then extends the glucose chain by up to seven additional UDPG-donated glucose residues to form a glycogen "primer." Only at this point does glycogen synthase commence glycogen synthesis by extending the primer. Analysis of glycogen granules suggests that each glycogen molecule is associated with only one molecule each of glycogenin and glycogen synthase.

C | Glycogen Branching Enzyme Transfers Seven-Residue Glycogen Segments

Glycogen synthase generates only α(1→4) linkages to yield α-amylose. Branching to form glycogen is accomplished by a separate enzyme, **amylo-(1,4→1,6)-transglycosylase (branching enzyme),** which is distinct from glycogen debranching enzyme (Section 16-1B). A branch is created by transferring a 7-residue segment from the end of a chain to the C6-OH group of a glucose residue on the same or another glycogen chain (Fig. 16-9). Each transferred segment must come from a chain of at least 11

■ **Figure 16-9 | The branching of glycogen.** Branches are formed by transferring a 7-residue terminal segment from an α(1 → 4)-linked glucan chain to the C6-OH group of a glucose residue on the same or another chain.

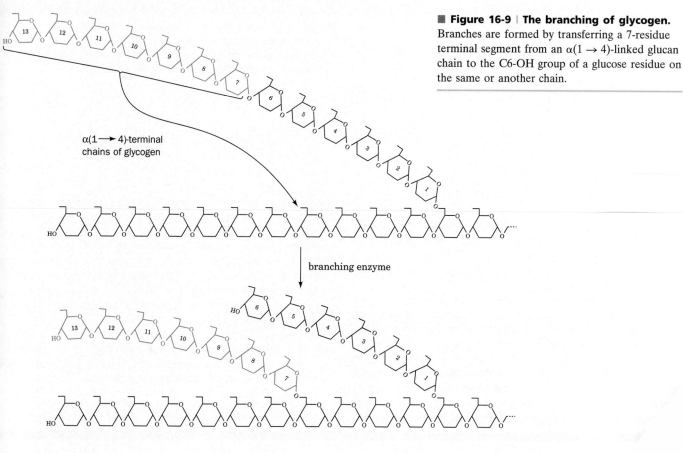

α(1 → 4)-terminal chains of glycogen

branching enzyme

■ **CHECK YOUR UNDERSTANDING**

Describe the enzymatic synthesis of glycogen. Why must opposing biosynthetic and degradative pathways differ in at least one enzyme?

residues, and the new branch point must be at least 4 residues away from other branch points. The branching pattern of glycogen has been optimized by evolution for the efficient storage and mobilization of glucose (Box 16-3).

BOX 16-3 PERSPECTIVES IN BIOCHEMISTRY

Optimizing Glycogen Structure

The function of glycogen in animal cells is to store the metabolic fuel glucose and to release it rapidly when needed. Glucose must be stored as a polymer, because glucose itself could not be stored without a drastic increase in intracellular osmotic pressure (Section 2-1D). It has been estimated that the total concentration of glucose residues stored as glycogen in a liver cell is ~0.4 M, whereas the concentration of glycogen is only ~10 nM. This huge difference mitigates osmotic stress.

To fulfill its biological function, the glycogen polymer must store the largest amount of glucose in the smallest possible volume while maximizing both the amount of glucose available for release by glycogen phosphorylase and the number of nonreducing ends (to maximize the rate at which glucose residues can be mobilized). All these criteria must be met by optimizing just two variables: the degree of branching and chain length.

In a glycogen molecule, shown schematically here,

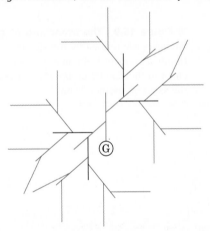

the glycogen chains, beginning with the innermost chain attached to glycogenin (G), have two branches (the outermost chains are unbranched). The entire molecule is roughly spherical and is organized in tiers. There are an estimated 12 tiers in mature glycogen (only 4 are shown above).

With two branches per chain, the number of chains in a given tier is twice the number of the preceding tier, and the outermost tier contains about half of the total glucose residues (regardless of the number of tiers). When the degree of branching increases, for example, to three branches per chain, the proportion of residues ~~~most tier increases, but so does the density of glucose ~~~ limits the maximum size of the glycogen ~~~ er of glucose residues it can accommodate. ~~~ound two branches per chain.

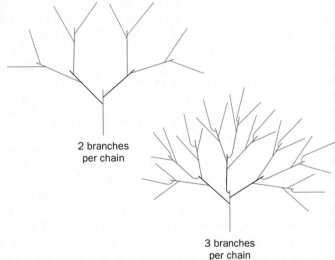

2 branches per chain

3 branches per chain

Mathematical analysis of the other variable, chain length, yields an optimal value of 13, which is in good agreement with the actual length of glycogen chains in cells (8–14 residues). Consider the two simplified glycogen molecules shown below, which contain the same number of glucose residues (the same total length of line segments) and the same branching pattern:

The molecule with the shorter chains packs more glucose in a given volume and has more points for phosphorylase attack, but only about half the amount of glucose can be released before debranching must occur (debranching is much slower than phosphorolysis). In the less dense molecule, the longer chains increase the number of residues that can be continuously phosphorylyzed; however, there are fewer points of attack. Thirteen residues is apparently a compromise for mobilizing the largest amount of glucose in the shortest time.

Amylopectin (Section 8-2C), which is chemically similar to glycogen, is a much larger molecule and has longer chains. Amylose lacks branches altogether. Evidently, starch, unlike glycogen, is not designed for rapid mobilization of metabolic fuel.

[Figures adapted from Meléndez-Hevia, E., Waddell, T.G., and Shelton E.D., *Biochem. J.* **295**, 477–483 (1993).]

3 Control of Glycogen Metabolism

glycogen synthesis and breakdown proceed simultaneously, all that is accomplished is the wasteful hydrolysis of UTP. Glycogen metabolism must therefore be controlled according to cellular needs. *The regulation of glycogen metabolism involves allosteric control as well as hormonal control by covalent modification of the pathway's regulatory enzymes.*

LEARNING OBJECTIVES

■ Understand that the opposing processes of glycogen breakdown and synthesis are reciprocally regulated by allosteric interactions and covalent modification of key enzymes.
■ Understand that glycogen metabolism is ultimately under hormonal control.

A | Glycogen Phosphorylase and Glycogen Synthase Are under Allosteric Control

As we saw in Sections 14-1E and 15-4B, the net flux, J, of reactants through a step in a metabolic pathway is the difference between the forward and reverse reaction velocities, v_f and v_r. However, the flux varies dramatically with substrate concentration as the reaction approaches equilibrium ($v_f \approx v_r$). The flux through a near-equilibrium reaction is therefore all but uncontrollable. *Precise flux control of a pathway is possible when an enzyme functioning far from equilibrium is opposed by a separately controlled enzyme. Then, v_f and v_r vary independently and v_r can be larger or smaller than v_f, allowing control of both rate and direction.* Exactly this situation occurs in glycogen metabolism through the opposition of the glycogen phosphorylase and glycogen synthase reactions.

Both glycogen phosphorylase and glycogen synthase are under allosteric control by effectors that include ATP, G6P, and AMP. Muscle glycogen phosphorylase is activated by AMP and inhibited by ATP and G6P. Glycogen synthase, on the other hand, is activated by G6P. This suggests that when there is high demand for ATP (low [ATP], low [G6P], and high [AMP]), glycogen phosphorylase is stimulated and glycogen synthase is inhibited, which favors glycogen breakdown. Conversely, when [ATP] and [G6P] are high, glycogen synthesis is favored.

In vivo, this allosteric scheme is superimposed on an additional control system based on covalent modification. For example, phosphorylase *a* is active even without AMP stimulation (Section 16-1A), and glycogen synthase is essentially inactive (Section 16-2B) unless it is dephosphorylated and G6P is present. *Thus, covalent modification (phosphorylation and dephosphorylation) of glycogen phosphorylase and glycogen synthase provides a more sophisticated control system that modulates the responsiveness of the enzymes to their allosteric effectors.*

B | Glycogen Phosphorylase and Glycogen Synthase Undergo Control by Covalent Modification

The interconversion of the *a* and *b* forms of glycogen synthase and glycogen phosphorylase is accomplished through enzyme-catalyzed phosphorylation and dephosphorylation (Section 12-3B), a process that is under hormonal control (Section 13-2). **Enzymatically interconvertible enzyme systems** can therefore respond to a greater number of effectors than simple allosteric systems. Furthermore, a set of kinases and phosphatases linked in cascade fashion has enormous potential for signal amplification and flexibility in response to different metabolic signals. Note that the correlation between phosphorylation and enzyme activity varies with the enzyme. For example, glycogen phosphorylase is activated by phosphorylation ($b \rightarrow a$), whereas glycogen synthase is inactivated by phosphorylation ($a \rightarrow b$). Conversely, dephosphorylation inactivates glycogen phosphorylase and activates glycogen synthase.

See Guided Exploration 15
Control of glycogen metabolism.

Glycogen Phosphorylase Is Activated by Phosphorylation. The ca
cade that governs the enzymatic interconversion of glycogen phosphor
lase involves three enzymes (Fig. 16-10):

1. *Phosphorylase kinase,* which specifically phosphorylates Ser 14
   glycogen phosphorylase *b*.
2. *Protein kinase A (PKA;* Section 13-3C), which phosphorylates a
   thereby activates phosphorylase kinase.
3. *Phosphoprotein phosphatase-1 (PP1;* Section 13-2D), which d
   phosphorylates and thereby deactivates both glycogen phosphor
   lase *a* and phosphorylase kinase.

Phosphorylase *b* is sensitive to allosteric effectors, but phosphorylase
is much less so, as discussed in Section 12-3B (Fig. 12-16). In the resti
cell, the concentrations of ATP and G6P are high enough to inhibit pho
phorylase *b*. The level of phosphorylase activity is therefore largely dete
mined by the fraction of enzyme present as phosphorylase *a*. The stea
state fraction of phosphorylated enzyme depends on the relative activiti
of phosphorylase kinase, PKA, and PP1. Recall that PKA is activated l
cAMP, a second messenger that is made by **adenylate cyclase** on hormon
stimulated activation of a heterotrimeric **G protein** (Section 13-3C). L
us examine the factors that regulate the activities of phosphorylase kina
and PP1 before we return to the regulation of glycogen synthase activit

Phosphorylase Kinase Is Activated by Phosphorylation and by Ca²
Phosphorylase kinase is a 1300-kD protein with four nonidentical subuni
known as α, β, γ, and δ. The γ subunit contains the catalytic site, and t
other three subunits have regulatory functions. *Phosphorylase kinase*
*maximally activated by Ca²⁺ and by the phosphorylation of its α and β su
units by PKA.*

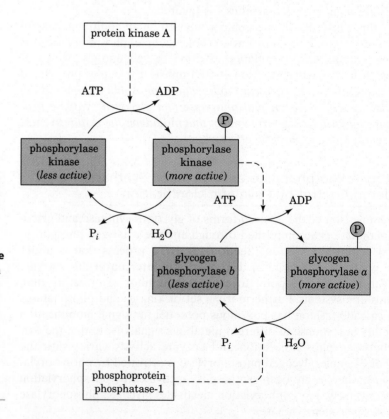

■ **Figure 16-10** | **The glycogen phosphorylase
interconvertible enzyme system.** Conversion
of phosphorylase *b* (the less active form) to
phosphorylase *a* (the more active form) is
accomplished through phosphorylation catalyzed
by phosphorylase kinase, which is itself subject to
activation through phosphorylation by protein
kinase A (PKA). Both glycogen phosphorylase *a*
and phosphorylase kinase are dephosphorylated
by phosphoprotein phosphatase-1.

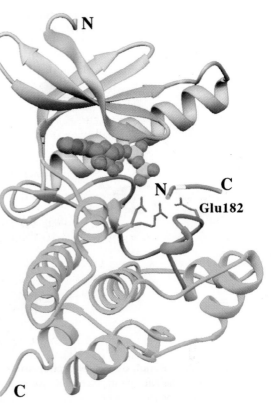

Figure 16-11 | X-Ray structure of the γ subunit of rabbit muscle phosphorylase kinase in complex with ATP and a heptapeptide analog of the enzyme's natural substrate. The N-terminal domain is pink, the C-terminal domain is cyan, the activation loop is light blue, and the heptapeptide is orange, with its residue to be phosphorylated (Ser) white. The ATP is shown in space-filling form and the side chains of the catalytically essential Arg 148, Asp 149, and Glu 182 are shown in stick form, all colored according to atom type (C green, N blue, O red, and P yellow). Note the structural similarities and differences between this protein and other protein kinases, for example, the C subunit of protein kinase A (Fig. 13-22) and the tyrosine kinase domain of the insulin receptor (Fig. 13-5). [After an X-ray structure by Louise Johnson, Oxford University, U.K. PDBid 2PHK.]

The γ subunit of phosphorylase kinase contains a 386-residue kinase domain, which is 36% identical in sequence to the PKA C subunit (Fig. 13-22) and has a similar structure (Fig. 16-11). The γ subunit is not subject to phosphorylation, as are many other protein kinases, because the Ser, Thr, or Tyr residue that is phosphorylated to activate those other kinases is replaced by a Glu residue in the γ subunit. The negative charge of the Glu is thought to mimic the presence of a phosphate group and interact with a conserved Arg residue near the active site. However, full catalytic activity of the γ subunit is prevented by an autoinhibitory C-terminal segment, which binds to and blocks the kinase's active site, much like the R subunit blocks the activity of the C subunit of protein kinase A. An inhibitory segment in the β subunit may also block the activity of the γ subunit.

Autoinhibition of phosphorylase kinase is relieved by PKA-catalyzed phosphorylation of both the α and β subunits. This presumably causes the β inhibitor segment to move aside (the way in which phosphorylation of the α subunit modulates the enzyme's behavior is not understood). However, full activity of the γ subunit also requires Ca^{2+} binding to the δ subunit, which is **calmodulin (CaM;** Section 13-4B; CaM functions both as a free-floating protein and as a subunit of other proteins). Ca^{2+} concentrations as low as 10^{-7} M activate phosphorylase kinase by inducing a conformational change in CaM that causes it to bind to and extract the γ subunit's autoinhibitor segment from its catalytic site.

The conversion of glycogen phosphorylase *b* to glycogen phosphorylase *a* through the action of phosphorylase kinase increases the rate of glycogen breakdown. The physiological significance of the Ca^{2+} trigger for this activation is that muscle contraction is also triggered by a transient increase in the level of cytosolic Ca^{2+} (Section 7-2B). The rate of glycogen breakdown is thereby linked to the rate of muscle contraction. This is critical because glycogen breakdown provides fuel for glycolysis to generate the ATP required for muscle contraction. Since Ca^{2+} release occurs in response to nerve impulses, whereas the phosphorylation of phosphorylase kinase ultimately occurs in response to the presence of certain hormones, these two signals act synergistically in muscle cells to stimulate glycogenolysis.

Phosphoprotein Phosphatase-1 Is Inhibited by Phosphoprotein Inhibitor-1. A steady state for many phosphorylated enzymes is maintained by a balance between phosphorylation, as catalyzed by a corresponding kinase, and hydrolytic dephosphorylation, as catalyzed by a phosphatase. Phosphoprotein phosphatase-1 (PP1) removes the phosphoryl groups from glycogen phosphorylase *a* and the α and β subunits of phosphorylase kinase (Fig. 16-10), as well as those of other proteins involved in glycogen metabolism (see below).

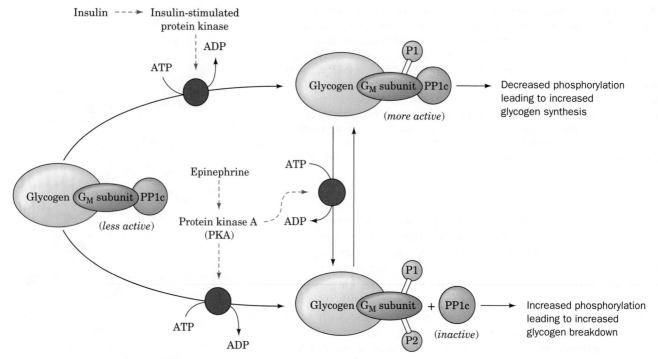

■ **Figure 16-12** | **Regulation of phosphoprotein phosphatase-1 in muscle.** The antagonistic effects of insulin and epinephrine on glycogen metabolism in muscle occur through their effects on the phosphoprotein phosphatase-1 catalytic subunit, PP1c, via its glycogen-bound G_M subunit. Green circles and dashed arrows indicate activation.

PP1 is controlled differently in muscle and in liver. In muscle, the catalytic subunit of PP1 (called **PP1c**) is active only when it is bound to glycogen through its glycogen-binding G_M **subunit.** The activity of PP1c and its affinity for the G_M subunit are regulated by phosphorylation of the G_M subunit at two separate sites (Fig. 16-12). Phosphorylation of site 1 by an **insulin-stimulated protein kinase** (a homolog of PKA and the γ subunit of phosphorylase kinase) activates PP1c, whereas phosphorylation of site 2 by PKA (which can also phosphorylate site 1) causes PP1c to be released into the cytoplasm, where it cannot dephosphorylate the glycogen-bound enzymes of glycogen metabolism.

In the cytosol, phosphoprotein phosphatase-1 is also inhibited by its binding to the protein **phosphoprotein phosphatase inhibitor 1.** The latter protein provides yet another example of control by covalent modification. It too is activated by PKA and deactivated by phosphoprotein phosphatase-1 (Fig. 16-13, *lower left*). *The concentration of cAMP therefore controls the fraction of an enzyme in its phosphorylated form, not only by increasing the rate at which it is phosphorylated, but also by decreasing the rate at which it is dephosphorylated.* In the case of glycogen phosphorylase, an increase in [cAMP] not only increases the enzyme's rate of activation, but also decreases its rate of deactivation.

In liver, PP1 is also bound to glycogen, but through the intermediacy of a glycogen-binding subunit named G_L. In contrast to G_M, G_L is not subject to control via phosphorylation. The activity of the PP1 · G_L complex is controlled by its binding to phosphorylase *a*. Both the R and T forms of phosphorylase *a* strongly bind PP1, but only in the T state is the Ser 14 phosphoryl group accessible for hydrolysis (in the R state, the Ser 14 phosphoryl group is buried at the dimer interface; Fig. 12-15). Consequently

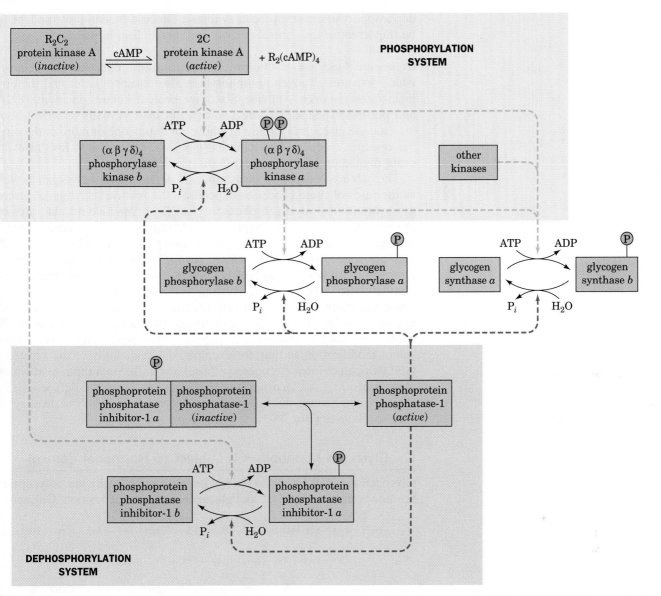

Figure 16-13 | The major phosphorylation and dephosphorylation systems that regulate glycogen metabolism in muscle. Activated enzymes are shaded green, and deactivated enzymes are shaded pink. Dashed arrows indicate facilitation of a phosphorylation or dephosphorylation reaction. 🔊 **See the Animated Figures.**

when phosphorylase a is in its active R form, it effectively sequesters PP1. However, under conditions where phosphorylase a shifts to the T state (see below), PP1 hydrolyzes the now exposed Ser 14 phosphoryl group, thereby converting phosphorylase a to phosphorylase b, which has only a low affinity for the PP1 · G_L complex. One effect of phosphorylase a dephosphorylation, therefore, is to relieve the inhibition of PP1. Since liver cells contain 10 times more glycogen phosphorylase than PP1, the phosphatase is not released until more than ~90% of the glycogen phosphorylase is in the b form. Only then can PP1 dephosphorylate its other target proteins, including glycogen synthase.

Glucose is an allosteric inhibitor of phosphorylase a (Fig. 12-16). Consequently, when the concentration of glucose is high, phosphorylase a converts to its T form, thereby leading to its dephosphorylation and the dephosphorylation of glycogen synthase. Glucose is therefore thought to be important in the control of glycogen metabolism in the liver.

Glycogen Synthase Is Elaborately Regulated. Phosphorylase kinase, which activates glycogen phosphorylase, also phosphorylates and thereby inactivates glycogen synthase. Six other protein kinases, including PKA and phosphorylase kinase, are known to at least partially deactivate human muscle glycogen synthase by phosphorylating one or more of the nine Ser residues on each of its subunits (Fig. 16-13). The reason for this elaborate regulation of glycogen synthase is unclear.

The balance between net synthesis and degradation of glycogen as well as the rates of these processes depend on the relative activities of glycogen synthase and glycogen phosphorylase. To a large extent, the rates of the phosphorylation and dephosphorylation of these enzymes control glycogen synthesis and breakdown. The two processes are linked by PKA and phosphorylase kinase, which, through phosphorylation, activate glycogen phosphorylase as they inactivate glycogen synthase (Fig. 16-13). They are also linked by PP1, which in liver is inhibited by phosphorylase *a* and therefore unable to activate (dephosphorylate) glycogen synthase unless it first inactivates (also by dephosphorylation) phosphorylase *a*. Of course, control by allosteric effectors is superimposed on control by covalent modification so that, for example, the availability of the substrate G6P (which activates glycogen synthase) also influences the rate at which glucose residues are incorporated into glycogen. Inherited deficiencies of enzymes can disrupt the fine control of glycogen metabolism, leading to various diseases (Box 16-2).

C | Glycogen Metabolism Is Subject to Hormonal Control

Glycogen metabolism in the liver is largely controlled by the polypeptide hormones insulin (Fig. 5-1) and **glucagon** acting in opposition. Glucagon

$$\overset{+}{H_3N}-His-Ser-Gln-Gly-Thr-Phe-Thr-Ser-Asp-Tyr-10$$

$$Ser-Lys-Tyr-Leu-Asp-Ser-Arg-Arg-Ala-Gln-20$$

$$Asp-Phe-Val-Gln-Trp-Leu-Met-Asn-Thr-COO^-\ 29$$

Glucagon

like insulin, is synthesized by the pancreas in response to the concentration of glucose in the blood. In muscles and various tissues, control is exerted by insulin and by the adrenal hormones **epinephrine** and **norepinephrine** (Section 13-1B). These hormones affect metabolism in their target tissues by ultimately stimulating covalent modification (phosphorylation) of regulatory enzymes. They do so by binding to transmembrane **receptors** on the surface of cells. Different cell types have different complements of receptors and therefore respond to different sets of hormones. The responses involve the release inside the cell of molecules collectively known as **second messengers,** that is, intracellular mediators of the externally received hormonal message. Different receptors cause the release of different second messengers. cAMP, identified by Earl Sutherland in the 1950s, was the first second messenger discovered. Ca^{2+}, as released from intracellular reservoirs into the cytosol, is also a common second messenger. Receptors and second messengers are discussed in greater depth in Chapter 13.

When hormonal stimulation increases the intracellular cAMP concentration, PKA activity increases, increasing the rates of phosphorylation of many proteins and decreasing their dephosphorylation rates as well. Because of the cascade nature of the regulatory system diagrammed in Fig. 16-13, *a small change in [cAMP] results in a large change in the fraction of phosphorylated enzymes.* When a large fraction of the glycogen metabolism enzymes are phosphorylated, the metabolic flux is in the direction of glycogen breakdown, since glycogen phosphorylase is active and glycogen synthase is inactive. When [cAMP] decreases, phosphorylation rates decrease, dephosphorylation rates increase, and the fraction of enzymes in their dephospho forms increases. The resulting activation of glycogen synthase and inhibition of glycogen phosphorylase cause the flux to shift to net glycogen synthesis.

Glucagon binding to its receptor on liver cells, which generates intracellular cAMP, results in glucose mobilization from stored glycogen (Fig. 16-14). Glucagon is released from the pancreas when the concentration of circulating glucose decreases to less than ~5 mM, such as during exercise or several hours after a meal has been digested. Glucagon is therefore critical for the liver's function in supplying glucose to tissues that depend primarily on glycolysis for their energy needs. Muscle cells do not respond to glucagon because they lack the appropriate receptor.

Epinephrine and norepinephrine, which are often called the "fight or flight" hormones, are released into the bloodstream by the adrenal glands in response to stress. There are two types of receptors for these hormones: the β-adrenoreceptor (β-adrenergic receptor), which is linked to the adenylate

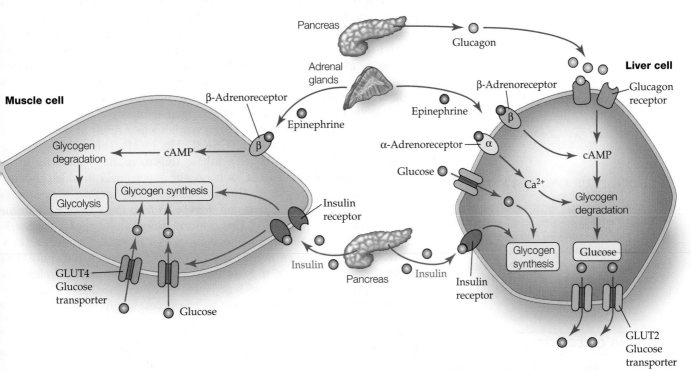

■ Figure 16-14 | Hormonal control of glycogen metabolism.
Epinephrine binding to β-adrenoreceptors on liver and muscle cells increases intracellular [cAMP], which promotes glycogen degradation to G6P for glycolysis (in muscle) or to glucose for export (in liver). The liver responds similarly to glucagon. Epinephrine binding to α-adrenoreceptors on liver cells leads to increased cytosolic [Ca²⁺], which also promotes glycogen degradation. When circulating glucose is plentiful, insulin stimulates glucose uptake and glycogen synthesis in muscle cells. The liver responds both to insulin and directly to increased glucose by increasing glycogen synthesis.

cyclase system, and the **α-adrenoreceptor (α-adrenergic receptor),** whose sec ond messenger causes intracellular $[Ca^{2+}]$ to increase (Section 13-4A). Muscl cells, which have the β-adrenoreceptor (Fig. 16-14), respond to epinephrine by breaking down glycogen for glycolysis, thereby generating ATP and help ing the muscles cope with the stress that triggered the epinephrine release.

Liver cells respond to epinephrine directly and indirectly. Epinephrine pro motes the release of glucagon from the pancreas, and glucagon binding to it receptor on liver cells stimulates glycogen breakdown as described above Epinephrine also binds directly to both α- and β-adrenoreceptors on the sur faces of liver cells (Fig. 16-14). Binding to the β-adrenoreceptor results in in creased intracellular cAMP, which leads to glycogen breakdown. Epinephrine binding to the α-adrenoreceptor stimulates an increase in intracellular $[Ca^{2+}]$ which reinforces the cells' response to cAMP (recall that phosphorylase ki nase, which activates glycogen phosphorylase and inactivates glycogen syn thase, is fully active only when phosphorylated and in the presence of in creased $[Ca^{2+}]$). In addition, glycogen synthase is inactivated through phosphorylation catalyzed by several Ca^{2+}-dependent protein kinases.

Insulin and Epinephrine Are Antagonists. Insulin is released from the pancreas in response to high levels of circulating glucose (e.g., immedi ately after a meal). Hormonal stimulation by insulin increases the rate o glucose transport into the many types of cells that have both insulin recep tors and insulin sensitive glucose transporters called GLUT4 on their surface (e.g., muscle and fat cells, but not liver and brain cells). In addition [cAMP] decreases, causing glycogen metabolism to shift from glycogen breakdown to glycogen synthesis (Fig. 16-14). The mechanism of insulin action is very complex (Sections 13-4D and 22-2), but one of its targe enzymes appears to be PP1. As outlined in Fig. 16-12, insulin activate insulin-stimulated protein kinase in muscle to phosphorylate site 1 on the glycogen-binding G_M subunit of PP1 so as to activate this protein and thu dephosphorylate the enzymes of glycogen metabolism. The storage of glu cose as glycogen is thereby promoted through the inhibition of glycogen breakdown and the stimulation of glycogen synthesis.

In liver, insulin stimulates glycogen synthesis as a result of the inhibition of **glycogen synthase kinase 3β: (GSK3β:** Fig. 13-31). This action decrease the phosphorylation of glycogen synthase, thus increasing its activity. In ad dition, it is thought that glucose itself, may be a messenger to which glycogen metabolism system responds. *Glucose inhibits phosphorylase a by binding to the enzyme's inactive T state and thereby shifting the T ⇌ R equilibrium toward the T state* (Fig. 12-16). This conformational shift exposes the Ser 1 phosphoryl group to dephosphorylation. An increase in glucose con centration therefore promotes inactivation of glycogen phosphorylase *a* through its conversion to phosphorylase *b*. The subsequent release of phosphoprotein phosphatase-1 activates glycogen synthase. Thus when glucose is plentiful, the liver can store the excess as glycogen.

■ **CHECK YOUR UNDERSTANDING**

Why does a phosphorylation/dephosphoryla tion system allow more sensitive regulation of a metabolic process than a simple allosteric system?

How does regulation of glycogen metabolism differ between liver and muscle?

LEARNING OBJECTIVES

■ Appreciate that glucose can be synthesized from lactate, pyruvate, and amino acids.
■ Understand that gluconeogenesis is mostly the reverse of glycolysis with the few endergonic reactions bypassed by hydrolysis.
■ Understand that glycolysis and gluconeogenesis must be reciprocally regulated.

4 Gluconeogenesis

When dietary sources of glucose are not available and when the liver has ex hausted its supply of glycogen, glucose is synthesized from noncarbohydrate precursors by **gluconeogenesis.** In fact, gluconeogenesis provides a substantia fraction of the glucose produced in fasting humans, even within a few hour of eating. Gluconeogenesis occurs in liver and, to a lesser extent, in kidney.

The noncarbohydrate precursors that can be converted to glucose include the glycolysis products lactate and pyruvate, citric acid cycle intermediates and the carbon skeletons of most amino acids. First, however, all these substances must be converted to the four-carbon compound **oxaloacetate** *(at right)*, which itself is a citric acid cycle intermediate (Section 17-1). The only amino acids that cannot be converted to oxaloacetate in animals are leucine and lysine because their breakdown yields only acetyl-CoA (Section 21-4E) and because *there is no pathway in animals for the net conversion of acetyl-CoA to oxaloacetate.* Likewise, fatty acids cannot serve as glucose precursors in animals because most fatty acids are degraded completely to acetyl-CoA (Section 20-2). However, fatty acid breakdown generates much of the ATP that powers gluconeogenesis.

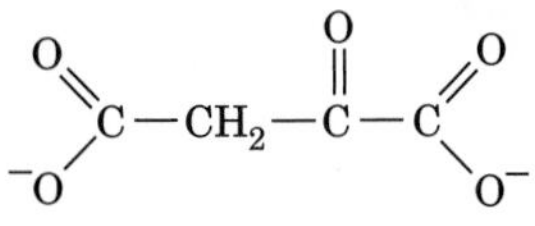

For convenience, we consider gluconeogenesis to be the pathway by which pyruvate is converted to glucose. Most of the reactions of gluconeogenesis are glycolytic reactions that proceed in reverse (Fig. 16-15).

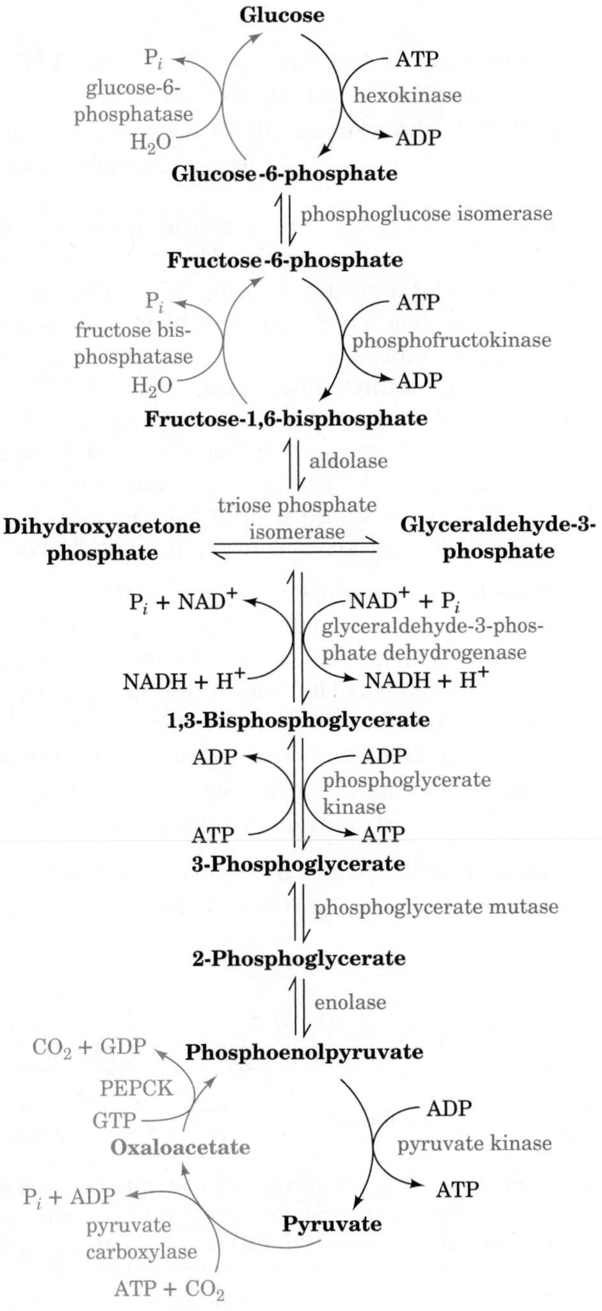

Oxaloacetate

■ **Figure 16-15 | Comparison of the pathways of gluconeogenesis and glycolysis.** The red arrows represent the steps that are catalyzed by different enzymes in gluconeogenesis. The other seven reaction steps of gluconeogenesis are catalyzed by glycolytic enzymes that function near equilibrium. *See the Animated Figures.*

However, the glycolytic enzymes hexokinase, phosphofructokinase, and pyruvate kinase catalyze reactions with large negative free energy changes. These reactions must therefore be replaced in gluconeogenesis by reactions that make glucose synthesis thermodynamically favorable.

A | Pyruvate Is Converted to Phosphoenolpyruvate in Two Steps

We begin our examination of the reactions unique to gluconeogenesis with the conversion of pyruvate to phosphoenolpyruvate (PEP). Because this step is the reverse of the highly exergonic reaction catalyzed by pyruvate kinase (Section 15-2J), it requires free energy input. This is accomplished by first converting the pyruvate to oxaloacetate. Oxaloacetate is a "high-energy" intermediate because its exergonic decarboxylation provides the free energy necessary for PEP synthesis. The process requires two enzymes (Fig. 16-16):

1. **Pyruvate carboxylase** catalyzes the ATP-driven formation of oxaloacetate from pyruvate and HCO_3^-.

2. **PEP Carboxykinase (PEPCK)** converts oxaloacetate to PEP in a reaction that uses GTP as a phosphoryl-group donor.

Pyruvate Carboxylase Has a Biotin Prosthetic Group. Pyruvate carboxylase is a tetrameric protein of identical ~1160-residue subunits, each of which has a **biotin** prosthetic group. Biotin (Fig. 16-17a) functions as a CO_2 carrier by forming a carboxyl substituent at its **ureido group** (Fig. 16-17b). Biotin is covalently bound to an enzyme Lys residue to form a **biocytin** (alternatively, **biotinyllysine**) residue (Fig. 16-17b). The biotin ring system is therefore at the end of a 14-Å-long flexible arm. Biotin, which was first identified in 1935 as a growth factor in yeast, is an essential human nutrient. Its nutritional deficiency is rare, however, because it occurs in many foods and is synthesized by intestinal bacteria.

The pyruvate carboxylase reaction occurs in two phases (Fig. 16-18):

Phase I The cleavage of ATP to ADP acts to dehydrate bicarbonate via the formation of a "high-energy" carboxyphosphate intermediate. The reaction of the resulting CO_2 with biotin is exergonic. The biotin-bound carboxyl group is therefore "activated" relative to bicarbonate and can be transferred to another molecule without further free energy input.

Phase II The activated carboxyl group is transferred from carboxybiotin to pyruvate in a three-step reaction to form oxaloacetate.

These two reaction phases occur on different subsites of the same enzyme; the 14-Å arm of biocytin transfers the biotin ring between the two sites.

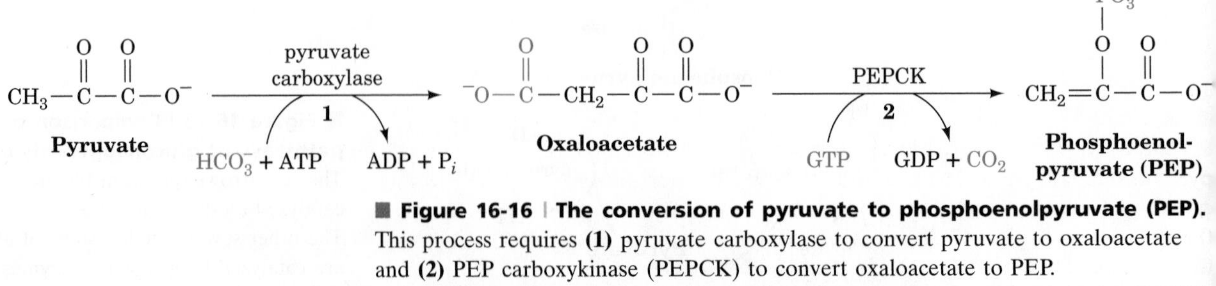

■ **Figure 16-16** | **The conversion of pyruvate to phosphoenolpyruvate (PEP).** This process requires (**1**) pyruvate carboxylase to convert pyruvate to oxaloacetate and (**2**) PEP carboxykinase (PEPCK) to convert oxaloacetate to PEP.

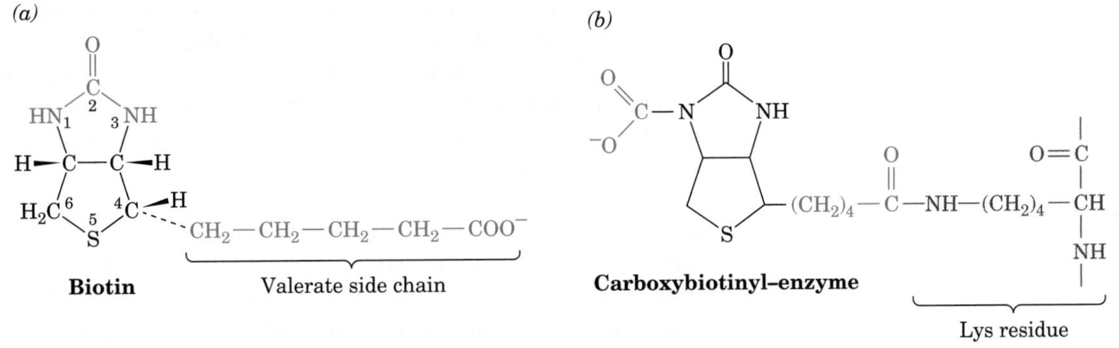

(a)

Biotin | Valerate side chain

(b)

Carboxybiotinyl–enzyme

Lys residue

■ Figure 16-17 | Biotin and carboxybiotinyl–enzyme.
(*a*) Biotin consists of an imidazoline ring that is cis-fused to a tetrahydrothiophene ring bearing a valerate side chain. Positions 1, 2, and 3 constitute a ureido group. (*b*) Biotin is covalently attached to carboxylases by an amide linkage between its valeryl carboxyl group and an ε-amino group of an enzyme Lys side chain. The carboxybiotinyl–enzyme forms when N1 of the biotin ureido group is carboxylated.

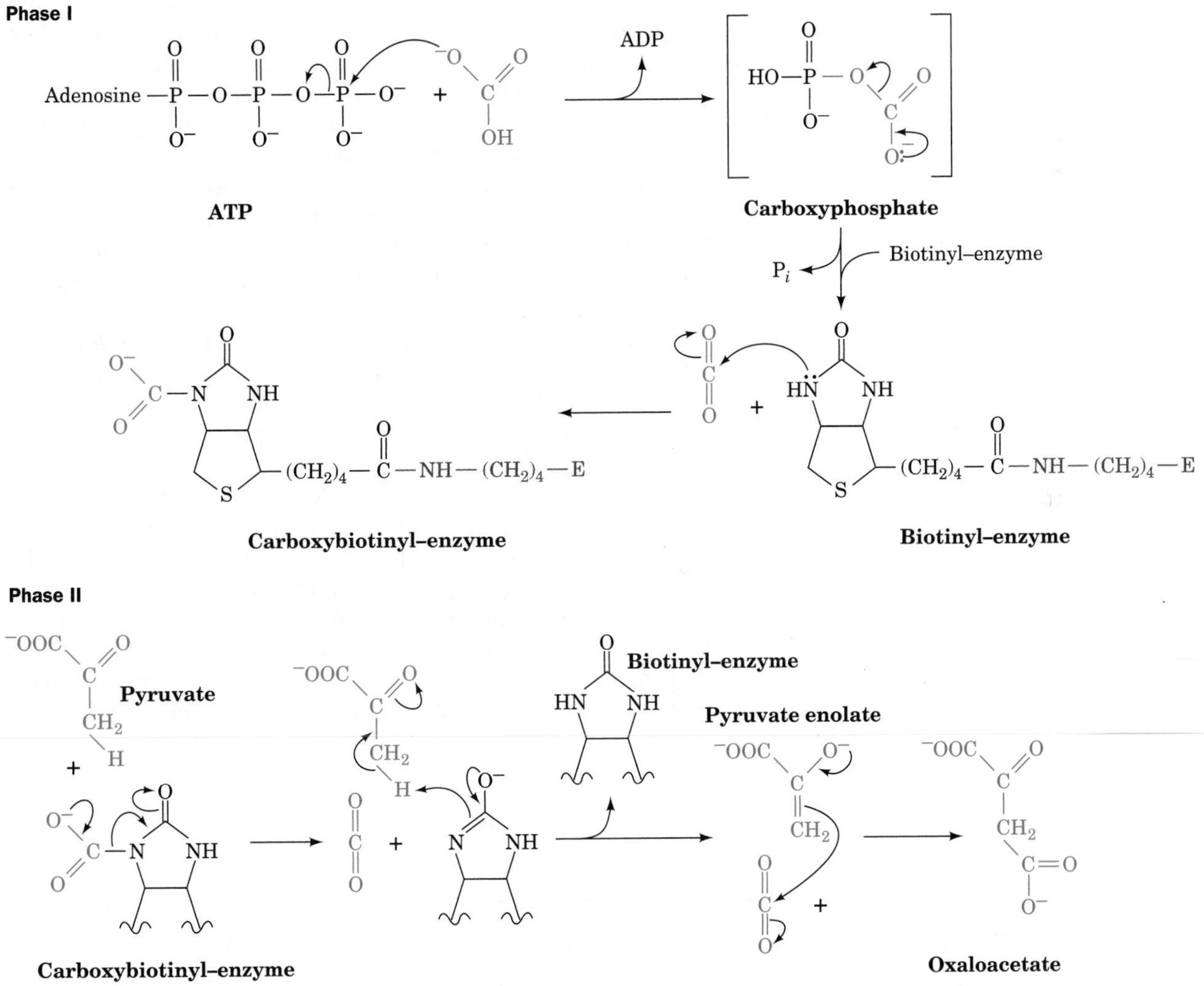

Phase I

ATP

Carboxyphosphate

Carboxybiotinyl–enzyme

Biotinyl–enzyme

Phase II

Pyruvate

Carboxybiotinyl–enzyme

Biotinyl–enzyme

Pyruvate enolate

Oxaloacetate

■ Figure 16-18 | The two-phase reaction mechanism of pyruvate carboxylase. Phase I is a three-step reaction in which carboxyphosphate is formed from bicarbonate and ATP, followed by the generation of CO_2, which then carboxylates biotin. Phase II is a three-step reaction in which CO_2 is produced at the active site via the elimination of the biotinyl–enzyme, which accepts a proton from pyruvate to generate pyruvate enolate. This enolate, in turn, nucleophilically attacks the CO_2, yielding oxaloacetate. [After Knowles, J.R., *Annu. Rev. Biochem.* **58**, 217 (1989).]

Oxaloacetate is both a precursor for gluconeogenesis and an intermediate of the citric acid cycle (Section 17-3). When the citric acid cycle substrate acetyl-CoA accumulates, it allosterically activates pyruvate carboxylase, thereby increasing the amount of oxaloacetate that can participate in the citric acid cycle. When citric acid cycle activity is low, oxaloacetate instead enters the gluconeogenic pathway.

PEP Carboxykinase Catalyzes the Formation of PEP. PEPCK, a monomeric ~610-residue enzyme, catalyzes the GTP-requiring decarboxylation/phosphorylation of oxaloacetate to form PEP and GDP (Fig. 16-19). Note that the CO_2 that carboxylates pyruvate to yield oxaloacetate is eliminated in the formation of PEP. The favorable decarboxylation reaction drives the formation of the enol that GTP phosphorylates. *Oxaloacetate can therefore be considered as "activated" pyruvate, with CO_2 and biotin facilitating the activation at the expense of ATP.*

Gluconeogenesis Requires Metabolite Transport between Mitochondria and Cytosol. The generation of oxaloacetate from pyruvate or citric acid cycle intermediates occurs only in the mitochondrion, whereas the enzymes that convert PEP to glucose are cytosolic. The cellular location of PEPCK varies: In some species, it is mitochondrial; in some, it is cytosolic; and in some (including humans) it is equally distributed between the two compartments. In order for gluconeogenesis to occur, either oxaloacetate must leave the mitochondrion for conversion to PEP or the PEP formed there must enter the cytosol.

PEP is transported across the mitochondrial membrane by specific membrane transport proteins. There is, however, no such transport system for oxaloacetate. *In species with cytosolic PEPCK, oxaloacetate must first be converted either to aspartate* (Fig. 16-20, Route 1) *or to **malate*** (Fig. 16-20, Route 2), for which mitochondrial transport systems exist. The difference between the two routes involves the transport of NADH **reducing equivalents** (in the transport of reducing equivalents, the electrons—but not the electron carrier—cross the membrane). The **malate dehydrogenase** route (Route 2) results in the transport of reducing equivalents from the mitochondrion to the cytosol, since it uses mitochondrial NADH and produces cytosolic NADH. The **aspartate aminotransferase** route (Route 1) does not involve NADH. Cytosolic NADH is required for gluconeogenesis, so, under most conditions, the route through malate is a necessity. However, when the gluconeogenic precursor is lactate, its oxidation to pyruvate generates cytosolic NADH, and either transport system can then be used. All the reactions shown in Fig. 16-20 are freely reversible, so that

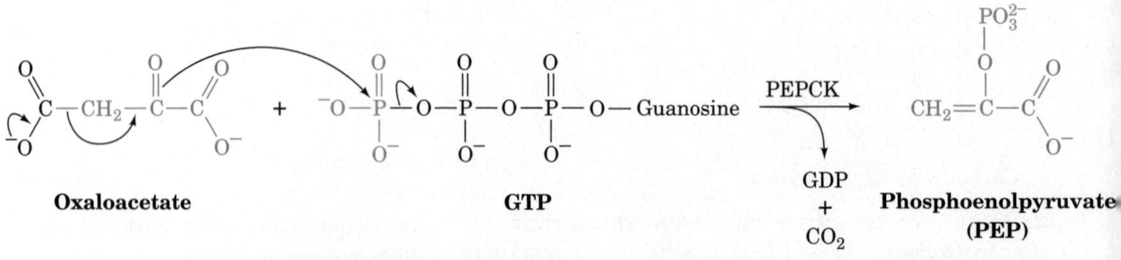

Oxaloacetate + GTP $\xrightarrow{\text{PEPCK}}$ GDP + CO_2 + Phosphoenolpyruvate (PEP)

■ **Figure 16-19 | The PEPCK mechanism.** Decarboxylation of oxaloacetate (a β-keto acid) forms a resonance-stabilized enolate anion whose oxygen atom attacks the γ-phosphoryl group of GTP, forming PEP and GDP.

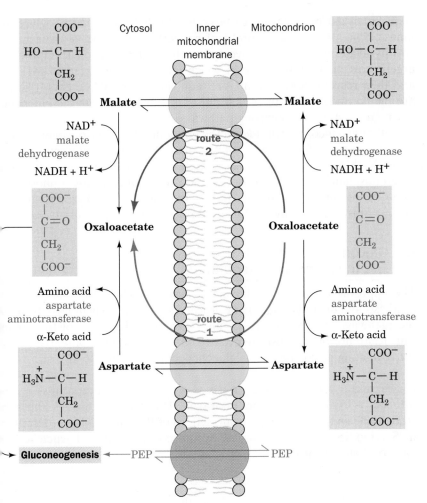

■ **Figure 16-20** │ **The transport of PEP and oxaloacetate from the mitochondrion to the cytosol.** PEP is directly transported between the compartments. Oxaloacetate, however, must first be converted to either aspartate through the action of aspartate aminotransferase (Route 1) or to malate by malate dehydrogenase (Route 2). Route 2 involves the mitochondrial oxidation of NADH followed by the cytosolic reduction of NAD^+ and therefore also transfers NADH reducing equivalents from the mitochondrion to the cytosol. ☜ **See the Animated Figures.**

under appropriate conditions, the malate–aspartate shuttle system also operates to transport NADH reducing equivalents into the mitochondrion for oxidative phosphorylation (Section 18-1B). Liver has a variation of Route 1 in which aspartate entering the cytosol is deaminated via the urea cycle before undergoing a series of reactions that yield oxaloacetate (Section 21-3A).

B │ Hydrolytic Reactions Bypass Irreversible Glycolytic Reactions

The route from PEP to fructose-1,6-bisphosphate (FBP) is catalyzed by the enzymes of glycolysis operating in reverse. However, *the glycolytic reactions catalyzed by phosphofructokinase (PFK) and hexokinase are endergonic in the gluconeogenesis direction and hence must be bypassed by different gluconeogenic enzymes.* FBP is hydrolyzed by **fructose-1,6-bisphosphatase (FBPase).** The resulting fructose-6-phosphate (F6P) is isomerized to G6P, which is then hydrolyzed by glucose-6-phosphatase, the same enzyme that converts glycogen-derived G6P to glucose (Section 16-1C) and which is present only in liver and kidney. Note that these two hydrolytic reactions release P_i rather than reversing the ATP → ADP reactions that occur at this point in the glycolytic pathway.

The net energetic cost of converting two pyruvate molecules to one glucose molecule by gluconeogenesis is six ATP equivalents: two each at the steps catalyzed by pyruvate carboxylase, PEPCK, and phosphoglycerate kinase. Since the energetic profit of converting one glucose molecule to two pyruvate molecules via glycolysis is two ATP, (Section 15-1), the energetic cost of the futile cycle in which glucose is converted to pyruvate and then resynthesized is four ATP equivalents. Such free energy losses are the thermodynamic price that must be paid to maintain the independent regulation of two opposing pathways.

Although glucose is considered the endpoint of the gluconeogenic pathway, it is possible for pathway intermediates to be directed elsewhere, for example, through the transketolase and transaldolase reactions of the pentose phosphate pathway (Section 15-6C) to produce ribose-5-phosphate. The G6P produced by gluconeogenesis may not be hydrolyzed to glucose but may instead be converted to G1P for incorporation into glycogen.

C | Gluconeogenesis and Glycolysis Are Independently Regulated

The opposing pathways of gluconeogenesis and glycolysis, like glycogen synthesis and degradation, do not proceed simultaneously *in vivo*. Instead, the pathways are reciprocally regulated to meet the needs of the organism. There are three substrate cycles and therefore three potential points for regulating glycolytic versus gluconeogenic flux (Fig. 16-21).

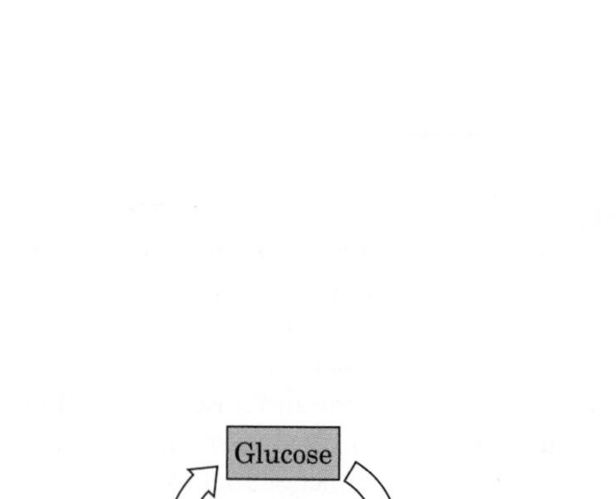

Fructose-2,6-Bisphosphate Activates Phosphofructokinase and Inhibits Fructose-1,6-Bisphosphatase. The net flux through the substrate cycle created by the opposing actions of PFK and FBPase (described in Section 15-4B) is determined by the concentration of fructose-2,6-bisphosphate (F2,6P).

$$^{-2}O_3P-OH_2C \quad O \quad O-PO_3^{2-}$$

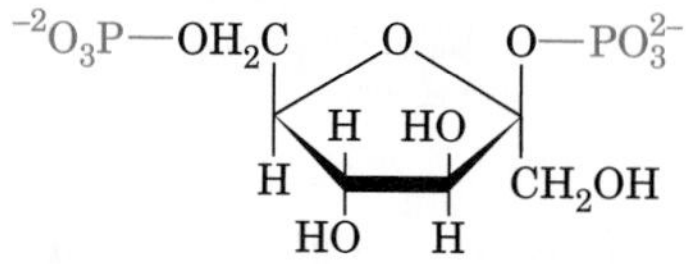

β-D-Fructose-2,6-bisphosphate (F2,6P)

F2,6P, which is not a glycolytic intermediate, is an extremely potent allosteric activator of PFK and an inhibitor of FBPase.

The concentration of F2,6P in the cell depends on the balance between its rates of synthesis and degradation by **phosphofructokinase-2 (PFK-2)** and **fructose bisphosphatase-2 (FBPase-2),** respectively (Fig. 16-22). These enzyme activities are located on different domains of the same ~100-kD homodimeric protein. The bifunctional enzyme is regulated by a variety of allosteric effectors and by phosphorylation and dephosphorylation as catalyzed by PKA and a phosphoprotein phosphatase. Thus, the balance between gluconeogenesis and glycolysis is under hormonal control.

For example, when [glucose] is low, glucagon stimulates the production of cAMP in liver cells. This activates PKA to phosphorylate the bifunctional enzyme at a specific Ser residue, which inactivates the enzyme's PFK-2 activity and activates its FBPase-2 activity. The net result is a decrease in [F2,6P], which shifts the balance between the PFK and FBPase reactions in favor of FBP hydrolysis and hence increases gluconeogenic flux (Fig. 16-23). The concurrent increases in gluconeogenesis and glycogen breakdown allow the liver to release glucose into the circulation. Conversely, when the blood [glucose] is high, cAMP levels decrease, and the resulting increase in [F2,6P] promotes glycolysis.

■ **Figure 16-21 | Substrate cycles in glucose metabolism.** The interconversions of glucose and G6P, F6P and FBP, and PEP and pyruvate are catalyzed by different enzymes in the forward and reverse directions so that all reactions are exergonic (the ΔG values for the reactions in liver are given in kJ · mol⁻¹). [ΔG's obtained from Newsholme, E.A. and Leech, A.R., *Biochemistry for the Medical Sciences,* p. 448, Wiley (1983).]

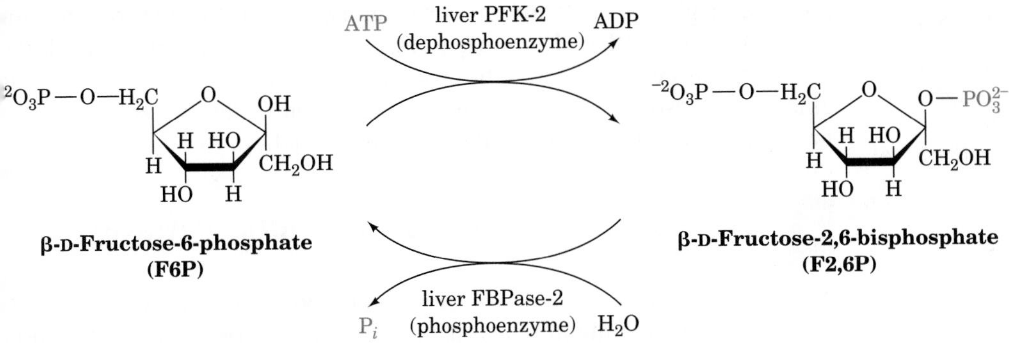

$$^{-2}O_3P-O-H_2C \quad O \quad OH$$

β-D-Fructose-6-phosphate
(F6P)

liver PFK-2
(dephosphoenzyme)
ATP → ADP

liver FBPase-2
(phosphoenzyme)
P_i → H_2O

$$^{-2}O_3P-O-H_2C \quad O \quad O-PO_3^{2-}$$

β-D-Fructose-2,6-bisphosphate
(F2,6P)

■ **Figure 16-22 | The formation and degradation of β-D-fructose-2, 6-bisphosphate (F2,6P).** The enzymatic activities of phosphofructokinase-2 (PFK-2) and fructose bisphosphatase-2 (FBPase-2) occur on different domains of the same protein molecule. The phosphorylation of the liver enzyme inactivates PFK-2 while activating FBPase-2.

In muscle, which is not a gluconeogenic tissue, the F2,6P control system functions quite differently from that in liver due to the presence of different PFK-2/FBPase-2 isozymes. For example, hormones that stimulate glycogen breakdown in heart muscle lead to phosphorylation of a site on the bifunctional enzyme that activates rather than inhibits PFK-2. The resulting increase in F2,6P stimulates glycolysis so that glycogen breakdown and glycolysis are coordinated. The skeletal muscle isozyme lacks a phosphorylation site altogether and is therefore not subject to cAMP-dependent control.

Other Allosteric Effectors Influence Gluconeogenic Flux. Acetyl-CoA activates pyruvate carboxylase (Section 16-4A), but there are no known allosteric effectors of PEPCK, which together with pyruvate carboxylase reverses the pyruvate kinase reaction. Pyruvate kinase, however, is allosterically inhibited in the liver by alanine, a major gluconeogenic precursor. Alanine is converted to pyruvate by the transfer of its amino group to an α-keto acid to yield a new amino acid and the α-keto acid pyruvate,

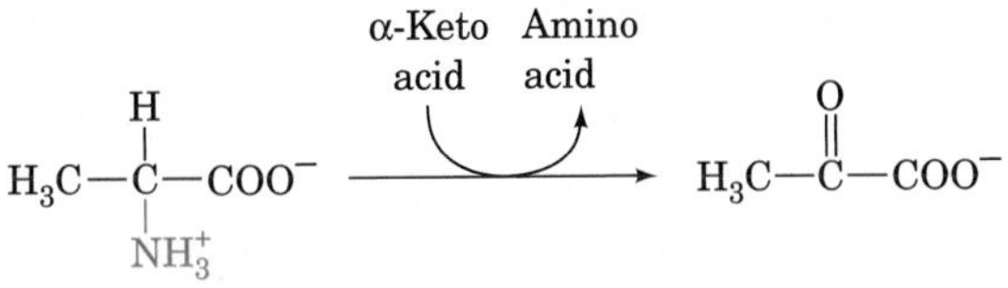

$$H_3C-\underset{\underset{NH_3^+}{|}}{\overset{\overset{H}{|}}{C}}-COO^- \quad \xrightarrow[\text{acid}]{\overset{\text{α-Keto Amino}}{\text{acid}}} \quad H_3C-\overset{\overset{O}{\|}}{C}-COO^-$$

Alanine   Pyruvate

a process termed **transamination** (which is discussed in Section 21-2A). Liver pyruvate kinase is also inactivated by phosphorylation, further increasing gluconeogenic flux. Since phosphorylation also activates glycogen phosphorylase, the pathways of gluconeogenesis and glycogen breakdown both flow toward G6P, which is converted to glucose for export from the liver.

The activity of hexokinase (or glucokinase, the liver isozyme) is also controlled, as we shall see in Section 22-1D. The activity of glucose-6-phosphatase is controlled as well but this process is complex and poorly understood.

The regulation of glucose metabolism occurs not only through allosteric effectors, but also through long-term changes in the amounts of enzymes synthesized. Pancreatic and adrenal hormones influence the rates of transcription and the stabilities of the mRNAs encoding many of the regulatory

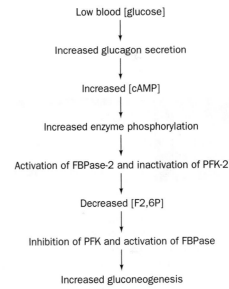

Low blood [glucose]
↓
Increased glucagon secretion
↓
Increased [cAMP]
↓
Increased enzyme phosphorylation
↓
Activation of FBPase-2 and inactivation of PFK-2
↓
Decreased [F2,6P]
↓
Inhibition of PFK and activation of FBPase
↓
Increased gluconeogenesis

■ **Figure 16-23 | Sequence of metabolic events linking low blood [glucose] to gluconeogenesis in liver.**

■ **CHECK YOUR UNDERSTANDING**

Describe the reactions of gluconeogenesis.
Why is the malate–aspartate shuttle system
important for gluconeogenesis?
Describe the role of fructose-2,6-bisphosphate
in regulating gluconeogenesis.

LEARNING OBJECTIVE

■ Understand that the formation of glycosidic
bonds in carbohydrates requires the energy
of activated nucleotide sugars.

proteins of glucose metabolism. For example, insulin inhibits transcription
of the gene for PEPCK, whereas high concentrations of intracellular
cAMP promote the transcription of the genes for PEPCK, FBPase, and
glucose-6-phosphatase, and repress transcription of the genes for glucokinase, PFK, and the PFK-2/FBPase-2 bifunctional enzyme.

5 Other Carbohydrate Biosynthetic Pathways

The liver, by virtue of its mass and its metabolic machinery, is primarily
responsible for maintaining a constant level of glucose in the circulation.
Glucose produced by gluconeogenesis or from glycogen breakdown is released from the liver for use by other tissues as an energy source. Of
course, glucose has other uses in the liver and elsewhere, for example, in
the synthesis of lactose (Box 16-4).

Nucleotide Sugars Power the Formation of Glycosidic Bonds. Glucose
and other monosaccharides (principally mannose, N-acetylglucosamine, fucose, galactose, N-acetylneuraminic acid, and N-acetylgalactosamine) occur
in glycoproteins and glycolipids. Formation of the glycosidic bonds that link
sugars to each other and to other molecules requires free energy input un-
der physiological conditions ($\Delta G^{\circ\prime} = 16$ kJ · mol^{-1}). This free energy, as we

BOX 16-4 PERSPECTIVES IN BIOCHEMISTRY

Lactose Synthesis

Like sucrose in plants, lactose is a disaccharide that is synthesized
for later use as a metabolic fuel, in this case, after digestion by
very young mammals. Lactose, or milk sugar, is produced in the
mammary gland by **lactose synthase.** In this reaction, the donor
sugar is UDP–galactose, which is formed by the epimerization of
UDP–glucose (Fig. 15-28). The acceptor sugar is glucose:

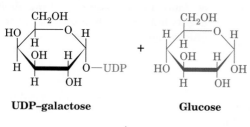

UDP–galactose   **Glucose**

| lactose synthase

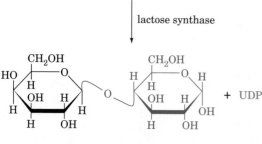

Lactose
[β-galactosyl-(1⟶4)-glucose]

Thus, both saccharide units of lactose are ultimately derived from
glucose.

Lactose synthase consists of two subunits:

1. **Galactosyltransferase,** the catalytic subunit, occurs in many
   tissues, where it catalyzes the reaction of UDP–galactose
   and N-acetylglucosamine to yield **N-acetyllactosamine,**

N-Acetyllactosamine

a constituent of many complex oligosaccharides.

2. **α-Lactalbumin,** a mammary gland protein with no catalytic
   activity, alters the specificity of galactosyltransferase so that
   it uses glucose as an acceptor, rather than N-acetylglucosamine, to form lactose instead of N-acetyllactosamine.

Synthesis of α-lactalbumin, whose sequence is ~37% identical to
that of lysozyme (which also participates in reactions involving
sugars), is triggered by hormonal changes at parturition (birth),
thereby promoting lactose synthesis for milk production.

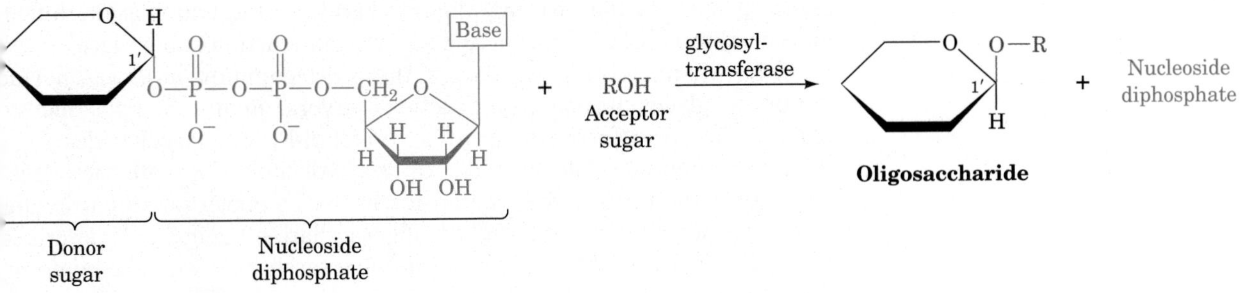

Figure 16-24 | Role of nucleotide sugars. These compounds are the glycosyl donors in oligosaccharide biosynthetic reactions as catalyzed by glycosyltransferases.

have seen in glycogen synthesis (Section 16-2A), is acquired through the synthesis of a **nucleotide sugar** from a nucleoside triphosphate and a monosaccharide, thereby releasing PP_i, whose exergonic hydrolysis drives the reaction. The nucleoside diphosphate at the sugar's anomeric carbon atom is a good leaving group and thereby facilitates formation of a glycosidic bond to a second sugar in a reaction catalyzed by a glycosyltransferase (Fig. 16-24). In mammals, most glycosyl groups are donated by UDP–sugars, but fucose and mannose are carried by GDP, and sialic acid by CMP. In plants, starch is built from glucose units donated by **ADP–glucose,** and cellulose synthesis relies on ADP–glucose or **CDP–glucose.**

O-Linked Oligosaccharides Are Posttranslationally Formed. Nucleotide sugars are the donors in the synthesis of O-linked oligosaccharides and in the processing of the N-linked oligosaccharides of glycoproteins (Section 8-3C). O-Linked oligosaccharides are synthesized in the Golgi apparatus by the serial addition of monosaccharide units to a completed polypeptide chain (Fig. 16-25). Synthesis begins with the transfer, as catalyzed by **GalNAc transferase,** of N-acetylgalactosamine (GalNAc) from UDP–GalNAc to a Ser or Thr residue on the polypeptide. The location of the glycosylation site is thought to be specified only by the secondary or tertiary structure of the polypeptide. Glycosylation continues with the stepwise addition of sugars such as galactose, sialic acid, N-acetylglucosamine, and fucose. In each case, the sugar residue is transferred from its nucleotide sugar derivative by a corresponding glycosyltransferase.

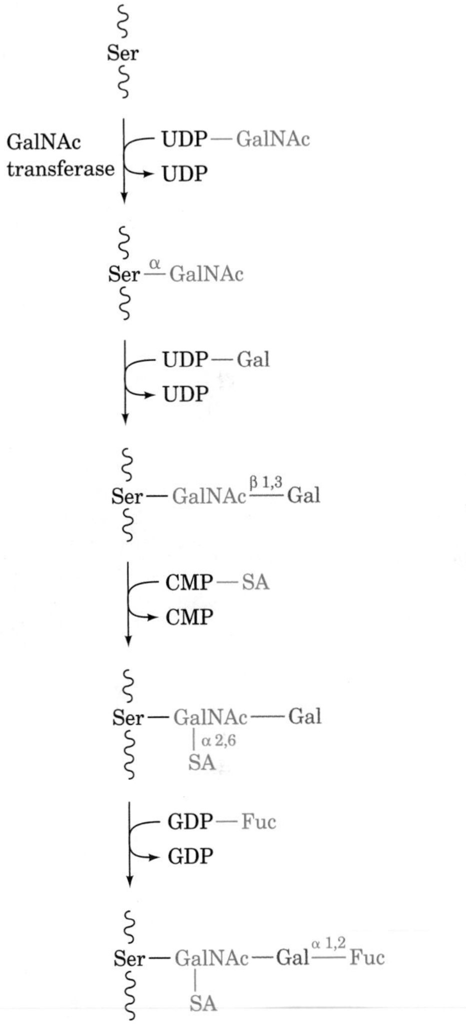

N-Linked Oligosaccharides Are Constructed on Dolichol Carriers. The synthesis of N-linked oligosaccharides is more complicated than that of O-linked oligosaccharides. In the early stages of N-linked oligosaccharide synthesis, sugar residues are sequentially added to a lipid carrier, **dolichol pyrophosphate** (Fig. 16-26). **Dolichol** is a long-chain polyisoprenoid containing 17 to 21 isoprene units in animals and 14 to 24 units in fungi and

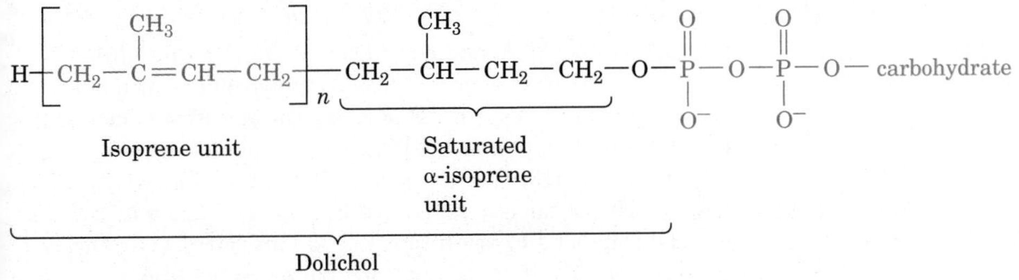

Figure 16-25 | Synthesis of an O-linked oligosaccharide chain. This pathway shows the proposed steps in the assembly of a carbohydrate moiety in canine submaxillary mucin. SA is sialic acid.

Figure 16-26 | Dolichol pyrophosphate glycoside. The carbohydrate precursors of N-linked glycosides are synthesized as oligosaccharides attached to dolichol, a long-chain polyisoprenol ($n = 14–24$) in which the α-isoprene unit is saturated.

plants. It anchors the growing oligosaccharide to the endoplasmic reticulum membrane, where the initial glycosylation reactions take place.

Although nucleotide sugars are the most common monosaccharide donors in glycosyltransferase reactions, several mannosyl and glucosyl residues are transferred to growing dolichol-PP-oligosaccharides from their corresponding dolichol-P derivatives. Dolichol phosphate "activates" a sugar residue for subsequent transfer, as does a nucleoside diphosphate.

The construction of an *N*-linked oligosaccharide begins, as is described in Section 8-3C, by the synthesis of an oligosaccharide with the composition (*N*-acetylglucosamine)$_2$(mannose)$_9$(glucose)$_3$. This occurs on a dolichol carrier in a 12-step process catalyzed by a series of specific glycosyltransferases (Fig. 16-27). Note that some of these reactions take place

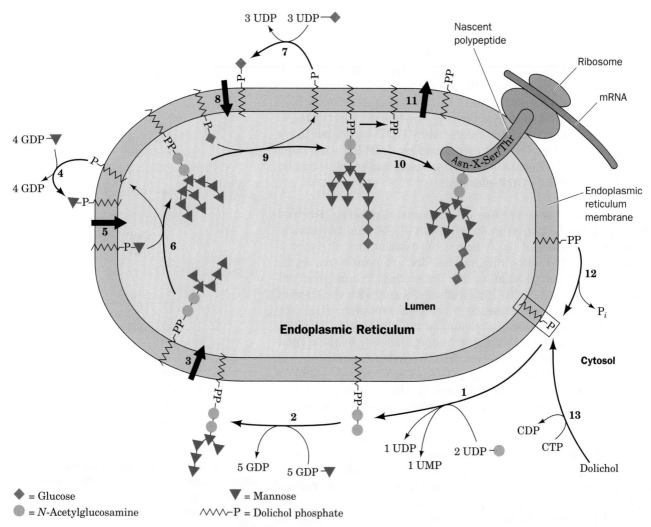

◆ = Glucose   ▼ = Mannose

● = *N*-Acetylglucosamine   ∿∿∿–P = Dolichol phosphate

■ **Figure 16-27 | The pathway of dolichol-PP-oligosaccharide synthesis.** **(1)** Addition of *N*-acetylglucosamine-1-P and a second *N*-acetylglucosamine to dolichol-P. **(2)** Addition of five mannosyl residues from GDP–mannose in reactions catalyzed by five different mannosyltransferases. **(3)** Membrane translocation of dolichol-PP-(*N*-acetylglucosamine)$_2$(mannose)$_5$ to the lumen of the endoplasmic reticulum (ER). **(4)** Cytosolic synthesis of dolichol-P-mannose from GDP–mannose and dolichol-P. **(5)** Membrane translocation of dolichol-P-mannose to the lumen of the ER. **(6)** Addition of four mannosyl residues from dolichol-P-mannose in reactions catalyzed by four different mannosyltransferases. **(7)** Cytosolic synthesis of dolichol-P-glucose from UDPG and dolichol-P. **(8)** Membrane translocation of dolichol-P-glucose to the lumen of the ER. **(9)** Addition of three glucosyl residues from dolichol-P-glucose. **(10)** Transfer of the oligosaccharide from dolichol-PP to the polypeptide chain at an Asn residue in the sequence Asn-X-Ser/Thr, releasing dolichol-PP. **(11)** Translocation of dolichol-PP to the cytoplasmic surface of the ER membrane. **(12)** Hydrolysis of dolichol-PP to dolichol-P. **(13)** Dolichol-P can also be formed by phosphorylation of dolichol by CTP. [Modified from Abeijon, C. and Hirschberg, C.B., *Trends Biochem. Sci.* **17**, 34 (1992).] ♫ **See the Animated Figures.**

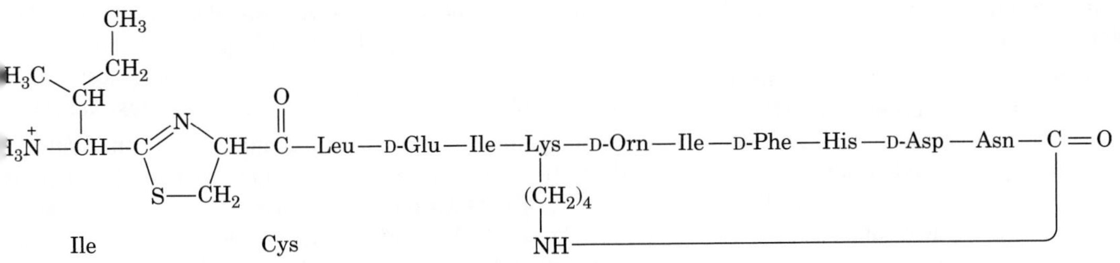

Bacitracin

Figure 16-28 | The chemical structure of bacitracin. Note that this dodecapeptide has four D-amino acid residues and two unusual intrachain linkages. "Orn" represents the nonstandard amino acid ornithine (Fig. 21-9).

on the lumenal surface of the endoplasmic reticulum, whereas others occur on its cytoplasmic surface. Hence, on four occasions (Reactions 3, 5, 8, and 11 in Fig. 16-27), dolichol and its attached hydrophilic group are translocated, via unknown mechanisms, across the endoplasmic reticulum membrane. In the final steps of the process, the oligosaccharide is transferred to the Asn residue in a segment of sequence Asn-X-Ser/Thr (where X is any residue except Pro and possibly Asp) on a growing polypeptide chain. The resulting dolichol pyrophosphate is hydrolyzed to dolichol phosphate and P_i, a process similar to the pyrophosphatase cleavage of PP_i to 2 P_i. Further processing of the oligosaccharide takes place, as described in Section 8-3C, first in the endoplasmic reticulum and then in the Golgi apparatus (Fig. 8-19), where certain monosaccharide residues are trimmed away by specific glycosylases and others are added by specific nucleotide sugar–requiring glycosyltransferases.

Bacitracin Interferes with the Dephosphorylation of Dolichol Pyrophosphate. A number of compounds block the actions of specific glycosylation enzymes, including **bacitracin** (Fig. 16-28), a cyclic polypeptide that is a widely used antibiotic. Bacitracin forms a complex with dolichol pyrophosphate that inhibits its dephosphorylation (Fig. 16-27, Reaction 12), thereby preventing the synthesis of glycoproteins from dolichol-linked oligosaccharide precursors. Bacitracin is clinically useful because it inhibits bacterial cell wall synthesis (which also involves dolichol-linked oligosaccharides) but does not affect animal cells since it cannot cross cell membranes (bacterial cell wall synthesis is an extracellular process).

■ **CHECK YOUR UNDERSTANDING**

Explain the group transfer reaction of glycosidic bond formation by describing the attacking nucleophile, the atom attacked, and the leaving group.

SUMMARY

1. Glycogen breakdown requires three enzymes. Glycogen phosphorylase converts the glucosyl units at the nonreducing ends of glycogen to glucose-1-phosphate (G1P). Debranching enzyme transfers an $\alpha(1\rightarrow4)$-linked trisaccharide to a nonreducing end and hydrolyzes the $\alpha(1\rightarrow6)$ linkage. Phosphoglucomutase converts G1P to glucose-6-phosphate (G6P). In liver, G6P is hydrolyzed by glucose-6-phosphatase to glucose for export to the tissues.

2. Glycogen synthesis requires a different pathway in which G1P is activated by reaction with UTP to form UDP–glucose. Glycogen synthase adds glucosyl units to the nonreducing ends of a growing glycogen molecule that has been primed by glycogenin. Branching enzyme removes an $\alpha(1\rightarrow4)$-linked

7-residue segment and reattaches it through an $\alpha(1\rightarrow6)$ linkage to form a branched chain.

3. Glycogen metabolism is controlled in part by allosteric effectors such as AMP, ATP, and G6P. Covalent modification of glycogen phosphorylase and glycogen synthase shifts their $T \rightleftharpoons R$ equilibria and therefore alters their sensitivity to allosteric effectors.

4. The ratio of phosphorylase a (more active) to phosphorylase b (less active) depends on the activity of phosphorylase kinase, which is regulated by the activity of protein kinase A (PKA), a cAMP-dependent enzyme, and on the activity of phosphoprotein phosphatase-1 (PP1). Glycogen phosphory-

lase is activated by phosphorylation, whereas glycogen synthase is activated by dephosphorylation.

5. Hormones such as glucagon, epinephrine, and insulin control glycogen metabolism. Hormone signals that generate cAMP as a second messenger or that elevate intracellular Ca^{2+}, which binds to the calmodulin subunit of phosphorylase kinase, promote glycogen breakdown. Insulin stimulates glycogen synthesis in part by activating phosphoprotein phosphatase-1.

6. Compounds that can be converted to oxaloacetate can subsequently be converted to glucose. The conversion of pyruvate to glucose by gluconeogenesis requires enzymes that bypass

the three exergonic steps of glycolysis: Pyruvate carboxylase and PEP carboxykinase (PEPCK) bypass pyruvate kinase fructose-1,6-bisphosphatase (FBPase) bypasses phosphofructokinase, and glucose-6-phosphatase bypasses hexokinase.

7. Gluconeogenesis is regulated by changes in enzyme synthesis and by allosteric effectors, including fructose-2,6-bisphosphate (F2,6P), which inhibits FBPase and activates phosphofructokinase (PFK) and whose synthesis depends on the phosphorylation state of the bifunctional enzyme phosphofructokinase-2/fructose bisphosphatase-2 (PFK-2/FBPase-2).

8. Formation of glycosidic bonds requires nucleotide sugars.

KEY TERMS

glycogenolysis **532**
phosphorolysis **533**
debranching **533**

glycogen storage disease **538**
nucleotide sugar **561**

interconvertible enzyme **545**
gluconeogenesis **552**

reducing equivalent **556**
dolichol **561**

PROBLEMS

1. Indicate the energy yield or cost, in ATP equivalents, for the following processes:

   (a) glycogen (3 residues) → 6 pyruvate

   (b) 3 glucose → 6 pyruvate

   (c) 6 pyruvate → 3 glucose

2. Write the balanced equation for (a) the sequential conversion of glucose to pyruvate and of pyruvate to glucose and (b) the catabolism of six molecules of G6P by the pentose phosphate pathway followed by conversion of ribulose-5-phosphate back to G6P by gluconeogenesis.

3. Phosphoglucokinase catalyzes the phosphorylation of the C6-OH group of G1P. Why is this enzyme important for the normal function of phosphoglucomutase?

4. The free energy of hydrolysis of an $\alpha(1 \rightarrow 4)$ glycosidic bond is -15.5 kJ·mol^{-1}, whereas that of an $\alpha(1 \rightarrow 6)$ glycosidic bond is -7.1 kJ·mol^{-1}. Use these data to explain why glycogen debranching includes three reactions [breaking and reforming $\alpha(1 \rightarrow 4)$ bonds and hydrolyzing $\alpha(1 \rightarrow 6)$ bonds], whereas glycogen branching requires only two reactions [breaking $\alpha(1 \rightarrow 4)$ bonds and forming $\alpha(1 \rightarrow 6)$ bonds].

5. Calculations based on the volume of a glucose residue and the branching pattern of cellular glycogen indicate that a glycogen molecule could have up to 28 branching tiers before becoming impossibly dense. What are the advantages of such a molecule and why is it not found *in vivo*?

6. One molecule of dietary glucose can be oxidized through glycolysis and the citric acid cycle to generate a maximum of 32 molecules of ATP. Calculate the fraction of this energy that is lost when the glucose is stored as glycogen before it is catabolized.

7. Glucose binds to glycogen phosphorylase and competitively inhibits the enzyme. What is the physiological advantage of this?

8. Many diabetics do not respond to insulin because of a deficiency of insulin receptors on their cells. How does this affect (a) the levels of circulating glucose immediately after a meal and (b) the rate of glycogen synthesis in muscle?

9. Glucose-6-phosphatase is located inside the endoplasmic reticulum. Describe the probable symptoms of a defect in G6P transport across the endoplasmic reticulum membrane.

10. Individuals with McArdle's disease often experience a "second wind" resulting from cardiovascular adjustments that allow glucose mobilized from liver glycogen to fuel muscle contraction. Explain why the amount of ATP derived in the muscle from circulating glucose is less than the amount of ATP that would be obtained by mobilizing the same amount of glucose from muscle glycogen.

11. A sample of glycogen from a patient with liver disease is incubated with P_i, normal glycogen phosphorylase, and normal debranching enzyme. The ratio of G1P to glucose formed in the reaction mixture is 100. What is the patient's most probable enzymatic deficiency?

CASE STUDIES

Case 22 (available at www.wiley.com/college/voet)
Carrier-Mediated Uptake of Lactate in Rat Hepatocytes

Focus concept: The structural characteristics of the lactate transport protein in hepatocytes are determined.

Prerequisites: Chapters 10, 15, and 16

- Transport proteins

- Major carbohydrate metabolic pathways including glycolysis and gluconeogenesis

Case 26
The Role of Specific Amino Acids in the Peptide Hormone Glucagon in Receptor Binding and Signal Transduction

Focus concept: Amino acid side chains important in glucagon binding and signal transduction are identified.

Prerequisites Chapters: 4, 13, and 16

- Amino acid structure

- Signal transduction via G proteins

SELECTED READINGS

Bollen, M., Keppens, S., and Stalmans, W., Specific features of glycogen metabolism in the liver, *Biochem. J.* **336,** 19–31 (1998). [Describes the activities of the enzymes involved in glycogen synthesis and degradation and discusses the mechanisms for regulating the processes.]

Brosnan, J.T., Comments on metabolic needs for glucose and the role of gluconeogenesis, *Eur. J. Clin. Nutr.* **53,** S107–S111 (1999). [A very readable review that discusses possible reasons why carbohydrates are used universally as metabolic fuels and why glucose is stored as glycogen.]

Browner, M.F. and Fletterick, R.J., Phosphorylase: a biological transducer, *Trends Biochem. Sci.* **17,** 66–71 (1992).

Burda, P. and Aebi, M., The dolichol pathway of N-linked glycosylation, *Biochim. Biophys. Acta* **1426,** 239–257 (1999).

Chen, Y.-T., Glycogen storage diseases, *in* Scriver, C.R., Beaudet, A.L., Sly, W.S., and Valle, D. (Eds.), *The Metabolic and Molecular Bases of Inherited Disease* (8th ed.), pp. 1521–1552, McGraw-Hill (2001). [Begins with a review of glycogen metabolism.]

Croniger, C.M., Olswang, Y., Reshef, L., Kalhan, S.C., Tilghman, S.M., and Hanson, R.W., Phosphoenolpyruvate carboxykinase revisited. Insights into its metabolic role, *Biochem. Mol. Biol. Educ.* **30,** 14–20 (2002); *and* Croniger, C.M., Chakravarty, K., Olswang, Y., Cassuto, H., Reshef, L., and Hanson, R.W., Phosphoenolpyruvate carboxykinase revisited. II. Control of PEPCK-C gene expression, *Biochem. Mol. Biol. Educ.* **30,** 353–362 (2002).

Meléndez-Hevia, E., Waddell, T.G., and Shelton, E.D., Optimization of molecular design in the evolution of metabolism: the glycogen molecule, *Biochem. J.* **295,** 477–483 (1993).

Nordlie, R.C., Foster, J.D., and Lange, A.J., Regulation of glucose production by the liver, *Annu. Rev. Nutr.* **19,** 379–406 (1999).

Okar, D.A., Manzano, À., Navarro-Sabatè, A., Riera, L., Bartrons, R., and Lange, A.J., PFK-2/FBPase-2: Maker and breaker of the essential biofactor fructose-2,6-bisphosphate, *Trends Biochem. Sci.* **26,** 30–35 (2001).

Roach, P.J. and Skurat, A.V., Self-glucosylating initiator proteins and their role in glycogen biosynthesis, *Prog. Nucleic Acid Res. Mol. Biol.* **57,** 289–316 (1997). [Discusses glycogenin.]

Whelan, W.J., Why the linkage of glycogen to glycogenin was so hard to determine. *Biochem. Mol. Biol. Educ.* **35,** 313–315 (2007).

17

Citric Acid Cycle

The synthesis and degradation of numerous biological materials depends on the flow of molecules and energy through the citric acid cycle, which has been likened to a metabolic water wheel. [Al Zwiazek/SUPERSTOCK.

■ CHAPTER CONTENTS

1 Overview of the Citric Acid Cycle

2 Synthesis of Acetyl-Coenzyme A

  A. Pyruvate Dehydrogenase Is a Multienzyme Complex

  B. The Pyruvate Dehydrogenase Complex Catalyzes Five Reactions

3 Enzymes of the Citric Acid Cycle

  A. Citrate Synthase Joins an Acetyl Group to Oxaloacetate

  B. Aconitase Interconverts Citrate and Isocitrate

  C. NAD^+-Dependent Isocitrate Dehydrogenase Releases CO_2

  D. α-Ketoglutarate Dehydrogenase Resembles Pyruvate Dehydrogenase

  E. Succinyl-CoA Synthetase Produces GTP

  F. Succinate Dehydrogenase Generates $FADH_2$

  G. Fumarase Produces Malate

  H. Malate Dehydrogenase Regenerates Oxaloacetate

4 Regulation of the Citric Acid Cycle

  A. Pyruvate Dehydrogenase Is Regulated by Product Inhibition and Covalent Modification

  B. Three Enzymes Control the Rate of the Citric Acid Cycle

5 Reactions Related to the Citric Acid Cycle

  A. Other Pathways Use Citric Acid Cycle Intermediates

  B. Some Reactions Replenish Citric Acid Cycle Intermediates

  C. The Glyoxylate Cycle Shares Some Steps with the Citric Acid Cycle

■ MEDIA RESOURCES

(available at www.wiley.com/college/voet)

Guided Exploration 16. Citric acid cycle overview

Interactive Exercise 18. Conformational changes in citrate synthase

Animated Figure 17-1. Overview of oxidative fuel metabolism

Animated Figure 17-2. Reactions of the citric acid cycle

Animated Figure 17-16. Regulation of the citric acid cycle

Animated Figure 17-17. Amphibolic functions of the citric acid cycle

Case Study 21. Characterization of Pyruvate Carboxylase from *Methanobacterium thermoautotrophicum*

In the preceding two chapters, we examined the catabolism of glucose and its biosynthesis, storage, and mobilization. Although glucose is a source of energy for nearly all cells, it is not the only metabolic fuel, nor is glycolysis the only energy-yielding catabolic pathway. Cells that rely exclusively on glycolysis to meet their energy requirements actually waste most of the chemical potential energy of carbohydrates. When glucose is converted to lactate or ethanol, a relatively reduced product leaves the cell. If the end product of glycolysis is instead further oxidized, the cell can recover considerably more energy.

The oxidation of an organic compound requires an electron acceptor, such as NO_3^-, SO_4^{2-}, Fe^{3+}, or O_2, all of which are exploited as oxidants in different organisms. In aerobic organisms, the electrons produced by oxidative metabolism are ultimately transferred to O_2. Oxidation of metabolic fuels is carried out by the citric acid cycle, a sequence of reactions that arose sometime after levels of atmospheric oxygen became significant, about 3 billion years ago. As the reduced carbon atoms of metabolic fuels are oxidized to CO_2, electrons are transferred to electron carriers that are subsequently reoxidized by O_2. In this chapter, we examine the oxidation reactions of the citric acid cycle itself. In the following chapter, we examine the fate of the electrons and see how their energy is used to drive the synthesis of ATP.

■ **Figure 17-1** | **Overview of oxidative fuel metabolism.** Acetyl groups derived from carbohydrates, amino acids, and fatty acids enter the citric acid cycle, where they are oxidized to CO_2. 🎬 **See the Animated Figures.**

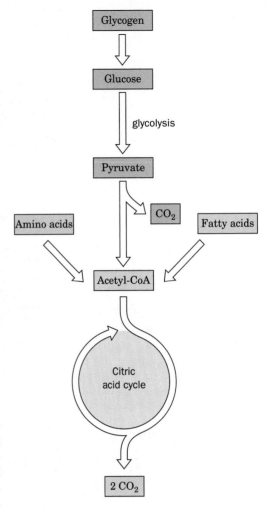

It is sometimes convenient to think of the citric acid cycle as an addendum to glycolysis. Pyruvate derived from glucose can be split into CO_2 and a two-carbon fragment that enters the cycle for oxidation as acetyl-CoA (Fig. 17-1). However, it is really misleading to think of the citric acid cycle as merely a continuation of carbohydrate catabolism. *The citric acid cycle is a central pathway for recovering energy from several metabolic fuels, including carbohydrates, fatty acids, and amino acids, that are broken down to acetyl-CoA for oxidation.* In fact, under some conditions, the principal function of the citric acid cycle is to recover energy from fatty acids. We shall also see that the citric acid cycle supplies the reactants for a variety of biosynthetic pathways.

We begin this chapter with an overview of the citric acid cycle. Next, we explore how acetyl-CoA, its starting compound, is formed from pyruvate. After discussing the reactions catalyzed by each of the enzymes of the cycle, we consider the regulation of these enzymes. Finally, we examine the links between citric acid cycle intermediates and other metabolic processes.

1 Overview of the Citric Acid Cycle

The **citric acid cycle** (Fig. 17-2) is an ingenious series of eight reactions that oxidizes the acetyl group of acetyl-CoA to two molecules of CO_2 in a manner that conserves the liberated free energy in the reduced compounds NADH and $FADH_2$. The cycle is named after the product of its first reaction, **citrate.** One complete round of the cycle yields two molecules of CO_2, three NADH, one $FADH_2$, and one "high-energy" compound (GTP or ATP).

The citric acid cycle first came to light in the 1930s, when Hans Krebs, building on the work of others, proposed a circular reaction scheme for the interconversion of certain compounds containing two or three carboxylic acid groups (that is, di- and tricarboxylates). At the time, many of the citric acid cycle intermediates were already well known as plant products: **citrate** from citrus fruit, **aconitate** from monkshood (*Aconitum*), **succinate** from amber (*Succinum*), **fumarate** from the herb *Fumaria,* and **malate** from apple (*Malus*). Two other intermediates, **α-ketoglutarate** and **oxaloacetate,** are known by their chemical names because they were synthesized before they were identified in living organisms. Krebs was the first to show how the metabolism of these compounds was linked to the oxidation of metabolic fuels. His discovery of the citric acid cycle, in 1937, ranks as one of the most important achievements of metabolic chemistry (Box 17-1). Although the enzymes and intermediates of the citric acid cycle are now well established, many investigators continue to explore the molecular mechanisms of the enzymes and how the enzymes are regulated for optimal performance under varying metabolic conditions in different organisms.

Before we examine each of the reactions in detail, we should emphasize some general features of the citric acid cycle:

1. The circular pathway, which is also called the **Krebs cycle** or the **tricarboxylic acid (TCA) cycle,** oxidizes acetyl groups from many

---

LEARNING OBJECTIVE

■ Understand that the citric acid cycle is a multistep catalytic process that converts acetyl groups derived from carbohydrates, fatty acids, and amino acids to CO_2, and produces NADH, $FADH_2$, and GTP.

See Guided Exploration 16
Citric Cycle Overview

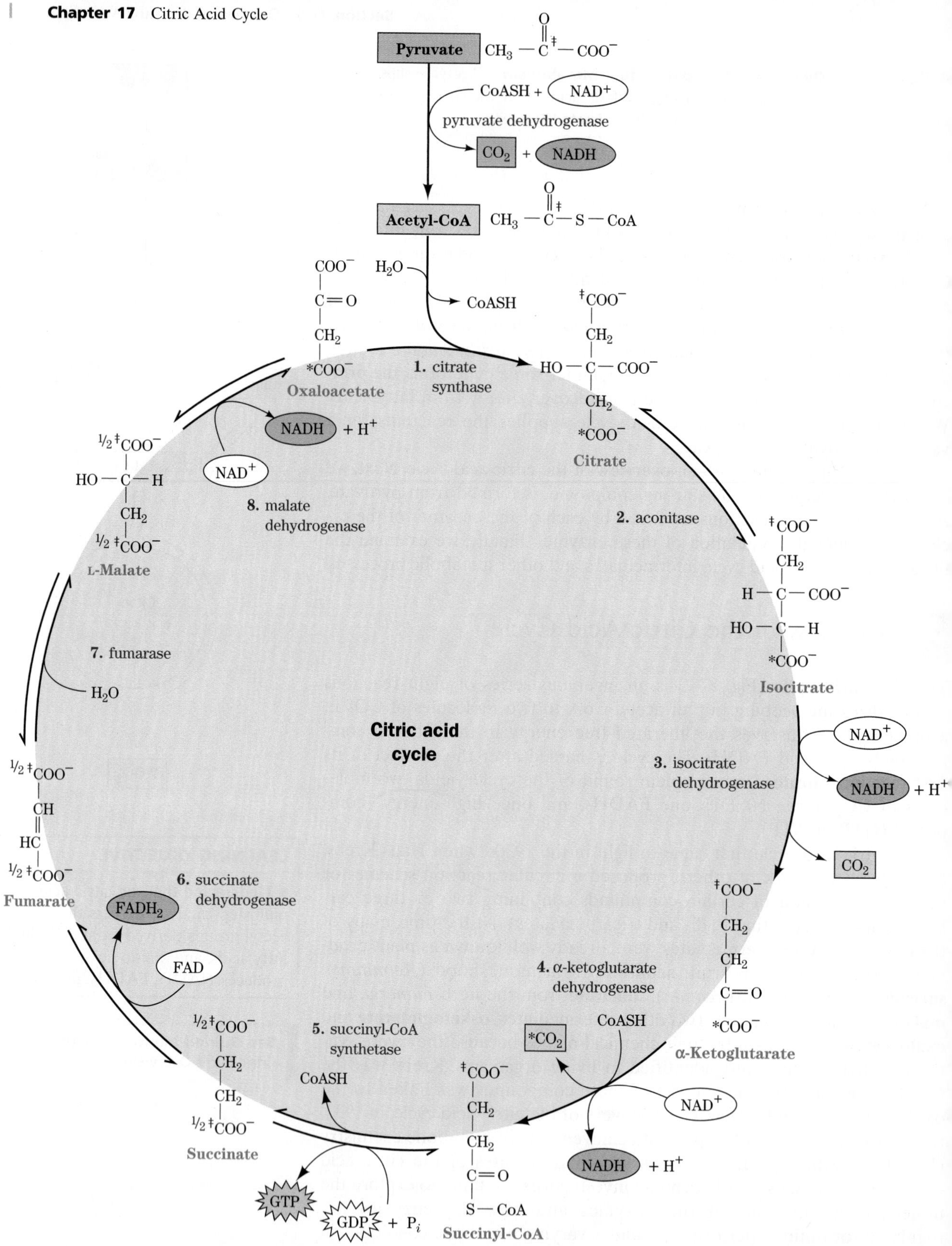

■ **Figure 17-2 | The reactions of the citric acid cycle.** The reactants and products of this catalytic cycle are boxed. The pyruvate → acetyl-CoA reaction (*top*) supplies the cycle's substrate via carbohydrate metabolism but is not considered to be part of the cycle. An isotopic label at C4 of oxaloacetate (*) becomes C1 of α-ketoglutarate and is released as CO_2 in Reaction 4. An isotopic label at C1 of acetyl-CoA (‡) becomes C5 of α-ketoglutarate and is scrambled in Reaction 5 between C1 and C4 of succinate ($\frac{1}{2}$‡).

🔁 **See the Animated Figures.**

BOX 17-1 PATHWAYS OF DISCOVERY

Hans Krebs and the Citric Acid Cycle

Hans Krebs (1900–1981)

Hans Krebs worked in Otto Warburg's laboratory from 1926 until 1930 and later declared that he had learned more from Warburg (see Box 15-1) than from any other teacher. Krebs applied Warburg's tissue-slice technique to the study of biosynthetic reactions (Warburg himself was interested primarily in oxidative and degradative reactions). Over a period of years, Krebs investigated synthetic pathways for urea, uric acid, and purines as well as oxidative pathways. He was forced to leave his native Germany for England in 1933, but unlike many other German emigrant scientists, he was able to bring much of his laboratory equipment with him. In England, Krebs continued to work on a series of metabolic reactions that he named the citric acid cycle.

The cycle was discovered not through sudden inspiration but through a series of careful experiments spanning the years 1932 to 1937. Krebs became interested in the "combustion" phase of fuel use, namely, what occurs after the fermentation of glucose to lactate. Until the 1930s, the mechanism of glucose oxidation and its relationship to cellular respiration (oxygen uptake) was a mystery. Krebs understood that the stoichiometry of the overall process (glucose + 6 O_2 → 6 CO_2 + 6 H_2O) required a multistep pathway. He was also aware that other researchers had examined the ability of muscle tissue to rapidly oxidize various dicarboxylates (α-ketoglutarate, succinate, and malate) and a tricarboxylate (citrate), but none of these substances had a clear relationship to any foodstuffs.

In 1935, Albert Szent-Györgyi found that cellular respiration was dramatically accelerated by small amounts of succinate, fumarate, malate, or oxaloacetate. In fact, the addition of any of these compounds stimulated O_2 uptake and CO_2 production far in excess of what would be expected for their oxidation. In other words, the compounds acted catalytically to boost the combustion of other compounds in the cell. At about the same time, Carl Martius and Franz Knoop showed that citrate could be converted to α-ketoglutarate. Soon, Krebs had an entire sequence of reactions for converting citrate to oxaloacetate: citrate → aconitate → isocitrate → α-ketoglutarate → succinate → fumarate → malate →

oxaloacetate. However, in order for this sequence of reactions to work catalytically, it must repeatedly return to its starting point; that is, the first compound must be regenerated. And there was still no obvious link to glucose metabolism!

Krebs believed that citrate and the other intermediates were involved in glucose combustion because they appeared to burn at the same rate as foodstuffs and were the only substances that did so. In addition, earlier work had shown that the three-carbon compound malonate not only blocks the conversion of succinate to fumarate, it blocks all combustion by living cells. In 1937, Martius and Knoop provided Krebs with a key piece of information: oxaloacetate and pyruvate could be converted to citrate in the presence of hydrogen peroxide.

Krebs now had the missing link: Pyruvate is a product of glucose metabolism, and its reaction with oxaloacetate to form citrate closed off the linear series of reactions to form a cycle. The idea of a circular pathway was not new to Krebs. He and Kurt Henseleit had elucidated the four-step urea cycle in 1932 (Section 21-3). Krebs quickly showed that the reaction of pyruvate with oxaloacetate to form citrate took place in living tissue and that the rates of citrate synthesis and breakdown were high enough to account for the observed fuel combustion in a variety of tissue types.

Remarkably, Krebs' initial report on the citric acid cycle was rejected by *Nature*, a leading journal, before being accepted for publication in the less prestigious *Enzymologia*. In his report, Krebs established the major outlines of the pathway, although some details were later revised. For example, the mechanism of citrate formation (which involves acetyl-CoA rather than pyruvate) and the participation of succinyl-CoA in the cycle were not immediately appreciated. Coenzyme A was not discovered until 1945, and only in 1951 was acetyl-CoA shown to be the intermediate that condenses with oxaloacetate to form citrate. Work by Krebs and others established that the citric acid cycle plays a major role in the oxidation of amino acids and fatty acids. In fact, the pathway accounts for approximately two-thirds of the energy derived from metabolic fuels. Krebs also recognized the role of the citric acid cycle in supplying precursors for synthetic reactions.

[Krebs, H.A. and Johnson, W.A., The role of citric acid in intermediate metabolism in animal tissues, *Enzymologia* **4**, 148–156 (1937).]

---

sources, not just pyruvate. Because it accounts for the major portion of carbohydrate, fatty acid, and amino acid oxidation, the citric acid cycle is often considered the "hub" of cellular metabolism.

2. The net reaction of the citric acid cycle is

$$3\,NAD^+ + FAD + GDP + P_i + acetyl\text{–}CoA \longrightarrow$$
$$3\,NADH + FADH_2 + GTP + CoA + 2\,CO_2$$

The oxaloacetate that is consumed in the first step of the citric acid cycle is regenerated in the last step of the cycle. Thus, *the citric acid cycle acts as a multistep catalyst that can oxidize an unlimited number of acetyl groups.*

3. In eukaryotes, all the enzymes of the citric acid cycle are located in the mitochondria, so all substrates, including NAD^+ and GDP, must be generated in the mitochondria or be transported into mitochondria from the cytosol. Similarly, all the products of the citric acid cycle must be consumed in the mitochondria or transported into the cytosol.

4. The carbon atoms of the two molecules of CO_2 produced in one round of the cycle are not the two carbons of the acetyl group that began the round (Fig. 17-2). These acetyl carbon atoms are lost in subsequent rounds of the cycle. However, the net effect of each round of the cycle is the oxidation of one acetyl group to 2 CO_2.

5. Citric acid cycle intermediates are precursors for the biosynthesis of other compounds (e.g., oxaloacetate for gluconeogenesis; Section 16-4).

6. The oxidation of an acetyl group to 2 CO_2 requires the transfer of four pairs of electrons. The reduction of 3 NAD^+ to 3 NADH accounts for three pairs of electrons; the reduction of FAD to $FADH_2$ accounts for the fourth pair. Much of the free energy of oxidation of the acetyl group is conserved in these reduced coenzymes. Energy is also recovered as GTP (or ATP). In Section 18-3C, we shall see that approximately 10 ATP are formed when the four pairs of electrons are eventually transferred to O_2.

■ **CHECK YOUR UNDERSTANDING**

Explain why the citric acid cycle is considered to be the hub of cellular metabolism.
What are the substrates and products of the net reaction corresponding to one turn of the citric acid cycle?

2 Synthesis of Acetyl-Coenzyme A

Acetyl groups enter the citric acid cycle as part of the "high-energy" compound acetyl-CoA (recall that thioesters have high free energies of hydrolysis; Section 14-2D). Although acetyl-CoA can also be derived from fatty acids (Section 20-2) and some amino acids (Section 21-4), we shall focus here on the production of acetyl-CoA from pyruvate derived from carbohydrates.

As we saw in Section 15-3, the end product of glycolysis under anaerobic conditions is lactate or ethanol. However, under aerobic conditions, when the NADH generated by glycolysis is reoxidized in the mitochondria, the final product is pyruvate. A transport protein imports pyruvate along with H^+ (i.e., a pyruvate–H^+ symport) into the mitochondrion for further oxidation.

LEARNING OBJECTIVE

■ Understand that pyruvate dehydrogenase is a multienzyme complex that catalyzes a five-part reaction in which pyruvate releases CO_2 and the remaining acetyl group becomes linked to coenzyme A.

A | Pyruvate Dehydrogenase Is a Multienzyme Complex

Multienzyme complexes are groups of noncovalently associated enzymes that catalyze two or more sequential steps in a metabolic pathway. Virtually all organisms contain multienzyme complexes, which represent a step forward in the evolution of catalytic efficiency because they offer the following advantages:

1. Enzymatic reaction rates are limited by the frequency with which enzymes collide with their substrates (Section 11-3D). When a series of reactions occurs within a multienzyme complex, the distance that substrates must diffuse between active sites is minimized, thereby enhancing the reaction rate.

2. The channeling of metabolic intermediates between successive enzymes in a metabolic pathway reduces the opportunity for these

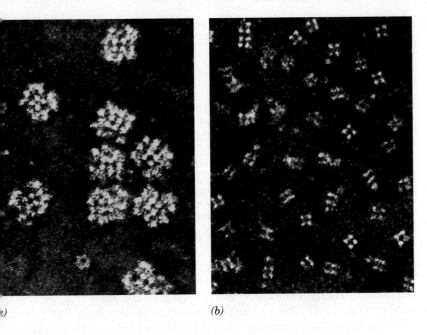

(b)

■ **Figure 17-3** | **Electron micrographs of the *E. coli* pyruvate dehydrogenase multienzyme complex.** (*a*) The intact complex. (*b*) The dihydrolipoyl transacetylase (E_2) core complex. [Courtesy of Lester Reed, University of Texas at Austin.]

intermediates to react with other molecules, thereby minimizing side reactions.

3. The reactions catalyzed by a multienzyme complex can be coordinately controlled.

Acetyl-CoA is formed from pyruvate through oxidative decarboxylation by a multienzyme complex named **pyruvate dehydrogenase.** This complex contains multiple copies of three enzymes: **pyruvate dehydrogenase (E_1), dihydrolipoyl transacetylase (E_2),** and **dihydrolipoyl dehydrogenase (E_3).**

The *E. coli* pyruvate dehydrogenase complex is an ~4600-kD particle with a diameter of about 300 Å (Fig. 17-3*a*). The core of the particle is made of 24 E_2 proteins arranged in a cube (Figs. 17-3*b* and 4*a*), which is surrounded by 24 E_1 proteins and 12 E_3 proteins (Fig. 17-4*b,c*). In mammals, yeast, and some bacteria, the pyruvate dehydrogenase complex is even larger and more complicated, although it catalyzes the same reactions using homologous enzymes and similar mechanisms. In these ~10,000-kD complexes, which are among the largest known multifunctional particles in cells, the E_2 core consists of 60 subunits arranged with

(a)　　　*(b)*　　　*(c)*

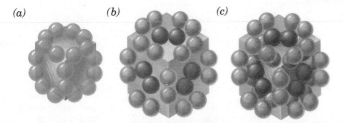

■ **Figure 17-4** | **Structural organization of the *E. coli* pyruvate dehydrogenase multienzyme complex.** (*a*) The dihydrolipoyl transacetylase (E_2) core. The 24 E_2 proteins (*green spheres*) associate as trimers at the corners of a cube. (*b*) The 24 pyruvate dehydrogenase (E_1) proteins (*orange spheres*) form dimers that associate with the E_2 core (*shaded cube*) along its 12 edges. The 12 dihydrolipoyl dehydrogenase (E_3) proteins (*purple spheres*) form dimers that attach to the six faces of the E_2 cube. (*c*) Parts *a* and *b* combined form the entire 60-subunit complex.

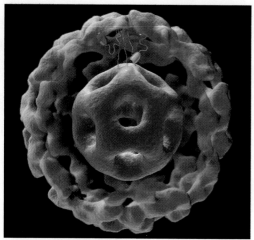

■ **Figure 17-5 | Model of the *Bacillus stearothermophilus* pyruvate dehydrogenase complex.** This ~500-Å-diameter cutaway surface diagram is based on cryoelectron microscopic images of a complex consisting of a core of 60 E_2 subunits (*gray-green*) surrounded by an outer shell of 60 E_1 subunits (*purple*) separated by an ~90-Å-wide annular gap. Three full-length E_2 subunits are schematically represented in red, green, and yellow to indicate their catalytic domains (embedded in the E_2 core), their peripheral subunit-binding domains (embedded in the E_3 shell) that bind the E_1 (and E_3) subunits, and their lipoyl domains, all connected by flexible polypeptide linkers (Section 17-2B). Here the red lipoyl domain is shown visiting an E_1 active site (*white dot*), whereas the green and yellow lipoyl domains occupy intermediate positions in the annular region between the E_2 core and E_1 shell. In a normal pyruvate dehydrogenase complex, E_3 subunits would take the place of some of the E_1 subunits. Indeed, a complex of 60 E_3 subunits and 60 E_2 subunits closely resembles the E_1E_2 complex. [Courtesy of Jacqueline Milne, National Institutes of Health, Bethesda, MD.]

dodecahedral symmetry [Fig. 17-5; a dodecahedron is a regular polyhedron with I symmetry (Fig. 6-34c) that has 20 vertices and 12 pentagonal faces] surrounded by a shell consisting of ~45 E_1 $\alpha_2\beta_2$ heterotetramers and ~ E_3 homodimers. E_1 and E_3 competitively bind to mutually exclusive sites on E_2 in a random distribution. Mammalian complexes, in addition contain ~12 copies. of **E_3 binding protein,** which facilitates the binding of E_3 to the E_2 core, and several copies of a kinase and a phosphatase that function to regulate the activity of the complex (Section 17-4A).

B | The Pyruvate Dehydrogenase Complex Catalyzes Five Reactions

The pyruvate dehydrogenase complex catalyzes five sequential reactions with the overall stoichiometry

$$\text{Pyruvate} + \text{CoA} + \text{NAD}^+ \longrightarrow \text{acetyl-CoA} + \text{CO}_2 + \text{NADH}$$

Five different coenzymes are required: thiamine pyrophosphate (TPP; Section 15-3B), **lipoamide,** coenzyme A (Fig. 14-10), FAD (Fig. 14-12), and NAD^+ (Fig. 11-4). The coenzymes and their mechanistic functions are listed in Table 17-1. The sequence of reactions catalyzed by the pyruvate dehydrogenase complex is as follows (Fig. 17-6):

1. Pyruvate dehydrogenase (E_1), a TPP-requiring enzyme, decarboxylates pyruvate with the formation of a hydroxyethyl-TPP intermediate.

Table 17-1 | The Coenzymes and Prosthetic Groups of Pyruvate Dehydrogenase

Cofactor	Location	Function
Thiamine pyrophosphate (TPP)	Bound to E_1	Decarboxylates pyruvate yielding a hydroxyethyl-TPP carbanion
Lipoic acid	Covalently linked to a Lys on E_2 (lipoamide)	Accepts the hydroxyethyl carbanion from TPP as an acetyl group
Coenzyme A (CoA)	Substrate for E_2	Accepts the acetyl group from lipoamide
Flavin adenine dinucleotide (FAD)	Bound to E_3	Reduced by lipoamide
Nicotinamide adenine dinucleotide (NAD^+)	Substrate for E_3	Reduced by FADH_2

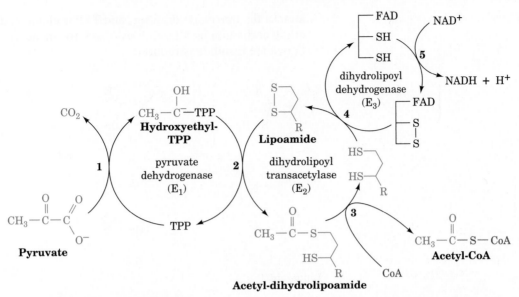

■ **Figure 17-6** | **The five reactions of the pyruvate
dehydrogenase multienzyme complex.** E_1 (pyruvate
dehydrogenase) contains TPP and catalyzes Reactions 1 and 2. E_2
(dihydrolipoyl transacetylase) contains lipoamide and catalyzes
Reaction 3. E_3 (dihydrolipoyl dehydrogenase) contains FAD and a
redox-active disulfide and catalyzes Reactions 4 and 5.

This reaction is identical to that catalyzed by yeast pyruvate decarboxylase (Fig. 15-20). Recall (Section 15-3B) that the ability of TPP's thiazolium ring to add to carbonyl groups and act as an electron sink makes
it the coenzyme most utilized in α-keto acid decarboxylation reactions.

2. The hydroxyethyl group is transferred to the next enzyme, dihydrolipoyl transacetylase (E_2), which contains a lipoamide group.
Lipoamide consists of **lipoic acid** linked via an amide bond to the
ε-amino group of a Lys residue (Fig. 17-7). The reactive center of
lipoamide is a cyclic disulfide that can be reversibly reduced to yield
dihydrolipoamide. The hydroxyethyl group derived from pyruvate

$$\begin{array}{c} \overbrace{}^{\text{Lipoic acid}} \qquad \overbrace{}^{\text{Lys}} \end{array}$$

S—CH$_2$
   CH$_2$
S—CH
    CH$_2$—CH$_2$—CH$_2$—CH$_2$—C—NH—(CH$_2$)$_4$—CH

Lipoamide

⇅ 2 H$^+$ + 2 e$^-$

HS—CH$_2$
   CH$_2$
HS—CH
    CH$_2$—CH$_2$—CH$_2$—CH$_2$—C—NH—(CH$_2$)$_4$—CH

Dihydrolipoamide

■ **Figure 17-7** | **Interconversion of lipoamide
and dihydrolipoamide.** Lipoamide consists of
lipoic acid covalently joined to the ε-amino group
of a Lys residue via an amide bond.

attacks the lipoamide disulfide, and TPP is eliminated. The hydroxy-ethyl carbanion is thereby oxidized to an acetyl group as the lipoamide disulfide is reduced:

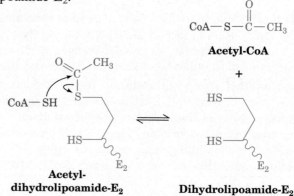

Lipoamide-E$_2$

TPP • E$_1$

Acetyl-dihydrolipoamide-E$_2$

3. E$_2$ then catalyzes a transesterification reaction in which the acetyl group is transferred to CoA, yielding acetyl-CoA and dihydrolipoamide-E$_2$:

Acetyl-CoA

+

Acetyl-dihydrolipoamide-E$_2$ **Dihydrolipoamide-E$_2$**

4. Acetyl-CoA has now been formed, but the lipoamide group of E$_2$ must be regenerated. Dihydrolipoyl dehydrogenase (E$_3$) reoxidizes dihydrolipoamide to complete the catalytic cycle of E$_2$. Oxidized E$_3$ contains a reactive Cys—Cys disulfide group and a tightly bound FAD. The oxidation of dihydrolipoamide is a disulfide interchange reaction:

E$_3$ (oxidized)   **E$_3$ (reduced)**

5. Finally, reduced E$_3$ is reoxidized. The sulfhydryl groups are reoxidized by a mechanism in which FAD funnels electrons to NAD$^+$ yielding NADH:

E$_3$ (oxidized)

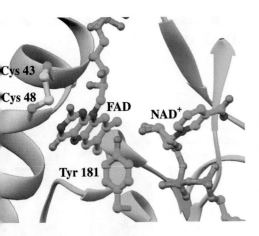

■ **Figure 17-8** | **Active site of dihydrolipoamide dehydrogenase (E$_3$).** In this X-ray structure of the enzyme from *Pseudomonas putida*, the redox-active portions of the bound NAD$^+$ and FAD cofactors, the side chains of Cys 43 and Cys 48 forming the redox-active disulfide bond, and the side chain of Tyr 181 are shown in ball-and-stick form with C green, N blue, O red, P magenta, and S yellow. Note that the side chain of Tyr 181 is interposed between the flavin and the nicotinamide rings. [Based on an X-ray structure by Wim Hol, University of Washington. PDBid 1LVL.]

The X-ray structure of dihydrolipoyl dehydrogenase together with mechanistic information indicate that the reaction catalyzed by dihydrolipoamide dehydrogenase (E$_3$) is more complex than Reactions 4 and 5 in Fig. 17-6 suggest. The enzyme's redox-active disulfide bond occurs between Cys 43 and Cys 48, which reside on a highly conserved segment of the enzyme's polypeptide chain. The disulfide bond links successive turns in a distorted segment of an α helix (in an undistorted helix, the C$_\alpha$ atoms of Cys 43 and Cys 48 would be too far apart to permit the disulfide bond to form). The enzyme's flavin group is almost completely buried in the protein, which prevents the surrounding solution from interfering with the electron-transfer reaction catalyzed by the enzyme. The nicotinamide ring of NAD$^+$ binds on the side of the flavin opposite the disulfide. In the absence of NAD$^+$, the phenol side chain of Tyr 181 covers the nicotinamide-binding pocket so as to shield the flavin from contact with the solution (Fig. 17-8). The Tyr side chain apparently moves aside to allow the nicotinamide ring to bind near the flavin ring.

FAD prosthetic groups in proteins have reduction potentials of around 0 V (Table 14-5), which makes FADH$_2$ unsuitable for donating electrons to NAD$^+$($\mathscr{E}°' = -0.315$ V). Evidence suggests that the FAD group in dihydrolipoamide dehydrogenase never becomes fully reduced as FADH$_2$. Due to the precise positioning of the flavin and nicotinamide ring, electrons are rapidly transferred from the enzyme disulfide through FAD to NAD$^+$, so a reduced flavin anion (FADH$^-$) has but a transient existence. Thus, *FAD appears to function more as an electron conduit than as a source or sink of electrons.*

A Swinging Arm Transfers Intermediates. How are reaction intermediates channeled between E$_2$ (the core of the pyruvate dehydrogenase complex) and the E$_1$ and E$_3$ proteins on the outside? The key is the lipoamide group of E$_2$. The lipoic acid residue and the side chain of the Lys residue to which it is attached have a combined length of about 14 Å. This **lipoyllysyl arm** (*at right*) apparently acts as a long tether that swings the disulfide group from E$_1$ (where it picks up a hydroxyethyl group), to the E$_2$ active site (where the hydroxyethyl group is transferred to form acetyl-CoA), and from there to E$_3$ (where the reduced disulfide is reoxidized). The domains of E$_2$ that carry the lipoyllysyl arms are linked to the rest of the E$_2$ protein by a highly flexible Pro- and Ala-rich segment that contributes to the mobility of the lipoyllysyl arm. Because of the flexibility and reach of the lipoyllysyl arms, one E$_1$ protein can acetylate numerous E$_2$ proteins, and one E$_3$ protein can reoxidize

**Lipoyllysyl arm
(fully extended)**

BOX 17-2 BIOCHEMISTRY IN HEALTH AND DISEASE

Arsenic Poisoning

The toxicity of arsenic has been known since ancient times. As(III) compounds such as **arsenite** (AsO_3^{3-}) and **organic arsenicals** are toxic because they bind to sulfhydryl compounds (including lipoamide) that can form bidentate adducts:

Arsenite   **Dihydro-lipoamide**

Organic arsenical

The inactivation of lipoamide-containing enzymes by arsenite, especially the pyruvate dehydrogenase and α-ketoglutarate dehydrogenase complexes, brings respiration to a halt. However, organic arsenicals are more toxic to microorganisms than they are to humans, apparently because of differences in the sensitivities of their various enzymes to the compounds. This differential toxicity is the basis for the early twentieth century use of organic arsenicals in the treatment of **syphilis** (a bacterial disease) and trypanosomiasis (a parasitic disease). These compounds were actually the first antibiotics, although, not surprisingly, they produced severe side effects.

Arsenic is often suspected as a poison in untimely deaths. It was long thought that Napoleon Bonaparte died from arsenic poisoning while in exile on the island of St. Helena, a suspicion that is strongly supported by the recent finding that a lock of his hair contains high levels of arsenic. But was it murder or environmental pollution? Arsenic-containing dyes were used in wallpaper at the time, and it was eventually determined that in damp weather, fungi convert the arsenic to a volatile compound. Surviving samples of the wallpaper from Napoleon's room in fact contain arsenic. Napoleon's arsenic poisoning may therefore have been unintentional.

Napoleon Bonaparte [© Victoria and Albert Museum/Art Resource.

Charles Darwin
[© Photo Researchers.]

Charles Darwin may also have been an unwitting victim of chronic arsenic poisoning. In the years following his epic voyage on the *Beagle*, Darwin was plagued by eczema, vertigo, headaches, gout, and nausea—all symptoms of arsenic poisoning. Fowler's solution, a widely used nineteenth century "tonic," contained 10 mg of arsenite per mL. Many individuals, quite possibly Darwin himself, took this "medication" for years.

■ **CHECK YOUR UNDERSTANDING**

Describe the five reactions of the pyruvate dehydrogenase multienzyme complex.

LEARNING OBJECTIVE

■ Become familiar with the reactions catalyzed by the eight enzymes of the citric acid cycle, including those that generate CO_2, GTP, and the reduced coenzymes NADH and $FADH_2$.

several dihydrolipoamide groups. The lipoyllysyl arms probably protrude into the space between the E_2 core and the E_1E_3 outer shell (Fig. 17-5) and swing around in order to "visit" the active sites of E_1, E_2, and E_3. The entire pyruvate dehydrogenase complex can be inactivated by the reaction of the lipoamide group with certain arsenic-containing compounds (see Box 17-2).

3 Enzymes of the Citric Acid Cycle

In this section, we discuss the eight enzymes of the citric acid cycle. The elucidation of the mechanisms for each of these enzymes is the result of an enormous amount of experimental work. Even so, there remain questions about the mechanistic details of the enzymes and their regulatory properties.

(b)

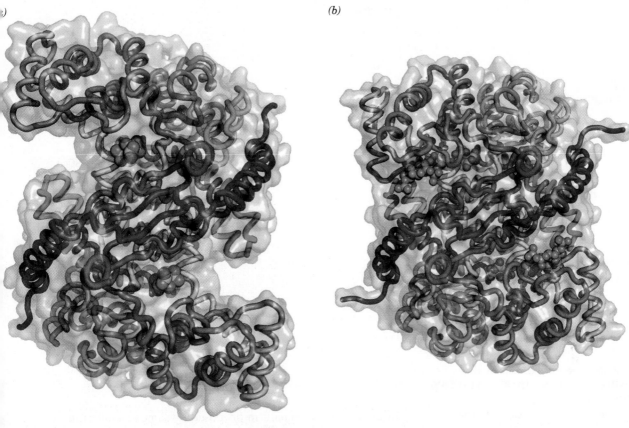

Figure 17-9 | Conformational changes in citrate synthase.
(a) The open conformation. (b) The closed, substrate-binding
conformation. In both forms, the homodimeric protein is viewed
along its twofold axis and is represented by its transparent molecular
surface with its polypeptide chains drawn in worm form colored in
rainbow order from blue at their N-termini to red at their C-termini.
The reaction product citrate, which is bound to both enzymatic
forms, and coenzyme A, which is also bound to the closed form, are
shown in space-filling form with citrate C cyan, CoA C green, N
blue, O red, and P orange. The large conformational shift between
the open and closed forms entails 18° rotations of the small
domains (*upper left and lower right*) relative to the large domains,
resulting in relative interatomic movements of up to 15 Å. [Based
on X-ray structures by James Remington and Robert Huber,
Max-Planck-Institut für Biochemie, Martinsried, Germany. PDBids
1CTS and 2CTS.] **See Interactive Exercise 18.**

A | Citrate Synthase Joins an Acetyl Group to Oxaloacetate

Citrate synthase catalyzes the condensation of acetyl-CoA and oxaloacetate. This initial reaction of the citric acid cycle is the point at which
carbon atoms (from carbohydrates, fatty acids, and amino acids) are "fed
into the furnace" as acetyl-CoA. The citrate synthase reaction proceeds
with an Ordered Sequential kinetic mechanism in which oxaloacetate
binds before acetyl-CoA.

X-Ray studies show that the free enzyme (a homodimer) is in an
"open" form, with two domains that form a cleft containing the substrate-
binding site (Fig. 17-9a). When substrate binds, the smaller domain undergoes a remarkable 18° rotation, which closes the cleft (Fig. 17-9b). The existence of the "open" and "closed" forms explains the enzyme's Ordered
Sequential kinetic behavior. *The conformational change generates the
acetyl-CoA binding site and seals the oxaloacetate binding site so that solvent cannot reach the bound substrate.* We have seen similar conformational changes in adenylate kinase (Fig. 14-9) and hexokinase (Fig. 15-2),
which prevent ATP hydrolysis.

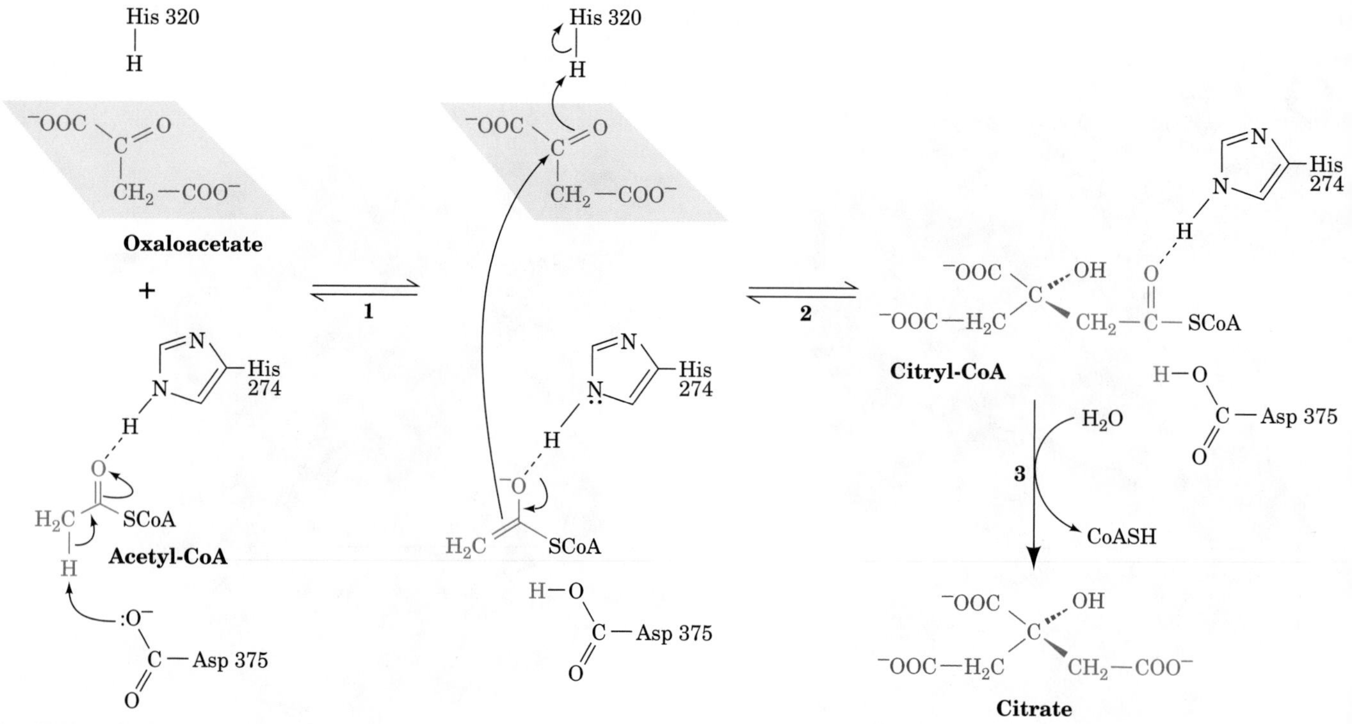

■ **Figure 17-10** | **The mechanism of the citrate synthase reaction.** His 274 and His 320 in their neutral forms and Asp 375 have been implicated as general acid–base catalysts. The rate-limiting step (**1**) is the formation of the acetyl-CoA enolate, which is stabilized by a hydrogen bond to the His 274. (**2**) The acetyl-CoA enolate then nucleophilically attacks oxaloacetate's carbonyl carbon. (**3**) The resulting intermediate, citryl-CoA, is hydrolyzed to yield citrate and CoA. [Mostly after Remington, *J.S., Curr. Opin. Struct. Biol.* **2,** 732 (1992).]

In the reaction mechanism proposed by James Remington, three ionizable side chains of citrate synthase participate in catalysis (Fig. 17-10):

1. The enol of acetyl-CoA is generated in the rate-limiting step of the reaction when Asp 375 (a base) removes a proton from the methyl group. His 274 forms a hydrogen bond with the enolate oxygen.

2. **Citryl-CoA** is formed in a concerted acid–base catalyzed step, in which the acetyl-CoA enolate (a nucleophile) attacks oxaloacetate. His 320 (an acid) donates a proton to oxaloacetate's carbonyl group. The citryl-CoA intermediate remains bound to the enzyme. Citrate synthase is one of the few enzymes that can directly form a carbon–carbon bond without the assistance of a metal ion cofactor.

3. Citryl-CoA is hydrolyzed to citrate and CoA. This hydrolysis provides the reaction's thermodynamic driving force ($\Delta G^{\circ\prime} = -31.5 \text{ kJ} \cdot \text{mol}^{-1}$). We shall see later why this reaction requires such a large, seemingly wasteful, expenditure of free energy.

B | Aconitase Interconverts Citrate and Isocitrate

Aconitase catalyzes the reversible isomerization of citrate and **isocitrate** with *cis*-aconitate as an intermediate:

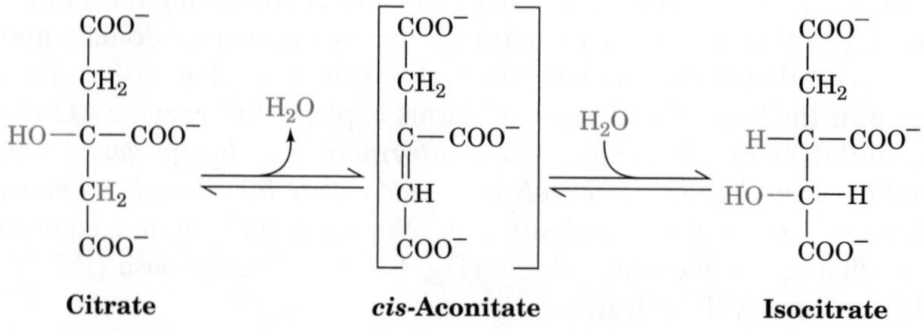

Citrate   *cis*-Aconitate   Isocitrate

he reaction begins with a dehydration step in which a proton and an OH
roup are removed. Since citrate has two carboxymethyl groups sub-
ituent to its central C atom, it is prochiral rather than chiral. Thus,
though water might conceivably be eliminated from either of the two
arboxymethyl arms, aconitase removes water only from citrate's lower
pro-R) arm (i.e., such that the product molecule has the R configuration;
ox 4-2).

Aconitase contains a **[4Fe–4S] iron–sulfur cluster** (an arrangement of
our iron atoms and four sulfur atoms, Section 18-2C) that presumably
oordinates the OH group of citrate to facilitate its elimination.
on–sulfur clusters normally participate in redox processes; aconitase is
n intriguing exception.

The second stage of the aconitase reaction is rehydration of the dou-
le bond of *cis*-aconitate to form isocitrate. Although addition of water
cross the double bond of *cis*-aconitate could potentially yield four
ereoisomers, aconitase catalyzes the stereospecific addition of OH^- and
H^+ to produce only one isocitrate stereoisomer. The ability of an enzyme
o differentiate its substrate's *pro-R* and *pro-S* groups was not appreciated
ntil 1948, when Alexander Ogston pointed out that aconitase can distin-
uish between the two $-CH_2COO^-$ groups of citrate when it is bound to
e enzyme (Section 11-1B).

| NAD$^+$-Dependent Isocitrate Dehydrogenase Releases CO_2

socitrate dehydrogenase catalyzes the oxidative decarboxylation of iso-
itrate to α-ketoglutarate. This reaction produces the first CO_2 and NADH
f the citric acid cycle. Note that this CO_2 began the citric acid cycle as a
omponent of oxaloacetate, not of acetyl-CoA (Fig. 17-2). (Mammalian tis-
ues also contain an isocitrate dehydrogenase isozyme that uses NADP$^+$
s a cofactor.)

NAD$^+$-dependent isocitrate dehydrogenase, which also requires a
Mn^{2+} or Mg^{2+} cofactor, catalyzes the oxidation of a secondary alcohol
isocitrate) to a ketone **(oxalosuccinate)** followed by the decarboxylation
f the carboxyl group β to the ketone (Fig. 17-11). Mn^{2+} helps polarize
he newly formed carbonyl group. The isocitrate dehydrogenase reaction
echanism is similar to that of phosphogluconate dehydrogenase in the
entose phosphate pathway (Section 15-6A).

The oxalosuccinate intermediate of the isocitrate dehydrogenase reac-
on exists only transiently, and its existence was therefore difficult to
onfirm. However, an enzymatic reaction can be slowed by mutating
atalytically important residues—in this case, Tyr 160 and Lys 230—to

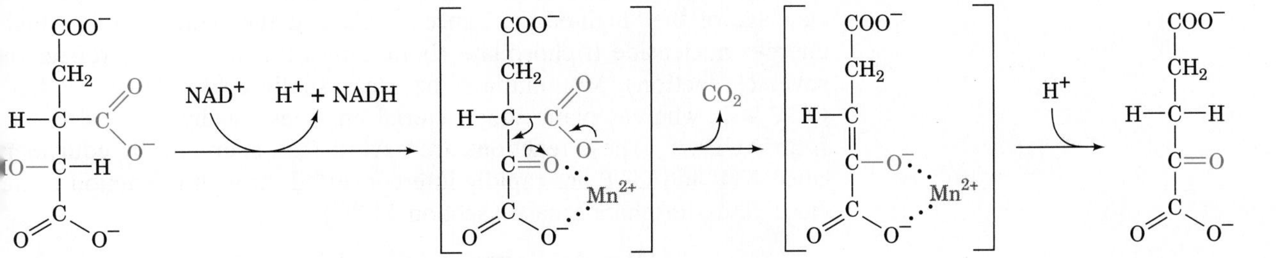

Figure 17-11 | The reaction mechanism of isocitrate dehydrogenase.
Oxalosuccinate is shown in brackets because it does not dissociate from the enzyme.

create kinetic "bottlenecks" so that reaction intermediates accumulate. Accordingly, crystals of the mutant isocitrate dehydrogenase were expose to the substrate isocitrate and immediately visualized via X-ray crystallo graphy using rapid measurement techniques that require the highly intens X-rays generated by a synchrotron. These studies revealed the oxalosuc cinate intermediate in the active site of the enzyme.

D | α-Ketoglutarate Dehydrogenase Resembles Pyruvate Dehydrogenase

α-Ketoglutarate dehydrogenase catalyzes the oxidative decarboxylation c an α-keto acid (α-ketoglutarate). This reaction produces the second CO_2 and NADH of the citric acid cycle:

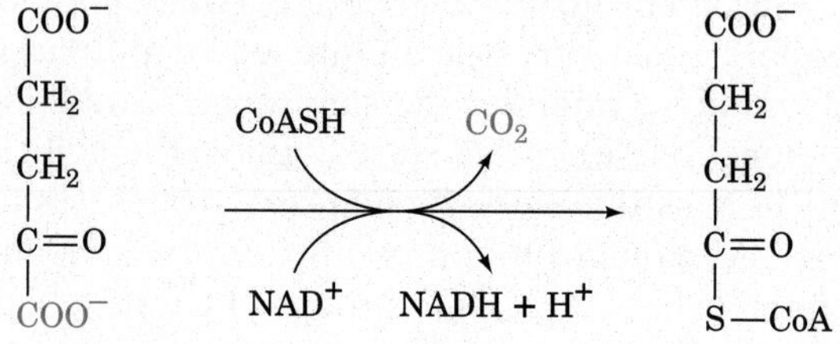

α-Ketoglutarate   **Succinyl-CoA**

Again, this CO_2 entered the citric acid cycle as a component of oxaloac etate rather than of acetyl-CoA (Fig. 17-2). Thus, although each round o the citric acid cycle oxidizes two C atoms to CO_2, the C atoms of the en tering acetyl groups are not oxidized to CO_2 until subsequent rounds o the cycle.

The α-ketoglutarate dehydrogenase reaction chemically resembles th reaction catalyzed by the pyruvate dehydrogenase multienzyme complex α-Ketoglutarate dehydrogenase is a multienzyme complex containin **α-ketoglutarate dehydrogenase (E₁), dihydrolipoyl transsuccinylase (E₂)** and **dihydrolipoyl dehydrogenase (E₃).** Indeed, this E₃ is identical to th E₃ of the pyruvate dehydrogenase complex (a third member of the **2-keto acid dehydrogenase** family of multienzyme complexes is **branched-chain α-keto acid dehydrogenase,** which participates in the degradation o isoleucine, leucine, and valine; Section 21-4). The reactions catalyzed b the α-ketoglutarate dehydrogenase complex occur by mechanisms identi cal to those of the pyruvate dehydrogenase complex. Again, the produc is a "high-energy" thioester, in this case, **succinyl-CoA.**

E | Succinyl-CoA Synthetase Produces GTP

Succinyl-CoA synthetase (also called **succinate thiokinase**) couples th cleavage of the "high-energy" succinyl-CoA to the synthesis of a "high energy" nucleoside triphosphate (both names for the enzyme reflect th reverse reaction). Mammalian enzymes usually synthesize GTP from GDP + P_i, whereas plant and bacterial enzymes usually synthesize ATP from ADP + P_i. These reactions are nevertheless energetically equivalen since ATP and GTP are rapidly interconverted through the action of nu cleoside diphosphate kinase (Section 14-2C):

$$GTP + ADP \rightleftharpoons GDP + ATP \qquad \Delta G^{\circ\prime} = 0$$

How does succinyl-CoA synthetase couple the exergonic cleavage o succinyl-CoA ($\Delta G^{\circ\prime} = -32.6 \text{ kJ} \cdot \text{mol}^{-1}$) to the endergonic formation of a nucleoside triphosphate ($\Delta G^{\circ\prime} = 30.5 \text{ kJ} \cdot \text{mol}^{-1}$) from the corresponding ucleoside diphosphate and P_i? This question was answered by an experiment with isotopically labeled ADP. In the absence of succinyl-CoA, the spinach enzyme catalyzes the transfer of the γ-phosphoryl group from TP to [^{14}C]ADP, producing [^{14}C]ATP. Such an isotope-exchange reaction suggests the participation of a phosphoryl-enzyme intermediate that mediates the reaction sequence

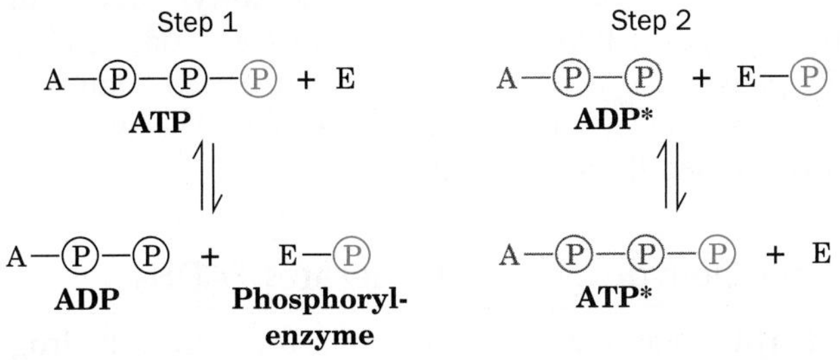

his information led to the isolation of a kinetically active phosphoryl-enzyme in which the phosphoryl group is covalently linked to the N3 position of a His residue. A three-step mechanism for succinyl-CoA synthetase is shown in Fig. 17-12.

1. Succinyl-CoA reacts with P_i to form **succinyl-phosphate** and CoA.
2. The phosphoryl group is then transferred from succinyl-phosphate to a His residue on the enzyme, releasing succinate.
3. The phosphoryl group on the enzyme is transferred to GDP, forming GTP.

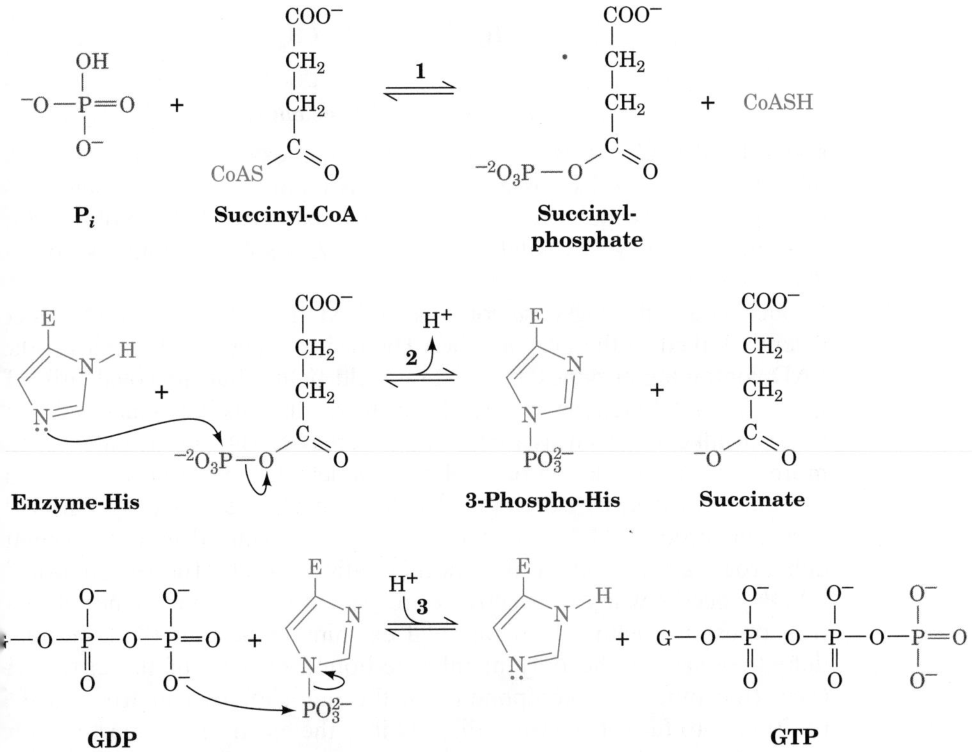

Figure 17-12 | The reaction catalyzed by succinyl-CoA synthetase.
(1) Formation of succinyl-phosphate, a "high-energy" acyl phosphate. (2) Formation of phosphoryl-His, a "high-energy" intermediate. (3) Transfer of the phosphoryl group to GDP, forming GTP.

Note that in each of these steps, *the energy of succinyl-CoA is conserved through the formation of "high-energy" compounds: first, succinyl-phosphate, then a 3-phospho-His residue, and finally GTP.* The process is reminiscent of passing a hot potato. The reaction catalyzed by succinyl-CoA synthetase is another example of substrate-level phosphorylation (ATP synthesis that does not directly depend on the presence of oxygen).

By this point in the citric acid cycle, one acetyl equivalent has been completely oxidized to two CO_2. Two NADH and one GTP (equivalent to one ATP) have also been generated. In order to complete the cycle, succinate must be converted back to oxaloacetate. This is accomplished by the cycle's remaining three reactions.

F | Succinate Dehydrogenase Generates FADH$_2$

Succinate dehydrogenase catalyzes the stereospecific dehydrogenation of succinate to fumarate:

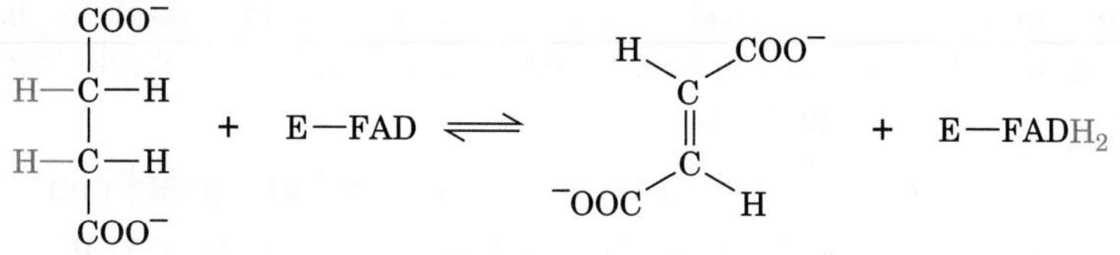

Succinate   **Fumarate**

This enzyme is strongly inhibited by malonate,

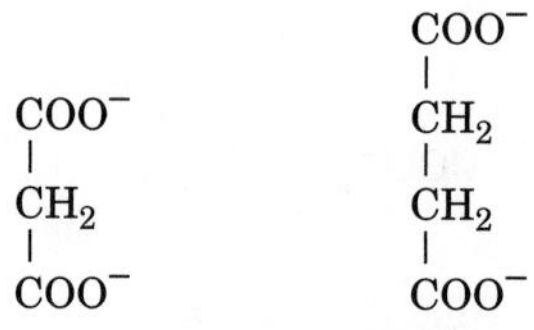

Malonate   **Succinate**

a structural analog of succinate and a classic example of a competitive inhibitor. When Krebs was formulating his theory of the citric acid cycle, the inhibition of cellular respiration by malonate provided one of the clues that succinate plays a catalytic role in oxidizing substrates and is not just another substrate.

Succinate dehydrogenase contains an FAD prosthetic group that is covalently linked to the enzyme via a His residue (Fig. 17-13; in most other FAD-containing enzymes, the FAD is held tightly but noncovalently). In general, FAD functions biochemically to oxidize alkanes (such as succinate) to alkenes (such as fumarate), whereas NAD^+ participates in the more exergonic oxidation of alcohols to aldehydes or ketones (e.g., in the reaction catalyzed by isocitrate dehydrogenase). The dehydrogenation of succinate produces FADH$_2$, which must be reoxidized before succinate dehydrogenase can undertake another catalytic cycle. The reoxidation of FADH$_2$ occurs when its electrons are passed to the mitochondrial electron transport chain, which we shall examine in Section 18-2. Succinate dehydrogenase is the only membrane-bound enzyme of the citric acid cycle (the others are components of the mitochondrial matrix), so it is positioned to funnel electrons directly into the electron transport machinery of the mitochondrial membrane.

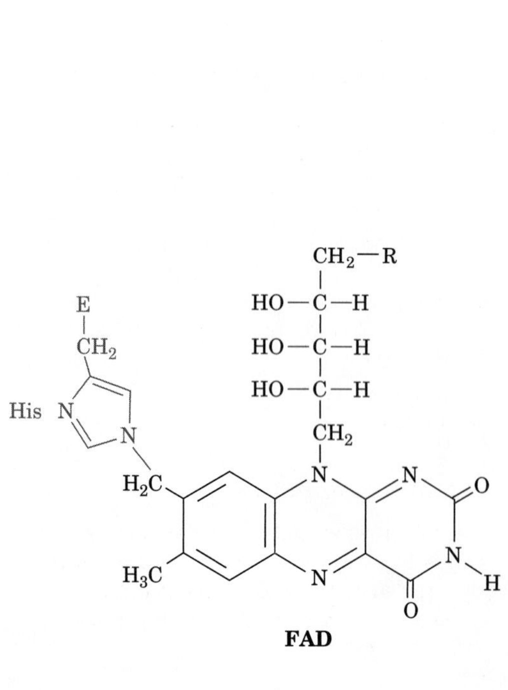

■ **Figure 17-13 | The covalent attachment of FAD to a His residue of succinate dehydrogenase.** R represents the ADP moiety.

FAD

Fumarase Produces Malate

Fumarase (fumarate hydratase) catalyzes the hydration of the double bond of fumarate to form malate. The hydration reaction proceeds via a carbanion transition state. OH^- addition occurs before H^+ addition:

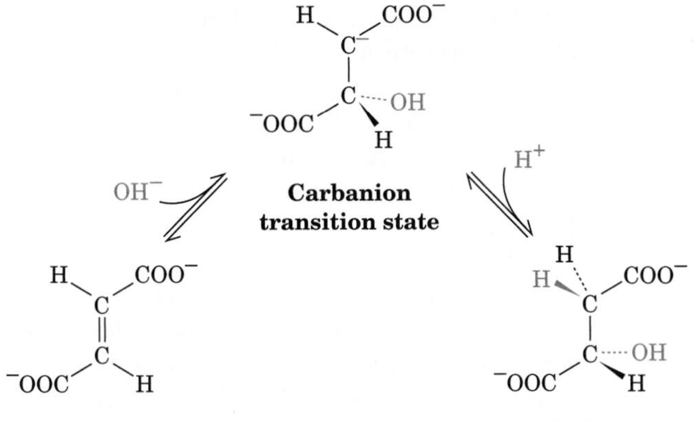

Malate Dehydrogenase Regenerates Oxaloacetate

Malate dehydrogenase catalyzes the final reaction of the citric acid cycle, the regeneration of oxaloacetate. The hydroxyl group of malate is oxidized in an NAD^+-dependent reaction:

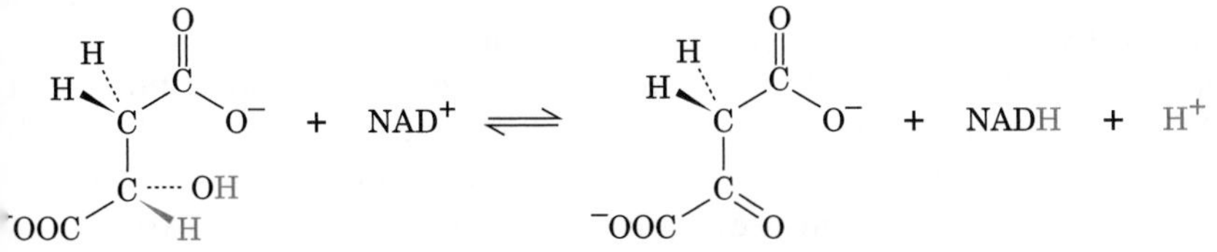

Transfer of the hydride ion to NAD^+ occurs by the same mechanism used for hydride ion transfer in lactate dehydrogenase and alcohol dehydrogenase (Section 15-3). X-Ray crystallographic comparisons of the NAD^+-binding domains of these three enzymes indicate that they are remarkably similar, consistent with the proposal that all NAD^+-binding domains evolved from a common ancestor.

The $\Delta G^{\circ\prime}$ value for the malate dehydrogenase reaction is $+29.7 \, kJ \cdot mol^{-1}$; therefore, the concentration of oxaloacetate at equilibrium (and under cellular conditions) is very low relative to malate. Recall, however, that the reaction catalyzed by citrate synthase, the first reaction of the citric acid cycle, is highly exergonic ($\Delta G^{\circ\prime} = -31.5 \, kJ \cdot mol^{-1}$) because of the cleavage of the thioester bond of citryl-CoA. We can now understand the necessity for such a seemingly wasteful process. It allows citrate formation to be exergonic even at the low oxaloacetate concentrations present in cells and thus helps keep the citric acid cycle rolling.

4 Regulation of the Citric Acid Cycle

The capacity of the citric acid cycle to generate energy for cellular needs is closely regulated. The availability of substrates, the need for citric acid cycle intermediates as biosynthetic precursors, and the demand for ATP will influence the operation of the cycle. There is some evidence that the

■ **CHECK YOUR UNDERSTANDING**

Draw the structures of the eight intermediates of the citric acid cycle and name the enzymes that catalyze their interconversions.

Which steps of the citric acid cycle release CO_2 as a product? Which steps produce NADH or $FADH_2$? Which step produces GTP?

Write the net equations for oxidation of pyruvate, the acetyl group of acetyl-CoA, and glucose to CO_2 and H_2O.

LEARNING OBJECTIVE

■ Understand how the need for energy regulates the citric acid cycle capacity at the pyruvate dehydrogenase step and at the three rate-controlling steps of the cycle.

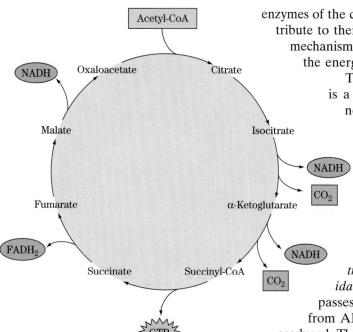

Figure 17-14 | Products of the citric acid cycle. For every two carbons that are oxidized to CO_2, electrons are recovered in the form of three NADH and one $FADH_2$. One GTP (or ATP) is also produced.

enzymes of the citric acid cycle are physically associated, which might contribute to their coordinated regulation. Before we examine the various mechanisms for regulating the citric acid cycle, let us briefly consider the energy-generating capacity of the cycle.

The oxidation of one acetyl group to two molecules of CO_2 is a four-electron pair process (but keep in mind that it is not the carbon atoms of the incoming acetyl group that are oxidized). For every acetyl-CoA that enters the cycle, three molecules of NAD^+ are reduced to NADH, which accounts for three of the electron pairs, and one molecule of FAD is reduced to $FADH_2$, which accounts for the fourth electron pair. In addition, one GTP (or ATP) is produced (Fig. 17-14).

The electrons carried by NADH and $FADH_2$ are funneled into the electron-transport chain, which culminates with the reduction of O_2 to H_2O. The energy of electron transport is conserved in the synthesis of ATP by oxidative phosphorylation (Section 18-3). For every NADH that passes its electrons on, approximately 2.5 ATP are produced from ADP + P_i. For every $FADH_2$, approximately 1.5 ATP are produced. Thus, one turn of the citric acid cycle ultimately generates approximately 10 ATP. We will see in Section 18-3C why these values are only approximations.

When glucose is converted to two molecules of pyruvate by glycolysis, two molecules of ATP are generated and two molecules of NAD^+ are reduced (Section 15-1). The NADH molecules yield approximately 5 molecules of ATP on passing their electrons to the electron-transport chain. When the two pyruvate molecules are converted to two acetyl-CoA by the pyruvate dehydrogenase complex, the two molecules of NADH produced in that process also eventually give rise to ~5 ATP. Two turns of the citric acid cycle (one for each acetyl group) generate ~20 ATP. Thus, one molecule of glucose can potentially yield ~32 molecules of ATP under aerobic conditions, when the citric acid cycle is operating. In contrast, only 2 molecules of ATP are produced per glucose molecule under anaerobic conditions.

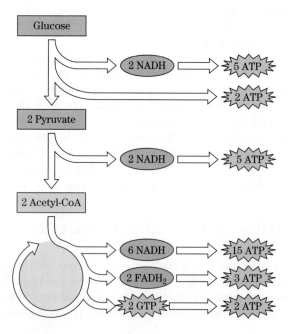

A | Pyruvate Dehydrogenase Is Regulated by Product Inhibition and Covalent Modification

Given the large amount of ATP that can potentially be generated from carbohydrate catabolism via the citric acid cycle, it is not surprising that the entry of acetyl units derived from carbohydrate sources is regulated. The decarboxylation of pyruvate by the pyruvate dehydrogenase complex is irreversible, and since there are no other pathways in mammals for the synthesis of acetyl-CoA from pyruvate, it is crucial that the reaction be precisely controlled. Two regulatory systems are used:

1. *Product inhibition by NADH and acetyl-CoA.* These compounds compete with NAD^+ and CoA for binding sites on their respective enzymes. They also drive the reversible transacetylase (E_2) and dihydrolipoyl dehydrogenase (E_3) reactions backward (Fig. 17-6). High $[NADH]/[NAD^+]$ and $[acetyl\text{-}CoA]/[CoA]$ ratios therefore maintain E_2 in the acetylated form, incapable of accepting the hydroxyethyl group from the TPP on E_1. This, in turn, ties up the TPP on the E_1 subunit in its hydroxyethyl form, decreasing the rate of pyruvate decarboxylation.

2. *Covalent modification by phosphorylation/dephosphorylation of E_1.* In eukaryotes, the products of the pyruvate dehydrogenase reaction, NADH and acetyl-CoA, also activate the pyruvate dehydrogenase kinase associated with the enzyme complex. The resulting phosphorylation of a specific dehydrogenase Ser residue inactivates the pyruvate dehydrogenase complex (Fig. 17-15). Insulin, the hormone that signals fuel abundance, reverses the inactivation by activating pyruvate dehydrogenase phosphatase, which removes the phosphate groups from pyruvate dehydrogenase. Recall that insulin also activates glycogen synthesis by activating phosphoprotein phosphatase (Section 16-3B). Thus, in response to increases in blood [glucose], insulin promotes the synthesis of acetyl-CoA as well as glycogen.

Other regulators of the pyruvate dehydrogenase system include pyruvate and ADP, which inhibit pyruvate dehydrogenase kinase, and Ca^{2+}, which inhibits pyruvate dehydrogenase kinase and activates pyruvate dehydrogenase phosphatase. In contrast to the glycogen metabolism control system (Section 16-3B), pyruvate dehydrogenase activity is unaffected by cAMP.

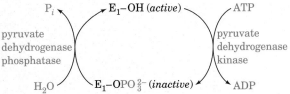

■ **Figure 17-15** | **Covalent modification of eukaryotic pyruvate dehydrogenase.** E_1 is inactivated by the specific phosphorylation of one of its Ser residues in a reaction catalyzed by pyruvate dehydrogenase kinase. This phosphoryl group is hydrolyzed through the action of pyruvate dehydrogenase phosphatase, thereby reactivating E_1.

B | Three Enzymes Control the Rate of the Citric Acid Cycle

To understand how a metabolic pathway is controlled, we must identify the enzymes that catalyze its rate-determining steps, the *in vitro* effectors of the enzymes, and the *in vivo* concentrations of these substances. *A proposed mechanism of flux control must operate within the physiological concentration range of the effector.*

Identifying the rate-determining steps of the citric acid cycle is more difficult than it is for glycolysis because most of the cycle's metabolites are present in both mitochondria and cytosol and we do not know their distribution between these two compartments (recall that identifying a pathway's rate-determining steps requires determining the ΔG of each of its reactions from the concentrations of its substrates and products). However, we shall assume that the compartments are in equilibrium and use the total cell concentrations of these substances to estimate their

Table 17-2	Standard Free Energy Changes ($\Delta G^{\circ\prime}$) and Physiological Free Energy Changes (ΔG) of Citric Acid Cycle Reactions		
Reaction	**Enzyme**	**$\Delta G^{\circ\prime}$** **(kJ · mol^{-1})**	**ΔG** **(kJ · mol^{-1})**
1	Citrate synthase	−31.5	Negative
2	Aconitase	~5	~0
3	Isocitrate dehydrogenase	−21	Negative
4	α-Ketoglutarate dehydrogenase	−33	Negative
5	Succinyl-CoA synthetase	−2.1	~0
6	Succinate dehydrogenase	+6	~0
7	Fumarase	−3.4	~0
8	Malate dehydrogenase	+29.7	~0

mitochondrial concentrations. Table 17-2 gives the standard free energy changes for the eight citric acid cycle enzymes and estimates of the physiological free energy changes for the reactions in heart muscle or liver tissue. We can see that *three of the enzymes are likely to function far from equilibrium under physiological conditions (negative ΔG): citrate synthase, NAD$^+$-dependent isocitrate dehydrogenase, and α-ketoglutarate dehydrogenase.* These are therefore the rate-determining enzymes of the cycle.

In heart muscle, where the citric acid cycle is active, the flux of metabolites through the citric acid cycle is proportional to the rate of cellular oxygen consumption. *Because oxygen consumption, NADH reoxidation, and ATP production are tightly coupled (Section 18-3), the citric acid cycle must be regulated by feedback mechanisms that coordinate NADH production with energy expenditure.* Unlike the rate-limiting enzymes of glycolysis and glycogen metabolism, which regulate flux by elaborate systems of allosteric control, substrate cycles, and covalent modification, the regulatory enzymes of the citric acid cycle seem to control flux primarily by three simple mechanisms: (1) substrate availability, (2) product inhibition, and (3) competitive feedback inhibition by intermediates further along the cycle. Some of the major regulatory mechanisms are diagramed in Fig. 17-16. There is no single flux-control point in the citric acid cycle; rather, flux control is distributed among several enzymes.

Perhaps the most crucial regulators of the citric acid cycle are its substrates, acetyl-CoA and oxaloacetate, and its product, NADH. Both acetyl-CoA and oxaloacetate are present in mitochondria at concentrations that do not saturate citrate synthase. The metabolic flux through the enzyme therefore varies with substrate concentration and is controlled by substrate availability. We have already seen that the production of acetyl-CoA from pyruvate is regulated by the activity of pyruvate dehydrogenase. The concentration of oxaloacetate, which is in equilibrium with malate, fluctuates with the [NADH]/[NAD$^+$] ratio according to the equilibrium expression

$$K = \frac{[\text{oxaloacetate}][\text{NADH}]}{[\text{malate}][\text{NAD}^+]}$$

If, for example, the muscle workload and respiration rate increase, mitochondrial [NADH] decreases. The consequent increase in [oxaloacetate] stimulates the citrate synthase reaction, which controls the rate of citrate formation.

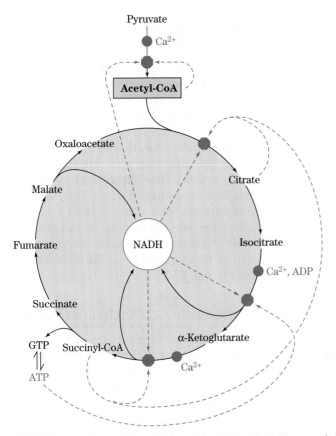

Figure 17-16 | Regulation of the citric acid cycle. This diagram of the citric acid cycle, which includes the pyruvate dehydrogenase reaction, indicates points of inhibition (*red octagons*) and the pathway intermediates that function as inhibitors (*dashed red arrows*). ADP and Ca^{2+} (*green dots*) are activators. ✎ **See the animated Figures.**

Aconitase functions close to equilibrium, so the rate of citrate consumption depends on the activity of NAD^+-dependent isocitrate dehydrogenase, which is strongly inhibited *in vitro* by its product NADH. Citrate synthase is also inhibited by NADH but is less sensitive than isocitrate dehydrogenase to changes in [NADH].

Other instances of product inhibition in the citric acid cycle are the inhibition of citrate synthase by citrate (citrate competes with oxaloacetate) and the inhibition of α-ketoglutarate dehydrogenase by NADH and succinyl-CoA. Succinyl-CoA also competes with acetyl-CoA in the citrate synthase reaction (competitive feedback inhibition). This interlocking system helps keep the citric acid cycle coordinately regulated and the concentrations of its intermediates within reasonable bounds.

Additional Regulatory Mechanisms. *In vitro* studies of citric acid cycle enzymes have identified a few allosteric activators and inhibitors. ADP is an allosteric activator of isocitrate dehydrogenase, whereas ATP inhibits the enzyme. Ca^{2+}, in addition to its many other cellular functions, regulates the citric acid cycle at several points. It activates pyruvate dehydrogenase phosphatase (Fig. 17-15), which in turn activates the pyruvate dehydrogenase complex to produce acetyl-CoA. Ca^{2+} also activates both isocitrate dehydrogenase and α-ketoglutarate dehydrogenase (Fig. 17-16). Thus Ca^{2+}, the signal that stimulates muscle contraction, also stimulates the production of the ATP to fuel it.

■ **CHECK YOUR UNDERSTANDING**

Which steps of the citric acid cycle regulate flux through the cycle?
Describe the role of Ca^{2+}, acetyl-CoA, and NADH in regulating pyruvate dehydrogenase and the citric acid cycle.

LEARNING OBJECTIVES

▪ Understand that the citric acid cycle provides metabolites for other pathways and can be replenished by other pathways.
▪ Understand that some organisms use the glyoxylate cycle, a variant of the citric acid cycle, for the net conversion of acetyl-CoA to oxaloacetate.

5 Reactions Related to the Citric Acid Cycle

At first glance, a metabolic pathway appears to be either catabolic, with the release and conservation of free energy, or anabolic, with a requirement for free energy. The citric acid cycle is catabolic, of course, because it involves degradation and is a major free-energy conservation system in most organisms. Cycle intermediates are required in only catalytic amounts to maintain the degradative function of the cycle. However, several biosynthetic pathways use citric acid cycle intermediates as starting materials for anabolic reactions. The citric acid cycle is therefore **amphibolic** (both anabolic and catabolic). In this section, we examine some of the reactions that feed intermediates into the citric acid cycle or draw them off; we also examine the **glyoxylate cycle,** a variation of the citric acid cycle that occurs only in plants and converts acetyl-CoA to oxaloacetate. Some of the reactions that use and replenish citric acid cycle intermediates are summarized in Fig. 17-17.

A | Other Pathways Use Citric Acid Cycle Intermediates

Reactions that utilize and therefore drain citric acid cycle intermediates are called **cataplerotic reactions** (emptying; Greek: *cata*, down + *plerotikos*, to fill). These reactions serve not only to synthesize important products but also to avoid the inappropriate buildup of citric acid cycle intermediates in the mitochondrion, for example, when there is a high rate of breakdown of amino acids to citric acid cycle intermediates. Cataplerotic reactions occur in the following pathways:

1. **Glucose biosynthesis** (gluconeogenesis) utilizes oxaloacetate (Section 16-4). Because gluconeogenesis takes place in the cytosol, oxaloacetate must be converted to malate or aspartate for transport

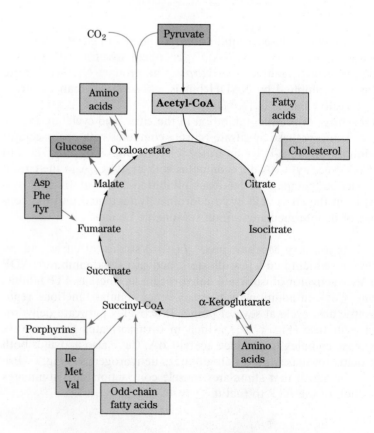

■ Figure 17-17 | Amphibolic functions of the citric acid cycle. The diagram indicates the positions at which intermediates are drawn off by cataplerotic reactions for use in anabolic pathways (*red arrows*) and the points where anaplerotic reactions replenish cycle intermediates (*green arrows*). Reactions involving amino acid transamination and deamination are reversible, so their direction varies with metabolic demand.
🖭 **See the Animated Figures.**

out of the mitochondrion (Fig. 16-20). Since the citric acid cycle is a cyclical pathway, any of its intermediates can be converted to oxaloacetate and used for gluconeogenesis.

2. **Fatty acid biosynthesis** is a cytosolic process that requires acetyl-CoA. Acetyl-CoA is generated in the mitochondrion and is not transported across the mitochondrial membrane. *Cytosolic acetyl-CoA is therefore generated by the breakdown of citrate, which can cross the membrane, in a reaction catalyzed by* **ATP-citrate lyase** (Section 20-4A). This reaction uses the free energy of ATP to "undo" the citrate synthase reaction:

$$ATP + citrate + CoA \longrightarrow ADP + P_i + oxaloacetate + acetyl-CoA$$

3. **Amino acid biosynthesis** uses α-ketoglutarate and oxaloacetate as starting materials. For example, α-ketoglutarate is converted to glutamate by reductive amination catalyzed by a **glutamate dehydrogenase** that utilizes either NADH or NADPH:

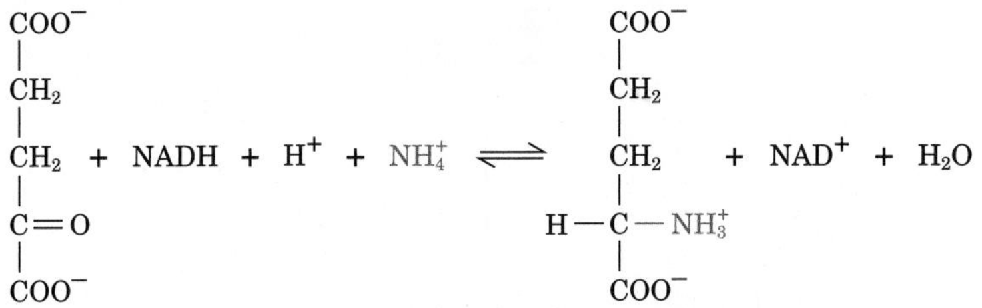

α-Ketoglutarate   Glutamate

Oxaloacetate undergoes transamination with alanine to produce aspartate and pyruvate (Section 21-2A):

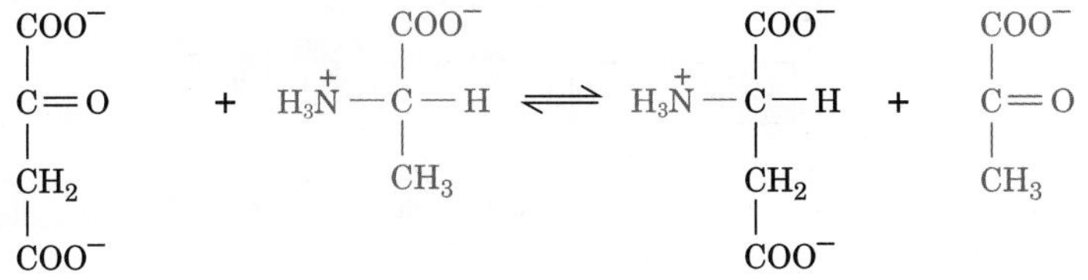

Oxaloacetate   **Alanine**   **Aspartate**   **Pyruvate**

Some Reactions Replenish Citric Acid Cycle Intermediates

In aerobic organisms, the citric acid cycle is the major source of free energy, and hence the catabolic function of the citric acid cycle cannot be interrupted: Cycle intermediates that have been siphoned off must be replenished. The replenishing reactions are called **anaplerotic reactions** (filling up; Greek: *ana*, up + *plerotikos*, to fill). The most important of these reactions is catalyzed by pyruvate carboxylase, which produces oxaloacetate from pyruvate:

$$Pyruvate + CO_2 + ATP + H_2O \longrightarrow oxaloacetate + ADP + P_i$$

(This is also one of the first steps of gluconeogenesis; Section 16-4A). Pyruvate carboxylase "senses" the need for more citric acid cycle intermediates through its activator, acetyl-CoA. *Any decrease in the rate of the cycle caused by insufficient oxaloacetate or other intermediates allows the concentration of acetyl-CoA to rise.* This activates pyruvate carboxylase, which replenishes oxaloacetate. The reactions of the citric acid cycle convert the oxaloacetate to citrate, α-ketoglutarate, succinyl-CoA, and so on, until all the intermediates are restored to appropriate levels.

An increase in the concentrations of citric acid cycle intermediates supports increased flux of acetyl groups through the cycle. For example, flux

through the citric acid cycle may increase as much as 60- to 100-fold i
muscle cells during intense exercise. Not all of this increase is due to el
vated concentrations of cycle intermediates (which only increase abou
fourfold), because other regulatory mechanisms (as described in Sectio
17-4B) also promote flux through the rate-controlling steps of the cycle

During exercise, some of the pyruvate generated by increased glycolyti
flux is directed toward oxaloacetate synthesis as catalyzed by pyruvate ca
boxylase. Pyruvate can also accept an amino group from glutamate (
transamination reaction) to generate alanine (the amino acid counterpar
of pyruvate) and the citric acid cycle intermediate α-ketoglutarate (th
ketone counterpart of glutamate). Both of these mechanisms help the ci
ric acid cycle efficiently catabolize the acetyl groups derived—also fro
pyruvate—by the reactions of the pyruvate dehydrogenase complex.

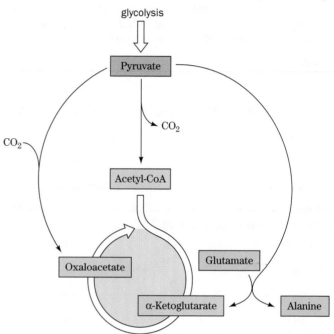

The end result is increased production of ATP to power muscle contractior

Other metabolites that feed into the citric acid cycle are succinyl-CoA
a product of the degradation of odd-chain fatty acids (Section 20-2E) an
certain amino acids (Section 21-4), and α-ketoglutarate and oxaloacetate
which are formed by the reversible transamination of certain amino acids
as indicated above. The links between the citric acid cycle and other meta
bolic pathways offer some clues to its evolution (Box 17-3).

C | The Glyoxylate Cycle Shares Some Steps with the Citric Acid Cycle

*Plants, bacteria, and fungi, but not animals, possess enzymes that mediat
the net conversion of acetyl-CoA to oxaloacetate, which can be used fo
gluconeogenesis.* In plants, these enzymes constitute the glyoxylate cycl
(Fig. 17-18), which operates in two cellular compartments: the mitochondrio
and the **glyoxysome,** a membrane-bounded plant organelle that is a spe
cialized peroxisome. Most of the enzymes of the glyoxylate cycle are the
same as those of the citric acid cycle.

The glyoxylate cycle consists of five reactions (Fig. 17-18):

Reactions 1 and 2. Glyoxysomal oxaloacetate is condensed with
acetyl-CoA to form citrate, which is isomerized to
isocitrate as in the citric acid cycle. Since the

glyoxysome contains no aconitase, Reaction 2 presumably takes place in the cytosol.

Reaction 3. Glyoxysomal **isocitrate lyase** cleaves the isocitrate to succinate and **glyoxylate** (hence the cycle's name).

Reaction 4. **Malate synthase,** a glyoxysomal enzyme, condenses glyoxylate with a second molecule of acetyl-CoA to form malate.

Reaction 5. Glyoxysomal malate dehydrogenase catalyzes the oxidation of malate to oxaloacetate by NAD^+.

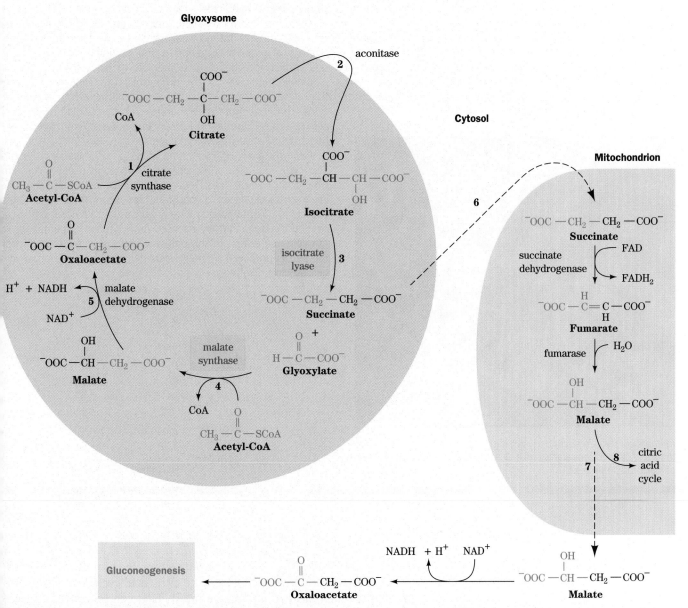

Figure 17-18 | The glyoxylate cycle. The cycle results in the net conversion of two acetyl-CoA to succinate in the glyoxysome, which can be converted to malate in the mitochondrion for use in gluconeogenesis. Isocitrate lyase and malate synthase, enzymes unique to glyoxysomes (which occur only in plants), are boxed in blue. (**1**) Glyoxysomal citrate synthase catalyzes the condensation of oxaloacetate with acetyl-CoA to form citrate. (**2**) Cytosolic aconitase catalyzes the conversion of citrate to isocitrate. (**3**) Isocitrate lyase catalyzes the cleavage of isocitrate to succinate and glyoxylate. (**4**) Malate synthase catalyzes the condensation of glyoxylate with acetyl-CoA to form malate. (**5**) Glyoxysomal malate dehydrogenase catalyzes the oxidation of malate to oxaloacetate, completing the cycle. (**6**) Succinate is transported to the mitochondrion, where it is converted to malate via the citric acid cycle. (**7**) Malate is transported to the cytosol, where malate dehydrogenase catalyzes its oxidation to oxaloacetate, which can then be used in gluconeogenesis. (**8**) Alternatively, malate can continue in the citric acid cycle, making the glyoxylate cycle anaplerotic.

BOX 17-3 PERSPECTIVES IN BIOCHEMISTRY

Evolution of the Citric Acid Cycle

The citric acid cycle is ubiquitous in aerobic organisms and plays a central role in energy metabolism in these cells. However, an eight-step catalytic cycle such as the citric acid cycle is unlikely to have arisen all at once and must have evolved from a simpler set of enzyme-catalyzed reactions. Clues to its origins can be found by examining the metabolism of cells that resemble early life-forms. Such organisms emerged before significant quantities of atmospheric oxygen became available some 3 billion years ago. These cells may have used sulfur as their ultimate oxidizing agent, reducing it to H_2S. Their modern-day counterparts are anaerobic autotrophs that harvest free energy by pathways that are independent of the pathways that oxidize carbon-containing compounds.

These organisms therefore do not use the citric acid cycle to generate reduced cofactors that are subsequently oxidized by molecular oxygen. However, all organisms must synthesize the small molecules from which they can build proteins, nucleic acids, carbohydrates, and lipids.

The task of divining an organism's metabolic capabilities has been facilitated through bioinformatics. By comparing the sequences of prokaryotic genomes and assigning functions to various homologous genes, it is possible to reconstruct the central metabolic pathways for the organisms. This approach has been fruitful because many "housekeeping" genes, which encode enzymes that make free energy and molecular building blocks available to the cell, are highly conserved among different species and hence are relatively easy to recognize.

Genomic analysis reveals that many prokaryotes lack the citric acid cycle. However, these organisms do contain genes for some citric acid cycle enzymes. The last four reactions of the cycle, leading from succinate to oxaloacetate, appear to be the most highly conserved. This pathway fragment constitutes a mechanism for accepting electrons that are released during sugar fermentation. For example, the reverse of this pathway could regenerate NAD^+ from the NADH produced by the glyceraldehyde-3-phosphate dehydrogenase step of glycolysis.

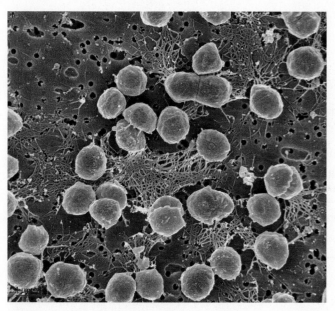

Methanococcus jannaschii, an organism without a citric acid cycle. [Courtesy of B. Boonyaratanakornkit, D.S. Clark, and G. Vrdoljak, University of California at Berkeley.]

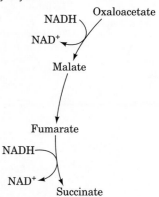

The glyoxylate cycle therefore results in the net conversion of two acetyl-CoA to succinate instead of to four molecules of CO_2 as would occur in the citric acid cycle. The succinate produced in Reaction 3 is transported to the mitochondrion where it enters the citric acid cycle and is converted to malate, which has two alternative fates: (1) It can be converted to oxaloacetate in the mitochondrion, continuing the citric acid cycle and thereby making the glyoxylate cycle an anaplerotic process (Section 17-5B) or (2) it can be transported to the cytosol, where it is converted to oxaloacetate for entry into gluconeogenesis.

The overall reaction of the glyoxylate cycle can be considered to be the formation of oxaloacetate from two molecules of acetyl-CoA:

$$2 \text{ Acetyl-CoA} + 2\,NAD^+ + FAD \longrightarrow$$
$$\text{oxaloacetate} + 2 \text{ CoA} + 2\,NADH + FADH_2 + 2\,H$$

e resulting succinate could then be used as a starting material
r the biosynthesis of other compounds.

Many archaeal cells have a **pyruvate:ferredoxin oxidoreductase**
at converts pyruvate to acetyl-CoA (but without producing
ADH). In a primitive cell, the resulting acetyl groups could have
ondensed with oxaloacetate (by the action of a citrate synthase),
entually giving rise to an oxidative sequence of reactions resem-
ing the first few steps of the modern citric acid cycle.

Oxaloacetate Acetyl-CoA

Citrate

Isocitrate

—NAD⁺

CO_2 NADH

α-Ketoglutarate

ne α-ketoglutarate produced in this way can be converted to glu-
mate and other amino acids.

The reductive and oxidative branches of the citric acid cycle out-
ed so far function in modern bacterial cells such as *E. coli* cells
hen they are growing anaerobically, suggesting that similar path-
ays could have filled the metabolic needs of early cells. The evo-
tion of a complete citric acid cycle in which the two branches
e linked and both proceed in an oxidative direction (clockwise)
ould have required an enzyme such as α-ketoglutarate:ferredoxin
ductase (a homolog of pyruvate:ferredoxin oxidoreductase) to
k α-ketoglutarate and succinate.

Interestingly, a primitive citric acid cycle that operated in the reverse (counterclockwise) direction could have provided a route for
fixing CO_2 (that is, incorporating CO_2 into biological molecules).

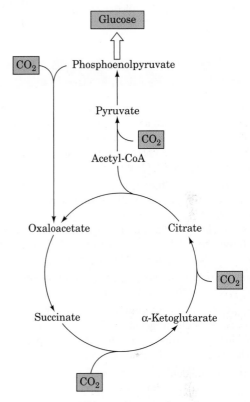

The genes encoding enzymes that catalyze the steps of such a
pathway have been identified in several modern autotrophic bacteria. This reductive pathway, which occurs in some deeply rooted
archaeal species, possibly predates the CO_2-fixing pathway used in
some photosynthetic bacteria and in the chloroplasts of green
plants (Section 19-3A).

ocitrate lyase and malate synthase occur only in plants. These enzymes
nable germinating seeds to convert their stored triacylglycerols, through
cetyl-CoA, to glucose. It had long been assumed that this was a require-
ent of germination. However, a mutant of *Arabidopsis thaliana* (an
ilseed plant) lacking isocitrate lyase, and hence unable to convert lipids
 carbohydrate, nevertheless germinated. This process was only inhibited
hen the mutant plants were subjected to low light conditions. Therefore,
 now appears that the glyoxylate cycle's importance in seedling growth
 its anaplerotic function in providing four-carbon units to the citric acid
ycle, which can then oxidize the triacylglycerol-derived acetyl-CoA.

Organisms that lack the glyoxylate pathway cannot undertake the net
 nthesis of glucose from acetyl-CoA. This is the reason humans cannot
 onvert fats (that is, fatty acids, which are catabolized to acetyl-CoA) to
 arbohydrates (that is, glucose).

Some human pathogens use the glyoxylate cycle, sometimes to gre advantage. For example, *Mycobacterium tuberculosis,* which causes tube culosis, can persist for years in the lung without being attacked by t immune system. During this period, the bacterium subsists largely lipids, using the citric acid cycle to produce precursors for amino acid sy thesis and using the glyoxylate cycle to produce carbohydrate precursor Drugs that are designed to inhibit the bacterial isocitrate lyase can ther fore potentially limit the pathogen's survival. The virulence of the yea *Candida albicans,* which often infects immunosuppressed individuals, ma also depend on activation of the glyoxylate cycle when the yeast cells ta up residence inside macrophages.

■ **CHECK YOUR UNDERSTANDING**

Explain how a catalytic cycle can supply precursors for other metabolic pathways without depleting its own intermediates. Describe the reactions of the glyoxylate cycle.

SUMMARY

1. The eight enzymes of the citric acid cycle function in a multistep catalytic cycle to oxidize an acetyl group to two CO_2 molecules with the concomitant generation of three NADH, one $FADH_2$, and one GTP. The free energy released when the reduced coenzymes ultimately reduce O_2 is used to generate ATP.

2. Acetyl groups enter the citric acid cycle as acetyl-CoA. The pyruvate dehydrogenase multienzyme complex, which contains three types of enzymes and five types of coenzymes, generates acetyl-CoA from the glycolytic product pyruvate. The lipoyllysyl arm of E_2 acts as a tether that swings reactive groups between enzymes in the complex.

3. Citrate synthase catalyzes the condensation of acetyl-CoA and oxaloacetate in a highly exergonic reaction.

4. Aconitase catalyzes the isomerization of citrate to isocitrate, and isocitrate dehydrogenase catalyzes the oxidative decarboxylation of isocitrate to α-ketoglutarate to produce the citric acid cycle's first CO_2 and NADH.

5. α-Ketoglutarate dehydrogenase catalyzes the oxidative decarboxylation of α-ketoglutarate to produce succinyl-CoA and the citric acid cycle's second CO_2 and NADH.

6. Succinyl-CoA synthetase couples the cleavage of succinyl-CoA to the synthesis of GTP (or in some organisms, ATP) via a phosphoryl-enzyme intermediate.

7. The citric acid cycle's remaining three reactions, catalyzed succinate dehydrogenase, fumarase, and malate dehydroge ase, regenerate oxaloacetate to continue the citric acid cyc

8. Entry of glucose-derived acetyl-CoA into the citric acid cyc is regulated at the pyruvate dehydrogenase step by produ inhibition (by NADH and acetyl-CoA) and by covale modification.

9. The citric acid cycle itself is regulated at the steps catalyze by citrate synthase, NAD^+-dependent isocitrate dehydroge ase, and α-ketoglutarate dehydrogenase. Regulation accomplished mainly by substrate availability, product inhib tion, and feedback inhibition.

10. Cataplerotic reactions deplete citric acid cycle intermediat Some citric acid cycle intermediates are substrates for gluc neogenesis, fatty acid biosynthesis, and amino acid biosynthes

11. Anaplerotic reactions such as the pyruvate carboxylase rea tion replenish citric acid cycle intermediates.

12. The glyoxylate cycle, which operates only in plants, bacteri and fungi, requires the glyoxysomal enzymes isocitrate lya and malate synthase. This variation of the citric acid cycle pe mits net synthesis of glucose from acetyl-CoA.

KEY TERMS

citric acid cycle **567**	lipoyllysyl arm **575**	glyoxylate cycle **588**	anaplerotic reaction **589**
multienzyme complex **570**	amphibolic pathway **588**	cataplerotic reaction **588**	glyoxysome **590**

PROBLEMS

1. (a) Explain why obligate anaerobes contain some citric acid cycle enzymes. (b) Why don't these organisms have a complete citric acid cycle?

2. The first organisms on earth may have been chemoautotrophs in which the citric acid cycle operated in reverse to "fix" atmospheric CO_2 in organic compounds. Complete a catalytic

cycle that begins with the hypothetical overall reactic succinate + $2 CO_2 \rightarrow$ citrate.

3. Which one of the five steps of the pyruvate dehydrogena complex reaction is most likely to be metabolically irr versible? Explain.

4. Explain why an individual with a deficiency of pyruva

dehydrogenase phosphatase (PDP) is unable to tolerate exercise.

4. The CO_2 produced in one round of the citric acid cycle does not originate in the acetyl carbons that entered that round. (a) If acetyl-CoA is labeled with ^{14}C at its carbonyl carbon, how many rounds of the cycle are required before $^{14}CO_2$ is released? (b) How many rounds are required if acetyl-CoA is labeled at its methyl group?

5. Explain why metabolic acidosis (Box 2-1) may result from the accumulation of some citric acid cycle intermediates.

7. The branched-chain α-keto acid dehydrogenase complex, which participates in amino acid catabolism, contains the same three types of enzymes as are in the pyruvate dehydrogenase and the α-ketoglutarate dehydrogenase complexes. Draw the reaction product when valine is deaminated as in the glutamate ⇌ α-ketoglutarate reaction (Section 17-5A) and then is acted on by the branched-chain α-keto acid dehydrogenase.

8. Refer to Table 14-5 to explain why FAD rather than NAD^+ is used in the succinate dehydrogenase reaction.

9. Malonate is a competitive inhibitor of succinate in the succinate dehydrogenase reaction. Explain why increasing the oxaloacetate concentration can overcome malonate inhibition.

10. Why is it advantageous for citrate, the product of Reaction 1 of the citric acid cycle, to inhibit phosphofructokinase, which catalyzes the third reaction of glycolysis?

11. Anaplerotic reactions permit the citric acid cycle to supply intermediates to biosynthetic pathways while maintaining the proper levels of cycle intermediates. Write the equation for the net synthesis of citrate from pyruvate.

12. Many amino acids are broken down to intermediates of the citric acid cycle. (a) Why can't these amino acid "remnants" be directly oxidized to CO_2 by the citric acid cycle? (b) Explain why amino acids that are broken down to pyruvate can be completely oxidized by the citric acid cycle.

13. Certain microorganisms with an incomplete citric acid cycle decarboxylate α-ketoglutarate to produce **succinate semialde-**

hyde. A dehydrogenase then converts succinate semialdehyde to succinate.

| α-Ketoglutarate | Succinate semialdehyde | Succinate |

These reactions can be combined with other standard citric acid cycle reactions to create a pathway from citrate to oxaloacetate. Compare the ATP and reduced cofactor yield of the standard and alternate pathways.

14. Given the following information, calculate the physiological ΔG of the isocitrate dehydrogenase reaction at 25°C and pH 7.0: $[NAD^+]/[NADH] = 8$, $[α\text{-ketoglutarate}] = 0.1$ mM, and $[isocitrate] = 0.02$ mM. Assume standard conditions for CO_2 ($\Delta G^{\circ\prime}$ is given in Table 17-2). Is this reaction a likely site for metabolic control?

15. Although animals cannot synthesize glucose from acetyl-CoA, if a rat is fed ^{14}C-labeled acetate, some of the label appears in glycogen extracted from its muscles. Explain.

CASE STUDY

Case 21 (available at www.wiley.com/college/voet)
Characterization of Pyruvate Carboxylase from Methanobacterium thermoautotrophicum

Focus concept: Pyruvate carboxylase is discovered in a bacterium that was previously thought not to contain the enzyme.

Prerequisite: Chapter 17

• Citric acid cycle reactions and associated anaplerotic reactions
• Glyoxylate cycle reactions

REFERENCES

astmond, P.J. and Graham, I.A., Re-examining the role of the glyoxylate cycle in oilseeds, *Trends Plant Sci.* **6**, 72–77 (2001).

uynen M.A., Dandekar, T., and Bork, P., Variation and evolution of the citric-acid cycle: a genomic perspective, *Trends Microbiol.* **7**, 281–291 (1999). [Discusses how genome studies can allow reconstruction of metabolic pathways, even when some enzymes appear to be missing.]

Milne, J.L.S., Wu, X., Borgnia, M.J., Lengyel, J.S., Brooks, B.R., Shi, D., Perham, R.N., and Subramaniam, S., Molecular structure of a 9-MDa icosahedral pyruvate dehydrogenase subcomplex containing the E_2 and E_3 enzymes using cryoelectron microscopy, *J. Biol. Chem.* **281**, 4364–4370 (2006).

Owen, O.E., Kalhan, S.C., and Hanson, R.W., The key role of anaplerosis and cataplerosis for citric acid cycle function, *J. Biol. Chem.* **277**, 30409–30412 (2002). [Describes the influx (anaplerosis) and efflux (cataplerosis) of citric acid cycle intermediates in different organ systems.]

Perham, R.N., Swinging arms and swinging domains in multifunctional enzymes: catalytic machines for multistep reactions, *Annu. Rev. Biochem.* **69**, 961–1004 (2000). [An authoritative review on multienzyme complexes.]

18

Electron Transport and Oxidative Phosphorylation

A resting human body consumes approximately 420 kilojoules of energy per hour, power requirement that is only slightly greater than that of a 100-watt lightbulb. The body's energy needs are largely met by the electrochemical events in mitochondria, which support a relatively modest voltage of approximately 0.2 V (a household power outlet in the United States supplies 110 V) but a current of about 500 amp, representing the transmembrane movement of approximately 3×10^{21} protons per second. It is this movement that powers ATP synthesis. [Image State/Alamy Images]

■ CHAPTER CONTENTS

1 The Mitochondrion
   A. Mitochondria Contain a Highly Folded Inner Membrane
   B. Ions and Metabolites Enter Mitochondria via Transporters

2 Electron Transport
   A. Electron Transport Is an Exergonic Process
   B. Electron Carriers Operate in Sequence
   C. Complex I Accepts Electrons from NADH
   D. Complex II Contributes Electrons to Coenzyme Q
   E. Complex III Translocates Protons via the Q Cycle
   F. Complex IV Reduces Oxygen to Water

3 Oxidative Phosphorylation
   A. The Chemiosmotic Theory Links Electron Transport to ATP Synthesis
   B. ATP Synthase Is Driven by the Flow of Protons
   C. The P/O Ratio Relates the Amount of ATP Synthesized to the Amount of Oxygen Reduced
   D. Oxidative Phosphorylation Can be Uncoupled from Electron Transport

4 Control of Oxidative Metabolism
   A. The Rate of Oxidative Phosphorylation Depends on the ATP and NADH Concentrations
   B. Aerobic Metabolism Has Some Disadvantages

■ MEDIA RESOURCES

(available at www.wiley.com/college/voet)
Guided Exploration 17. Electron transport and oxidative phosphorylation overview
Guided Exploration 18. The Q cycle
Guided Exploration 19. F_1F_0-ATP synthase and the binding change mechanism
Interactive Exercise 19. Complex III
Interactive Exercise 20. Cytochrome *c* residues involved in intermolecular complex formation
Interactive Exercise 21. Bovine heart cytochrome *c* oxidase
Interactive Exercise 22. F_1-ATP synthase
Animated Figure 18-8. The mitochondrial electron transport chain
Animated Figure 18-20. Coupling of electron transport and ATP synthesis
Animated Figure 18-24. The binding change mechanism of ATP synthesis
Animated Figure 18-29. Coordinated control of glycolysis and the citric acid cycle
Kinemage 5. Cytochrome *c*
Case Study 24. Uncoupling Proteins in Plants
Case Study 27. Regulation of Sugar and Alcohol Metabolism in *Saccharomyces cerevisiae*
Case Study 33. Modification of Subunit c from Bovine Mitochondrial ATPase

Aerobic organisms consume oxygen and generate carbon dioxide in the process of oxidizing metabolic fuels. The complete oxidation of glucose ($C_6H_{12}O_6$), for example, by molecular oxygen

$$C_6H_{12}O_6 + 6\,O_2 \longrightarrow 6\,CO_2 + 6\,H_2O$$

an be broken down into two half-reactions that the metabolic machinery arries out. In the first, glucose carbon atoms are oxidized:

$$C_6H_{12}O_6 + 6\,H_2O \longrightarrow 6\,CO_2 + 24\,H^+ + 24\,e^-$$

nd in the second, molecular oxygen is reduced:

$$6\,O_2 + 24\,H^+ + 24\,e^- \longrightarrow 12\,H_2O$$

Ve have already seen that the first half-reaction is mediated by the enzymatic reactions of glycolysis and the citric acid cycle (the breakdown of atty acids—the other major type of metabolic fuel—also requires the citic acid cycle). In this chapter, we describe the pathway by which the elecrons from reduced fuel molecules are transferred to molecular oxygen in ukaryotes. We also examine how the energy of fuel oxidation is conserved nd used to synthesize ATP.

As we have seen, the 12 electron pairs released during glucose oxidaon are not transferred directly to O_2. Rather, they are transferred to the oenzymes NAD^+ and FAD to form 10 NADH and 2 $FADH_2$ (Fig. 18-1) n the reactions catalyzed by the glycolytic enzyme glyceraldehyde--phosphate dehydrogenase (Section 15-2F), pyruvate dehydrogease (Section 17-2B), and the citric acid cycle enzymes isocitrate ehydrogenase, α-ketoglutarate dehydrogenase, succinate ehydrogenase, and malate dehydrogenase (Section 17-3). *The lectrons then pass into the **mitochondrial electron-transport hain**, a system of linked electron carriers.* The following vents occur during the electron-transport process:

1. By transferring their electrons to other substances, the NADH and $FADH_2$ are reoxidized to NAD^+ and FAD so that they can participate in additional substrate oxidation reactions.

2. The transferred electrons participate in the sequential oxidation–reduction of multiple **redox centers** (groups that undergo oxidation–reduction reactions) in four enzyme complexes before reducing O_2 to H_2O.

3. During electron transfer, protons are expelled from the mitochondrion, producing a proton gradient across the mitochondrial membrane. *The free energy stored in this electrochemical gradient drives the synthesis of ATP from ADP and P_i through **oxidative phosphorylation**.*

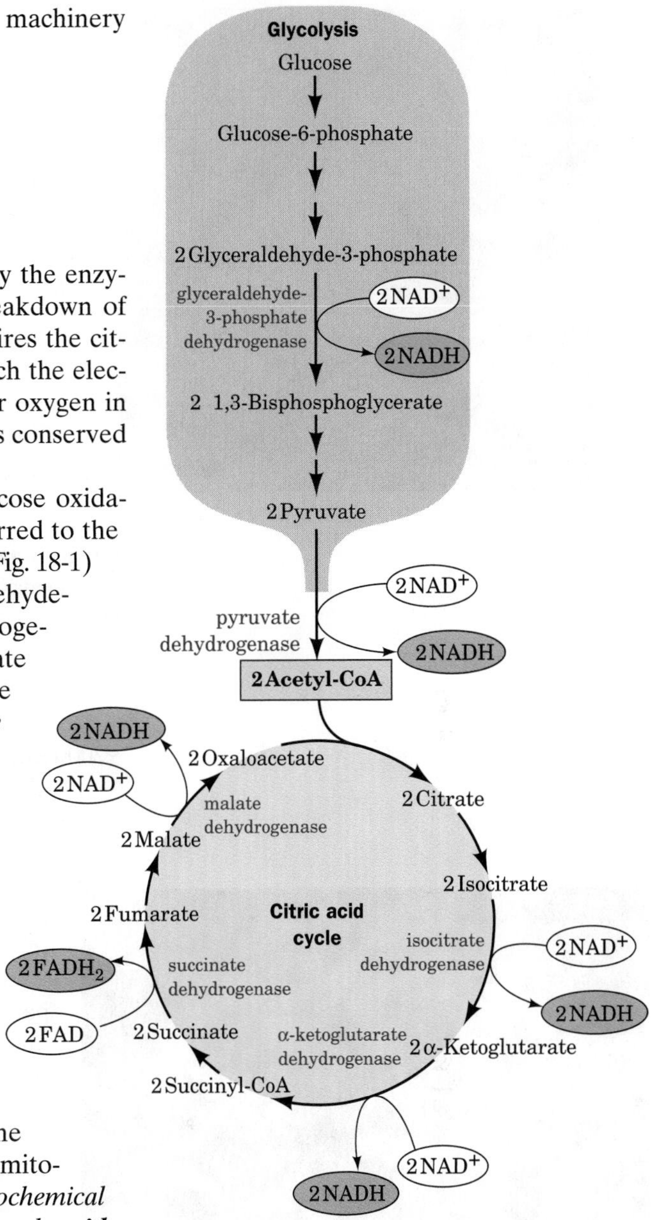

■ Figure 18-1 | The sites of electron transfer that form NADH and FADH₂ in glycolysis and the citric acid cycle.

1 The Mitochondrion

The mitochondrion (Greek: *mitos,* thread + *chondros,* granule) is the site f eukaryotic oxidative metabolism. Mitochondria contain pyruvate ehydrogenase, the citric acid cycle enzymes, the enzymes catalyzing fatty cid oxidation (Section 20-2), and the enzymes and redox proteins nvolved in electron transport and oxidative phosphorylation. It is thereore with good reason that the mitochondrion is often described as the ell's "power plant."

A | Mitochondria Contain a Highly Folded Inner Membrane

Mitochondria vary in size and shape, depending on their source and metaolic state, but they are often ellipsoidal with dimensions of around 0.5 × .0 μm, about the size of a bacterium. A eukaryotic cell typically contains

LEARNING OBJECTIVES

■ Understand that a highly folded inner membrane separates the mitochondrial matrix from the outer membrane.
■ Understand that transport proteins are required to import reducing equivalents, ADP, and P_i into the mitochondria.

(a)

(b)

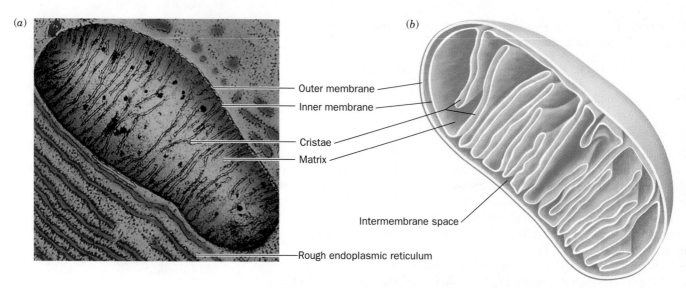

Outer membrane

Inner membrane

Cristae

Matrix

Intermembrane space

Rough endoplasmic reticulum

■ **Figure 18-2** | **The mitochondrion.** (*a*) An electron micrograph of an animal mitochondrion. [© K.R. Porter/Photo Researchers.] (*b*) Cutaway diagram of a mitochondrion.

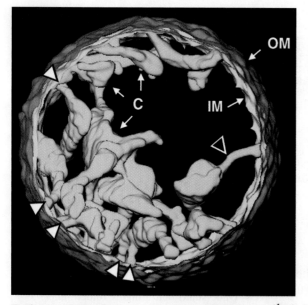

OM

C

IM

■ **Figure 18-3** | **Electron microscopy–based three-dimensional image reconstruction of a rat liver mitochondrion.** The outer membrane (OM) is red, the inner membrane (IM) is yellow, and the cristae (C) are green. The arrowheads point to tubular regions of the cristae that connect them to the inner membrane and to each other. [Courtesy of Carmen Mannella, Wadsworth Center, Albany, New York.]

~2000 mitochondria, which occupy roughly one-fifth of its total cell volume. A mitochondrion is bounded by a smooth outer membrane and contains an extensively invaginated inner membrane (Fig. 18-2). The number of invaginations, called **cristae** (Latin: crests), reflects the respiratory activity of the cell. The proteins mediating electron transport and oxidative phosphorylation are bound in the inner mitochondrial membrane, so the respiration rate varies with membrane surface area.

The inner membrane divides the mitochondrion into two compartments, the **intermembrane space** and the internal **matrix.** The matrix is a gel-like solution that contains extremely high concentrations of the soluble enzymes of oxidative metabolism as well as substrates, nucleotide cofactors, and inorganic ions. The matrix also contains the mitochondrial genetic machinery—DNA, RNA, and ribosomes—that generates several (but by no means all) mitochondrial proteins.

Two-dimensional electron micrographs of mitochondria such as Fig. 18-2a suggest that mitochondria are discrete kidney-shaped organelles. In fact, some mitochondria adopt a tubular shape that extends throughout the cytosol. Furthermore, mitochondria are highly variable structures. For example, the cristae may not resemble baffles and the intercristal spaces may not communicate freely with the mitochondrion's intermembrane space. Electron microscopy-based three-dimensional image reconstruction methods have revealed that cristae can range in shape from simple tubular entities to more complicated lamellar assemblies that merge with the inner membrane via narrow tubular structures (Fig. 18-3). Evidently, cristae form microcompartments that restrict the diffusion of substrates and ions between the intercristal and intermembrane spaces. This has important functional implications because it would result in a locally greater pH gradient across cristal membranes than across inner membranes that are not part of cristae, thereby significantly influencing the rate of oxidative phosphorylation (Section 18-3).

| Ions and Metabolites Enter Mitochondria via Transporters

Like bacterial outer membranes, the outer mitochondrial membrane contains porins, proteins that permit the free diffusion of molecules of up to 10 kD (Section 10-2B). *The intermembrane space is therefore equivalent to the cytosol in its concentrations of metabolites and ions.* The inner membrane, which is ~75% protein by mass, is considerably richer in proteins than is the outer membrane (Fig. 18-4). It is freely permeable only to O_2, CO_2, and H_2O and contains, in addition to respiratory chain proteins, numerous transport proteins that control the passage of metabolites such as ATP, ADP, pyruvate, Ca^{2+}, and phosphate. *The controlled impermeability of the inner mitochondrial membrane to most ions and metabolites permits the generation of ion gradients across this barrier and results in the compartmentalization of metabolic functions between cytosol and mitochondria.*

Cytosolic Reducing Equivalents Are "Transported" into Mitochondria. The NADH produced in the cytosol by glycolysis must gain access to the mitochondrial electron-transport chain for aerobic oxidation. However, the inner mitochondrial membrane lacks an NADH transport protein. *Only the electrons from cytosolic NADH are transported into the mitochondrion by one of several ingenious "shuttle" systems.* We have already discussed the **malate–aspartate shuttle** (Fig. 16-20), in which, when run in reverse, cytosolic oxaloacetate is reduced to malate for transport into the mitochondrion. When malate is reoxidized in the matrix, it gives up the reducing equivalents that originated in the cytosol.

In the **glycerophosphate shuttle** (Fig. 18-5) of insect flight muscle (the tissue with the largest known sustained power output—about the same power-to-weight ratio as a small automobile engine), **3-phosphoglycerol dehydrogenase** catalyzes the oxidation of cytosolic NADH by dihydroxyacetone phosphate to yield NAD^+, which re-enters glycolysis. The electrons of the resulting **3-phosphoglycerol** are transferred to **flavoprotein dehydrogenase** to form $FADH_2$. This enzyme, which is situated on the inner mitochondrial membrane's outer surface, supplies electrons directly to the electron-transport chain (Section 18-2D).

A Translocator Exchanges ADP and ATP. Most of the ATP generated in the **mitochondrial matrix** through oxidative phosphorylation is used in the cytosol. The inner mitochondrial membrane contains an **ADP–ATP translocator** (also called the

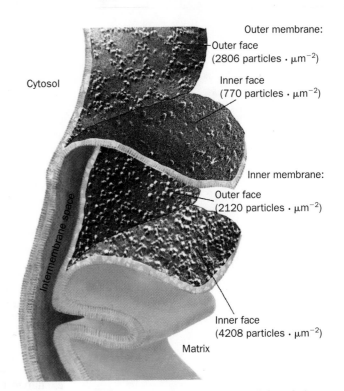

■ **Figure 18-4** | **Electron micrographs of the inner and outer mitochondrial membranes that have been split to expose the inner surfaces of their bilayer leaflets.** Note that the inner membrane contains about twice the density of embedded particles as does the outer membrane. The particles are the portions of integral membrane proteins that were exposed when the bilayers were split. [Courtesy of Lester Packer, University of California at Berkeley.]

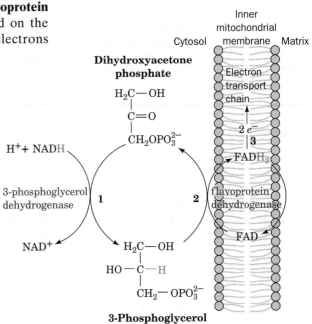

■ **Figure 18-5** | **The glycerophosphate shuttle.** The electrons of cytosolic NADH are transported to the mitochondrial electron-transport chain in three steps (shown in red as hydride transfers): (**1**) Cytosolic oxidation of NADH by dihydroxyacetone phosphate catalyzed by 3-phosphoglycerol dehydrogenase. (**2**) Oxidation of 3-phosphoglycerol by flavoprotein dehydrogenase with reduction of FAD to $FADH_2$. (**3**) Reoxidation of $FADH_2$ with passage of electrons into the electron-transport chain.

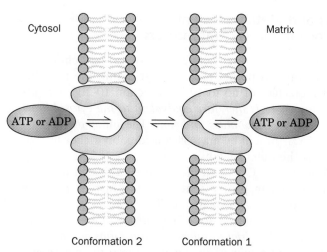

■ Figure 18-6 | Conformational mechanism of the ADP–ATP translocator. An adenine nucleotide–binding site located in the intersubunit contact area of the translocator dimer is alternately exposed to the two sides of the membrane.

■ CHECK YOUR UNDERSTANDING

Describe how shuttle systems transport reducing equivalents into the mitochondria.
Explain how the free energy of the proton gradient drives the transport of ATP, ADP, and P_i.

LEARNING OBJECTIVES

■ Understand that the free energy of electron transport from NADH to O_2 can drive the synthesis of approximately 2.5 ATP.
■ Understand that electron carriers are arranged so that electrons travel from Complexes I and II via coenzyme Q to Complex III, and from there via cytochrome *c* to Complex IV.
■ Understand the reactions catalyzed by Complexes I, III, and IV, and their mechanisms of proton translocation.

adenine nucleotide translocase) that transports ATP out of the matrix in exchange for ADP produced in the cytosol by ATP hydrolysis.

The ADP–ATP translocator, a dimer of identical 30-kD subunits, has one binding site for which ADP and ATP compete. It has two major conformations: one with its ATP–ADP-binding site facing the inside of the mitochondrion, and the other with the site facing outward (Fig. 18-6). The translocator must bind ligand to change from one conformation to the other at a physiologically reasonable rate. Thus it functions as an exchanger by importing one ADP for every ATP that is exported. In this respect, it differs from the glucose transporter (Fig. 10-13), which can change its conformation in the absence of ligand. Note that the export of ATP (net charge −4) and the import of ADP (net charge −3) results in the export of one negative charge per transport cycle. This **electrogenic** antiport is driven by the membrane potential difference, $\Delta\Psi$, across the inner mitochondrial membrane (positive outside), which is a consequence of the transmembrane proton gradient.

Phosphate Must Be Imported into the Mitochondrion. ATP is synthesized from ADP + P_i in the mitochondrion but is utilized in the cytosol. The P_i is returned to the mitochondrion by the **phosphate carrier**, an electroneutral P_i–H symport that is driven by ΔpH. The transmembrane proton gradient generated by the electron-transport machinery of the inner mitochondrial membrane thus not only provides the thermodynamic driving force for ATP synthesis (Section 18-3), it also motivates the transport of the raw materials—ADP and P_i—required for the process.

2 Electron Transport

The electron carriers that ferry electrons from NADH and $FADH_2$ to O_2 are associated with the inner mitochondrial membrane. Some of these redox centers are mobile, and others are components of integral membrane protein complexes. The sequence of electron carriers roughly reflects their relative reduction potentials, so that the overall process of electron transport exergonic. We begin this section by examining the thermodynamics of electron transport. We then consider the molecular characteristics of the various electron carriers.

Electron Transport Is an Exergonic Process

We can estimate the thermodynamic efficiency of electron transport by inspecting the standard reduction potentials of the redox centers. As we saw in our thermodynamic considerations of oxidation–reduction reactions (Section 14-3), an oxidized substrate's affinity for electrons increases with its standard reduction potential, $\mathscr{E}^{\circ\prime}$ (Table 14-5 lists the standard reduction potentials of some biologically important half-reactions). The standard reduction potential difference, $\Delta\mathscr{E}^{\circ\prime}$, for a redox reaction involving any two half-reactions is expressed

$$\Delta\mathscr{E}^{\circ\prime} = \mathscr{E}^{\circ\prime}_{(e^- \, acceptor)} - \mathscr{E}^{\circ\prime}_{(e^- \, donor)}$$

For the reaction that occurs in mitochondria, that is, the oxidation of NADH by O_2, the half-reactions are

$$NAD^+ + H^+ + 2\,e^- \rightleftharpoons NADH \qquad \mathscr{E}^{\circ\prime} = -0.315 \text{ V}$$

and

$$\tfrac{1}{2}O_2 + 2\,H^+ + 2\,e^- \rightleftharpoons H_2O \qquad \mathscr{E}^{\circ\prime} = 0.815 \text{ V}$$

Since the O_2/H_2O half-reaction has the greater standard reduction potential and therefore the higher affinity for electrons, the NADH half-reaction is reversed so that NADH is the electron donor in this couple and O_2 the electron acceptor. The overall reaction is

$$\tfrac{1}{2}O_2 + NADH + H^+ \rightleftharpoons H_2O + NAD^+$$

so that

$$\Delta\mathscr{E}^{\circ\prime} = 0.815 \text{ V} - (-0.315 \text{ V}) = 1.130 \text{ V}$$

The standard free energy change for the reaction can then be calculated from Eq. 14-7:

$$\Delta G^{\circ\prime} = -n\mathscr{F}\Delta\mathscr{E}^{\circ\prime}$$

For NADH oxidation, $\Delta G^{\circ\prime} = -218 \text{ kJ} \cdot \text{mol}^{-1}$. In other words, the oxidation of 1 mol of NADH by O_2 (the transfer of 2 mol e^-) under standard biochemical conditions is associated with the release of 218 kJ of free energy.

Because the standard free energy required to synthesize 1 mol of ATP from ADP + P_i is 30.5 kJ $\cdot$ mol^{-1}, the oxidation of NADH by O_2 is theoretically able to drive the formation of several moles of ATP. In mitochondria, the coupling of NADH oxidation to ATP synthesis is achieved by an electron-transport chain in which electrons pass through three protein complexes. *This allows the overall free energy change to be broken into three smaller parcels, each of which contributes to ATP synthesis by oxidative phosphorylation. Oxidation of one NADH results in the synthesis of approximately 2.5 ATP* (we shall see later why the relationship is not strictly stoichiometric). The thermodynamic efficiency of oxidative phosphorylation is therefore 2.5 $\times$ 30.5 kJ $\cdot$ mol^{-1} $\times$ 100/218 kJ $\cdot$ mol^{-1} = 35% under standard biochemical conditions. However, under physiological conditions in active mitochondria (where the reactant and product concentrations as well as the pH deviate from standard conditions), this thermodynamic efficiency is thought to be ~70%. In comparison, the energy efficiency of a typical automobile engine is <30%.

B | Electron Carriers Operate in Sequence

See Guided Exploration 17
Electron transport and oxidative
phosphorylation overview.

*Oxidation of NADH and FADH$_2$ is carried out by the electron-transport
chain, a set of protein complexes containing redox centers with progressively
greater affinities for electrons (increasing standard reduction potentials).
Electrons travel through this chain from lower to higher standard reduction
potentials* (Fig. 18-7). Electrons are carried from **Complexes I** and **II** to
Complex III by **coenzyme Q** (**CoQ** or **ubiquinone**; so named because of
its ubiquity in respiring organisms), and from Complex III to **Complex IV**
by the peripheral membrane protein **cytochrome c.**

Complex I catalyzes oxidation of NADH by CoQ:

$$\text{NADH} + \text{CoQ } (oxidized) \rightarrow \text{NAD}^+ + \text{CoQ } (reduced)$$
$$\Delta\mathscr{E}^{\circ\prime} = 0.360 \text{ V} \qquad \Delta G^{\circ\prime} = -69.5 \text{ kJ} \cdot \text{mol}^{-1}$$

Complex III catalyzes oxidation of CoQ (reduced) by cytochrome c:

$$\text{CoQ } (reduced) + 2 \text{ cytochrome } c \ (oxidized) \rightarrow$$
$$\text{CoQ } (oxidized) + 2 \text{ cytochrome } c \ (reduced)$$
$$\Delta\mathscr{E}^{\circ\prime} = 0.190 \text{ V} \qquad \Delta G^{\circ\prime} = -36.7 \text{ kJ} \cdot \text{mol}^{-1}$$

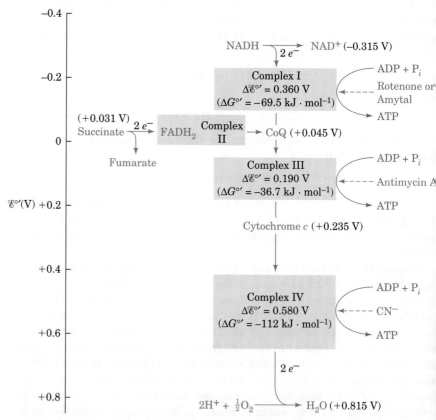

■ **Figure 18-7 | Overview of electron transport in the mitochondrion.** The
standard reduction potentials of its most mobile components (*green*) are indicated, as
are the points where sufficient free energy is released to synthesize ATP (*blue*) and
the sites of action of several respiratory inhibitors (*red*). Complexes I, III, and IV do
not directly synthesize ATP but sequester the free energy necessary to do so by
pumping protons outside the mitochondrion to form a proton gradient.

omplex IV catalyzes oxidation of reduced cytochrome c by O_2, the terminal
electron acceptor of the electron-transport process:

$$2 \text{ Cytochrome } c \text{ (reduced)} + \tfrac{1}{2} O_2 \rightarrow 2 \text{ cytochrome } c \text{ (oxidized)} + H_2O$$

$$\Delta\mathscr{E}^{\circ\prime} = 0.580 \text{ V} \qquad \Delta G^{\circ\prime} = -112 \text{ kJ} \cdot \text{mol}^{-1}$$

s an electron pair successively traverses Complexes I, III, and IV, suffi-
ent free energy is released at each step to power ATP synthesis.

Complex II catalyzes the oxidation of FADH$_2$ by CoQ:

$$FADH_2 + CoQ \text{ (oxidized)} \rightarrow FAD + CoQ \text{ (reduced)}$$

$$\Delta\mathscr{E}^{\circ\prime} = 0.085 \text{ V} \qquad \Delta G^{\circ\prime} = -16.4 \text{ kJ} \cdot \text{mol}^{-1}$$

*This redox reaction does not release sufficient free energy to synthesize
ATP; it functions only to inject the electrons from FADH$_2$ into the electron-
transport chain.*

Inhibitors Reveal the Workings of the Electron-Transport Chain. The
sequence of events in electron transport was elucidated largely through
the use of specific inhibitors and later corroborated by measurements of
the standard reduction potentials of the redox components. The rate at
which O_2 is consumed by a suspension of mitochondria is a sensitive measure of the activity of the electron-transport chain. Compounds that inhibit
electron transport, as judged by their effect on O_2 consumption, include
rotenone (a plant toxin used by Amazonian Indians to poison fish and
which is also used as an insecticide), **amytal** (a barbiturate), **antimycin A**
(an antibiotic), and **cyanide.**

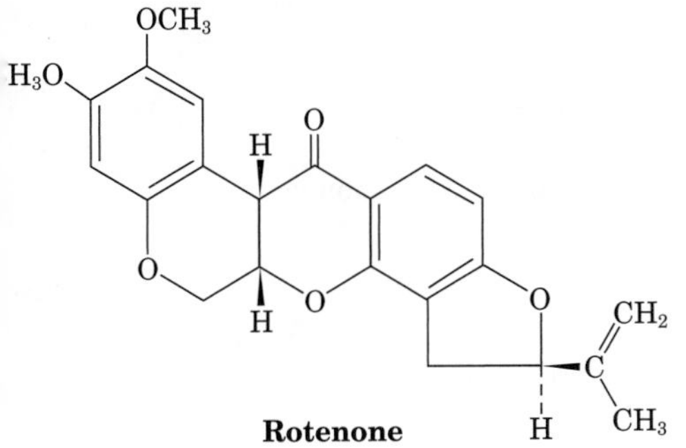

Rotenone

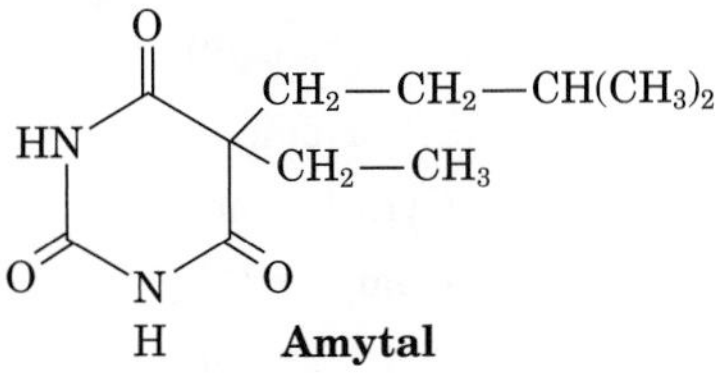

Amytal

Cyanide

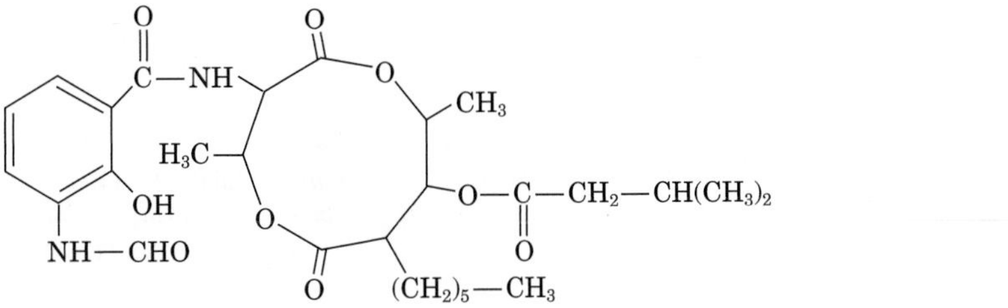

Antimycin A

Adding rotenone or amytal to a suspension of mitochondria blocks
electron transport in Complex I; antimycin A blocks Complex III, and
CN^- blocks electron transport in Complex IV (Fig. 18-7). Each of these
inhibitors also halts O_2 consumption. Oxygen consumption resumes
following addition of a substance whose electrons enter the electron-
transport chain "downstream" of the block. For example, the addition of
succinate to rotenone-blocked mitochondria restores electron transport
and O_2 consumption. Experiments with inhibitors of electron transport
thus reveal the points of entry of electrons from various substrates.

Each of the four respiratory complexes of the electron-transport chain
consists of several protein components that are associated with a variety
of redox-active prosthetic groups with successively increasing reduction

Table 18-1	Reduction Potentials of Electron-Transport Chain Components in Resting Mitochondria	
Component		$\mathscr{E}^{\circ\prime}$ **(V)**
NADH		−0.315
Complex I (NADH–CoQ oxidoreductase; ~900 kD, 46 subunits):		
FMN		−0.340
[2Fe–2S]N1a		−0.380
[2Fe–2S]N1b		−0.250
[4Fe–4S]N3, 4, 5, 6a, 6b, 7		−0.250
[4Fe–4S]N2		−0.100
Succinate		0.031
Complex II (succinate–CoQ oxidoreductase; ~120 kD, 4 subunits):		
FAD		−0.040
[2Fe–2S]		−0.030
[4Fe–4S]		−0.245
[3Fe–4S]		0.060
Heme b_{560}		−0.080
Coenzyme Q		0.045
Complex III (CoQ–cytochrome c oxidoreductase; ~450 kD, 9–11 subunits):		
Heme b_H (b_{562})		0.030
Heme b_L (b_{566})		−0.030
[2Fe–2S]		0.280
Heme c_1		0.215
Cytochrome c		0.235
Complex IV (cytochrome c oxidase; ~410 kD, 8–13 subunits):		
Heme a		0.210
Cu_A		0.245
Cu_B		0.340
Heme a_3		0.385
O_2		0.815

Source: Mainly Wilson, D.F., Erecinska, M., and Dutton, P.L., *Annu. Rev. Biophys. Bioeng.* **3,** 205 and 208 (1974); *and* Wilson, D.F., *in* Bittar, E.E. (Ed.), *Membrane Structure and Function* Vol. 1, p. 160, Wiley (1980).

potentials (Table 18-1). The complexes are all laterally mobile within the inner mitochondrial membrane and may associate to form "supercomplexes" with variable composition. In the following sections, we examine the structures of Complexes I through IV and the molecules that transfer electrons between them. Their relationships are summarized in Fig. 18-8.

C | Complex I Accepts Electrons from NADH

Complex I **(NADH–coenzyme Q oxidoreductase),** which passes electrons from NADH to CoQ, may be the largest protein complex in the inner mitochondrial membrane, containing, in mammals, 46 subunits with a total mass of ~900 kD. Electron microscopy shows an L-shaped protein with one arm embedded in the inner mitochondrial membrane and the other extending into the matrix (Fig. 18-9).

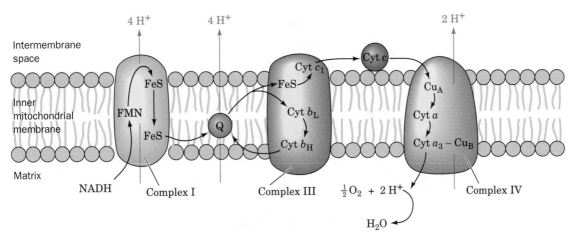

4 H⁺ · · · 4 H⁺ · · · 2 H⁺

Intermembrane
space

Inner
mitochondrial
membrane

Matrix

NADH · · · Complex I · · · Complex III · · · $\frac{1}{2}O_2 + 2 H^+$ · · · Complex IV · · · H₂O

Figure 18-8 | The mitochondrial electron-transport chain. This diagram indicates the pathways of electron transfer (*black*) and proton translocation (*red*). Electrons are transferred between Complexes I and III by the membrane-soluble coenzyme Q (Q)
and between Complexes III and IV by the peripheral membrane protein cytochrome *c*. Complex II (not shown) transfers electrons from succinate to coenzyme Q. **See the Animated Figures.**

Complex I Contains Multiple Coenzymes. Complex I contains one molecule of **flavin mononucleotide** (**FMN,** a redox-active prosthetic group that differs from FAD only by the absence of the AMP group) and eight or nine **iron–sulfur clusters.** Iron–sulfur clusters occur as the prosthetic groups of **iron–sulfur proteins** (also called **nonheme iron proteins**). The two most common types, designated **[2Fe–2S]** and **[4Fe–4S] clusters** (*at right*) consist of equal numbers of iron and sulfide ions and are both coordinated to four protein Cys sulfhydryl groups. Note that the Fe atoms in both types of clusters are each coordinated by four S atoms, which are more or less tetrahedrally disposed around the Fe.

Iron–sulfur clusters can undergo one-electron oxidation and reduction. *The oxidized and reduced states of all iron–sulfur clusters differ by one formal charge regardless of their number of Fe atoms.* This is because the Fe atoms in each cluster form a conjugated system and thus can have oxidation states between the normal +2 and +3 values for individual Fe ions.

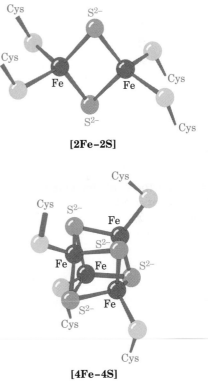

[2Fe–2S]

[4Fe–4S]

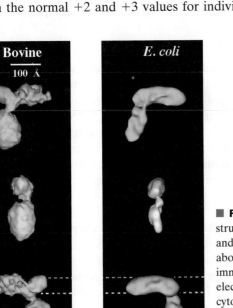

Bovine · · · *E. coli*

100 Å

(a) · · · (b)

Figure 18-9 | Cryoelectron microscopy–based images of Complex I. The structures from (*a*) bovine heart mitochondria and (*b*) *E. coli* were determined at 22 and 34 Å resolution, respectively. Successive views, top to bottom, are rotated by 90° about the vertical axis. The boundaries of the lipid bilayer in which the complex is immersed are indicated by the dashed lines. The vertical arm, which contains the electron-transport groups, protrudes into the mitochondrial matrix or bacterial cytoplasm. [Courtesy of Nikolaus Grigorieff, Brandeis University. The *E. coli* structure was determined by Vincent Guénebaut and Kevin Leonard, European Molecular Biology Laboratory, Heidelberg, Germany.]

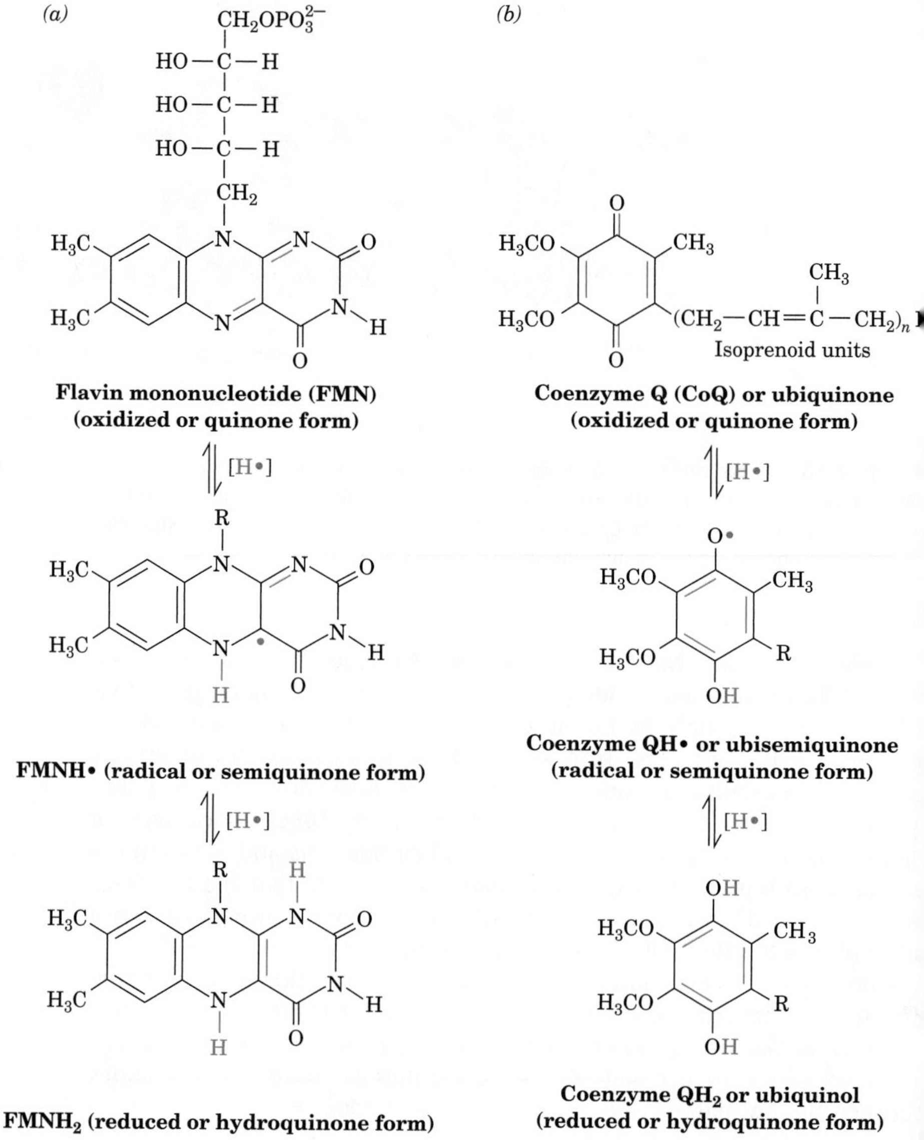

(a)

Flavin mononucleotide (FMN)
(oxidized or quinone form)

$\updownarrow$ [H•]

FMNH• (radical or semiquinone form)

$\updownarrow$ [H•]

FMNH$_2$ (reduced or hydroquinone form)

(b)

Coenzyme Q (CoQ) or ubiquinone
(oxidized or quinone form)

$\updownarrow$ [H•]

Coenzyme QH• or ubisemiquinone
(radical or semiquinone form)

$\updownarrow$ [H•]

Coenzyme QH$_2$ or ubiquinol
(reduced or hydroquinone form)

■ **Figure 18-10** | **The oxidation states of FMN and coenzyme Q.** Both (a) FMN and (b) coenzyme Q form stable semiquinone free-radical states.

FMN and CoQ can each adopt three oxidation states (Fig. 18-10). They are capable of accepting and donating either one or two electrons because their semiquinone forms are stable (these semiquinones are stable **free radicals,** molecules with an unpaired electron). FMN is tightly bound to proteins; however, CoQ has a hydrophobic tail that makes it soluble in the inner mitochondrial membrane's lipid bilayer. In mammals, this tail consists of 10 C_5 isoprenoid units (Section 9-1F) and hence the coenzyme is designated **Q$_{10}$.** In other organisms, CoQ may have only 6 **(Q$_6$)** or 8 **(Q$_8$)** isoprenoid units.

Electrons Follow a Multistep Path through Complex I. Complex I from *Thermus thermophilus* consists of 14 subunits with an aggregate molecular mass of 550 kD. The X-ray structure of its 8-subunit hydrophilic (extramembranous) arm, determined by Leonid Sazanov, reveals that this minimal model of Complex I is a Y-shaped assembly that is 140 Å high (Fig. 18-11a). This subcomplex contains all of the enzyme's redox centers: an FMN, seven [4Fe–4S] clusters, and two [2Fe–2S] clusters. The FMN is located at the end of a solvent-exposed cavity that presumably forms the

(a)

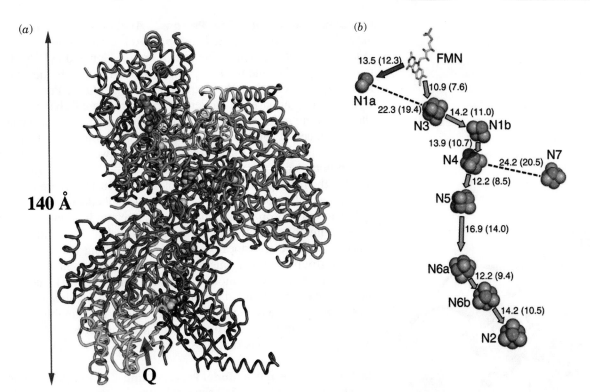

140 Å

Q

(b)

Figure 18-11 | X-ray structure of the hydrophilic domain of Complex I from *Thermus thermophilus*. (*a*) Side view with the transmembrane arm presumably beneath and extending to the right (upside down relative to Fig. 18-9*b, lower structure*). The eight subunits are drawn in worm form in different colors. The FMN (*upper left*) and the nine iron–sulfur clusters are shown in space-filling form with C green, N blue, O red, P orange, S yellow, and Fe red-brown. The likely CoQ-binding site (Q) is indicated by a gray arrow. (*b*) The arrangement of redox groups viewed similarly to Part *a*. The FMN (stick model with C yellow) and the two [Fe–S] and seven [4Fe–4S] clusters (space-filling models) are shown together with their center-to-center distances in angstroms (shortest edge-to-edge distances are indicated in parentheses). Blue arrows represent the main path of electrons after their transfer from NADH to FMN. [Part *a* based on an X-ray structure by and Part *b* courtesy of Leonid Sazanov, Medical Research Council, Cambridge, U.K. PDBid 2FUG.]

NADH-binding site. The CoQ-binding site appears to be in a cavity near the end of a chain of [4Fe–4S] clusters that is located at the presumed interface with Complex I's membrane-embedded arm.

The transit of electrons from NADH to CoQ presumably occurs by a stepwise mechanism, according to the reduction potential of the various redox centers in Complex I (Table 18-1). This process involves the transient reduction of each group as it binds electrons and its reoxidation when it passes the electrons to the next group. The spatial arrangement of the groups indicates the likely path of the electrons (Fig. 18-11*b*). Note that redox centers do not need to come into contact in order to transfer an electron. An electron's quantum mechanical properties enable it to quickly "tunnel" (jump) between protein-embedded redox groups that are separated by less than ~14 Å. Because electron transfer rates decrease exponentially with the distance between redox centers (they exhibit an ~10-fold decrease for each 1.7 Å increase in distance), electron transfers over distances longer than ~14 Å always involve chains of redox centers.

NADH can participate in only a two-electron transfer reaction. In contrast, the cytochromes of Complex III (see below), to which reduced CoQ passes its electrons, are capable of only one-electron reactions. *FMN and CoQ, which can transfer one or two electrons at a time, therefore provide an electron conduit between the two-electron donor NADH and the one-electron acceptors, the cytochromes.*

Complex I Translocates Four Protons. *As electrons are transferred between the redox centers of Complex I, four protons are translocated from the matrix to the intermembrane space.* The fate of protons donated by NADH is uncertain: They may be among those pumped across the membrane or used in the reduction of CoQ to its hydroquinone form, $CoQH_2$. Proton pumping in Complex I is apparently driven by conformational changes induced by changes in the redox state of the protein. These conformational changes alter the pK values of ionizable side chains so that protons are taken up or released as electrons are transferred. Coupling between electron transport and proton pumping is not well understood because the redox groups are all located in the hydrophilic arm of Complex I (Fig. 18-11), whereas proton transport necessarily occurs across the membrane-embedded arm.

Because a proton is simply an atomic nucleus, it cannot be transported across a membrane in the same way as ions such as Na^+ and K^+. However, a proton can be translocated by "hopping" along a chain of hydrogen bonded groups in a transmembrane channel, just as it "jumps" between hydrogen-bonded water molecules in solution (Fig. 2-15). Such an arrangement of hydrogen-bonded groups in the protein has been described as a **proton wire** and may include water molecules. Presumably, Complex I includes a proton wire that pumps four protons across the membrane for every pair of electrons that passes from NADH to CoQ.

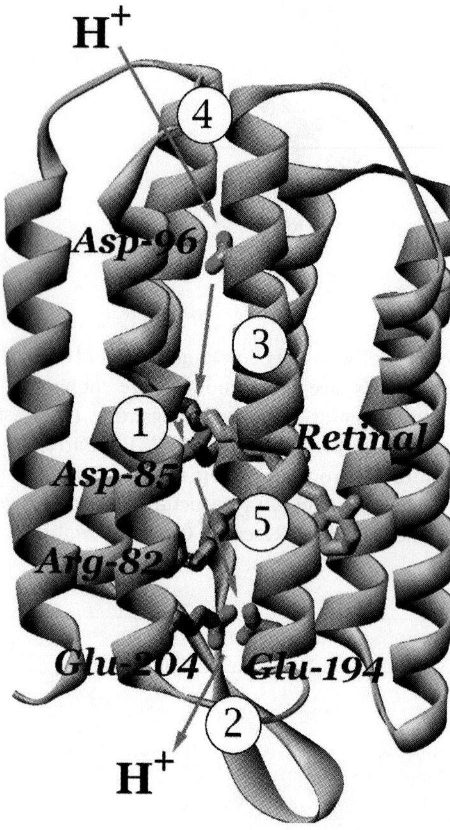

Bacteriorhodopsin Is a Model Proton Pump. A useful model for proton-translocating complexes is bacteriorhodopsin, an integral membrane protein from *Halobacterium salinarium* that contains seven transmembrane helical segments surrounding a central polar channel (Fig. 9-22). Bacteriorhodopsin is a light-driven proton pump: It obtains the free energy required for pumping protons through the absorbance of light by its retinal prosthetic group. The retinal is linked to the protein via a protonated Schiff base to the side chain of Lys 216.

On absorbing light, the all-*trans*-retinal isomerizes to its 13-*cis* configuration:

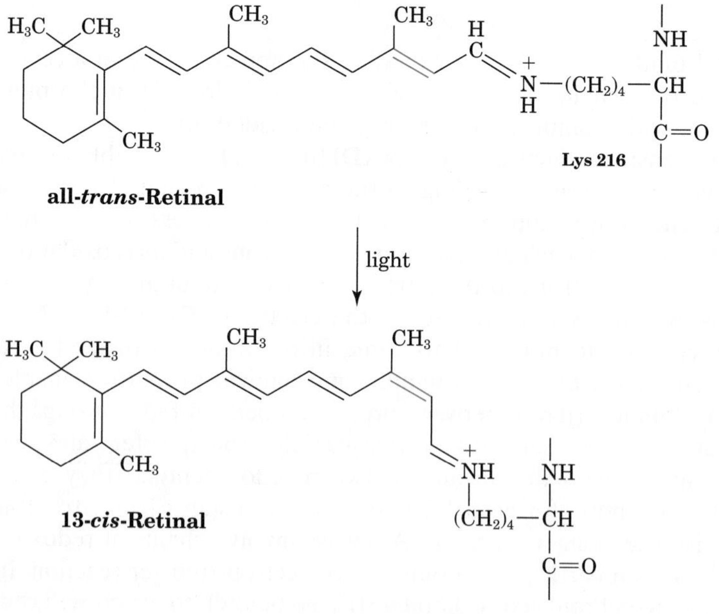

Figure 18-12 | **Proton translocation in bacteriorhodopsin.** The retinal prosthetic group in Schiff base linkage to Lys 216 of the seven-transmembrane helix protein is shown in purple. The side chains of amino acids that participate in light-driven proton translocation are shown in stick form with C gray, N blue, and O red. The arrows with their associated numbers indicate the order of proton-transfer steps during the photochemical cycle: (**1**) deprotonation of the Schiff base and protonation of Asp 85; (**2**) proton release to the extracellular surface; (**3**) reprotonation of the Schiff base and deprotonation of Asp 96; (**4**) reprotonation of Asp 96 from the cytoplasmic surface; and (**5**) deprotonation of Asp 85 and reprotonation of the proton release site. [Courtesy of Janos Lanyi, University of California at Irvine. PDBid 1C3W.]

This structural change initiates a sequence of protein conformational adjustments that restore the system to its ground state over a period of ~10 ms. These conformational changes alter the pK's of several amino acid side chains (Fig. 18-12). Specifically, the pK of Asp 85 increases so that it can ceive a proton from the Schiff base. Asp 85 then transfers the proton to the extracellular medium via a hydrogen-bonded network that includes Arg 82, Glu 194, Glu 204, and several water molecules. Water molecules also move into position to form a hydrogen-bonded network that reprotonates the Schiff base with an intracellular proton via Asp 96, whose pK decreases. The net result is that a proton appears to move from the cytosol to the cell exterior (the proton that leaves the cytosol is not the same proton that enters the extracellular space).

The various amino acid side chains involved in proton transport in bacteriorhodopsin move by ~1 Å or less, but this is enough to alter their pK values and to sequentially make and break hydrogen bonds so as to allow a proton to pass along the proton wire. The vectorial (one-way) nature of this process arises from the unidirectional series of conformational changes made by the photoexcited retinal as it relaxes to its ground state. Electron transfers between the various redox cofactors of Complex I likely motivate a similar sequence of conformational and pK changes.

Complex II Contributes Electrons to Coenzyme Q

Complex II **(succinate–coenzyme Q oxidoreductase),** which contains the citric acid cycle enzyme succinate dehydrogenase (Section 17-3F), passes electrons from succinate to CoQ. Its redox groups include succinate dehydrogenase's covalently bound FAD (Fig. 17-13) to which electrons are initially passed, one [4Fe–4S] cluster, a [3Fe–4S] cluster (essentially a [4Fe–4S] complex that lacks one Fe atom), one [2Fe–2S] cluster, and one **cytochrome b_{560}** (cytochromes are discussed in Box 18-1).

The free energy for electron transfer from succinate to CoQ (Fig. 18-7) is insufficient to drive ATP synthesis. The complex is nevertheless important because it allows relatively high-potential electrons to enter the electron-transport chain by bypassing Complex I.

Note that Complexes I and II, despite their names, do not operate in series. But both accomplish the same result: the transfer of electrons to CoQ from reduced substrates (NADH or succinate). *CoQ, which diffuses in the lipid bilayer among the respiratory complexes, therefore serves as a sort of collection point for electrons.* As we shall see in Section 20-2C, the first step in fatty acid oxidation generates electrons that enter the electron-transport chain at the level of CoQ. CoQ also collects electrons from the FADH$_2$ produced by the glycerophosphate shuttle (Fig. 18-5).

Complex II Contains a Linear Chain of Redox Cofactors. The X-ray structures of mitochondrial Complex II and the closely related *E. coli* Complex II have been determined (Fig. 18-13). The *E. coli* Complex II is a 360-kD mushroom-shaped homotrimer

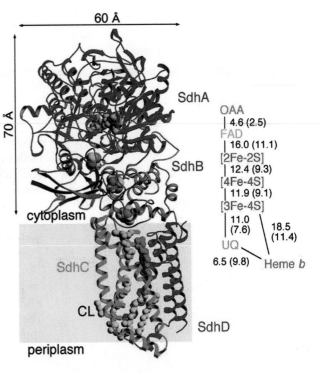

Figure 18-13 | X-Ray structure of *E. coli* Complex II. A protomer of the trimeric complex as viewed parallel to the membrane with the cytoplasm above. SdhA, SdhB, SdhC, and SdhD are respectively purple, brown, green, and blue. The bound oxaloacetate inhibitor (OAA; *dark green*), the FAD (*yellow-green*), the Fe–S clusters (*Fe red and S green*), the ubiquinone (*green*), and the heme *b* (*magenta*) are drawn in space-filling form as are bound cardiolipin (CL) molecules (*gray*). The center-to-center and edge-to-edge (in parentheses) distances in angstroms between redox centers are shown. The inferred position of the membrane is indicated by the light blue shading. [Courtesy of So Iwata, Imperial College London, U.K. PDBid 1NEK.]

BOX 18-1 PERSPECTIVES IN BIOCHEMISTRY

Cytochromes Are Electron-Transport Heme Proteins

Cytochromes, whose function was elucidated in 1925 by David Keilin, are redox-active proteins that occur in all organisms except a few types of obligate anaerobes. These proteins contain heme groups that alternate between their Fe(II) and Fe(III) oxidation states during electron transport.

The heme groups of the reduced Fe(II) cytochromes have prominent visible absorption spectra consisting of three peaks: the α, β, and γ **(Soret)** bands. The spectrum for cytochrome c is shown in Fig. a.

The wavelength of the α peak, which varies characteristically with the reduced cytochrome species (it is absent in oxidized cytochromes), is used to differentiate the various cytochromes in mitochondrial membranes (*top right of Fig. a and Fig. b*).

Each group of cytochromes contains a differently substituted heme group coordinated with the redox-active iron atom. The b-type cytochromes contain **protoporphyrin IX,** which also occurs in myoglobin and hemoglobin (Section 7-1A). The heme group of c-type cytochromes differs from protoporphyrin IX in that its vinyl groups have added Cys sulfhydryls across their double bonds to form thioether linkages to the protein. Heme a contains a long hydrophobic tail of isoprene units attached to the porphyrin, as well as a formyl group in place of a methyl substituent in hemes b and c. The

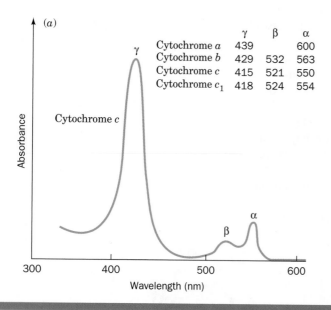

	γ	β	α
Cytochrome a	439		600
Cytochrome b	429	532	563
Cytochrome c	415	521	550
Cytochrome c_1	418	524	554

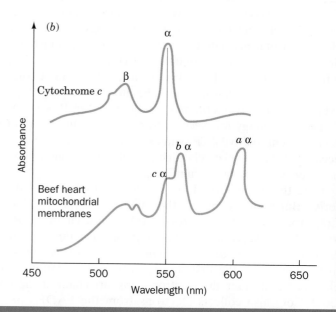

whose protomers each consist of two hydrophilic subunits, a flavoprotein **(SdhA)** and an iron–sulfur subunit **(SdhB),** that occupy the cytoplasm (the equivalent of the mitochondrial matrix), and two hydrophobic membrane-anchor subunits, **SdhC** and **SdhD,** which each have three transmembrane helices and which collectively bind one b-type heme and one ubiquinone. SdhA binds both the substrate (whose binding site is occupied by the inhibitor oxaloacetate in the X-ray structure) and the FAD prosthetic group, whereas SdhB binds the complex's three iron–sulfur clusters. The substrate- and ubiquinone-binding sites are connected by a >40-Å-long chain of redox centers with the sequence substrate–FAD—[2Fe–2S]—[4Fe–4S]—[3Fe–4S]—Q (top to bottom in Fig. 18-13). The heme b, which is not located in this direct electron-transfer pathway, apparently fine-tunes the system's electronic properties so as to suppress

xial ligands of the heme iron also vary with the cytochrome type. In cytochromes a and b, both ligands are His residues, whereas in cytochromes c, one is His and the other is the S atom of Met.

Within each group of cytochromes, different heme group environments may be characterized by slightly different α peak wavelengths. For this reason, it is convenient to identify cytochromes by the wavelength (in nm) at which its α band absorbance is maximal (e.g., cytochrome b_{560} in Complex II). Cytochromes are also identified nondescriptively with either numbers or letters.

Reduced heme groups are highly reactive entities; they can transfer electrons over distances of 10 to 20 Å at physiologically

significant rates. Hence cytochromes, in a *sense*, have the opposite function of enzymes: Instead of persuading unreactive substrates to react, they must prevent their hemes from transferring electrons nonspecifically to other cellular components. This, no doubt, is why these hemes are almost entirely enveloped by protein. However, cytochromes must also provide a path for electron transfer to an appropriate partner. Since electron transfer occurs far more efficiently through bonds than through space, protein structure appears to be an important determinant of the rate of electron transfer between proteins.

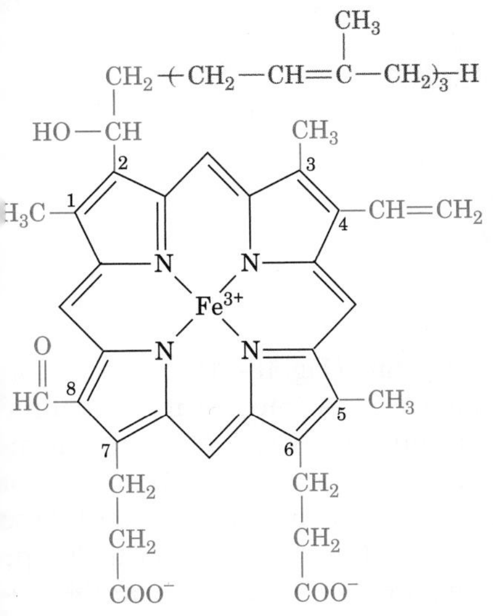

Heme a

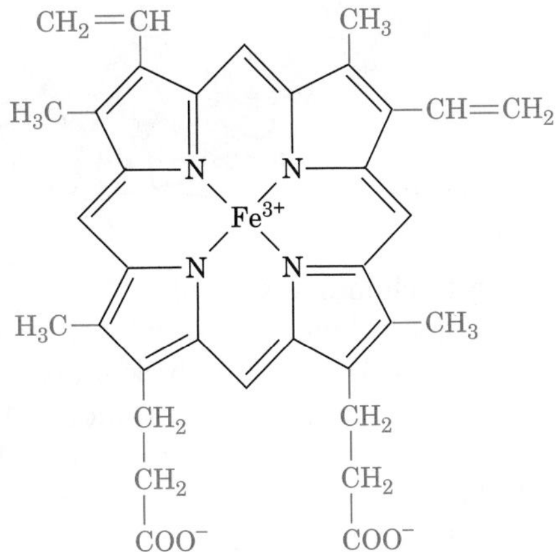

Heme b
(iron–protoporphyrin IX)

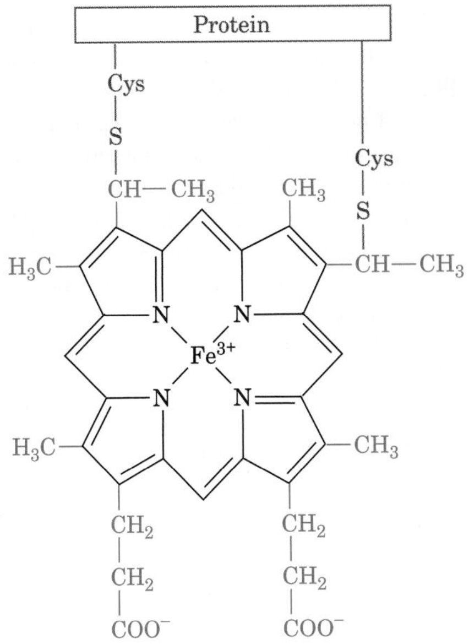

Heme c

side reactions that form damaging **reactive oxygen species** such as H_2O_2 (Section 18-4B). The [2Fe–2S] cluster labeled N1a in Complex I (Fig. 18-11b) may have a similar role.

E | Complex III Translocates Protons via the Q Cycle

Complex III (also known as **coenzyme Q–cytochrome c oxidoreductase** or **cytochrome bc_1**) passes electrons from reduced CoQ to cytochrome c. It contains two **b-type cytochromes,** one **cytochrome c_1,** and one [2Fe–2S] cluster in which one of the Fe atoms is coordinated by two His residues rather than two Cys residues (and which is known as a **Rieske center** after its discoverer, John Rieske). Complex III from yeast mitochondria is a 419-kD homodimer with 9 subunits (11 in the 485-kD bovine heart

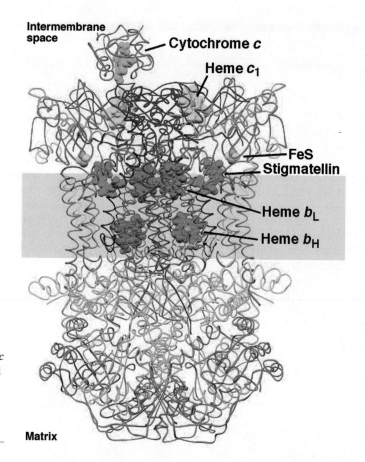

■ Figure 18-14 | X-Ray structure of yeast Complex III in complex with cytochrome c and the inhibitor stigmatellin. The homodimeric complex is viewed from within the plane of the membrane with the intermembrane space above. The nine different subunits in each protomer, which collectively have 12 transmembrane helices, are differently colored with cytochrome b green, cytochrome c_1 purple, the ISP magenta, and cytochrome c red. The four different heme groups, the [2Fe–2S] cluster, and stigmatellin are drawn in space-filling form in different colors but with all Fe atoms orange. The inferred position of the membrane is indicated by the blue shading. Note that only one cytochrome c is bound to the homodimeric Complex III. [Based on an X-ray structure by Carola Hunte, Max Planck Institute for Biophysics, Frankfurt am Main, Germany. PDBid 1KYO.] ♨ **See Interactive Exercise 19.**

See Guided Exploration 18
The Q cycle.

mitochondrial Complex III). Its X-ray structure (Fig. 18-14) reveals a pear-shaped dimer whose widest part extends ~75 Å into the mitochondrial matrix. The ~40-Å-thick transmembrane portion consists of 12 transmembrane helices per protomer (14 in bovine heart Complex III), most of which are tilted with respect to the plane of the membrane. Eight of these helices belong to the **cytochrome b** subunit, which binds both b-type cytochrome hemes, b_{562} (or b_H, for high potential, which lies near the matrix) and b_{566} (or b_L, for low potential, which lies near the intermembrane space). The cytochrome c_1 subunit is anchored by a single transmembrane helix, with its globular head, which contains a c-type heme, extending into the intermembrane space. The **iron–sulfur protein (ISP)**, which contains the Rieske center, is similarly anchored by a single transmembrane helix and extends into the intermembrane space. The two ISPs of the dimeric complex are intertwined so that the [2Fe–2S] cluster in the ISP of one protomer interacts with the cytochrome b and cytochrome c_1 subunits of the other protomer.

Electrons from Coenzyme Q Follow Two Paths. Complex III functions to permit one molecule of $CoQH_2$, a two-electron carrier, to reduce two molecules of cytochrome c, a one-electron carrier. This occurs by a surprising bifurcation of the flow of electrons from $CoQH_2$ to cytochrome c_1 and to cytochrome b (in which the flow is cyclic). It is this so-called **Q cycle** that permits Complex III to pump protons from the matrix to the intermembrane space.

The essence of the Q cycle is that *$CoQH_2$ undergoes a two-cycle reoxidation in which the semiquinone, $CoQ^{\cdot -}$, is a stable intermediate.* This involves two independent binding sites for coenzyme Q: Q_o, which binds $CoQH_2$ and is located between the Rieske [2Fe–2S] center and heme b_L in roximity to the intermembrane space; and Q_i, which binds both $CoQ^{-\bullet}$ and CoQ and is located near heme b_H in proximity to the matrix. In the first cycle (Fig. 18-15, *top*), $CoQH_2$ from Complex I (**1** and **2**) binds to the Q_o site, where it transfers one of its electrons to the ISP (**3**), releasing its two protons into the intermembrane space and yielding $CoQ^{-\bullet}$. The ISP goes on to reduce cytochrome c_1, whereas the $CoQ^{-\bullet}$ transfers its remaining electron to cytochrome b_L (**4**), yielding fully oxidized CoQ. Cytochrome b_L then reduces cytochrome b_H (**6**). The CoQ from Step 4 is released from the Q_o site and rebinds to the Q_i site (**5**), where it picks up the electron from cytochrome b_H (**7**), reverting to the semiquinone form, $CoQ^{-\bullet}$. Thus, the reaction for this first cycle is

$$CoQH_2 + \text{cytochrome } c_1 \, (Fe^{3+}) \rightarrow$$
$$CoQ^{-\bullet} + \text{cytochrome } c_1 \, (Fe^{2+}) + 2\,H^+ \, (\textit{intermembrane})$$

In the second cycle (Fig. 18-15, *bottom*), another $CoQH_2$ from Complex repeats Steps 1 through 6: One electron reduces the ISP and then cytochrome c_1, and the other electron sequentially reduces cytochrome b_L

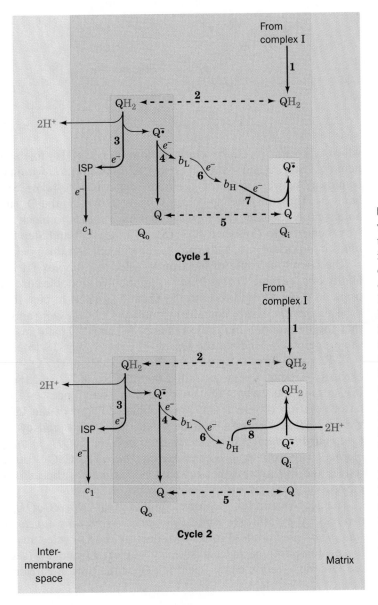

Figure 18-15 | The Q cycle. The Q cycle, which is mediated by Complex III, results in the translocation of H^+ from the matrix to the intermembrane space as driven by the transport of electrons from cytochrome b to cytochrome c. The overall cycle is actually two cycles, the first requiring Reactions 1 through 7 and the second requiring Reactions 1 through 6 and 8. (**1**) Coenzyme QH_2 is supplied by Complex I on the matrix side of the membrane. (**2**) QH_2 diffuses to the cytosolic side of the membrane, where it binds in the Q_o site on the cytochrome b subunit of Complex III. (**3**) QH_2 reduces the Rieske iron–sulfur protein (ISP), forming $Q^{-\bullet}$ semiquinone and releasing 2 H^+. The ISP goes on to reduce heme c_1. (**4**) $Q^{-\bullet}$ reduces heme b_L to form coenzyme Q. (**5**) Q diffuses to the matrix side, where, in Cycle 1 only, it binds in the Q_i site on cytochrome b. (**6**) Heme b_L reduces heme b_H. (**7**, Cycle 1 only) Q is reduced to $Q^{-\bullet}$ by heme b_H. (**8**, Cycle 2 only) $Q^{-\bullet}$ bound in the Q_i site is reduced to QH_2 by heme b_H. The net reaction is the transfer of two electrons from QH_2 to cytochrome c_1 and the translocation of four protons from the matrix to the intermembrane space [After Trumpower, B.L., *J. Biol. Chem.* **265**, 11410 (1990).]

and then cytochrome b_H. This second electron then reduces the $CoQ^{\bar{\cdot}}$ a the Q_i site produced in the first cycle (**8**), yielding $CoQH_2$. The proton consumed in this last step originate in the mitochondrial matrix. The reaction for the second cycle is therefore

$$CoQH_2 + CoQ^{\bar{\cdot}} + \text{cytochrome } c_1 (Fe^{3+}) + 2\,H^+\,(matrix) \rightarrow$$
$$CoQ + CoQH_2 + \text{cytochrome } c_1 (Fe^{2+}) + 2\,H^+\,(intermembrane$$

For every two $CoQH_2$ that enter the Q cycle, one $CoQH_2$ is regener ated. The combination of both cycles, in which two electrons are transferred from $CoQH_2$ to cytochrome c_1, results in the overall reaction

$$CoQH_2 + 2\,\text{cytochrome } c_1 (Fe^{3+}) + 2\,H^+\,(matrix) \rightarrow$$
$$CoQ + 2\,\text{cytochrome } c_1 (Fe^{2+}) + 4\,H^+\,(intermembrane$$

How does the structure of Complex III support the operation of the Q cycle? First, X-ray studies provide direct evidence for the independen existence of the Q_o and Q_i sites. The antifungal agent **stigmatellin,**

Stigmatellin

which is known to inhibit electron flow from $CoQH_2$ to the ISP and to heme b_L (Steps 3 and 4 of both cycles), binds in a pocket within cytochrome b midway between the iron positions of the Rieske [2Fe–2S] center and heme b_L. Thus, this binding pocket is likely to overlap the Q_o site. Similarly, antimycin A (Section 18-2B), which has been shown to block electron flow from heme b_H to CoQ or $CoQ^{\bar{\cdot}}$ (Step 7 of Cycle 1 and Step 8 of Cycle 2), binds in a pocket near heme b_H, thereby identifying this pocket as site Q_i.

The circuitous route of electron transfer in Complex III is tied to the ability of coenzyme Q to diffuse within the hydrophobic core of the membrane in order to bind to both the Q_o and Q_i sites. In fact, the mitochondrial membrane likely contains a pool of CoQ, $CoQ^{\bar{\cdot}}$, and $CoQH_2$, so that the ubiquinone molecule released from the Q_o site may not be the same one that rebinds to the Q_i site in Cycle 1 (Fig. 18-15).

X-Ray structures of cytochrome bc_1 also explain why Q_o-bound $CoQ^{\bar{\cdot}}$ exclusively reduces heme b_L rather than the Rieske [2Fe–2S] cluster of the ISP, despite the greater reduction potential difference ($\Delta\mathscr{E}$) favoring the latter reaction (Table 18-1). The globular domain of the ISP can swing via an ~20-Å hinge motion between the Q_o site and cytochrome c_1. *Consequently, the ISP acquires an electron from $CoQH_2$ in the Q_o site and mechanically delivers it to the heme c_1 group. The $CoQ^{\bar{\cdot}}$* product cannot reduce the ISP (after it has reduced cytochrome c_1) because the ISP has moved too far away for this to occur.

The net reaction for the Q cycle indicates that *when $CoQH_2$ is oxidized, two reduced cytochrome c molecules and four protons appear on the outer side of the membrane.* Proton transport by the Q cycle thus differs from the proton-pumping mechanism of Complexes I and IV (see below): In the Q cycle, a redox center itself (CoQ) is the proton carrier.

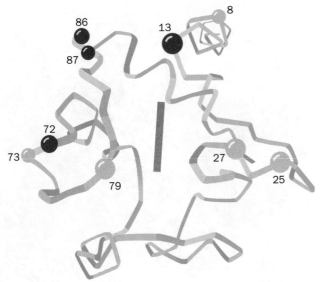

■ Figure 18-16 | Ribbon diagram of cytochrome *c* showing the Lys residues involved in intermolecular complex formation. Dark and light blue balls, respectively, mark the position of Lys residues whose ε-amino groups are strongly and less strongly protected by cytochrome c_1 or cytochrome *c* oxidase against acetylation. Note that these Lys residues form a ring around the heme (*solid bar*) on one face of the protein. [After Mathews, F.S., *Prog. Biophys. Mol. Biol.* **45**, 45 (1986).] 🔗 **See Interactive Exercise 20 and Kinemage Exercise 5.**

Cytochrome *c* Is a Soluble Electron Carrier. The electrons that flow to cytochrome c_1 are transferred to cytochrome *c*, which, unlike the other cytochromes of the respiratory electron-transport chain, is a peripheral membrane protein. It shuttles electrons between Complexes III and IV on the outer surface of the inner mitochondrial membrane. The evolution and structure of cytochrome *c* are discussed in Sections 5-4A and 6-2D. Several highy conserved Lys residues in cytochrome *c* lie in a ring around the exposed edge of its otherwise buried heme group (Fig. 18-16). These positively charged residues constitute binding sites for complementary negatively charged groups on cytochrome c_1 and cytochrome *c* oxidase. Such interactions presumably serve to align redox groups for optimal electron transfer.

The X-ray structure shown in Fig. 18-14 reveals that the association between cytochrome bc_1 and cytochrome *c* is particularly tenuous, because its interfacial area (880 Å^2) is significantly less than that exhibited by protein–protein complexes known to have low stability (typically < 1600 Å^2). Such a small interface is well suited for fast binding and release. This interface involves only two cytochrome *c* Lys residues, Lys 86 and Lys 79, which respectively contact Glu 235 and Ala 164 of cytochrome c_1. Other pairs of charged and often conserved residues surround the contact site but they are not close enough for direct polar interactions. Perhaps these interactions are mediated by water molecules that are not seen in the X-ray structure. The closest approach between the heme groups of the contacting proteins is 4.5 Å between atoms of their respective vinyl side chains, which accounts for the rapid rate of electron transfer between the two redox centers.

F | Complex IV Reduces Oxygen to Water

Cytochrome *c* oxidase (Complex IV) catalyzes the one-electron oxidations of four consecutive reduced cytochrome *c* molecules and the concomitant four-electron reduction of one O_2 molecule:

$$4\,\text{Cytochrome } c\,(\text{Fe}^{2+}) + 4\,\text{H}^+ + \text{O}_2 \rightarrow 4\,\text{cytochrome } c\,(\text{Fe}^{3+}) + 2\,\text{H}_2\text{O}$$

Mammalian Complex IV is an ~410-kD homodimer whose component protomers are each composed of 13 subunits. The X-ray structure of

■ **Figure 18-17 | X-Ray structure of the bovine heart cytochrome c oxidase homodimer.** The homodimeric complex is viewed from within the plane of the membrane with the intermembrane space at the top. The 13 different subunits in each protomer, which collectively have 28 transmembrane helices, are differently colored. The protein's bound heme groups and Cu ions are drawn in space-filling form with C magenta, N blue, O red, Fe orange, and Cu cyan. [Based on an X-ray structure by Shinya Yoshikawa, Himeji Institute of Technology, Hyogo, Japan. PDBid 1V54.] *See Interactive Exercise 21.*

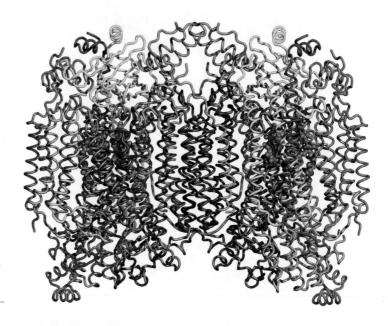

Complex IV from bovine heart mitochondria, determined by Shinya Yoshikawa, reveals that ten of its subunits are transmembrane proteins that contain a total of 28 membrane-spanning α helices (Fig. 18-17). The core of Complex IV consists of its three largest and most hydrophobic subunits, I, II, and III (green, yellow, and purple in Fig. 18-17), which are encoded by mitochondrial DNA (the remaining subunits are nuclearly encoded and must be transported into the mitochondrion). A concave area on the surface of the protein that faces the intermembrane space contains numerous acidic amino acids that can potentially interact with the ring of Lys residues on cytochrome c, the electron donor for Complex IV.

Complex IV contains four redox centers: **cytochrome a, cytochrome a₃,** a copper atom known as **Cu$_B$,** and a pair of copper atoms known as the **Cu$_A$ center** (Fig. 18-18). The Cu$_A$ center, which is bound to Subunit II, lies 8 Å above the membrane surface. Its two copper ions are bridged by the sulfur atoms of two Cys residues, giving it a geometry similar to that of a [2Fe–2S] cluster. The other redox groups—Cu$_B$ and cytochromes a and a₃—all bind to Subunit I and lie ~13 Å below the membrane surface.

Spectroscopic studies have shown that electron transfer in Complex IV is linear, proceeding from cytochrome c to the Cu$_A$ center, then to heme a, and finally to heme a₃ and Cu$_B$. The Fe of heme a₃ lies only 4.9 Å from Cu$_B$; these redox groups really form a single binuclear complex. Electrons

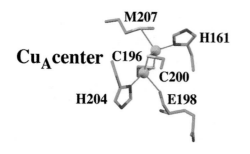

■ **Figure 18-18 | The redox centers of bovine heart cytochrome c oxidase.** The view is similar to that in Fig. 18-17. The Fe and Cu ions are represented by orange and cyan spheres. Their liganding heme and protein groups are drawn in stick form colored according to atom type (heme C magenta, protein C green, N blue, O red, and S yellow). The peroxy group that bridges the Cu$_B$ and heme a₃ Fe ions is shown in ball-and-stick form in red. Coordination bonds are drawn as gray lines. Note that the side chains of His 240 and Tyr 244 are joined by a covalent bond (*lower right*). [Based on an X-ray structure by Shinya Yoshikawa, Himeji Institute of Technology, Hyogo, Japan. PDBid 2OCC.]

ppear to travel between the redox centers of Complex IV via a hydrogen-bonded network, involving amino acid side chains, the polypeptide backbone, and the propionate side chains of the heme groups.

Cytochrome *c* Oxidase Catalyzes a Four-Electron Redox Reaction. The reduction of O_2 to 2 H_2O by cytochrome *c* oxidase takes place at the cytochrome a_3–Cu_B binuclear complex and requires the nearly simultaneous input of four electrons. However, the fully reduced Fe(II)–Cu(I) binuclear complex can readily contribute only three electrons to its bound O_2 in reaching its fully oxidized Fe(IV)–Cu(II) state [cytochrome a_3 assumes its Fe(IV) or **ferryl** oxidation state during the reduction of O_2; see below]. What is the source of the fourth electron?

X-Ray structures of cytochrome *c* oxidase clearly indicate that the His 240 ligand of Cu_B is covalently bonded to the side chain of a conserved Tyr residue (Tyr 244; Fig. 18-18, *lower right*). This places the Tyr phenolic —OH group close to the heme a_3–ligated O_2 such that *Tyr 244 can supply the fourth electron by transiently forming a tyrosyl radical* (TyrO·). Tyrosyl radicals have been implicated in several other enzyme-mediated redox processes, including the generation of O_2 from H_2O in photosynthesis (Section 19-2C) and in the **ribonucleotide reductase** reaction (which converts NDP to dNDP; Section 23-3A). In cytochrome *c* oxidase, the Tyr phenolic —OH group is within hydrogen-bonding distance of the enzyme-bound O_2 and hence is a likely H^+ donor during O—O bond cleavage. The formation of the covalent cross-link is expected to lower both the reduction potential and the p*K* of Tyr 244, thereby facilitating both radical formation and proton donation.

A proposed reaction sequence for cytochrome *c* oxidase, which was elucidated through the use of a variety of spectroscopic techniques, is shown in Fig. 18-19:

1 and 2. The oxidized binuclear complex $[Fe(III)_{a3}$—OH^- $Cu(II)_B]$ is reduced to its $[Fe(II)_{a3}$ $Cu(I)_B]$ state by two consecutive one-electron transfers from cytochrome *c* via cytochrome *a* and Cu_A. A proton from the matrix is concomitantly acquired and an H_2O is released in this process. Tyr 244 (Y—OH) is in its phenolic state.

3. O_2 binds to the reduced binuclear complex so as to ligand its Fe(II)$_{a3}$ atom. It binds to the heme with much the same configuration it has in oxymyoglobin (Fig. 7-3).

4. Internal electron redistribution rapidly yields the oxyferryl complex $[Fe(IV)$=O^{2-} HO^-—$Cu(II)]$ in which Tyr 244 has donated an electron and a proton to the complex and thereby assumed its neutral radical state (Y—O·). This is known as compound P because it was once thought to be a peroxy compound.

5. A third one-electron transfer from cytochrome *c* together with the acquisition of two protons reconverts Tyr 244 to its phenolic state, yielding compound F (for ferryl) and releasing an H_2O.

6. A fourth and final electron transfer and proton acquisition yields the oxidized $[Fe(III)_{a3}$—OH^- $Cu(II)_B]$ complex, thereby completing the catalytic cycle.

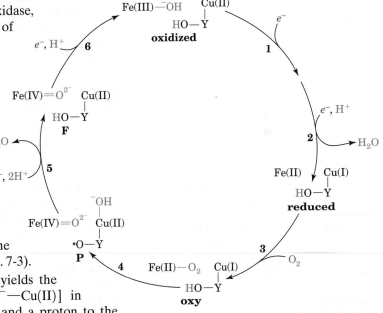

■ **Figure 18-19** | **Proposed reaction sequence for cytochrome c oxidase.** A total of four electrons ultimately donated by four cytochrome *c* molecules, together with four protons, are required to reduce O_2 to H_2O at the cytochrome a_3–Cu_B binuclear complex. The numbered steps are discussed in the text. The entire reaction is extremely fast; it goes to completion in ~1 ms at room temperature. [Modified from Babcock, G.T., *Proc. Natl. Acad. Sci.* **96**, 12971 (1999).]

CHECK YOUR UNDERSTANDING

Describe the route followed by electrons from glucose to O_2.

Discuss why several ATP molecules can be synthesized from the free energy released by electron transport from NADH to O_2.

Position the four electron-transport complexes on a graph showing their relative reduction potentials, and indicate the path of electron flow.

List the types of prosthetic groups in Complexes I, II, III, and IV and state whether they are one- or two-electron carriers.

Describe the different mechanisms for translocating protons during electron transport.

Cytochrome *c* Oxidase Has Two Proton-Translocating Channels. The reaction catalyzed by cytochrome *c* oxidase contributes to the transmembrane proton gradient in two ways. First, four so-called **chemical** or **scalar** protons are taken up from the matrix during the reduction of O_2 by cytochrome *c* oxidase to yield 2 H_2O, thereby depleting the matrix $[H^+]$. Second, the four-electron reduction reaction is coupled to the translocation of four so-called **pumped** or **vectorial** protons from the matrix to the intermembrane space. Note that for each turnover of the enzyme,

$$8\,H^+_{matrix} + O_2 + 4\,\text{cytochrome}\ c\,(Fe^{2+}) \rightarrow$$
$$4\,\text{cytochrome}\ c\,(Fe^{3+}) + 2\,H_2O + 4\,H^+_{intermembrane}$$

a total of eight positive charges are lost from the matrix, thus contributing to the membrane potential difference that drives ATP synthesis (Section 18-3).

X-Ray structures of cytochrome *c* oxidase reveal the presence of two channels that lead from the matrix to the vicinity of the O_2-reducing center, which could potentially transport protons via a proton wire mechanism. The **K-channel** (so named because it contains an essential Lys residue) leads from the matrix side of the protein to Tyr 244, the residue that forms a free radical as described above. Since this channel does not appear to be connected to the intermembrane space, it is thought to supply the chemical protons for O_2 reduction. The **D-channel** (named for a key Asp residue) extends from the matrix to the vicinity of the heme a_3–Cu_B center, where it connects to the so-called **exit channel,** which communicates with the intermembrane space. Apparently, the D-channel, in series with the exit channel, functions to pump vectorial protons from the matrix to the intermembrane space. Moreover, the D-channel also functions as a conduit for the chemical protons that are required for the second part of the reaction cycle (steps 5 and 6 of Fig. 18-19). Despite the foregoing, the mechanism that couples O_2 reduction to proton pumping in Complex IV remains an enigma.

3 Oxidative Phosphorylation

The endergonic synthesis of ATP from ADP and P_i in mitochondria is catalyzed by an **ATP synthase** (also known as **Complex V**) that is driven by the electron-transport process. *The free energy released by electron transport through Complexes I–IV must be conserved in a form that the ATP synthase can use.* Such energy conservation is referred to as **energy coupling.**

The physical characterization of energy coupling proved to be surprisingly elusive; many sensible and often ingenious ideas failed to withstand the test of experimental scrutiny. For example, one theory—now abandoned—was that electron transport yields a "high-energy" intermediate, such as phosphoenolpyruvate (PEP) in glycolysis (Section 15-2J), whose subsequent breakdown drives ATP synthesis. No such intermediate has ever been identified. In fact, ATP synthesis is coupled to electron transport through the formation of a transmembrane proton gradient during electron transport by Complexes I, III, and IV. In this section, we explore this coupling mechanism and the operation of ATP synthase.

LEARNING OBJECTIVES

■ Understand that the chemiosmotic theory invokes a proton gradient to link electron transport to ATP synthesis.

■ Understand that ATP synthase consists of an F_1 component that catalyzes ATP synthesis by a binding change mechanism, and an F_0 component that includes a *c*-ring whose rotation is driven by the dissapation of the proton gradient and drives conformational changes in the F_1 component.

■ Understand that for every two electrons that enter the electron-transport chain as NADH and reduce one oxygen atom, approximately 2.5 ATP molecules are produced, giving a P/O ratio of 2.5.

■ Understand that agents that dissipate the proton gradient can uncouple electron transport and ATP synthesis.

A | The Chemiosmotic Theory Links Electron Transport to ATP Synthesis

The **chemiosmotic theory,** proposed in 1961 by Peter Mitchell, spurred considerable controversy before becoming widely accepted (Box 18-2). Mitchell's theory states that *the free energy of electron transport is conserved*

BOX 18-2 PATHWAYS OF DISCOVERY

Peter Mitchell and the Chemiosmotic Theory

Peter Mitchell (1920–1992)

One of the most dramatic paradigm shifts in biochemistry came about through the work of Peter Mitchell, whose chemiosmotic hypothesis linked biological electron transport to ATP synthesis. Mitchell was primarily a theoretical biochemist, although he also generated experimental data to support his hypothesis. He once compared the human mind to a garden planted with facts and ideas that are constantly being rearranged. However, he promoted his own ideas, which were highly controversial, with great tenacity and very little flexibility.

Mitchell graduated from the University of Cambridge in 1942 and conducted research there, laying the groundwork for the chemiosmotic theory. Mitchell continued his work after 1955 at the University of Edinburgh. He was captivated by the idea of compartmentation in living cells and by the vectorial, or one-way, aspect of metabolic processes. Initially, he chose to study phosphate transport in bacteria because this process was linked both to metabolism and to transmembrane transport. He realized that the vectorial nature of membrane transport must be due to the presence of membrane-associated systems that were driven by chemical forces.

Mitchell also became interested in the respiratory chain, an idea formulated by David Keilin at Cambridge, because this too was a clearly vectorial biological phenomenon. Mitchell reasoned that there must be enzymes that, like transporters, convert a substrate on one side of a membrane to a product on the other side. Other researchers had already discovered that the activity of the respiratory chain generated a pH gradient. Mitchell's genius was to explain how this pH gradient could drive ATP synthesis. In his seminal paper of 1961, Mitchell proposed that the respiratory chain, associated with the cristae in the mitochondrion, generates a protonmotive force due to electrical and pH differences across the membrane. This force drives an ATPase, working in reverse, to catalyze the condensation of phosphate with ADP to produce ATP.

Mitchell's hypothesis, elegant as it was, met strong resistance from other biochemists for several reasons. First, chemiosmosis was a theoretical notion without direct experimental evidence. Second, the study of oxidative phosphorylation was dominated by a few powerful laboratories that were not inclined to welcome new theories. In particular, metabolic studies since the mid-1940s had been focused on the activities of soluble enzymes. Mitchell's theory was not a product of this classic biochemical approach but instead came through an understanding of membrane physiology. Furthermore, the prevailing theories about the connection between electron transport and ATP synthesis centered on a phos-

phorylated compound as a high-energy intermediate. Fritz Lipmann (Box 14-3) had proposed that a high-energy phosphate group might become attached to some component of the respiratory chain. This hypothesis was later amended to invoke a soluble phosphorylated intermediate. The search for the elusive compound lasted some 20 years, and the investment of time and money may have made some researchers hesitant to abandon this theory in favor of Mitchell's seemingly outrageous proposal. In the meantime, a third theory was proposed, in which electron transport was coupled to ATP synthesis through protein conformational changes, with the observed pH gradient presumed to be simply a by-product of this process.

Mitchell's chemiosmotic hypothesis did not garner significant support until about 10 years after its publication. During this period of sometimes acrimonious debate, Mitchell became ill, moved to Cornwall, and renovated a manor house, part of which became a private laboratory, known as Glynn Research, that was funded by Mitchell's family fortune. Here, he and his lifelong collaborator, Jennifer Moyle, produced experimental evidence to support the chemiosmotic theory. Ultimately, Mitchell was proven correct by other researchers who demonstrated the proton-pumping activity of purified mitochondrial components reconstituted in liposomes. Mitchell was awarded a Nobel Prize in Chemistry in 1978.

Mitchell succeeded in changing the prevailing views of a central feature of aerobic metabolism, although it was a long battle. He later expressed sadness that his work was taken for granted, as if it had been "self-evident from the beginning." Oddly, Mitchell stubbornly resisted altering any of his own ideas. For example, he never wavered in his belief that protons participate directly in ADP phosphorylation in the active site of ATP synthase. And for many years, Mitchell refused to acknowledge proton pumping (as we now know occurs in Complexes I and IV). Instead, he insisted that the source of the proton gradient was a "redox loop" in which two electrons are transferred from the positive to the negative side of the membrane and combine with two protons to reduce a quinone to a quinol. The quinol then diffuses back across the bilayer to be reoxidized at the positive side, where the protons are released. The redox loop mechanism, which requires two "active sites," does occur during the Q cycle in mitochondrial Complex III and in certain bacterial systems, but it cannot account for the entire protonmotive force that is the heart of the chemiosmotic mechanism.

Mitchell, P., Coupling of phosphorylation to electron and hydrogen transfer by a chemiosmotic type of mechanism, *Nature* **191**, 144–148 (1961).

Prebble, J., Peter Mitchell and the ox phos wars, *Trends Biochem. Sci.* **27**, 209–212 (2002).

by pumping H^+ from the mitochondrial matrix to the intermembrane space to create an electrochemical H^+ gradient across the inner mitochondrial membrane. The electrochemical potential of this gradient is harnessed to synthesize

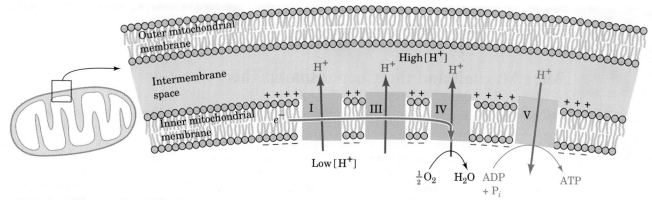

■ **Figure 18-20** | **The coupling of electron transport and ATP synthesis.** Electron transport (*green arrow*) generates a proton electrochemical gradient across the inner mitochondrial membrane. H$^+$ is pumped out of the mitochondrion during electron transport (*blue arrows*) and its exergonic return powers the synthesis of ATP (*red arrows*). Note that the intermembrane space is topologically equivalent to the cytosol because the outer mitochondrial membrane is permeable to H$^+$. ⟲ **See the Animated Figures.**

ATP (Fig. 18-20). Several key observations are explained by the chemiosmotic theory:

1. Oxidative phosphorylation requires an intact inner mitochondrial membrane.

2. The inner mitochondrial membrane is impermeable to ions such as H$^+$, OH$^-$, K$^+$, and Cl$^-$, whose free diffusion would discharge an electrochemical gradient.

3. Electron transport results in the transport of H$^+$ out of intact mitochondria (the intermembrane space is equivalent to the cytosol), thereby creating a measurable electrochemical gradient across the inner mitochondrial membrane.

4. Compounds that increase the permeability of the inner mitochondrial membrane to protons, and thereby dissipate the electrochemical gradient, allow electron transport (from NADH and succinate oxidation) to continue but inhibit ATP synthesis; that is, they "uncouple" electron transport from oxidative phosphorylation. Conversely, increasing the acidity outside the inner mitochondrial membrane stimulates ATP synthesis.

An entirely analogous process occurs in bacteria, whose electron-transporting machinery is located in their plasma membranes (Box 18-3).

Electron Transport Generates a Proton Gradient. *Electron transport, as we have seen, causes Complexes I, III, and IV to transport protons across the inner mitochondrial membrane from the matrix, a region of low [H$^+$], to the intermembrane space (which is in contact with the cytosol), a region of high [H$^+$]* (Fig. 18-8). The free energy sequestered by the resulting electrochemical gradient (also called the **protonmotive force; pmf**) powers ATP synthesis.

The free energy change of transporting a proton from one side of the membrane to the other has a chemical as well as an electrical component, since H$^+$ is an ion (Section 10-1). ΔG is therefore expressed by Eq. 10-3, which in terms of pH is

$$\Delta G = 2.3\,RT[\text{pH}\,(side\,1) - \text{pH}\,(side\,2)] + Z\mathcal{F}\Delta\Psi \qquad [18\text{-}1]$$

where Z is the charge on the proton (including sign), $\mathcal{F}$ is the Faraday constant, and $\Delta\Psi$ is the membrane potential. The sign convention for $\Delta\Psi$ is

BOX 18-3 PERSPECTIVES IN BIOCHEMISTRY

Bacterial Electron Transport and Oxidative Phosphorylation

t comes as no surprise that aerobic bacteria (such as those pictured below), whose ancestors gave rise to mitochondria, use similar machinery to oxidize reduced coenzymes and conserve their energy in ATP synthesis. In bacteria, the components of the respiratory electron-transport chain are located in the plasma membrane, and protons are pumped from the cytosol to the outside of the plasma membrane. Protons flow back into the cell via an ATP synthase, whose catalytic component is oriented toward the cytosol. This is exactly the arrangement expected if bacteria and mitochondria are evolutionarily related.

The oxidation of $CoQH_2$ is universal in aerobic organisms. In mitochondria, CoQ collects electrons donated by NADH (via Complex I), succinate (via Complex II), and fatty acids. In aerobic bacteria, CoQ is the collection point for electrons extracted by dehydrogenases specific for a wide variety of substrates. In bacteria, as in mitochondria, electrons flow from CoQ through cytochrome-based oxidoreductases before reaching O_2 (*below, right*). In some species, two protein complexes (analogous to mitochondrial Complexes III and IV) carry out this process. In other species, including *E. coli*, a single type of enzyme, **quinol oxidase,** uses the electrons donated by CoQ to reduce O_2.

The advantage of a multicomplex electron-transport pathway is that it affords more opportunities for proton translocation across the bacterial membrane, so the ATP yield per electron is greater. However, the shorter electron-transport pathways may confer a selective advantage in the presence of toxins that inactivate the bacterial counterpart of mitochondrial Complex III. Multiple routes for electron transport probably also allow bacteria to adjust oxidative phosphorylation to the availability of different energy sources and to balance ATP synthesis against the regeneration of various reduced coenzymes. For example, in facultative anaerobic bacteria (which can grow in either the absence or presence of O_2), when energy needs are met through anaerobic fermentation, electron transport can be adjusted to regenerate NAD^+ without synthesizing ATP by oxidative phosphorylation.

A variety of cytochrome-containing protein complexes occur in bacterial plasma membranes. Some of these proteins represent more streamlined versions of the mitochondrial complexes since they lack the additional subunits encoded by the nuclear genome of eukaryotes. However, this is not a universal feature of respiratory complexes, and many bacterial proteins (e.g., **cytochrome d**) have no counterparts encoded by either the mitochondrial or nuclear genomes.

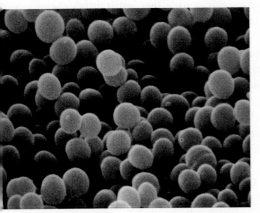

Staphylococcus aureus. [© Tony Brain/Photo Researchers.]

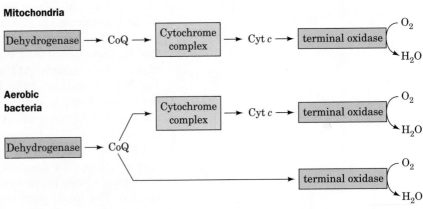

that when a proton is transported from a negative region to a positive region, $\Delta\Psi$ is positive. Since the pH outside the mitochondrion (*side 2*) is less than the pH of the matrix (*side 1*), *the export of protons from the mitochondrial matrix (against the proton gradient) is an endergonic process.*

The measured membrane potential across the inner membrane of a liver mitochondrion, for example, is 0.168 V (inside negative). The pH of its matrix is 0.75 units higher than that of its intermembrane space. ΔG for proton transport out of this mitochondrial matrix is therefore 21.5 $kJ \cdot mol^{-1}$. Because formation of the proton gradient is an endergonic process, discharge of the gradient is exergonic. This free energy is harnessed by ATP synthase to drive the phosphorylation of ADP.

An ATP molecule's estimated physiological free energy of synthesis, around +40 to +50 kJ·mol^{-1}, is too large for ATP synthesis to be driven by the passage of a single proton back into the mitochondrial matrix; at least two protons are required. In fact, most experimental measurements (which are difficult to precisely quantitate) indicate that around three protons are required per ATP synthesized.

B | ATP Synthase Is Driven by the Flow of Protons

ATP synthase, also known as **proton-pumping ATP synthase** and **F_1F_0-ATPase,** is a multisubunit transmembrane protein with a total molecular mass of 450 kD. Efraim Racker discovered that mitochondrial ATP synthase is composed of two functional units, **F_0** and **F_1.** F_0 is a water-insoluble transmembrane protein containing as many as eight different types of subunits. F_1 is a water-soluble peripheral membrane protein, composed of five types of subunits, that is easily and reversibly dissociated from F_0 by treatment with urea. Solubilized F_1 hydrolyzes ATP but cannot synthesize it (hence the name ATPase).

Electron micrographs of the inner mitochondrial membrane reveal that its matrix surface is studded with molecules of ATP synthase whose F_1 component is connected to the membrane-embedded F_0 component by a protein stalk, thereby giving F_1 a lollipop-like appearance (Fig. 18-21a). Similar entities have been observed lining the inner surface of the bacterial plasma membrane and in chloroplasts (Section 19-2D). Higher resolution cryoelectron micrography-based images of the ATP synthase from bovine heart mitochondria reveal that its F_1 and F_0 components are joined by both an ~50-Å-long central stalk and a less substantial peripherally located connector (Fig. 18-21b).

The F_1 Component Has Pseudo-Threefold Symmetry. The F_1 component of mitochondrial ATP synthase has the subunit composition $\alpha_3\beta_3\gamma\delta\varepsilon$. The X-ray structure of the 3440-residue (371-kD) F_1 subunit from bovine heart mitochondria, determined by John Walker and Andrew Leslie, reveals that it consists of an 80-Å-high and 100-Å-wide spheroid that is mounted on a 30-Å-long stem (Fig. 18-22a). The α and β subunits, which are 20% identical in sequence and have nearly identical folds, are arranged alternately, like the segments of an orange, around the upper portion of a 90-Å-long α helix formed by the C-terminal segment of the γ subunit (Fig. 18-22b). The lower portion of the helix forms an antiparallel coiled coil

■ **Figure 18-21** | **Structure of ATP synthase.** (*a*) An electron micrograph of cristae from a mitochondrion showing their F_1 "lollipops" projecting into the matrix. [From Parsons, D.F., *Science* **140,** 985 (1963). Copyright © 1963 American Association for the Advancement of Science. Used by permission.] (*b*) Cryoelectron microscopy–based image of F_1F_0-ATPase from bovine heart mitochondria. [Courtesy of John Rubinstein, University of Toronto, Canada, and John Walker and Richard Henderson, MRC Laboratory of Molecular Biology, Cambridge, U.K.]

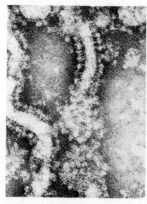

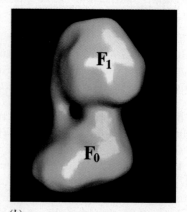

(*a*)   (*b*)

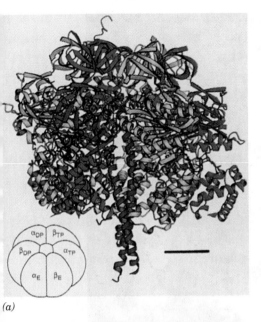

(a)

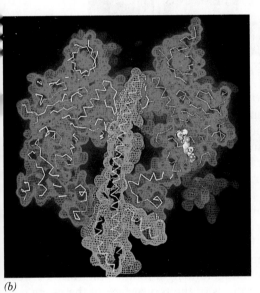

(b)

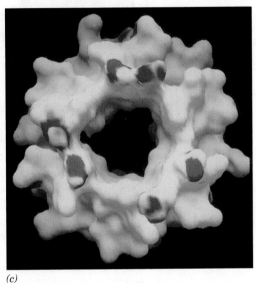

(c)

■ **Figure 18-22 | X-Ray structure of F₁-ATP synthase from bovine heart mitochondria.** (*a*) A ribbon diagram in which the α, β, and γ subunits are red, yellow, and blue, respectively. The inset drawing indicates the orientation of these subunits in this view. The bar is 20 Å long. (*b*) Cross section through the electron density map of the protein (the α and β subunits are blue, and the γ subunit is orange). The superimposed C$_\alpha$ backbones of these subunits are yellow, and a bound AMPPNP is represented in space-filling form (C yellow, N blue, O red). (*c*) Pseudosymmetrical arrangement of the α₃β₃ assembly as viewed from the top of Parts *a* and *b*. The surface is colored according to its electrical potential, with positive potentials blue, negative potentials red, and neutral potentials white. Note the absence of charge on the inner surface of this sleeve. The portion of the γ subunit's C-terminal helix that contacts the sleeve is similarly devoid of charge. [From Abrahams, J.P., Leslie, A.G.W., Lutter, R., and Walker, J.E., *Nature* **370,** 623 and 627 (1994). PDBid 1BMF.] ⟡ **See Interactive Exercise 22.**

with the N-terminal segment of the γ subunit. This coiled coil, along with the δ and ε subunits that are wrapped around it, links F₁ to F₀.

The cyclic arrangement and structural similarities of F₁'s α and β subunits give it both pseudo-threefold and pseudo-sixfold rotational symmetry (Fig. 18-22*c*). Nevertheless, the protein is asymmetric due to the presence of the γ subunit but, more importantly, because each pair of α and β subunits adopts a different conformation, each with a different substrate affinity. Thus one β subunit (designated β$_{TP}$ in Fig. 18-22*a*) binds a molecule of the nonhydrolyzable ATP analog AMPPNP, the second (β$_{DP}$) binds ADP, and the third (β$_E$) has an empty and distorted binding site. Only the β subunits catalyze the ATP synthesis reaction although the α subunits also bind AMPPNP.

The F₀ Component Includes a Transmembrane Ring. The F₀ component of bacterial and mitochondrial F₁F₀-ATPases consists of multiple

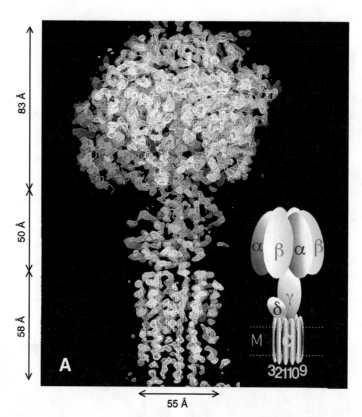

■ **Figure 18-23** | **X-Ray structure of the yeast mitochondrial F₁–c₁₀ complex.** This low-resolution (3.9 Å) electron density map (*pink*) shows the complex as viewed from within the inner mitochondrial membrane with the matrix above. The C_α backbone of bovine F_1 (with α orange, β yellow, and γ green) is superimposed on the electron density map. The inset indicates the location of the subunits of the complex, with the dashed lines indicating the presumed position of the inner mitochondrial membrane (M) and with the *c* subunits numbered. [Courtesy of Andrew Leslie and John Walker, Medical Research Council, Cambridge, U.K. PDBid 1QO1.]

subunits. In *E. coli,* three transmembrane subunits—*a, b,* and *c*—form an $a_1b_2c_{9-12}$ complex. Mitochondrial F_0 contains additional subunits whose functions are unclear. The *c* subunits, each of which contains two α helices, associate to form a ring that is embedded in the membrane.

A low-resolution X-ray structure of yeast F_1 in complex with its *c*-ring oligomer (Fig. 18-23) reveals that its α and β subunits have conformations and bound nucleotides similar to those in bovine F_1 (Fig. 18-22). The yeast *c* oligomer consists of 10 subunits (a number which may differ from that in *E. coli*) that associate side by side so as to form two concentric rings of α helices. Modeling studies indicate that the δ subunit contacts both the base of the γ subunit and the *c*-ring, forming a footlike interface between F_0 and F_1 such that about two-thirds of the top surface of the *c*-ring contacts the base of the F_1 stalk (Fig. 18-23).

The sequence of the *a* subunit suggests that this highly hydrophobic 271-residue protein forms five transmembrane helices. The 156-residue *b* subunit consists of a single transmembrane helix anchoring a polar domain that homodimerizes to form a parallel α-helical coiled coil that extends from the periphery of the *c*-ring into the matrix where it contacts the $\delta\alpha_3\beta_3$ assembly (the peripherally located connector in Fig. 18-21*b*).

See Guided Exploration 19
F_1F_0-ATP synthase and the binding change mechanism.

ATP Is Synthesized by the Binding Change Mechanism. The mechanism of ATP synthesis by proton-translocating ATP synthase can be conceptually broken down into three phases:

1. Translocation of protons carried out by F_0.
2. Catalysis of formation of the phosphoanhydride bond of ATP carried out by F_1.
3. Coupling of the dissipation of the proton gradient with ATP synthesis, which requires interaction of F_1 and F_0.

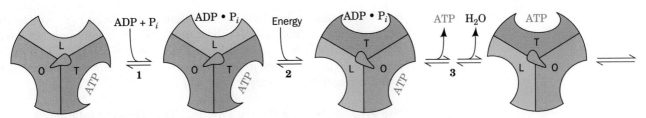

Figure 18-24 | The binding change mechanism for ATP synthase. F_1 has three chemically identical but conformationally distinct interacting $\alpha\beta$ protomers: O, the open conformation, has very low affinity for ligands and is catalytically inactive; L binds ligands loosely and is catalytically inactive; T binds ligands tightly and is catalytically active. ATP synthesis occurs in three steps: (**1**) ADP and P_i bind to site L. (**2**) An energy-dependent conformational change converts binding site L to T, T to O, and O to L. (**3**) ATP is synthesized at site T and ATP is released from site O. The enzyme returns to its initial state after two more passes of this reaction sequence. The free energy that drives the conformational change is transmitted to the catalytic $\alpha_3\beta_3$ assembly via the rotation of the $\gamma\delta$ assembly ($\gamma\varepsilon$ in *E. coli*), here represented by the centrally located asymmetric object (*green*). [After Cross, R.L., *Annu. Rev. Biochem.* **50**, 687 (1980).] ✷ **See the Animated Figures.**

Considerable evidence supports a mechanism for ATP formation proposed by Paul Boyer. According to this **binding change mechanism**, F_1 has three interacting catalytic protomers ($\alpha\beta$ units), each in a different conformational state: one that binds substrates and products loosely (L state), one that binds them tightly (T state), and one that does not bind them at all (open or O state). *The free energy released on proton translocation is harnessed to interconvert these three states.* The phosphoanhydride bond of ATP is synthesized only in the T state, and ATP is released only in the O state. The reaction involves three steps (Fig. 18-24):

1. ADP and P_i bind to the loose (L) binding site (β_{DP} in Fig. 18-22*a*).

2. A free energy–driven conformational change converts the L site to a tight (T) binding site (β_{TP}) that catalyzes the formation of ATP. This step also involves conformational changes of the other two protomers that convert the ATP-containing T site to an open (O) site (β_E) and convert the O site to an L site.

3. ATP is synthesized at the T site on one subunit while ATP dissociates from the O site on another subunit. The reaction forming ATP is essentially at equilibrium under the conditions at the enzyme's active site. The free energy supplied by the proton flow primarily facilitates the release of the newly synthesized ATP from the enzyme; that is, it drives the T → O transition, thereby disrupting the enzyme–ATP interactions that had previously promoted the spontaneous formation of ATP from ADP + P_i in the T site.

How is the free energy of proton transfer coupled to the synthesis of ATP? The cyclic nature of the binding change mechanism led Boyer to propose that *the binding changes are driven by the rotation of the catalytic assembly, $\alpha_3\beta_3$, with respect to other portions of the F_1F_0-ATPase.* This hypothesis is supported by the X-ray structure of F_1. Thus, the closely fitting nearly circular arrangement of the α and β subunits' inner surface about the γ subunit's helical C-terminus is reminiscent of a cylindrical bearing rotating in a sleeve (Figs. 18-22*b,c*). Indeed, the contacting hydrophobic surfaces in this assembly are devoid of the hydrogen-bonding and ionic interactions that would interfere with their free rotation (Fig. 18-22*c*); that is, the bearing and sleeve appear to be "lubricated." Moreover, the central cavity in the $\alpha_3\beta_3$ assembly (Fig. 18-22*b*) would permit the passage of the γ subunit's N-terminal helix within the core of this particle during rotation. Finally, the conformational differences between F_1's three catalytic sites appear to be correlated with the position of the γ subunit. *Apparently the γ subunit, which rotates within the fixed $\alpha_3\beta_3$ assembly, acts as a molecular camshaft in linking the proton gradient–driven F_0 engine to the conformational changes in the catalytic sites of F_1.*

The F_1F_0-ATPase Is a Rotary Engine. The proposed rotation of the $\alpha_3\beta_3$ assembly with respect to the γ subunit engendered by the binding change mechanism has led to the model of the F_1F_0-ATPase diagrammed in Fig. 18-25. A rotational engine must have both a rotor (which rotates) and a stator (which is stationary). In the F_1F_0-ATPase, the rotor is proposed to be an assembly of the *c*-ring with the γ and (*E. coli*) ε subunits, whereas the ab_2 unit and the (*E. coli*) δ subunit together with the $\alpha_3\beta_3$ spheroid form the stator. The rotation of the *c*-ring in the membrane relative to the stationary *a* subunit is driven by the migration of protons from the outside to the inside as we discuss below (here "outside" refers to the mitochondrial intermembrane space or the bacterial exterior, whereas "inside" refers to the mitochondrial matrix or the bacterial cytoplasm). The $b_2\delta$ assembly presumably functions to hold the $\alpha_3\beta_3$ spheroid in position while the γ subunit rotates inside it.

In the model for proton-driven rotation of the F_0 subunit that is diagrammed in Fig. 18-25, protons from the outside enter a hydrophilic channel between the *a* subunit and the *c*-ring, where they bind to a *c* subunit. The *c*-ring then rotates nearly a full turn (while protons bind to successive *c* subunits as they pass this input channel) until the subunit reaches a second hydrophilic channel between the *a* subunit and the *c*-ring that opens into the inside, where the proton is released (in an alternative

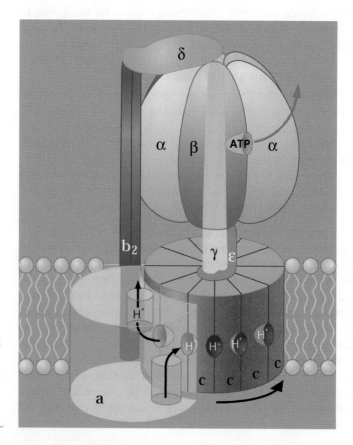

■ **Figure 18-25** | **Model of the *E. coli* F_1F_0-ATPase.** The $\gamma\varepsilon-c_{12}$ ring complex is the rotor and the $ab_2-\alpha_3\beta_3\delta$ complex is the stator. Rotational motion is imparted to the rotor by the passage of protons from the outside (periplasmic space, *bottom*) to the inside (cytoplasm, *top*). Protons entering from the outside bind to a *c* subunit where it interacts with the *a* subunit, and exit to the inside after the *c*-ring has made a nearly full rotation as indicated (*black arrows*), so that the *c* subunit again contacts the *a* subunit. The $b_2\delta$ complex presumably functions to prevent the $\alpha_3\beta_3$ assembly from rotating with the γ subunit. Note that the *E. coli* ε subunit is the homolog of the mitochondrial δ subunit, the *E. coli* δ subunit is the homolog of the mitochondrial subunit known as **OSCP**, and the mitochondrial ε subunit has no counterpart in either bacterial or chloroplast ATP synthases. [Courtesy of Richard Cross, State University of New York, Syracuse, New York.]

(a)   (b)

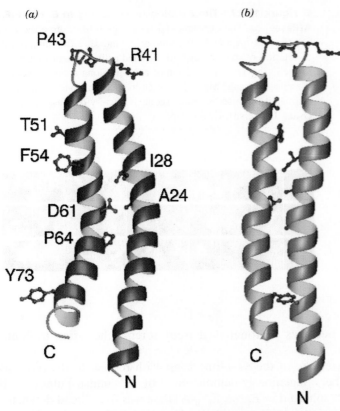

■ **Figure 18-26** | **NMR structure of the *c* subunit of *E. coli* F₁F₀-ATPase.**
(*a*) At pH 8, Asp 61 (D61) is deprotonated. (*b*) At pH 5, D61 is protonated. Selected
side chains are shown to aid in the comparison of the two structures. Note that the
C-terminal helix in the pH 8 structure is rotated 140° clockwise, as viewed from the
top of the drawing, relative to that in the pH 5 structure. [Courtesy of Mark Girvin,
Albert Einstein College of Medicine. PDBid 1COV.]

model, the protons are released through putative channels between the
C-terminal helices of adjacent *c* subunits, channels that are occluded when
the *a* and *c* subunits are in contact). Thus, the F₁F₀-ATPase, which generates 3 ATP per turn and (at least in yeast) has 10 *c* subunits in its F₀
assembly, ideally forms 3/10 = 0.3 ATP for every proton it passes from
outside to inside.

How does the passage of protons through this system induce the rotation of the *c*-ring and hence the synthesis of ATP? Each *c* subunit consists
of two α helices of different lengths that are connected by a four-residue
polar loop and arranged in an antiparallel coiled coil. Protons most likely
bind to Asp 61 of each *c* subunit, an invariant residue whose protonation
and deprotonation alter the subunit's conformation (Fig. 18-26). Evidently,
when a *c* subunit binds a proton as it passes the input channel, its conformation changes, which causes it to mechanically push against the *a* subunit so as to induce the *c*-ring to rotate in the direction indicated in Fig.
18-25. This process is augmented by the interaction between Asp 61 on the
c subunit and the invariant Arg 210 on the *a* subunit. These two residues
have been shown to become juxtaposed at some point during the *c*-ring's
rotation cycle. It has therefore been proposed that the electrostatic attraction between the cationic Arg 210 and the anionic Asp 61 helps rotate the
c-ring so as to bring the two residues into opposition but, as this occurs,

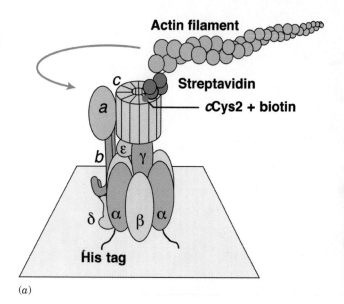

(a)

■ **Figure 18-27** | **The rotation of the c-ring in E. coli F₁F₀-ATPase.** (a) The experimental system used to observe the rotation. See the text for details. The blue arrow indicates the observed direction of rotation of the fluorescently labeled actin filament that was linked to the c-ring. (b) The rotation of a 3.6-μm-long actin filament in the presence of 5 mM MgATP as seen in successive video images taken through a fluorescence microscope. [Courtesy of Masamitsu Futai, Osaka University, Osaka, Japan.]

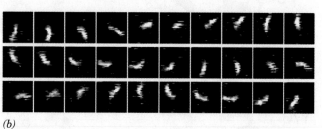

(b)

Asp 61 becomes protonated, thereby forcing the c-ring to continue its rotation.

The rotation of the $\gamma\varepsilon$–c-ring rotor with respect to the ab_2–$\alpha_3\beta_3\delta$ stator has been ingeniously demonstrated by Masamitsu Futai (Fig. 18-27a). The $\alpha_3\beta_3$ spheroid of E. coli F_1F_0-ATPase was fixed, head down, to a glass surface as follows. Six consecutive His residues (a so-called **His tag**) were mutagenically appended to the N-terminus of the α subunit, which is located at the top of the $\alpha_3\beta_3$ spheroid as it is drawn in Fig. 18-22a. The His-tagged assembly was applied to a glass surface coated with horseradish peroxidase (which, like most proteins, sticks to glass) conjugated with **Ni^{2+}-nitriloacetic acid** [Ni^{2+}-$N(CH_2COOH)_3$, which tightly binds His tags], thereby binding the F_1F_0-ATPase to the surface with its F_0 side facing away from the surface. The Glu 2 residues of this assembly's c subunits, which are located on the side of the c-ring facing away from F_1, had been mutagenically replaced by Cys residues, which were then covalently linked to biotin (Section 16-4A). A fluorescently labeled and biotinylated (at one end) filament of the muscle protein **actin** (Section 7-2C) was then attached to the c subunit through the addition of a bridging molecule of **streptavidin,** a bacterial protein that avidly binds biotin to each of four binding sites.

The E. coli F_1F_0-ATPase can work in reverse, that is, it can pump protons from the inside to the outside at the expense of ATP hydrolysis (this enables the bacterium to maintain its proton gradient under anaerobic conditions, which it uses to drive various processes). Thus, the foregoing preparation was observed under a fluorescence microscope as a 5 mM MgATP solution was infused over it. *Many of the actin filaments were seen to rotate (Fig. 18-27b), and always in a counterclockwise direction when viewed looking down on the glass surface (from the outside).* This would permit the γ subunit to sequentially interact with the β subunits in the direction

$$\beta_E(\text{O-state}) \rightarrow \beta_{DP}(\text{L-state}) \rightarrow \beta_{TP}(\text{T-state})$$

(Figs. 18-22a and 18-24), the direction expected for ATP hydrolysis. Similar experiments revealed that the γ subunit rotates mostly in increments of 120°. Presumably, electrostatic interactions between the γ and β subunits of F_1 act as a catch that temporarily holds the γ subunit in place. As the c-ring rotates, strain builds up and causes the γ subunit to snap to the next β subunit. In addition, when a magnetic bead was instead attached to the γ subunit of immobilized F_1-ATPase and an external magnetic field was rotated in the clockwise direction so as to force the γ subunit to follow, ATP was synthesized from ADP + P_i.

C | The P/O Ratio Relates the Amount of ATP Synthesized to the Amount of Oxygen Reduced

ATP synthesis is tightly coupled to the proton gradient; that is, ATP synthesis requires the discharge of the proton gradient, and the proton gradient cannot be discharged without the synthesis of ATP. The proton gradient is established through the activity of the electron-transporting complexes of the inner mitochondrial membrane. Therefore, it is possible to express the amount of ATP synthesized in terms of substrate molecules oxidized. Experiments with isolated mitochondria show that the oxidation of NADH is associated with the synthesis of approximately 3 ATP, and the oxidation of $FADH_2$ with approximately 2 ATP. Oxidation of the nonphysiological compound **tetramethyl-*p*-phenylenediamine,**

Tetramethyl-*p*-phenylenediamine (TMPD), reduced form **TMPD, oxidized form**

which donates an electron pair directly to Complex IV, yields approximately 1 ATP. These stoichiometric relationships are called **P/O ratios** because they relate the amount of ATP synthesized (P) to the amount of oxygen reduced (O).

Experimentally determined P/O ratios are compatible with the chemiosmotic theory and the known structure of ATP synthase. The flow of two electrons through Complexes I, III, and IV results in the translocation of 10 protons into the intermembrane space (Fig. 18-8). Influx of these 10 protons through the F_1F_0-ATPase, which contains 10 c subunits in eukaryotes (Fig. 18-23), results in one complete rotation of the c-ring–γ subunit rotor relative to the $\alpha_3\beta_3$ spheroid, enough to drive the synthesis of ~3 ATP. Electrons that enter the electron-transport chain as $FADH_2$ at Complex II bypass Complex I and therefore lead to the transmembrane movement of only 6 protons, enough to synthesize ~2 ATP (corresponding to approximately two-thirds of a full rotation of the ATP synthase rotary engine). The transit of two electrons through Complex IV alone contributes 2 protons to the gradient, enough for ~1 ATP (around one-third of a rotation).

In actively respiring mitochondria, *P/O ratios are almost certainly not integral numbers.* This is also consistent with the chemiosmotic theory. Oxidation of a physiological substrate contributes to the transmembrane proton gradient at several points, but the gradient is tapped at only a single point, the F_1F_0-ATPase. Therefore, the number of protons translocated out of the mitochondrion by any component of the electron-transport chain need not be an integral multiple of the number of protons required to synthesize ATP from ADP + P_i. Moreover, the proton gradient is dissipated to some extent by the nonspecific leakage of protons back into the matrix and by the consumption of protons for other purposes, such as the transport of P_i into the matrix (Section 18-1B). Taking P_i transport into account gives a stoichiometry of four protons consumed per ATP synthesized from ADP + P_i. Thus, as Peter Hinkle has experimentally demonstrated, the P/O ratios above are actually closer to 2.5, 1.5, and 1. Consequently, the number of ATPs that are synthesized per molecule of glucose oxidized is 2.5 ATP/NADH × 10 NADH/glucose + 1.5 ATP/FADH$_2$ × 2 FADH$_2$/glucose + 2 ATP/glucose from the citric acid cycle + 2 ATP/glucose from glycolysis = 32 ATP/glucose.

D | Oxidative Phosphorylation Can Be Uncoupled from Electron Transport

Electron transport (the oxidation of NADH and FADH$_2$ by O$_2$) and oxidative phosphorylation (the proton gradient–driven synthesis of ATP) are normally tightly coupled. *This coupling depends on the impermeability of the inner mitochondrial membrane, which allows an electrochemical gradient to be established across the membrane by H^+ translocation during electron transport.* Virtually the only way for H^+ to re-enter the matrix is through the F$_0$ portion of ATP synthase. In the resting state, when oxidative phosphorylation is minimal, the electrochemical gradient across the inner mitochondrial membrane builds up to the extent that it prevents further proton pumping and therefore inhibits electron transport. When ATP synthesis increases, the electrochemical gradient dissipates, allowing electron transport to resume.

Over the years, compounds such as **2,4-dinitrophenol (DNP)** have been found to "uncouple" electron transport and ATP synthesis. DNP is a lipophilic weak acid that readily passes through membranes in its neutral, protonated state. In a pH gradient, it binds protons on the acidic side of the membrane, diffuses through the membrane, and releases the protons on the membrane's alkaline side, thereby acting as a proton-transporting ionophore (Section 10-2A) and dissipating the gradient (Fig. 18-28). The chemiosmotic theory provides a rationale for understanding the action of such **uncouplers.** *The presence in the inner mitochondrial membrane of an agent that increases its permeability to H^+ uncouples oxidative phosphorylation from electron transport by providing a route for the dissipation of the proton electrochemical gradient that does not require ATP synthesis.* Uncoupling therefore allows electron transport to proceed

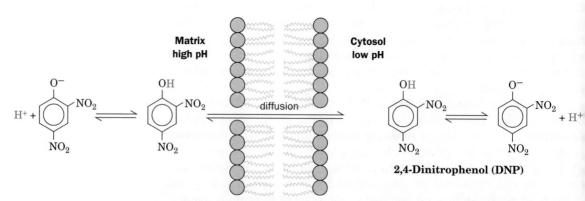

■ **Figure 18-28** | **Action of 2,4-dinitrophenol.** A proton-transporting ionophore such as DNP uncouples oxidative phosphorylation from electron transport by discharging the electrochemical proton gradient generated by electron transport.

unchecked even when ATP synthesis is inhibited. Consequently, in the 1920s, DNP was used as a "diet pill," a practice that was effective in inducing weight loss but often caused fatal side effects. Under physiological conditions, *the dissipation of an electrochemical H^+ gradient, which is generated by electron transport and uncoupled from ATP synthesis, produces heat* (see Box 18-4).

■ **CHECK YOUR UNDERSTANDING**

Summarize the chemiosmotic theory.
Describe the overall structure of the F_1 and F_0 components of ATP synthase.
Summarize the steps of the binding change mechanism.
Describe how protons move from the intermembrane space into the matrix. How is proton translocation linked to ATP synthesis?
Explain why the P/O ratio for a given substrate is not necessarily an integer.
Explain how oxidative phosphorylation is linked to electron transport and how the two processes can be uncoupled.

4 Control of Oxidative Metabolism

An adult woman requires some 1500 to 1800 kcal (6300–7500 kJ) of metabolic energy per day. This corresponds to the free energy of hydrolysis of over 200 mol of ATP to ADP and P_i. Yet the total amount of ATP present in the body at any one time is <0.1 mol; obviously, this sparse supply of ATP must be continually recycled. As we have seen, when carbohydrates serve as the energy supply and aerobic conditions prevail, this recycling involves glycogenolysis, glycolysis, the citric acid cycle, and oxidative phosphorylation.

Of course, the need for ATP is not constant. There is a 100-fold change in the rate of ATP consumption between sleep and vigorous activity. *The activities of the pathways that produce ATP are under strict coordinated control so that ATP is never produced more rapidly than necessary.* We have already discussed the control mechanisms of glycolysis, glycogenolysis, and the citric acid cycle (Sections 15-4, 16-3, and 17-4). In this section, we discuss the mechanisms that control the rate of oxidative phosphorylation.

LEARNING OBJECTIVES

■ Understand that the rate of oxidative phosphorylation is coordinated with the cell's other oxidative pathways.
■ Understand that although aerobic metabolism is efficient, it leads to the production of reactive oxygen species.

A | The Rate of Oxidative Phosphorylation Depends on the ATP and NADH Concentrations

In our discussions of metabolic pathways, we have seen that most of their reactions function close to equilibrium. The few irreversible reactions constitute potential control points of the pathways and usually are catalyzed by regulatory enzymes that are under allosteric control. In the case of oxidative phosphorylation, the pathway from NADH to cytochrome c functions near equilibrium:

$$\tfrac{1}{2}\text{NADH} + \text{cytochrome } c\,(Fe^{3+}) + \text{ADP} + P_i \rightleftharpoons$$
$$\tfrac{1}{2}\text{NAD}^+ + \text{cytochrome } c\,(Fe^{2+}) + \text{ATP} \qquad \Delta G' \approx 0$$

and hence

$$K_{eq} = \left(\frac{[\text{NAD}^+]}{[\text{NADH}]}\right)^{1/2} \frac{[c^{2+}]}{[c^{3+}]} \frac{[\text{ATP}]}{[\text{ADP}][P_i]}$$

This pathway is therefore readily reversed by the addition of its product, ATP. However, *the cytochrome c oxidase reaction (the terminal step of the electron-transport chain) is irreversible and is therefore a potential control site.* Cytochrome c oxidase, in contrast to most regulatory enzyme systems, appears to be controlled primarily by the availability of one of its substrates, reduced cytochrome c (c^{2+}). Since c^{2+} is in equilibrium with the rest of the coupled oxidative phosphorylation system, the concentration of c^{2+} ultimately depends on the intramitochondrial ratios of [NADH]/[NAD$^+$] and [ATP]/[ADP][P_i] (the latter quantity is known as the **ATP mass action ratio**). We can see, by rearranging the foregoing equilibrium expression,

$$\frac{[c^{2+}]}{[c^{3+}]} = \left(\frac{[\text{NADH}]}{[\text{NAD}^+]}\right)^{1/2} \frac{[\text{ADP}][P_i]}{[\text{ATP}]} K_{eq}$$

BOX 18-4 PERSPECTIVES IN BIOCHEMISTRY

Uncoupling in Brown Adipose Tissue Generates Heat

Heat generation is the physiological function of **brown adipose tissue (brown fat).** This tissue is unlike typical (white) adipose tissue in that it contains numerous mitochondria whose cytochromes cause its brown color. Newborn mammals that lack fur, such as humans, as well as hibernating mammals, all contain brown fat in their neck and upper back that generates heat by **nonshivering thermogenesis.** Other sources of heat are the ATP hydrolysis that occurs during muscle contraction (in shivering or any other movement) and the operation of ATP-hydrolyzing substrate cycles (see Section 15-4B).

[© K.M. Highfill/Photo Researchers.]

The mechanism of heat generation in brown fat involves the regulated uncoupling of oxidative phosphorylation. Brown fat mitochondria contain a proton channel known as **uncoupling protein** (**UCP1,** also called **thermogenin;** see below). In cold-adapted animals, UCP1 constitutes up to 15% of the protein in the inner mitochondrial membranes of brown fat. The flow of protons through UCP1 is inhibited by physiological concentrations of purine nucleotides (ADP, ATP, GDP, GTP), but this inhibition can be overcome by free fatty acids.

Thermogenesis in brown fat mitochondria is under hormonal control (see dia-

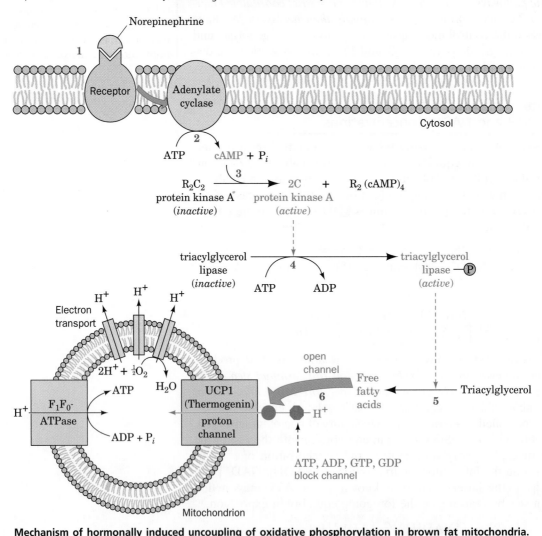

Mechanism of hormonally induced uncoupling of oxidative phosphorylation in brown fat mitochondria.

gram). Norepinephrine (**1**; noradrenaline) induces the production of the second messenger cAMP (**2**) and thereby activates protein kinase A (**3**; Section 13-3C). The kinase then activates **hormone-sensitive triacylglycerol lipase** (**4**) by phosphorylating it. The activated lipase hydrolyzes triacylglycerols (**5**) to yield free fatty acids that counteract the inhibitory effect of the purine nucleotides on UCP1 (**6**). The resulting flow of protons through UCP1 dissipates the proton gradient across the inner mitochondrial membrane. This allows substrate oxidation to proceed (and generate heat) without the synthesis of ATP.

Adult humans lack brown fat, but the mitochondria of ordinary adipose tissue and muscle appear to contain uncoupling proteins known as **UCP2** and **UCP3.** These proteins may help regulate metabolic rates, and variations in UCP levels or activity might explain why some people seem to have a "fast" or "slow" metabolism. UCPs are being studied as targets for treating obesity, since increasing the activity of UCPs could uncouple respiration from ATP synthesis, thus permitting stored metabolic fuels (especially fat) to be metabolized.

Uncoupling proteins may also play a role in maintaining body temperature, and their function may not be limited to the animal kingdom. Some plants express uncoupling proteins in response to cold stress or to increase flower temperature, possibly to enhance the vaporization of scent to attract pollinators.

that the higher the $[NADH]/[NAD^+]$ ratio and the lower the ATP mass action ratio, the higher the concentration of reduced cytochrome c and thus the higher the cytochrome c oxidase activity.

How is this system affected by changes in physical activity? In an individual at rest, the rate of ATP hydrolysis to ADP and P_i is minimal and the ATP mass action ratio is high; the concentration of reduced cytochrome c is therefore low and the rate of oxidative phosphorylation is minimal. Increased activity results in hydrolysis of ATP to ADP and P_i, thereby decreasing the ATP mass action ratio and increasing the concentration of reduced cytochrome c. This results in an increase in the rate of electron transport and ADP phosphorylation.

The concentrations of ATP, ADP, and P_i in the mitochondrial matrix depend on the activities of the transport proteins that import these substances from the cytosol. Thus, the ADP–ATP translocator and the P_i transporter may play a part in regulating oxidative phosphorylation. There is also some evidence that Ca^{2+} stimulates the electron-transport complexes and possibly ATP synthase itself. This is consistent with the many other instances in which Ca^{2+} directly stimulates oxidative metabolic processes.

Mitochondria contain an 84-residue protein, called **IF$_1$** that functions to regulate ATP synthase. In actively respiring mitochondria, in which the matrix pH is relatively high, IF_1 exists as an inactive tetramer. However, below pH 6.5, the protein dissociates into dimers and in this form inhibits the ATPase activity of the F_1 component by binding to the interface between its α_{DP} and β_{DP} subunits so as to trap the ATP bound to the β_{DP} subunit. This appears to be a mechanism to prevent ATP hydrolysis when respiratory activity (and therefore the proton gradient) is temporarily interrupted by lack of O_2. Otherwise, the F_1F_0-ATPase would reverse its direction of rotation as driven by the hydrolysis of ATP (then generated by glycolysis), thus depriving the cell of its remaining energy resources.

Pathways of Oxidative Metabolism Are Coordinately Controlled. The primary sources of the electrons that enter the mitochondrial electron-transport chain are glycolysis, fatty acid degradation, and the citric acid cycle. For example, 10 molecules of NAD^+ are converted to NADH per molecule of glucose oxidized (Fig. 18-1). Not surprisingly, the control of glycolysis and the citric acid cycle is coordinated with the demand for oxidative phosphorylation. An adequate supply of electrons to feed the electron transport chain is provided by regulation of the control points of glycolysis and the citric acid cycle (phosphofructokinase, pyruvate dehydrogenase, citrate synthase, isocitrate dehydrogenase, and α-ketoglutarate dehydrogenase) by adenine nucleotides or NADH or both, as well as by certain metabolites (Fig. 18-29).

One particularly interesting regulatory effect is the inhibition of phosphofructokinase (PFK) by citrate. When demand for ATP decreases, [ATP] increases and [ADP] decreases. Because isocitrate dehydrogenase is activated by ADP and α-ketoglutarate dehydrogenase is inhibited by ATP, the citric acid cycle slows down. This causes the citrate concentration to build up. Citrate leaves the mitochondrion via a specific transport system and, *once in the cytosol, acts to restrain further carbohydrate breakdown by inhibiting PFK.* The citrate concentration also builds up when the acetyl-CoA concentration increases, which occurs, as we shall see in Chapter 20, during the oxidation of fatty acids. The inhibition of glycolysis by fatty acid oxidation is called the **glucose–fatty acid cycle** or **Randle cycle** (after its discoverer, Phillip Randle) although it is not, in fact, a cycle. The Randle cycle allows fatty acids to be utilized as the major fuel for oxidative metabolism in heart muscle, while conserving glucose for organs such as the brain, which require it.

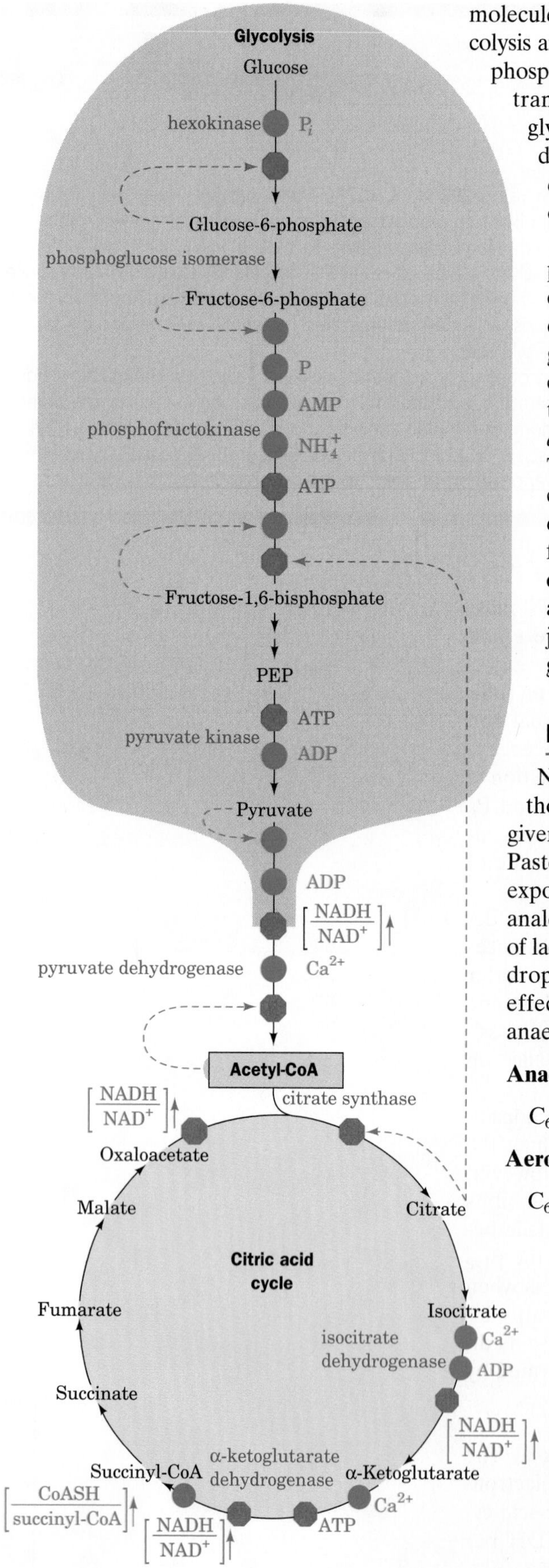

B | Aerobic Metabolism Has Some Disadvantages

Not all organisms carry out oxidative phosphorylation. However, those that do are able to extract considerably more energy from a given amount of a metabolic fuel. This principle is illustrated by the Pasteur effect (Section 15-3C): When anaerobically growing yeast are exposed to oxygen, their glucose consumption drops precipitously. An analogous effect is observed in mammalian muscle; the concentration of lactic acid (the anaerobic product of muscle glycolysis; Section 15-3A), drops dramatically when cells switch to aerobic metabolism. These effects are easily understood by examining the stoichiometries of anaerobic and aerobic breakdown of glucose (Section 17-4):

Anaerobic glycolysis:

$$C_6H_{12}O_6 + 2\,ADP + 2\,P_i \rightarrow 2\,\text{lactate} + 2\,H^+ + 2\,H_2O + 2\,ATP$$

Aerobic metabolism of glucose:

$$C_6H_{12}O_6 + 32\,ADP + 32\,P_i + 6\,O_2 \rightarrow 6\,CO_2 + 38\,H_2O + 32\,ATP$$

■ **Figure 18-29 | The coordinated control of glycolysis and the citric acid cycle.** The diagram shows the effects of ATP, ADP, AMP, P_i, Ca^{2+}, and the [NADH]/[NAD$^+$] ratio (the vertical arrows indicate increases in this ratio). Here a green dot signifies activation and a red octagon represents inhibition. [After Newsholme, E.A. and Leech, A.R., *Biochemistry for the Medical Sciences,* pp. 316, 320, Wiley (1983).]
🖭 **See the Animated Figures.**

BOX 18-5 BIOCHEMISTRY IN HEALTH AND DISEASE

Oxygen Deprivation in Heart Attack and Stroke

As outlined in Box 7-1, organisms larger than 1 mm thick require circulatory systems to deliver nutrients to cells and dispose of cellular wastes. In addition, the circulatory fluid in most larger organisms contains proteins specialized for oxygen transport (e.g., hemoglobin). The sophistication of oxygen-delivery systems and their elaborate regulation are consistent with their essential nature and their long period of evolution.

What happens during oxygen deprivation? Consider two common causes of human death, **myocardial infarction** (heart attack) and **stroke,** which result from interruption of the blood (O_2) supply to a portion of the heart or the brain, respectively. In the absence of O_2, a cell, which must then rely only on glycolysis for ATP production, rapidly depletes its stores of phosphocreatine (a source of rapid ATP production; Section 14-2C) and glycogen. As the rate of ATP production falls below the level required by membrane ion pumps for maintaining proper intracellular ion concentrations, osmotic balance is disrupted so that the cell and its membrane-enveloped organelles begin to swell. The resulting overstretched membranes become permeable, thereby leaking their enclosed contents. For this reason, a useful diagnostic criterion for myocardial infarction is the presence in the blood of heart-specific enzymes, such as the H-type isozyme of lactate dehydrogenase (Section 14-1C), which leak out of necrotic (dead) heart tissue. Moreover, the decreased intracellular pH that accompanies anaer-

obic glycolysis (because of lactic acid production) permits the released lysosomal enzymes (which are active only at acidic pH) to degrade the cell contents. Thus, O_2 deprivation leads not only to cessation of cellular activity but to irreversible cell damage and cell death. Rapidly respiring tissues, such as the heart and brain, are particularly susceptible to damage by oxygen deprivation.

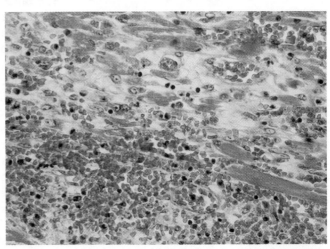

Necrotic tissue resulting from a heart attack. [© CNRI/Photo Researchers.]

Thus, *aerobic metabolism is up to 16 times more efficient than anaerobic glycolysis in producing ATP.*

Aerobic metabolism has its drawbacks, however. Many organisms and tissues depend exclusively on aerobic metabolism and suffer irreversible damage during oxygen deprivation (Box 18-5). Oxidative metabolism is also accompanied by the production of low levels of reactive oxygen metabolites that, over time, may damage cellular components. Evidently, the organisms that have existed during the last 3 billion years (the period in which the earth's atmosphere has contained significant amounts of O_2) exhibit physiological and biochemical adaptations that permit them to take advantage of the oxidizing power of O_2 while minimizing the potential dangers of oxygen itself.

Partial Oxygen Reduction Produces Reactive Oxygen Species (ROS).
Although the four-electron reduction of O_2 by cytochrome *c* oxidase is nearly always orchestrated with great rapidity and precision, *O_2 is occasionally only partially reduced, yielding oxygen species that readily react with a variety of cellular components.* The best known reactive oxygen species is the **superoxide radical:**

$$O_2 + e^- \rightarrow O_2^- \cdot$$

Superoxide radical is a precursor of other reactive species. Protonation of $O_2^- \cdot$ yields $HO_2 \cdot$, a much stronger oxidant than $O_2^- \cdot$. The most potent oxygen species in biological systems is probably the hydroxyl radical, which forms from the relatively harmless hydrogen peroxide (H_2O_2):

$$H_2O_2 + Fe^{2+} \rightarrow \cdot OH + OH^- + Fe^{3+}$$

The hydroxyl radical also forms through the reaction of superoxide with H_2O_2:

$$O_2^- \cdot + H_2O_2 \rightarrow O_2 + H_2O + \cdot OH$$

Although most free radicals are extremely short-lived (the half-life of $O_2^- \cdot$ is 1×10^{-6} s, and that of $\cdot OH$ is 1×10^{-9} s), they readily extract electrons from other molecules, converting them to free radicals and thereby initiating a chain reaction.

The random nature of free-radical attacks makes it difficult to characterize their reaction products, but all classes of biological molecules are susceptible to oxidative damage caused by free radicals. The oxidation of polyunsaturated lipids in cells may disrupt the structures of biological membranes, and oxidative damage to DNA may result in point mutations. Enzyme function may also be compromised through radical reactions with amino acid side chains. Because the mitochondrion is the site of the bulk of the cell's oxidative metabolism, its lipids, DNA, and proteins probably bear the brunt of free radical–related damage.

Several degenerative diseases, including **Parkinson's, Alzheimer's, and Huntington's diseases,** are associated with oxidative damage to mitochondria. Such observations have led to the free-radical theory of aging, which holds that *free-radical reactions arising during the course of normal oxidative metabolism are at least partially responsible for the aging process.* In fact, individuals with congenital defects in their mitochondrial DNA suffer from a variety of symptoms typical of old age, including neuromotor difficulties, deafness, and dementia. Their genetic defects may make their mitochondria all the more susceptible to the reactive oxygen species generated by the electron-transport machinery.

Cells Are Equipped with Antioxidant Mechanisms. **Antioxidants** destroy oxidative free radicals such as $O_2^- \cdot$ and $\cdot OH$. In 1969, Irwin Fridovich discovered that the enzyme **superoxide dismutase (SOD),** which is present in nearly all cells, catalyzes the conversion of $O_2^- \cdot$ to H_2O_2.

$$2 O_2^- \cdot + 2 H^+ \rightarrow H_2O_2 + O_2$$

Mitochondrial and bacterial SOD are both Mn-containing tetramers; eukaryotic cytosolic SOD is a dimer containing copper and zinc ions. The rate of nonenzymatic superoxide breakdown is $\sim 2 \times 10^5 M^{-1} \cdot s^{-1}$, whereas the rate of the Cu,Zn-SOD–catalyzed reaction is $\sim 2 \times 10^9 M^{-1} \cdot s^{-1}$. This rate enhancement, which is close to the diffusion-controlled limit (Section 12-1B), is apparently accomplished by electrostatic guidance of the negatively charged superoxide substrate into the enzyme's active site (Fig. 18-30). The active-site Cu ion lies at the bottom of a deep pocket in each enzyme subunit. A hydrogen-bonded network of Glu 123, Glu 133, Lys 136, and Thr 137 at the entrance to the pocket facilitates the diffusion of $O_2^- \cdot$ to a site between the Cu ion and Arg 143.

SOD is considered a first-line defense against reactive oxygen species. The H_2O_2 produced in the reaction, which can potentially react to yield other reactive oxygen species, is degraded to water and oxygen by enzymes such as **catalase,** which catalyzes the reaction

$$2 H_2O_2 \rightarrow 2 H_2O + O_2$$

Figure 18-30 Electrostatic effects in human Cu,Zn-superoxide dismutase. In this cross section of the active site channel of Cu,Zn-SOD, the molecular surface is represented by a dot surface that is colored according to charge: red, most negative; yellow, negative; green, neutral; light blue, positive; dark blue, most positive. The electrostatic field vectors are represented by similarly colored arrows. The Cu and Zn ions at the active site are represented by orange and silver dotted spheres. The O_2^-·-binding site is located between the Cu ion and the side chain of Arg 143. [Courtesy of Elizabeth Getzoff, The Scripps Research Institute, La Jolla, California.]

nd glutathione peroxidase (Box 15-4), which uses glutathione (GSH) as he reducing agent:

$$2\,GSH + H_2O_2 \rightarrow GSSG + 2\,H_2O$$

he latter enzyme also catalyzes the breakdown of organic hydroperoxdes. Some types of glutathione peroxidase require Se for activity; this is ne reason why Se appears to have antioxidant activity.

Other potential antioxidants are plant-derived compounds such as scorbate (vitamin C; Section 6-1C) and α-tocopherol (vitamin E; Section -1F). These compounds may help protect plants from oxidative damage uring photosynthesis, a process in which H_2O is oxidized to O_2. Their eficacy as antioxidants in humans, however, is disputed.

■ **CHECK YOUR UNDERSTANDING**

What control mechanisms link glycolysis, the citric acid cycle, and oxidative phosphorylation?
Describe the advantages and disadvantages of oxygen-based metabolism.

SUMMARY

1. Electrons from the reduced coenzymes NADH and $FADH_2$ pass through a series of redox centers in the electron-transport chain before reducing O_2. During electron transfer, protons are translocated out of the mitochondrion to form an electrochemical gradient whose free energy drives ATP synthesis.

2. The mitochondrion contains soluble and membrane-bound enzymes for oxidative metabolism. Reducing equivalents are imported from the cytosol via a shuttle system. Specific transporters mediate the transmembrane movements of ADP, ATP, and P_i.

3. Electrons flow from redox centers with more negative reduction potentials to those with more positive reduction potentials. Inhibitors have been used to reveal the sequence of electron carriers and the points of entry of electrons into the electron-transport chain.

4. Electron transport is mediated by one-electron carriers (Fe–S clusters, cytochromes, and Cu ions) and two-electron carriers (CoQ, FMN, FAD).

5. Complex I transfers two electrons from NADH to CoQ while translocating four protons to the intermembrane space.

6. Complex II transfers electrons from succinate through FAD to CoQ.

7. Complex III transfers two electrons from $CoQH_2$ to two molecules of cytochrome c. The concomitant operation of the Q cycle translocates four protons to the intermembrane space.

8. Complex IV reduces O_2 to $2\,H_2O$ using four electrons donated by four cytochrome c and four protons from the matrix. Two protons are translocated to the intermembrane space for every two electrons that reduce oxygen.

9. As explained by the chemiosmotic theory, protons translocated into the intermembrane space during electron transport through Complexes I, III, and IV establish an electrochemical gradient across the inner mitochondrial membrane.

10. The influx of protons through the F_0 component of ATP synthase (F_1F_0-ATPase) drives its F_1 component to synthesize ATP from ADP + P_i via the binding change mechanism, a process that is mechanically driven by the F_0-mediated rotation of F_1's γ subunit with respect to its catalytic $\alpha_3\beta_3$ assembly.

11. The P/O ratio, the number of ATPs synthesized per oxygen reduced, need not be an integral number.

12. Agents that discharge the proton gradient can uncouple oxidative phosphorylation from electron transport.

13. Oxidative phosphorylation is controlled by the ratio [NADH]/[NAD⁺] and by the ATP mass action ratio. Glycolysis and the citric acid cycle are coordinately regulated according to the need for oxidative phosphorylation.

14. Aerobic metabolism is more efficient than anaerobic metabolism. However, aerobic organisms must guard against damage caused by reactive oxygen species.

KEY TERMS

redox center **597**
cristae **598**
intermembrane space **598**
mitochondrial matrix **599**
malate–aspartate shuttle **599**
glycerophosphate shuttle **599**
ADP–ATP translocator **599**

electrogenic transport **600**
coenzyme Q (ubiquinone) **602**
iron–sulfur protein **605**
free radical **606**
proton wire **608**
cytochrome **609**
Q cycle **612**

energy coupling **618**
chemiosmotic theory **618**
protonmotive force (pmf) **620**
F₁F₀-ATPase **622**
binding change
  mechanism **625**
P/O ratio **629**

uncoupler **630**
ATP mass action ratio **631**
glucose–fatty acid cycle **634**
superoxide radical **635**
antioxidant **636**

PROBLEMS

1. Explain why a liver cell mitochondrion contains fewer cristae than a mitochondrion from a heart muscle cell.

2. How many ATPs are synthesized for every cytoplasmic NADH that participates in the glycerophosphate shuttle in insect flight muscle? How does this compare to the ATP yield when NADH reducing equivalents are transferred into the matrix via the malate–aspartate shuttle?

3. Calculate $\Delta G^{\circ\prime}$ for the oxidation of free FADH₂ by O₂. What is the maximum number of ATPs that can be synthesized, assuming standard conditions and 100% conservation of energy?

4. The O₂-consumption curve of a dilute, well-buffered suspension of mitochondria containing an excess of ADP and Pᵢ takes the form

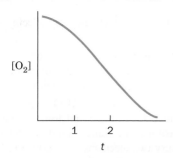

Sketch the curves obtained when (a) amytal is added at time $t = 1$; (b) amytal is added at $t = 1$ and succinate is added at $t = 2$; (c) CN⁻ is added at $t = 1$ and succinate is added at $t = 2$; (d) oligomycin (which binds to F₀ and prevents ATP synthesis) is added at $t = 1$ and DNP is added at $t = 2$.

5. Why is it possible for electrons to flow from a redox center with a more positive $\mathscr{E}^{\circ\prime}$ to one with a more negative $\mathscr{E}^{\circ\prime}$ within an electron-transfer complex?

6. Bombarding a suspension of mitochondria with high-frequency sound waves (**sonication**) produces **submitochondrial particles** derived from the inner mitochondrial membrane. These membranous vesicles seal inside out, so that the intermembrane space of the mitochondrion becomes the lumen of the submitochondrial particle. (a) Diagram the process of electron transfer and oxidative phosphorylation in these particles. (b) Assuming all the substrates for oxidative phosphorylation are present in excess, does ATP synthesis increase or decrease with an increase in the pH of the fluid in which the submitochondrial particles are suspended?

7. The difference in pH between the internal and external surfaces of the inner mitochondrial membrane is 1.4 pH units (external side acidic). If the membrane potential is 0.06 V (inside negative), what is the free energy released on transporting 1 mol of protons back across the membrane? How many protons must be transported to provide enough free energy for the synthesis of 1 mol of ATP (assuming standard biochemical conditions)?

8. Consider the mitochondrial ADP–ATP translocator and the Pᵢ–H⁺ symport protein. (a) How do the activities of the two transporters affect the electrochemical gradient across the mitochondrial membrane? (b) What thermodynamic force drives the two transport systems?

9. Dicyclohexylcarbodiimide (DCCD) is a reagent that reacts with Asp or Glu residues.

Dicyclohexylcarbodiimide (DCCD)

Explain why the reaction of DCCD with the *c* subunits of F₁F₀-ATPase blocks its ATP-synthesizing activity.

10. How do the P/O ratios for NADH differ in ATP synthase that contain 9 and 12 *c* subunits?

11. Explain why compounds such as DNP increase metabolic rates

12. What is the advantage of hormones activating a lipase to stimulate nonshivering thermogenesis in brown fat rather than activating UCP1 directly (see Box 18-4)?

13. Describe the changes in [NADH]/[NAD$^+$] and [ATP]/[ADP] that occur during the switch from anaerobic to aerobic metabolism. How do these ratios influence the activity of glycolysis and the citric acid cycle?

14. Activated neutrophils and macrophages (types of white blood cells) fight invading bacteria by releasing superoxide. These cells contain an **NADPH oxidase** that catalyzes the reaction

$$2\,O_2 + NADPH \rightarrow 2\,O_2^- \cdot\; + NADP^+ + H^+$$

Explain why flux through the glucose-6-phosphate dehydrogenase reaction increases in these cells.

CASE STUDIES

Case 24 (available at www.wiley.com/college/voet)
Uncoupling Proteins in Plants

Focus concept: Uncoupling proteins in plants uncouple oxidative phosphorylation in order to generate heat in the developing plant.

Prerequisite: Chapter 18

• Electron transport and oxidative phosphorylation

• Mechanisms of uncoupling agents, such as 2,4-dinitrophenol

Case 27
Regulation of Sugar and Alcohol Metabolism in Saccharomyces cerevisiae

Focus concept: The regulation of carbohydrate metabolic pathways in yeast serves as a good model for regulation of the same pathways in multicellular organisms.

Prerequisites: Chapters 15, 16, 17, and 18

• The major pathways associated with carbohydrate metabolism, including glycolysis, the citric acid cycle, oxidative phosphorylation, pentose phosphate pathway and gluconeogenesis

• The various fates of pyruvate via alcoholic fermentation and aerobic respiration

Case 33
Modification of Subunit c from Bovine Mitochondrial ATPase

Focus concept: Modification of Lys 43 in the mitochondrial ATPase, once thought to be the structural basis of Batten disease, has been found in bovine mitochondria, indicating that this modification is completely normal.

Prerequisites: Chapters 5 and 18

• Mechanism of ATP synthesis in oxidative phosphorylation

• Protein structure/function relationships

REFERENCES

Beinert, H., Holm, R.H., and Münck, E., Iron-sulfur clusters: Nature's modular, multipurpose structures, *Science* **277**, 653–659 (1997).

Boyer, P.D., Catalytic site forms and controls in ATP synthase catalysis, *Biochim. Biophys. Acta* **1458**, 252–262 (2000). [A description of the steps of ATP synthesis and hydrolysis, along with experimental evidence and alternative explanations, by the author of the binding change mechanism.]

Crofts, A.R., The cytochrome bc_1 complex: Function in the context of structure, *Annu. Rev. Physiol.* **66**, 689–733 (2004).

Frey, T.G. and Mannella, C.A., The internal structure of mitochondria, *Trends Biochem. Sci.* **23**, 319–324 (2000).

Hinkle, P.C., P/O ratios of mitochondrial oxidative phosphorylation, *Biochim. Biophys. Acta* **1706**, 1–11 (2005).

Hosler, J.P., Ferguson-Miller, S., and Mills, D.A., Energy transduction: Proton transfer through the respiratory complexes, *Annu. Rev. Biochem.* **75**, 165–187 (2006). [A review that focuses on cytochrome c oxidase.]

Kühlbrandt, W., Bacteriorhodopsin—the movie, *Nature* **406**, 569– 570 (2000).

Lange, C. and Hunte, C., Crystal structure of the yeast cytochrome bc_1 complex with its bound substrate cytochrome c, *Proc. Natl. Acad. Sci.* **99**, 2800–2805 (2002).

Lanyi, J.K., Bacteriorhodopsin, *Annu. Rev. Physiol.* **66**, 665–688 (2004).

Nicholls, D.G. and Ferguson, S.J., *Bioenergetics 3*, Academic Press (2002). [An authoritative monograph devoted almost entirely to the mechanism of oxidative phosphorylation and the techniques used to elucidate it.]

Noji, H. and Yoshida, M., The rotary machine in the cell, ATP synthase, *J. Biol. Chem.* **276**, 1665–1668 (2001).

Pebay-Peyroula, E., Dahout-Gonzalez, C., Kahn, R., Trézéguet, V., Lauquin, G.J.-M., and Brandolin, G., Structure of mitochondrial ADP/ATP carrier in complex with carboxyatractyloside, *Nature* **426**, 39–44 (2003). [Reports the 2.2-Å-resolution structure of the bovine carrier monomer and proposes a mechanism in which conformational changes in each monomer of the dimeric complex allow simultaneous transport of ADP into and ATP out of the matrix.]

Sazanov, L.A. and Hinchcliffe, P., Structure of the hydrophilic domain of respiratory Complex I from *Thermus thermophilus*, *Science* **311**, 1430–1436 (2006).

Schultz, B.E. and Chan, S.I., Structures and proton-pumping strategies of mitochondrial respiratory enzymes, *Annu. Rev. Biophys. Biomol. Struct.* **30**, 23–65 (2001).

Stock, D., Gibbons, C., Arechaga, I., Leslie, A.G.W., and Walker, J.E., The rotary mechanism of ATP synthase, *Curr. Opin. Struct. Biol.* **10**, 692–679 (2000).

Walker, J.E. (Ed.), The Mechanism of F_1F_0-ATPase, *Biochim. Biophys. Acta* **1458**, 221–514 (2002). [A series of authoritative reviews.]

Yankovskaya, V., Horsefield, R., Törnroth, S., Luna-Chavez, C., Miyoshi, H., Léger, C., Byrne, B., Cecchini, G., and Iwata, S., Architecture of succinate dehydrogenase and reactive oxygen species generation, *Science* **299**, 700–704 (2003). [X-Ray structure of *E. coli* Complex II.]

19

Photosynthesis

Plants, such as these trees, can survive literally on water, air, and light. They oxidize H_2O to O_2 and convert CO_2 from air into carbohydrates in a process that is driven by light. [Michael Busselle/Stone/Getty Images.]

■ CHAPTER CONTENTS

1 Chloroplasts
  A. The Light Reactions Take Place in the Thylakoid Membrane
  B. Pigment Molecules Absorb Light

2 The Light Reactions
  A. Light Energy Is Transformed to Chemical Energy
  B. Electron Transport in Photosynthetic Bacteria Follows a Circular Path
  C. Two-Center Electron Transport Is a Linear Pathway That Produces O_2 and NADPH
  D. The Proton Gradient Drives ATP Synthesis by Photophosphorylation

3 The Dark Reactions
  A. The Calvin Cycle Fixes CO_2
  B. Calvin Cycle Products Are Converted to Starch, Sucrose, and Cellulose
  C. The Calvin Cycle Is Controlled Indirectly by Light
  D. Photorespiration Competes with Photosynthesis

■ MEDIA RESOURCES

(available at www.wiley.com/college/voet)
Guided Exploration 20. Two-center photosynthesis (Z-scheme) overview
Interactive Exercise 23. Light-harvesting complex LH-2
Interactive Exercise 24. *Rb. sphaeroides* reaction center
Interactive Exercise 25. Ferredoxin
Interactive Exercise 26. Ferredoxin–NADP$^+$ reductase
Animated Figure 19-6. Electronic states of chlorophyll
Animated Figure 19-26. The Calvin cycle
Animated Figure 19-28. Mechanism of RuBP carboxylase
Kinemage 8-2. Photosynthetic reaction center

The notion that plants obtain nourishment from such insubstantia things as light and air was not validated until the eighteenth cen tury. Evidence that plants produce a vital substance—O_2—was no obtained until Joseph Priestly noted that the air in a jar in which a can dle had burnt out could be "restored" by introducing a small plant int the jar. In the presence of sunlight, plants and cyanobacteria consume CO and H_2O and produce O_2 and "fixed" carbon in the form of carbohydrate

$$CO_2 + H_2O \xrightarrow{\text{light}} (CH_2O) + O_2$$

Photosynthesis, in which light energy drives the reduction of carbon, i essentially the reverse of oxidative carbohydrate metabolism. Photo synthetically produced carbohydrates therefore serve as an energy source for the organism that produces them as well as for nonphotosynthetic or ganisms that directly or indirectly consume photosynthetic organisms. It i estimated that photosynthesis annually fixes $\sim10^{11}$ tons of carbon, which represents the storage of over 10^{18} kJ of energy. The process by which ligh energy is converted to chemical energy has its roots early in evolution and its complexity is consistent with its long history. Our discussion fo cuses first on purple photosynthetic bacteria, because of the relative sim plicity of their photosynthetic machinery, and then on plants, whose chloroplasts are the site of photosynthesis.

Early in the twentieth century, it was mistakenly thought that ligh absorbed by photosynthetic pigments directly reduced CO_2, which the

Solutions to Problems

1. A   Thiol (sulfhydryl) group

   B   Carbonyl group

   C   Amide linkage

   D   Phosphoanhydride (pyrophosphoryl) linkage

   E   Phosphoryl group (P_i)

   F   Hydroxyl group

2. The cell membrane must be semipermeable so that the cell can retain essential compounds while allowing nutrients to enter and wastes to exit.

3. Concentration = (number of moles)/(volume)

   Volume = $(4/3)\pi r^3 = (4/3)\pi(5 \times 10^{-7}\,\text{m})^3$
   $= 5.24 \times 10^{-19}\,\text{m}^3 = 5.24 \times 10^{-16}\,\text{L}$

   Moles of protein = (2 molecules)/
   $(6.022 \times 10^{23}\,\text{molecules}\cdot\text{mol}^{-1}) = 3.32 \times 10^{-24}\,\text{mol}^{-1}$

   Concentration = $(3.32 \times 10^{-24}\,\text{mol})/(5.24 \times 10^{-16}\,\text{L})$
   $= 6.3 \times 10^{-9}\,\text{M} = 6.3\,\text{nM}$

4. Number of molecules = (molar conc.)(volume)
   $(6.022 \times 10^{23}\,\text{molecules}\cdot\text{mol}^{-1})$
   $= (1.0 \times 10^{-3}\,\text{mol}\cdot\text{L}^{-1})(5.24 \times 10^{-16}\,\text{L})$
   $(6.022 \times 10^{23}\,\text{molecules}\cdot\text{mol}^{-1})$
   $= 3.2 \times 10^5\,\text{molecules}$

5. (a) Liquid water; (b) ice has less entropy at the lower temperature.

6. (a) Decreases; (b) increases; (c) increases; (d) no change.

7. (a) $T = 273 + 10 = 283\,\text{K}$

   $\Delta G = \Delta H - T\Delta S$

   $\Delta G = 15\,\text{kJ} - (283\,\text{K})(0.050\,\text{kJ}\cdot\text{K}^{-1})$
   $= 15 - 14.15\,\text{kJ} = 0.85\,\text{kJ}$

   ΔG is greater than zero, so the reaction is not spontaneous.

   (b) $T = 273 + 80 = 353\,\text{K}$

   $\Delta G = \Delta H - T\Delta S$

   $\Delta G = 15\,\text{kJ} - (353\,\text{K})(0.050\,\text{kJ}\cdot\text{K}^{-1})$
   $= 15 - 17.65\,\text{kJ} = -2.65\,\text{kJ}$

   ΔG is less than zero, so the reaction is spontaneous.

8. $K_{eq} = e^{-\Delta G^{\circ\prime}/RT} = e^{-(-20.900\,\text{J}\cdot\text{mol}^{-1})/(8.314\,\text{J}\cdot\text{K}^{-1}\cdot\text{mol}^{-1})(298\,\text{K})}$
   $= 4.6 \times 10^3$

9. $\Delta G^{\circ\prime} = -RT\ln K_{eq} = -RT\ln([\text{C}][\text{D}]/[\text{A}][\text{B}])$
   $= -(8.314\,\text{J}\cdot\text{K}^{-1}\cdot\text{mol}^{-1})(298\,\text{K})\ln[(3)(5)/(10)(15)]$
   $= 5700\,\text{J}\cdot\text{mol}^{-1} = 5.7\,\text{kJ}\cdot\text{mol}^{-1}$

   Since $\Delta G^{\circ\prime}$ is positive, the reaction is endergonic under standard conditions.

10. From Eq. 1-17, $K_{eq} = [\text{G6P}]/[\text{G1P}] = e^{-\Delta G^{\circ\prime}/RT}$

    $[\text{G6P}]/[\text{G1P}] = e^{-(-7100\,\text{J}\cdot\text{mol}^{-1})/(8.314\,\text{J}\cdot\text{K}^{-1}\cdot\text{mol}^{-1})(298\,\text{K})}$

    $[\text{G6P}]/[\text{G1P}] = 17.6$

    $[\text{G1P}]/[\text{G6P}] = 0.057$

11. $\Delta G = \Delta H - T\Delta S$

    $\Delta G = -7000\,\text{J}\cdot\text{mol}^{-1} - (298\,\text{K})(-25\,\text{J}\cdot\text{K}^{-1}\cdot\text{mol}^{-1})$

    $\Delta G = -7000 + 7450\,\text{J}\cdot\text{mol}^{-1} = 450\,\text{J}\cdot\text{mol}^{-1}$

    The reaction is not spontaneous because $\Delta G > 0$. The temperature must be decreased in order to decrease the value of the $T\Delta S$ term.

12. In order for ΔG to have a negative value (a spontaneous reaction), $T\Delta S$ must be greater than ΔH.

    $T\Delta S > \Delta H$

    $T > \Delta H/\Delta S$

    $T > 7000\,\text{J}\cdot\text{mol}^{-1}/20\,\text{J}\cdot\text{K}^{-1}\cdot\text{mol}^{-1}$

    $T > 350\,\text{K or }77°\text{C}$

13. (a) False. A spontaneous reaction only occurs in one direction. (b) False. Thermodynamics does not specify the rate of a reaction. (c) True. (d) True. A reaction is spontaneous so long as $\Delta S > \Delta H/T$.

14. This strategy will NOT work because Reaction 1 has a negative enthalpy change, releasing heat, and will therefore become more favorable with decreasing temperature, whereas Reaction 2, which has a positive enthalpy change, will become less favorable. Thus decreasing the temperature will favor Reaction 1, not Reaction 2. In order to make Reaction 2 more favorable, the temperature must be raised.

    To calculate the amount that the temperature must be raised, Equation 1-18 may be used as follows:

    $$\ln K_{eq} = \frac{-\Delta H^\circ}{R}\left(\frac{1}{T}\right) + \frac{\Delta S^\circ}{R}$$

    $$\ln\frac{K_1^{T_1}}{K_1^{T_2}} = \frac{-\Delta H_1^\circ}{R}\left(\frac{1}{T_1} - \frac{1}{T_2}\right)$$

    $$\ln\frac{K_2^{T_1}}{K_2^{T_2}} = \frac{-\Delta H_2^\circ}{R}\left(\frac{1}{T_1} - \frac{1}{T_2}\right)$$

    On subtraction of the previous two equations, and taking into account that $K_2^{T_1}/K_1^{T_1} = 1$, we get

    $$\ln\left[\frac{K_1^{T_1}K_2^{T_2}}{K_1^{T_2}K_2^{T_1}}\right] = \ln\frac{K_2^{T_2}}{K_1^{T_2}} = \frac{\Delta H_2^\circ - \Delta H_1^\circ}{R}\left(\frac{1}{T_1} - \frac{1}{T_2}\right)$$

    We would like $K_2^{T_2}/K_1^{T_2} = 10$. Substituting in all values and solving for T_2 we get

    $$\ln\frac{K_2^{T_2}}{K_1^{T_2}} = \ln 10 = 2.3 = \frac{28,000 + 28,000}{8.31}\left(\frac{1}{298} - \frac{1}{T_2}\right)$$

    Solving for T_2 we get

    $$T_2 = \frac{1}{\dfrac{1}{298} - \dfrac{2.3 \times 8.31}{56,000}} = 332\,\text{K}$$

    Hence to increase K_2/K_1 from 1 to 10, the temperature must be raised from 298 K to 332 K.

CHAPTER 2

1. (a) Donors: NH1, NH$_2$ at C2, NH9; acceptors: N3, O at C6, N7. (b) Donors: NH1, NH$_2$ at C4; acceptors: O at C2, N3. (c) Donors: NH$_3^+$ group, OH group; acceptors: COO$^-$ group, OH group.

2. A protonated (and therefore positively charged) nitrogen would promote the separation of charge in the adjacent C—H bond so that the C would have a partial negative charge and the H would have a partial positive charge. This would make the H more likely to be donated to a hydrogen bond acceptor group.

3. From most soluble (most polar) to least soluble (least polar): c, b, e, a, d.

4. (a) Water; (b) water; (c) micelle.

5. The waxed car is a hydrophobic surface. To minimize its interaction with the hydrophobic molecules (wax), each water drop minimizes its surface area by becoming a sphere (the geometrical shape with the lowest possible ratio of surface to volume). Water does not bead on glass, because the glass presents a hydrophilic surface with which the water molecules can interact. This allows the water to spread out.

6. Water molecules move from inside the dialysis bag to the surrounding seawater by osmosis. Ions from the seawater diffuse into the dialysis bag. At equilibrium, the compositions of the solutions inside and outside the dialysis bag are identical. If the membrane were solute-impermeable, essentially all the water would leave the dialysis bag.

7. (a)
COO$^-$
|
CH
‖
HC
|
COO$^-$

(b)
COO$^-$
|
H—C—H
|
NH$_3^+$

(c)
COO$^-$
|
H—C—H
|
NH$_2$

(d)
COO$^-$
|
H—C—CH$_2$—COO$^-$
|
NH$_3^+$

8. (a) pH 4, NH$_4^+$; pH 8, NH$_4^+$; pH 11, NH$_3$.
(b) pH 4, H$_2$PO$_4^-$; pH 8, HPO$_4^{2-}$; pH 11, HPO$_4^{2-}$.

9. The increase in [H$^+$] due to the addition of HCl is (50 mL) (1 mM)/(250 mL) = 0.2 mM = 2×10^{-4} M. Because the [H$^+$] of pure water, 10^{-7} M, is relatively insignificant, the pH of the solution is equal to $-\log(2 \times 10^{-4})$ or 3.7.

10. (a) $(0.010 \text{ L})(5 \text{ mol} \cdot \text{L}^{-1} \text{ NaOH})/(1 \text{ L}) =$
0.05 M NaOH ≡ 0.05 M OH$^-$

[H$^+$] = K_w/[OH$^-$] = $(10^{-14})/(0.05) = 2 \times 10^{-13}$ M
pH = $-\log$[H$^+$] = $-\log(2 \times 10^{-13}) = 12.7$

(b) $(0.020 \text{ L})(5 \text{ mol} \cdot \text{L}^{-1} \text{ HCl})/(1 \text{ L}) =$
0.1 M HCl ≡ 0.1 M H$^+$

Since the contribution of 0.01 L × 100 mM/(1 L) = 1 mM glycine is insignificant in the presence of 0.1 M HCl,
pH = $-\log$[H$^+$] = $-\log(0.1) = 1.0$

(c) pH = pK + log([acetate]/[acetic acid])
[acetate] = (5 g) (1 mol/82 g)/(1 L) = 0.061 M
[acetic acid] = (0.01 L) (2 mol · L^{-1})/(1 L) = 0.02 M
pH = 4.76 + log(0.061/0.02) = 4.76 + 0.48 = 5.24

11. The standard free energy change can be calculated using Eq. 1-16 and the value of K from Table 2-4.

$\Delta G^{\circ\prime} = -RT \ln K$
$= -(8.314 \text{ J} \cdot \text{K}^{-1} \cdot \text{mol}^{-1})(298 \text{ K}) \ln (3.39 \times 10^{-8})$
$= 42,600 \text{ J} \cdot \text{mol}^{-1} = 42.6 \text{ kJ} \cdot \text{mol}^{-1}$

12. The pK corresponding to the equilibrium between H$_2$PO$_4^-$ (HA) and HPO$_4^{2-}$ (A$^-$) is 6.82 (Table 2-4). The concentration of A$^-$ is (50 mL)(2.0 M)/(200 mL) = 0.5 M, and the concentration of HA is (25 mL)(2.0 M)/(200 mL) = 0.25 M. Substitute these values into the Henderson–Hasselbalch equation (Eq. 2-9):

$$pH = pK + \log \frac{[\text{A}^-]}{[\text{HA}]}$$

$$pH = 6.82 + \log \frac{0.5}{0.25}$$

$$pH = 6.82 + \log 2$$

$$pH = 6.82 + 0.30 = 7.12$$

13. Use the Henderson–Hasselbalch equation (Eq. 2-9) and solve for pK:

$$pH = pK + \log \frac{[\text{A}^-]}{[\text{HA}]}$$

$$pK = pH - \log \frac{[\text{A}^-]}{[\text{HA}]}$$

$$pK = 6.5 - \log \frac{0.2}{0.1}$$

$$pK = 6.5 - 0.3 = 6.2$$

14. Let HA = sodium succinate and A$^-$ = disodium succinate.
[A$^-$] + [HA] = 0.050 M, so [A$^-$] = 0.050 M − [HA]
From Eq. 2-9 and Table 2-4,
log([A]/[HA]) = pH − pK = 6.0 − 5.64 = 0.36
[A$^-$]/[HA] = antilog 0.36 = 2.29
(0.050 M − [HA])/[HA] = 2.29
[HA] = 0.015 M
[A$^-$] = 0.050 M − 0.015 M = 0.035 M
grams of sodium succinate =
(0.015 mol · L^{-1})(140 g · mol^{-1}) × (1 L) = 2.1 g
grams of disodium succinate =
(0.035 mol · L^{-1})(162 g · mol^{-1}) × (1 L) = 5.7 g

15. At pH 4, essentially all the phosphoric acid is in the H$_2$PO$_4^-$ form, and at pH 9, essentially all is in the HPO$_4^{2-}$ form (Fig. 2-18). Therefore, the concentration of OH$^-$ required is equivalent to the concentration of the acid: (0.100 mol · L^{-1} phosphoric acid)(0.1 L) = 0.01 mol NaOH required = (0.01 mol) (1 L/5 mol NaOH) = 0.002 L = 2 mL.

16. (a) Succinic acid; (b) ammonia; (c) HEPES.

17. The dissociation of TrisH$^+$ to its basic form and H$^+$ is associated with a large, positive enthalpy change. Consequently, heat is taken up by the reactant on dissociation. When the temperature is lowered, there is less heat available for this process, shifting the equilibrium constant toward the associated form (the effect of temperature on the equilibrium constant of a reaction is given by Eq. 1-18). To avoid this problem, the buffer should be prepared at the same temperature as its planned use.

3. (a) Carboxylic acid groups are stronger acids than ammonium groups and therefore lose their protons at lower pH values. This can be seen in Fig. 2-17, where the carboxylic acid group of CH_3COOH is 50% dissociated to $CH_3COO^- + H^+$ at pH 4.7 while it is not until pH 9.25 that the ammonium ion is 50% dissociated to NH_3.

(b) $H_3N^+CH_2COOH \rightleftharpoons H_3N^+CH_2COO^- + H^+ \rightleftharpoons$
$$H_2NCH_2COO^- + H^+$$

(c) The pK values of glycine's two ionizable groups are sufficiently different so that the Henderson–Hasselbalch equation (Section 2-2B) adequately describes the behavior of the solution of the diacid and the monodissociated species.

$$pH = pK + \log\frac{[A^-]}{[HA]}$$

$$2.65 = pK + \log\frac{0.02}{0.01}$$

$$pK = 2.65 - 0.3$$

$$pK = 2.35$$

(d)

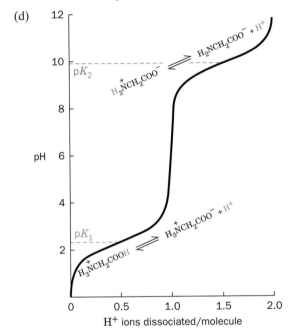

CHAPTER 3

1. (a) Yes; (b) no; (c) no; (d) yes.

2. Since the haploid genome contains 21% G, it must contain 21% C (because G = C) and 58% A + T (or 29% A and 29% T, because A = T). Each cell is diploid, containing 90,000 kb or 9×10^7 bases. Therefore,

$$A = T = (0.29)(9 \times 10^7) = 2.61 \times 10^7 \text{ bases}$$
$$C = G = (0.21)(9 \times 10^7) = 1.89 \times 10^7 \text{ bases}$$

3. The DNA contains 40 bases in all. Since G = C, there are 7 cytosine residues. The remainder $(40 - 14 = 26)$ must be adenine and thymine. Since A = T, there are 13 adenine residues. There are no uracil residues (U is a component of RNA but not DNA).

4. (a)

5.

Hypoxanthine   **Adenine**

Hypoxanthine   **Cytosine**

(b)

6. The high pH eliminates hydrogen bonds between bases, making it easier to separate the strands of DNA.

7. The number of possible sequences of four different nucleotides is 4^n where n is the number of nucleotides in the sequence. Therefore, (a) $4^1 = 4$, (b) $4^2 = 16$, (c) $4^3 = 64$, and (d) $4^4 = 256$.

8. 5'-A C G T-3'   5'-C G A A T C-3'
   3'-T G C A G C-5' + 3'-T T A G-5'

9. (a) *Alu*I, *Eco*RV, *Hae*III, *Pvu*II; (b) *Hpa*II and *Msp*I; (c) *Bam*HI and *Bgl*II; *Hpa*II and *Taq*I; *Sal*I and *Xho*I.

10. (a) Newly synthesized chains would be terminated less frequently, so the bands representing truncated fragments on the sequencing gel would appear faint.

(b) Chain termination would occur more frequently, so longer fragments would be less abundant.

(c) The amount of DNA synthesis would decrease and the resulting gel bands would appear faint.

(d) No effect.

11. The *C. elegans* genome contains 97,000 kb, so
$$f = 5/97{,}000 = 5.2 \times 10^{-5}.$$
Using Eq. 3-2,
$$N = \log(1 - P)/\log(l - f)$$
$$N = \log(1 - 0.99)/\log(1 - 5.2 \times 10^{-5})$$
$$N = -2/(-2.24 \times 10^{-5}) = 8.91 \times 10^{4}$$

12. The desired clones are colorless when grown in the presence of ampicillin and X-gal. Nontransformed bacteria cannot grow in the presence of ampicillin, because they lack the amp^{R} gene carried by the plasmid. Clones transformed with the plasmid only are blue, since they have an intact *lacZ* gene and produce β-galactosidase, which cleaves the chromogenic substrate X-gal. Clones that contain the plasmid with the foreign DNA insert are colorless because the insert interrupts the *lacZ* gene.

13. (a) Only single DNA strands of variable length extending from the remaining primer would be obtained. The number of these strands would increase linearly with the number of cycles rather than geometrically.

(b) PCR would yield a mixture of DNA segments whose lengths correspond to the distance between the position of the primer with a single binding site and the various sites where the multispecific primer binds.

(c) The first cycle of PCR would yield only the new strand that is complementary to the intact DNA strand, since DNA synthesis cannot proceed when the template is broken. However, since the new strand has the same sequence as the broken strand, PCR can proceed normally from the second cycle on.

(d) DNA synthesis would terminate at the breaks in the first cycle of PCR.

14. ATAGGCATAGGC and CTGACCAGCGCC.

15. (a) The genomic library contains DNA sequences corresponding to all the organism's DNA, which includes genes and nontranscribed sequences. A cDNA library represents only the DNA sequences that are transcribed into mRNA.

(b) Different cell types express different sets of genes. Therefore, the populations of mRNA molecules used to construct the cDNA libraries also differ.

16. (a) If an individual is homozygous (has two copies of the same allele) at a locus, then only one peak will appear in the electrophoretogram (for example, the D3S1358 locus from Suspect 2).

(b) Suspect 3, whose alleles exactly match those from the blood stain, is the most likely source of the blood.

(c) Analysis of each of the three STR loci in this example shows a match between the sample and Suspect 3, and no matches with the other suspects. In practice, however, multiple loci are analyzed in order to minimize the probability of obtaining a match by chance.

(d) The peak heights are lower for Suspect 1 compared to Suspect 4, suggesting that less DNA was available for PCR amplification from Suspect 1.

CHAPTER 4

1. Gly and Ala; Ser and Thr; Val, Leu, and Ile; Asn and Gln; Asp and Glu.

2. $^{+}H_3N-CH_2-CH_2-COO^-$

3. Hydrogen bond donors: α-amino group, amide nitrogen. Hydrogen bond acceptors: α-carboxylate group, amide carbonyl

4.

5. The first residue can be one of five residues, the second one of the remaining four, etc.
$$N = 5 \times 4 \times 3 \times 2 \times 1 = 120$$

6. (a) +1; (b) 0; (c) −1; (d) −2.

7. (a) $pI = (2.35 + 9.87)/2 = 6.11$
(b) $pI = (6.04 + 9.33)/2 = 7.68$
(c) $pI = (2.10 + 4.07)/2 = 3.08$

8. The polypeptide would be even less soluble than free Tyr, because most of the amino and carboxylate groups that interact with water and make Tyr at least slightly soluble are lost in forming the peptide bonds in poly(Tyr).

9.

10.

11. Replace with CH_3 to give D-Ala

12.

13. (2*S*,3*S*)-Isoleucine

14. (a) Glutamate; (b) aspartate

5. (a) Serine (N-acetylserine); (b) lysine (5-hydroxylysine); (c) methionine (N-formylmethionine).

6.

$$H_3\overset{+}{N}-CH-\overset{O}{\overset{\|}{C}}-NH-CH-\overset{O}{\overset{\|}{C}}-NH-CH-\overset{O}{\overset{\|}{C}}-NH-CH-\overset{O}{\overset{\|}{C}}-NH-CH-\overset{O}{\overset{\|}{C}}-NH-CH-COO^-$$

with side chains:
CH_3 | $H-\overset{|}{C}-OH$ / CH_3 | CH_2 / $H-\overset{|}{C}-CH_3$ / CH_3 | CH_2 / COO^- | CH_3 | $(CH_2)_4$ / NH_3^+

(a) The pK's of the ionizable side chains (Table 4-1) are 3.90 (Asp) and 10.54 (Lys); assume that the terminal Lys carboxyl group has a pK of 3.5 and the terminal Ala amino group has a pK of 8.0 (Section 4-1D). The pI is approximately midway between the pK's of the two ionizations involving the neutral species (the pK of Asp and the N-terminal pK):

$$pI \approx \tfrac{1}{2}(3.90 + 8.0) \approx 5.95$$

(b) The net charge at pH 7.0 is 0 (as drawn above).

7. At position A8, duck insulin has a Glu residue, whereas human insulin has a Thr residue. Since Glu is negatively charged at physiological pH and Thr is neutral, human insulin has a higher pI than duck insulin. (The other amino acids that differ between the proteins do not affect the pI because they are uncharged.)

CHAPTER 5

1. Peptide B, because it contains more Trp and other aromatic residues.

2. Since $A = \varepsilon cl$, $A = (0.4\ \text{mL}\cdot\text{mg}^{-1}\cdot\text{cm}^{-1})(2.0\ \text{mg}\cdot\text{mL}^{-1})$ $(1\ \text{cm}) = 0.8$

3. Lowering the pH from 7.0 to 5.0 would promote the precipitation of protein Q because the protein will be least soluble when its net charge is zero (when pH = pI).

4. (a) Leu, His, Arg. (b) Lys, Val, Glu.

5. (a)

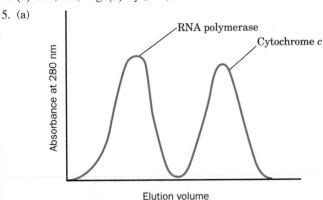

6. The protein behaves like a larger protein during gel filtration, suggesting that it has an elongated shape. The mass determined

by SDS-PAGE is more accurate since the mobility of a denatured SDS-coated protein depends only on its size.

7. The protein contains two 60-kD polypeptides and two 40-kD polypeptides. Each 40-kD chain is disulfide bonded to a 60-kD chain. The 100-kD units associate noncovalently to form a protein with a molecular mass of 200 kD.

8. Because protein 1 has a greater proportion of hydrophobic residues (Ala, Ile, Pro, Val) than do proteins 2 and 3, hydrophobic interaction chromatography could be used to isolate it.

9. (a)

Purification step	mg total protein	μmol Mb	Specific activity (μmol Mb/mg total protein)	% yield	Fold purification
1. Crude extract	1550	0.75	4.8×10^{-4}	100	1
2. DEAE-cellulose chromatography	550	0.35	6.4×10^{-4}	47	1.3
3. Affinity chromatography	5.0	0.28	5.9×10^{-2}	80 from Affinity chromatography (37 overall)	123-fold overall, 92-fold from Affinity chromatography

(b) The DEAE chromatography step results in only a 47% yield, while the affinity chromatography step results in an 80% yield from the step before it. The DEAE chromatography step therefore results in the greatest loss of Mb.

(c) The DEAE chromatography step results in a 1.3-fold purification, while the affinity chromatography step results in a 92-fold purification from the previous step. The affinity chromatography step therefore results in the greatest purification of Mb.

(d) The affinity chromatography step is the best choice for a one-step purification of Mb in this example.

10. Dansyl chloride reacts with primary amino groups, including the ε-amino group of Lys residues.

11. (a) Gly; (b) Thr; (c) none (the N-terminal amino group is acetylated and hence unreactive with Edman's reagent)

12. Thermolysin would yield the most fragments (9) and endopeptidase V8 would yield the fewest (2).

13. (a) The positive charges are caused by the protonation of basic side chains (H, K, and R) and the N-terminal amino groups of the protein.

(b) There is 1 H, 6 K, 11 R, and 1 NH$_2$ at the N-terminus. Therefore, the maximum number of positive charges that can be obtained is 19.

(c) From Sample Calculation 5-1 we see that
$$M = (p_2 - 1)(p_1 - 1)/(p_2 - p_1)$$
Therefore
$$M = (1789.2 - 1)(1590.6 - 1)/(1789.2 - 1590.6)$$
$$= (1788.2)(1589.6)/198.6$$
$$= 14{,}312.8$$

(b)

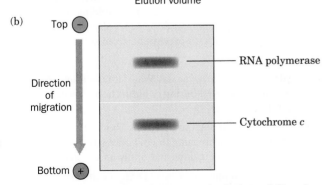

(d) Peak 5 is p_1 in our calculation. From Sample Calculation 5-1,

$$p_1 = (M + z)/z$$
$$1590.6 = (14312.8 + z)/z$$
$$1590.6z - z = 14312.8$$
$$z(1590.6 - 1) = 14312.8$$
$$z = 14312.8/1589.6 = 9.00$$

The charge on the fifth peak in the mass spectrum is 9.00.

14. Gln–Ala–Phe–Val–Lys–Gly–Tyr–Asn–Arg–Leu–Glu

15. Asp–Met–Leu–Phe–Met–Arg–Ala–Tyr–Gly–Asn

16. (a) There is one Met, so CNBr would produce two peptides.

(b) There are four possible sites for chymotrypsin to hydrolyze the peptide: following Phe, Tyr (twice), and Trp. This would yield five peptides.

(c) Four Cys residues form two disulfide bonds.

(d) Arbitrarily choosing one Cys residue, there are three ways it can make a disulfide bond with the remaining three Cys residues. After choosing one of them, there is only one way that the remaining two Cys residues can form a disulfide bond. Thus there are $3 \times 1 = 3$ possible arrangements of the disulfide bonds.

17. Ala—Val—Cys—Arg—Thr—Gly—Cys—Lys—Asn—Phe—Leu

Tyr—Lys—Cys—Phe—Arg—His—Thr—Lys—Cys—Ser

18. Arg–Ile–Pro–Lys–Cys–Arg–Lys–Phe–Gln–Gln–Ala–Gln–His–Leu–Arg–Ala–Cys–Gln–Gln–Trp–Leu–His–Lys–Gln–Ala–Asn–Gln–Ser–Gly–Gly–Gly–Pro–Ser

19. Because the side chain of Gly is only an H atom, it often occurs in a protein at a position where no other residue can fit. Consequently, Gly can take the place of a larger residue more easily than a larger residue, such as Val, can take the place of Gly.

20. (a) Position 6 (Gly) and Position 9 (Val) appear to be invariant.

(b) Conservative substitutions occur at Position 1 (Asp and Lys, both charged), Position 10 (Ile and Leu, similar in structure and hydrophobicity), and Position 2 (all uncharged bulky side chains). Positions 5 and 8 appear to tolerate some substitution.

(c) The most variable positions are 3, 4, and 7, where a variety of residues appear.

CHAPTER 6

1.

2. (a) 3.6_{13}; (b) steeper.

3. (100 residues)(1 α-helical turn/3.6 residues)

(5.1 Å/keratin turn) = 142 Å

4. (a) The first and fourth side chains of the two helices of a coiled coil form buried hydrophobic interacting surfaces, but the remaining side chains are exposed to the solvent and therefore tend to be polar or charged.

(b) Although the residues at positions 1 and 4 in both sequences are hydrophobic, Trp and Tyr are much larger than Ile and Val and would therefore not fit as well in the area of contact between the two polypeptides in a coiled coil.

5. A fibrous protein such as α keratin does not have a discrete globular core. Most of the residues in its coiled coil structure are exposed to the solvent. The exception is the strip of nonpolar side chains at the interface of the two coils.

6. The reducing conditions promote cleavage of the disulfide bonds that cross-link α keratin molecules. This helps the larvae digest the wool clothing that they eat.

7. Collagen's primary structure is its amino acid sequence, which is a repeating triplet of mostly Gly–Pro–Hyp. Its secondary structure is the left-handed helical conformation characteristic of its repeating sequence. Its tertiary structure is essentially the same as its secondary structure, since most of the protein consists of one type of secondary structure. Collagen's quaternary structure is the arrangement of its three chains in a right-handed triple helix.

8. Because collagen has such an unusual amino acid composition (almost two-thirds consists of Gly and Pro or Pro derivatives), it contains relatively fewer of the other amino acids and is therefore not as good a source of amino acids as proteins containing a greater variety of amino acids.

9. Yes, although such irregularity should not be construed as random.

10. (a) Gln; (b) Ser; (c) Ile; (d) Cys. See Table 6-1.

11. (a) C_4 and D_2; (b) C_6 and D_3.

12. (a) Phe. Ala and Phe are both hydrophobic, but Phe is much larger and might not fit as well in Val's place.

(b) Asp. Replacing a positively charged Lys residue with an oppositely charged Asp residue would be more disruptive.

(c) Glu. The amide-containing Asn would be a better substitute for Gln than the acidic Glu.

(d) His. Pro's constrained geometry is best approximated by Gly, which lacks a side chain, rather than a residue with a bulkier side chain such as His.

13. A polypeptide synthesized in a living cell has a sequence that has been optimized by natural selection so that it folds properly (with hydrophobic residues on the inside and polar residues on the outside). The random sequence of the synthetic peptide cannot direct a coherent folding process, so hydrophobic side chains on different molecules aggregate, causing the polypeptide to precipitate from solution.

14. No.

15. Hydrophobic effects, van der Waals interactions, and hydrogen bonds are destroyed during denaturation. Covalent cross-links are retained.

16. At physiological pH, the positively charged Lys side chains repel each other. Increasing the pH above the pK (>10.5) would neutralize the side chains and allow an α helix to form.

17. The molecular mass of O_2 is 32 D. Hence the ratio of the masses of hemoglobin and 4 O_2, which is equal to the ratio of their

volumes, is $65,000/(4 \times 32) = 508$. The 70-kg office worker has a volume of $70 \text{ kg} \times 1 \text{ cm}^3/\text{g} \times (1000 \text{ g/kg}) \times (1 \text{ m}/100 \text{ cm})^3 = 0.070 \text{ m}^3$. Hence the ratio of the volumes of the office and the office worker is $(4 \times 4 \times 3)/0.070 = 686$. These ratios are similar in magnitude, which you may not have expected.

8. Peptide c is most likely to form an α helix with its three charged residues (Lys, Glu, and Arg) aligned on one face of the helix. Peptide a has adjacent basic residues (Arg and Lys), which would destabilize a helix. Peptide b contains Gly and Pro, both of which are helix-breaking (Table 6-1). The presence of Gly and Pro would also inhibit the formation of β strands, so peptide b is least likely to form a β strand.

9. In a protein crystal, the residues at the end of a polypeptide chain may experience fewer intramolecular contacts and therefore tend to be less ordered (more mobile in the crystal). If their disorder prevents them from generating a coherent diffraction pattern, it may be impossible to map their electron density.

CHAPTER 7

1.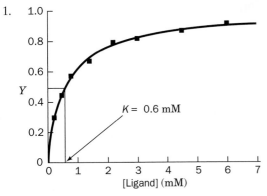

2. Set b describes sigmoidal binding to an oligomeric protein and hence represents cooperative binding.

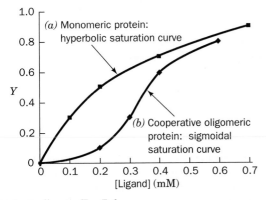

3. According to Eq. 7-6,

$$Y_{O_2} = \frac{pO_2}{K + pO_2}$$

When $pO_2 = 10$ torr,

$$Y_{O_2} = \frac{10}{2.8 + 10} = 0.78$$

When $pO_2 = 1$ torr,

$$Y_{O_2} = \frac{1}{2.8 + 1} = 0.26$$

The difference in Y_{O_2} values is $0.78 - 0.26 = 0.52$. Therefore, in active muscle cells, myoglobin can transport a significant amount of O_2 by diffusion from the cell surface to the mitochondria.

4. (a) Hyperventilation eliminates CO_2, but it does not significantly affect the O_2 concentration, since the hemoglobin in arterial blood is already essentially saturated with oxygen.

(b) The removal of CO_2 also removes protons, according to the reaction

$$H^+ + HCO_3^- \rightleftharpoons H_2O + CO_2$$

The resulting increase in blood pH would increase the O_2 affinity of hemoglobin through the Bohr effect. The net result would be that less oxygen could be delivered to the tissues until the CO_2 balance was restored. Thus, hyperventilation has the opposite of the intended effect (note that since hyperventilation suppresses the urge to breathe, doing so may cause the diver to lose consciousness due to lack of O_2 and hence drown).

5. (a) Vitamin O is useless because the body's capacity to absorb oxygen is not limited by the amount of oxygen available but by the ability of hemoglobin to bind and transport O_2. Furthermore, oxygen is normally introduced into the body via the lungs, so it is unlikely that the gastrointestinal tract would have an efficient mechanism for extracting oxygen.

(b) The fact that oxygen delivery in vertebrates requires a dedicated O_2-binding protein (hemoglobin) indicates that dissolved oxygen by itself cannot attain the high concentrations required. Moreover, a few drops of vitamin O would make an insignificant contribution to the amount of oxygen already present in a much larger volume of blood.

6. (a) Lower; (b) higher. The Asp 99$\beta \rightarrow$ His mutation of hemoglobin Yakima disrupts a hydrogen bond at the α_1–β_2 interface of the T state (Fig. 7-9a), causing the T $\rightleftharpoons$ R equilibrium to shift toward R state (lower p_{50}). The Asn 102$\beta \rightarrow$ Thr of hemoglobin Kansas causes the opposite shift in the T $\rightleftharpoons$ R equilibrium by abolishing an R-state hydrogen bond (Fig. 7-9b).

7. The increased BPG helps the remaining erythrocytes deliver O_2 to tissues. However, BPG stabilizes the T conformation of hemoglobin, so it promotes sickling and therefore aggravates the disease.

8. (a) Because the mutation destabilizes the T conformation of hemoglobin Rainier, the R (oxy) conformation is more stable. Therefore, the oxygen affinity of hemoglobin Rainier is greater than normal.

(b) The ion pairs that normally form in deoxyhemoglobin absorb protons. The absence of these ion pairs in hemoglobin Rainier decreases the Bohr effect (in fact, the Bohr effect in hemoglobin Rainier is about half that of normal hemoglobin).

(c) Because the R conformation of hemoglobin Rainier is more stable than the T conformation, even when the molecule is not oxygenated, O_2-binding cooperativity is reduced. The Hill coefficient of hemoglobin Rainier is therefore less than that for normal hemoglobin.

9. As the crocodile remains under water without breathing, its metabolism generates CO_2 and hence the HCO_3^- content of its

blood increases. The HCO_3^- preferentially binds to the croco-dile's deoxyhemoglobin, which allosterically prompts the he-moglobin to assume the deoxy conformation and thus release its O_2. This helps the crocodile stay under water long enough to drown its prey.

10. (a)

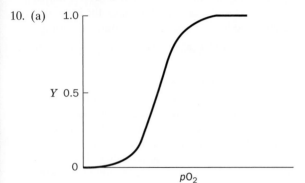

(b) The Hill coefficient most likely has a value between 1 (no cooperativity) and 2 (perfect cooperativity between the two subunits).

11. Myosin is both fibrous and globular. Its two heads are globu-lar, with several layers of secondary structure. Its tail, however, consists of a lengthy, fibrous coiled coil.

12. Because many myosin heads bind along a thin filament where it overlaps a thick filament, and because the myosin molecules do not execute their power strokes simultaneously, the thick and thin filaments can move past each other by more than 100 Å in the interval between power strokes of an individual myosin molecule.

13. In the absence of ATP, each myosin head adopts a conforma-tion that does not allow it to release its bound actin molecule. Consequently, thick and thin filaments form a rigid cross-linked array.

14. Microfilaments consist entirely of actin subunits that are as-sembled in a head-to-tail fashion so that the polarity of the subunits is preserved in the fully assembled fiber. In keratin filaments, however, successive heterodimers align in an an-tiparallel fashion, so that in a fully assembled intermediate fil-ament, half the molecules are oriented in one direction and half are oriented in the opposite direction (Fig. 6-16).

15. (a) 150–200 kD; (b) 150–200 kD; (c) ~23 kD and 53–75 kD.

16. The loops are on the surface of the domain, so they can toler-ate more amino acid substitutions. Amino acid changes in the β sheets would be more likely to destabilize the domain.

17. The antigenic site in the native protein usually consists of sev-eral peptide segments that are no longer contiguous when the tertiary structure of the protein is disrupted.

18. (a) Fab fragments are monovalent and therefore cannot cross-link antigens to produce a precipitate. (b) A small antigen has only one antigenic site and therefore cannot bind more than one antibody to produce a precipitate. (c) When antibody is in great excess, most antibodies that are bound to antigen bind only one per immunoglobulin molecule. When antigen is in ex-cess, most immunoglobulins bind to two independent antigens.

CHAPTER 8

1. (a) 4; (b) 8; (c) 16.

2. (a) and (d)

3. Tagatose is derived from galactose.

4.

5. (a) Yes; (b) no (its symmetric halves are superimposable); (c) no.

6.

   L-Fucose

   L-Fucose is the 6-deoxy form of L-galactose.

7. (a) α-D-glucose-(1 → 1)-α-D-glucose or α-D-glucose-(1 → 1)-β-D-glucose. (b) The numerous hydrogen-bonding —OH groups of the disaccharide act as substitutes for water molecules.

8. 19

9.

10. One

11. Amylose (it has only one nonreducing end from which glucose can be mobilized).

12. Glucosamine is a building block of certain glycosaminoglycan components of proteoglycans (Fig. 8-12). Boosting the body's supply of glucosamine might slow the progression of the dis-ease osteoarthritis, which is characterized by the degradation of proteoglycan-rich articular (relating to a joint) cartilage.

13. −200

14.

5.

Gal

GlcNAc

Fuc

6. (a) There are four types of methylated glucose molecules, corresponding to (1) the residue at the reducing end of the glycogen molecule, (2) residues at the nonreducing ends, (3) residues at the $\alpha(1 \rightarrow 6)$ branch points, and (4) residues from the linear $\alpha(1 \rightarrow 4)$-linked segments of glycogen. Type 4 is the most abundant type of residue.

(b)

CHAPTER 9

1. *trans*-Oleic acid has a higher melting point because, in the solid state, its hydrocarbon chains pack together more tightly than those of *cis*-oleic acid.

2. Of the $4 \times 4 = 16$ pairs of fatty acid residues at C1 and C3, only 10 are unique because a molecule with different substituents at C1 and C3 is identical to the molecule with the reverse substitution order. However, C2 may have any of the four substituents for a total of $4 \times 10 = 40$ different triacylglycerols.

3. The triacylglycerol containing the stearic acid residues yields more energy since it is fully reduced.

4.

5. (a) Palmitic acid and 2-oleoyl-3-phosphatidylserine;

(b) oleic acid and 1-palmitoyl-3-phosphatidylserine;

(c) phosphoserine and 1-palmitoyl-2-oleoyl-glycerol;

(d) serine and 1-palmitoyl-2-oleoyl-phosphatidic acid.

6. All except choline can form hydrogen bonds.

7. No; the two acyl chains of the "head group" are buried in the bilayer interior, leaving a head group of diphosphoglycerol.

8. Both DNA and phospholipids have exposed phosphate groups that are recognized by the antibodies.

9. Steroid hormones, which are hydrophobic, can diffuse through the cell membrane to reach their receptors.

10. Eicosanoids synthesized from arachidonic acid are necessary for intercellular communication. Cultured cells do not need such communication and therefore do not require linoleic acid.

11. Triacylglycerols lack polar head groups, so they do not orient themselves in a bilayer with their acyl chains inward and their glycerol moiety toward the surface.

12. The large oligosaccharide head groups of gangliosides would prevent efficient packing of the lipids in a bilayer.

13. (a) Saturated; (b) long-chain. By increasing the proportion of saturated and long-chain fatty acids, which have higher melting points, the bacteria can maintain constant membrane fluidity at the higher temperature.

14. (a) (1 turn/5.4 Å)(30 Å) = 5.6 turns

(b) (3.6 residues/turn)(5.6 turns) = 20 residues

(c) The additional residues form a helix, which partially satisfies backbone hydrogen bonding requirements, where the lipid head groups do not offer hydrogen bonding partners.

15. No. Although the β strand could span the bilayer, a single strand would be unstable because its backbone could not form the hydrogen bonds it would form with water in aqueous solution.

16. (a) Inner; (b) outer. See Fig. 9-32.

17. (a) Both the intra- and extracellular portions will be labeled. (b) Only the extracellular portion will be labeled. (c) Only the intracellular portion will be labeled.

18. The mutant signal peptidase would cleave many preproteins within their signal peptides, which often contain Leu-Leu sequences. This would not affect translocation into the ER, since signal peptidase acts after the signal peptide enters the ER lumen. Proteins lacking the Leu-Leu sequence would retain their signal peptides. These proteins, and those with abnormally cleaved signal sequences, would be more likely to fold abnormally and therefore function abnormally.

19. In order for a neuron to repeatedly release neurotransmitters, the components of its exocytotic machinery must be recycled. Following the fusion of synaptic vesicles with the plasma membrane, the four-helix SNARE complex is disassembled so that the Q-SNAREs remain in the plasma membrane while portions of the membrane containing R-SNAREs can be used to re-form synaptic vesicles. This recycling process would not be possible if the R- and Q-SNAREs remained associated, and the neuron would eventually be unable to release neurotransmitters.

CHAPTER 10

1. (a) Nonmediated; (b) mediated; (c) nonmediated; (d) mediated.

2. The less polar a substance, the faster it can diffuse through the lipid bilayer. From slowest to fastest: C, A, B.

3. $\Delta G = RT \ln \dfrac{[\text{Glucose}]_{in}}{[\text{Glucose}]_{out}}$

$= (8.3145 \text{ J} \cdot \text{K}^{-1} \cdot \text{mol}^{-1})(298 \text{ K}) \ln \dfrac{(0.003)}{(0.005)}$

$= -1270 \text{ J} \cdot \text{mol}^{-1} = -1.27 \text{ kJ} \cdot \text{mol}^{-1}$

4. (a) $\Delta G = RT \ln([Na^+]_{in}/[Na^+]_{out})$
$= (8.314 \text{ J} \cdot \text{K}^{-1} \cdot \text{mol}^{-1})(310 \text{ K})$
$(\ln[10 \text{ mM}/150 \text{ mM}])$
$= (8.314)(310)(-2.71) \text{ J} \cdot \text{mol}^{-1}$
$= -6980 \text{ J} \cdot \text{mol}^{-1} = -7.0 \text{ kJ} \cdot \text{mol}^{-1}$

(b) $\Delta G = RT \ln([Na^+]_{in}/[Na^+]_{out}) + Z_A\mathcal{F}\Delta\Psi$
$= -6980 + (1)(96,485 \text{ C} \cdot \text{mol}^{-1})(-0.06 \text{ J} \cdot \text{C}^{-1})$
$= -6980 \text{ J} \cdot \text{mol}^{-1} - 5790 \text{ J} \cdot \text{mol}^{-1}$
$= -12,770 \text{ J} \cdot \text{mol}^{-1} = -12.8 \text{ kJ} \cdot \text{mol}^{-1}$

5. Use Equation 10-3 and let $Z = 2$ and $T = 310$ K:

(a) $\Delta G = RT \ln\dfrac{[Ca^{2+}]_{in}}{[Ca^{2+}]_{out}} + Z\mathcal{F}\Delta\Psi$
$= (8.314 \text{ J} \cdot \text{K}^{-1} \cdot \text{mol}^{-1})(310 \text{ K})\ln(10^{-7})/(10^{-3})$
$+ (2)(96,485 \text{ J} \cdot \text{V}^{-1} \cdot \text{mol}^{-1})(-0.050 \text{ V})$
$= -23,700 \text{ J} \cdot \text{mol}^{-1} - 9600 \text{ J} \cdot \text{mol}^{-1}$
$= -33,300 \text{ J} \cdot \text{mol}^{-1} = -33.3 \text{ kJ} \cdot \text{mol}^{-1}$

The negative value of ΔG indicates a thermodynamically favorable process.

(b) $\Delta G = RT \ln\dfrac{[Ca^{2+}]_{in}}{[Ca^{2+}]_{out}} + Z\mathcal{F}\Delta\Psi$
$= (8.314 \text{ J} \cdot \text{K}^{-1} \cdot \text{mol}^{-1})(310 \text{ K})\ln(10^{-7})/(10^{-3})$
$+ (2)(96,485 \text{ J} \cdot \text{V}^{-1} \cdot \text{mol}^{-1})(+0.150 \text{ V})$
$= -23,700 \text{ J} \cdot \text{mol}^{-1} + 28,900 \text{ J} \cdot \text{mol}^{-1}$
$= +5,200 \text{ J} \cdot \text{mol}^{-1} = +5.2 \text{ kJ} \cdot \text{mol}^{-1}$

The positive value of ΔG indicates a thermodynamically unfavorable process.

6. K^+ transport ceases because the ionophore–K^+ complex cannot diffuse through the membrane when the lipids are immobilized in a gel-like state.

7. The number of ions to be transported is

$(10 \text{ mM})(100 \text{ } \mu\text{m}^3)(N)$
$= (0.010 \text{ mol} \cdot \text{L}^{-1})(10^{-13} \text{ L})(6.02 \times 10^{23} \text{ ions} \cdot \text{mol}^{-1})$
$= 6.02 \times 10^8 \text{ ions}$

Since there are 100 ionophores, each must transport 6.02×10^6 ions. The time required is $(6.02 \times 10^6 \text{ ions})(1 \text{ s}/10^4 \text{ ions}) = 602 \text{ s} = 10$ min.

8. (a) The data do not indicate the involvement of a transport protein, since the rate of transport does not approach a maximum as [X] increases.

(b) To verify that a transport protein is involved, increase [X] to demonstrate saturation of the transporter at high [X], or add a structural analog of X to compete with X for binding to the transporter, resulting in a lower flux of X.

9. In the absence of ATP, Na^+ extrusion by the $(Na^+$–$K^+)$–ATPase would cease, so no glucose could enter the cell by the Na^+–glucose symport. The glucose in the cell would then exit via the passive-mediated glucose transporter, and the cellular [glucose] would decrease until it matched the extracellular [glucose] (of course, the cell would probably osmotically burst before this could occur).

10. The hyperbolic curve for glucose transport into pericytes indicates a protein-mediated sodium-dependent process. The transport protein has binding sites for sodium ions. At low [Na^+], glucose transport is directly proportional to [Na^+]. However, at high [Na^+], all Na^+ binding sites on the transport protein are occupied, and thus glucose transport reaches a maximum velocity. Glucose transport into endothelial cells is not sodium-dependent and occurs at a high rate whether or not Na^+ is present. There is not enough information in the figure to determine whether glucose transport into endothelial cells is protein-mediated.

11. (a) No; there is no glycerol backbone.

(b) Miltefosine is amphipathic and therefore cannot cross the parasite cell membrane by diffusion. Since it is not a normal cell component, it probably does not have a dedicated active transporter. It most likely enters the cell via a passive transport protein.

(c) This amphipathic molecule most likely accumulates in membranes, with its hydrophobic tail buried in the bilayer and its polar head group exposed to the solvent.

(d) The protein recognizes the phosphocholine head group, which also occurs in some sphingolipids and some glycerophospholipids. Since the protein does not bind all phospholipids or triacylglycerols, it does not recognize the hydrocarbon tail.

12. (a) A transporter similar to a porin would be inadequate since even a large β barrel would be far too small to accommodate the massive ribosome. Likewise, a transport protein with alternating conformations would not be up to the task due to its small size relative to the ribosome. In addition, neither type of protein would be suited for transporting a particle across two membranes. (In fact, ribosomes and other large particles move between the nucleus and cytoplasm via nuclear pores, which are constructed from many different proteins and form a structure that is much larger than the ribosome and spans both nuclear membranes.

(b) Ribosomal transport might appear to be a thermodynamically favorable process, since the concentration of ribosomes is greater in the nucleus, where they are synthesized. However, free energy would ultimately be required to establish a pore (which would span two membrane thicknesses) for the ribosome to pass through. (In fact, the nucleocytoplasmic transport of all but very small substances requires the activity of GTPases that escort particles through the nuclear pore assembly and help ensure that transport proceeds in one direction.)

13. (a) Acetylcholine binding triggers the opening of the channel, an example of a ligand-gated transport protein.

(b) Na^+ ions flow into the muscle cell, where their concentration is low.

(c) The influx of positive charges causes the membrane potential to increase.

14. (a) pH $= -\log[H^+] = -\log(0.15) = 0.82$

The pH of the secreted HCl is over 6 pH units lower than the cytosolic pH, which corresponds to a [H^+] of $\sim 4 \times 10^{-8}$ M

(b) $CO_2 + H_2O \rightleftharpoons HCO_3^- + H^+$

(c)
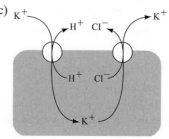

5. Overexpression of an MDR transporter would increase the ability of the cancer cell to excrete anticancer drugs. Higher concentrations of the drugs or different drugs would then be required to kill the drug-resistant cells.

CHAPTER 11

1. b

2. (a) isomerase (alanine racemase); (b) lyase (pyruvate decarboxylase); (c) oxidoreductase (lactate dehydrogenase); (d) ligase (glutamine synthetase).

3. As shown in Table 11-1, the only relationship between the rates of catalyzed and uncatalyzed reactions is that the catalyzed reaction is faster than the uncatalyzed reaction. The absolute rate of an uncatalyzed reaction does not correlate with the degree to which it is accelerated by an enzyme.

4. There are three transition states ($X^\ddagger$) and two intermediates (I). The reaction is not thermodynamically favorable because the free energy of the products is greater than that of the reactants.

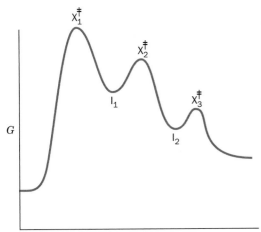

5. The tighter S binds to the enzyme, the greater the value of $\Delta G_E^\ddagger$. As $\Delta G_E^\ddagger$ approaches $\Delta G_N^\ddagger$ the rate of the enzyme-catalyzed reaction approaches the rate of the nonenzymatic reaction.

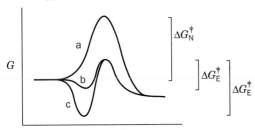

6. At 25°C, every 10-fold increase in rate corresponds to a decrease of about 5.7 kJ·mol^{-1} in $\Delta G^\ddagger$. For the nuclease, with a rate enhancement on the order of 10^{14}, $\Delta G^\ddagger$ is lowered about 14×5.7 kJ·mol^{-1}, or about 80 kJ·mol^{-1}. Alternatively, since the rate enhancement, k, is given by $k = e^{\Delta\Delta G_{cat}^\ddagger/RT}$,

$$\ln k = \ln(10^{14}) = \Delta\Delta G_{cat}^\ddagger/8.3145 \times (273 + 25)$$

Hence, $\Delta\Delta G_{cat}^\ddagger = 80$ kJ·mol^{-1}.

7. Glu has a pK of ~4 and, in its ionized form, acts as a base catalyst. Lys has a pK of ~10 and, in its protonated form, acts as an acid catalyst.

8. The active form of the enzyme contains the thiolate ion. The increased pK would increase the nucleophilicity of the thiolate and thereby increase the rate of the reaction catalyzed by the active form of the enzyme. However, at physiological pH, there would be less of the active form of the enzyme and therefore the overall rate would be decreased.

9. DNA lacks the 2′-OH group required for the formation of the 2′,3′-cyclic reaction intermediate.

10. Two such analogs are

Furan-2-carboxylate   **Thiophene-2-carboxylate**

Both of these molecules are planar, particularly at the C atom to which the carboxylate is bonded, as is true of the transition state for the proline racemase reaction.

11. The preferential binding of the transition state to an enzyme is an important (often the most important) part of an enzyme's catalytic mechanism. Hence, the substrate-binding site is the catalytic site.

12. The lysozyme active site is arranged to cleave oligosaccharides between the fourth and fifth residues. Moreover, since the lysozyme active site can bind at least six monosaccharide units, (NAG)$_6$ would be more tightly bound to the enzyme than (NAG)$_4$, and this additional binding free energy would be applied to distorting the D ring to its half-chair conformation, thereby facilitating the reaction.

13. Asp 101 and Arg 114 form hydrogen bonds with the substrate molecule (Fig. 11-19). Ala cannot form these hydrogen bonds, so the substituted enzyme is less active.

14.

Tosyl-L-alanine chloromethylketone   or

Tosyl-L-valine chloromethylketone

15. Yes. An enzyme decreases the activation energy barrier for both the forward and the reverse directions of a reaction.

16.

17. The observation that subtilisin and chymotrypsin are genetically

unrelated indicates that their active site geometries arose by convergent evolution. Assuming that evolution has optimized the catalytic efficiencies of these enzymes and that there is only one optimal arrangement of catalytic groups, any similarities between the active sites of subtilisin and chymotrypsin must be of catalytic significance. Conversely, any differences are unlikely to be catalytically important.

18. (a) Little or no effect; (b) catalysis would be much slower because the mutation disrupts the function of the catalytic triad.

19. Activated factor IXa leads, via several steps, to the activation of the final coagulation protease, thrombin. The absence of factor IX therefore slows the production of thrombin, delaying clot formation, and causing the bleeding of hemophilia. Although activated factor XIa also leads to thrombin production, factor XI plays no role until it is activated by thrombin itself. By this point, coagulation is already well underway, so a deficiency of factor XI does not significantly delay coagulation.

20. As a digestive enzyme, chymotrypsin's function is to indiscriminately degrade a wide variety of ingested proteins, so that their component amino acids can be recovered. Broad substrate specificity would be dangerous for a protease that functions outside of the digestive system, since it might degrade proteins other than its intended target.

21. If the soybean trypsin inhibitor were not removed from tofu, it would inhibit the trypsin in the intestine. At best, this would reduce the nutritional value of the meal by rendering its protein indigestible. It might very well also lead to intestinal upset.

CHAPTER 12

1. (a) $v = k[A]$
$k = v/[A]$
$k = (5\ \mu M \cdot min^{-1})/(20\ mM)$
$= (0.005\ mM \cdot min^{-1})/(20\ mM)$
$= 2.5 \times 10^{-4}\ min^{-1}$

(b) The reaction has a molecularity of 1.

2. From Eq. 12-7, $[A] = [A]_o\ e^{-kt}$. Since $t_{1/2} = 0.693/k$, $k = 0.693/14\ d = 0.05\ d^{-1}$. (a) 7 μmol; (b) 5 μmol; (c) 3.5 μmol; (d) 0.3 μmol.

3. $v = k[A]^2$
$v = (10^{-6}\ M^{-1} \cdot s^{-1})(0.010\ M)(0.010\ M)$
$v = 10^{-10}\ M \cdot s^{-1}$

4. For Reaction A, only a plot of 1/[reactant] versus t gives a straight line, so the reaction is second order. The slope, k, is $0.15\ mM^{-1} \cdot s^{-1}$. For Reaction B, only a plot of ln[reactant] versus t gives a straight line, so the reaction is first order. The negative of the slope, k, is $0.17\ s^{-1}$.

Time (s)	Reaction A 1/[reactant] (mM⁻¹)	Reaction B ln[reactant]
0	0.16	1.69
1	0.32	1.53
2	0.48	1.36
3	0.62	1.16
4	0.77	0.99
5	0.91	0.83

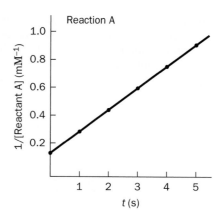

Reaction A

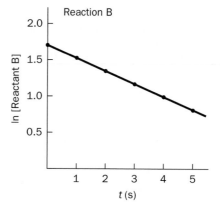

Reaction B

5.

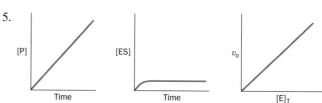

6. Enzyme activity is measured as an initial reaction velocity, the velocity before much substrate has been depleted and before much product has been generated. It is easier to measure the appearance of a small amount of product from a baseline of zero product than to measure the disappearance of a small amount of substrate against a background of a high concentration of substrate.

7. $v_o = V_{max}[S]/(K_M + [S])$

$v_o/V_{max} = [S]/(K_M + [S])$

$0.95 = [S]/(K_M + [S])$

$[S] = 0.95 K_M + 0.95[S]$

$0.05[S] = 0.95\ K_M$

$[S] = (0.95/0.05)K_M = 19\ K_M$

8. Acetylcholinesterase, carbonic anhydrase, catalase, and fumarase.

9. Set A corresponds to $[S] > K_M$, and set B corresponds to $[S] < K_M$. Ideally, a single data set should include $[S]$ values that are both larger and smaller than K_M.

Set A [S] (mM)	v_o (μM·s^{-1})	Set B [S] (mM)	v_o (μM·s^{-1})
2	0.42	0.12	0.17
1	0.38	0.10	0.15
0.67	0.34	0.08	0.13
0.50	0.32	0.07	0.11

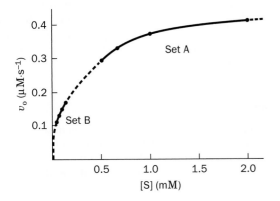

0. Construct a Lineweaver–Burk plot.

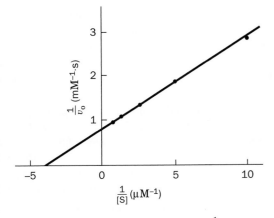

$K_M = -1/x\text{-intercept} = -1/(-4\ \mu\text{M}^{-1}) = 0.25\ \mu\text{M}$

$V_{max} = 1/y\text{-intercept} = 1/(0.8\ \text{mM}^{-1}\cdot\text{s}) = 1.25\ \text{mM}\cdot\text{s}^{-1}$

11. Comparing the two data points, since a 100-fold increase in substrate concentration only produces a 10-fold increase in reaction velocity, it appears that when [S] = 100 mM, the velocity is close to V_{max}. Therefore, assume that $V_{max} \approx 50\ \mu\text{M}\cdot\text{s}^{-1}$ and use the other data point to estimate K_M using the Michaelis–Menten equation:

$$v_o = \frac{V_{max}[S]}{K_M + [S]}$$

$$K_M + [S] = \frac{V_{max}[S]}{v_o}$$

$$K_M = \frac{V_{max}[S]}{v_o} - [S]$$

$$K_M = \frac{(50\ \mu\text{M}\cdot\text{s}^{-1})(1\ \mu\text{M})}{(5\ \mu\text{M}\cdot\text{s}^{-1})} - (1\ \mu\text{M}) = 9\ \mu\text{M}$$

The true V_{max} must be greater than the estimated value, so the value of K_M is an underestimate of the true K_M.

12. The experimentally determined K_M would be greater than the true K_M because the actual substrate concentration is less than expected.

13. The enzyme concentration is comparable to the lowest substrate concentration and therefore does not meet the requirement that [E] ≪ [S]. You could fix this problem by decreasing the amount of enzyme used for each measurement.

14. Velocity measurements can be made using any convenient unit of change per unit of time. K_M is, by definition, a substrate concentration (the concentration when $v_o = V_{max}/2$), so its value does not reflect how the velocity is measured.

15. (a, b) It is not necessary to know [E]$_T$. The only variables required to determine K_M and V_{max} (for example, by constructing a Lineweaver–Burk plot) are [S] and v_o. (c) The value of [E]$_T$ is required to calculate k_{cat} since $k_{cat} = V_{max}/[E]_T$.

16. (a) N-Acetyltyrosine ethyl ester, which has the lower value of K_M, has greater apparent affinity for chymotrypsin. (b) The value of V_{max} is not related to the value of K_M, so no conclusion can be drawn.

17. Product P will be more abundant because enzyme A has a much lower K_M for the substrate than enzyme B. Because V_{max} is approximately the same for the two enzymes, the relative efficiency of the enzymes depends almost entirely on their K_M values.

18. (a, b) A* will appear only if the reaction follows a Ping Pong mechanism, since only a double-displacement reaction can exchange an isotope from P back to A in the absence of B. Hence, in a reaction that has a sequential mechanism, A will not become isotopically labeled.

19. The lines of the double-reciprocal plots intersect to the left of the $1/v_o$ axis (on the $1/[S]$ axis). Hence, inhibition is mixed (with $\alpha = \alpha'$).

[S]	1/[S]	$1/v_o$	$1/v_o$ with I
1	1.00	0.7692	1.2500
2	0.50	0.5000	0.8333
4	0.25	0.3571	0.5882
8	0.125	0.2778	0.4545
12	0.083	0.2500	0.4167

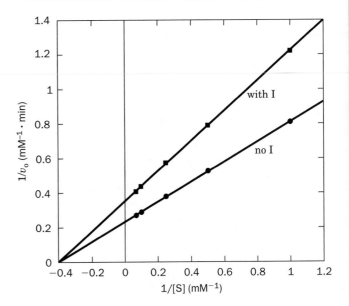

20. From Eq. 12-32, α is 3.

$$\alpha = 3 = 1 + [I]/K_I = 1 + 5\text{ mM}/K_I$$
$$K_I = 2.5\text{ mM}$$

21. (a) Inhibition is most likely mixed (noncompetitive) with $\alpha = \alpha'$ since it is reversible and only V_{max} is affected.

(b) Since $V_{max}^{app} = 0.8\ V_{max}$, 80% of the enzyme remains uninhibited. Therefore, 20% of the enzyme molecules have bound inhibitor.

(c) As indicated in Table 12-2 for mixed inhibition, $V_{max}^{app} = V_{max}/\alpha'$. Thus,

$$\alpha' = \frac{V_{max}}{V_{max}^{app}} = \frac{1}{0.8} = 1.25$$

From Eq. 12-32,

$$1.25 = 1 + \frac{[I]}{K_I'}$$

$$K_I' = \frac{5\text{ nM}}{1.25 - 1} = 20\text{ nM}$$

22. By irreversibly reacting with chymotrypsin's active site, DIPF would decrease $[E]_T$. The apparent V_{max} would decrease since $V_{max} = k_{cat}[E]_T$. K_M would not be affected since the uninhibited enzyme would bind substrate normally.

23. (a) If an irreversible inhibitor is present, the enzyme solution's activity would be exactly 100 times lower when the sample is diluted 100-fold. Dilution would not significantly change the enzyme's degree of inhibition. (b) For reversible inhibition, $K_I = [E][I]/[EI]$ so that $[E]/[EI] = K_I/[I]$. Hence, if a reversible inhibitor is present, dilution would lower the concentrations of both the enzyme and inhibitor so that the degree of dissociation of the inhibitor from the enzyme would increase. The enzyme solution's activity would therefore not be exactly 100 times less than the undiluted sample, but would be somewhat greater than that value because the proportion of uninhibited enzyme would be greater at the lower concentration.

24. Enzyme Y is more efficient at low [S]; enzyme X is more efficient at high [S].

25.

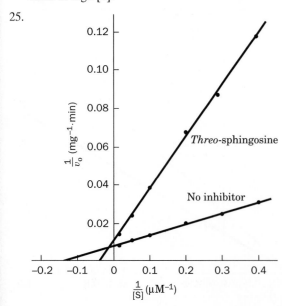

(a) K_M is determined from the x-intercept ($= -1/K_M$). In the absence of inhibitor, $K_M = 1/0.14\ \mu M^{-1} = 7\ \mu M$. In the presence of inhibitor, $K_M^{app} = 1/0.04\ \mu M^{-1} = 25\ \mu M$. V_{max} is determined from the y-intercept ($= 1/V_{max}$). In the absence of inhibitor, $V_{max} = 1/0.008\text{ mg}^{-1} \cdot \text{min} = 125\text{ mg} \cdot \text{min}^{-1}$. In the presence of inhibitor, $V_{max}^{app} = 1/0.01\text{ mg}^{-1} \cdot \text{min} = 100\text{ mg} \cdot \text{min}^{-1}$.

(b) The lines in the double-reciprocal plots intersect very close to the $1/v_o$ axis. Hence, *threo*-sphingosine is most likely a competitive inhibitor. Competitive inhibition is likely also because of the structural similarity between the inhibitor and the substrate, which allows them to compete for binding to the enzyme active site.

CHAPTER 13

1. (a) Yes, because the binding of Src's SH3 domain to the linker that connects its SH2 domain to the N-terminal lobe of its PTK domain is required for Src to maintain its autoinhibited conformation. Hence, the deletion of this SH3 domain would constitutively activate Src, thereby driving the cell with this mutation to a state of unrestrained proliferation.

(b) No, because the phosphorylation of Tyr 416 is required for the activation of Src and hence the Y416F mutation would inhibit the mutant cell's proliferation.

(c) Yes, because the phosphorylation of Tyr 527 is required for the autoinhibition of Src via the binding of its SH2 domain and hence the Y527F mutant Src would be constitutively activated.

(d) No, because replacing the wild-type Glu at position 253 of Src with Pro would make the 250 to 253 segment of Src into a normal Pro-X-X-Pro binding target for the SH3 domain, thereby stabilizing Src's autoinhibited conformation.

2. In the presence of the viral protein, the cell would undergo more cycles of cell division in response to the growth factor.

3. Cell transformation results from several genetic changes in a cell. Thus, a single oncogene supplied to an otherwise normal cell will be insufficient to transform it. However, an immortalized cell already has some of the genetic changes necessary for transformation (malignant cells are also immortal). In such cells, the additional oncogene may be all they require to complete their transformation.

4. Because the GTP analog cannot be hydrolyzed, G_α remains active. Analog binding to G_s therefore increases cAMP production. Analog binding to G_i decreases cAMP production.

5. When $G_{s\alpha}$ catalyzes the hydrolysis of its bound GTP to GDP + P_i, the Arg side chain that cholera toxin ADP-ribosylates functions to stabilize the transition state's developing negative charge. The ADP-ribosylated $G_{s\alpha}$ therefore hydrolyzes its bound GTP at a greatly reduced rate and hence remains activated far longer than normal $G_{s\alpha}$. Mutating this Arg will have a similar effect. Consequently, in cells in which a $G_{s\alpha} \cdot$ GTP functions to induce cell proliferation, mutating this Arg will drive the cell into a state of unrestrained proliferation, a requirement for the malignant transformation of the cell. The gene encoding such a $G_{s\alpha}$ subunit is a proto-oncogene and the mutation of its Arg residue converts it to an oncogene. Cholera toxin does not

cause cancer because the $G_{s\alpha}$ it ADP-ribosylates only mediates the intestinal cell's secretion of digestive fluid, not its rate of proliferation. Moreover, cholera toxin does not pass through the intestine to the other tissues and hence does not affect other cells. However, even if it did so, its effect would only last as long as the cholera infection, whereas a mutation permanently affects the cell in which it has occurred and all its progeny.

6. No. Although the diacylglycerol second messengers are identical, phosphatidylethanolamine does not generate an IP_3 second messenger that triggers the release of Ca^{2+}, which in turn alters protein kinase C activity.

7. Pertussis toxin ADP ribosylates $G_{i\alpha}$ so as to prevent it from exchanging its bound GDP for GTP and hence from releasing $G_{\beta\gamma}$ upon interacting with its cognate activated GPCRs. The PLC-β isozymes, which are activated through their association with free $G_{\beta\gamma}$, are effectively inhibited by pertussis toxin as a consequence of the reduction in the $G_{\beta\gamma}$ concentration that it causes.

8. The C1 domain of PKC binds to membrane-bound DAG, whereas its C2 domain binds membrane-bound phosphatidylserine in a Ca^{2+}-mediated manner. The simultaneous binding of both of these domains to the membrane conformationally extracts the adjacent N-terminal pseudosubstrate from PKC's active site, thereby activating it. If the pseudosubstrate were relocated to the PKC's C-terminus, the simultaneous binding to the membrane of C1 and C2, which are on the N-terminal side of the protein kinase, would be unlikely to conformationally extract the pseudosubstrate from the protein kinase's active site. Hence the protein kinase would remain inhibited even when C1 and C2 were both bound to the membrane.

9. (a) Diacylglycerol kinase converts DAG to phosphatidic acid (Section 9-1C).

(b) Activation of the kinase converts the nonpolar DAG to a more amphiphilic molecule that can no longer activate protein kinase C. In effect, the kinase limits the activity of one of the second messengers produced during signaling by the phosphoinositide pathway.

10. Li^+ blocks the conversion of phosphorylated inositol species to inositol, thereby preventing the recycling of IP_3 and its degradation products back to inositol. This in turn prevents the synthesis of phosphatidylinositol and PIP_2, the precursor of the IP_3 second messenger.

CHAPTER 14

1. C, D, A, E, B

2. (a) Since $\Delta G^{\circ\prime} = -RT \ln K$,

$$K = e^{-\Delta G^{\circ\prime}/RT}$$
$$K = e^{-(7500 \text{ J}\cdot\text{mol}^{-1})/(8.3145 \text{ J}\cdot\text{K}^{-1}\cdot\text{mol}^{-1})(298 \text{ K})}$$
$$K = 0.048$$

(b) $\Delta G = \Delta G^{\circ\prime} + RT \ln \dfrac{[B]}{[A]}$

$$\Delta G = 7500 \text{ J}\cdot\text{mol}^{-1}$$
$$+ (8.3145 \text{ J}\cdot\text{K}^{-1}\cdot\text{mol}^{-1})(310 \text{ K})\ln\dfrac{(0.0001)}{(0.0005)}$$
$$\Delta G = 7500 \text{ J}\cdot\text{mol}^{-1} - 4150 \text{ J}\cdot\text{mol}^{-1}$$
$$\Delta G = 3350 \text{ J}\cdot\text{mol}^{-1} = 3.35 \text{ kJ}\cdot\text{mol}^{-1}$$

The reaction is not spontaneous since $\Delta G > 0$.

(c) The reaction can proceed in the cell if the product B is the substrate for a second reaction such that the second reaction continually draws off B, causing the first reaction to continually produce more B from A.

3. b

4. The theoretical maximum yield of ATP is equivalent to ($\Delta G^{\circ\prime}$ for fuel oxidation)/($\Delta G^{\circ\prime}$ for ATP synthesis).

(a) $(-2850 \text{ kJ}\cdot\text{mol}^{-1})/(-30.5 \text{ kJ}\cdot\text{mol}^{-1}) \approx 93$ ATP

(b) $(-9781 \text{ kJ}\cdot\text{mol}^{-1})/(-30.5 \text{ kJ}\cdot\text{mol}^{-1}) \approx 320$ ATP

5. At pH 6, the phosphate groups are more ionized than they are at pH 5, which increases their electrostatic repulsion and therefore increases the magnitude of ΔG for hydrolysis (makes it more negative).

6. The exergonic hydrolysis of PP_i by pyrophosphatase ($\Delta G^{\circ\prime} = -19.2 \text{ kJ}\cdot\text{mol}^{-1}$) drives fatty acid activation.

7. Calculating ΔG for the reaction ATP + creatine $\rightleftharpoons$ phosphocreatine + ADP, using Eq. 14-1:

$$\Delta G = \Delta G^{\circ\prime} + RT \ln\left(\dfrac{[\text{phosphocreatine}][\text{ADP}]}{[\text{creatine}][\text{ATP}]}\right)$$

$$= 12.6 \text{ kJ}\cdot\text{mol}^{-1} + (8.3145 \text{ J}\cdot\text{K}^{-1}\cdot\text{mol}^{-1})(298 \text{ K})$$
$$\ln\left(\dfrac{(2.5 \text{ mM})(0.15 \text{ mM})}{(1 \text{ mM})(4 \text{ mM})}\right)$$

$$= 12.6 \text{ kJ}\cdot\text{mol}^{-1} - 5.9 \text{ kJ}\cdot\text{mol}^{-1} = 6.7 \text{ kJ}\cdot\text{mol}^{-1}$$

Since $\Delta G > 0$, the reaction will proceed in the opposite direction as written above, that is, in the direction of ATP synthesis.

8. Using the data in Table 14-4, we calculate $\Delta G^{\circ\prime}$ for the adenylate kinase reaction.

	$\Delta G^{\circ\prime}$
ATP + $H_2O \rightarrow$ AMP + PP_i	$-45.6 \text{ kJ}\cdot\text{mol}^{-1}$
2 ADP + 2 $P_i \rightarrow$ 2 ATP + 2 H_2O	$2 \times 30.5 \text{ kJ}\cdot\text{mol}^{-1}$
	$= 61.0 \text{ kJ}\cdot\text{mol}^{-1}$
$PP_i + H_2O \rightarrow 2 P_i$	$-19.2 \text{ kJ}\cdot\text{mol}^{-1}$
2 ADP $\rightarrow$ ATP + AMP	$-3.8 \text{ kJ}\cdot\text{mol}^{-1}$

Since ΔG for a reaction at equilibrium is zero, Eq. 14-1 becomes $\Delta G^{\circ\prime} = -RT \ln K_{eq}$ so that $K_{eq} = e^{-\Delta G^{\circ\prime}/RT}$.

$$K_{eq} = \dfrac{[\text{ATP}][\text{AMP}]}{[\text{ADP}]^2} = e^{-\Delta G^{\circ\prime}/RT}$$

$$[\text{AMP}] = \dfrac{(5 \times 10^{-4}\,\text{M})^2}{(5 \times 10^{-3}\,\text{M})}$$
$$\times e^{-(-3800 \text{ J}\cdot\text{mol}^{-1})/(8.3145 \text{ J}\cdot\text{K}^{-1}\cdot\text{mol}^{-1})(298 \text{ K})}$$

$$[\text{AMP}] = 2.3 \times 10^{-4} \text{ M} = 0.23 \text{ mM}$$

9. The more positive the reduction potential, the greater the oxidizing power. From Table 14-5,

Compound	$\mathscr{E}^{\circ\prime}$ (V)
SO_4^{2-}	-0.515
Acetoacetate	-0.346
NAD^+	-0.315
Pyruvate	-0.185
Cytochrome b (Fe^{3+})	0.077

10. The balanced equation is

2 cyto c (Fe^{3+}) + ubiquinol →

2 cyto c (Fe^{2+}) + ubiquinone + 2H$^+$

Using the data in Table 14-5,

$\Delta\mathscr{E}^{\circ\prime} = \mathscr{E}^{\circ\prime}_{(e^- \text{ acceptor})} - \mathscr{E}^{\circ\prime}_{(e^- \text{ donor})} = 0.235 \text{ V} - 0.045 \text{ V}$
$= 0.190 \text{ V}$
$\Delta G^{\circ\prime} = -n\mathscr{F}\Delta\mathscr{E}^{\circ\prime} = -(2)(96,485 \text{ J} \cdot \text{V}^{-1} \cdot \text{mol}^{-1})(0.190 \text{ V})$
$= -36.7 \text{ kJ} \cdot \text{mol}^{-1}$

11. Using the data in Table 14-5:

(a) $\Delta\mathscr{E}^{\circ\prime} = \mathscr{E}^{\circ\prime}_{(e^- \text{ acceptor})} - \mathscr{E}^{\circ\prime}_{(e^- \text{ donor})} = \mathscr{E}^{\circ\prime}_{(\text{fumarate})} - \mathscr{E}^{\circ\prime}_{(\text{NAD}^+)}$
$= 0.031 \text{ V} - (-0.315 \text{ V}) = 0.346 \text{ V}$. Because $\Delta\mathscr{E}^{\circ\prime} > 0$,
$\Delta G^{\circ\prime} < 0$ and the reaction will spontaneously proceed as written.

(b) $\Delta\mathscr{E}^{\circ\prime} = \mathscr{E}^{\circ\prime}_{(e^- \text{ acceptor})} - \Delta\mathscr{E}^{\circ\prime}_{(e^- \text{ donor})} = \mathscr{E}^{\circ\prime}_{(\text{cyto } b)} - \mathscr{E}^{\circ\prime}_{(\text{cyto } a)} =$
$0.077 \text{ V} - (0.290 \text{ V}) = -0.213 \text{ V}$. Because $\Delta\mathscr{E}^{\circ\prime} < 0$,
$\Delta G^{\circ\prime} > 0$ and the reaction will spontaneously proceed in the opposite direction from that written.

12. Using the data in Table 14-5, for the oxidation of free FADH$_2$ ($\mathscr{E}^{\circ\prime} = -0.219 \text{ V}$) by ubiquinone ($\mathscr{E}^{\circ\prime} = 0.045 \text{ V}$),

$\Delta\mathscr{E}^{\circ\prime} = \mathscr{E}^{\circ\prime}_{(\text{ubiquinone})} - \mathscr{E}^{\circ\prime}_{(\text{FADH}_2)}$
$= (0.045 \text{ V}) - (-0.219 \text{ V}) = 0.264 \text{ V}$
$\Delta G^{\circ\prime} = -n\mathscr{F}\Delta\mathscr{E}^{\circ\prime} = -(2)(96,485 \text{ J} \cdot \text{V}^{-1} \cdot \text{mol}^{-1})$
$(0.264 \text{ V}) = -50.9 \text{ kJ} \cdot \text{mol}^{-1}$

This is more than enough free energy to drive the synthesis of ATP from ADP + P$_i$ ($\Delta G^{\circ\prime} = +30.5 \text{ kJ} \cdot \text{mol}^{-1}$; Table 14.4).

13. $Z \xrightarrow{B} W \xrightarrow{C} Y \xrightarrow{A} X$

14. (a) The step catalyzed by enzyme Y is likely to be the major flux-control point, since this step operates farthest from equilibrium (it is an irreversible step). (b) Inhibition of enzyme Z would cause the concentration of D, the reaction's product, to decrease, and it would cause C, the reaction's substrate, to accumulate. The concentrations of A and B would not change because the steps catalyzed by enzymes X and Y would not be affected. The accumulated C would not be transformed back to B since the step catalyzed by enzyme Y is irreversible.

CHAPTER 15

1. (a) Reactions 1, 3, 7, and 10; (b) Reactions 2, 5, and 8; (c) Reaction 6; (d) Reaction 9; (e) Reaction 4.

2. C1 of DHAP and C1 of GAP are achiral but become chiral in FBP (as C3 and C4). There are four stereoisomeric products that differ in configuration at C3 and C4: fructose-1,6-bisphosphate, psicose-1,6-bisphosphate, tagatose-1,6-bisphosphate, and sorbose-1,6-bisphosphate (see Fig. 8-2).

3. The Zn^{2+} polarizes the carbonyl oxygen of the substrate to stabilize the enolate intermediate of the reaction.

4. (a) Glucose + 2 NAD$^+$ + 2 ADP + 2 P$_i$ →
2 pyruvate + 2 NADH + 2 ATP + 2 H$_2$O

(b) Glucose + 2 NAD$^+$ + 2 ADP + 2 AsO$_4^{3-}$ →
2 pyruvate + 2 NADH + 2 ADP—AsO$_3^{2-}$ + 2 H$_2$O
2 ADP—AsO$_3^{2-}$ + 2 H$_2$O → 2 ADP + 2 AsO$_4^{3-}$

Overall: Glucose + 2 NAD$^+$ → 2 pyruvate + 2 NADH

(c) Arsenate is a poison because it uncouples ATP generation from glycolysis. Consequently, glycolytic energy generation cannot occur.

5. ribulose-5-phosphate isomerase reaction: ribulose-5-phosphate epimerase reaction:

1,2-Enediolate intermediate   **2,3-Enediolate intermediate**

6. (a) ΔG values differ from $\Delta G^{\circ\prime}$ values because $\Delta G = \Delta G^{\circ\prime} + RT \ln[\text{Products}]/[\text{Reactants}]$ and cellular reactants and products are not in their standard states.

(b) Yes. The same *in vivo* conditions that decrease the magnitude of ΔG relative to $\Delta G^{\circ\prime}$ may also decrease ΔG for ATP synthesis.

7. When [GAP] = 10^{-4} M, [DHAP] = 5.5×10^{-4} M. According to Eq. 1-17,

$K = e^{-\Delta G^{\circ\prime}/RT}$

$\dfrac{[\text{GAP}][\text{DHAP}]}{[\text{FBP}]} = e^{-(22,800 \text{ J} \cdot \text{mol}^{-1})/(8.3145 \text{ J} \cdot \text{K}^{-1} \cdot \text{mol}^{-1})(310 \text{ K})}$

$\dfrac{(10^{-4})(5.5 \times 10^{-4})}{[\text{FBP}]} = 1.4 \times 10^{-4}$

$[\text{FBP}] = 3.8 \times 10^{-4} \text{ M}$

$[\text{FBP}]/[\text{GAP}] = (3.8 \times 10^{-4} \text{ M})/(10^{-4} \text{ M}) = 3.8$

8. For the coupled reaction

Pyruvate + NADH + H$^+$ ⟶ lactate + NAD$^+$

$\Delta\mathscr{E}^{\circ\prime} = (-0.185 \text{ V}) - (-0.315 \text{ V}) = 0.130 \text{ V}$. According to Eq. 14-8

$\Delta\mathscr{E} = \Delta\mathscr{E}^{\circ\prime} - \dfrac{RT}{n\mathscr{F}} \ln\left(\dfrac{[\text{lactate}][\text{NAD}^+]}{[\text{pyruvate}][\text{NADH}]}\right)$

and $\Delta G = -n\mathscr{F}\Delta\mathscr{E}$ (Eq. 14-7). Since two electrons are transferred in the above reaction, $n = 2$.

(a) $\Delta\mathscr{E} = 0.130 \text{ V} - \dfrac{RT}{nF} \ln(1) = 0.130 \text{ V}$

$\Delta G = -(2)(96,485 \text{ J} \cdot \text{V}^{-1} \cdot \text{mol}^{-1})(0.130 \text{ V})$
$= -25.1 \text{ kJ} \cdot \text{mol}^{-1}$

(b) $RT/n\mathscr{F} = (8.3145 \text{ J} \cdot \text{K}^{-1} \cdot \text{mol}^{-1})(298 \text{ K})/$
$(2)(96,485 \text{ J} \cdot \text{V}^{-1} \cdot \text{mol}^{-1}) = 0.01284 \text{ V}$
$\Delta\mathscr{E} = 0.130 \text{ V} - 0.01284 \text{ V} \ln(160 \times 160)$
$\Delta\mathscr{E} = 0.130 \text{ V} - 0.130 \text{ V} = 0$
$\Delta G = 0$

(c) $\Delta\mathscr{E} = 0.130 \text{ V} - 0.01284 \text{ V} \ln(1000 \times 1000)$
$\Delta\mathscr{E} = 0.130 \text{ V} - 0.177 \text{ V} = -0.047 \text{ V}$
$\Delta G = -(2)(96,485 \text{ J} \cdot \text{V}^{-1} \cdot \text{mol}^{-1})(-0.047 \text{ V})$
$= 9.1 \text{ kJ} \cdot \text{mol}^{-1}$

(d) At the concentration ratios of Part a, ΔG is negative and the reaction proceeds as written. As [lactate]/[pyruvate] increases, the reaction ΔG increases even though [NAD$^+$]/[NADH] also increases so that in Part b the reaction is at equilibrium ($\Delta G = 0$) and in Part c ΔG is positive and the reaction proceeds spontaneously in the opposite direction.

9. (a) Pyruvate kinase regulation is important for controlling the flux of metabolites, such as fructose (in liver), which enter glycolysis after the PFK step.

   (b) FBP is the product of the third reaction of glycolysis, so it acts as a feed-forward activator of the enzyme that catalyzes Step 10. This regulatory mechanism helps ensure that once metabolites pass the PFK step of glycolysis, they will continue through the pathway.

0. The three glucose molecules that proceed through glycolysis yield 6 ATP. The bypass through the pentose phosphate pathway results in a yield of 5 ATP.

1. The label will appear at C1 and C3 of F6P (see Fig. 15-30).

2. (a) Transketolase transfers 2-carbon units from a ketose to an aldose, so the products are a 3-carbon sugar and a 7-carbon sugar. (b) The products are a 4-carbon sugar and a 7-carbon sugar. The order of binding does matter. The ketose binds first and transfers the 2-carbon unit to the TPP on the enzyme. The aldose then binds and accepts the 2-carbon unit.

3. Even when the flux of glucose through glycolysis and hence the citric acid cycle is blocked, glucose can be oxidized by the pentose phosphate pathway, with the generation of CO_2.

4. The liver enzyme is far more sensitive than the brain enzyme to the three activators. It is possible that liver PFK-1 is subject to a greater degree of regulation than brain PFK-1. Fuel must be supplied to the brain continuously and thus glycolysis is always active, but the liver has a wide variety of physiological roles and is more likely to regulate cellular pathways.

5. (a)

   COO$^-$ H   O
   | \\ //
   C=O   C
   | |
   CH$_3$ +   H—C—OH
                     CH$_2$OPO$_3^{2-}$

   Pyruvate   **GAP**

   (b) The pyruvate product of the aldolase reaction is not further modified. The GAP product is converted to pyruvate by the actions of the glycolytic enzymes glyceraldehyde-3-phosphate dehydrogenase, phosphoglycerate kinase, phosphoglycerate mutase, enolase, and pyruvate kinase.

   (c) One ATP is consumed when glucose is converted to glucose-6-phosphate. One ATP is generated by the phosphoglycerate kinase reaction and one by the pyruvate kinase reaction (these quantities are not doubled because only one three-carbon fragment of glucose follows this route), for a net yield of one ATP per glucose. The standard glycolytic pathway generates two ATP per glucose.

CHAPTER 16

1. (a) +9 ATP, (b) +6 ATP, (c) −18 ATP.

2. (a) The overall reaction for glycolysis is

   Glucose + 2 NAD$^+$ + 2 ADP + 2 P$_i$ $\longrightarrow$
        2 pyruvate + 2 NADH + 4 H$^+$ + 2 ATP + 2 H$_2$O

The overall reaction for gluconeogenesis is

2 Pyruvate + 2 NADH + 4 H$^+$ + 4 ATP + 2 GTP + 6 H$_2$O
     $\longrightarrow$ glucose + 2 NAD$^+$ + 4 ADP + 2 GDP + 6 P$_i$

For the two processes operating sequentially,

2 ATP + 2 GTP + 4 H$_2$O $\longrightarrow$ 2 ADP + 2 GDP + 4 P$_i$

(b) The reaction for catabolism of 6 G6P by the pentose phosphate pathway is

6 G6P + 12 NADP$^+$ + 6 H$_2$O $\longrightarrow$
         6 Ru5P + 12 NADPH + 12 H$^+$ + 6 CO$_2$

Ru5P can be converted to G6P by transaldolase, transketolase, and gluconeogenesis:

6 Ru5P + H$_2$O $\longrightarrow$ 5 G6P + P$_i$

The net equation is therefore

G6P + 12 NADP$^+$ + 7 H$_2$O $\longrightarrow$
         12 NADPH + 12 H$^+$ + 6 CO$_2$ + P$_i$

3. Phosphoglucokinase activity generates G1,6P, which is necessary to "prime" phosphoglucomutase that has become dephosphorylated and thereby inactivated through the loss of its G1,6P reaction intermediate.

4. The overall free energy change for debranching is

Breaking $\alpha(1 \rightarrow 4)$ bond	$\Delta G^{\circ\prime} = -15.5 \text{ kJ} \cdot \text{mol}^{-1}$
Forming $\alpha(1 \rightarrow 4)$ bond	$+15.5 \text{ kJ} \cdot \text{mol}^{-1}$
Hydrolyzing $\alpha(1 \rightarrow 6)$ bond	$-7.1 \text{ kJ} \cdot \text{mol}^{-1}$
Total	$\Delta G^{\circ\prime} = -7.1 \text{ kJ} \cdot \text{mol}^{-1}$

The overall free energy change for branching is

Breaking $\alpha(1 \rightarrow 4)$ bond	$\Delta G^{\circ\prime} = -15.5 \text{ kJ} \cdot \text{mol}^{-1}$
Forming $\alpha(1 \rightarrow 6)$ bond	$+7.1 \text{ kJ} \cdot \text{mol}^{-1}$
Total	$\Delta G^{\circ\prime} = -8.4 \text{ kJ} \cdot \text{mol}^{-1}$

Assuming that $\Delta G^{\circ\prime}$ is close to ΔG, the sum of the two reactions of branching has $\Delta G < 0$, but debranching would be endergonic ($\Delta G > 0$) without the additional step of hydrolyzing the $\alpha(1 \rightarrow 6)$ bond to form glucose.

5. A glycogen molecule with 28 tiers would represent the most efficient arrangement for storing glucose, and its outermost tier would contain considerably more glucose residues than a glycogen molecule with only 12 tiers. However, densely packed glucose residues would be inaccessible to phosphorylase. In fact, such a dense glycogen molecule could not be synthesized because glycogen synthase and branching enzyme would have no room to operate (see Box 16-3 for a discussion of glycogen structure).

6. In the course of glucose catabolism, a detour through glycogen synthesis and glycogen breakdown begins and ends with G6P. The energy cost of this detour is 1 ATP equivalent, consumed in the UDP–glucose pyrophosphorylase step. The overall energy lost is therefore 1/32 or ~3%.

7. This mechanism allows glycogen phosphorylase activity to be regulated by the concentration of glucose so that glycogen is not broken down when glucose is already plentiful.

8. (a) Circulating [glucose] is high because cells do not respond to the insulin signal to take up glucose.

   (b) Insulin is unable to activate phosphoprotein phosphatase-1 in muscle, so glycogen synthesis is not stimulated. Moreover, glycogen synthesis is much reduced by the lack of available glucose in the cell.

9. A defect in G6P transport would have the symptoms of glucose-6-phosphatase deficiency: accumulation of glycogen and hypoglycemia.

10. The conversion of circulating glucose to lactate in the muscle generates 2 ATP. If muscle glycogen could be mobilized, the energy yield would be 3 ATP, since phosphorolysis of glycogen bypasses the hexokinase-catalyzed step that consumes ATP in the first stage of glycolysis.

11. The deficiency is in branching enzyme (Type IV glycogen storage disease). The high ratio of G1P to glucose indicates abnormally long chains of $\alpha(1 \rightarrow 4)$-linked residues with few $\alpha(1 \rightarrow 6)$-linked branch points (the normal ratio is ~10).

CHAPTER 17

1. (a) Because citric acid cycle intermediates such as citrate and succinyl-CoA are precursors for the biosynthesis of other compounds, anaerobes must be able to synthesize them.

    (b) These organisms do not need a complete citric acid cycle, which would yield reduced coenzymes that must be reoxidized.

2. Citrate can be cleaved to generate an acetyl group and oxaloacetate. The oxaloacetate can then be converted to succinate to complete the cycle.

3. The decarboxylation step is most likely to be metabolically irreversible since the CO_2 product is rapidly hydrated to bicarbonate. The reverse reaction, a carboxylation, requires the input of free energy to become favorable (Section 16-4A). The other four reactions are transfer reactions or oxidation–reduction reactions (transfer of electrons) that are more easily reversed.

4. PDP removes the phosphate group that inactivates the pyruvate dehydrogenase complex. A deficiency of PDP leads to less pyruvate dehydrogenase activity in muscle cells, making it difficult for the muscle to increase flux through the citric acid cycle in order to meet the energy demands of exercise.

5. (a) The labeled carbon becomes C4 of the succinyl moiety of succinyl-CoA. Because succinate is symmetrical, the label appears at C1 and C4 of succinate. When the resulting oxaloacetate begins the second round, the labeled carbons appear as $^{14}CO_2$ in the isocitrate dehydrogenase and the α-ketoglutarate dehydrogenase reactions (see Fig. 17-2).

    (b) The labeled carbon becomes C3 of the succinyl moiety of succinyl-CoA and hence appears at C2 and C3 of succinate, fumarate, malate, and oxaloacetate. Neither C2 nor C3 of oxaloacetate is released as CO_2 in the second round of the cycle. However, the ^{14}C label appears at C1 and C2 of the succinyl moiety of succinyl-CoA in the second round and therefore appears at all four positions of the resulting oxaloacetate. Thus, in the third round, ^{14}C is released as $^{14}CO_2$.

6. Citric acid cycle intermediates are all acids and as such represent a source of hydrogen ions that would lead to a decrease in blood pH (acidosis).

7.

8. NAD^+ ($\mathscr{E}^{\circ\prime} = -0.315$ V) does not have a high enough reduction potential to support oxidation of succinate to fumarate ($\mathscr{E}^{\circ\prime} = +0.031$ V); that is, the succinate dehydrogenase reac-

tion has insufficient free energy to reduce NAD^+. Enzyme bound FAD ($\mathscr{E}^{\circ\prime} \approx 0$) is more suitable for oxidizing succinate

9. Competitive inhibition can be overcome by adding more substrate, in this case succinate. Oxaloacetate overcomes malonate inhibition because it is converted to succinate by the reaction of the citric acid cycle.

10. The phosphofructokinase reaction is the major flux-control point for glycolysis. Inhibiting phosphofructokinase slows the entire pathway, so the production of acetyl-CoA by glycolysis followed by the pyruvate dehydrogenase complex can be decreased when the citric acid cycle is operating at maximum capacity and the citrate concentration is high. As citric acid cycle intermediates are consumed in synthetic pathways, the citrate concentration drops, relieving phosphofructokinase inhibition and allowing glycolysis to proceed in order to replenish the citric acid cycle intermediate

11. To synthesize citrate, pyruvate must be converted to oxaloacetate by pyruvate carboxylase:

    Pyruvate + CO_2 + ATP + H_2O $\longrightarrow$
    $$\text{oxaloacetate} + \text{ADP} + P$$

    A second pyruvate is converted to acetyl-CoA by pyruvate dehydrogenase:

    Pyruvate + CoASH + NAD^+ $\longrightarrow$
    $$\text{acetyl-CoA} + CO_2 + \text{NADH}$$

    The acetyl-CoA then combines with oxaloacetate to produce citrate:

    Oxaloacetate + acetyl-CoA + H_2O $\longrightarrow$
    $$\text{citrate} + \text{CoASH} + H$$

    The net reaction is

    2 Pyruvate + ATP + NAD^+ + 2 H_2O $\longrightarrow$
    $$\text{citrate} + \text{ADP} + P_i + \text{NADH} + H$$

12. (a) The citric acid cycle is a multistep catalyst. Degrading an amino acid to a citric acid cycle intermediate boosts the catalytic activity of the cycle but does not alter the stoichiometry of the overall reaction (acetyl-CoA $\rightarrow$ 2 CO_2). In order to undergo oxidation, the citric acid cycle intermediate must exit the cycle and be converted to acetyl-CoA to reenter the cycle as a substrate. (b) Pyruvate derived from the degradation of an amino acid can be converted to acetyl-CoA by the pyruvate dehydrogenase complex; these amino acid carbons can then be completely oxidized by the citric acid cycle.

13. The alternate pathway bypasses the succinyl-CoA synthetase reaction of the standard citric acid cycle, a step that is accompanied by the phosphorylation of ADP. The alternate pathway therefore generates one less ATP than the standard citric acid cycle. There is no difference in the number of reduced cofactors generated.

14. For the reaction isocitrate + NAD^+ $\rightleftharpoons$ α-ketoglutarate + NADH + CO_2 + H^+, we assume $[H^+]$ and $[CO_2]$ = 1 According to Eq. 14-1,

$$\Delta G = \Delta G^{\circ\prime} + RT \ln\left(\frac{[\text{NADH}][\alpha\text{-ketoglutarate}]}{[NAD^+][\text{isocitrate}]}\right)$$

$$= -21 \text{ kJ} \cdot \text{mol}^{-1} + (8.3145 \text{ J} \cdot \text{K} \cdot \text{mol}^{-1})$$

$$(298 \text{ K}) \ln\left[\frac{(1)(0.1)}{(8)(0.02)}\right]$$

$$= -21 \text{ kJ} \cdot \text{mol}^{-1} - 1.16 \text{ kJ} \cdot \text{mol}^{-1} = -22.16 \text{ kJ} \cdot \text{mol}^{-1}$$

With such a large negative free energy of reaction under physiological conditions, isocitrate dehydrogenase is likely to be a metabolic control point.

5. Animals cannot carry out the net synthesis of glucose from acetyl-CoA (to which acetate is converted). However, ^{14}C-labeled acetyl-CoA enters the citric acid cycle and is converted to oxaloacetate. Some of this oxaloacetate may exchange with the cellular pool of oxaloacetate to be converted to glucose through gluconeogenesis and subsequently taken up by muscle and incorporated into glycogen.

CHAPTER 18

1. Mitochondria with more cristae have more surface area and therefore more proteins for electron transport and oxidative phosphorylation. Tissues with a high demand for ATP synthesis (such as heart) contain mitochondria with more cristae than tissues with lower demand for oxidative phosphorylation (such as liver).

2. When NADH participates in the glycerophosphate shuttle, the electrons of NADH flow to FAD and then to CoQ, bypassing Complex I. Thus, about 1.5 ATP are synthesized per NADH. About 2.5 ATP are produced when NADH participates in the malate–aspartate shuttle.

3. The relevant half-reactions (Table 14-5) are

$$FAD + 2 H^+ + 2 e^- \rightleftharpoons FADH_2 \qquad \mathscr{E}' = -0.219 \text{ V}$$
$$\tfrac{1}{2} O_2 + 2 H^+ + 2 e^- \rightleftharpoons H_2O \qquad \mathscr{E}^{\circ\prime} = -0.815 \text{ V}$$

Since the O_2/H_2O half-reaction has the more positive $\mathscr{E}^{\circ\prime}$, the FAD half-reaction is reversed and the overall reaction is

$$\tfrac{1}{2} O_2 + FADH_2 \rightleftharpoons H_2O + FAD$$
$$\Delta\mathscr{E}^{\circ\prime} = 0.815 \text{ V} - (-0.219 \text{ V}) = 1.034 \text{ V}$$

Since $\Delta G^{\circ\prime} = -n\mathscr{F}\Delta\mathscr{E}^{\circ\prime}$,

$$\Delta G^{\circ\prime} = -(2)(96{,}485 \text{ J} \cdot \text{V}^{-1} \cdot \text{mol}^{-1})(1.034 \text{ V})$$
$$= -200 \text{ kJ} \cdot \text{mol}^{-1}$$

The maximum number of ATP that could be synthesized under standard conditions is therefore $200 \text{ kJ} \cdot \text{mol}^{-1}/30.5 \text{ kJ} \cdot \text{mol}^{-1}$ = 6.6 mol ATP/mol $FADH_2$ oxidized by O_2.

4. *(a)*   *(b)*

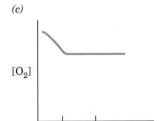

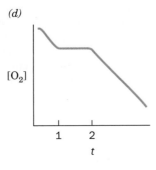

5. (a) O_2 consumption ceases because amytal blocks electron transport in Complex I.

(b) Electrons from succinate bypass the amytal block by entering the electron-transport chain at Complex II and thereby restore electron transport through Complexes III and IV.

(c) CN^- blocks electron transport in Complex IV, after the point of entry of succinate.

(d) Oligomycin blocks oxidative phosphorylation and hence O_2 consumption. DNP uncouples electron transport from oxidative phosphorylation and thereby permits O_2 consumption to resume.

5. $\mathscr{E}$ may differ from $\mathscr{E}^{\circ\prime}$, depending on the redox center's microenvironment and the concentrations of reactants and products. In addition, the tight coupling between successive electron transfers within a complex may "pull" electrons so that the overall process is spontaneous.

6. (a)

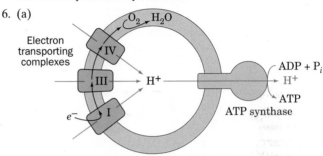

(b) An increase in external pH (decrease in $[H^+]$) increases the electrochemical potential across the mitochondrial membrane and therefore leads to an increase in ATP synthesis.

7. For the transport of a proton from outside to inside (Eq. 18-1),

$$\Delta G = 2.3RT[\text{pH } (side\ 1) - \text{pH } (side\ 2)] + Z\mathscr{F}\Delta\Psi$$

The difference in pH is -1.4. Since an ion is transported from the positive to the negative side of the membrane, $\Delta\Psi$ is negative.

$$\Delta G = (2.3)(8.314 \text{ J} \cdot \text{K}^{-1} \cdot \text{mol}^{-1})(298 \text{ K})(-1.4) +$$
$$(1)(96{,}485 \text{ J} \cdot \text{V}^{-1} \cdot \text{mol}^{-1})(-0.06 \text{ V})$$
$$\Delta G = -7980 \text{ J} \cdot \text{mol}^{-1} - 5790 \text{ J} \cdot \text{mol}^{-1} = 13.8 \text{ KJ} \cdot \text{mol}^{-1}$$

Since $\Delta G^{\circ\prime}$ for ATP synthesis is $30.5 \text{ kJ} \cdot \text{mol}^{-1}$ and $30.5/13.8 = 2.2$, between two and three moles of protons must be transported to provide the free energy to synthesize one mole of ATP under standard biochemical conditions.

8. (a) The import of ADP (net charge -3) and the export of ATP (net charge -4) represents a loss of negative charge inside the mitochondria. This decreases the difference in electrical charge across the membrane, since the outside is positive due to the translocation of protons during electron transport. Consequently, the electrochemical gradient is diminished by the activity of the ADP–ATP translocator. The activity of the P_i–H^+ symport protein diminishes the proton gradient by allowing protons from the intermembrane space to re-enter the matrix.

(b) Both transport systems are driven by the free energy of the electrochemical proton gradient.

9. The protonation and subsequent deprotonation of Asp 61 of the F_1F_0-ATPase's *c* subunits induces the rotation of the *c*-ring, which in turn, mechanically drives the synthesis of ATP. DCCD

reacts with Asp 61 in a manner that prevents it from binding a proton and thereby prevents the synthesis of ATP.

10. In an ATP synthase with more c subunits, more proton translocation events are required to drive one complete rotation of the c ring. Consequently, more substrate oxidation (O_2 consumption) is required to synthesize three ATP (the yield of one cycle of the rotary engine), and the P/O ratio is lower.

11. DNP and related compounds dissipate the proton gradient required for ATP synthesis. The dissipation of this gradient decreases the rate of synthesis of ATP, decreasing the ATP mass action ratio. Decreasing this ratio relieves the inhibition of the electron transport chain, causing an increase in metabolic rate.

12. Hormones stimulate the release of fatty acids from stored triacylglycerols, which activates UCP1 and also provides the fuel whose oxidation yields electrons for the heat-generating electron transfer process. This cascade also amplifies the effect of the hormone.

13. The switch to aerobic metabolism allows ATP to be produced by oxidative phosphorylation. The phosphorylation of ADP increases the [ATP]/[ADP] ratio, which then increases the [NADH]/[NAD$^+$] ratio because a high ATP mass action ratio slows electron transport. The increases in [ATP] and [NADH] inhibit their target enzymes in glycolysis and the citric acid cycle (Fig. 18-29) and thereby slow those processes.

14. Glucose is shunted through the pentose phosphate pathway to provide NADPH, whose electrons are required to reduce O_2 to $O_2^-\cdot$.

CHAPTER 19

1. The color of the seawater indicates that the photosynthetic pigments of the algae absorb colors of visible light other than red.

2. $2 H_2O + 2 NADP^+ \longrightarrow 2 NADPH + 2 H^+ + O_2$

3. The order of action is water–plastoquinone oxidoreductase (Photosystem II), plastoquinone–plastocyanin oxidoreductase (cytochrome b_6f), and plastocyanin–ferredoxin oxidoreductase (Photosystem I).

4. The label appears as $^{18}O_2$:

$$H_2^{18}O + CO_2 \xrightarrow{\text{light}} (CH_2O) + {}^{18}O_2$$

5. (a) The energy per photon is $E = hc/\lambda$, so the energy per mole of photons ($\lambda = 700$ nm) is

$$
\begin{aligned}
E &= Nhc/\lambda \\
&= (6.022 \times 10^{23} \text{ mol}^{-1})(6.626 \times 10^{-34} \text{ J} \cdot \text{s}) \\
&\quad (2.998 \times 10^8 \text{ m} \cdot \text{s}^{-1})/(7 \times 10^{-7} \text{ m}) \\
&= 1.71 \times 10^5 \text{ J} \cdot \text{mol}^{-1} \\
&= 171 \text{ kJ} \cdot \text{mol}^{-1}
\end{aligned}
$$

(b) $(171 \text{ kJ} \cdot \text{mol}^{-1})/(30.5 \text{ kJ} \cdot \text{mol}^{-1}) = 5.6$

Five moles of ATP could theoretically be synthesized (at least under standard biochemical conditions).

6. (a) The relevant half-reactions are (Table 14-5):

$$O_2 + 4 e^- + 4 H^+ \rightarrow 2 H_2O \qquad \mathscr{E}^{\circ\prime} = 0.815 \text{ V}$$
$$NADP^+ + H^+ + 2 e^- \rightarrow NADPH \qquad \mathscr{E}^{\circ\prime} = -0.320 \text{ V}$$

The overall reaction is

$$2 NADP^+ + 2 H_2O \rightarrow 2 NADPH + O_2 + 2 H^+$$
$$\Delta\mathscr{E}^{\circ\prime} = -0.320 \text{ V} - (0.815 \text{ V}) = -1.135 \text{ V}$$
$$
\begin{aligned}
\Delta G^{\circ\prime} &= -n\mathscr{F}\Delta\mathscr{E}^{\circ\prime} \\
&= -(4)(96,485 \text{ J} \cdot \text{V}^{-1} \cdot \text{mol}^{-1})(-1.135 \text{ V}) \\
&= 438 \text{ kJ} \cdot \text{mol}^{-1}
\end{aligned}
$$

(b) One mole of photons of red light ($\lambda = 700$ nm) has an energy of 171 kJ. Therefore, $438/171 = 2.6$ moles of photons are theoretically required to drive the oxidation of H_2O by $NADP^+$ to form one mole of O_2.

(c) The energy of a mole of photons of UV light ($\lambda = 220$ nm) is

$$
\begin{aligned}
E &= Nhc/\lambda \\
&= (6.022 \times 10^{23} \text{ mol}^{-1})(6.626 \times 10^{-34} \text{ J} \cdot \text{s}) \\
&\quad (2.998 \times 10^8 \text{ ms}^{-1})/(2.2 \times 10^{-7} \text{ m}) \\
&= 544 \text{ kJ} \cdot \text{mol}^{-1}
\end{aligned}
$$

The number of moles of 220-nm photons required to produce one mole of O_2 is $438/544 = 0.8$.

7. Both systems mediate cyclic electron flows. The photooxidized bacterial reaction center passes electrons through a series of electron carriers so that electrons return to the reaction center (e.g., P960$^+$) and restore it to its original state. During cyclic electron flow in PSI, electrons from photooxidized P700 are transferred to cytochrome b_6f and, via plastoquinone and plastocyanin, back to P700$^+$. In both cases, there is no net change in the redox state of the reaction center, but the light-driven electron movements are accompanied by the transmembrane movement of protons.

8. When cyclic electron flow occurs, photoactivation of PSI drives electron transport independently of the flow of electrons derived from water. Thus, the oxidation of H_2O by PSII is not linked to the number of photons consumed by PSI.

9. (a) The buildup of the proton gradient is indicative of a high level of activity of the photosystems. A steep gradient could therefore trigger photoprotective activity to prevent further photooxidation when the proton-translocating machinery is operating at maximal capacity. (b) Photooxidation would not be a good protective mechanism since it might interfere with the normal redox balance among the electron-carrying groups in the thylakoid membrane. Releasing the energy by exciton transfer or fluorescence (emitting light of a longer wavelength) could potentially funnel light energy back to the overactive photosystems. Dissipation of the excess energy via internal conversion to heat would be the safest mechanism, since the photosystems do not have any way to harvest thermal energy to drive chemical reactions.

10. (a) An uncoupler dissipates the transmembrane proton gradient by providing a route for proton translocation other than ATP synthase. Therefore, chloroplast ATP production would decrease. (b) The uncoupler would not affect NADP$^+$ reduction since light-driven electron transfer reactions would continue regardless of the state of the proton gradient.

11. An increase in [O_2] increases the oxygenase activity of RuBP carboxylase–oxygenase and therefore lowers the efficiency of CO_2 fixation.

. After the light is turned off, ATP and NADPH levels fall as those substances are used up in the Calvin cycle without being replaced by the light reactions. 3PG builds up because it cannot pass through the phosphoglycerate kinase reaction in the absence of ATP. The RuBP level drops because it is consumed by the RuBP carboxylase reaction (which requires neither ATP nor NADPH) and its replenishment is blocked by the lack of ATP for the phosphoribulokinase reaction.

. The net synthesis of 2 GAP from 6 CO_2 in the initial stage of the Calvin cycle (Fig. 19-26) consumes 18 ATP and 12 NADPH (equivalent to 30 ATP). The conversion of 2 GAP to glucose-6-phosphate (G6P) by gluconeogenesis does not require energy input (Section 16-4B), nor does the isomerization of G6P to glucose-1-phosphate (G1P). The activation of G1P to its nucleotide derivative consumes 2 ATP equivalents (Section 16-5), but ADP is released when the glucose residue is incorporated into starch. These steps represent an overall energy investment of $18 + 30 + 1 = 49$ ATP.

Starch breakdown by phosphorolysis yields G1P, whose subsequent degradation by glycolysis yields 3 ATP, 2 NADH (equivalent to 5 ATP), and 2 pyruvate. Complete oxidation of 2 pyruvate to 6 CO_2 by the pyruvate dehydrogenase reaction and the citric acid cycle (Section 17-1) yields 8 NADH (equivalent to 20 ATP), 2 $FADH_2$ (equivalent to 3 ATP), and 2 GTP (equivalent to 2 ATP). The overall ATP yield is therefore $3 + 5 + 20 + 3 + 2 = 33$ ATP.

The ratio of energy spent to energy recovered is $49/33 = 1.5$.

. These plants store CO_2 by CAM. At night, CO_2 reacts with PEP to form malate. By morning, so much malate (malic acid) has accumulated that the leaves have a sour taste. During the day, the malate is converted to pyruvate + CO_2. The leaves therefore become less acidic and hence tasteless. Late in the day, when all the malate is consumed, the leaves become slightly basic, that is, bitter.

HAPTER 20

. A defect in carnitine palmitoyl transferase II prevents normal transport of activated fatty acids into the mitochondria for β oxidation. Tissues such as muscle that use fatty acids as metabolic fuels therefore cannot generate ATP as needed. The problem is more severe during a fast because other fuels, such as dietary glucose, are not readily available.

L-Glycerol   **L-Glycerol-3-phosphate**

Dihydroxyacetone phosphate

3. The first three steps of β oxidation resemble the reactions that convert succinate to oxaloacetate (Sections 17-3F to 17-3H).

Succinate   **Fumarate**

L-Malate   **Oxaloacetate**

4. (a) Six cycles are required.

(b) 3 Acetyl-CoA, 3 propionyl-CoA, and 1 methylpropionyl-CoA.

5. There are not as many usable nutritional calories per gram in unsaturated fatty acids as there are in saturated fatty acids. This is because oxidation of fatty acids containing double bonds yields fewer reduced coenzymes whose oxidation drives the synthesis of ATP. In the oxidation of fatty acids with a double bond at an odd-numbered carbon, the enoyl-CoA isomerase reaction bypasses the acyl-CoA dehydrogenase reaction and therefore does not generate $FADH_2$ (equivalent to 1.5 ATP). A double bond at an even-numbered carbon must be reduced by NADPH (equivalent to the loss of 2.5 ATP).

6. Oxidation of odd-chain fatty acids generates succinyl-CoA, an intermediate of the citric acid cycle. Because the citric acid cycle operates as a multistep catalyst to convert acetyl groups to CO_2, increasing the concentration of a cycle intermediate can increase the catalytic activity of the cycle.

7. Palmitate oxidation produces 106 ATP and glucose catabolism produces 32 ATP (Section 17-4). Assuming a free energy cost of $30.5 \text{ kJ} \cdot \text{mol}^{-1}$ to synthesize ATP, palmitate catabolism has an efficiency of

$$106 \times 30.5/9781 \times 100 = 33\%$$

Glucose catabolism has an efficiency of

$$32 \times 30.5/2850 \times 100 = 34\%$$

Thus, the two processes have very nearly the same overall efficiency.

8. 3-Ketoacyl-CoA transferase is required to convert ketone bodies to acetyl-CoA. If the liver contained this enzyme, it would be unable to supply ketone bodies as fuels for other tissues.

9. Palmitate (C_{16}) synthesis requires 14 NADPH. The transport of 8 acetyl-CoA to the cytosol by the tricarboxylate transport system supplies 8 NADPH (Fig. 20-24), which represents $8/14 \times 100 = 57\%$ of the required NADPH.

10. The label does not appear in palmitate because $^{14}CO_2$ is released in Reaction 2b of fatty acid synthesis (Fig. 20-26).

11. The breakdown of glucose by glycolysis generates the dihydroxyacetone phosphate that becomes the glycerol backbone of triacylglycerols (Fig. 20-29).

12. This fatty acid (**linolenate**) cannot be synthesized by animals because it contains a double bond closer than 6 carbons from its noncarboxylate end.

13. The synthesis of stearate (18:0) from mitochondrial acetyl-CoA requires 9 ATP to transport 9 acetyl-CoA from the mitochondria to the cytosol. Seven rounds of fatty acid synthesis consume 7 ATP (in the acetyl-CoA carboxylase reaction) and 14 NADPH (equivalent to 35 ATP). Elongation of palmitate to stearate requires 1 NADH and 1 NADPH (equivalent to 5 ATP). The energy cost is therefore $9 + 7 + 35 + 5 = 56$ ATP.

(a) The degradation of stearate to 9 acetyl-CoA consumes 2 ATP (in the acyl-CoA synthetase reaction) but generates, in eight rounds of β oxidation, 8 FADH$_2$ (equivalent to 12 ATP) and 8 NADH (equivalent to 20 ATP). Thus, the energy yield is $12 + 20 - 2 = 30$ ATP. This represents only about half of the energy consumed in synthesizing stearate (30 ATP versus 56 ATP).

(b) The complete oxidation of the 9 acetyl-CoA to CO$_2$ by the citric acid cycle yields an additional 9 GTP (equivalent to 9 ATP), 27 NADH (equivalent to 67.5 ATP), and 9 FADH$_2$ (equivalent to 13.5 ATP) for a total of $30 + 9 + 67.5 + 13.5 = 120$ ATP. Thus, more than twice the energy investment of synthesizing stearate is recovered (120 ATP versus 56 ATP).

14. (a)

$$H_3C-\overset{O}{\overset{\|}{\underset{14}{C}}}-CH_2-\overset{O}{\overset{\|}{\underset{14}{C}}}-O^-$$

Acetoacetate

See Fig. 20-21.

(b)

$$\begin{array}{c} \overset{OH}{\overset{|}{\underset{14}{CH}}}-(CH_2)_{14}-CH_3 \\ H_2N-C-H \\ | \\ CH_2OH \end{array}$$

Sphinganine

See Fig. 20-35.

15. Statins inhibit the HMG-CoA reductase reaction, which produces mevalonate, a precursor of cholesterol. Although lower cholesterol levels induce the synthesis of HMG-CoA reductase to make up for the loss in activity, some decrease in activity may still be present. Because mevalonate is also the precursor of ubiquinone (coenzyme Q), supplementary ubiquinone may be necessary.

CHAPTER 21

1. Proteasome-dependent proteolysis requires ATP to activate ubiquitin in the first step of linking ubiquitin to the target protein (Fig. 21-2) and for denaturing the protein as it enters the proteasome.

2. The urea cycle transforms excess nitrogen from protein breakdown to an excretable form, urea. In a deficiency of a urea cycle enzyme, the preceding urea cycle intermediates may build up to a toxic level. A low-protein diet minimizes the amount of nitrogen that enters the urea cycle and therefore reduces the concentrations of the toxic intermediates.

3. An individual consuming a high-protein diet uses amino acids as metabolic fuels. As the amino acid skeletons are converted to glucogenic or ketogenic compounds, the amino groups are disposed of as urea, leading to increased flux through the urea cycle. During starvation, proteins (primarily from muscle) are degraded to provide precursors for gluconeogenesis. Nitrogen from these protein-derived amino acids must be eliminated, which demands a high level of urea cycle activity.

4. Glutamate dehydrogenase, glutamine synthetase, and carbamoyl phosphate synthetase.

5. (a)

$$H_2N-\overset{O}{\overset{\|}{C}}-NH_2 + H_2O \rightleftharpoons 2\,NH_3 + CO_2$$

(b) The NH$_3$ produced by the action of urease can combine with protons in gastric fluid to form NH$_4^+$. This could reduce the concentration of protons and therefore increase the pH.

6. Since the three reactions converting tiglyl-CoA to acetyl-CoA and propionyl-CoA are analogous to those of fatty acid oxidation (β oxidation; Fig. 20-12), the reactions are:

$$CH_3-CH=\overset{O}{\overset{\|}{\underset{\underset{CH_3}{|}}{C}}}-C-SCoA$$

Tiglyl-CoA

H$_2$O ↘ | (a hydratase)

$$CH_3-\overset{H}{\overset{|}{\underset{\underset{OH}{|}}{C}}}-CH-\overset{O}{\overset{\|}{C}}-SCoA$$
$$\qquad\qquad\quad\underset{CH_3}{|}$$

NAD$^+$ ↘ | (a dehydrogenase)

NADH ↙

$$CH_3-\overset{O}{\overset{\|}{C}}-\overset{}{\underset{\underset{CH_3}{|}}{CH}}-\overset{O}{\overset{\|}{C}}-SCoA$$

CoASH ↘ | (a thiolase)

$$CH_3-\overset{O}{\overset{\|}{C}}-SCoA \quad + \quad CH_3-CH_2-\overset{O}{\overset{\|}{C}}-SCoA$$

Acetyl-CoA   **Propionyl-CoA**

7.

bond to be cleaved

8. (a) Ala, Arg, Asn, Asp, Cys, Gln, Glu, Gly, His, Met, Pro, Ser, and Val

(b) Leu and Lys

(c) Ile, Phe, Thr, Trp, and Tyr

9. Tryptophan can be considered a member of this group since one of its degradation products is alanine, which is converted to pyruvate by deamination.

10. In the absence of uridylyl-removing enzyme, adenylyltransferase·P_{II} will be fully uridylylated, since there is no mechanism for removing the uridylyl groups once they are attached. Uridylylated adenylyltransferase·P_{II} adenylylates glutamine synthetase, which activates it. Hence, the defective *E. coli* cells will have a hyperactive glutamine synthetase and thus a higher than normal glutamine concentration. Reactions requiring glutamine will therefore be accelerated, thereby depleting glutamate and the citric acid cycle intermediate α-ketoglutarate. Consequently, biosynthetic reactions requiring transamination, as well as energy metabolism, will be suppressed.

11. Since only plants and microorganisms synthesize aromatic amino acids, herbicides that inhibit these pathways do not affect amino acid metabolism in animals.

12. The pigment coloring skin and hair is melanin, which is synthesized from tyrosine. When tyrosine is in short supply, as when dietary protein is not available, melanin cannot be synthesized in normal amounts, and the skin and hair become depigmented.

CHAPTER 22

1. Hyperinsulinemia would result in a decrease in blood glucose. The decrease in [glucose] for the brain would cause loss of brain function (leading to coma and death).

2. ATP generating pathways such as glycolysis and fatty acid oxidation require an initial investment of ATP (the hexokinase and phosphofructokinase steps of glycolysis and the acyl-CoA synthetase activation step that precedes β oxidation). This "priming" cannot occur when ATP has been exhausted.

3. (a) GLUT2 has a higher K_M than GLUT1 so that the rate of glucose entry into liver cells can vary directly with the concentration of glucose in the blood. A transporter with a high K_M is less likely to be saturated with its ligand and therefore would not limit the rate of transport. (b) Type I glycogen storage disease results from a deficiency of glucose-6-phosphatase so that glucose-6-phosphate produced by glycogenolysis can-

not exit the cell as glucose. A defect in the glucose-transport protein GLUT2 would similarly prevent the exit of glucose (a passive transporter can operate in either direction). In both cases, the buildup of intracellular glucose-6-phosphate prevents glycogen breakdown, and glycogen accumulates.

4. (a) Because fatty acids, like glucose, are metabolic fuels, it makes sense for them to stimulate insulin release, which is a signal of abundant fuel. (b) Elevated levels of circulating fatty acids occur during an extended fast, when dietary glucose and glucose mobilized from glycogen stores are no longer available. Insulin release would be inappropriate for these conditions. A combination of abundant fatty acids and glucose, indicating the fed state, would serve as a better trigger for insulin release.

5. At high altitude, less oxygen is available for aerobic metabolism, so glycolysis, an anaerobic pathway, would become relatively more important in active muscles. An increase in GLUT1 would increase the intracellular glucose concentration, and an increase in PFK would increase the flux of glucose through the pathway.

6. (a) In the absence of MCAD, fatty acids cannot be fully oxidized to acetyl-CoA (Section 20-2C). Since ketone bodies are synthesized from acetyl-CoA (Section 20-3), ketogenesis is impaired.

(b) In normal individuals, acetyl-CoA activates pyruvate carboxylase (Section 17-5B), which converts pyruvate to oxaloacetate. This increases the capacity of the citric acid cycle to metabolize acetyl-CoA. When glucose levels are low, the oxaloacetate is used for gluconeogenesis (Section 16-4). In MCAD deficiency, lack of fatty acid–derived acetyl-CoA keeps pyruvate carboxylase activity low, thereby limiting the synthesis of glucose and contributing to hypoglycemia.

7. Insulin activates ATP-citrate lyase, which is the enzyme that converts citrate to oxaloacetate and acetyl-CoA (Section 20-4A). The activity of this enzyme is essential for making acetyl units available for fatty acid biosynthesis in the cytosol. The acetyl units, generated from pyruvate in the mitochondria, combine with oxaloacetate to form citrate, which can then be transported from the mitochondria to the cytosol for reconversion to acetyl-CoA.

8. Insulin promotes the uptake of glucose via the increase in GLUT4 receptors on the adipocyte surface. A source of glucose is necessary to supply the glycerol-3-phosphate backbone of triacylglycerols.

9. Ingesting glucose while in the resting state causes the pancreas to release insulin. This stimulates the liver, muscle, and adipose tissue to synthesize glycogen, fat, and protein from the excess nutrients while inhibiting the breakdown of these metabolic fuels. Hence, ingesting glucose before a race will gear the runner's metabolism for resting rather than for running.

10. During starvation, the synthesis of glucose from liver oxaloacetate depletes the supply of citric acid cycle intermediates and thus decreases the ability of the liver to metabolize acetyl-CoA via the citric acid cycle.

11. The leptin produced by the normal mouse will enter the circulation of the *ob/ob* mouse, resulting in decreases in its appetite and weight.

12. Adipose tissue synthesizes and releases the polypeptide hormones adiponectin, leptin, and resistin.

13. Since PYY_{3-36} is a peptide hormone, it would be digested if taken orally. Introducing it directly into the bloodstream avoids degradation.

14. An intermediate in the biosynthesis of triacylglycerols is diacylglycerol (DAG), a second messenger responsible for activating PKC.

15. Physical inactivity would lead to a decreased need for ATP in muscle, which would be reflected by a decreased AMP to ATP ratio. A decrease in this ratio would lead to a decrease in AMPK activity. AMPK activity is positively associated with glucose uptake by cells due to an increase in GLUT4 activity. GLUT4 activity is also increased by insulin. A decrease in AMPK would lead to a decrease in GLUT4 activity, making insulin's job more difficult.

CHAPTER 23

1. (a) 7 ATP;
   (b) 8 ATP;
   (c) 7 ATP.

2. PRPP and FGAR accumulate because they are substrates of Reactions 2 and 5 in the IMP biosynthetic pathway (Fig. 23-1). XMP also accumulates because the GMP synthetase reaction is blocked (Fig. 23-3). Although glutamine is a substrate of carbamoyl phosphate synthetase II (the first enzyme of UMP synthesis; Fig. 23-5), the other substrates of that enzyme do not accumulate.

3. (a) The recovered deoxycytidylate would be equally labeled in its base and ribose components (i.e., the same labeling pattern as in the original cytidine). (b) The recovered deoxycytidylate would be unequally labeled in its base and ribose components because the separated ^{14}C-cytosine and ^{14}C-ribose would mix with the different-sized pools of unlabeled cellular cytosine and ribose before recombining as the deoxycytidylate that becomes incorporated into DNA. [This experiment established that deoxyribonucleotides, in fact, are synthesized from their corresponding ribonucleotides (alternative a).]

4. Hydroxyurea destroys the tyrosyl radical that is essential for the activity of ribonucleotide reductase. Tumor cells are generally fast-growing and cannot survive without this enzyme, which supplies dNTPs for nucleic acid synthesis. In contrast, most normal cells grow slowly, if at all, and hence have less need for nucleic acid synthesis.

5. dATP inhibits ribonucleotide reductase, thereby preventing the synthesis of the deoxynucleotides required for DNA synthesis.

6. FdUMP and methotrexate kill rapidly proliferating cells, such as cancer cells and those of hair follicles. Consequently, hair falls out.

7. The mutant cells grow because the medium contains the thymidine they are unable to make. Normal cells, however, continue to synthesize their own thymidine and thereby convert their limited supply of THF to DHF. The methotrexate inhibits dihydrofolate reductase, so THF cannot be regenerated. With-

out a supply of THF for the synthesis of nucleotides and amino acids, the cells die.

8. The synthesis of histidine and methionine requires THF. The cell's THF is converted to DHF by the thymidylate synthase reaction, but in the presence of methotrexate THF cannot be regenerated.

9. The conversion of dUMP to dTMP is a reductive methylation. In the thymidylate synthase reaction shown in Fig. 23-15, THF is oxidized to DHF, so that DHFR must subsequently reduce the DHF to THF. Organisms that lack DHFR use an alternative mechanism for converting dUMP to dTMP in which the FAD cofactor of the enzyme, rather than the folate, undergoes oxidation.

10. (a) Trimethoprim binds to bacterial dihydrofolate reductase but does not permanently inactivate the enzyme. Therefore, it is not a mechanism-based inhibitor. (b) Allopurinol is oxidized by xanthine oxidase to a product that irreversibly binds to the enzyme. It is therefore a mechanism-based inhibitor of xanthine oxidase.

11. In von Gierke's disease (glucose-6-phosphatase deficiency) glucose-6-phosphate accumulates in liver cells, thereby stimulating the pentose phosphate pathway. The resulting increase in ribose-5-phosphate production boosts the concentration of PRPP, which in turn stimulates purine biosynthesis. High levels of uric acid derived from the breakdown of these excess purines causes gout.

12.

Nicotinamide

Nicotinamide mononucleotide (NMN)

Nicotinamide adenine dinucleotide (NAD⁺)

CHAPTER 24

1. Since amino acids have an average molecular mass of ~110 D, the 50-kD protein contains 50,000 D ÷ 110 D/residue = ~455 residues. These residues are encoded by 455 × 3 = 1365 nucleotides. In B-DNA, the rise per base pair is 3.4 Å, so the contour length of 1365 bp is 3.4 Å/bp × 1365 bp = 4641 Å, or

0.46 μm. In A-DNA, the contour length would be 1365 bp × 2.9 Å/bp = 3959 Å, or 0.40 μm.

2. (a) Hypoxanthine pairs with cytosine in much the same way as does guanine.

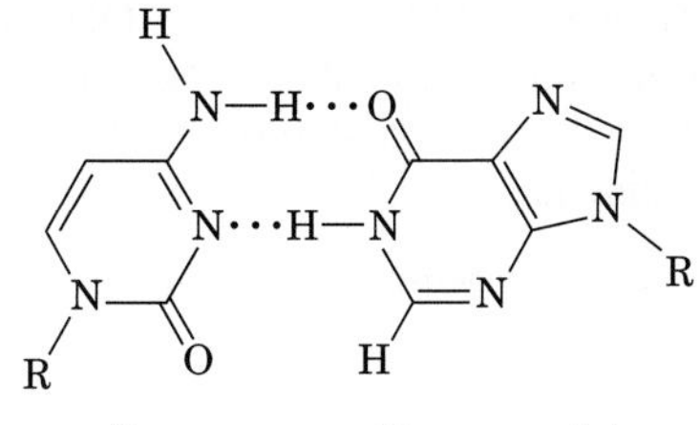

C　　　　**Hypoxanthine**

(b)

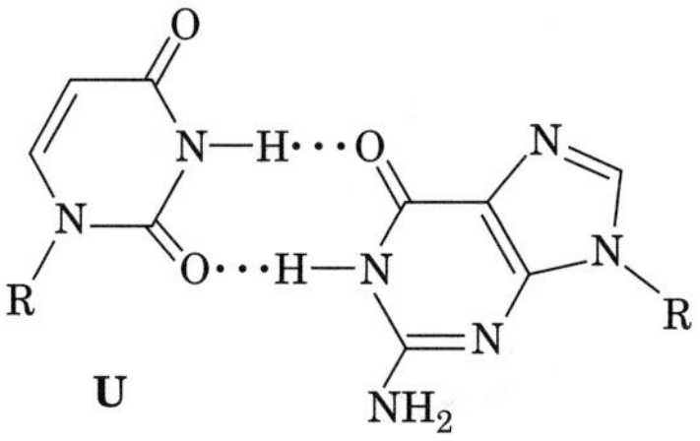

U　　　　　**G**

3. (a)

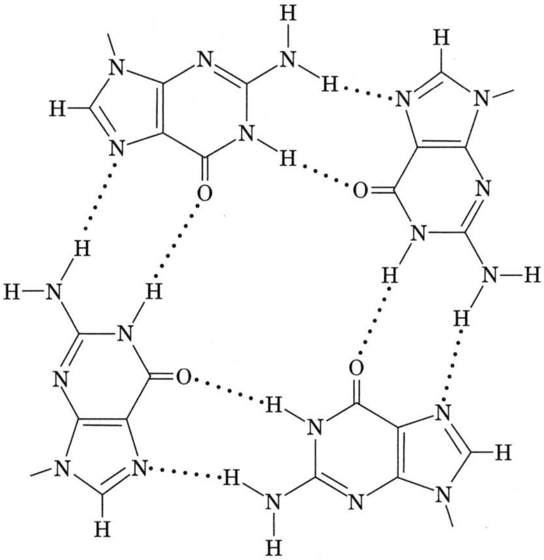

(b)

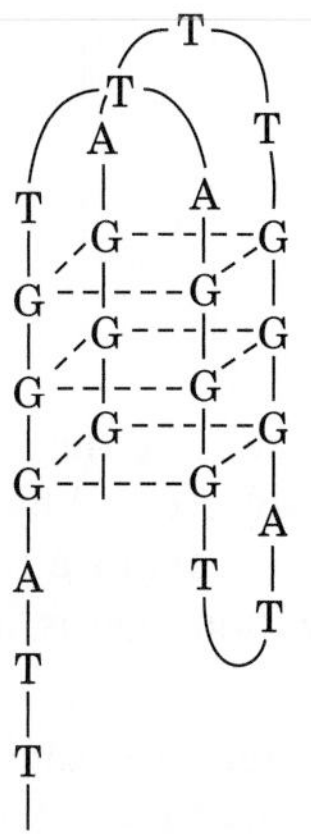

4. The decarboxylation of the amino acid ornithine, an intermediate of the urea cycle (Fig. 21-9), generates 1,4-diaminobutane (also known as putrescine).

$$^{+}H_3N-(CH_2)_4-NH_3^{+}$$

This cationic molecule interacts electrostatically with the negatively charged phosphate groups of DNA.

5. The enzyme has no effect on the supercoiling of DNA since cleaving the C2′—C3′ bond of ribose does not sever the sugar–phosphate chain of DNA.

6. In the B-DNA to Z-DNA transition, a right-handed helix with one turn per 10.4 base pairs converts to a left-handed helix with one turn per 12 base pairs. Since a right-handed duplex helix has a positive twist, the twist decreases:

$$\Delta T = -\frac{100}{10.4} + \frac{-100}{12} = -17.9 \text{ turns}$$

The linking number must remain constant ($\Delta L = 0$) since no covalent bonds are broken. Hence, the change in writhing number is $\Delta W = -\Delta T = 17.9$ turns.

7. The segment with 20% A residues (i.e., 40% A · T base pairs) contains 60% G · C base pairs and therefore melts at a higher temperature than a segment with 30% A residues (i.e., 40% G · C base pairs).

8. (a) Its T_m decreases because the charges on the phosphate groups are less shielded from each other at lower ionic strength and hence repel each other more strongly, thereby destabilizing the double helix. (b) The nonpolar solvent diminishes the hydrophobic forces that stabilize double-stranded DNA and hence lowers the T_m.

9. (a) As the temperature increases, the stacked bases melt apart so that their ultraviolet absorbance increases (the hyperchromic effect). (b) The broad shape of the poly(A) melting curve indicates noncooperative changes, as expected for a single-stranded RNA. The sharp melting curve for DNA reflects the cooperativity of strand separation.

10.
```
        A U U G G  C
        | | | | |    A
      A A U A G C C  U
```

11.
```
            G
        C     G
        A — T
        C — G
        C — G
        T — A
        G — C
        A — T
   5'-T C A   T G C-3'
      | | |   | | |
   3'-A G T   A C G-5'
        T — A
        C — G
        A — T
        G — C
        G — C
        T — A
      G     C
        C
```

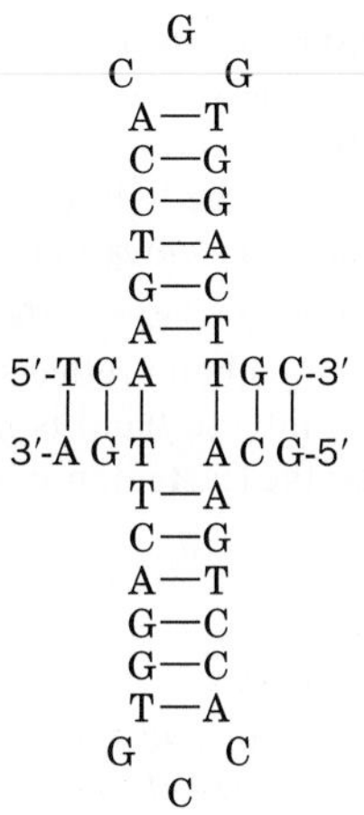

12.

Top (−)

28S RNA

16S RNA

Direction
of
migration

5S RNA

Bottom (+)

13. The target sequence consists of 6 symmetry-related base pairs. Since there are 4 possible base pairs (A · T, T · A, G · C, and C · G), the probability that any two base pairs are randomly related by symmetry is 1/4. Hence, the probability of finding all 6 pairs of base pairs by random chance is $(1/4)^6 = 2.4 \times 10^{-4}$.

14. (a) A 6-nt sequence would be expected to occur, on average, every $4^6 = 4096$ nt in single-stranded DNA. However, in double-stranded DNA, it would be expected to occur at twice this frequency, that is, every $4096/2 = 2048$ bp. Thus the expected number of copies of a 6-bp sequence in the *E. coli* genome is 4,639,000 bp/2048 bp = 2265.

(b) A 12-bp sequence would be expected to occur, on average, every $4^{12}/2 = 8,388,608$ bp, which is nearly twice as large as the number of base pairs in the *E. coli* genome. Thus the *trp* repressor is unlikely to bind specifically to any other site in the *E. coli* chromosome.

15. (a) The contour length is 5×10^7 bp $\times 3.4$ Å/bp = 1.7×10^8 Å = 17 mm.

(b) A nucleosome, which binds ~200 bp, compresses the DNA to an 80-Å-high supercoil. The length of the DNA is therefore (80 Å/200 bp) $\times$ (5×10^7 bp) = 2×10^7 Å = 2 mm.

(c) In the 30-nm fiber, 18.9 nucleosomes cover 316 Å. The length of the DNA is (316 Å/18.9 nucleosomes) $\times$ (1 nucleosome/200 bp) $\times$ (5×10^7 bp) = 4.2×10^6 Å = 0.42 mm.

16. Experiment 1. The restriction enzyme failed to digest the genomic DNA, leaving the DNA too large to enter the gel during electrophoresis.

Experiment 2. The hybridization conditions were too "relaxed," resulting in nonspecific hybridization of the probe to all the DNA fragments. This problem could be corrected by boiling the blot to remove the probe and repeating the hybridization at a higher temperature and/or lower salt concentration.

Experiment 3. The probe hybridized with three different mouse genes. The different intensity of each band reflects the relatedness of the sequences. The most intense band is most similar to the human *rxr-1* gene, whereas the least intense band is least similar to the *rxr-1* gene.

CHAPTER 25

1. Okazaki fragments are 1000 to 2000 nt long, and the *E. coli* chromosome contains 4.6×10^6 bp. Therefore, *E. coli* chromosomal replication requires 2300 to 4600 Okazaki fragments.

2. As indicated in Fig. *a* (*below*), nucleotides would be added to a polynucleotide strand by attack of the 3′-OH of the incoming nucleotide on the 5′ triphosphate group of the growing strand with the elimination of PP$_i$. The hydrolytic removal of a mispaired nucleotide by the 5′ → 3′ exonuclease activity (Fig. *b*, *below*) would leave only an OH group or monophosphate group at the 5′ end of the DNA chain. This would require an additional activation step before further chain elongation could commence.

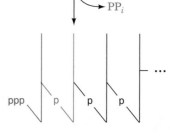

(*a*) 3′ → 5′ Polymerase

(*b*) 5′ → 3′ Exonuclease

3. The drug would inhibit DNA synthesis because the polymerization reaction is accompanied by the release and hydrolysis of PP$_i$. Failure to hydrolyze the PP$_i$ would remove the thermodynamic driving force for polymerization, that is, it would be reversible.

4. PP$_i$ is the product of the polymerization reaction catalyzed by DNA polymerase. This reaction also requires a template DNA strand and a primer with a free 3′ end.

(a) There is no primer strand, so no PP_i is produced.

(b) There is no primer strand, so no PP_i is produced.

(c) PP_i is produced.

(d) No PP_i is produced because there is no 3′ end that can be extended.

(e) PP_i is produced.

(f) PP_i is produced.

5. The 5′ → 3′ exonuclease activity is essential for DNA replication because it removes RNA primers and replaces them with DNA. Absence of this activity would be lethal.

6. The Klenow fragment, which lacks 5′ → 3′ exonuclease activity (and therefore cannot catalyze nick translation), is used to ensure that all the replicated DNA chains have the same 5′ terminus, a necessity if a sequence is to be assigned according to fragment length.

7. AT-rich DNA is less stable than GC-rich DNA and therefore would more readily melt apart, a requirement for initiating replication.

8. DNA gyrase adds negative supercoils to relieve the positive supercoiling that helicase-catalyzed unwinding produces ahead of the replication fork.

9. Mismatch repair and other repair systems correct most of the errors missed by the proofreading functions of DNA polymerases.

0. The *E. coli* replication system can fully replicate only circular DNAs. Bacteria do not have a mechanism (e.g., telomerase-catalyzed extension of telomeres) for replicating the extreme 3′ ends of linear template strands.

1. (a)

5BU
(enol tautomer)   **Guanine**

(b) When 5BU incorporated into DNA pairs with G, the result is an A · T → G · C transition after two more rounds of DNA replication:

$$A \cdot T \rightarrow A \cdot 5BU \rightarrow G \cdot 5BU \rightarrow G \cdot C$$

2. Base excision repair. The deaminated base can be recognized because hypoxanthine does not normally occur in DNA.

3. The cytosine derivative base-pairs with adenine, generating a C · G → T · A transition.

Adenine

14. The triphosphatase destroys nucleotides containing the modified base before they can be incorporated into DNA during replication.

15. When 5-methylcytosine residues deaminate, they form thymine residues.

5-Methyl-C   **T**

Since thymine is a normal DNA base, the repair systems cannot determine whether such a T or its opposing G is the mutated base. Consequently, only about half of the deaminated 5-methylcytosines are correctly repaired.

16. (a) Loss of the helicase DnaB, which unwinds DNA for replication, would be lethal.

(b) Loss of Pol I would prevent the excision of RNA primers and would therefore be lethal.

(c) SSB prevents reannealing of separated single strands. Loss of SSB would be lethal.

(d) RecA protein mediates the SOS response and homologous recombination. Loss of RecA would be harmful but not necessarily lethal.

17. *E. coli* contains a low concentration of dUTP, which DNA polymerase incorporates into DNA in place of dTTP. The resulting uracil bases are rapidly excised by uracil–DNA glycosylase followed by nucleotide excision repair (NER), which temporarily causes a break in the DNA chain. DNA that is isolated before DNA polymerase I and DNA ligase can complete the repair process would be fragmented. However, in the absence of a functional uracil–DNA glycosylase, the inappropriate uracil residues would remain in place, and hence leading strand DNA would be free of breaks. The lagging strand, being synthesized discontinuously, would still contain breaks, although fewer than otherwise.

18. Pol V is less processive than Pol III. When the progress of Pol III is arrested by the presence of a thymine dimer, Pol V can take over, allowing replication to continue at a high rate, although with a greater incidence of mispairings. The damage is minimal, however, since Pol V soon dissociates from the DNA, allowing the more accurate Pol III to resume replicating DNA.

CHAPTER 26

1. (a) Cordycepin is the 3′-deoxy analog of adenosine.

(b) Because it lacks a 3′-OH group, the cordycepin incorporated into a growing RNA chain cannot support further chain elongation in the 5′ → 3′ direction.

2. The top strand is the sense strand. Its TATGAT segment differs by only one base from the TATAAT consensus sequence of the promoter's −10 sequence; its TTTACA sequence differs by only one base from the TTGACA consensus sequence of the promoter's −35 sequence and is appropriately located ~25 nt to the 5′ side of the −10 sequence; and the initiating G

nucleotide is the only purine that is located ~10 nt downstream of the −10 sequence.

5′ CAACGTAACAC**TTTACA**GCGGCGCGTCATTTGA**TATGAT**GCGCCCC**G**CTTCCCGATA 3′

−35 region	−10 region	start point

3. The probe should have a sequence complementary to the consensus sequence of the 6-nt Pribnow box: 5′-ATTATA-3′.

4. Promoter elements for RNA polymerase II include sequences at −27 (the TATA box) and between −50 and −100. The insertion of 10 bp would separate the promoter elements by the distance of the turn of the DNA helix, thereby diminishing the binding of proteins required for transcription initiation. However, the protein-binding sites would still be on the same side of the helix. Inserting 5 bp (half of a helical turn) would move the protein-binding sites to opposite sides of the helix, making it even more difficult to initiate transcription.

5. G · C base pairs are more stable than A · T base pairs. Hence, the more G · C base pairs that the promoter contains, the more difficult it is to form the open complex during transcription initiation.

6. Transcription of an rRNA gene yields a single rRNA molecule that is incorporated into a ribosome. In contrast, transcription of a ribosomal protein gene yields an mRNA that can be translated many times to produce many copies of its corresponding protein. The greater number of rRNA genes relative to ribosomal protein genes helps ensure the balanced synthesis of rRNA and proteins necessary for ribosome assembly.

7. The cell lysates can be applied to a column containing a matrix with immobilized poly(dT). The poly(A) tails of processed mRNAs will bind to the poly(dT) while other cellular components are washed away. The mRNAs can be eluted by decreasing the salt concentration to destabilize the A · T base pairs.

8. (a) The phosphate groups of the phosphodiester backbone of the mRNA will be labeled at all sites where α-[^{32}P]ATP is used as a substrate by RNA polymerase.

   (b) ^{32}P will appear only at the 5′ end of mRNA molecules that have A as the first residue (this residue retains its α and β phosphates). In all other cases where β-[^{32}P]ATP is used as a substrate for RNA synthesis, the β and γ phosphates are released as PP$_i$ (see Fig. 26-6).

   (c) No ^{32}P will appear in the RNA chain. During polymerization, the β and γ phosphates are released as PP$_i$. The terminal (γ) phosphate of an A residue at the 5′ end of an RNA molecule is removed during the capping process.

9. DNA polymerase needs a primer; poly(A) polymerase uses the pre-mRNA as a primer; tRNA nucleotidyl transferase uses the immature tRNA as a primer; and RNA polymerase does not require a primer. Both DNA polymerase and RNA polymerase require a DNA template, but neither poly(A) polymerase nor tRNA nucleotidyl transferase uses a template. The four polymerases use different sets of nucleotides: DNA polymerase uses all four dNTPS; RNA polymerase uses all four NTPs; poly(A) polymerase uses only ATP; and tRNA nucleotidyl transferase uses ATP and CTP.

10. The active site of poly(A) polymerase is narrower because it does not need to accommodate a template strand.

11. The mechanism of RNase hydrolysis requires a free 2′-OH group to form a 2′,3′-cyclic phosphate intermediate (Figure 11-10). Nucleotide residues lacking a 2′-OH group would therefore be resistant to RNase-catalyzed hydrolysis.

12. The mRNA splicing reaction, which requires no free energy input and results in no loss of phosphodiester bonds, is theoretically reversible *in vitro*. However, the degradation of the excised intron makes the reaction irreversible in the cell.

13. The intron must be large enough to include a spliceosome binding site(s).

14. Inhibition of snRNA processing interferes with mRNA splicing. As a result, host mRNA cannot be translated, so the host ribosomes will synthesize only viral proteins.

CHAPTER 27

1. A 4-nt insertion would add one codon and shift the gene's reading frame by one nucleotide. The proper reading frame could be restored by deleting a nucleotide. Gene function, however, would not be restored if (a) the 4-nt insertion interrupted the codon for a functionally critical amino acid; (b) the 4-nt insertion created a codon for a structure-breaking amino acid; (c) the 4-nt insertion introduced a Stop codon early in the gene; or (d) the 1-nt deletion occurred far from the 4-nt insertion so that even though the reading frame was restored, a long stretch of frame-shifted codons separated the insertion and deletion points.

2. The possible codons are UUU, UUG, UGU, GUU, UGG, GUG, GGU, and GGG. The encoded amino acids are Phe, Leu, Cys, Val, Trp, and Gly (Table 27-1).

3. An amber mutation results from any of the point mutations XAG, UXG, or UAX to UAG. The XAG codons specify Gln, Lys, and Glu; the UXG codons specify Leu, Ser, and Trp; and the UAX codons that are not Stop codons both specify Tyr. Hence some of the codons specifying these amino acids can undergo a point mutation to UAG.

4. (a) Each ORF begins with an initiation codon (ATG) and ends with a Stop codon (TGA):

   ATGCTCAACTATATGTGA encodes *vir-2* and

   ATGCCGCATGCTCTGTTAATCACATATAGTTGA
   on the complementary strand encodes *vir-1*.

   (b) *vir-1*: MPHALLITYS; *vir-2*: MLNYM.

   (c) *vir-1*: MPHALLIPYS; *vir-2*: MLNYMGLTEHAA.

5. There are four exons (the underlined bases)

   TATAATACGCGCAATACAATCTACAGCTTC<u>GCGTA</u>
   <u>AATCGCAG</u>GTAAGTTGTAATAAATATAAGTGAGT
   ATGATAGG<u>GCTTTGGACCGATAGATGCGACCCTG</u>
   <u>CAG</u>GTAAGTATAGATTAATTAAGCACAGG<u>CATGCA</u>
   <u>GGGATATCCTCCAAACAG</u>GTAAGTAACCTTACGG
   TCAATTAATTAGG<u>CAGTAGATGAATAAACGATAT</u>
   <u>CGATCGGTTACAG</u>TAGTCTGAT

   The mature mRNA, which has a 5′ cap and a 3′ poly(A) tail, therefore has the sequence

   GCGUAAAUCGUAGGCUUUGGACCGAUAG**AUG**
   CGACCCUGGAGCAUGCAGGGAUAUCCUCCAAA
   UAGCAGUAGA**UGA**AUAAACGAUAUCGAUCGG
   UUAGGU

The initiation codon and termination codon are shown in bold-face. The encoded protein has the sequence

MRPWSMQGYPPNSSR

6. Gly and Ala; Val and Leu; Ser and Thr, Asn and Gln; and Asp and Glu.

7. The assembly of functional ribosomes requires equal amounts of the rRNA molecules, so it is advantageous for the cell to synthesize the rRNAs all at once.

8. Ribosomes cannot translate double-stranded RNA, so the base pairing of a complementary antisense RNA to an mRNA prevents its translation.

9. Only newly synthesized bacterial polypeptides have fMet at their N-terminus. Consequently, the appearance of fMet in a mammalian system signifies the presence of invading bacteria. Leukocytes that recognize the fMet residue can therefore combat these bacteria through phagocytosis.

10. Prokaryotic ribosomes can select an initiation codon located anywhere on the mRNA molecule as long as it lies just downstream of a Shine–Dalgarno sequence. In contrast, eukaryotic ribosomes usually select the AUG closest to the 5′ end of the mRNA. Eukaryotic ribosomes therefore cannot recognize a translation initiation site on a circular mRNA.

11. As expected, the correctly charged tRNAs (Ala–tRNA^{Ala} and Gln–tRNA^{Gln}) bind to EF-Tu with approximately the same affinity, so they are delivered to the ribosomal A site with the same efficiency. The mischarged Ala–tRNA^{Gln} binds to EF-Tu much more loosely, indicating that it may dissociate from EF-Tu before it reaches the ribosome. The mischarged Gln–tRNA^{Ala} binds to EF-Tu much more tightly, indicating that EF-Tu may not be able to dissociate from it at the ribosome. These results suggest that either a higher or a lower binding affinity could affect the ability of EF-Tu to carry out its function, which would decrease the rate at which mischarged aminoacyl–tRNAs bind to the ribosomal A site during translation.

12. eIF2 is a G protein that delivers the initiator tRNA to the 40S ribosomal subunit and then hydrolyzes its bound GTP to GDP. The GEF eIF2B helps eIF2 release GDP in order to bind GTP so that it can participate in another round of translation initiation.

13. By inducing the same conformational changes that occur during correct tRNA–mRNA pairing, paromomycin can mask the presence of an incorrect codon–anticodon match. Without proofreading at the aminoacyl–tRNA binding step, the ribosome synthesizes a polypeptide with the wrong amino acids, which is likely to be nonfunctional or toxic to the cell.

14. (a) Transpeptidation involves the nucleophilic attack of the amino group of the aminoacyl–tRNA on the carbonyl carbon of the peptidyl–tRNA. As the pH increases, the amino group becomes more nucleophilic (less likely to be protonated).

   (b) As the pH increases, residue A2486 would be less likely to be protonated and therefore less likely to stabilize the negatively charged oxyanion of the tetrahedral reaction intermediate. Thus, the mechanistic embellishment is inconsistent with the observed effect.

15. The enzyme hydrolyzes peptidyl–tRNA molecules that dissociate from a ribosome before normal translation termination takes place. Because peptide synthesis is prematurely halted, the resulting polypeptide, which is still linked to tRNA, is likely to be nonfunctional. Peptidyl–tRNA hydrolase is necessary for recycling the amino acids and the tRNA.

16. Aminoacylation occurs via pyrophosphate cleavage of ATP, and hence the aminoacylation of 100 tRNAs requires 200 ATP equivalents; translation initiation requires 1 GTP (1 ATP equivalent); 99 cycles of elongation require 99 GTP (99 ATP equivalents) for EF-Tu action; 99 cycles of ribosomal translocation require 99 GTP (99 ATP equivalents) for EF-G action; and translation termination requires 1 GTP (1 ATP equivalent), bringing the total energy cost to 200 + 1 + 99 + 99 + 1 = 400 ATP equivalents.

17.

	Start	Lys	Pro	Ala
5′-AGGAGCUX$_{-4}$	^A_GUG	AA^A_G	CCX	GCX -

Shine–Dalgarno sequence.
3–10 base pairs with G · U's allowed

Gly	Thr	Glu	Asn	Ser	Stop
GGX	ACX	GA^A_G	AA^U_C	UCX	UAA
				or	UAG - 3′
				AG^U_C	UGA

CHAPTER 28

1. Virtually all the DNA sequences in *E. coli* are present as single copies, so the renaturation of *E. coli* DNA is a straightforward process of each fragment reassociating with its complementary strand. In contrast, the human genome contains many repetitive DNA sequences. The many DNA fragments containing these sequences find each other to form double-stranded regions (renature) much faster than the single-copy DNA sequences that are also present, giving rise to a biphasic renaturation curve.

2. Because genes encoding proteins with related functions often occur in operons, the identification of one or several genes in an operon may suggest functions for the remaining genes in that operon.

3. (a) O_1 is the primary repressor-binding site, so *lac* repressor cannot stably bind to the operator in its absence and repression cannot occur.

   (b) Both O_2 and O_3 are secondary repressor-binding sequences. If one is absent, the other can still function, resulting in only a small loss of repressor effectiveness.

   (c) In the absence of both O_2 and O_3, the repressor can bind only to O_1, which partially interferes with transcription but does not repress transcription as fully as when a DNA loop forms through the cooperative binding of *lac* repressor to O_1 and either O_2 or O_3.

4. In the absence of β-galactosidase (the product of the *lacZ* gene), lactose is not converted to the inducer allolactose. Consequently, *lac* enzymes, including galactoside permease, are not synthesized.

5. Since operons other than the *lac* operon maintain their sensitivity to the absence of glucose, the defect is probably not in the gene that encodes CAP. Instead, the defect is probably located in the portion of the *lac* operon that binds CAP–cAMP.

6. In eukaryotes, transcription takes place in the nucleus and translation occurs in the cytoplasm. Hence, in eukaryotes,

ribosomes are never in contact with nascent mRNAs, an essential aspect of the attenuation mechanism in prokaryotes.

7. Deletion of the leader peptide sequence from *trpL* would eliminate sequence 1 of the attenuator. Consequently, the 2·3 hairpin rather than the 3·4 terminator hairpin would form. Transcription would therefore continue into the remainder of the *trp* operon, which would then be regulated solely by *trp* repressor.

8. Red–green color blindness is conferred by a mutation in an X-linked gene so that female carriers of this condition, who do not appear to be red–green colorblind, have one wild-type gene and one mutated gene for this condition. In placental mammals such as humans, females are mosaics of clones of cells in which only one of their two X chromosomes is transcriptionally active. Hence in a female carrier of red–green color blindness, the transcriptionally active X chromosome in some of these clones will contain the wild-type gene and the others will contain the mutated gene. The former type of retinal clone is able to differentiate red and green light, whereas the latter type of retinal clone is unable to do so. Apparently, these retinal clones are small enough so that a narrow beam of light is necessary to separately interrogate them.

9.

Acetyllysine   **Methyllysine**   **Methylarginine**

In acetyllysine, the cationic side chain of Lys has been converted to a polar but uncharged side chain. In methyllysine and methylarginine, the hydrophobic methyl group partially masks the cationic character of the Lys or Arg side chain.

10. Histone and DNA methylation requires *S*-adenosylmethionine (SAM), which becomes *S*-adenosylhomocysteine after it gives up its methyl group (Fig. 21-18). *S*-Adenosylhomocysteine is converted back to methionine, the precursor of SAM, in a reaction in which the methyl group is donated by the folic acid derivative tetrahydrofolate (THF; Fig. 21-18). A shortage of this cofactor could limit cellular production of SAM, which would result in the undermethylation of histones and DNA.

11. The product is a citrulline residue (Fig. 21-9).

12. Transcriptionally active chromatin has a more open structure due to histone modifications that help make the DNA more accessible to transcription factors and RNA polymerase as well as nucleases.

13. A sequence located downstream of the gene's promoter (i.e., within the coding region) could regulate gene expression if it were recognized by the appropriate transcription factor such that the resulting DNA–protein complex successfully recruited RNA polymerase to the promoter.

14. The susceptibility of RNA to degradation *in vivo* makes it possible to regulate gene expression by adjusting the rate of mRNA degradation. If mRNA were very stable, it might continue to direct translation even when the cell no longer needed the encoded protein.

15. A 22-bp segment of RNA, incorporating all four nucleotides, has 4^{22} or 1.8×10^{13} possible unique sequences. An RNA half this size would have only 4^{11} or 4.2×10^6 possible sequences. The shorter the siRNA, the greater is the probability that it could hybridize with more than one complementary mRNA, thereby making it less efficient in silencing a specific gene. (In the 3.2×10^9-bp human genome, a sequence of 16 bp has a high probability of randomly occurring at least once.)

16. Since there are 65 V_H, 27 D, and 6 J_H segments that can be used to assemble the coding sequence of the variable region of the heavy chain, somatic recombination could theoretically generate $65 \times 27 \times 6 = 10530$ heavy chain genes (junctional flexibility would increase this number). Since each immunoglobulin molecule contains two identical heavy chains and two identical light chains, the possible number of immunoglobulins would be $10530 \times 2000 = {\sim}21$ million.

17. The imprecise joining of V, D, and J segments, along with nucleotide addition or removal at the junction, can generate a Stop codon (yielding a truncated and hence nonfunctional immunoglobulin) or create a shift in the reading frame (yielding a misfolded and nonfunctional protein).

18. In multicellular organisms, apoptosis of damaged cells minimizes damage to the entire organism. For a single-celled organism, survival of a genetically damaged cell is preferable in a Darwinian sense to its death.

19. The *esc* gene is apparently a maternal-effect gene. Thus, the proper distribution of the *esc* gene product in the fertilized egg, which is maternally specified, is sufficient to permit normal embryonic development regardless of the embryo's genotype.

Glossary

umbers and Greek letters are alphabetized as if they were spelled out.

. See Absorbance.

site. See aminoacyl site.

–tRNA. See aminoacyl–tRNA.

RS. See aminoacyl–tRNA synthetase.

BC transporter. A member of a large family of transmembrane roteins that use the free energy of ATP to mediate the transport f polar or nonpolar substances across a membrane.

BO blood group antigens. The oligosaccharide components of ycolipids on the surfaces of erythrocytes and other cells.

bsolute configuration. The spatial arrangement of chemical roups around a chiral center.

bsorbance (A). A function of the amount of light transmitted hrough a solution (I) relative to the incident light (I_0) at a given avelength: $A = \log(I_0/I)$. Also called optical density.

bsorptivity (ε). A constant that relates the absorbance of a olution to the concentration of the solute at a given wavelength. lso called the extinction coefficient.

cceptor stem. The base-paired region of a tRNA molecule hat contains the 5′ end and the 3′ end, to which an amino acid is ttached.

ccessory pigment. A molecule in the photosynthetic system hat absorbs light at wavelengths other than those absorbed by hlorophyll.

cid. A substance that can donate a proton.

cid–base catalysis. A catalytic mechanism in which partial roton transfer from an acid or partial proton abstraction by a ase lowers the free energy of a reaction's transition state. See lso general acid catalysis and general base catalysis.

cidic solution. A solution whose pH is less than 7.0 ($[H^+] >$ 0^{-7} M).

cidosis. A pathological condition in which the pH of the blood rops below its normal value of 7.4.

ction potential. The wave of transient depolarization and epolarization that constitutes the electrical signal generated by nerve cell.

ctive site. The region of an enzyme in which catalysis takes lace.

ctive transport. The transmembrane movement of a substance om low to high concentrations by a protein that couples this ndergonic transport to an exergonic process such as ATP ydrolysis.

ctivity. A solute's concentration, corrected for its nonideal ehavior at concentrations greater than infinite dilution.

cyl-carrier protein. A phosphopantetheine-containing protein hat binds the intermediates of fatty acid synthesis as thioesters.

Acyl–enzyme intermediate. An intermediate of peptide bond hydrolysis in which the carbonyl carbon of the scissile bond is covalently bound to the enzyme nucleophile that attacked it.

Acyl group. A portion of a molecule with the formula —COR, where R is an alkyl group.

Adenylate cyclase system. A signal transduction pathway in which hormone binding to a cell-surface receptor activates a G protein that in turn stimulates adenylate cyclase to synthesize the second messenger 3′,5′-cyclic AMP (cAMP) from ATP.

Adenylylation. Addition of an adenylyl (AMP) group.

Adipocyte. Fat cell, which is specialized for the synthesis and storage of triacylglycerols from free fatty acids.

Adipose tissue. Fat cells; distributed throughout an animal's body.

ADP–ATP translocator. A membrane transport protein with an adenine nucleotide–binding site that alternately allows ADP to enter and ATP to exit the mitochondrial matrix.

Adrenoreceptor. A cell surface receptor that binds and responds to adrenal hormones such as epinephrine and norepinephrine. Also called an adrenergic receptor.

Aerobe. An organism that uses O_2 as an oxidizing agent for nutrient breakdown.

Affinity chromatography. A procedure in which a molecule is separated from a mixture of other molecules by its ability to bind specifically to an immobilized ligand. See also metal chelate affinity chromatography.

Affinity labeling. A technique in which a labeled substrate analog reacts irreversibly with, and can thereby be used to identify, a group in an enzyme's active site.

Agarose. Linear carbohydrate polymers, made by red algae, that form a loose mesh.

Agonist. A substance that binds to a receptor so as to evoke a cellular response.

Alcoholic fermentation. A metabolic pathway that synthesizes ethanol from pyruvate through decarboxylation and reduction.

Alditol. A sugar produced by reduction of an aldose or ketose to a polyhydroxy alcohol.

Aldol cleavage. A carbon–carbon cleavage reaction of an aldol (an aldehyde or ketone with a β hydroxyl group) that yields smaller carbonyl compounds.

Aldonic acid. A sugar produced by oxidation of an aldose aldehyde group to a carboxylic acid group.

Aldose. A sugar whose carbonyl group is an aldehyde.

Alkalosis. A pathological condition in which the pH of the blood rises above its normal value of 7.4.

Allele. An alternate form of a gene; diploid organisms contain two alleles for each gene, which may or may not be identical.

Allosteric effector. A small molecule whose binding to a protein affects the function of another site on the protein.

Allosteric interaction. The binding of ligand at one site in a macromolecule that affects the binding of other ligands at other sites in the molecule. See also cooperative binding.

αα motif. A protein motif consisting of two α helices packed against each other with their axes inclined.

α-amino acid. See amino acid.

α anomer. See anomers.

α/β barrel. A β barrel in which successive parallel β strands are connected by α helices such that a barrel of α helices surrounds the β barrel.

α carbon. The carbon atom of an amino acid to which the amino and carboxylic acid groups are attached.

α cell. A pancreatic islet cell that secretes the hormone glucagon in response to low blood glucose levels.

α-glycoside. See glycoside.

α helix. A regular secondary structure of polypeptides, with 3.6 residues per right-handed turn, a pitch of 5.4 Å, and hydrogen bonds between each backbone N—H group and the backbone C=O group that is four residues earlier.

Alternative splicing. The tissue-specific patterns of splicing of a given pre-mRNA that result in variations in the excision and retention of exons and introns.

Alzheimer's disease. A neurodegenerative disease characterized by the precipitation of β amyloid protein in the brain.

Ames test. A method for assessing the mutagenicity of a compound from its ability to cause genetically defective strains of bacteria to revert to normal growth.

Amido group. A portion of a molecule with the formula —CONH—.

Amino acid. A compound consisting of a carbon atom to which are attached a primary amino group, a carboxylic acid group, a side chain (R group), and an H atom. Also called an α-amino acid.

Amino group. A portion of a molecule with the formula —NH_2, —NHR, or —NR_2, where R is an alkyl group. Amino groups are usually protonated at physiological pH.

Amino sugar. A sugar in which one or more OH groups are replaced by an amino group, which is often acetylated.

Amino terminus. The end of a polypeptide that has a free amino group. Also called the N-terminus.

Aminoacyl site (A site). The ribosomal site where a tRNA with an attached aminoacyl group binds during protein synthesis.

Aminoacyl–tRNA (aa–tRNA). The covalent ester complex between an "activated" amino acid and a tRNA molecule.

Aminoacyl–tRNA synthetase (aaRS). An enzyme that catalyzes the ATP-dependent esterification of an amino acid to a tRNA with high specificity for the amino acid and the tRNA molecule.

Amphibolic. A term to describe a metabolic process that can be either catabolic or anabolic.

Amphipathic substance. See amphiphilic substance.

Amphiphilic substance. A substance that contains both polar and nonpolar regions and is therefore both hydrophilic and hydrophobic. Also called an amphipathic substance.

Amyloid. Insoluble extracellular aggregates of fibrous protein that characterize such diseases as Alzheimer's disease and the transmissible spongiform encephalopathies.

Anabolism. The reactions by which biomolecules are synthesized from simpler components.

Anaerobe. An organism that does not use O_2 as an oxidizing agent for nutrient breakdown. An obligate anaerobe cannot grow in the presence of O_2, whereas a facultative anaerobe can grow in the presence or absence of O_2.

Anaplerotic reaction. A reaction that replenishes the intermediates of a metabolic pathway.

Androgen. A steroid that functions primarily as a male sex hormone.

Anemia. A condition caused by insufficient red blood cells.

Angina. Chest pain due to insufficient blood supply to the heart.

Anion exchanger. A cationic matrix used to bind anionic molecules in ion exchange chromatography.

Anneal. To maintain conditions that allow loose base pairing between complementary single polynucleotide strands so that properly paired double-stranded segments form.

Anomeric carbon. The carbonyl carbon of a monosaccharide, which becomes a chiral center when the sugar cyclizes to a hemiacetal or hemiketal.

Anomers. Sugars that differ only in the configuration around the anomeric carbon. In the α anomer, the OH substituent of the anomeric carbon is on the opposite side of the ring from the CH_2OH group at the chiral center that designates the D or L configuration. In the β anomer, the OH substituent is on the same side.

Antagonist. A substance that binds to a receptor but does not elicit a cellular response.

Antenna chlorophyll. A chlorophyll group that absorbs light energy and passes it on to a photosynthetic reaction center by exciton transfer.

Anti conformation. A purine or pyrimidine nucleotide conformation in which the ribose and the base point away from each other. See also syn conformation.

Antibody. A protein produced by an animal's immune system in response to the introduction of a foreign substance (an antigen); it contains at least one pair each of identical heavy and light chains. Also called an immunoglobulin (Ig).

Anticodon. The sequence of three nucleotides in tRNA that recognizes an mRNA codon through complementary base pairing.

Anticodon arm. The conserved stem–loop structure in a tRNA molecule that includes the anticodon.

Antigen. A substance that elicits an immune response (production of antibodies) when introduced into an animal; it is specifically recognized by an antibody.

Antioxidant. A substance that destroys an oxidative free radical such as $O_2^-\cdot$ or OH·.

Antiparallel. Running in opposite directions.

Antiport. A transmembrane channel that simultaneously moves two molecules or ions in opposite directions. See also symport and uniport.

Antisense RNA. A single-stranded RNA molecule that forms a double-stranded structure with a complementary mRNA so as to block its translation into protein.

Antisense strand. The DNA strand that serves as a template for transcription; it is complementary to the RNA. Also called the noncoding strand.

AP site. An apurinic or apyrimidinic site; the deoxyribose residue remaining after the removal of a base from a DNA strand.

Apoenzyme. An enzyme that is inactive due to the absence of a cofactor.

Apolipoprotein. The protein component of a lipoprotein. Also called an apoprotein.

Apoprotein. A protein without the prosthetic group or metal ion that renders it fully functional. See also apoenzyme and apolipoprotein.

Apoptosis. Cell death by a regulated process in which the cell shrinks and fragments into membrane-bounded portions for phagocytosis by other cells. See also necrosis.

Aptamer. A nucleic acid whose conformation allows it to bind a particular ligand with high specificity and high affinity.

Aquaporin. A tetrameric membrane protein that mediates the rapid diffusion of water molecules but not protons or other ions across a membrane.

Archaea. One of the two major groups of prokaryotes (the other eubacteria). Also known as archaebacteria.

Archaebacteria. See archaea.

Assay. A laboratory technique for detecting, and in many cases quantifying, a macromolecule or its activity.

Asymmetric center. See chiral center.

Atherosclerosis. A disease characterized by the formation of cholesterol-containing fibrous plaques in the walls of blood vessels, leading to loss of elasticity and blockage of blood flow.

ATP mass action ratio. The ratio [ATP]/[ADP][P_i], which influences the rate of electron transport and oxidative phosphorylation.

ATP synthase. See F_1F_0-ATPase.

ATPase. An enzyme that catalyzes the hydrolysis of ATP to ADP + P_i.

Attenuation. A mechanism in prokaryotes for regulating gene expression in which the availability of an amino acid determines whether an operon (consisting of genes for the enzymes that synthesize the amino acid) is transcribed.

Attenuator. A prokaryotic control element that governs transcription of an operon according to the availability of an amino acid synthesized by the proteins encoded by the operon.

Autocatalytic reaction. A reaction in which a product molecule can act as a catalyst for the same reaction; the reactant molecule therefore appears to catalyze its own reaction.

Autoimmune disease. A disease in which the immune system has lost some of its self-tolerance and produces antibodies against certain self-antigens.

Autolysis. An autocatalytic process in which a molecule catalyzes its own degradation.

Autophosphorylation. The kinase-catalyzed phosphorylation of itself or an identical molecule.

Autoradiography. A process in which X-ray film records the positions of radioactive entities, such as proteins or nucleic acids, that have been immobilized in a matrix such as a nitrocellulose membrane or an electrophoretic gel.

Autotroph. An organism that can synthesize all its cellular components from simple molecules using the energy obtained from sunlight (photoautotroph) or from the oxidation of inorganic compounds (chemolithotroph).

Axial substituent. A group that extends perpendicularly from the plane of the ring to which it is bonded. See also equatorial substituent.

BAC. See bacterial artificial chromosome.

Backbone. The atoms that form the repeating linkages between successive residues of a polymeric molecule, exclusive of the side chains. Also called the main chain.

Bacteria. The organisms comprising the two major groups of prokaryotes, the archaea and the eubacteria.

Bacterial artificial chromosome (BAC). A plasmid-derived DNA molecule that can replicate in a bacterial cell. BACs are commonly used as cloning vectors.

Bacteriophage. A virus specific for bacteria. Also known as a phage.

Barr body. The condensed and darkly staining inactive X chromosome in the nucleus of a female mammalian cell.

Base. (1) A substance that can accept a proton. (2) A purine or pyrimidine component of a nucleoside, nucleotide, or nucleic acid.

Base excision repair (BER). The removal and replacement of a damaged nucleotide in DNA that is initiated by the removal of the base.

Base pair. The specific hydrogen-bonded association between nucleic acid bases. The Watson–Crick base pairs are A·T and G·C.

Basic helix–loop–helix (bHLH) motif. A eukaryotic protein motif that includes a basic DNA-binding region followed by two amphipathic helices connected by a loop. The second helix, which mediates protein dimerization, is often continuous with a leucine zipper motif.

Basic solution. A solution whose pH is greater than 7.0 ([H^+] < 10^{-7} M).

Beer–Lambert law. The equation that describes the relationship between a solute's absorbance (A) and its concentration (c): $A = \varepsilon c l$ where ε is the solute's molar absorptivity and l is the length of the light path.

BER. See base excision repair.

Beriberi. A disease caused by a deficiency of thiamine (vitamin B_1), which is a precursor of the cofactor thiamine pyrophosphate.

βαβ motif. A protein motif consisting of an α helix connecting two parallel strands of a β sheet.

β anomer. See anomers.

β barrel. A protein motif consisting of a β sheet rolled into a cylinder.

β bend. See reverse turn.

β bulge. An irregularity in a β sheet resulting from an extra residue that is not hydrogen bonded to a neighboring chain.

β cell. A pancreatic islet cell that secretes the hormone insulin in response to high blood glucose levels.

β-glycoside. See glycoside.

β hairpin. A protein motif in which two antiparallel β stands are connected by a reverse turn.

β oxidation. A series of enzyme-catalyzed reactions in which fatty acids are progressively degraded by the removal of two-carbon units as acetyl-CoA.

β sheet. A regular secondary structure in which extended polypeptide chains form interstrand hydrogen bonds. In parallel β sheets, the polypeptide chains all run in the same direction; in antiparallel β sheets, neighboring chains run in opposite directions.

bHLH motif. See basic helix–loop–helix motif.

Bilayer. An ordered, double layer of amphiphilic molecules in which polar segments point toward the two solvent-exposed surfaces and the nonpolar segments associate in the center.

Bile acid (bile salt). An amphiphilic cholesterol derivative that acts as a detergent to solubilize lipids for digestion and absorption.

Binding change mechanism. The mechanism whereby the subunits of the F_1F_0-ATP synthase adopt three successive conformations to convert $ADP + P_i$ to ATP as driven by the dissipation of the transmembrane proton gradient.

Bioavailability. A measure of the fraction of a drug that reaches its target tissue, which depends on the drug's dosage and pharmacokinetics.

Biochemical standard state. A set of conditions including unit activity of the species of interest, a temperature of 25°C, a pressure of 1 atm, and a pH of 7.0.

Biofilm. A surface-associated aggregate of bacterial cells and extracellular polysaccharides that protect the cells from environmental assault.

Bioinformatics. The study of biological information in the form of molecular sequences and structures; e.g., structural bioinformatics.

Biopterin. A pterin derivative that functions as a cofactor in the hydroxylation of phenylalanine to produce tyrosine.

Blastoderm. The single layer of cells surrounding a yolk-like core that forms during the early development of an insect larva.

Blunt ends. The fully base-paired ends of a DNA fragment that has been cleaved by a restriction endonuclease that cuts the DNA strands at opposing sites.

Bohr effect. The decrease in O_2 binding affinity of hemoglobin in response to a decrease in pH.

bp. Base pair, the unit of length used for DNA molecules. Thousands of base pairs (kilobase pairs) are abbreviated kb.

Bradford assay. A spectroscopic technique for determining protein concentration in solution from the absorbance of a dye bound to the protein.

Branch migration. The movement of a crossover point in a Holliday junction during DNA recombination.

Breathing. The small conformational fluctuations of a protein molecule.

Bromodomain. A protein module that binds acetylated Lys residues in histones.

Buffer. A solution of a weak acid and its conjugate base in approximately equal quantities. Such a solution resists changes in pH on the addition of acid or base.

Buffering capacity. The ability of a buffer solution to resist pH changes on addition of acid or base. Buffers are most useful when the pH is within one unit of its component acid's pK.

C-terminus. See carboxyl terminus.

C value. A measure of the quantity of an organism's unique genetic material.

C-value paradox. The occurrence of exceptions to the rule that an organism's DNA content (C value) is correlated to the complexity of its morphology and metabolism.

Cahn–Ingold–Prelog system (*RS* system). A system for unambiguously describing the configurations of molecules with one or more asymmetric centers by assigning a priority ranking to the substituent groups of each asymmetric center.

Calvin cycle. The sequence of photosynthetic dark reactions in which ribulose-5-phosphate is carboxylated, converted to three-carbon carbohydrate precursors, and regenerated. Also called the reductive pentose phosphate cycle.

Calmodulin (CaM). A small Ca^{2+}-binding protein that binds to other proteins in the presence of Ca^{2+} and thereby regulates their activities.

CaM. See calmodulin.

CAM. See crassulacean acid metabolism.

cAMP. 3′,5′-Cyclic AMP, an intracellular second messenger.

Cap. A 7-methylguanosine residue that is posttranscriptionally appended to the 5′ end of a eukaryotic mRNA.

Capillary electrophoresis (CE). Electrophoretic procedures carried out in small diameter capillary tubes.

Carbamate. The product of a reaction between CO_2 and an amino group: $-NH-COO^-$.

Carbohydrate. A compound with the formula $(C \cdot H_2O)_n$ where $n \geq 3$. Also called a saccharide.

Carbonyl group. A portion of a molecule with the formula $>C=O$

Carboxyl group. A portion of a molecule with the formula $-COOH$. Carboxyl groups are usually ionized at physiological pH.

Carboxyl terminus. The end of a polypeptide that has a free carboxylate group. Also called the C-terminus.

Carcinogen. An agent that damages DNA so as to induce a mutation that leads to uncontrolled cell proliferation (cancer).

Caspase. A heterotetrameric cysteine protease that hydrolyzes cellular proteins, including caspase zymogens, as part of the process of apoptosis.

Catabolism. The degradative metabolic reactions in which nutrients and cell constituents are broken down for energy and raw materials.

Catabolite repression. A phenomenon in which the presence of glucose prevents the expression of genes involved in the metabolism of other fuels.

Catalyst. A substance that promotes a chemical reaction without itself undergoing permanent change. A catalyst increases the rate at which a reaction approaches equilibrium but does not affect the free energy change of the reaction.

Catalytic perfection. The ability of an enzyme to catalyze a reaction as fast as diffusion allows it to bind its substrates.

Catalytic triad. The hydrogen-bonded Ser, His, and Asp residues that participate in catalysis in serine proteases.

Cataplerotic reaction. A reaction that drains the intermediates of a metabolic pathway.

Catecholamine. A hydroxylated tyrosine derivative, such as dopamine, norepinephrine, or epinephrine.

Catenate. To interlink circular DNA molecules like the links of a chain.

Cation exchanger. An anionic matrix used to bind cationic molecules in ion exchange chromatography.

CCAAT box. A eukaryotic promoter element with the consensus sequence CCAAT that is located 70 to 90 nucleotides upstream from the transcription start site.

cDNA. See complementary DNA.

CE. See capillary electrophoresis.

Cell cycle. The sequence of events between eukaryotic cell divisions; it includes mitosis and cell division (M phase), a gap stage (G_1 phase), a period of DNA synthesis (S phase), and a second gap stage (G_2 phase) before the next M phase.

Cellular immunity. Immunity mediated by T lymphocytes (T cells).

Central dogma of molecular biology. The paradigm that DNA directs its own replication as well as its transcription to RNA, which is then translated into a polypeptide. The flow of information is from DNA to RNA to protein.

Centromere. The eukaryotic chromosomal region that attaches to the mitotic spindle during cell division; it contains high concentrations of repetitive DNA.

Ceramide. A sphingosine derivative with an acyl group attached to its amino group.

Cerebroside. A ceramide with a sugar residue as a head group.

C_4 plant. A plant in which photosynthesis relies on CO_2 that has been concentrated by incorporating it into oxaloacetate (a C_4 compound).

Chain-terminator procedure. A technique for determining the nucleotide sequence of a DNA using dideoxy nucleotides so as to yield a collection of daughter strands of all different lengths. Also called the dideoxy method.

Channeling. The transfer of an intermediate product from one enzyme active site to another in such a way that the intermediate remains protected by the protein.

Chaotropic agent. A substance that increases the solubility of nonpolar substances in water and thereby tends to denature proteins.

Chaperone. See molecular chaperone.

Chargaff's rules. The observation, first made by Erwin Chargaff, that DNA has equal numbers of adenine and thymine residues and equal numbers of guanine and cytosine residues.

Chemical potential. The partial molar free energy of a substance.

Chemiosmotic theory. The postulate that the free energy of electron transport is conserved by the formation of a transmembrane proton gradient. The electrochemical potential of this gradient is used to drive ATP synthesis.

Chemolithotroph. An autotrophic organism that obtains energy from the oxidation of inorganic compounds.

Chimera. See recombinant.

Chiral center. An atom whose substituents are arranged such that it is not superimposable on its mirror image. Also called an asymmetric center.

Chirality. The property of being asymmetric. A chiral molecule cannot be superimposed on its mirror image.

Chloroplasts. The plant organelles in which photosynthesis takes place.

Chromatin. The complex of DNA and protein that comprises the eukaryotic chromosomes.

Chromatin-remodeling complex. An ATP-dependent multisubunit protein in eukaryotes that transiently disrupts DNA–histone interactions so as to alter the accessibility of DNA in nucleosomes.

Chromatography. A technique for separating the components of a mixture of molecules based on their partition between a mobile solvent phase and a porous matrix (stationary phase).

Chromodomain. A protein module that binds methylated Lys residues in histones.

Chromophore. A light-absorbing group or molecule.

Chromosome. The complex of protein and a single DNA molecule that comprises some or all of an organism's genome.

Chylomicrons. Lipoprotein particles that transport dietary triacylglycerols and cholesterol from the intestines to the tissues.

Cis conformation. An arrangement of the peptide group in which successive C_α atoms are on the same side of the peptide bond.

Cis peptide. A conformation in which successive C_α atoms are on the same side of the peptide bond.

Cistron. An archaic term for a gene.

Citric acid cycle. A set of eight enzymatic reactions, arranged in a cycle, in which free energy in the form of ATP, NADH, and $FADH_2$ is recovered from the oxidation of the acetyl group of acetyl-CoA to CO_2. Also called the Krebs cycle and the tricarboxylic acid (TCA) cycle.

Clathrin. A three-legged protein that polymerizes to form a polyhedral structure defining the shape of membranous vesicles that travel between the plasma membrane and intracellular organelles such as the Golgi apparatus.

Clinical trials. A three-phase series of tests of a drug's safety, effectiveness, and side effects in human subjects.

Clone. A collection of identical cells derived from a single ancestor.

Cloning. The production of exact copies of a DNA segment or the organism that harbors it.

Cloning vector. A DNA molecule such as a plasmid, virus, or artificial chromosome that can accommodate a segment of foreign DNA for cloning.

Closed system. A thermodynamic system that can exchange energy but not matter with its surroundings.

Coated vesicle. A membranous intracellular transport vesicle that is encased by clathrin or another coat protein.

Coding strand. See sense strand.

Codon. The sequence of three nucleotides in DNA or RNA that specifies a single amino acid.

Coenzyme. A small organic molecule that is required for the catalytic activity of an enzyme. A coenzyme may be either a cosubstrate or a prosthetic group.

Coenzyme Q. An isoprenoid that functions in electron-transport pathways as a lipid-soluble electron carrier. Also called ubiquinone.

Cofactor. A small organic molecule (coenzyme) or metal ion that is required for the catalytic activity of an enzyme.

Coiled coil. An arrangement of polypeptide chains in which two α helices wind around each other, as in α keratin.

Cointegrate. The product of the fusion of two plasmids, which occurs as an intermediate in transposition.

Colligative property. A physical property, such as freezing point depression or osmotic pressure, that depends on the concentration of a dissolved substance rather than on its chemical nature.

Colony hybridization. A procedure in which DNA from multiple cell colonies is transferred to a membrane or filter and incubated with a DNA or RNA probe to test for the presence of a desired DNA fragment in the cell colonies. Also called *in situ* hybridization.

Combinatorial chemistry. A method for rapidly and inexpensively synthesizing large numbers of related compounds by systematically varying a portion of their structure.

Compartmentation. The division of a cell into smaller functionally discrete systems.

Competitive inhibition. A form of enzyme inhibition in which a substance competes with the substrate for binding to the enzyme active site and thereby appears to increase K_M.

Complementary DNA (cDNA). A DNA molecule, usually synthesized by the action of reverse transcriptase, that is complementary to an mRNA molecule.

Composite transposon. A genetic sequence that may include a variety of genes and is flanked by IS-like elements; such transposons apparently arose by the association of two independent IS elements.

Condensation reaction. The formation of a covalent bond between two molecules, during which the elements of water are lost; the reverse of hydrolysis.

Conjugate acid. The compound that forms when a base accepts a proton.

Conjugate base. The compound that forms when an acid donates a proton.

Conjugate redox pair. An electron donor and acceptor that form a half-reaction. Also called a redox couple.

Conservative replication. A hypothetical mode of DNA duplication in which the parental molecule remains intact and both strands of the daughter duplex are newly synthesized.

Conservative substitution. A change of an amino acid residue in a protein to one with similar properties, e.g., Leu to Ile or Asp to Glu.

Constant region. The C-terminal portion of an antibody (immunoglobulin) subunit, which does not exhibit the high sequence variability of the antigen-recognizing (variable) region of the antibody.

Constitutive enzyme. An enzyme that is synthesized at a more or less steady rate and that is required for basic cell function. Also called a housekeeping enzyme. See also inducible enzyme.

Contact inhibition. The inhibition of proliferation in cultured animal cells when the cells touch each other.

Contour length. The end-to-end length of a stretched-out polymer molecule.

Contour map. A map containing lines (contours) that trace positions of equal value of some property of the map (e.g., height above sea level, electron density).

Convergent evolution. The independent development of similar characteristics in unrelated species or proteins.

Cooperative binding. A situation in which the binding of a ligand at one site on a macromolecule affects the affinity of other sites for the same ligand. Both negative and positive cooperativity occur. See also allosteric interaction.

Corepressor. A substance that acts together with a protein repressor to block gene transcription.

Cori cycle. An interorgan metabolic pathway in which lactate produced by glycolysis in the muscles is transported via the bloodstream to the liver, where it is used for gluconeogenesis. The resulting glucose returns to the muscles.

Cosubstrate. A coenzyme that is only transiently associated with an enzyme so that it functions as a substrate.

Coupled enzymatic reaction. A technique in which the activity of an enzyme is measured by the ability of a second enzyme to use the product of the first enzymatic reaction to produce a detectable product.

Covalent catalysis. A catalytic mechanism in which the transient formation of a covalent bond between the catalyst and a reactant lowers the free energy of a reaction's transition state.

CpG island. A cluster of CG dinucleotides located just upstream of many vertebrate genes; such sequences occur elsewhere in the genome at only one-fifth their randomly expected frequency.

Crassulacean acid metabolism (CAM). A variation of the C_4 photosynthetic cycle in which CO_2 is temporarily stored as malate.

Cristae. The invaginations of the inner mitochondrial membrane.

Cross talk. The interactions of different signal transduction pathways through activation of the same signaling components, generation of a common second messenger, or similar patterns of target protein phosphorylation.

ryoelectron microscopy (cryo-EM). A technique in electron microscopy in which a sample is rapidly frozen to very low temperatures so that it retains its native shape to a greater extent than in conventional electron microscopy.

3′-endo. A ribose conformation in which C3′ is displaced toward the same side of the ring as C5′.

₃ plant. A plant in which photosynthesis proceeds by the incorporation of CO_2 into three-carbon compounds.

2′-endo. A ribose conformation in which C2′ is displaced toward the same side of the ring as C5′.

urved arrow convention. A notation for indicating the movement of an electron pair in a chemical reaction by drawing a curved arrow emanating from the electrons and pointing to the electron-deficient center that attracts the electron pair.

yanosis. A bluish skin color indicating the presence of deoxyhemoglobin in the arterial blood.

yclic symmetry. A type of symmetry in which the asymmetric units of a symmetric object are related by a single axis of rotation.

yclin. A member of a family of proteins that participate in regulating the stages of the cell cycle and whose concentrations change dramatically over the course of the cell cycle.

ytochrome. A redox-active protein that carries electrons via a prosthetic Fe-containing heme group.

ytochrome P450. Heme-containing monooxygenases that catalyze the addition of OH groups to drugs and toxins in order to detoxify them and facilitate their excretion.

ytoplasm. The entire contents of a cell excluding the nucleus.

ytoskeleton. The network of intracellular fibers that gives a cell its shape and structural rigidity.

ytosol. The contents of a cell excluding its nucleus and other membrane-bounded organelles.

). Dalton, a unit of molecular mass; 1/12th the mass of a ²C atom.

) arm. A conserved stem–loop structure in a tRNA molecule that usually contains the modified base dihydrouridine.

Dark reactions. The portion of photosynthesis in which NADPH and ATP produced by the light reactions are used to incorporate CO_2 into carbohydrates.

ldNTP. An abbreviation for any dideoxynucleoside triphosphate.

Deamination. The hydrolytic removal of an amino group.

Debranching. The enzymatic removal of side chains from a branched polymer such as glycogen.

Degenerate code. A code in which more than one "word" encodes the same entity.

Δ𝒢. Electromotive force. Change in reduction potential.

Δ𝐺‡. See free energy of activation.

ΔΨ. See membrane potential.

Denature. To disrupt the native conformation of a polymer.

Deoxy sugar. A saccharide produced by replacement of an OH group by H.

Deoxynucleotide. See deoxyribonucleotide.

Deoxyribonucleic acid. See DNA.

Deoxyribonucleotide. A nucleotide in which the pentose is 2′-deoxyribose. Also known as a deoxynucleotide.

Depolarization. The loss of membrane potential that occurs during electrical signaling in cells such as neurons.

Desaturase. An enzyme that introduces double bonds into a fatty acid.

Desensitization. A cell's or organism's adaptation to a long-term stimulus through a reduced response to the stimulus.

Dextrorotatory. Rotating the plane of plane-polarized light clockwise from the point of view of the observer; the opposite of levorotatory.

Diabetes mellitus. A disease in which the pancreas does not secrete sufficient insulin (also called type I, insulin-dependent, or juvenile-onset diabetes) or in which the body has insufficient response to circulating insulin (type II, non-insulin-dependent, or maturity-onset diabetes). Diabetes is characterized by elevated levels of glucose in the blood.

Dialysis. A procedure in which solvent molecules and solutes smaller than the pores in a semipermeable membrane freely exchange with the bulk medium, while larger solutes are retained, thereby changing the solution in which the larger molecules are dissolved.

Diazotroph. A bacterium that can fix nitrogen.

Dideoxy method. See chain-terminator procedure.

Diet-induced thermogenesis. See thermogenesis.

Diffraction pattern. The record of the destructive and constructive interferences of radiation scattered from an object. In X-ray crystallography, this takes the form of a series of discrete spots resulting from a collimated beam of X-rays scattering from a single crystal.

Diffusion. The transport of molecules through their random movement.

Diffusion-controlled limit. The theoretical maximum rate of an enzymatic reaction in solution, about 10^8 to $10^9\ M^{-1} \cdot s^{-1}$.

Dihedral angle. See torsion angle.

Dihedral symmetry. A type of symmetry in which the asymmetric units are related by a twofold rotational axis that intersects another rotation axis at a right angle.

Dimer. An assembly consisting of two monomeric units (protomers).

Dinucleotide binding fold. A protein structural motif consisting of two βαβαβ units, which binds a dinucleotide such as NAD^+. Also called a Rossmann fold.

Dipeptide. A polypeptide consisting of two amino acids.

Diphosphoryl (pyrophosphoryl) group. Two phosphoryl groups linked by a phosphoanhydride bond $(-O_3P-O-PO_3-)^{2-}$.

Diploid. Having two equivalent sets of chromosomes.

Dipolar ion. A compound bearing oppositely charged groups. Also called a zwitterion.

Disaccharide. A carbohydrate consisting of two monosaccharides linked by a glycosidic bond.

Dissociation constant (K). The ratio of the products of the concentrations of the dissociated species to those of their parent compounds at equilibrium.

Disulfide bond. A covalent —S—S— linkage.

DNA. Deoxyribonucleic acid. A polymer of deoxynucleotides whose sequence of bases encodes genetic information in all living cells.

DNA chip. See DNA microarray.

DNA fingerprinting. A technique for distinguishing individuals on the basis of DNA polymorphisms, such as the number of short tandem repeats (STR).

DNA glycosylase. An enzyme that initiates base excision repair of DNA by cleaving the glycosidic bond that links a nucleotide base to ribose.

DNA library. A set of cloned DNA fragments representing some or all of an organism's genome.

DNA microarray. A set of DNA segments of known sequence that are immobilized on a solid support for the purpose of hybridizing with nucleic acids in test samples. Also called a DNA chip.

dNTP. A deoxyribonucleoside triphosphate.

Dolichol. An isoprenoid that serves as a lipid-soluble carrier of an N-linked oligosaccharide during its synthesis in the endoplasmic reticulum.

Domain. A group of one or a few polypeptide segments of about 40–200 residues that folds into a globular unit.

Double-displacement reaction. A reaction in which a substrate binds and a product is released in the first stage, and another substrate binds and another product is released in the second stage.

Double-reciprocal plot. See Lineweaver–Burk plot.

Drug–drug interactions. Increases or decreases in the bioavailability of a drug caused by the metabolic effects of another drug.

$\mathcal{E}$. See reduction potential.

$\mathcal{E}°'$. Reduction potential under biochemical standard conditions.

E site. See exit site.

EC classification. The Enzyme Commission's system for classifying and numbering enzymes according to the type of reaction catalyzed.

Edman degradation. A procedure for the stepwise removal and identification of the N-terminal residues of a polypeptide.

EF hand. A widespread helix–loop–helix structural motif that forms a Ca^{2+}-binding site.

Eicosanoids. C_{20} compounds derived from the C_{20} fatty acid arachidonic acid and which act as local mediators. Prostaglandins, prostacyclins, thromboxanes, leukotrienes, and lipoxins are eicosanoids.

Electrochemical cell. A device in which two half-reactions occur in separate compartments linked by a wire for transporting electrons and a salt bridge for maintaining electrical neutrality; the simultaneous activity of the half-reactions forms a complete oxidation–reduction reaction.

Electrochemical potential. The partial molar free energy of a substance (chemical potential) in the presence of an electrical potential.

Electrogenic transport. The transmembrane movement of a charged substance in a way that generates a charge difference across the membrane.

Electromotive force (emf). $\Delta\mathcal{E}$. Change in reduction potential.

Electron crystallography. A technique for determining molecular structure, in which the electron beam of an electron microscope used to elicit diffraction from a two-dimensional crystal of the molecules of interest.

Electron density. The arrangement of electrons that gives rise to a diffraction pattern in X-ray crystallography.

Electron-transport chain. A series of membrane-associated electron carriers that pass electrons from reduced coenzymes (NADH and $FADH_2$) to molecular oxygen so as to recover free energy for the synthesis of ATP.

Electrophile. A group that contains an unfilled valence electron shell, or contains an electron-deficient atom. An electrophile (electron-lover) reacts readily with a nucleophile (nucleus-lover).

Electrophoresis. See gel electrophoresis.

Electrospray ionization (ESI). A method for vaporizing macromolecules for their mass spectrometry in which a macromolecular solution is sprayed from a narrow capillary at high voltage to produce fine, highly charged droplets that rapidly evaporate leaving the now charged macromolecule in the gas phase.

Electrostatic catalysis. A catalytic mechanism in which the distribution of charges about the catalytic site lowers the free energy of a reaction's transition state.

Elementary reaction. A simple one-step chemical process, several of which may occur in sequence in a chemical reaction.

ELISA. See enzyme-linked immunosorbent assay.

Elongase. An enzyme that adds acetyl units to a fatty acid previously synthesized by fatty acid synthase.

Elongation factor. A protein that interacts with tRNA and/or the ribosome during polypeptide synthesis.

Eluant. The solution used to wash material through a chromatographic column.

Elution. The process of dislodging a molecule that has bound to a chromatographic matrix.

Emergent property. A property of a complex system that is not attributable to any of its individual components but becomes apparent when all components are present.

emf. Electromotive force. Change in reduction potential.

Enantiomers. Molecules that are nonsuperimposable mirror images of one another. Enantiomers are a type of stereoisomer.

Endergonic process. A process that has an overall positive free energy change (a nonspontaneous process).

Endocrine gland. A tissue in higher animals that synthesizes and releases hormones into the bloodstream.

Endocytosis. The internalization of extracellular material through the formation of a vesicle that buds off from the plasma membrane the opposite of exocytosis. See also receptor-mediated endocytosis.

Endoglycosidase. An enzyme that catalyzes the hydrolysis of the glycosidic bonds between two monosaccharide units within a polysaccharide.

Endonuclease. An enzyme that catalyzes the hydrolysis of the phosphodiester bonds between two nucleotide residues within a polynucleotide strand.

Endopeptidase. An enzyme that catalyzes the hydrolysis of a peptide bond within a polypeptide chain.

Endoplasmic reticulum (ER). A labyrinthine membranous organelle in eukaryotic cells in which membrane lipids are synthesized and some proteins undergo posttranslational modification.

Endosome. A membrane-bounded vesicle that receives materials that the cell ingests via receptor-mediated endocytosis and passes them to lysosomes for degradation.

Enediol intermediate. A reaction intermediate containing a carbon–carbon double bond and a hydroxyl group attached to each carbon.

Energy coupling. The conservation of the free energy of electron transport in a form that can be used to synthesize ATP from ADP + P_i.

"Energy-rich" compound. See "High-energy" compound.

Enhanceosome. A complex containing several transcription factors that regulates gene expression in eukaryotes.

Enhancer. A eukaryotic DNA sequence located some distance from the transcription start site, where an activator of transcription may bind.

Enthalpy (H). A thermodynamic quantity, $H = U + PV$, that is equivalent to the heat absorbed at constant pressure (q_P).

Entropy (S). A measure of the degree of randomness or disorder of a system. It is defined as $S = k_B \ln W$, where k_B is the Boltzmann constant and W is the number of equivalent ways the system can be arranged in its particular state.

Enzyme. A biological catalyst. Most enzymes are proteins; a few are RNA.

Enzyme-linked immunosorbent assay (ELISA). A technique in which a molecule is detected, and in many cases quantified, by its ability to bind an antibody to which an enzyme with an easily detected reaction product is attached.

Enzyme saturation. A state in which the substrate concentration is so high that essentially all the enzyme molecules are in the ES form.

Epigenetics. The inheritance of patterns of gene expression that are maintained from generation to generation independent of DNA's base sequence. This occurs, for example, through the methylation of DNA.

Epimers. Sugars that differ only by the configuration at one C atom (excluding the anomeric carbon).

Equatorial substituent. A group that extends largely in the plane of the ring to which it is bonded. See also axial substituent.

Equilibrium. The point in a process at which the forward and reverse reaction rates are exactly balanced so that it undergoes no net change.

Equilibrium constant (K_{eq}). The ratio, at equilibrium, of the product of the concentrations of reaction products to that of its reactants. K_{eq} is related to $\Delta G°$ for the reaction: $\Delta G° = -RT \ln K_{eq}$. Usually abbreviated K.

ER. See endoplasmic reticulum.

Erythrocyte. A red blood cell, which functions to transport O_2 to the tissues. It is essentially a membranous sack of hemoglobin.

Erythrocyte ghost. Membranous particles derived from erythrocytes, which retain their original shape but are devoid of cytoplasm.

ES complex. The enzyme–substrate complex, whose formation is a key component of the Michaelis–Menten model of enzyme action. Also called the Michaelis complex.

ESI. See electrospray ionization.

Essential amino acid. An amino acid that an animal cannot synthesize and must therefore obtain in its diet.

Essential fatty acid. A fatty acid that an animal cannot synthesize and must therefore obtain in its diet.

EST. See expressed sequence tag.

Ester group. A portion of a molecule with the formula —COOR, where R is an alkyl group.

Estrogen. A steroid that functions primarily as a female sex hormone.

Ether. A molecule with the formula ROR′, where R and R′ are alkyl groups.

Eubacteria. One of the two major groups of prokaryotes (the other is archaea).

Euchromatin. The transcriptionally active, relatively uncondensed chromatin in a eukaryotic cell.

Eukarya. See eukaryote.

Eukaryote. An organism consisting of a cell (or cells) whose genetic material is contained in a membrane-bounded nucleus.

Evolution. The gradual alteration of an organism or one of its components as a result of genetic changes that are passed from parent to offspring.

Exciton transfer. A mode of decay of an energetically excited molecule, in which electronic energy is transferred to a nearby unexcited molecule. Also known as resonance energy transfer.

Exergonic process. A process that has an overall negative free energy change (a spontaneous process).

Exit site (E site). The ribosomal binding site that accommodates a tRNA molecule that has previously transferred its peptidyl group to an incoming aminoacyl–tRNA and is ready to dissociate from the ribosome.

Exocytosis. The release outside the cell of a vesicle's contents through the fusion of the vesicle membrane with the plasma membrane; the opposite of endocytosis.

Exoglycosidase. An enzyme that catalyzes the hydrolytic excision of a monosaccharide unit from the end of a polysaccharide.

Exon. A portion of a gene that appears in both the primary and mature mRNA transcripts. Also called an expressed sequence.

Exonuclease. An enzyme that catalyzes the hydrolytic excision of a nucleotide residue from one end of a polynucleotide strand.

Exopeptidase. An enzyme that catalyzes the hydrolytic excision of an amino acid residue from one end of a polypeptide chain.

Expressed sequence. See exon.

Expressed sequence tag (EST). A cDNA segment corresponding to a cellular mRNA, that can be used to identify genes that are transcribed.

Expression vector. A plasmid containing the transcription and translation control sequences required for the production of a foreign DNA gene product (RNA or protein) in a host cell.

Extinction coefficient. See absorptivity.

Extrinsic protein. See peripheral protein.

$\mathscr{F}$. Faraday, the electrical charge of one mole of electrons.

F_1F_0-ATPase. A multisubunit protein consisting of a proton-translocating membrane-embedded component (F_0) linked to a soluble catalytic component (F_1) that catalyzes ATP synthesis in the presence of a protonmotive force. Also called ATP synthase.

Fab fragment. A proteolytic fragment of an antibody molecule that contains the antigen-binding site. See also Fc fragment.

Facilitated diffusion. See passive-mediated transport.

Familial hypercholesterolemia. See hypercholesterolemia.

Fat. A mixture of triacylglycerols that is solid at room temperature.

Fatty acid. A carboxylic acid with a long-chain hydrocarbon side group.

Fc fragment. A proteolytic fragment of an antibody molecule that contains the two C-terminal domains of its two heavy chains. See also Fab fragment.

Fe–S cluster. See iron–sulfur cluster.

Feedback inhibition. The inhibition of an early step in a reaction sequence by the product of a later step.

Feedforward activation. The activation of a later step in a reaction sequence by the product of an earlier step.

Fermentation. An anaerobic catabolic process.

Fibrous protein. A protein characterized by a stiff, elongated conformation, that tends to form fibers.

First-order reaction. A reaction whose rate is proportional to the concentration of a single reactant.

Fischer convention. A system for describing the absolute configurations of chiral molecules by relating their structures to that of D- or L-glyceraldehyde.

Fischer projection. A graphical convention for specifying molecular configuration in which horizontal lines represent bonds that extend above the plane of the paper and vertical lines represent bonds that extend below the plane of the paper.

5′ end. The terminus of a polynucleotide whose C5′ is not esterified to another nucleotide residue.

Flip-flop. See transverse diffusion.

Flipase. An enzyme that catalyzes the translocation of a membrane lipid across a lipid bilayer (a flip-flop).

Fluid mosaic model. A model of biological membranes in which integral membrane proteins float and diffuse laterally in a fluid lipid bilayer.

Fluorescence. A mode of decay of an excited molecule, in which electronic energy is emitted in the form of a photon.

Fluorescence recovery after photobleaching (FRAP). A technique for assessing the diffusion of membrane components from the rate at which the fluorescently labeled component moves into an area previously bleached by a pulse of laser light.

Fluorophore. A fluorescent group or molecule.

Flux. (1) The rate of flow of metabolites through a metabolic pathway. (2) The rate of transport per unit area.

fMet. The formylated methionine that initiates ribosomal polypeptide synthesis in prokaryotes.

Footprinting. A procedure in which the DNA sequence to which a protein binds is identified by determining which bases are protected by the protein from chemical or enzymatic modification.

Fractional saturation (Y). The fraction of a protein's ligand-binding sites that are occupied by ligand. For example, Y_{O_2} is the fractional saturation of a protein's oxygen-binding sites.

Fractionation procedure. A laboratory technique for separating the components of a mixture of molecules through differences in their chemical and physical properties.

Frameshift mutation. An insertion or deletion of nucleotides in DNA that alters the sequential reading (the frame) of sets of three nucleotides (codons) during translation.

FRAP. See fluorescence recovery after photobleaching.

Free energy (G). A thermodynamic quantity, $G = H - TS$, whose change at constant pressure is indicative of the spontaneity of a process. For spontaneous processes, $\Delta G < 0$, whereas for a process at equilibrium, $\Delta G = 0$. Also called Gibbs free energy.

Free energy of activation ($\Delta G^{\ddagger}$). The free energy of the transition state minus the free energies of the reactants in a chemical reaction.

Free radical. A molecule with an unpaired electron.

Functional group. A portion of a molecule that participates in interactions with other substances. Common functional groups in biochemistry are acyl, amido, amino, carbonyl, carboxyl, diphosphoryl (pyrophosphoryl), ester, ether, hydroxyl, imino, phosphoryl, and sulfhydryl groups.

Furanose. A sugar with a five-membered ring.

Futile cycle. See substrate cycle.

G. See free energy.

$G^{\ddagger}$. The free energy of the transition state. See also free energy of activation.

G protein. A guanine nucleotide–binding protein, most of which are involved in signal transduction, that is inactive when it binds GDP and active when it binds GTP. The GTPase activity of the G protein limits its own activity. Heterotrimeric G proteins consist of three subunits, which dissociate to form G_α (to which GTP binds) and $G_{\beta\gamma}$ components on activation.

G-quartet. A cyclic tetramer of hydrogen-bonded guanine groups. Stacks of G-quartets result from the antiparallel association of G-rich telomeric DNA hairpin structures.

Ganglioside. A ceramide whose head group is an oligosaccharide containing at least one sialic acid residue.

Gap genes. See segmentation genes.

Gap junction. An intercellular channel for ions and small molecules that is formed by protein complexes in the membranes of apposed cells.

Gastrulation. The stage of embryonic development in which cells migrate to form a triple-layered structure.

ates and fences model. A model for membrane structure at includes cytoskeletal proteins that prevent or limit the free iffusion of other membrane proteins.

ating. The opening and closing of a transmembrane channel in sponse to a signal such as mechanical stimulation, ligand binding, resence of a signaling molecule, or a change in membrane voltage.

el electrophoresis. A procedure in which macromolecules are eparated on the basis of charge or size by their differential igration through a gel-like matrix under the influence of an pplied electric field. In polyacrylamide gel electrophoresis PAGE), the matrix is cross-linked polyacrylamide. Agarose gels re used to separate molecules of very large masses, such as NAs. See also SDS-PAGE and pulsed-field gel electrophoresis.

el filtration chromatography. A procedure in which acromolecules are separated on the basis of their size and shape. lso called size exclusion or molecular sieve chromatography.

ene. A unique sequence of nucleotides that encodes a olypeptide or RNA; it may include nontranscribed and ontranslated sequences, some of which have regulatory functions.

ene cluster. A region of DNA containing multiple copies of enes, usually tRNA or rRNA genes, whose products are equired in large amounts.

ene duplication. An event, such as aberrant crossover, that ives rise to two copies of a gene on the same chromosome, each f which can then evolve independently.

ene expression. The decoding, via transcription and translation, f the information contained in a gene to yield a functional RNA r protein product.

ene knockout. A genetic engineering process that deletes or nactivates a specific gene in an animal.

ene product. The RNA or protein that is encoded by a gene nd that is the end point of the gene's expression through ranscription and translation.

ene therapy. The transfer of genetic material to the cells of an ndividual in order to produce a therapeutic effect.

eneral acid catalysis. A catalytic mechanism in which partial roton transfer from an acid lowers the free energy of a eaction's transition state.

eneral base catalysis. A catalytic mechanism in which partial roton abstraction by a base lowers the free energy of a eaction's transition state.

eneral transcription factor (GTF). One of a set of eukaryotic roteins that are required for the synthesis of all mRNAs.

enetic anticipation. A pattern of inheritance of a genetic lisease, in which the age of onset of symptoms decreases with ach generation.

enetic code. The correspondence between the sequence of ucleotides in a nucleic acid and the sequence of amino acids in polypeptide; a series of three nucleotides (a codon) specifies n amino acid.

Genetic engineering. See recombinant DNA technology.

Genome. The complete set of genetic instructions in an rganism.

Genomic library. A set of cloned DNA fragments representing n organism's entire genome.

Genomics. The study of the size, organization, and gene content of organisms' genomes.

Genotype. An organism's genetic characteristics.

Gibbs free energy. See free energy.

Globin. The polypeptide components of myoglobin and hemoglobin.

Globoside. A ceramide whose head group is a neutral oligosaccharide.

Globular protein. A water-soluble protein characterized by a compact, highly folded structure.

Glucocorticoid. A steroid hormone that affects a range of metabolic pathways and the inflammatory response.

Glucogenic amino acid. An amino acid whose degradation yields a gluconeogenic precursor. See also ketogenic amino acid.

Gluconeogenesis. The synthesis of glucose from noncarbohydrate precursors.

Glucose–alanine cycle. An interorgan metabolic pathway that transports nitrogen to the liver in which pyruvate produced by glycolysis in the muscles is converted to alanine and transported to the liver. There the alanine is converted back to pyruvate and its amino group is used to synthesize urea for excretion. The pyruvate is converted, via gluconeogenesis, to glucose, which is returned to the muscles.

Glucose–fatty acid cycle. The downregulation of glycolysis by fatty acid oxidation, caused by the acetyl-CoA–induced inhibition of phosphofructokinase by citrate. Also called the Randle cycle.

Glycan. See polysaccharide.

Glycerophosphate shuttle. A metabolic pathway that uses the interconversion of dihydroxyacetone phosphate and 3-phosphoglycerol to transport cytosolic reducing equivalents into the mitochondria.

Glycerophospholipid. An amphiphilic lipid in which two fatty acyl groups are attached to a glycerol-3-phosphate whose phosphate group is linked to a polar group. Also called a phosphoglyceride.

Glycoconjugate. A molecule, such as a glycolipid or glycoprotein, that contains covalently linked carbohydrate.

Glycoforms. Glycoproteins that differ in the sequence, location, and number of covalently attached carbohydrates.

Glycogen. An $\alpha(1 \rightarrow 6)$ branched polymer of $\alpha(1 \rightarrow 4)$-linked glucose residues that serves as a glucose storage molecule in animals.

Glycogen storage disease. An inherited disorder of glycogen metabolism affecting the size and structure of glycogen molecules or their mobilization in the muscle and/or liver.

Glycogenolysis. The enzymatic degradation of glycogen to glucose-6-phosphate.

Glycolipid. A lipid to which carbohydrate is covalently attached.

Glycolysis. The 10-reaction pathway by which glucose is broken down to 2 pyruvate with the concomitant production of 2 ATP and the reduction of 2 NAD^+ to 2 NADH.

Glycomics. The study of the structures and functions of all of a cell's carbohydrates, including large glycans and the small oligosaccharides of glycoproteins.

Glycoprotein. A protein to which carbohydrate is covalently attached.

Glycosaminoglycan. An unbranched polysaccharide consisting of alternating residues of uronic acid and hexosamine.

Glycoside. A molecule containing a saccharide and another molecule linked by a glycosidic bond to the anomeric carbon in the α configuration (α-glycoside) or β configuration (β-glycoside).

Glycosidic bond. The covalent linkage (acetal or ketal) between the anomeric carbon of a saccharide and an alcohol (*O*-glycosidic bond) or an amine (*N*-glycosidic bond). Glycosidic bonds link the monosaccharide residues of a polysaccharide.

Glycosylation. The attachment of carbohydrate chains to a protein through *N*- or *O*-glycosidic linkages.

Glyoxylate pathway. A variation of the citric acid cycle in plants that allows acetyl-CoA to be converted quantitatively to gluconeogenic precursors.

Glyoxysome. A membrane-bounded plant organelle in which the reactions of the glyoxylate cycle take place. It is a specialized type of peroxisome.

Golgi apparatus. A eukaryotic organelle consisting of a set of flattened membranous sacs in which newly synthesized proteins and lipids are modified.

Gout. A disease characterized by elevated levels of uric acid, usually the result of impaired uric acid excretion. Its most common manifestation is painful arthritic joint inflammation caused by the deposition of sodium urate.

GPCR. G protein–coupled receptor, a cell-surface protein with seven transmembrane helices that interacts with an associated G protein on ligand binding.

GPI-linked protein. A protein that is anchored in a membrane via a covalently linked glycosylphosphatidylinositol (GPI) group.

Gram-negative bacterium. A bacterium that does not take up Gram stain, indicating that its cell wall is surrounded by a complex outer membrane that excludes Gram stain.

Gram-positive bacterium. A bacterium that takes up Gram stain, indicating that its outermost layer is a cell wall.

Grana (*sing.* granum). The stacked disks of the thylakoid in a chloroplast.

gRNA. See guide RNA.

Group I intron. An intron in an rRNA molecule whose self-splicing reaction requires a guanine nucleotide and generates a cyclized intron product.

Group II intron. An intron in a eukaryotic rRNA molecule whose self-splicing reaction does not require a free nucleotide and generates a lariat intron product.

Growth factor. A protein hormone that stimulates the proliferation and differentiation of its target cells.

GTF. See general transcription factor.

GTPase. An enzyme that catalyzes the hydrolysis of GTP to GDP + P$_i$.

Guide RNA (gRNA). Small RNA molecules that pair with an immature mRNA to direct its posttranscriptional editing.

H. See enthalpy.

Half-life. See half-time.

Half-reaction. The single oxidation or reduction process, involving an electron donor and its conjugate electron acceptor, that occurs in electrical cells but requires direct contact with another such reaction to form a complete oxidation–reduction reaction.

Half-time ($t_{1/2}$). The time required for half the reactant initially present to undergo reaction. Also called half-life.

Halobacteria. Bacteria that thrive in (and may require) high salinity.

Haploid. Having one set of chromosomes.

HAT. See histone acetyltransferase.

Haworth projection. A representation of a sugar ring in which ring bonds that project in front of the plane of the paper are represented by heavy lines and ring bonds that project behind the plane of the paper are drawn as light lines.

HDL. High density lipoprotein; see lipoprotein.

Heat shock protein (Hsp). See molecular chaperone.

Helicase. An enzyme that unwinds a double-stranded nucleic acid.

Helix cap. A protein structural element in which the side chain of a residue preceding or succeeding a helix folds back to form a hydrogen bond with the backbone of one of the helix's four terminal residues.

Helix–turn–helix (HTH) motif. An ~20-residue protein motif that forms two α helices that cross at an angle of ~120°. This motif, which occurs in numerous prokaryotic DNA-binding proteins, binds in DNA's major groove to specific base sequences.

Heme. A porphyrin derivative whose central Fe(II) atom is the site of reversible oxygen binding (in myoglobin and hemoglobin) or oxidation–reduction (in cytochromes).

Hemiacetal. The product of the reaction between an alcohol and the carbonyl group of an aldehyde.

Hemiketal. The product of the reaction between an alcohol and the carbonyl group of a ketone.

Hemolytic anemia. Loss of red blood cells through their lysis (destruction) in the bloodstream.

Henderson–Hasselbalch equation. The mathematical expression of the relationship between the pH of a solution of a weak acid and its pK: pH = pK + log([A$^-$]/[HA]).

Heptad repeat. A sequence of seven residues that is repeated in the same polymer.

Heterochromatin. Highly condensed, nonexpressed eukaryotic DNA.

Heterogeneous nuclear RNA (hnRNA). Eukaryotic mRNA primary transcripts whose introns have not yet been excised.

Heterologous DNA. A segment of DNA consisting of imperfectly complementary strands.

Heterolytic cleavage. Cleavage of a bond in which one of two chemically bonded atoms acquires both of the electrons that formed the bond.

Heteropolysaccharide. A polysaccharide consisting of more than one type of monosaccharide.

Heterotrimeric G protein. See G protein.

Heterotroph. An organism that obtains free energy from the oxidation of organic compounds produced by other organisms.

Heterozygous. Having one each of two gene variants.

Hexose monophosphate shunt. See pentose phosphate pathway.

"High-energy" intermediate. A substance whose degradation is highly exergonic (yields at least as much free energy as is required to synthesize ATP from ADP + P_i; ≥30.5 kJ · mol^{-1} under standard biochemical conditions). Also called an "energy-rich" compound.

High-performance liquid chromatography (HPLC). An automated chromatographic procedure for fractionating molecules using precisely fabricated matrix materials and pressurized flows of precisely mixed solvents.

Highly repetitive DNA. Clusters of nearly identical sequences of up to 10 bp that are repeated thousands of times; these sequences are present at >10^6 copies per haploid genome. Also known as short tandem repeats (STRs).

Hill coefficient. The exponent in the Hill equation. It provides a measure of the degree of cooperative binding of a ligand to a molecule.

Hill equation. A mathematical expression for the degree of saturation of ligand binding to a molecule with multiple binding sites as a function of the ligand concentration.

Histone acetyltransferase (HAT). An enzyme that catalyzes the sequence-specific acetylation of histones so as to regulate gene transcription.

Histone code. The correlation between the pattern of histone modification and the transcriptional activity of the associated DNA.

Histones. Highly conserved basic proteins that constitute the protein core to which DNA is bound to form a nucleosome.

HIV. Human immunodeficiency virus, the causative agent of acquired immunodeficiency syndrome (AIDS).

HMG protein. A member of the high mobility group (HMG) of nonhistone chromosomal proteins whose abundant charged groups give them high electrophoretic mobility.

hnRNA. See heterogeneous nuclear RNA.

Holliday junction. The four-stranded structure that forms as an intermediate in DNA recombination.

Holoenzyme. A catalytically active enzyme–cofactor complex.

Homeobox. See homeodomain.

Homeodomain. An ~60-amino acid DNA-binding motif common to many genes that specify the identities and fates of embryonic cells; such genes encode transcription factors. Also called a homeobox.

Homeostasis. The maintenance of a steady state in an organism.

Homeotic selector genes. Insect genes that specify the identities of body segments.

Homolactic fermentation. The reduction of pyruvate to lactate with the concomitant oxidation of NADH to NAD$^+$.

Homologous end-joining. A pathway in which DNA with double-strand breaks is repaired nonmutagenically through recombination with an intact homologous chromosome.

Homologous proteins. Proteins that resemble each other due to their evolution from a common ancestor.

Homologous recombination. See recombination.

Homolytic cleavage. Cleavage of a bond in which each participating atom acquires one of the electrons that formed the bond.

Homopolysaccharide. A polysaccharide consisting of one type of monosaccharide unit.

Homozygous. Having two identical copies of a particular gene.

Hoogsteen base pair. A form of base pairing in which thymine or uracil atom N3 hydrogen bonds to adenine atom N7 and adenine N6 hydrogen bonds to thymine or uracil O4. See also Watson–Crick base pair.

Hormone. A substance (e.g., a peptide or a steroid) that is secreted by one tissue into the bloodstream and which induces a physiological response (e.g., growth and metabolism) in other tissues.

Hormone response element (HRE). A DNA sequence to which a hormone–receptor complex binds so as to enhance or repress the transcription of an associated gene.

Hormone-sensitive lipase. An adipose tissue enzyme that releases fatty acids from triacylglycerols in response to a hormonally generated increase in cAMP. Also known as hormone-sensitive triacylglycerol lipase.

Housekeeping enzyme. See constitutive enzyme.

Hox gene. A gene encoding a transcription factor that includes a homeodomain.

HPLC. See high-performance liquid chromatography.

HRE. See hormone response element.

Hsp. Heat shock protein. See molecular chaperone.

HTH motif. See helix–turn–helix motif.

Humoral immunity. Immunity mediated by antibodies (immunoglobulins) produced by B lymphocytes (B cells).

Hybridization. The formation of double-stranded segments of complementary DNA and/or RNA sequences.

Hybridoma. The cell clones produced by the fusion of an antibody-producing lymphocyte and an immortal myeloma cell. These are the cells that produce monoclonal antibodies.

Hydration. The molecular state of being surrounded by and interacting with several layers of solvent water molecules, that is, solvated by water.

Hydrogen bond. A largely electrostatic interaction between a weakly acidic donor group such as O—H or N—H and a weakly basic acceptor atom such as O or N.

Hydrolase. An enzyme that catalyzes a hydrolytic reaction.

Hydrolysis. The cleavage of a covalent bond accomplished by adding the elements of water; the reverse of a condensation.

Hydronium ion. A proton associated with a water molecule, H_3O^+.

Hydropathy. A measure of the combined hydrophobicity and hydrophilicity of an amino acid residue; it is indicative of the likelihood of finding that residue in a protein interior.

Hydrophilic substance. A substance whose high polarity allows it to readily interact with water molecules and thereby dissolve in water.

Hydrophobic collapse. A driving force in protein folding, resulting from the tendency of hydrophobic residues to avoid contact with water and hence form the protein core.

Hydrophobic effect. The tendency of water to minimize its contacts with nonpolar substances, thereby inducing the substances to aggregate.

Hydrophobic interaction chromatography. A procedure in which molecules are selectively retained on a nonpolar matrix by virtue of their hydrophobicity.

Hydrophobic substance. A substance whose nonpolar nature reduces its ability to be solvated by water molecules. Hydrophobic substances tend to be soluble in nonpolar solvents but not in water.

Hydroxide ion. OH^-, a product of the ionization of a water molecule.

Hydroxyl group. A portion of a molecule with the formula —OH.

Hyperammonemia. Elevated levels of ammonia in the blood, a toxic situation.

Hyperbolic curve. The graphical representation of the mathematical equation that describes the noncooperative binding of a ligand to a molecule or the rate of a reaction catalyzed by a Michealis–Menten enzyme.

Hypercholesterolemia. High levels of cholesterol in the blood, a risk factor for heart disease. Familial hypercholesterolemia usually results from an inherited defect in the LDL receptor.

Hyperchromic effect. The increase in DNA's ultraviolet absorbance resulting from the loss of stacking interactions as the DNA denatures.

Hyperglycemia. Elevated levels of glucose in the blood.

Hypervariable residue. An amino acid residue occupying a position in a protein that is occupied by many different residues among evolutionarily related proteins. The opposite of a hyper-variable residue is an invariant residue.

Hypoxia. A condition in which the oxygen level in the blood is lower than normal.

I-cell disease. A hereditary deficiency in a lysosomal hydrolase that leads to the accumulation of glycosaminoglycan and glycolipid inclusions in the lysosomes.

IDL. Intermediate density lipoprotein; see lipoprotein.

IEF. See isoelectric focusing.

Ig. Immunoglobulin. See antibody.

Imaginal disk. A patch of apparently undifferentiated but developmentally committed cells in an insect larva that ultimately gives rise to a specific external structure in the adult.

Imino group. A portion of a molecule with the formula $\rangle C{=}NH$.

Immune system. The cells and organs that respond to microbial infection by producing antibodies and by killing pathogens and infected host cells.

Immunoaffinity chromatography. A procedure in which a molecule is separated from a mixture of other molecules by its ability to bind specifically to an immobilized antibody.

Immunoassay. A procedure for detecting, and in some cases quantifying the activity of, a macromolecule by using an antibody or mixture of antibodies that reacts specifically with that substance.

Immunoblot. A technique in which a molecule immobilized on a membrane filter can be detected through its ability to bind to an antibody directed against it. A Western blot is an immunoblot to detect an immobilized protein after electrophoresis.

Immunofluorescence microscopy. A technique in microscopy in which a fluorescence-tagged antibody is used to reveal the presence of the antigen to which it binds.

Immunoglobulin (Ig). See antibody.

Immunoglobulin fold. A disulfide-linked domain consisting of a sandwich of a three-stranded and a four-stranded antiparallel β sheet that occurs in antibody molecules.

Imprinting. The differential expression of maternal and paternal genes according to their patterns of DNA methylation.

in silico. In a computer simulation (electronic circuits are mainly silicon-based).

in situ. In place.

in situ **hybridization.** See colony hybridization.

in vitro. In the laboratory (literally, in glass).

in vivo. In a living organism.

Inactivator. An inhibitor that reacts irreversibly with an enzyme so as to inactivate it.

Indirect readout. The ability of a DNA-binding protein to detect its target base sequence though the sequence-dependent conformation and/or flexibility of its DNA backbone rather than through direct interaction with its bases.

Induced fit. An interaction between a protein and its ligand, which induces a conformational change in the protein that increases the protein's affinity for the ligand.

Inducer. A substance that facilitates gene expression.

Inducible enzyme. An enzyme that is synthesized only when required by the cell. See also constitutive enzyme.

Inhibition constant (K_I). The dissociation constant for an enzyme–inhibitor complex.

Inhibitor. A substance that reduces an enzyme's activity by affecting its substrate binding or turnover number.

Initiation factor. A protein that interacts with mRNA and/or the ribosome and which is required to initiate translation.

Inorganic compound. A compound that lacks the element carbon.

Insertion sequence. A simple transposon that is flanked by short inverted repeats. Also called an IS element.

Insertion/deletion mutation. A genetic change resulting from the addition or loss of nucleotides; also called an indel.

Insulator. A segment of DNA that delimits the effective range of a transcription-regulating element.

Insulin resistance. The decreased ability of cells to respond to insulin by increasing their glucose uptake.

Integral protein. A membrane protein that is embedded in the lipid bilayer and can be separated from it only by treatment with agents that disrupt membranes. Also called an intrinsic protein.

Intercalation agent. A substance, usually a planar aromatic cation, that slips in between the stacked bases of a double-stranded polynucleotide.

Interconvertible enzyme. An enzyme that undergoes covalent modification/demodification, usually phosphorylation/dephosphorylation, so as to modulate its activity.

Interfacial activation. The increase in activity when a lipid-specific enzyme contacts the lipid–water interface.

Intermembrane space. The compartment between the inner and outer mitochondrial membranes. Because of the porosity of the outer membrane, the intermembrane space is equivalent to the cytosol in its small-molecule composition.

Internal conversion. A mode of decay of an excited molecule, in which electronic energy is converted to heat (the kinetic energy of molecular motion).

Intervening sequence. See intron.

Intrinsic protein. See integral protein.

Intron. A portion of a gene that is transcribed but excised prior to translation. Also called an intervening sequence.

Invariant residue. A residue in a protein that is the same in all evolutionarily related proteins. The opposite of an invariant residue is a hypervariable residue.

Ion exchange chromatography. A fractionation procedure in which ions are selectively retained by a matrix bearing oppositely charged groups.

Ion pair. An electrostatic interaction between two ionic groups of opposite charge. In proteins, it is also called a salt bridge.

Ionophore. An organic molecule, often an antibiotic, that increases the permeability of a membrane to a particular ion. A carrier ionophore diffuses with its ion through the membrane, whereas a channel-forming ionophore forms a transmembrane pore.

Iron–sulfur protein. A protein that contains a prosthetic group consisting most commonly of equal numbers of iron and sulfur ions (i.e., [2Fe–2S] and [4Fe–4S]) and that usually participates in oxidation–reduction reactions.

IS element. See insertion sequence.

Isoaccepting tRNA. A tRNA that carries the same amino acid as another tRNA.

Isoelectric focusing (IEF). Electrophoresis through a stable pH gradient such that a charged molecule migrates to a position corresponding to its isoelectric point.

Isoelectric point (pI). The pH at which a molecule has no net charge and hence does not migrate in an electric field.

Isoforms. See isozymes.

Isolated system. A thermodynamic system that cannot exchange matter or energy with its surroundings.

Isomerase. An enzyme that catalyzes an isomerization reaction.

Isopeptide bond. An amide linkage between an α-carboxylate group of an amino acid and the ε-amino group of Lys, or between the α-amino group of an amino acid and the β- or γ-carboxylate group of Asp or Glu.

Isoprenoid. A lipid containing five-carbon units with the same carbon skeleton as isoprene.

Isoschizomers. Restriction endonucleases that cleave at the same nucleotide sequence.

Isozymes. Enzymes that catalyze the same reaction but are encoded by different genes. Also called isoforms.

Jaundice. A yellowing of the skin and whites of the eyes as a result of the deposition of the heme degradation product bilirubin in those tissues. It is a symptom of liver dysfunction, bile-duct obstruction, or a high rate of red cell destruction.

Junk DNA. See selfish DNA.

K. See dissociation constant and equilibrium constant.

k. See rate constant.

k_B. Boltzmann constant $(1.3807 \times 10^{-23}\ \mathrm{J \cdot K^{-1}})$; it is equivalent to R/N, where R is the gas constant and N is Avogadro's number.

kb. Kilobase pair; 1 kb = 1000 base pairs (bp).

k_{cat}. The catalytic constant for an enzymatic reaction, equivalent to the ratio of the maximal velocity (V_{max}) and the enzyme concentration $([E]_T)$. Also called the turnover number.

k_{cat}/K_M. The apparent second-order rate constant for an enzyme-catalyzed reaction; it is a measure of an enzyme's catalytic efficiency.

kD. Kilodaltons; 1000 daltons (D).

K_{eq}. See equilibrium constant.

Ketogenesis. The synthesis of ketone bodies from acetyl-CoA.

Ketogenic amino acid. An amino acid whose degradation in animals yields compounds that can be converted to fatty acids or ketone bodies. See also glucogenic amino acid.

Ketone bodies. Acetoacetate, D-β-hydroxybutyrate, and acetone; these compounds are produced from acetyl-CoA by the liver for use as metabolic fuels in peripheral tissues.

Ketose. A sugar whose carbonyl group is a ketone.

Ketosis. A potentially pathological condition in which ketone bodies are produced in excess of their utilization.

K_I. See inhibition constant.

Kinase. An enzyme that transfers a phosphoryl group between ATP and another molecule.

Kinase cascade. A set of reactions in which kinase-catalyzed phosphorylation activates the next kinase in a series, thereby amplifying the effect of the initial kinase.

K_M. See Michaelis constant.

K_M^{app}. The apparent (observed) Michaelis constant for an enzyme-catalyzed reaction, which may differ from the true value due to the presence of an enzyme inhibitor.

k_{-1}. The rate constant for a reverse reaction, e.g., the breakdown of the ES complex to E + S.

Krebs cycle. See citric acid cycle.

k_2. The rate constant for the second step of a simple enzyme-catalyzed reaction that follows Michaelis–Menten kinetics, that is, the conversion of the ES complex to E + P.

K_w. The ionization constant of water; equal to 10^{-14}.

L. See linking number.

Lactose intolerance. The inability to digest the disaccharide lactose due to a deficiency of the enzyme β-galactosidase (lactase).

Lagging strand. A newly synthesized DNA strand that extends $3' \rightarrow 5'$ in the direction of travel of the replication fork. This strand is synthesized as a series of discontinuous fragments that are later joined.

Lateral diffusion. The movement of a lipid within one leaflet of a bilayer.

LBHB. See low-barrier hydrogen bond.

LDL. Low density lipoprotein; see lipoprotein.

Lead compound. A drug molecule that serves as the starting point for the development of more effective drug molecules.

Leader peptide. See signal peptide.

Leader sequence. (1) A nucleotide sequence that precedes the coding region of an mRNA. (2) A signal sequence.

Leading strand. A newly synthesized DNA strand that extends $5' \rightarrow 3'$ in the direction of travel of the replication fork. This strand is synthesized continuously.

Lectin. A protein that binds to a specific saccharide.

Lesch–Nyhan syndrome. A genetic disease caused by the deficiency of hypoxanthine–guanine phosphoribosyltransferase (HGPRT), an enzyme required for purine salvage reactions. Affected individuals produce excessive uric acid and exhibit neurological abnormalities.

Leucine zipper. A protein structural motif in which two α helices, each with a hydrophobic strip along one side, associate as a coiled coil. This motif, which has a Leu at nearly every seventh residue, mediates the association of many types of DNA-binding proteins.

Leukocyte. White blood cell.

Levorotatory. Rotating the plane of polarized light counterclockwise from the point of view of the observer; the opposite of dextrorotatory.

LHC. See light-harvesting complex.

Ligand. (1) A small molecule that binds to a larger molecule. (2) A molecule or ion bound to a metal ion.

Ligand-gated channel. A channel whose opening and closing (gating) is controlled by the binding of a specific molecule (ligand).

Ligase. An enzyme that catalyzes bond formation coupled with the hydrolysis of ATP.

Ligation. The joining together of two molecules such as two DNA segments.

Light-harvesting complex (LHC). A pigment-containing membrane protein that collects light energy and transfers it to a photosynthetic reaction center.

Light reactions. The portion of photosynthesis in which specialized pigment molecules capture light energy and are thereby oxidized. Electrons are transferred to generate NADPH and a transmembrane proton gradient that drives ATP synthesis.

Limited proteolysis. A technique in which a polypeptide is incompletely digested by proteases.

Lineweaver–Burk plot. A graph of a rearrangement of the Michaelis–Menten equation to a linear form that permits the determination of K_M and V_{max}. Also called a double-reciprocal plot.

Linker DNA. The ~55-bp segment of DNA that links nucleosome core particles in chromatin.

Linking number (L). The number of times that one strand of a covalently closed circular double-stranded DNA winds around the other; it cannot be changed without breaking covalent bonds.

Lipid. Any member of a broad class of biological molecules that are largely or wholly hydrophobic and therefore tend to be insoluble in water but soluble in organic solvents such as hexane.

Lipid bilayer. See bilayer.

Lipid-linked protein. A protein that is anchored to a biological membrane via a covalently attached lipid such as a farnesyl, geranylgeranyl, myristoyl, palmitoyl, or glycosylphosphatidylinositol group.

Lipid raft. A semicrystalline region of a cell membrane containing tightly packed glycosphingolipids and cholesterol.

Lipid storage disease. A defect in a lipid-degrading enzyme that causes the substrate for the enzyme to accumulate in lysosomes.

Lipoprotein. A globular particle consisting of a nonpolar lipid core surrounded by an amphiphilic coat of protein, phospholipid, and cholesterol. Lipoproteins, which transport lipids between tissues via the bloodstream, are classified by their density as high, low, intermediate, and very low density lipoproteins (HDL, LDL, IDL, and VLDL).

Liposome. A synthetic vesicle bounded by a single lipid bilayer.

Lipoyllysyl arm. An extended structure, consisting of lipoic acid linked to a lysine side chain, that delivers intermediates between active sites in multienzyme complexes such as the pyruvate dehydrogenase complex.

London dispersion forces. The weak attractive forces between electrically neutral molecules in close proximity, which arise from electrostatic interactions among their fluctuating dipoles.

Low-barrier hydrogen bond (LBHB). An unusually short and strong hydrogen bond that forms when the donor and acceptor groups have nearly equal pK values so that the hydrogen atom is equally shared between them.

Lung surfactant. The amphipathic protein and lipid mixture that prevents collapse of the lung alveoli (microscopic air spaces) on the expiration of air.

Lyase. An enzyme that catalyzes the elimination of a group to form a double bond.

Lymphocyte. Types of white blood cells that mediate the immune response. Mammalian B lymphocytes develop in the bone marrow, and T lymphocytes in the thymus.

Lysis. The disintegration of cells by rupturing their cell walls.

Lysophospholipid. A glycerophospholipid derivative lacking a fatty acyl group at position C2 that acts as a detergent to disrupt cell membranes.

Lysosome. A membrane-bounded organelle in a eukaryotic cell that contains a battery of hydrolytic enzymes and which functions to digest ingested material and to recycle cell components.

Macronutrient. A nutrient that is required in relatively large amounts, such as proteins, carbohydrates, and fats. See also micronutrient.

Main chain. See backbone.

Major groove. The groove on a DNA double helix onto which the glycosidic bonds of a base pair form an angle of >180°. In B-DNA, this groove is wider than the minor groove.

Malaria. A mosquito-borne disease caused by protozoa of the genus Plasmodia, most notably *Plasmodium falciparum,* which reside in red blood cells during much of their life cycle.

Malate–aspartate shuttle. A metabolic circuit that uses the malate and aspartate transporters and the interconversion of malate, oxaloacetate, and aspartate to ferry reducing equivalents into the mitochondrion.

Malignant tumor. A mass of cells that proliferate uncontrollably; cancer.

Mass spectrometry. A technique for identifying molecules by measuring the mass-to-charge ratios of molecular ions in the gas phase.

Maternal-effect genes. Insect genes whose mRNA or protein products are deposited by the mother in the ovum and which define the polarity of the embryonic body.

Matrix. The gel-like solution of enzymes, substrates, cofactors, and ions in the interior of the mitochondrion.

Mechanism-based inhibitor. A molecule that chemically inactivates an enzyme only after undergoing part or all of its normal catalytic reaction. Also called a suicide substrate.

Mechanosensitive channel. A channel whose opening and closing (gating) is controlled by stimuli such as touch, sound, and changes in osmotic pressure.

Mediated transport. The transmembrane movement of a substance through the action of a specific carrier protein; the opposite of nonmediated transport.

Melting temperature (T_m). The midpoint temperature of the melting curve for the thermal denaturation of a macromolecule.

Membrane-enveloped virus. A virus produced by budding from the surface of a host cell such that the viral particle is surrounded by a membrane derived from the host cell.

Membrane potential ($\Delta\Psi$). The electrical potential difference across a membrane.

Memory B cell. A B cell that can recognize its corresponding antigen and rapidly proliferate to produce specific antibodies weeks to years after the antigen was first encountered.

Mercaptan. A compound containing an —SH group.

Messenger RNA (mRNA). A ribonucleic acid whose sequence is complementary to that of a protein-coding gene in DNA. In the ribosome, mRNA directs the polymerization of amino acids to form a polypeptide with the corresponding sequence.

Metabolic fuel. A molecule that can be oxidized to provide free energy for an organism.

Metabolic syndrome. An obesity-related disorder that includes insulin resistance, hypertension, and atherosclerosis.

Metabolism. The total of all degradative and biosynthetic cellular reactions.

Metabolite. A reactant, intermediate, or product of a metabolic reaction.

Metabolomics. The study of all the metabolites produced by a cell under a given set of conditions, including their concentrations and functions.

Metal chelate affinity chromatography. A procedure in which a molecule bearing metal-chelating groups is separated from a mixture of other molecules by its ability to bind to metal ions attached to a chromatographic matrix.

Metal ion catalysis. A catalytic mechanism that requires the presence of a metal ion to lower the free energy of a reaction's transition state.

Metalloenzyme. An enzyme that contains a tightly bound metal ion cofactor, typically a transition metal ion such as Fe^{2+}, Zn^{2+}, or Mn^{2+}.

Methanogen. An organism that produces CH_4.

Micelle. A globular aggregate of amphiphilic molecules in aqueous solution that are oriented such that polar segments form the surface of the aggregate and the nonpolar segments form a core that is out of contact with the solvent.

Michaelis complex. See ES complex.

Michaelis constant (K_M). For an enzyme that follows the Michaelis–Menten model, $K_M = (k_{-1} + k_2)/k_1$; K_M is equal to the substrate concentration at which the reaction velocity is half-maximal.

Michaelis–Menten equation. A mathematical expression that describes the activity of an enzyme in terms of the substrate concentration ([S]), the enzyme's maximal velocity (V_{max}), and its Michaelis constant (K_M): $v_0 = V_{max}[S]/(K_M + [S])$.

Micro RNA (miRNA). See short interfering RNA.

Microarray. See DNA microarray.

Microfilament. A 70-Å-diameter cytoskeletal element composed of actin.

Microheterogeneity. The variability in carbohydrate composition in glycoproteins.

Micronutrient. A nutrient that is required in relatively small amounts, including vitamins and minerals. See also macronutrient.

Mineral. An inorganic substance required for metabolic activity, including sodium, potassium, chloride, and calcium. Minerals such as iron, copper, and zinc, which are required in small amounts, are known as trace elements.

Mineralocorticoid. A steroid hormone that regulates the excretion of salt and water by the kidneys.

Minor groove. The groove on a DNA double helix onto which the glycosidic bonds of a base pair form an angle of <180°. In B-DNA, this groove is narrower than the major groove.

(–) end. The end of a polymeric filament where growth is slower. See also (+) end.

miRNA. Micro RNA. See short interfering RNA.

Mismatch repair (MMR). A postreplication process, in which mispaired nucleotides are excised and replaced, that distinguishes between the parental (correct) and daughter (incorrect) strands of DNA.

Mitochondria (*sing.* mitochondrion). The double-membrane-enveloped eukaryotic organelles in which aerobic metabolic reactions occur, including those of the citric acid cycle, fatty acid oxidation, and oxidative phosphorylation.

Mitochondrial matrix. See matrix.

Mixed inhibition. A form of enzyme inhibition in which an inhibitor binds to both the enzyme and the enzyme–substrate complex and thereby differently affects K_M and V_{max}. Also called noncompetitive inhibition.

MMR. See mismatch repair.

Moderately repetitive DNA. Segments of hundreds to thousands of base pairs that are present at $<10^6$ copies per haploid genome.

Modification methylase. A bacterial enzyme that methylates a specific sequence of DNA as part of a restriction–modification system.

Molecular chaperone. A protein that binds to unfolded or misfolded proteins so as to promote normal folding and the formation of native quaternary structure. Also known as a heat shock protein (Hsp).

Molecular cloning. See recombinant DNA technology.

Molecular sieve chromatography. See gel filtration chromatography.

Molecular weight. See M_r.

Molecularity. The number of molecules that participate in an elementary chemical reaction.

Molten globule. A collapsed but conformationally mobile intermediate in protein folding that has much of the native protein's secondary structure but little of its tertiary structure.

Monocistronic mRNA. The RNA transcript of a single gene.

Monoclonal antibody. A single type of antibody molecule produced by a clone of hybridoma cells, which are derived by the fusion of a myeloma cell with a lymphocyte producing that antibody.

Monomer. (1) A structural unit from which a polymer is built up. (2) A single subunit or protomer of a multisubunit protein.

Monoprotic acid. An acid that can donate only one proton.

Monosaccharide. A carbohydrate consisting of a single saccharide (sugar).

Morphogen. A substance whose distribution in an embryo directs, in part, the embryo's developmental pattern.

Motif. See supersecondary structure.

Motor protein. An intracellular protein that couples the free energy of ATP hydrolysis to molecular movement relative to another protein that often acts as a track for the linear movement of the motor protein.

M_r. Relative molecular mass. A dimensionless quantity that is defined as the ratio of the mass of a particle to 1/12th the mass of a ^{12}C atom. Also known as molecular weight. It is numerically equal to the grams/mole of a compound.

mRNA. See messenger RNA.

Multienzyme complex. A group of noncovalently associated enzymes that catalyze two or more sequential steps in a metabolic pathway.

Multiple myeloma. A disease in which a cancerous B cell proliferates and produces massive quantities of a single antibody known as a myeloma protein.

Multisubunit protein. A protein consisting of more than one polypeptide chain (subunit).

Mutagen. An agent that induces a mutation in an organism.

Mutase. An enzyme that catalyzes the transfer of a functional group from one position to another on a molecule.

Mutation. A heritable alteration in an organism's genetic material.

Myocardial infarction. The death of heart tissue caused by the loss of blood supply (a heart attack).

Myofibril. The bundle of fibers that are arranged in register in striated muscle cells.

Myristoylation. The attachment of a myristoyl group to a protein to form a lipid-linked protein.

N-end rule. The correlation between the identity of a polypeptide's N-terminal residue and its half-life in the cell.

N-glycosidic bond. See glycosidic bond.

N-linked oligosaccharide. An oligosaccharide linked via a glycosidic bond to the amide group of a protein Asn residue in the sequence Asn-X-Ser/Thr.

N-terminus. See amino terminus.

Native structure. The fully folded conformation of a macromolecule.

Natural selection. The evolutionary process by which the continued existence of a replicating entity depends on its ability to survive and reproduce under the existing conditions.

ncRNA. See noncoding RNA.

NDP. A ribonucleoside diphosphate.

Near-equilibrium reaction. A reaction whose ΔG value is close to zero, so that it can operate in either direction depending on the substrate and product concentrations.

Necrosis. Trauma-induced cell death that results in the unregulated disintegration of the cell and the release of proinflammatory substances. See also apoptosis.

Negative cooperativity. See cooperative binding.

NER. See nucleotide excision repair.

Nernst equation. An expression of the relationship between reduction potential difference ($\Delta\mathcal{E}$) and the concentrations of the electron donors and acceptors (A, B):
$$\Delta\mathcal{E} = \Delta\mathcal{E}° - RT/n\mathcal{F} \ln ([A_{red}][B_{ox}]/[A_{ox}][B_{red}]).$$

Neurotransmitter. A substance released by a nerve cell that alters the activity of another nerve cell.

Neutral drift. Evolutionary changes that become fixed at random rather than through natural selection.

Neutral solution. A solution whose pH is equal to 7.0 ($[H^+] = 10^{-7}$ M).

NHEJ. See nonhomologous end-joining.

Nick translation. The progressive movement of a single-strand break (nick) in duplex DNA through the coordinated actions of a $5' \rightarrow 3'$ exonuclease function that removes residues from the $5'$ side of the break and a polymerase function that adds residues to the $3'$ side.

Nitrogen assimilation. The incorporation of fixed nitrogen (e.g., ammonia) into a biological molecule such as an amino acid.

Nitrogen cycle. The series of reactions in which N_2 and ammonia are interconverted, often via nitrate and nitrite, by various organisms.

Nitrogen fixation. The process by which atmospheric N_2 is converted to a biologically useful form such as NH_3.

NMD. See nonsense-mediated decay.

NMR. See nuclear magnetic resonance.

Noncoding RNA (ncRNA). An RNA molecule, such as rRNA, RNA, or another small RNA, that is not translated.

Noncoding strand. See antisense strand.

Noncompetitive inhibition. (1) A synonym for mixed inhibition. (2) A special case of mixed inhibition in which the inhibitor binds the enzyme and enzyme–substrate complex with equal affinities ($K_I = K_I'$), thereby reducing the apparent value of V_{max} but leaving K_M unchanged.

Noncooperative binding. A situation in which binding of a ligand to a macromolecule does not affect the affinities of other binding sites on the same molecule.

Nonessential amino acid. An amino acid that animals can synthesize from common intermediates.

Nonhomologous end-joining (NHEJ). An error-prone pathway for repairing DNA with double-strand breaks.

Nonmediated transport. The transmembrane movement of a substance through simple diffusion; the opposite of mediated transport.

Nonpolar molecule. A molecule that lacks a group with a permanent dipole.

Nonreceptor tyrosine kinase. An intracellular tyrosine kinase that is indirectly activated by ligand binding to a receptor.

Nonrepetitive structure. A segment of a polymer in which the backbone has an ordered arrangement that is not characterized by a repeating conformation.

Nonsense codon. See Stop codon.

Nonsense-mediated decay (NMD). The degradation of an mRNA that contains a premature Stop codon.

Nonsense mutation. A mutation that converts a codon that specifies an amino acid to a Stop codon, thereby causing the premature termination of translation.

Nonsense suppressor tRNA. A mutated tRNA that recognizes a Stop codon so that its attached aminoacyl group is appended to the polypeptide chain; it mitigates the effect of a nonsense mutation in a structural gene.

Northern blotting. A procedure for identifying an RNA containing a particular base sequence through its ability to hybridize with a complementary single-stranded segment of DNA or RNA. See also Southern blotting.

nt. Nucleotide.

NTP. A ribonucleoside triphosphate.

Nuclear magnetic resonance (NMR). A spectroscopic method for characterizing atomic and molecular properties based on the signals emitted by radiofrequency-excited atomic nuclei in a magnetic field. It can be used to determine the three-dimensional molecular structure of a protein or nucleic acid.

Nuclease. An enzyme that hydrolytically degrades nucleic acids.

Nucleic acid. A polymer of nucleotide residues. The major nucleic acids are deoxyribonucleic acid (DNA) and ribonucleic acid (RNA). Also known as a polynucleotide.

Nucleolus (*pl.* nucleoli). The dark-staining region of the eukaryotic nucleus, where ribosomes are assembled.

Nucleophile. A group that contains unshared electron pairs that readily reacts with an electron-deficient group (electrophile). A nucleophile (nucleus-lover) reacts with an electrophile (electron-lover).

Nucleoside. A compound consisting of a nitrogenous base and a five-carbon sugar (ribose or deoxyribose) in N-glycosidic linkage.

Nucleosome. The complex of a histone octamer and ~200 bp of DNA that forms the lowest level of DNA organization in the eukaryotic chromosome.

Nucleosome core particle. The complex of histones and ~146 bp of DNA that forms a compact disk-shaped particle in which the DNA is wound in ~2 helical turns around the outside of the histone octamer.

Nucleotide. A compound consisting of a nucleoside esterified to one or more phosphate groups. Nucleotides are the monomeric units of nucleic acids.

Nucleotide excision repair (NER). A multistep process in which a portion of DNA containing a lesion is excised and replaced by normal DNA.

Nucleotide sugar. A saccharide linked to a nucleotide by a phosphate ester bond, the cleavage of which drives the formation of a glycosidic bond.

Nucleus. The membrane-enveloped organelle in which the eukaryotic cell's genetic material is located.

Nutrition. The intake and utilization of food as a source of raw materials and free energy.

O-glycosidic bond. See glycosidic bond.

O-linked oligosaccharide. An oligosaccharide linked via a glycosidic bond to the hydroxyl group of a protein Ser or Thr side chain.

Oil. A mixture of triacylglycerols that is liquid at room temperature.

Okazaki fragments. The short segments of DNA formed in the discontinuous lagging-strand synthesis of DNA.

Oligomer. (1) A short polymer consisting of a few linked monomer units. (2) A protein consisting of a few protomers (subunits).

Oligopeptide. A polypeptide containing a few amino acid residues.

Oligosaccharide. A polymeric carbohydrate containing a few monosaccharide residues.

Oligosaccharide processing. The cellular pathway in which a newly glycosylated protein undergoes the enzymatic removal and addition of monosaccharide residues.

Oncogene. A mutant version of a normal gene (a proto-oncogene), which may be acquired through viral infection; it interferes with the mechanisms that normally control cell growth and differentiation and thereby contributes to uncontrolled proliferation (cancer).

Open complex. The separated DNA strands at the transcription start site.

Open reading frame (ORF). A portion of the genome that potentially codes for a protein. This sequence of nucleotides begins with a Start codon, ends with a Stop codon, contains no internal Stop codons, is flanked by the proper control sequences, and exhibits the same codon-usage preference as other genes in the organism.

Open system. A thermodynamic system that can exchange matter and energy with its surroundings.

Operator. A DNA sequence at or near the transcription start site of a gene, to which a repressor binds so as to control transcription of the gene.

Operon. A prokaryotic genetic unit that consists of several genes with related functions that are transcribed as a single mRNA molecule.

Optical activity. The ability of a molecule to rotate the plane of polarized light.

Optical density. See absorbance.

Ordered mechanism. A sequential reaction with a compulsory order of substrate addition to the enzyme.

ORF. See open reading frame.

Organelle. A differentiated structure within a eukaryotic cell, such as a mitochondrion, ribosome, or lysosome, that performs specific functions.

Organic compound. A compound that contains the element carbon.

Orphan gene. A gene, usually identified through genome sequencing, with no known function.

Orthologous genes. Related genes in different species that have the same function.

Orthophosphate cleavage. The hydrolysis of ATP that yields $ADP + P_i$.

Osmosis. The movement of solvent across a semipermeable membrane from a region of low solute concentration to a region of high solute concentration.

Osmotic pressure. The pressure that must be applied to a solution containing a high concentration of solute to prevent the net flow of solvent across a semipermeable membrane separating it from a solution with a lower concentration of solute. The osmotic pressure of a 1 M solution of any solute separated from solvent by a semipermeable membrane is ideally 22.4 atm.

Overproducer. A genetically engineered organism that produces massive quantities of a foreign DNA gene product.

Oxidation. The loss of electrons. Oxidation of a substance is accompanied by the reduction of another substance.

Oxidative phosphorylation. The process by which the free energy obtained from the oxidation of metabolic fuels is used to generate ATP from $ADP + P_i$.

Oxidizing agent. A substance that can accept electrons from other substances, thereby oxidizing them and becoming reduced.

Oxidoreductase. An enzyme that catalyzes an oxidation–reduction reaction.

Oxonium ion. A resonance-stabilized carbocation such as occurs during the lysozyme-catalyzed hydrolysis of a glycoside.

Oxyanion hole. A structure in an enzyme active site that preferentially binds and thereby stabilizes the oxyanionic tetrahedral transition state of the reaction.

Oxygen debt. The postexertion continued elevation in O_2 consumption that is required to replenish the ATP consumed by the liver during operation of the Cori cycle.

Oxygenation. The binding of molecular oxygen, e.g., to a heme group.

P site. See peptidyl site.

P/O ratio. The ratio of the number of molecules of ATP synthesized from $ADP + P_i$ to the number of atoms of oxygen reduced.

PAGE. Polyacrylamide gel electrophoresis. See gel electrophoresis.

Pair-rule genes. See segmentation genes.

Palindrome. A word or phrase or a nucleotide sequence that reads the same forward or backward.

Palmitoylation. The attachment of a palmitoyl group to a protein to form a lipid-linked protein.

Paralogous genes. Related genes in the same organism derived from a gene duplication event.

Partial oxygen pressure (pO_2). The concentration of gaseous O_2 in units of pressure (e.g., torr).

Passive-mediated transport. The thermodynamically spontaneous carrier-mediated transmembrane movement of a substance from high to low concentration. Also called facilitated diffusion.

Pasteur effect. The greatly increased sugar consumption of yeast grown under anaerobic conditions compared to that of yeast grown under aerobic conditions.

Pathogen. A disease-causing microorganism.

PCR. See polymerase chain reaction.

Pellagra. The human disease resulting from a deficiency of the vitamin niacin (nicotinic acid), a precursor of the nicotinamide-containing cofactors NAD^+ and $NADP^+$.

Pentose phosphate pathway. A pathway for glucose degradation that yields ribose-5-phosphate and NADPH. Also called the hexose monophosphate shunt.

Peptidase. An enzyme that hydrolyzes peptide bonds. Also called a protease.

Peptide. A polypeptide of less than about 40 residues.

Peptide bond. An amide linkage between the α-amino group of one amino acid and the α-carboxylate group of another. Peptide bonds link the amino acid residues in a polypeptide.

Peptide group. The planar —CO—NH— group that encompasses the peptide bond between amino acid residues in a polypeptide.

Peptidoglycans. The cross-linked bag-shaped macromolecules consisting of polysaccharide and polypeptide chains that form bacterial cell walls.

Peptidyl site (P site). The ribosomal site that accommodates a tRNA with an attached peptidyl group during protein synthesis.

Peptidyl transferase. The catalytic activity of the ribosome, which carries out peptide bond synthesis by promoting the nucleophilic attack of an incoming aminoacyl group on the growing peptidyl group.

Peptidyl–tRNA. The covalent complex between a tRNA molecule and a growing polypeptide chain during protein synthesis.

Peripheral protein. A protein that is weakly associated with the surface of a biological membrane. Also called an extrinsic protein.

Periplasmic compartment. The space between the cell wall and the outer membrane of gram-negative bacteria.

Peroxisome. A eukaryotic organelle with specialized oxidative functions.

Perutz mechanism. A model for the cooperative binding of oxygen to hemoglobin, in which O_2 binding causes the protein to shift conformation from the deoxy (T state) to the oxy (R state).

PFGE. See pulsed-field gel electrophoresis.

p_{50}. For a gaseous ligand, the ligand concentration, in units of pressure (e.g., torr), at which a binding protein such as hemoglobin is half-saturated with ligand.

pH. A quantity used to express the acidity of a solution, equivalent to $-\log [H^+]$.

Phage. See bacteriophage.

Pharmacogenomics. The study of how an individual's genetic makeup influences a drug's effectiveness.

Pharmacokinetics. The behavior of a drug in the body over time, including its tissue distribution and rate of elimination or degradation.

Phenotype. An organism's physical characteristics.

ϕ (phi). The torsion angle that describes the rotation around the C_α—N bond in a peptide group; the dihedral angle made by the bonds connecting the C—N—C_α—C atoms in a peptide chain.

Phosphagen. A phosphoguanidine whose phosphoryl group-transfer potential is greater than that of ATP; these compounds can therefore phosphorylate ADP to generate ATP.

Phosphatase. An enzyme that hydrolyzes phosphoryl ester groups. See also protein phosphatase.

Phosphatidic acid. The simplest glycerophospholipid, consisting of two fatty acyl groups attached to glycerol-3-phosphate.

Phosphodiester bond. The linkage in which a phosphate group is esterified to two alcohol groups, e.g., the phosphate groups that join the adjacent nucleoside residues in a polynucleotide.

Phosphoglyceride. See glycerophospholipid.

Phosphoinositide pathway. A signal transduction pathway in which hormone binding to a cell-surface receptor induces phospholipase C to catalyze the hydrolysis of phosphatidylinositol-4,5-bisphosphate (PIP_2), which yields inositol-1,4,5-trisphosphate (IP_3) and 1,2-diacylglycerol (DAG), both of which are second messengers.

Phospholipase. An enzyme that hydrolyzes one or more bonds of a glycerophospholipid.

Phosphoprotein phosphatase. See protein phosphatase.

Phosphorolysis. The cleavage of a chemical bond by the substitution of a phosphate group rather than water.

Phosphoryl group. A portion of a molecule with the formula —PO_3H_2.

Phosphoryl group-transfer potential. A measure of the tendency of a phosphorylated compound to transfer its phosphoryl group to water; the opposite of its free energy of hydrolysis.

Photoautotroph. An autotrophic organism that obtains energy from sunlight.

Photon. A packet of light energy. See also Planck's law.

Photooxidation. A mode of decay of an excited molecule, in which oxidation occurs through the transfer of an electron to an acceptor molecule.

Photophosphorylation. The synthesis of ATP from ADP + P_i coupled to the dissipation of a proton gradient that has been generated through light-driven electron transport.

Photoreactivation. The conversion of pyrimidine dimers, a form of DNA damage, to monomers using light energy.

Photorespiration. The consumption of O_2 and evolution of CO_2 by plants (a dissipation of the products of photosynthesis), resulting from the competition between O_2 and CO_2 for binding to ribulose bisphosphate carboxylase.

Photosynthesis. The reduction of CO_2 to $(CH_2O)_n$ in plants and bacteria as driven by light energy.

Photosynthetic reaction center. The pigment-containing protein complex that undergoes photooxidation during the light reactions of photosynthesis.

Phylogenetic tree. A reconstruction of the probable paths of evolution of a set of related organisms, usually based on sequence variations in homologous proteins and nucleic acids; a sort of family tree.

Phylogeny. The study of the evolutionary relationships among organisms.

p*I*. See isoelectric point.

PIC. See preinitiation complex.

Ping Pong reaction. A group-transfer reaction in which one or more products are released before all substrates have bound to the enzyme.

Pitch. The distance a helix rises along its axis per turn; 5.4 Å for an α helix, 34 Å for B-DNA.

p*K*. A quantity used to express the tendency for an acid to donate a proton (dissociate); equal to $-\log K$, where K is the acid's dissociation constant. Also known as pK_a.

Planck's law. An expression for the energy (E) of a photon: $E = hc/\lambda = h\nu$, where c is the speed of light, λ is its wavelength, ν is its frequency, and h is Planck's constant (6.626×10^{-34} J·s).

Plaque. (1) A region of lysed cells on a "lawn" of cultured bacteria, which indicates the presence of infectious bacteriophage. (2) A deposit of insoluble material in an animal's tissues.

Plasmalogen. A glycerophospholipid in which the C1 substituent is attached via an ether rather than an ester linkage.

Plasmid. A small circular DNA molecule that autonomously replicates in a bacterial or yeast cell. Plasmids are often modified for use as cloning vectors.

PLP. Pyridoxal-5′-phosphate, a cofactor used mainly in transamination reactions.

(+) end. The end of a polymeric filament where growth is faster. See also (−) end.

pmf. See protonmotive force.

Point mutation. The substitution of one base for another in DNA. Point mutations may arise from mispairing during DNA replication or from chemical alterations of existing bases.

Polar molecule. A molecule with one or more groups that have permanent dipoles.

Polarimeter. A device that measures the optical rotation of a solution. It can be used to determine the optical activity of a substance.

Poly(A) tail. The sequence of adenylate residues that is posttranscriptionally appended to the 3' end of eukaryotic mRNAs.

Polyacrylamide gel electrophoresis (PAGE). See gel electrophoresis.

Polycistronic mRNA. The RNA transcript of a bacterial operon. It encodes several polypeptides.

Polycythemia. A condition characterized by an increased number of erythrocytes.

Polyelectrolyte. A macromolecule that bears multiple charged groups.

Polymer. A molecule consisting of numerous smaller units that are linked together in an organized manner. Polymers may be linear or branched and may contain one or more kinds of structural units (monomers).

Polymerase. An enzyme that catalyzes the addition of nucleotide residues to a polynucleotide through nucleophilic attack of the chain's 3'-OH group on the α-phosphoryl group of the incoming nucleoside triphosphate. DNA- and RNA-directed polymerases require a template molecule with which the incoming nucleotide must base pair.

Polymerase chain reaction (PCR). A procedure for amplifying a segment of DNA by repeated rounds of replication centered between primers that hybridize with the two ends of the DNA segment of interest.

Polymorphism. A variation in DNA or amino acid sequences between individuals.

Polynucleotide. See nucleic acid.

Polypeptide. A polymer consisting of amino acid residues linked in linear fashion by peptide bonds.

Polyprotic acid. A substance with more than one proton that can be donated. Polyprotic acids have multiple ionization states.

Polyribosome. An mRNA transcript bearing multiple ribosomes in the process of carrying out translation. Also called a polysome.

Polysaccharide. A polymeric carbohydrate containing multiple monosaccharide residues. Also called a glycan.

Polysome. See polyribosome.

Polyunsaturated fatty acid. A fatty acid that contains more than one double bond in its hydrocarbon chain.

Porphyrias. Genetic defects in heme biosynthesis that result in the accumulation of porphyrins.

Positive cooperativity. See cooperative binding.

Posttranscriptional modification. The removal or addition of nucleotide residues or their modification following the synthesis of RNA.

Posttranslational processing. The removal or derivatization of amino acid residues following their incorporation into a polypeptide, or the cleavage of a polypeptide.

pO_2. See partial oxygen pressure.

pre-mRNA. See heterogeneous nuclear RNA.

pre-rRNA. An immature rRNA transcript.

pre-tRNA. An immature tRNA transcript.

Prebiotic era. The period of time between the formation of the earth ~4.6 billion years ago and the appearance of living organisms at least 3.5 billion years ago.

Precursor. The entity that gives rise, through a process such as evolution or chemical reaction, to another entity.

Preinitiation complex (PIC). The assembly of eukaryotic transcription factors bound to DNA that renders the DNA available for transcription by RNA polymerase.

Prenylation. The attachment of an isoprenoid group to a protein to form a lipid-linked protein.

Preproprotein. A protein bearing both a signal peptide (preprotein) and a propeptide (proprotein).

Preprotein. A protein bearing a signal peptide that is cleaved off following the translocation of the protein through the endoplasmic reticulum membrane.

Pribnow box. The prokaryotic promoter element with the consensus sequence TATAAT that is centered at around the −10 position relative to the transcription start site.

Primary active transport. Transmembrane transport that is driven by the exergonic hydrolysis of ATP.

Primary structure. The sequence of residues in a polymer.

Primary transcript. The immediate product of transcription, which may be modified before becoming fully functional.

Primase. The RNA polymerase responsible for synthesizing the RNA segment that primes DNA synthesis.

Primer. An oligonucleotide that serves as a starting point for additional polymerization reactions catalyzed by DNA polymerase to form a polynucleotide. A primer base-pairs with a segment of a template polynucleotide strand so as to form a short double-stranded segment that can then be extended through template-directed polymerization.

Primosome. The protein complex that synthesizes the RNA primers in DNA synthesis.

Prion. A protein whose misfolding causes it to aggregate and produce the neurodegenerative symptoms of transmissible spongiform encephalopathies and related diseases. Misfolded prions induce properly folded prions to misfold and thereby act as infectious agents.

Probe. A labeled single-stranded DNA or RNA segment that can hybridize with a DNA or RNA of interest in a screening procedure.

Processive enzyme. An enzyme that catalyzes many rounds of a polymerization reaction without dissociating from the growing polymer.

Prochirality. A property of some nonchiral molecules such that they contain a group whose substitution by another group yields a chiral molecule.

Product inhibition. A case of enzyme inhibition in which product that accumulates during the course of the reaction competes with substrate for binding to the active site.

Proenzyme. An inactive precursor of an enzyme.

Prokaryote. A unicellular organism that lacks a membrane-bounded nucleus. All bacteria are prokaryotes.

Promoter. The DNA sequence at which RNA polymerase binds to initiate transcription.

Proofreading. An additional catalytic activity of an enzyme, which acts to correct errors made by the primary enzymatic activity.

Propeptide. A polypeptide segment of an immature protein that must be proteolytically excised to activate the protein.

Proprotein. The inactive precursor of a protein that, to become fully active, must undergo limited proteolysis to excise its propeptide.

Prostaglandin. See eicosanoids.

Prosthetic group. A cofactor that is permanently (often covalently) associated with an enzyme.

Protease. See peptidase.

Proteasome. A multiprotein complex with a hollow cylindrical core in which cellular proteins are degraded to peptides (recycled) in an ATP-dependent process.

Protein. A macromolecule that consists of one or more polypeptide chains.

Protein kinase. An enzyme that catalyzes the transfer of a phosphoryl group from ATP to the OH group of a protein Ser, Thr, or Tyr residue.

Protein phosphatase. An enzyme that catalyzes the hydrolytic excision of phosphoryl groups from proteins.

Proteoglycan. An extracellular aggregate of protein and glycosaminoglycan.

Proteomics. The study of all of a cell's proteins, including their quantitation, localization, modifications, interactions, and activities.

Proto-oncogene. The normal cellular analog of an oncogene; the mutation of a proto-oncogene may yield an oncogene that contributes to uncontrolled cell proliferation (cancer).

Protomer. One of two or more identical units of an oligomeric protein. A protomer may consist of one or more polypeptide chains.

Proton jumping. The sequential transfer of protons between hydrogen-bonded water molecules. Proton jumping is largely responsible for the rapid rate at which hydronium and hydroxyl ions appear to move through an aqueous solution.

Proton wire. A group of hydrogen-bonded protein groups and water molecules that serves as a conduit for protons to traverse a membrane via proton jumping.

Protonmotive force (pmf). The free energy of the electrochemical proton gradient that forms during electron transport.

Proximity effect. A catalytic mechanism in which a reaction's free energy of activation is reduced by the prior bringing together of its reacting groups.

PRPP. 5-Phosphoribosyl-α-pyrophosphate, an "activated" form of ribose that serves as a precursor in the synthesis of histidine, tyrosine, and purine and pyrimidine nucleotides.

Pseudo-first-order reaction. A bimolecular reaction whose rate appears to be proportional to the concentration of only a single reactant because the second reactant is present in large excess.

Pseudogene. An unexpressed sequence of DNA that is apparently the defective remnant of a duplicated gene.

ψ (psi). The torsion angle that describes the rotational position around the C_α—C bond in a peptide group; the dihedral angle made by the bonds connecting the N—C_α—C—N atoms in a peptide chain.

PSI. Photosystem I, the protein complex that reduces $NADP^+$ during the light reactions of photosynthesis.

PSII. Photosystem II, the protein complex that oxidizes H_2O to O_2 during the light reactions of photosynthesis.

Pulse-labeling. A technique for tracing metabolic fates, in which cells or a reacting system are exposed briefly to high levels of a labeled compound.

Pulsed-field gel electrophoresis (PFGE). An electrophoretic procedure in which electrodes arrayed around the periphery of an agarose slab gel are sequentially pulsed so that DNA molecules must continually reorient, thereby allowing very large molecules to be separated by size.

Purine nucleotide cycle. The conversion of aspartate to fumarate, which replenishes citric acid cycle intermediates, through the deamination of AMP to IMP.

Purines. Derivatives of the compound purine, a planar aromatic, heterocyclic compound. Adenine and guanine, two of the nitrogenous bases of nucleotides, are purines.

Pyranose. A sugar with a six-membered ring.

Pyrimidine dimer. The cyclobutane-containing structure resulting from UV irradiation of adjacent thymine or cytosine residues in DNA.

Pyrimidines. Derivatives of the compound pyrimidine, a planar aromatic, heterocyclic compound. Cytosine, uracil, and thymine, three of the nitrogenous bases of nucleotides, are pyrimidines.

Pyrophosphate cleavage. The hydrolysis of ATP that yields $AMP + PP_i$.

Pyrophosphoryl group. See diphosphoryl group.

q. The thermodynamic term for heat absorbed.

Q cycle. The cyclic flow of electrons accompanied by the transport of protons, involving a stable semiquinone intermediate of CoQ in Complex III of mitochondrial electron transport and in photosynthetic electron transport.

q_P. The thermodynamic term for heat absorbed at constant pressure.

Quantum (*pl.* quanta). A packet of energy. See also photon.

Quantum yield. The ratio of molecules reacted to photons absorbed in a light-induced reaction.

Quaternary structure. The spatial arrangement of a macromolecule's individual subunits.

R group. A symbol for a variable portion of an organic molecule, such as the side chain of an amino acid.

R state. One of two conformations of an allosteric protein; the other is the T state. The R state is usually the catalytically more active state.

Racemic mixture. A sample of a compound in which both enantiomers are present in equal amounts.

Radioimmunoassay (RIA). A technique for measuring the concentration of a molecule based on its ability to block the binding of a small amount of the radioactively labeled molecule to its corresponding antibody.

Radionuclide. A radioactive isotope.

Ramachandran diagram. A plot of ϕ versus ψ that indicates the sterically allowed conformations of a polypeptide.

Randle cycle. See glucose–fatty acid cycle.

Random coil. A totally disordered and rapidly fluctuating polymer conformation.

Random mechanism. A sequential reaction without a compulsory order of substrate addition to the enzyme.

Rate constant (k). The proportionality constant between the velocity of a chemical reaction and the concentration(s) of the reactant(s).

Rate-determining step. The step with the highest transition state free energy in a multistep reaction; the slowest step.

Rate enhancement. The ratio of the rates of a catalyzed to an uncatalyzed chemical reaction.

Rate equation. A mathematical expression for the time-dependent progress of a reaction as a function of reactant concentration.

Rational drug design. See structure-based drug design.

Reaction coordinate. The path of minimum free energy for the progress of a reaction.

Reaction order. The sum of the exponents of the concentration terms that appear in a reaction's rate equation.

Reading frame. The grouping of nucleotides in sets of three whose sequence corresponds to a polypeptide sequence.

Receptor. A binding protein that is specific for its ligand and elicits a discrete biochemical effect when its ligand is bound.

Receptor-mediated endocytosis. A process in which an extracellular ligand binds to a specific cell-surface receptor and the resulting receptor–ligand complex is engulfed by the cell.

Receptor tyrosine kinase. A hormone receptor whose intracellular domain is activated, as a result of hormone binding, to phosphorylate tyrosine residues on other proteins and/or on other subunits of the same receptor.

Recombinant. A DNA molecule constructed by combining DNA from different sources. Also called a chimera.

Recombinant DNA technology. The isolation, amplification, and modification of specific DNA sequences. Also called molecular cloning or genetic engineering.

Recombination. The exchange of polynucleotide strands between separate DNA segments. Homologous recombination occurs between DNA segments with extensive homology, whereas site-specific recombination occurs between two short, specific DNA sequences.

Recombination repair. A mechanism for repairing damaged DNA, in which recombination exchanges a portion of a damaged strand for a homologous segment that can then serve as a template for the replacement of the damaged bases.

Redox center. A group that can undergo an oxidation–reduction reaction.

Redox couple. See conjugate redox pair.

Reducing agent. A substance that can donate electrons, thereby reducing another substance and becoming oxidized.

Reducing equivalent. A term used to describe the number of electrons that are transferred from one molecule to another during a redox reaction.

Reducing sugar. A saccharide bearing an anomeric carbon that has not formed a glycosidic bond and can therefore reduce mild oxidizing agents.

Reduction. The gain of electrons. Reduction of a substance is accompanied by the oxidation of another substance.

Reduction potential ($\mathscr{E}$). A measure of the tendency of a substance to gain electrons.

Reductive pentose phosphate cycle. See Calvin cycle.

Regular secondary structure. A segment of a polymer in which the backbone adopts a regularly repeating conformation.

Release factor. A protein that recognizes a Stop codon and thereby helps induce ribosomes to terminate polypeptide synthesis.

Renaturation. The refolding of a denatured macromolecule so as to regain its native conformation.

Repetitive DNA. Stretches of DNA of up to several thousand bases that occur in multiple copies in an organism's genome; they are often arranged in tandem.

Replica plating. The transfer of yeast colonies, bacterial colonies, or phage plaques from a culture plate to another culture plate, a membrane, or a filter in a manner that preserves the distribution of the cells on the original plate.

Replication. The process of making an identical copy of a DNA molecule. During DNA replication, the parental polynucleotide strands separate so that each can direct the synthesis of a complementary daughter strand, resulting in two complete DNA double helices.

Replication fork. The branch point in a replicating DNA molecule at which the two strands of the parental molecule are separated and serve as templates for the synthesis of the daughter strands.

Replicon. A unit of eukaryotic DNA that is replicated from one replication origin.

Replisome. The DNA polymerase–containing protein assembly that catalyzes the synthesis of both the leading and lagging strands of DNA at the replication fork.

Repolarization. The recovery of membrane potential that occurs during electrical signaling in cells such as neurons.

Repressor. A protein that binds at or near a gene so as to prevent its transcription.

RER. See rough endoplasmic reticulum.

Residue. A term for a monomeric unit of a polymer.

Resonance energy transfer. See exciton transfer.

Respiratory distress syndrome. Difficulty in breathing in prematurely born infants, caused by alveolar collapse resulting from insufficient synthesis of lung surfactant.

Restriction endonuclease. A bacterial enzyme that recognizes a specific DNA sequence and cleaves the DNA as part of a restriction–modification system.

Restriction–modification system. A matched pair of bacterial enzymes that recognize a specific DNA sequence: a modification methylase that methylates bases in that sequence, and a restriction endonuclease that cleaves the DNA if it has not been methylated in that sequence. It is a defensive system that eliminates foreign (e.g., viral) DNA.

Reticulocyte. An immature red blood cell, which actively synthesizes hemoglobin.

Retrotransposon. A transposon whose sequence and mechanism of transposition suggest that it arose from a retrovirus.

Retrovirus. A virus whose genetic material is RNA that must be reverse-transcribed to double-stranded DNA during host cell infection.

Reverse transcriptase. A DNA polymerase that uses RNA as its template.

Reverse turn. A polypeptide conformation in which the chain makes an abrupt reversal in direction; usually consisting of four successive residues. Also called a β bend.

Rho factor. A prokaryotic helicase that separates DNA and RNA to promote transcription termination.

RIA. See radioimmunoassay.

Ribonucleic acid. See RNA.

Ribonucleoprotein. A complex of protein and RNA.

Ribonucleotide. A nucleotide in which the pentose is ribose.

Ribosomal RNA (rRNA). The RNA molecules that constitute the bulk of the ribosome, the site of polypeptide synthesis. rRNA provides structural scaffolding for the ribosome and catalyzes peptide bond formation.

Ribosome. The organelle that synthesizes polypeptides under the direction of mRNA. It consists of around two-thirds RNA and one-third protein.

Riboswitch. An mRNA structure that regulates gene expression through alterations in its structure triggered by the presence of the metabolite that is synthesized by the encoded protein.

Ribozyme. An RNA molecule that has catalytic activity.

Rickets. The vitamin D-deficiency disease in children that is characterized by stunted growth and deformed bones.

Rigor mortis. The stiffening of muscles after death.

RNA. Ribonucleic acid. A polymer of ribonucleotides. The major forms of RNA include messenger RNA (mRNA), transfer RNA (tRNA), and ribosomal RNA (rRNA).

RNA editing. The posttranscriptional insertion, deletion, or alteration of bases in mRNA.

RNA interference (RNAi). A form of posttranscriptional gene regulation in which a short double-stranded RNA segment triggers the degradation of the homologous mRNA molecule.

RNAi. See RNA interference.

RNAP. RNA polymerase, the enzyme that synthesizes RNA using a DNA template.

Rossmann fold. See dinucleotide binding fold.

Rotational symmetry. A type of symmetry in which the asymmetric units of a symmetric object can be brought into coincidence through rotation.

Rough endoplasmic reticulum (RER). That portion of the endoplasmic reticulum associated with ribosomes; it is the site of synthesis of membrane proteins and proteins destined for secretion or residence in certain organelles.

rRNA. See ribosomal RNA.

RS system. See Cahn–Ingold–Prelog system.

S. See entropy.

S. Svedberg, a unit for the sedimentation coefficient, equivalent to 10^{-13} s.

Saccharide. See carbohydrate.

Salt bridge. See ion pair.

Salting in. The increase in solubility of a protein (or other molecule) with increasing (low) salt concentration.

Salting out. The decrease in solubility of a protein (or other molecule) with increasing (high) salt concentration.

Salvage pathway. A metabolic pathway for converting free purines and pyrimidines to their nucleotide forms.

SAM. *S*-Adenosylmethionine, a nucleotide cofactor that functions mostly as a methyl group donor. Also called AdoMet.

Sarcomere. The repeating unit of a myofibril, consisting of thin and thick filaments that slide past each other during muscle contraction.

Saturated fatty acid. A fatty acid that does not contain any double bonds in its hydrocarbon chain.

Saturation. The state in which all of a macromolecule's ligand-binding sites are occupied by ligand. See also enzyme saturation and saturated fatty acid.

Schiff base. An imine that forms between an amine and an aldehyde or ketone.

SCID. See severe combined immunodeficiency disease.

Scrapie. See transmissible spongiform encephalopathy.

Screening. A technique for identifying clones that contain a desired gene.

Scurvy. A disease caused by vitamin C (ascorbic acid) deficiency, which results in inadequate formation of 4-hydroxyprolyl residues in collagen, thereby reducing the collagen's stability.

SDS-PAGE. Polyacrylamide gel electrophoresis (PAGE) in the presence of the detergent sodium dodecyl sulfate (SDS), which denatures and imparts a uniform charge density to polypeptides and thereby permits them to be fractionated on the basis of size rather than inherent charge.

Second messenger. An intracellular ion or molecule that acts as a signal for an extracellular event such as ligand binding to a cell-surface receptor.

Second-order reaction. A reaction whose rate is proportional to the square of the concentration of one reactant or to the product of the concentrations of two reactants.

Secondary active transport. Transmembrane transport that is driven by the energy stored in an electrochemical gradient, which itself is generated utilizing the free energy of ATP hydrolysis or electron transport.

Secondary structure. The local spatial arrangement of a polymer's backbone atoms without regard to the conformations of its substituent side chains. α helices and β sheets are common secondary structural elements of proteins.

Secretory pathway. The series of steps in which an integral membrane or secretory protein is recognized by the signal recognition particle as it emerges from the ribosome, is translocated across the endoplasmic reticulum membrane via a translocon, and is cleaved by a signal peptidase.

Sedimentation coefficient. A measure of a particle's rate of sedimentation in an ultracentrifuge, usually expressed in Svedberg units (S).

Segment polarity genes. See segmentation genes.

Segmentation genes. Insect genes that specify the correct number and polarity of body segments. Gap genes, pair-rule genes, and segment polarity genes are all segmentation genes.

Selectable marker. A gene whose product has an activity, such as antibiotic resistance, such that, under the appropriate conditions, cells harboring the gene can be distinguished from those that lack the gene.

Selfish DNA. Genomic DNA that has no apparent function. Also called junk DNA.

Semiconservative replication. The natural mode of DNA duplication in which each new duplex molecule contains one strand from the parent molecule and one newly synthesized strand.

Semidiscontinuous replication. The mode of DNA replication in which one strand is replicated as a continuous polynucleotide strand (the leading strand) while the other is replicated as a series of discontinuous fragments (Okazaki fragments) that are later joined (the lagging strand).

Sense strand. The DNA strand complementary to the strand that is transcribed; it has the same base sequence (except for the replacement of U with T) as the synthesized RNA. Also called the coding strand.

Sequential model of allosterism. A model for allosteric behavior in which the subunits of an oligomeric protein change conformation in a stepwise manner as the number of bound ligands increases.

Sequential reaction. A reaction in which all substrates must combine with the enzyme before a reaction can occur; it can proceed by an Ordered or Random mechanism.

Serine protease. A peptide-hydrolyzing enzyme characterized by a reactive Ser residue in its active site.

Severe combined immunodeficiency disease (SCID). An inherited disease that greatly impairs the immune system. One such defect is a deficiency of the enzyme adenosine deaminase.

Shear degradation. The fragmentation of DNA by the mechanical force of shaking or stirring.

Shine–Dalgarno sequence. A purine-rich sequence ~10 nucleotides upstream from the start codon of many prokaryotic mRNAs that is partially complementary to the 3′ end of the 16S rRNA. This sequence helps position the ribosome to initiate translation.

Short interfering RNA (siRNA). A naturally occurring RNA of 18 to 25 nucleotides that inhibits gene expression through RNA interference. Also known as micro RNA (miRNA).

Short tandem repeat (STR). See highly repetitive DNA.

Shotgun cloning. The cloning of an organism's genome in the form of a set of random fragments.

Sickle-cell anemia. An inherited disease in which erythrocytes are deformed and damaged by the presence of a mutant hemoglobin (Glu $6\beta \rightarrow$ Val) that in its deoxy form polymerizes into fibers.

σ factor. A component of the bacterial RNA polymerase holoenzyme that recognizes a gene's promoter and is released once chain initiation has occurred.

Sigmoidal curve. The S-shaped graphical representation of the cooperative binding of a ligand to a molecule.

Signal-gated channel. A channel whose opening and closing (gating) is controlled by the binding of an intracellular signaling molecule.

Signal peptide. A short (13–36 residues) N-terminal peptide sequence that targets a nascent secretory or transmembrane protein to the endoplasmic reticulum (in eukaryotes) or plasma membrane (in prokaryotes). This leader peptide is subsequently cleaved away by signal peptidase.

Signal recognition particle (SRP). A protein–RNA complex that binds to the signal peptide of a nascent transmembrane or secretory protein and escorts it to the endoplasmic reticulum (in eukaryotes) or plasma membrane (in prokaryotes) for translocation through the membrane.

Signal transduction. The transmittal of an extracellular signal to the cell interior by the binding of a ligand to a cell-surface receptor so as to elicit a cellular response through the activation of a sequence of intracellular events that often include the generation of second messengers.

Silencer. A DNA sequence some distance from the transcription start site, where a repressor of transcription may bind.

Single-displacement reaction. A reaction in which a group is transferred from one molecule to another in a concerted fashion (with no intermediates).

Single nucleotide polymorphism (SNP). A single base difference in the genomes of two individuals; such differences occur every 1250 bp on average in the human genome.

Single-strand binding protein (SSB). A tetrameric protein, many molecules of which coat single-stranded DNA during replication so as to prevent formation of double-stranded DNA.

siRNA. See short interfering RNA.

Site-directed mutagenesis. A technique in which a cloned gene is mutated in a specific manner.

Site-specific recombination. See recombination.

Size exclusion chromatography. See gel filtration chromatography.

Sliding filament model. A mechanism for muscle contraction in which interdigitated thin and thick filaments move past each other so as to shorten the overall length of a sarcomere.

Small nuclear ribonucleoprotein (snRNP). A complex of protein and small nuclear RNA that participates in mRNA splicing.

Small nuclear RNA (snRNA). Highly conserved 60- to 300-nt RNAs that participate in mRNA splicing.

Small nucleolar RNA (snoRNA). Eukaryotic RNA molecules of 70 to 100 nt that pair with immature rRNAs to direct their sequence-specific methylation.

SNARE. A membrane-associated protein that participates in vesicle fusion; SNAREs from the two fusing membranes form a bundle of four helices that holds the membranes in close proximity.

snoRNA. See small nucleolar RNA.

SNP. See single nucleotide polymorphism.

snRNA. See small nuclear RNA.

snRNP. See small nuclear ribonucleoprotein.

Soap. A salt of a long-chain fatty acid, which contains a polar head group and a long hydrophobic tail.

Solvation. The state of being surrounded by several layers of ordered solvent molecules. Hydration is solvation by water.

Somatic hypermutation. The greatly increased rate of mutation that occurs in the immunoglobulin genes of proliferating B lymphocytes and leads, over several cell generations, to antibodies with higher antigen affinity.

Somatic recombination. Genetic rearrangement that occurs in cells other than germline cells.

Sonication. Irradiation with high frequency sound waves. Such treatment is used to disrupt cells and subcellular membranous structures.

SOS response. A bacterial system that recognizes damaged DNA, halts its replication, and repairs the damage, although in an error-prone fashion.

Southern blotting. A procedure for identifying a DNA base sequence after electrophoresis, through its ability to hybridize with a complementary single-stranded segment of labeled DNA or RNA. See also Northern blotting.

Special pair. The set of two closely spaced chlorophyll groups in a photosynthetic system that undergo photooxidation.

Spherocytosis. A hereditary abnormality in the erythrocyte cytoskeleton that renders the cells rigid and spheroidal and which causes hemolytic anemia.

Sphingolipid. A derivative of the C_{18} amino alcohol sphingosine. Sphingolipids include the ceramides, cerebrosides, and gangliosides. Sphingolipids with phosphate head groups are called sphingophospholipids.

Sphingomyelin. The most common sphingolipid, consisting of a ceramide bearing a phosphocholine or phosphoethanolamine head group.

Spliceosome. A 60S particle containing proteins, snRNPs, and pre-mRNA; it carries out the splicing reactions whereby a pre-mRNA is converted to a mature mRNA.

Splicing. The usually ribonucleoprotein-catalyzed process by which introns are removed and exons are joined to produce a mature transcript. Some RNAs are self-splicing.

Spontaneous process. A thermodynamic process that occurs without the input of free energy from outside the system. Spontaneity is independent of the rate of a process.

Squelching. The inhibition of the activity of a transcription factor by another transcription factor that competes with it for binding to DNA.

SR. See SRP receptor.

SRP. See signal recognition particle.

SRP receptor (SR). The endoplasmic reticulum protein that serves as a docking point for the signal recognition particle (SRP) during the synthesis of a transmembrane or secretory protein.

SSB. See single-strand binding protein.

Stacking interactions. The stabilizing van der Waals interactions between successive (stacked) bases and base pairs in a polynucleotide.

Standard state. A set of conditions including unit activity of the species of interest, a temperature of 25°C, a pressure of 1 atm, and a pH of 0.0. See also biochemical standard state.

Starch. A mixture of linear and branched glucose polymers that serve as the principal energy reserves of plants.

STAT. A member of a family of proteins that function as signal transducers and activators of transcription (STAT) by binding to DNA in response to tyrosine phosphorylation.

State function. Quantities such as energy, enthalpy, entropy, and free energy, whose values depend only on the current state of the system, not on how they reached that state.

Steady state. A set of conditions in an open system under which the formation and degradation of individual components are balanced such that the system does not change over time.

Steady state assumption. A condition for the application of the Michaelis–Menten model to an enzymatic reaction, in which the concentration of the ES complex remains unchanged over the course of the reaction.

Stem–loop. A secondary structural element in a single-stranded nucleic acid, in which two complementary segments form a base-paired stem whose strands are connected by a loop of unpaired bases.

Stereoisomers. Chiral molecules with different configurations about at least one of their asymmetric centers but which are otherwise identical.

Steroid. Any of numerous naturally occurring lipids composed of four fused rings; many are hormones that are derived from cholesterol.

Sterol. An alcohol derivative of a steroid.

Sticky end. The single-stranded extension of a DNA fragment that has been cleaved at a specific sequence (often by a restriction endonuclease) in a staggered cut such that this single-stranded extension is complementary to those of similarly cleaved DNAs.

Stop codon. A sequence of three nucleotides that does not specify an amino acid but instead causes the termination of translation. Also called a nonsense codon.

STR. Short tandem repeat. See highly repetitive DNA.

Striated muscle. The voluntary or skeletal muscles, which have a striped microscopic appearance.

Stroma. The concentrated solution of enzymes, small molecules, and ions in the interior of a chloroplast; the site of carbohydrate synthesis.

Stromal lamellae. The membranous assemblies that connect grana in a chloroplast.

Strong acid. An acid that is essentially completely ionized in aqueous solution. A strong acid has a dissociation constant much greater than unity ($pK < 0$).

Structural bioinformatics. See bioinformatics.

Structural gene. A gene that encodes a protein.

Structure-based drug design. The synthesis of more effective drug molecules as guided by knowledge of the target molecule's structure and interactions with other drug molecules. Also called rational drug design.

Substrate. A reactant in an enzymatic reaction.

Substrate cycle. Two opposing metabolic reactions that function together to hydrolyze ATP, but provide a control point for regulating metabolic flux. Also called a futile cycle.

Substrate-level phosphorylation. The direct transfer of a phosphoryl group to ADP to generate ATP.

Subunit. One of several polymer chains that make up a macromolecule.

Sugar. A simple mono- or disaccharide.

Suicide substrate. See mechanism-based inhibitor.

Sulfhydryl group. A portion of a molecule with the formula —SH.

Supercoiling. The topological state of covalently closed circular double-helical DNA in which the double helix is twisted around itself. It arises through the over- or underwinding of the double helix. Also called superhelicity.

Superhelicity. See supercoiling.

Superoxide radical. O_2^-, a partially reduced oxygen species that can damage biomolecules through free radical reactions.

Supersecondary structure. A common grouping of secondary structural elements. Also called a motif.

Suppressor mutation. A mutation that cancels the effect of another mutation.

Surface labeling. A technique in which a lipid-insoluble protein-labeling reagent is used to identify the portion of a membrane protein that is exposed to solvent.

Surroundings. In thermodynamics, the universe other than the particular system that is of interest.

Symbiosis. A mutually dependent relationship between two organisms.

Symmetry model of allosterism. A model for allosteric behavior in which all the subunits of an oligomeric protein are constrained to change conformation in a concerted manner so as to maintain the symmetry of the oligomer.

Symport. A transmembrane channel that simultaneously transports two different molecules or ions in the same direction. See also antiport and uniport.

Syn conformation. A purine nucleotide conformation in which the ribose and the base are eclipsed. See also anti conformation.

Syncytium. A single cell containing multiple nuclei that results from repeated nuclear division without the formation of new plasma membranes.

Synonymous codons. Codons that specify the same amino acid.

System. In thermodynamics, the part of the universe that is of interest; the rest of the universe is the surroundings. See also closed system, isolated system, and open system.

Systems biology. The computer-based collection and analysis of data sets for the purpose of discerning relationships between dynamic or multifactorial biological entities.

T. See twist.

$t_{1/2}$. See half-time.

T state. One of two conformations of an allosteric protein; the other is the R state. The T state is usually the catalytically less active state.

T → R transition. A shift in conformation of an allosteric protein induced by ligand binding.

TAFs. TBP-associated factors, which, along with TBP, constitute the general transcription factor TFIID required for the transcription of eukaryotic structural genes.

TATA box. A eukaryotic promoter element with the consensus sequence TATAAAA located 10 to 27 nucleotides upstream from the transcription start site.

Tautomers. Isomers that differ only in the positions of their hydrogen atoms and double bonds.

Taxonomy. The study of biological classification.

Tay-Sachs disease. A fatal sphingolipid storage disease caused by a deficiency of hexosaminidase A, the lysosomal enzyme that breaks down ganglioside G_{M2}.

TBP. TATA-binding protein, a DNA-binding protein that is required for transcription of all eukaryotic genes.

TCA cycle. Tricarboxylic acid cycle. See citric acid cycle.

Telomerase. An RNA-containing DNA polymerase that, using the RNA as a template, catalyzes the repeated addition of a specific G-rich sequence to the 3′ end of a eukaryotic DNA molecule to form a telomere.

Telomere. The end of a linear eukaryotic chromosome, which consists of tandem repeats of a short G-rich sequence on the 3′-ending strand and its complementary sequence on the 5′-ending strand.

Tertiary structure. The entire three-dimensional structure of a single-chain polymer, including that of its side chains.

Tetrahedral intermediate. An intermediate of peptide bond hydrolysis in which the carbonyl carbon of the scissile bond has undergone nucleophilic attack so that it has four substituents.

Tetramer. An assembly consisting of four monomeric units.

Therapeutic index. The ratio of the dose of a drug that produces toxicity to the dose that produces the desired effect.

Thermodynamics. The study of the relationships among various forms of energy.

Thermogenesis. The generation of heat by muscle contraction (shivering) or by fuel oxidation without ATP synthesis (also called diet-induced thermogenesis).

Thermophile. An organism that thrives at high temperatures.

θ structure. The appearance of a circular DNA molecule undergoing replication by the progressive separation of its two strands.

THF. Tetrahydrofolate, a cofactor for reactions that transfer one-carbon units in various oxidation states.

Thick filament. The sarcomere element that is composed primarily of several hundred myosin molecules.

Thin filament. The sarcomere element that is composed primarily of actin, along with tropomyosin and troponin.

30-nm fiber. A condensed chromatin structure in which nucleosomes fold in a zigzag manner to form a fiber with a diameter of ~30 nm.

3′ end. The terminus of a polynucleotide whose C3′ is not esterified to another nucleotide residue.

Thylakoid. The innermost compartment in chloroplasts, which is formed by invaginations of the chloroplast's inner membrane. The thylakoid membrane is the site of the light reactions of photosynthesis.

Titration curve. The graphic presentation of the relationship between the pH of an acid- or base-containing solution and the degree of proton dissociation (roughly equal to the number of equivalents of strong base or strong acid that have been added to the solution).

T_m. See melting temperature.

TM protein. See transmembrane protein.

Topoisomerase. An enzyme that alters DNA supercoiling by catalyzing breaks in one or both strands, passing DNA through the break, and resealing the break.

Topology. The study of the geometric properties of an object that are not altered by deformations such as bending and stretching

Torsion angle. The dihedral angle described by the bonds between four successive atoms. The torsion angles ϕ and ψ indicate the backbone conformation of a peptide group in a polypeptide.

TPP. Thiamine pyrophosphate, a cofactor for reactions in which α-keto acids undergo decarboxylation.

TψC arm. A conserved stem–loop structure in a tRNA molecule that usually contains the sequence TψC, where ψ is pseudouridine.

Trace element. See mineral.

Trans conformation. An arrangement of the peptide group in which successive C_α atoms are on opposite sides of the peptide bond.

Trans peptide. A conformation in which successive C_α atoms are on opposite sides of the peptide bond.

Transamination. The transfer of an amino group from an amino acid to an α-keto acid to yield a new α-keto acid and a new amino acid.

Transcription. The process by which RNA is synthesized using a DNA template, thereby transferring genetic information from the DNA to the RNA. Transcription is catalyzed by RNA polymerase as facilitated by numerous other proteins.

Transcription factor. A protein that promotes the transcription of a gene by binding to DNA sequences at or near the gene or by interacting with other proteins that do so.

Transcriptomics. The study of all the mRNA molecules that a cell transcribes.

Transfer RNA (tRNA). The small L-shaped RNAs that deliver specific amino acids, which have been esterified to the tRNA's 3′ ends, to ribosomes according to the sequence of a bound mRNA. The proper tRNA is selected through the complementary base pairing of its three-nucleotide anticodon with the mRNA's codon, and the growing polypeptide is transferred to its aminoacyl group.

Transferase. An enzyme that catalyzes the transfer of a functional group from one molecule to another.

Transformation. (1) The permanent alteration of a bacterial cell's genetic message through the introduction of foreign DNA. (2) The genetic changes that convert a normal cell to a cancerous cell.

Transgene. A foreign gene that is stably expressed in a host organism.

Transgenic organism. An organism that stably expresses a foreign gene (transgene).

Transition. A mutation in which one purine (or pyrimidine) replaces another.

Transition state. A molecular assembly at the point of maximal free energy in the reaction coordinate diagram of a chemical reaction.

Transition state analog. A stable substance that geometrically and electronically resembles the transition state of a reaction.

Transition temperature. The temperature at which a lipid bilayer shifts from a gel-like solid to a more fluid liquid crystal form.

Translation. The process of transforming the information contained in the nucleotide sequence of an RNA to the corresponding amino acid sequence of a polypeptide as specified by the genetic code. Translation is catalyzed by ribosomes and requires the additional participation of messenger RNA, transfer RNA, and a variety of protein factors.

Translocation. (1) The movement of a polypeptide through a membrane during the synthesis of a secreted protein. (2) The movement, by one codon, of the ribosome relative to the mRNA after peptide bond synthesis.

Translocon. A multisubunit protein that forms an aqueous pore across the endoplasmic reticulum membrane for the purpose of translocating a protein as part of the secretory pathway.

Transmembrane (TM) protein. An integral protein that completely spans the membrane.

Transmissible spongiform encephalopathy (TSE). An invariably fatal neurodegenerative disease resulting from prion infection, such as scrapie in sheep.

Transpeptidation. The ribosomal process in which a tRNA-bound nascent polypeptide is transferred to a tRNA-bound aminoacyl group so as to form a new peptide bond, thereby lengthening the polypeptide by one residue at its C-terminus.

Transposable element. See transposon.

Transposition. The movement (copying) of genetic material from one part of the genome to another or, in some cases, from one organism to another.

Transposon. A genetic unit that can move (be copied) from one position to another in a genome; some transposons carry genes. Also called a transposable element.

Transverse diffusion. The movement of a lipid from one leaflet of a bilayer to the other. Also called flip-flop.

Transversion. A mutation in which a purine is replaced by a pyrimidine or vice versa.

Treadmilling. The addition of monomeric units to one end of a linear aggregate, such as an actin filament, and their removal from the opposite end such that the length of the aggregate remains unchanged.

Triacylglycerol. A lipid in which three fatty acids are esterified to a glycerol backbone. Also called a triglyceride.

Tricarboxylic acid (TCA) cycle. See citric acid cycle.

Triglyceride. See triacylglycerol.

Trimer. An assembly consisting of three monomeric units.

Tripeptide. A polypeptide containing three amino acids.

tRNA. See transfer RNA.

TSE. See transmissible spongiform encephalopathy.

Tumor suppressor. A protein whose loss or inactivation may lead to cancer.

Turnover number. See k_{cat}.

Twist (T). The number of complete revolutions that one strand of a covalently closed circular double-helical DNA makes around the duplex axis. It is positive for right-handed superhelical coils and negative for left-handed superhelical coils.

Two-dimensional (2D) gel electrophoresis. A technique in which proteins are first subjected to isoelectric focusing, which separates them by net charge, and then to SDS-PAGE in a perpendicular direction, which separates them by size.

Tyrosine kinase. An enzyme that catalyzes the ATP-dependent phosphorylation of a Tyr side chain.

U. The thermodynamic symbol for energy.

Ubiquinone. See coenzyme Q.

Ubiquitin. A small, highly conserved protein that is covalently attached to a eukaryotic intracellular protein so as to mark it for degradation by a proteasome.

Ultracentrifugation. A procedure that subjects macromolecules to a strong centrifugal force (in an ultracentrifuge), thereby separating them by size and/or density and providing a method for determining their mass and subunit structure.

Uncompetitive inhibition. A form of enzyme inhibition in which an inhibitor binds to the enzyme–substrate complex and thereby decreases its apparent K_M and its apparent V_{max} by the same factor.

Uncoupler. A substance that allows the proton gradient across a membrane to dissipate without ATP synthesis so that electron transport proceeds without oxidative phosphorylation.

Uniport. A transmembrane channel that transports a single molecule or ion. See also antiport and symport.

Unsaturated fatty acid. A fatty acid that contains at least one double bond in its hydrocarbon chain.

Urea cycle. A catalytic cycle in which amino groups donated by ammonia and aspartate combine with a carbon atom from HCO_3^- to form urea for excretion and which provides the route for the elimination of nitrogen from protein degradation.

Uridylylation. Addition of a uridylyl (UMP) group.

Uronic acid. A sugar produced by oxidation of an aldose primary alcohol group to a carboxylic acid group.

v. Reaction velocity, typically measured as the rate of appearance of product or disappearance of reactant.

Vacuole. An intracellular vesicle for storing water or other molecules.

van der Waals distance. The distance of closest approach between two nonbonded atoms.

van der Waals forces. The noncovalent associations between molecules that arise from the electrostatic interactions among permanent and/or induced dipoles.

van't Hoff plot. A graph of K_{eq} versus $1/T$ that is used to determine $\Delta H°$ and $\Delta S°$ and therefore $\Delta G°$ for a chemical reaction.

Variable arm. A nonconserved region of a tRNA molecule that contains 3 to 21 nucleotides and that may include a base-paired stem.

Variable region. The N-terminal portions of an antibody molecule, where antigen binding occurs and which are characterized by high sequence variability.

Variant. A naturally occurring mutant form.

Vector. See cloning vector.

Vesicle. A fluid-filled sac enclosed by a membrane.

Virulence. The disease-evoking power of a microorganism.

Virus. A nonliving entity that co-opts the metabolism of a host cell to reproduce.

Vitamin. A metabolically required substance that cannot be synthesized by an animal and must therefore be obtained from the diet.

VLDL. Very low density lipoprotein; see lipoprotein.

V_{max}. Maximal velocity of an enzymatic reaction.

V_{max}^{app}. The observed maximal velocity of an enzymatic reaction, which may differ from the true value due to the presence of an inhibitor.

v_o. Initial velocity of an enzymatic reaction.

Voltage-gated channel. A channel whose opening and closing (gating) is controlled by a change in membrane potential.

W. (1) See writhing number. (2) The number of energetically equivalent ways of arranging the components of a system.

w. The thermodynamic term for the work done by a system on its surroundings.

Water of hydration. The shell of relatively immobile water molecules that surrounds and interacts with (solvates) a dissolved molecule.

Watson–Crick base pair. A stable pairing of nucleotide bases, either adenine with thymine or guanine with cytosine, that occurs in DNA and, to a lesser extent, in RNA. See also Hoogsteen base pair.

Weak acid. An acid that is only partially ionized in aqueous solution. A weak acid has a dissociation constant less than unity ($pK > 0$).

Western blot. See immunoblot.

Wild type. The naturally occurring version of an organism or gene.

Wobble hypothesis. An explanation for the permissive tRNA–mRNA pairing at the third anticodon position that includes non-Watson–Crick base pairs. This allows many tRNAs to recognize two or three different (degenerate) codons.

Writhing number (W). The number of turns that the duplex axis of a covalently closed circular double-helical DNA makes around the superhelix axis. It is a measure of the DNA's superhelicity.

X-Ray crystallography. A method for determining three-dimensional molecular structures from the diffraction pattern produced by exposing a crystal of a molecule to a beam of X-rays.

Xenobiotic. A molecule that is not normally present in an organism.

Y. See fractional saturation.

YAC. See yeast artificial chromosome.

Yeast artificial chromosome (YAC). A linear DNA molecule that contains the chromosomal structures required for normal replication and segregation in a yeast cell. YACs are commonly used as cloning vectors.

Ylid. A molecule with opposite charges on adjacent atoms.

Y_{O_2}. See fractional saturation.

Z-scheme. A Z-shaped diagram indicating the sequence of events and their reduction potentials in the two-center photosynthetic electron-transport system of plants and cyanobacteria.

Zero-order reaction. A reaction whose rate does not vary with the concentration of any of its reactants.

Zinc finger. A protein structural motif, often involved in DNA binding, that consists of 25 to 60 residues that include His and/or Cys residues to which one or two Zn^{2+} ions are tetrahedrally coordinated.

Zwitterion. See dipolar ion.

Zymogen. The inactive precursor (proenzyme) of a proteolytic enzyme.

Index

Page numbers in **bold face** refer to a major discussion of the entry. F after a page number refers to a figure. T after a page number refers to a table. Positional and configurational designations in chemical names (e.g., 3-, α, *N-, p-, trans,* D-) are ignored in alphabetizing. Numbers and Greek letters are otherwise alphabetized as if they were spelled out.

A

A, *see* Adenine; Aminoacyl site
Aβ (amyloid-β protein), 169
A antigens, 242F
aaRSs, *see* Aminoacyl-tRNA synthetases
aa-tRNA, *see* Aminoacyl-tRNA
A bands, 198
Abasic sites, 921
ABCA1 (ATP-cassette binding protein A1), 729
ABC transporters, 311, **314–316**, 315F
Abdominal cavity, adipose tissue in, 796
Ab initio protein design, 163
ABO blood group antigens, 242
Abortive initiation, 948
Absolute configuration, 83
Absorbance, 95–96
Absorbance spectroscopy, 95
Absorption spectrum, 96
Absorptivity, 95
Abx (anteriobithorax) mutant, 1092
AC, *see* Adenylate cyclase
ACAT (acyl-CoA:cholesterol acyltransferase), 684F, 725
ACC (acetyl-CoA carboxylase), 805
Acceptor stem (tRNA), 991F
Accessory BChl, 648
Accessory pigments, 644–645
Acesulfame, 228
Acetal:
　cyclic, 225
　nonenzymatic acid-catalyzed hydrolysis, 344F
Acetaldehyde, 327
　from alcoholic fermentation, 505
　geometric specificity, 326
Acetamide, 319
Acetaminophen, 399, 719
Acetate, cholesterol biosynthesis from, **722–725**
Acetic acid, titration curve, 34F
Acetimidoquinone, 400
Acetoacetate:
　in amino acid degradation, 747F
　decarboxylation, 334F
　in ketogenesis, 698–699F
　in ketone body conversion to acetyl-CoA, 700F

from phenylalanine/tyrosine break-down, 760–761F
from tryptophan breakdown, 758, 760F
Acetoacetyl-ACP, in fatty acid synthesis, 705F
Acetoacetyl-CoA:
　in ketogenesis, 699, 699F
　in ketone body conversion to acetyl-CoA, 700F
Aceto-α-hydroxybutyrate, 772
Acetolactate, 772
Acetone, geometric specificity, 326
Acetyl-ACP, in fatty acid synthesis, 705F
Acetylcholine, hydrolysis, 349
Acetylcholinesterase, 349, 371T
Acetyl-CoA (acetyl-coenzyme A), 451–452, 468–469, 801, 1060. *See also* Ketone bodies
　in amino acid degradation, 747F
　in citric acid cycle, 568F, **570–573,** 584F, 585–587
　in fatty acid synthesis, 705F
　in glyoxylate cycle, 591F
　in ketogenesis, 699, 699F
　in ketone body conversion to acetyl-CoA, 700F
　mammalian metabolism, 792F, 793, 797
Acetyl-CoA-ACP transacylase, in fatty acid synthesis, 705F
Acetyl-CoA carboxylase (ACC), 805
Acetyl-coenzyme A, *see* Acetyl-CoA
N-Acetylglucosamine (NAG, GlcNAc), 232, 340, 343, 346, 347
N-Acetyl-D-glucosamine, 232F, 237F
N-Acetylglutamate, 747
N-Acetylglutamate synthase, 747
Acetyl-Lys binding sites, 1062F
ε-*N*-Acetyllysine, 86F
N-Acetylmuramic acid (NAM, MurNAc), 237F, 340, 343, 346
N-Acetylneuraminic acid (NANA), 225F
Acetyl phosphate, 461T, 465, 497
Acids, 32–34
　as buffering agents, 36
　conjugate bases, 32
　polyprotic, 35, 35F
　strength, 32–34
Acid-base catalysis (enzymes), **331–333**

Acid-base chemistry, **32–34**
　and proton jumping, 30–31
　standard state conventions, 17
Acidic solutions, 31
Acidosis, 36
Aconitase:
　in citric acid cycle, 568F, **578–579,** 587
　in glyoxylate cycle, 591F
　stereospecificity of, 325
Aconitate, 567
ACP (acyl-carrier protein), 703–704
Acquired immunodeficiency syndrome (AIDS), 377, 384–385
Acridine orange, as intercalating agent, 873F, 919
Acromegaly, 411
Actin, **207–209,** 628
　myosin-actin interaction, 203F
　structure, 202F, 203F
α-Actinin, 204
β-Actinin, 205
Actinomycin D, 954
Action potentials, 302–303
Action potential time course, 302F
Activation domains, 1068
Activation energy, **328–330**
Activators (regulatory proteins), 1067
Active membrane transport, 276, 297, **297–310**
　ATP-driven, **311–314**
　endergonic process, 311
　ion-gradient-driven, **316–318**
　sodium and potassium, 312F
Active site (enzymes), 323
Active transporters, 299, 311–318
Active transport systems, 316
Activity, 17
Activity site, 833
Acute intermittent porphyria, 778
Acute lymphoblastic leukemia, 751
Acute pancreatitis, 357
Acyclovir, 844
Acyl-carnitine, 687
Acyl-carrier protein (ACP), 703–704
Acyl-CoA:cholesterol acyltransferase (ACAT), 684F, 725
Acyl-CoA dehydrogenase, 688–689F
Acyl-CoA oxidase, 698
Acyl-CoA synthetases, 686, 687F

Acyl-dihydroxyacetone phosphate, in triacylglycerol biosynthesis, 710F

Acyl-dihydroxyacetone phosphate reductase, in triacylglycerol biosynthesis, 710F

Acyl-enzyme, tetrahedral intermediate, 357F

Acyl-enzyme intermediate, chymotrypsin, 354

1-Acylglycerol-3-phosphate acyltransferase, in triacylglycerol biosynthesis, 710F, 711

2-Acylglycerols, 678–679

Acyl phosphates, 465

N-Acylsphingosine, 714, 718F

Acyl thioester, 498

Adaptor, 418

ADAR2, 976

Addison's disease, 215T, 255

Adenine (A), 40, 41T
 base pairing, 46F, 49F, 851F, 866–868
 Chargaff's rules and, 44
 as common nucleotide, 42
 modified forms in tRNA, 992F
 oxidative deamination, 917F
 stacking interactions, 867F

Adenine nucleotide translocase, 599–600

Adenine phosphoribosyltransferase (APRT), 823

Adenine ribonucleotide synthesis, 821–822

Adenosine, 41T, 460, 840F

Adenosine-3′,5′-cyclic monophosphate, *see* cAMP

Adenosine-5′(β,γ-imido)triphosphate (AMPPNP, ADPNP), 202F, 415, 422F

Adenosine deaminase, 378, 841F

Adenosine diphosphate, *see* ADP

Adenosine monophosphate, *see* AMP

Adenosine triphosphate, *see* ATP

Adenosylcobalamin, 697

S-Adenosylhomocysteine, 754, 1063

S-Adenosylmethionine (SAM, AdoMet), 753–754, 966, 1055, 1063, 1064

Adenylate cyclase (AC), 428–429, 432–434, 432F, 434F, 546, 797, 801

Adenylate kinase, 467F, 513–514

Adenylic acid, *see* AMP

Adenylosuccinate, in IMP conversion to AMP/GMP, 822

Adenylosuccinate lyase:
 in IMP conversion to AMP/GMP, 821F
 in IMP synthesis, 819F

Adenylosuccinate synthetase, in IMP conversion to AMP/GMP, 821F

Adenylylation, 766

Adenylyltransferase, 766

ADH (alcohol dehydrogenase reaction), 327

Adipocytes, 248F, 796, 805

Adiponectin, 806, 806F

Adiponectin receptors, 806

Adipose tissue, 248, 454
 brown, 632
 mammalian metabolism in, 793, 794F, **795–796,** 797

A-DNA, 852T
 conformation, 856F–857

AdoMet, *see* *S*-Adenosylmethionine

ADP (adenosine diphosphate), 42
 citric acid cycle regulator, 585
 in glycolysis, 487F, 488

ADP-ATP translocator, 599–600

ADP-glucose, 42, 42F, 561

ADP-glucose pyrophosphorylase, 669

ADPNP, *see* Adenosine-5′(β,γ-imido) triphosphate

Adrenal cortex, 255

Adrenal glands, 255, 406F, 409–410, 799

Adrenaline, *see* Epinephrine

Adrenergic receptors (adrenoreceptors), 409, 551–552
 α-Adrenergic receptors, 409, 552
 β-Adrenergic receptors, 409, 551

Adrenocortical steroids, 410

Adult respiratory distress syndrome, 250

Adverse reactions, 397

Aequorea victoria, 87

Aerobes, 449

Aerobic metabolism, 7, 505, 567F. *See also* Citric acid cycle; Electron transport
 antioxidant mechanisms, **636–637**
 coordinated control, **633–634**
 electron transport in, 597
 in heart, 795
 physiological implications, **634–637**

Affinity chromatography, 97, 101F

Affinity chromatography nucleic acids, 872

Affinity labeling, 348

African sleeping sickness, 504

Agarose gel, 367
 for nucleic acid electrophoresis, 52, 872–873
 for protein chromatography, 98

Aging:
 and free radicals, 636
 and telomerase, 915

Agonists, 409

Agre, P., 306

AICAR (5-Aminoimidazole-4-carboxamide ribonucleotide), 774, 775F, 819F, 820

AICAR transformylase, in IMP synthesis, 819F

AIDS, *see* Acquired immunodeficiency syndrome

AIR carboxylase, in IMP synthesis, 819F, 820

AIR synthetase, in IMP synthesis, 819F

Akt protein, 443F

Ala, *see* Alanine

ALA (δ-aminolevulinic acid), in heme biosynthesis, 776F, 777

Alanine (Ala):
 α helix/β sheet propensities, 140T
 biosynthesis, 764–765F
 breakdown, 747F, 748–751
 as common amino acid, 93
 glucose–alanine cycle, **799,** 799F
 ionizable groups, 76T, 79F
 nonpolar side chain, 79, 79F
 side chain hydropathy, 156T
 transamination, 559
 from tryptophan breakdown, 758, 760F

Alanine transaminase (ALT), 742

Alanine tRNA (tRNA^Ala), 991

β-Alanine, in pyrimidine catabolism, 845F

Alber, T., 881

Alberts, B., 949

Albumin, 685

Alcaptonuria, 477, 762

Alcohol, functional group and linkages, 4T

Alcohol dehydrogenase, 324
 as bisubstrate reaction, 375
 in fructose metabolism, 517F

Alcohol dehydrogenase reaction (ADH), 327

Alcoholic fermentation, 322, **506–509**

Aldehyde, 4T, 330

Alditols, 224

Aldohexoses, 220F

Aldolase:
 in Calvin cycle, 665F
 enzymatic mechanism of, 493
 in glycolysis, 487F, **492–494,** 492F

Aldol cleavage, 492

Aldonic acids, 224

Aldopentoses, 220F

Aldoses, 220F

D-Aldoses, 220F

Aldosterone, 255F, 410

Aldotetroses, 220F

Aldotrioses, 220F

Alkalosis, 36

Alkylacylglycerophospholipids, 716–717

Alkylating agents, mutagenic effects, 918

O[6]-Alkylguanine-DNA alkyltransferase, 921

Alkyltransferases, 921

Allantoic acid, 842F–843

Allantoin, 842F–843

Allantoinase, in uric acid degradation, 842F

Allele, 66

Allis, D., 1060

1,6-Allolactase, 1047

Allopurinol, 843

D-Allose, 220F

Allosteric control:
 enzymes, 324, 386–390, 458
 glycogen phosphorylase, 543, 545
 glycogen synthase, 542–543, 545
 metabolic flux, 457
 phosphofructokinase, 512–513F

Allosteric effectors, 386, 559–560

Allosteric modifiers:
 structural change, 390
Allosteric proteins, **192–194**
Allosterism:
 interactions, allosteric, 192
 sequential model of, 193F
 symmetry model of, 193F
Alloxanthine, 843
Allysine, 139F
Almassy, R., 820
. (Soret) band, 610
β barrel (TIM barrel), 148, 149, 495–496
 helix, **129–132,** 129F, 132F, 265–267
 keratins, 134, 136
 proteins, 148
ALT (alanine transaminase), 742
Alternative name, 324
Alternative splicing, 973–975
Altman, S., 980
-Altrose, 220F
Alu elements, 1043F
Alu family, 1045
Alzheimer's disease, 169–170, 636, 1087
Amanita phalloides, 955
-Amanitin, 955
Amatoxins, 955
Amber codon, 990
Amber suppressor, 1028
Ames, B., 919
Ames test, 919F, 920
Amethopterin, 838
Amides, functional group and linkages, 4T
Amidophosphoribosyl transferase, in IMP
  synthesis, 818, 819F
Amines, 330
 functional group and linkages, 4T
 reaction with carboxylic acids, 3F
Amino acids:
 abbreviations, 76–77T, 81–82
 abundance, 93
 acid–base properties, **81**
 biologically active, **86–89,** 88F
 charged polar side chains, 77T, 78, 80–81
 as chemical messengers, 88
 classification and characteristics, **78–81**
 derivatives in proteins, **86–89,** 86F
 energy recovery by citric acid cycle, 567
 essential, 764T
 general properties, **74–78**
 genetic code specification, 989T
 glucogenic, 747
 hydrophobic effect, 80
 intracellular protein degradation,
  733–735
 ketogenic, 747–748
 nomenclature, 81–82, 82F
 nonessential, 764T
 nonpolar side chains, 76T, 79, 79F
 nutritive importance, 74
 occurrence, 76–77T
 peptide bonds, **78**

pK values of ionizable groups, 76–77T
 specification by codon, 986
 stereochemistry, **82–86**
 structures, **74–82,** 76T
 transport between tissues, 798–799
 uncharged polar side chains, 77T,
  79–80, 79F
α-Amino acids, 74F, 84F
D-Amino acids, **84,** 84–85
L-Amino acids, **84**
L-α-Amino acids, 84
Amino acid biosynthesis:
 citric acid cycle intermediates, 589
 essential amino acids, **769–774**
 mammalian metabolism, 792F–793
 nonessential amino acids, **764–769**
Amino acid breakdown, **747–763,** 747F
 branched-chain amino acids,
  757–758
 common intermediates, 747F
 mammalian metabolism, 792F–793,
  797–798
Amino acid catabolism, 739F
Amino acid deamination, **738–742**
 oxidative, **742**
 transamination, **738–742**
Amino acid derivatives, **86–89**
Amino acid metabolism, 86–89
 heme biosynthesis, **775–778**
 heme degradation, **778–780**
Amino acid residues, 78
 α helix/β sheet propensities, 140T
 conservative substitution, 116
 hydropathics, 156T
 hypervariable, 116
 invariant, 116
 pH effects, 332
 polypeptide chain interior, 81
Amino acid sequencing, see Protein
  sequencing
Amino acid stem (tRNA), 991F
Aminoacrylate, 749
Aminoacyl-adenylate, 994
Aminoacyl (A) site, 1006
Aminoacyl–tRNA (aa-tRNA), 994F–995,
  1009F, 1021
Aminoacyl–tRNA synthetases (aaRSs),
  994–998
 class I vs. class II, 994–995
 organisms lacking, 998
 proofreading (editing) step, 997–998
 and unique structural features of tRNA,
  995–997
p-Aminobenzoic acid, 754
γ-Aminobutyric acid (GABA), 88, 780
Aminoglycosides, 1024
5-Aminoimidazole-4-carboxamide
  ribotide, see AICAR
5-Aminoimidazole-4-(N-succinylocarbox-
  amide) ribotide (SACAIR), in IMP
  synthesis, 819F, 820

5-Aminoimidazole ribotide (AIR), in IMP
  synthesis, 819F, 820
β-Aminoisobutyrate, in pyrimidine
  catabolism, 845F
α-Amino-β-ketobutyrate, 749
α-Amino-β-ketobutyrate lyase, 748F–749
δ-Aminolevulinic acid (ALA), 776F, 777
δ-Aminolevulinic acid synthase, in heme
  biosynthesis, 776F
Aminopterin, 838
Amino sugars, 225
Amino terminus, see N-terminus
Aminotransferase, 739, 845F
Ammonia, 743
Ammonification, 788
Ammonium ion, titration curve, 34F
Ammonium sulfate, for protein salting
  out, 97F
AMP (adenosine monophosphate), 41T
 animal catabolism pathway, 840F
 from IMP, 821F
 synthesis, 819F, **821–822**
AMP deaminase, 840
AMP-dependent protein kinase (AMPK),
  703, 804–805F
Amphibolic pathways, 588
Amphipathic molecules, 28–29
Amphiphilic molecules, 28–29
AMPK, see AMP-dependent protein
  kinase
AMP nucleosidase, catalytic power, 323T
AMPPNP, see Adenosine-5'-(β,γ-imido)
  triphosphate
AmpR gene, 62
Amylase, 231
Amylo-1,6-glucosidase deficiency (Cori's
  disease), 538, 539
Amyloid, 168–169
Amyloid-β protein (Aβ), 169
Amyloidoses, 168
Amylopectin, 230, 544
α-Amylose, 230F, 231F, 544
Amylo-(1,4→1,6)-transglycosylase
  (branching enzyme), 538, **543–544**
Amylo-1,4→1,6-transglycosylase defi-
  ciency (Andersen's disease), 538
Amytal, 603
Anabolic steroids, 411
Anabolism, 448, 457
Anaerobes, 449
Anaerobic gylcolysis, 506
Anaerobic metabolism, 7, 505, 634–635,
  795. See also Fermentation
Anaerobiosis, 488
Analbuminemia, 685
Anaplerotic reactions, 589
Andersen's disease, 538, 539
Androgens, 255F, 410
Anencephaly, 755
Anfinsen, C., 159
Angelman syndrome (AS), 1067

Angina pectoris, 781
Animal cells, 8F
Anion channels, 305
Anion exchangers, in chromatography, 98
Anion-selective pore, 305
Ankyrin, 273F, 274
Ankyrin repeats, 274F
Annealing:
    of DNA, 866
    in DNA manipulation, 61
α Anomers, 222F–223F
Anomeric forms, 222–223
Antagonists, 409
ANT-C (antennapedia complex), 1094
Antenna chlorophyll, 643F
Antennapedia complex (ANT-C), 1094
Antennapedia mutant *(antp)*, 1092
Anteriobithorax mutant *(abx)*, 1092
Anterograde transport, 283
Anthranilate, 773
Antibiotics:
    arsenicals as, 576
    effects on protein synthesis, 1024–1025
    peptidoglycan-specific, 238
    transcription inhibitors, 953–955
    as transition state analogs, 339
    type II topoisomerase inhibitors, 865
Antibiotic-resistant transposons, 938
Antibodies, **209–215**
    binding of, to antigens, **212–214**
    defined, 209
    diversity of, **214**, 1081
    for immunoassays, 95
    interaction of, with antigen, 214F
    monoclonal, 212, 213
    structure, **209–212**
Anticodons, 987
    codon–anticodon interactions, **998–999**
    recognition by aminoacyl-tRNA
        synthetases, 995
Anticodon arm (tRNA), 991F
Anti conformation, 856F
Antifolates, 838
Antigen–antibody binding, **212–214**
Antigens, 95, 209, 214F
Antimycin A, 603
Antioxidants, 636
Antiparallel β sheet, 132–134
Antiparallel strands, DNA, 45
Antiport, 310
Antisense RNA, 1034, 1075
Antisense (noncoding) strand, 944, 945F
Antp (antennapedia) mutant, 1092
Ap$_5$A, 467
Apaf-1 (apoptosis protease-activating
    factor-1), 1090
AP endonuclease, 921
Apical domain, 277
ApoA-I (apolipoprotein A-I), 682
ApoB (apolipoprotein B), 975

ApoB-48 (apolipoprotein B-48), 975
ApoB-100 (apolipoprotein B-100),
    682, 975
Apoenzymes, 327
Apolipoproteins, 682
Apolipoprotein A-I (apoA-I), 682
Apolipoprotein B (apoB), 975
Apolipoprotein B-48 (apoB-48), 975
Apolipoprotein B-100 (apoB-100), 682, 975
Apoproteins, 682
Apoptosis, 420F, 924, 1086
    cellular death, 1082
    essential process, 1086–1087
    extrinsic and intrinsic pathways,
        1088–1089
    programmed cell death, 1086–1087
Apoptosis extrinsic pathway, 1089F
Apoptosis protease-activating factor-1
    (Apaf-1), 1090
Apoptosome, 1090, 1090F
Apoptotic bodies, 1087
Aβ precursor protein (βPP), 169
APRT (Adenine phosphoribosyltrans-
    ferase), 823
APS/Cbl complex, 442
AP sites, 921
Aptamers, 1055
Apurinic (AP) sites, 921
Apyrimidinic (AP) sites, 921
AQP1, 306, 307F
Aquaporins, **306–307**
    kidneys, 306
    lacrimal glands, 306
    salivary glands, 306
    water molecules, 306
Aquaporin AQP1, 306F
Arabidopsis thaliana, 593, 961F
D-Arabinose, 220F
Arachidic acid, 247T
Arachidonic acid, 247T, 259F
Archaea, 9F
Archaeal rhodopsin family, 266
Archaebacteria, 9
Architectural proteins, 1058
Arg, *see* Arginine
Arginase, in urea cycle, 744, 746
Arginine (Arg):
    α helix/β sheet propensities, 140T
    biosynthesis, 768–769
    breakdown, 747F, 751–752F
    charged polar side chain, 80
    genetic code specification, 988, 989T
    ionizable groups, 77T
    as NO precursor, 781
    side chain hydropathy, 156T
    in urea cycle, 744F
Argininosuccinase, in urea cycle, 746
Argininosuccinate, in urea cycle, 744F, 746
Argininosuccinate synthetase, in urea
    cycle, 744, 746

Arg residues, 306, 318
Aromatic amino acid decarboxylase, in
    neurotransmitter synthesis, 781F
Arrhenius, S., 32
ARS (autonomously replicating
    sequences), 912
Arsenate, 528
Arsenicals, 576
Arsenic poisoning, 576
Arsenite, 576
Arthritis, rheumatoid, 215T, 733
Artificial sweeteners, 228
AS (Angelman syndrome), 1067
Ascorbic acid, 137. *See also* Vitamin C
Asn, *see* Asparagine
Asn residues, 307
AsnRS, 998
Asp, *see* Aspartic acid
L-Asparaginase, 751
Asparagine (Asn):
    acid-base catalysis by, 332
    α helix/β sheet propensities, 140T
    biosynthesis, 764–765F
    breakdown, 747F, 751
    covalent catalysis by, 335
    genetic code specification, 989T
    ionizable groups, 77T
    side chain hydropathy, 156T
    uncharged polar side chain, 79
Asparagine synthetase, 765
Aspartame, 228, 762
Aspartate, 80. *See also* Aspartic acid
    from amino acid degradation, 738, 747F
    biosynthesis, 764–765F
    breakdown, 751
    reaction with carbamoyl phosphate, 386
    in urea cycle, 743, 744F
Aspartate aminotransferase, 556
Aspartate/ATCase reaction, 387F
Aspartate transaminase (AST), 742
Aspartate transcarbamoylase (ATCase),
    386–390
    conformational changes, 389F
    in UMP synthesis, 825F
Aspartic acid (Asp):
    α helix/β sheet propensities, 140T
    charged polar side chain, 80, 80F
    genetic code specification, 989T
    ionizable groups, 77T
    side chain hydropathy, 156T
Aspartic protease, 384
Aspartokinase, 770
Aspartyl phosphate residue, 312
Aspartyl-β-phosphate, 770
Aspartyl-tRNA synthetase (AspRS),
    996–997
Aspirin, 719
AspRS (aspartyl-tRNA synthetase),
    996–997
Assays, proteins, 95–97

Assimilation, 782, 786–788

AST (aspartate transaminase), 742

Asthma, 410, 435

Asturias, F., 1056, 1070

Asx, 82. *See also* Asparagine; Aspartic acid

Asymmetric centers, 83

Ataxia telangiectasia (ATM), 1084

ATCase, *see* Aspartate transcarbamoylase

Atherosclerosis, 727–728. *See also* Myocardial infarction

ATM (ataxia telangiectasia), 1084

ATP (adenosine triphosphate), 42. *See also* Electron transport; Oxidative phosphorylation
  AMP-to-ATP ratio, 804
  ATCase inhibition, 387
  biological importance, 460–461
  in Calvin cycle, 664, 665F
  chemical potential energy, 42
  coupled reactions involving, 463, 463T
  dissipation in dark reactions, 641, 664, 672–673F
  DNA ligase activation, 907F
  free energy of phosphate hydrolysis, 461T
  in fructose metabolism, 517F
  in galactose metabolism, 519F
  in gluconeogenesis, 553F, 554F, 557–558
  in glycolysis, 486–492, 487F, 490–491, 499, 503–504
  group transfer, **460–462**
  hydrolysis by type II topoisomerases, 863–864
  in mannose metabolism, 520F
  metabolic role overview, 451F
  and muscle contraction, 510, 795
  production control, **631–634**
  production in light reactions, 641, 647, 650–651F, 661–663
  regeneration, 464–465, 631
  and standard free energy, 462

ATPase(s), 165
  A-type, 311
  Ca^{2+}–, 313–314F
  F-type, 311
  P-type, 311
  $(Na^{+}$-$K^{+})$–, 311F–313, 316
  V-type, 311

ATP-cassette binding protein A1 (ABCA1), 729

ATP-citrate lyase, in fatty acid synthesis, 702

ATP-driven active transport, **311–314**

ATP driven complexes, 1056

ATP hydrolysis, 311, 313

ATP mass action ratio, 631

ATP synthase (F_1F_0-ATPase), 618, **622–629**
  binding change mechanism, 624–629
  chloroplasts, 661

F_0 component, 623–624

F_1 component, 622–623

ATR protein kinase, 1086

Attenuators, **1051–1054**

A-type ATPases, 311

Autocatalytic trypsinogen activation, 357

Autoimmune diseases, **214–215**, 811

Autoinhibitor segments, 433

Autolysis, 357

Automated DNA sequencing, **55–56**

Autonomously replicating sequences (ARS), 912

Autophosphorylation, 413

Autoradiography, 367
  colony hybridization application, 64
  protein purification application, 102
  sequencing gel, 55F

Autotrophs, 449

Avery, O., 48

Avidin, 481

Avogadro's number, 13

Azathioprine, 844

3′-Azido-3′-deoxy thymidine (AZT, zidovudine), 384

Azotobacter vinelandii, 783

AZT (3′-Azido-3′-deoxythymidine, zidovudine), 384

B

BACs, *see* Bacterial artificial chromosomes

Bacillus anthracis, 444–445

Bacillus stearothermophilus, 512

Bacitracin, 563

Backbone, proteins, 127–129

Bacteria. *See also specific headings, e.g.:* Photosynthetic bacteria
  cell walls, **235–238**, 236F, 237F
  evolutionary studies, **9–11**
  fatty acids, 247
  gene insertion sequences, 1043–1044
  lipid bilayer fluidity modification, 262–263
  lysozyme action, 339–340
  microfossil, 2F
  tetracycline-resistant, 1025
  transformed pneumococci, 48F

Bacterial artificial chromosomes (BACs), 61

Bacterial biofilms, 234

Bacterial oxalate transporter, 310

Bacteriochlorophyll *a* (BChl *a*), 642F

Bacteriochlorophyll *b* (BChl *b*), 642F

Bacteriophages, 51

Bacteriophage 434, repressor, 876–877F

Bacteriophage λ, 60, 63F

Bacteriophage SP01, 947

Bacteriophage T4:
  genetic code, 986
  wild-type reversion rate, 909

Bacteriopheophytin (BPheo), 647

Bacteriorhodopsin, 265F
  proton pumping in, 608–609
  structure, 265F–266

Baker's yeast *(Saccharomyces cerevisiae):*
  codon usage bias, 999
  DNA chips, 479F
  80S rRNA, 1008F
  proteins from, 94

Baltimore, D., 912

*Bam*HI–DNA complex, 876

B antigens, 242F

Banting, F., 475, 811, 812

Barcroft, J., 191

Barnett, J., 307

Barr bodies, 1057F

Bases, 32–34
  conjugate acids, 32
  nucleotide, *see* Nucleotide bases
  strength, 33–34

Base excision repair (BER), **921–923**

Base-flipping, 921

Base pairs (bp), 46, 47, 851F

Basic helix–loop–helix (bHLH), 726, 882–883

Basic solutions, 31

Basolateral domain, 277

Bassham, J., 663

Bcd (bicoid) gene, 1092

B cells (B lymphocytes), 209

BChl *a* (bacteriochlorophyll *a*), 642F

BChl *b* (bacteriochlorophyll *b*), 642F

Bcl-2 family, 1089

B-DNA, 849, 851, 852T
  conformation, 850, 856F–857
  dimer stacking energies, 868T

Beadle, G., 49

Becker muscular dystrophy (BMD), 205

Beer–Lambert law, 95

Behenic acid, 247T

Benson, A., 663

Benzoic acid, 686

BER (base excision repair), **921–923**

Berg, P., 997

Beriberi, 509

Berman, H., 138

Bernal, J. D., 125, 182, 697

Berson, S. A., 408

Best, C., 475, 811, 812

βαβ Motif, 146

β anomers, 223F

β (Soret) band, 610

β barrels, 148
  transmembrane protein, 267

β bends, 134

β bulge, 139

β cells, pancreatic, *see* Pancreatic β cells

β-clamp, 630, 906

β hairpin motif, 146

β keratins, 134–136

β oxidation, 686, **688–690,** 698

βPP, *see* Aβ precursor protein
β propeller, 431
β proteins, 148
β sheet, **132–134**, 132F, 133F
β subunit, 906
b_H (cytochrome b_{562}), 148, 612
BHA, 290–291, 290F, 291F
bHLH (basic helix–loop–helix), 726, 882–883
Bibliome, 478
Bicarbonate:
  as buffer, 36
  role in carbon dioxide transport, 189
Bicoid (bcd) gene, 1092
Bicoid protein, 1092
Bidirectional replication, 894
Bilayers, *see* Lipid bilayers
Bile acids, 678, 678F
  cholesterol conversion to, 725
  and lipid absorption, 630
Bile salts, 678, 678F
Bilirubin, in heme degradation, 778, 779F
Biliverdin, in heme degradation, 778, 779F
Bimolecular nucleophilic substitution reactions, 336–337
Bimolecular reactions, 336–337, 365
Binding change mechanism, 624–629
Bioavailability, and toxicity, 396
Biochemical constants, 13
Biochemical signaling:
  and heterotrimeric G proteins, **428–436**
  and metabolic regulation, 803–804
  and phosphoinositide pathway, **436–445**
  and receptor tyrosine kinases, **412–428**
Biochemistry, 1, 13
Biocytin, 318T, 554
Biofilms, 234
Bioinformatics, **151–154**
Biological membranes, *see* Membranes
Biomolecule bond energies, 25T
Biopterin, 760
Biosphere, energy flow in, 18F
Biosynthetic pathways, 452
Biotin, 480–481
Biotin group, 554, 555F
Biotinyllysine, 554, 555F
1,3-Bisphosphoglycerate (1,3-BPG), 465
  in Calvin cycle, 665F, 666
  free energy of phosphate hydrolysis, 461T
  in gluconeogenesis, 553F
  in glycolysis, 487F, 497–499
2,3-Bisphosphoglycerate (2,3-BPG):
  binding of, to fetal hemoglobin, 191
  and blood oxygen carrying capacity, 502
D-2,3-Bisphosphoglycerate (BPG), 191
Bisphosphoglycerate mutase, 502
2,3-Bisphosphoglycerate phosphatase, 502
Bisubstrate reactions (enzyme kinetics), **375–376**, 375F

Bithorax complex (BX-C), 1094
Bithorax mutant *(bx)*, 1092
b_L (cytochrome b_{566}), 612
Black, J., 844
Blackburn, E., 914
Blastocyst, 1066
Blastoderm, 1090
Blobel, G., 280, 1008
Bloch, K., 701, 721
Blood-brain barrier, 396
Blood buffering, 35–36
Blood coagulation:
  cascade, 358–359
  multidomain protein, 120F
Blood glucose:
  allowable levels, 794
  glucagon secretion and, 797
  and gluconeogenesis, 559F
  and liver glucose conversion to G6P, 796–797
  normal vs. non-insulin-dependent diabetics, 813F
Blood oxygen carrying capacity, 502
Bloodstream, 793
  fatty acid release into, 796
  triacylglycerol release into, 797
Blood types, 242
Blow, D., 351
Blue-green algae, *see* Cyanobacteria
Blunt ends, 52
Blunt end ligation, 908
B lymphocytes (B cells), 209
BMD (Becker muscular dystrophy), 205
Bohr, C., 189
Bohr effect, 189–190
Boltzmann constant (k_B), 13, 372
Bonaparte, N., 576
Bond energies, 25T
BoNT/A (botulinum neurotoxin A), 288
BoNT/G (botulinum neurotoxin G), 288
Bordetella pertussis, 435
Botulism, 288
Bovine carboxypeptidase A, 134F
Bovine chymotrypsinogen, hydropathic index plot, 157F
Bovine Complex I, 605F
Bovine cytochrome *c*, 612
Bovine cytochrome *c* oxidase, 616F
Bovine F_1-ATPase, 623F
Bovine insulin, 92F, 104
Bovine pancreatic RNase A, 333F
Bovine pancreatic trypsin inhibitor (BPTI), 356F
Bovine protein kinase A, 433F
Bovine rhodopsin, 429F
Bovine spongiform encephalopathy (BSE, mad cow disease), 169, 171
Boyer, H., 61
Boyer, P., 625
bp, *see* Base pairs

1,3-BPG, *see* 1,3-Bisphosphoglycerate
2,3-BPG, *see* 2,3-Bisphosphoglycerate
BPheo (bacteriopheophytin), 647
B protein, 971
BPTI (bovine pancreatic trypsin inhibitor), 356F
Bradford assay, 96
Brain:
  blood–brain barrier, 396
  mammalian metabolism in, **793–794**, 794F
Branched-chain amino acid degradation, 757–758
Branched-chain α-keto acid dehydrogenase, 580, 757
Branching enzyme (amylo-(1,4→1,6)-transglycosylase), 538, **543–544**
Branch migration, 927F, 928
Branden, C.-I., 667
Braunstein, A., 740
BRCA1, 934
BRCA2, 934
BRE, 959F
Breaker, R., 1055
Breathing, 158
Brenner, S., 986
Briggs, G. E., 369
Brittle bone disease, 137
Broad beans, 526
Broad-spectrum antibiotics, 1025
Brodsky, B., 138
Bromodomains, 1061–1063
5-Bromouracil (5BU), 940
Brønsted, J., 32
Brown, A., 366
Brown adipose tissue, 632
Brown fat, 632
BSE (bovine spongiform encephalopathy), 169
b-type cytochromes, 611–612
Bubonic plague, 426
Buchanan, J., 818
Buchner, E., 322
Buffers, **34–36**
Buffering capacity, 36
Bundle-sheath cells, 674
Bunick, G., 885
Burk, D., 373
Burley, S., 961, 962
αβ-trans-Butenoyl-ACP, 705F
N-Butyldeoxynojirimycin, 721
Butyramide, 319
Butyryl-ACP, in fatty acid synthesis, 705F
BX-C (bithorax complex), 1094
Bx (bithorax) mutant, 1092

C

C, *see* Cytosine
C2′-*endo* conformation, 856F
C3′-*endo* conformation, 856F

3G, 443F

$_3$ plants, 674

$_4$ cycle, 673–674

$_4$ plants, 674

Ca, *See under* Calcium

CA1P (2-carboxyarabinitol-1-
phosphate), 671

Ca^{2+} ion:
and calmodulin, 439–440
citric acid cycle control, 587
and glycogen breakdown control,
546–547
with metal-activated enzymes, 335
with proteins, 93
and tropomyosin, 207F
vitamin D control of, 256–257

Ca^{2+}–ATPase (Ca^{2+} pump), 313–314F

Cadmium (Cd^{2+}) ion, Zn^{2+} ion
replacement, 326

Caenorhabditis elegans, 418, 1075, 1076

Caffeine, 435

Cahn, R., 85

Cahn–Ingold–Prelog (*RS*) system, 85

CAIR (Carboxyaminoimidazole ribotide),
in IMP synthesis, 819F, 820

Cairns, J., 894, 919

CAK (cdk-activating kinase), 1082

Calcineurin (PP2B), 428

Calcium, and muscle contraction, 207.
See also under Ca

Calf thymus histones, 884T

Calmodulin (CaM), 438–440, 547

Calnexin, 1033

Calreticulin, 1033

Calvin, M., 663

Calvin cycle (reductive pentose phosphate
cycle), 663–669F, 664F, 665F
control, 670–671
free energy changes for reactions, 670T

CaM (calmodulin), 438–440, 547

CAM (crassulacean acid metabolism), 675

Cambillau, C., 679

Camels, fat storage in hump of, 677

cAMP (adenosine-3′,5′-cyclic monophosphate), 428, 546, 712

cAMP-dependent protein kinase (cAPK),
432, 546

CAM plants, 674–675

cAMP-phosphodiesterases
(cAMP-PDEs), 436

cAMP receptor protein, 1050–1051, 1051F

Cancer, 488
abnormal DNA methylation patterns, 1067
L-asparaginase as anticancer agent, 751
gangliosides and, 253
and oncogenes, 421
and telomerase, 915
thymidylate synthesis inhibition, 838
type II topoisomerases as anticancer
agent, 865

Candida albicans, 594

Cantor, C., 873

CAP (Cbl-associated protein), 443F

CAP (catabolite activator protein, cAMP
receptor protein), 1050–1051, 1051F

Cap-binding protein, 1014

Capillaries, oxygen transport in, 189–190

Capillary electrophoresis (CE), 103

cAPK (cAMP-dependent protein kinase),
432, 546

Capping, 915

Capping enzyme, 966

Cap structure, eukaryotic mRNA, 966F

CapZ, 205

Carbamate, 190, 745

N-Carbamoylaspartate, 386

Carbamoyl aspartate, in UMP synthesis,
825F

Carbamoyl phosphate, 460
reaction with aspartate, 386
in UMP synthesis, 825F
in urea cycle, 743, 744F, 745

Carbamoyl phosphate, in urea cycle, 695

Carbamoyl phosphate synthetase (CPS) I,
in urea cycle, 743, 745

Carbamoyl phosphate synthetase (CPS)
II, in UMP synthesis, 824–825F

Carbinolamine intermediate, 330

Carbohydrates, 219–242. *See also*
Glycoprotein(s); Monosaccharides;
Oligosaccharides; Polysaccharides
catabolism overview, 452F
defined, 219
energy recovery by citric acid cycle, 567
Fischer convention: D and L sugars, 221
in gangliosides, 253F
metabolism in liver, 796
from photosynthesis, 640–641, 663–675
and recognition events, 219, 241–242

Carbohydrate recognition markers, 286

Carbon, oxidation states of, 453

α Carbon, amino acids, 74–75, 83

Carbon—carbon bonds, 453

Carbon dioxide:
from C$_4$ cycle, 673–674
permeability to intermembrane
space, 599
from photorespiration, 671–675
in photosynthesis, 640–641, 663–664

Carbon fixation, by photosynthesis, 640

Carbonic anhydrase, 189
catalytic power, 323T
Michaelis–Menten parameters, 371T
Zn^{2+} role in, 336F

Carbon monoxide dehydrogenase, 693

Carboxymethylcysteine, 497

Carboxyaminoimidazole ribotide (CAIR),
in IMP synthesis, 819F, 820

2-Carboxyarabinitol-1-phosphate
(CA1P), 671

γ-Carboxyglutamate, 86F

Carboxyl group, 26F

Carboxylic acids:
functional group and linkages, 4T
reaction with amines, 3F

Carboxyl terminus, *see* C-terminus

Carboxymethylcysteine, 497

Carboxymethyl (CM) groups, in cation
exchangers, 98

Carboxypeptidase A:
β sheet, bovine, 134F
catalytic power, 323T

2-Carboxypropyl-CoA, 694, 694F

Carcinogens, **919–920**

Cardiac glycosides, 313

Cardiolipin, 716

Carnitine, 687

Carnitine palmitoyl transferase I, 687, 805

Carnitine palmitoyl transferase II, 687

β-Carotene, 69, 257, 645

Carotenoids, 643F, 645

Carriers, 297

Carrier ionophores, 297

Cartilage, 235

Caspases, apoptosis participation,
1087–1088

Caspases (cysteinyl aspartate-specific
proteases), 1087

Caspase-3, 1088

Caspase-7, 1088, 1088F

Caspase-8, 1088

Caspase-9, 1090

Caspase-10, 1088

Caspase-activated DNase, 1088

Cassette exons, 974

CAT (chloramphenicol acetyltransferase),
1068

Catabolism, 448
overview, 452F
purine ribonucleotides, **839–842**
thermodynamics, 457

Catabolite gene activator protein (CAP),
1050–1051, 1051F

Catabolite repression, **1050–1051**

Catalase, 324, 371T, 636

Catalysis:
electrostatic, 337
lysozyme mechanism, 344
proximity/orientation effects, 336–338

Catalysts, 6, 19. *See also* Enzymes

Catalytic constant, 371

Catalytic mechanism:
chymotrypsin, 352–357
lysozyme, 343–347

Catalytic perfection, 496

Catalytic triad, 350F–351

Cataracts:
and diabetes, 811F
and galactitol, 519

Catechol, 409, 780

Catecholamines, 409, 780–781F, 801
Catenation, 860F
CATH (database), 153
Cathepsins, 733
Cathepsin D, 286
Cation channels, 305–306
Cation exchanger, in chromatography, 98
Caveolae, 278
Caveolins, 278
CCAAT box, 959
CCVs (clathrin-coated vesicles), 284–285, 285F, 685
Cd^{2+} ion, Zn^{2+} ion replacement, 326
Cdks (cyclin-dependent protein kinases), 1082
Cdk2 (cyclin-dependent protein kinase 2), 1082
Cdk4/6-cyclin D complexes, 1086
Cdk7 (cyclin-dependent protein kinase 7), 1082
Cdk-activating kinase (CAK), 1082
cDNA (complementary DNA), 912
CDP–Diacylglycerol, 716
CDP–glucose, 561
CE (capillary electrophoresis), 103
CE (computer program), 153
Cech, T., 977–978
Celecoxib (Celebrex), 398, 719
Cells. *See also* Cancer; Eukaryotes; Prokaryotes
   components, 6–7F
   evolution, **5–7**
   lysing in protein purification, 94
   metabolic pathways in, 453–455
   microfilaments in nonmuscle, 207–209
Cell–cell recognition:
   cell-surface carbohydrates, 241–242
   gangliosides and, 253
Cell cycle, 883, 1081–1084
Cell cycle arrest, 1086
Cell membranes, 5–6, 8F. *See also* Membranes
Cell nucleus, 8F
Cell signaling, *see* Signal transduction
Cellular immunity, 209
Cellulase, 230
Cellulose, 228, **228–230,** 229F
Cell wall(s):
   bacterial, **235–238,** 236F, 237F
   Chaetomorpha, 229F
Central dogma of molecular biology, 49, 849, 942, 985
Centrioles, 8F
Centromeres, 1043
Ceramides, 252
   biosynthesis, 718F
   in sphingoglycolipid degradation, 720F
Cerebrosides, 252, 717, 718
CF_1CF_0 complex, 661

CFTR (cystic fibrosis transmembrane conductance regulator), 315–316
cGMP, 436
cGMP–PDEs, 436
CGN (cis Golgi network), 282
C_H (constant region), 212
C_H1, 212
C_H2, 212
C_H3, 212
Chain elongation:
   polypeptide synthesis, **1008–1010**
   RNA polymerase, **947–950**
Chain initiation:
   polypeptide synthesis, **1010–1014,** 1013F
Chain initiation codons, 990–991
Chain termination:
   polypeptide synthesis, **1026–1028,** 1026F
   RNA polymerase, **950–952**
Chain-terminator method, nucleic acid sequencing, **53–56,** 54F
Chair conformation, 342F
Chamberlin, M., 950
Changeux, J.-P., 193
Channels, 297
Channel-forming ionophores, 297
Channel-forming proteins, 267
Channeling, 745–746, 774
Chaotropic agents, 159, 263–264
Chaperones, molecular, 165–168
Chaperonins, 165–166
Chargaff, E., 44, 48
Chargaff's rules, 44, 47, 48
Charifson, P., 1088
Checkpoints, cell cycle, 1082
Chemical energy, transformation of light energy to, **645–647**
Chemical equilibria, *see* Equilibrium
Chemical evolution, **3–5**
Chemical kinetics, **364–366.** *See also* Enzyme kinetics
Chemical mutagenesis, **916–919**
Chemical potential, 16, 296
Chemical potential difference, membranes, 296
Chemical protons, 618
Chemiosmotic theory, **618–622**
Chemolithotrophs, 449
Cheng, Xiaodong, 1065
Chicken, muscle troponin, 204F
Chimera, 61
Chipman, D., 346
Chiral centers, 83
Chirality, 83
Chiral organic synthesis, 86
Chi sequence, 930
Chitin, 230
Chk2 (activated protein kinase), 1084
Chl *a* (chlorophyll *a*), 642F
Chl *b* (chlorophyll *b*), 642F
Chloramphenicol, 1025

Chloramphenicol acetyltransferase (CAT), 1068
Chloride ions, and transmembrane movement, 305
Chlorocruorins, 181
Chlorophylls, 642F, 643–645
   absorption spectra, 643F
   antenna, 643F
   electronic states, 646F
Chlorophyll *a* (Chl *a*), 642F
Chlorophyll *b* (Chl *b*), 642F
Chloroplasts, 8, **641–645,** 641F
   evolution, 10
   light-absorbing pigments, **643–645**
   oxygen generation, 655F
   oxygen yield per flash, 655F
   thylakoid membrane, **641–642**
Chloroquine, 394
Chocolate, 435
Cholecalciferol (Vitamin D_3), 256
Cholera toxin, 253, 435
Cholesterol, 254
   biosynthesis, **721–725**
   isotopic tracer studies, 476
   as membrane fluidity modulator, 262–263
   synthesis regulation, **725–727**
   transport, 683F, **727,** 729, 729F
   uses, 725
Cholesteryl esters, 254, 725
Cholesteryl stearate, 254
Choline, 349, 715, 249T
Chondroitin-4-sulfate, 232F
Chondroitin-6-sulfate, 232F
Chorea, 1045
Chorismate, 773
Chorismate mutase, catalytic power, 323T
Chou, P., 140, 163
Chromatin, 8F
   ATP-driven complexes, 1056
   electron micrograph, 887F
   higher level organization, **887–890**
   histones, **884,** 884T
   nucleosomes, **884–887,** 885F
   structure, 889F, **1055–1067**
Chromatin decondensation, 1060
Chromatin filaments, 887F–888
Chromatin-remodeling complexes, 1056–1058
Chromatography:
   affinity, 97, 101
   gel filtration, 97, **100–101**
   high-performance liquid (HPLC), 98
   hydrophobic interaction, 97
   hydroxyapatite, 872
   immunoaffinity, 101
   ion exchange, **97,** 99F
   metal chelate affinity, 101
   molecular sieve, **100–101**
   nucleic acids, **872**

proteins, **101**
size exclusion, **100–101**
chromodomains, 1064
chromophore, 96
chromosomes, 47, 883F
  eukaryotic, **883–890**
  histone-depleted metaphase, 888F
  histones, **884**, 884T
  recombination, 938F
  replication of linear, 914F
chromosome inactivation, 1057
chronic myelogenous leukemia (CML),
  424–425
chylomicrons, 681, 809
chylomicron remnants, 683
chymotrypsin, 1068
  activation effects on active site, 358
  active site, 348, 352F
  catalytic mechanism, **352–357**
  function, 348
  geometric specificity, 326
  polypeptide degradation, 738
  specificity, 107T, 351
  tosyl-L-phenylalanine chloromethyl-
    ketone binding, 348
  X-ray structure, 348–352
chymotrypsinogen, 351
  activation effects on active site, 358
  hydropathic index plot, bovine, 157F
cigarette smoking, protease inhibitor
  effects, 356
ciliated protozoa, alternative genetic code
  in, 991
Cinchona tree, 394
ciprofloxacin, 444, 865
circular duplex DNA, 857F
cis cisternae, 282
cis conformation, 127
cis Golgi network (CGN), 282
cisternae, 282
cisternal progression, 283
cistron, 945
citrate, 325, 567
  in amino acid degradation, 747F
  in citric acid cycle, 568F, 578–579, 584F
  in glyoxylate cycle, 591F
citrate synthase:
  citric acid cycle, **577–578**
  in citric acid cycle, 568F
  in glyoxylate cycle, 591F
citric acid cycle (Krebs cycle, tricarboxylic
  acid cycle, TCA cycle), 452
  acetyl-CoA synthesis, **570–574**
  aconitase, **578–579**, 587
  amino acid degradation, 747F
  amphibolic functions, 588F
  citrate synthase, **577–578**, 586
  coordinated control, 634F
  electron transport sites, 597F
  energy-producing capacity, 584

evolution, 592–593
fumarase, **583**
and gluconeogenesis, 556
glyoxylate cycle, **590–594**, 591F
α-ketoglutarate dehydrogenase in,
  585–587, 586T
malate dehydrogenase in, 568F, **583**
NAD$^+$-dependent isocitrate dehydrogenase in, **579–580**, 579F, 586–587
pathways using citric acid cycle
  intermediates, **588–589**
products of, 584F
purine nucleotide, 841
pyruvate dehydrogenase in, 568F,
  570–573
related reactions, **588–591**
replenishment of citric acid cycle
  intermediates, **589–590**
succinate dehydrogenase in, 568F,
  582, 582F
succinyl-CoA synthetase in, 568F,
  580–582, 581F
Citrulline, in urea cycle, 744F, 746
Citryl-CoA, 578
CJD (Cruetzfeldt–Jakob disease),
  169–170
CKIs (cyclin-dependent kinase
  inhibitors), 1083
Cl$^-$ (chloride), 299
C$_L$ (constant region), 212
Clamp loader, 906–907
Class I aminoacyl-tRNA synthetases,
  994–995
Class II aminoacyl-tRNA synthetases,
  994–995
Class II genes, 1067
Class II gene promoters, 1069
Classification number (enzymes), 324–325
Clathrin, 284
Clathrin-coated pits, 685
Clathrin-coated vesicles (CCVs), 284–285,
  285F, 685
Clathrin flexible cage, 285–286
Clathrin light chain (LCa), 275
Clathrin light chain (LCb), 275
Clay, and chemical evolution, 3
ClC Cl$^-$ channels, 305–306, 305F
Cl$^-$ channels, 305–306
Cleavage and polyadenylation specificity
  factor (CPSF), 966
Cleland, W. W., 375
Clinical trials, 396–398
Clones, 60
Cloned DNA, and selection, 61–62
Cloning, 51
  inclusion bodies, 94F
  shotgun, 63
  techniques, 60–62
Cloning vectors, 60–61
Closed systems, 18

Clostridium botulinim, 917
Clotting, *see* Blood coagulation
Clp, 737
ClpA, 737
ClpP, 737
ClpX, 737
CM (carboxymethyl) groups, in cation
  exchangers, 98
CML (chronic myelogenous leukemia),
  424–425
CMP (cytidine monophosphate), 41T, 845F
Cn3D (computer program), 154
Co^{2+}, as cofactor, 335
CoA, *see* Coenzyme A
Coactivators, 1061
Coagulation, *see* Blood coagulation
Coagulation cascade, 358–359
CoA moiety, 1061
CoASH, *see* Coenzyme A
Coated vesicles, 283
  clathrin, 284–285
  protein transportation, 283–285
Coatomer, 285
Cobalamin, 692
Cobalamin coenzymes, 693
Cobra venom enzyme, 251F
Cochaperones, 165
Cockayne syndrome (CS), 924
Coding (sense) strand, 945F
Codons, 986, 989T
  chain initiation, 990–991
  evolution, 990
  frequently used, 999
  phenotypically silent, 990
  Stop, 974, 990, 1026
  synonyms, 989–990
Codon–anticodon interactions, **998–999**
Coenzymes, **327–328**
Coenzyme A (CoA, CoASH), 451–452,
  468–469, 569. *See also* Acetyl-CoA
Coenzyme Q (ubiquinone), 257, 606F
Coenzyme Q$_6$, 606
Coenzyme Q$_8$, 606
Coenzyme Q$_{10}$, 606
Coenzyme Q–cytochrome *c* oxidoreduc-
  tase, *see* Complex III
Coenzyme QH·, 606F
Coenzyme QH$_2$, 606F, 621
Cofactors, **326–328**
  metal ions as, 335–336
  prosthetic groups, 327
Cohen, P., 743
Cohen, S., 61
Coils, polypeptides, 139
Coiled coil structure, 134–135, 135F
Cointegrate, 937F
Colipase, 679
Collagen, 98T, 136–139F, 232
Collagen diseases, 137
Colligative properties, 29

Collins, F., 56, 57

Collip, J., 812

Colony hybridization, 64F–65

Colony-stimulating factors, genetically engineered, 67T

Combinatorial chemistry, 395

Compartmentation, cells, 5, 6F

Competition, 309

Competitive enzyme inhibition, **377–381,** 379F–380F

Competitive inhibitors, 377, 379

Complementarity, 5, 5F
  electronic, 325
  geometric, 325

Complementary base pairing, DNA, 46F

Complementary DNA (cDNA), 912

Complex I (NADH–coenzyme Q oxidoreductase), 602–603, **604–609**
  coenzymes of, 605–606
  electrons in, 606–607
  hydrophilic domain of, 607F
  reduction potentials, 604F

Complex II (succinate–coenzyme Q oxidoreductase), 602–603, 604F, **609–611**

Complex III (coenzyme Q–cytochrome c oxidoreductase; cytochrome bc_1), 602–603, 604F, **611–615,** 649–650

Complex IV (cytochrome c oxidase), 602–603, **615–618**
  control, 631
  reduction potentials, 604F

Complex V (ATP synthase; proton-pumping ATP synthase; F_1F_0-ATPase), 618, **622–629**

Composite transposons, 936F

Concerted acid–base catalyzed reactions, 331

Condensation reactions, 3, 78, 78F

Congenital erythropoietic porphyria, 778

Conjugate acids, 32

Conjugate bases, 32

Conjugate redox pair, 471

Connexins, 307, 308

Connexons, 308

Conservative replication, 893

Conservative substitution, amino acid residues, 116

Constant region (C_H), 212

Constant region (C_L), 212

Constitutive enzymes, 950

Contour length, 883

Contour maps, 141–142

Controlled rotation mechanism, 860, 862–863

Convergent evolution, 352

Coomassie brilliant blue, 96

Cooperative oxygen binding, 186–194

Cooperativity:
  hemoglobin oxygen binding, **186–194**
  protein denaturation, 158
  synergy, 1069

Cooperman, B., 833

COPI, 284–285

COPII, 285

Coproporphyrinogen III, in heme biosynthesis, 776F

Coproporphyrinogen oxidase, in heme biosynthesis, 776F

CoQ, *see* Coenzyme Q

Cordycepin, 983

Core, two-domain, 1049

Core enzyme, 943, 947

Core histones, posttranslational modifications, 1059

Corepressors, 1051

Core promoter element, 958

Core proteins, 234–235F

Corey, R., 127, 130, 132

Cori, C., 533, 798

Cori, G., 533, 798

Cori cycle, **798,** 798F

Cori's disease, 538, 539

Corn:
  chloroplast, 641F
  evolution, 59F
  transposition in, 934–935

Corrin ring, 693

Cortex, 409

Cortisol, 255F, 410

Cosubstrates, 327
  nicotinamide adenine dinucleotide (NAD^+), 327
  nicotinamide adenine dinucleotide phosphate ($NADP^+$), 327

Coulomb (unit), 13

Coupled enzymatic reactions, 95

Coupled reactions, high-energy compounds in, **462–464**

Covalent bond energies, 25T

Covalent catalysis, **333–335**

Covalent modification:
  enzymes, 324
  glycogen phosphorylase, 534, **546**
  glycogen synthase, **545, 550**
  for metabolic flux control, 458
  protein phosphorylation, 390–393
  proteins, 93
  pyruvate dehydrogenase, 585

COX, 718

COX-1, 719

COX-2, 719

COX-3, 719

Coxibs, 719

CP43 (PsbC), 653

CP47 (PsbB), 653

CpG islands, 918, 958, 1040
  chromosome inactivation, 1057
  palindromes, 1065

CPSF (cleavage and polyadenylation specificity factor), 966

CPS I, 743–745

CPS II, 745

Cramer, W., 656

Crassulacean acid metabolism (CAM), 67.

Creatine kinase, 466, 513

Creatine phosphate, 460

Crick, F., 44, 49, 126, 200, 849–850F, 850, 893, 942, 986, 990

Cristae, 598

CrkII, 443F

Crohn's disease, 215T

Crossing-over, 927F

Cross talk, 421

Cruciforms, 891

Cruetzfeldt–Jakob disease (CJD), 169–170

Cryoelectron microscopy (cryo-EM), 1002

Cryptic splice sites, 974

CS (Cockayne syndrome), 924

CTCF, 1070

CTD (C-terminal domain), 391F, 955–956

C-terminal α helix, 1049

C-terminal cytoplasmic domain, 303

C-terminal domain (CTD), 391F, 955–956

C-terminus (carboxyl terminus), 78
  dynamics, 158
  as working end of polypeptide synthesis 1008–1009

CTP (cytidine triphosphate):
  ATCase inhibition, 387
  synthesis, **826**

CTP synthetase, 826–827F

c-type cytochromes, 150

CuA center, cytochrome c oxidase, 616

CuB, cytochrome c oxidase, 617

Cubic symmetry, 155F

Cu ion:
  as cofactor, 326, 335
  Cu_A center, 616
  Cu_B, cytochrome c oxidase, 617

Curie, E., 408

Curved arrow notation, 330

Cushing's syndrome, 256

Cutaneous anthrax, 444

C-value paradox, 1038

Cyanide (CN^-), 603

Cyanobacteria, 640, 643F, 645. *See also* Photosynthetic bacteria

Cyanogen bromide, 108F

Cyanosis, 194

Cyclic symmetry, 155

Cyclins, 1082–1084

Cyclin A, 1082

Cyclin-dependent kinase inhibitors (CKIs), 1083

Cyclin-dependent protein kinases (Cdks), 1082

Cyclin H, 1082

Cyclooxygenase, 718

Cyclopentanoperhydrophenanthrene, 254

Cyclosporin A, 428

Cys, *see* Cysteine
Cys$_2$–His$_2$ zinc finger, 158F
Cys$_2$–His$_2$ zinc finger, 879F–881
Cys$_6$ zinc finger, 879F–881
CysRS, 998
Cystathionine, 754
Cysteine (Cys):
  acid–base catalysis by, 332
  α helix/β sheet propensities, 140T
  biosynthesis, 769
  breakdown, 747F, 748–751
  covalent catalysis by, 335
  disulfide bonds, 80F
  genetic code specification, 989T
  as rare amino acid, 93
  side chain hydropathy, 156T
Cysteine proteases, 1087
Cysteinyl aspartate-specific proteases
    (caspases), 1087
Cystic fibrosis, 56
Cystic fibrosis transmembrane conduc-
    tance regulator (CFTR), 315–316
Cyt, *see* Cytosine
Cytidine, 41T, 845F
Cytidine deaminase, 845F, 976
Cytidine monophosphate (CMP),
    41T, 845F
Cytidine triphosphate, *see* CTP
Cytochromes:
  function, 610–611
  heme prosthetic group, 327
Cytochrome *a*, 616
Cytochrome *a*$_3$, 616
Cytochrome *b*, 611–612
Cytochrome *b*$_6$, 656
Cytochrome *b*$_6$*f* complex, 650–651F,
    656–657, 656F
Cytochrome *b*$_{559}$, 653
Cytochrome *b*$_{560}$, 610
Cytochrome *b*$_{562}$ (*b*$_H$), 148, 612
Cytochrome *b*$_{566}$ (*b*$_L$), 612
Cytochrome *bc*$_1$, *see* Complex III
Cytochrome *c*, 150, 151F, 602–603,
    649F–650, 1089–1090
  in apoptosis, 1089–1090
  electron transport, 602–605
  evolution, **114–117**, 119F
  isoelectric point, 98T
  occurrence, 150
  as peripheral membrane protein, 269
  phylogenetic tree, 116–117F
  side chain location, horse heart, 147F
  as soluble electron carrier, 615
  species, 114–115T
Cytochrome *c*$_1$, 611–612
Cytochrome *c* oxidase, *see* Complex IV
Cytochrome *c* reductase, *see* Complex III
Cytochrome *d*, 621
Cytochrome *f*, 656–657
Cytochrome P450, **398**, 398–400

Cytokines, 422, 1070
Cytokine receptors, 1071
Cytoplasm, 8
Cytoplasmic domains, 314
Cytoplasmic loops, 305
Cytosine (Cyt), 40, 41T, 1065
  base pairing, 46F, 851F, 866–868
  Chargaff's rules and, 44
  as common nucleotide, 42
  modified forms in tRNA, 992F
  oxidative deamination, 917F
  reaction with hydroxylamine, 940
Cytoskeleton, 8, 274
Cytosol, 8. *See also* Fatty acid biosynthesis;
    Gluconeogenesis; Glycolysis; Pentose
    phosphate pathway; Urea cycle
  acetyl-CoA transport from
    mitochondria, for fatty acid
    biosynthesis, **701–702**
  heme biosynthesis in, 776F
  metabolic functions, 455T
  metabolite transport between
    mitochondria and, in gluconeogenesis,
    556–557, 557F
Cytosolic (outer) faces, 283
Cytosolic palmitoyl-CoA, 805
Cytosolic reducing equivalents, 599

D

D (dalton), 13
D (Fischer convention), 83–84
D1 (PsbA), 652
D$_1$ proteins, 971
D2 (PsbD), 652
D$_2$ proteins, 971
D$_3$ proteins, 971
DAG, *see* 1,2-Diacylglycerol
Dalgarno, L., 1011
Dali (computer program), 153
Dalton (D), 13
Dam methyltransferase, 918
Danio rerio, 57T
Dansyl chloride, 105–106, 106F
Dark reactions, photosynthesis, 641,
    663–675
D Arm (tRNA), 991F
Darnell, J., 1071
Darst, S., 943
Darwin, C., 11, 59, 576
Darwinian evolution. *See* Evolution
Davies, D., 773
Davis, R., 61
Dawkins, R., 11
Dayhoff, M., 117
D-channel, 618
Dcm methyltransferase, 918
DCMU [3-(3,4-dichlorophenyl)-1,1-
    dimethylurea], 650
ddC (2′,3′-dideoxycytidine, Zalcitabine), 384
ddI (2′,3′-dideoxyinosine, Didanosine), 384

ddNTP, 54
Deadenylases, 1074
DEAE (diethylaminoethyl) groups, in
    anion exchangers, 98
Deamination, 732
Death ligand, 1088
Death receptor, 1088
5-Deazatetrahydrofolate (5dTHF), 820
Debranching enzyme, 231, 533, **536–537**
Decapping enzyme, 1074
Decoding, 1014
deDuve, C., 534
Deep View (computer program), 153
Degeneracy, codon, 999
Degenerate code, 986, 999T
Degradative pathways, 451–452
7-Dehydrocholesterol, 256
Dehydrogenases, sequential reaction
    mechanism, 375–376
Deletion mutations, 916–919
Δ^4-fatty acyl desaturase, 708
Δ^5-fatty acyl desaturase, 708
Δ^6-fatty acyl desaturase, 708
Δ^9-fatty acyl desaturase, 708
Demethylases, 1065
Denaturation:
  DNA, **864, 866,** 866F
  proteins, 94, **158–160**
Denatured (fully unfolded) proteins, 139
Denaturing conditions, 263–264
Denitrification, 788
5′-Deoxyadenosylcobalamin, 692, 693F
Deoxyhemoglobin, 183F
  bisphosphoglycerate (BPG)
    binding to, 191
  ion pairs and hydrogen bonds, 187F
Deoxyhemoglobin S, 196F
Deoxyribonucleic acid, *see* DNA
Deoxyribonucleotides, 40, 41F, **828–838**
β-D-2′-Deoxyribose, 40, 224, **828–834**
Deoxy sugars, 224
Deoxythymidine, 41T, 845F
Deoxythymidine monophosphate
    (deoxythymidylic acid, dTMP), 41T
Depolarization, 302
Depsipeptides, 955
Dermatan sulfate, 232F
Desaturases, 707–708
Desensitization, 430
Desert-dwelling succulent plants, 675
Detergents:
  membrane disruption, 263–264
  protein denaturation, 158–160
Development, molecular basis of,
    1090–1097
Dextrorotatory molecules, 84
DHAP, *see* Dihydroxyacetone phosphate
DHF (dihydrofolate), 835
DHFR (dihydrofolate reductase), 754,
    836–837F

Diabetes mellitus, 215T, 475, **811–814.** *See also* Insulin

1,2-Diacylglycerol (DAG), 251, 437–438, 679
  activation of protein kinase C by, 440–442
  in fatty acid synthesis, 714
  in triacylglycerol biosynthesis, 710F

Diacylglycerol acyltransferase, in triacylglycerol biosynthesis, 710F, 711

Diacylglycerophospholipids, synthesis, 714–716

Dialysis, 30F

Diazotrophs, 782–783

Dicer, 1075

3-(3,4-Dichlorophenyl)-1,1-dimethylurea (DCMU), 650

Dickerson, R., 45, 351

Didanosine (2′,3′-Dideoxyinosine, ddI), 384

2′,3′-Dideoxycytidine (ddC, Zalcitabine), 384

2′,3′-Dideoxyinosine (ddI, Didanosine), 384

2′,3′-Dideoxynucleoside triphosphate, 54

3,5–2,4-Dienoyl-CoA isomerase, 692

2,4-Dienoyl-CoA reductase, 690

Diethylaminoethyl (DEAE) groups, in anion exchangers, 98

Diet-induced thermogenesis, 808

Differential gene splicing, 58

Diffraction patterns, 141F

Diffusion, **29–30**
  facilitated, 276, 297
  lipid bilayers, 261F
  thermodynamics, 296–297

Diffusion-controlled limit, 371

Digestion, 74

Digitalin, 313

Digitalis, 313, 394

Digitoxin, 313

Dihedral angles, polypeptides, 128

Dihedral symmetry, 155

7,8-Dihydrobiopterin, 762

Dihydroceramide, 718F

Dihydroceramide reductase, 718F

Dihydrofolate (DHF), 835

Dihydrofolate reductase (DHFR), 754, 837F

Dihydrolipoamide, in citric acid cycle, 573

Dihydrolipoyl dehydrogenase (E$_3$), 571, 574F, 580

Dihydrolipoyl transacetylase (E$_2$), 571, 575–576

Dihydrolipoyl transsuccinylase, 580

Dihydroorotase, in UMP synthesis, 825–826, 825F

Dihydroorotate, in UMP synthesis, 825–826, 825F

Dihydroorotate dehydrogenase, in UMP synthesis, 825–826, 825F

Dihydropteridine reductase, 762–763F

Dihydrouracil, in pyrimidine catabolism, 845F

Dihydrouracil dehydrogenase, in pyrimidine catabolism, 845F

Dihydrouridine, 992, 992F

Dihydroxyacetone, 221

Dihydroxyacetone phosphate (DHAP):
  in Calvin cycle, 665F, 666
  in fructose metabolism, 517F
  in glycolysis, 487F, 492–494
  in triacylglycerol biosynthesis, 710F

Dihydroxyacetone phosphate acyltransferase, in triacylglycerol biosynthesis, 710F, 711

1α,25-Dihydroxycholecalciferol, 256

Dihydroxyphenylalanine (L-DOPA), synthesis from tyrosine, 780–781F

Dihydroxythymine, in pyrimidine catabolism, 845F

Diimine, 786

Diisopropylphosphofluoridate (DIPF), 348
  neurotoxicity, 349
  as serine protease inhibitor, 355

Dimers, 44

N^6,N^6-Dimethyladenine, 977

Dimethylallyl pyrophosphate, 722–723F

5-Dimethylamino-1-naphthalenesulfonyl chloride, 105–106, 106F

5,6-Dimethylbenzimidazole, 693

N^2,N^2-Dimethylguanosine, 992F

Dimethyl sulfate, mutagenic effects, 917

2,4-Dinitrophenol (DNP), 630–631

Dintzis, H., 1008

Dinucleotide-binding (Rossmann) fold, proteins, 150

Dipalmitoyl phosphatidylcholine (DPPC), 250, 261F

Dipeptides, 78

DIPF, *see* Diisopropylphosphofluoridate

Diphosphate ester, functional group and linkages, 4T

Diphosphatidylglycerol, 249T

Diploid organisms, 47

Dipolar ions, 75F

Dipole–dipole interactions, 25F, 25T

Direct repeats, 935F

Disaccharides, **227**

Dissociation constant (K):
  selected acids, 33T
  water, 31

Disulfide, functional group and linkages, 4T

Disulfide bonds:
  cleavage in protein sequencing, 106–107
  cysteine, 80F
  keratin, 136
  position determination, 112F
  and protein folding, 157–158

Diversity, 1079, 1081

Dihydropteridine reductase, 762–763F

DMD (Duchenne muscular dystrophy), 20

DNA (deoxyribonucleic acid), 39–40. *See also* B-DNA; Genes; Mutations; Nucleic acids; Nucleotides; RNA
  A-DNA, 852T
  base composition, **44**
  base pairing, 46F, 851F, **866–868**
  base stacking interactions, 867–868, 867
  complementary strands, 46F
  contour length, 883
  denaturation, **864,** 864F, **866**
  double helix, **44–47,** 45F, **849–864**
  dynamic nature of, and evolution, 58–59
  evolution, 871
  flexibility, **855–857**
  forensic testing, 66
  as genetic information carrier, **47–48**
  geometry, **849–864**
  Hoogsteen base pairs, 866F
  hybridization, 866
  ionic interactions, **868**
  lack of uracil in, 921
  melting curve, 866, 866F
  methylation, 918
  nontranscribed, **1043–1046,** 1056
  nucleotides, 42
  palindrome sequences, 51–52F
  renaturation, **866,** 866F
  repetitive sequences, 1043
  selfish (junk), 1046
  shear degradation, 883
  supercoiled, *see* Supercoiled DNA
  unexpressed, 1038
  Watson-Crick base pairs, 46, 851F
  Z-DNA, 852–853F, 852T, 854, 857

DnaA protein, 903

DnaB protein, 903

DNA catalog, 49–50

DNA chips, 479F–480

DNA damage, *see* Mutation

DNA-directed DNA polymerases, 894, 895F

DNA fingerprinting, 66

DNA glycosylases, 921

DnaG protein, 904

DNA gyrase, 863

DnaJ, 1028–1029

DnaK, 1028–1029

DNA libraries, **62–65**

DNA ligase, 61, 896, 907F

DNA manipulation:
  applications, 67–70
  genomic libraries, **62–65**
  polymerase chain reaction, 65–67, 65F

DNA methylation (eukaryotes), 1066–1067

DNA methylation levels (epigenetic reprogramming), 1066

DNA methylation sites, 1042

DNA methyltransferases (DNA MTases), 1065

NA microarrays, 479–480
NA MTases (DNA methyltransferases), 1065
NA photolyases, 920F
NA polymerases, 894, 895F, 949
NA polymerase I, see Pol I
NA polymerase II (Pol II), 902
NA polymerase III (Pol III), 902
NA polymerase IV, 926
NA polymerase V, 926
NA polymerase β (pol β), 910
NA polymerase γ (pol γ), 911
NA polymerase η (pol η), 925
NA-protein interactions, **874–883**
  eukaryotic transcription factors, **879–883**
  prokaryotic transcriptional control
    motifs, **876–879**
  restriction endonucleases, **875–876,**
    875F, 876F
NA recombination, see Recombination
NA repair, **920–926**. See also
  Recombination
  base excision repair (BER), **921–923**
  direct damage reversal, **920–921**
  introduction of errors, **925–926**
  mismatch repair, **924–925**
  nucleotide excision repair (NER),
    923–924
  and Pol I, 899–900
  by recombination, **932–934**
  SOS response, **926**
NA replication, 48, 48F, 58, 849. See also
  Eukaryotic DNA replication; Gene
  expression; Prokaryotic DNA
  replication
  complementarity and, 5
  overview, **894–896**
  postreplication repair, 932–933F
  replication forks, 894
  RNA primers, 896, 899F
  semiconservative, 893
  semidiscontinuous, 896
Nase, caspase-activated, 1088
Nase I, 899
NMT1 protein, 1066
NMT3a (DNA MTase), 1066
NMT3b (DNA MTase), 1066
NP (2,4-dinitrophenol), 630–631
NTPs, 53
  and replication fidelity, 909
  synthesis, 833–834
  use in PCR, 64, 65F
Docking protein, 279
Dolichol-PP-oligosaccharide synthesis
  pathway, 562F
Dolichol pyrophosphate, 561F–562
Domains:
  apical, 277
  basolateral, 277
  protein duplication, 120

protein evolution, 118
  proteins, **149–150,** 150F
Donohue, J., 44, 850
L-DOPA (dihydroxyphenylalanine),
  synthesis from tyrosine, 780–781F
Dopamine, 88, 780–781F
Dopamine β-hydroxylase, in
  neurotransmitter synthesis, 781F
Dosage compensation, 1057
Double blind tests, 397
Double-displacement reactions, 376
Double helix, **44–47,** 45F, **849–864**
Double-reciprocal plot, see Lineweaver-
  Burk plot
Double-stranded breaks (DSBs),
  925–926
Double-stranded DNA (dsDNA), 899
Double-stranded RNA, 1075, 1076
Doudna, J., 1030
Down's syndrome, 169
Doxorubicin, 865
DPE, 959F
DPPC (dipalmitoyl phosphatidylcholine),
  250, 261F
Drew, H., 45
Drosophila sp., 1070
  development, 1090–1091
  histone genes reiteration, 1042
Drosophila melanogaster:
  calmodulin, 439F
  development, 1090–1097
  genome sequencing, 57T
  26S proteasome, 735F
Drug design, **394–400**
  bioavailability and toxicity, 396
  clinical trials, 396–398
Drug–drug interactions, 398–400
Druker, B., 425
DSBs (double-stranded breaks), 925–926
DSCAM protein, 974
dsDNA (double-stranded DNA), 899
D segment, 1079
dTMP (deoxythymidine monophosphate),
  41T
Dual-specificity tyrosine phosphatases, 426
Duchenne muscular dystrophy
  (DMD), 205
dUTP diphosphohydrolase
  (dUTPase), 834F
Dwarfism, 411
Dystrophin, 205, 968

E

ℰ, see Reduction potential
E (exit) site, 1006
E. coli, see *Escherichia coli*
E₁, see Pyruvate dehydrogenase
E_1 (conformational state), 312
E-1 (low-affinity lactose binding site), 317
E1 (ubiquitin-activating enzyme), 734

E_2 (conformational state), 312
E₂ (dihydrolipoyl transacetylase), 571,
  575–576
E-2 (high-affinity lactose binding site), 317
E2s (ubiquitin-conjugating enzymes), 734
E2F family (of transcription factors), 1086
E3, see Ubiquitin-protein ligase
E₃ (dihydrolipoyl dehydrogenase), 571,
  574F, 580
E3a, 735
E₃ binding protein, 572
E4P, see Erythrose-4-phosphate
Early genes, 947
EC classification number, 324–325
*Eco*RI endonuclease, 52T, 875F–876
*Eco*RV endonuclease, 52T, 876, 876F
Edema, 256
Edema factor (EF), 444–445
Edidin, M., 270
Editing, RNA, 975
Edman, P., 109
Edman degradation, 106, **109–110,** 109F, 111
Edman's reagent, 109
eEF1A, 1025
eEF1B, 1025
eEF2, 1025–1026
EF (edema factor), 444–445
EF-G, 1022
EF hands, 438, 439F
EF-Ts, 1015
EF-Tu, 1015–1016, 1018
EGF (epidermal growth factor)
  receptor, 421
Ehlers–Danlos syndromes, 137
Eicosanoids, **258–259,** 259F
eIF2, 1013
eIF2B (initiation factor), 1077
eIF2 phosphatase, 1077
eIF4A, 1014
eIF4E, 1014
eIF4F, 1014
eIF4G, 1014
eIF5B, 1014
18S rRNA, 977, 1007
80S ribosome, 1008F
Eisenberg, D., 667
EJC (exon-junction protein complex), 1074
Eklund, H., 829
Elastase:
  function, 348
  polypeptide degradation, 738
  proelastase activation to, 358
  specificity, 107T
  substrate specificity, 351
  X-ray structure, 348–352
Elastin, 351
ELC (Essential light chains), 201
Electrical potential difference, 471
Electroblotting, 874

Electrochemical cells, 471F–472
Electrochemical gradients, 312, 316
Electrochemical potential, 296
Electrogenic antiport, 600
Electromagnetic radiation, 645
Electromotive force (emf), 472
Electron acceptors, 470–471
Electron beam, 266
Electron crystallography, 265, 266
Electron crystal structures, 308, 310F
Electron density, 142
Electron density maps, 141
Electron donors, 470–471
Electronic complementarity (enzymes), 325
Electron micrographs, 283F
Electron-transfer flavoprotein (ETF), 688
Electron-transfer reactions, 469, 474
Electron transport, 504
    bacteria, 621
    Complex I, 605
    Complex II, 609
    Complex III: Q cycle, 612–614
    Complex IV, 618
    Complex V (ATP synthase), **618–622**
    photosynthetic bacteria, **647–650**
    sequence of, 602–604, 647–662
    thermodynamics, 601
    two-center, photosynthesis, **650–663**
Electron-transport chain, **597–618**
    inhibitors, 603–604
    reduction potentials, 604F
Electrophoresis:
    agarose gel, 872–873
    capillary (CE), 103
    nucleic acids, **872–873,** 873F
    nucleic acid sequencing, **52–53,**
        52F, 54F, 55F
    polyacrylamide gel (PAGE), **101–103**
    protein purification, 101–103
    proteins, **101–103**
    pulsed-field gel (PFGE), **873**
    SDS-PAGE, 102–103
Electrospray ionization (ESI), 111F
Electrospray ionization mass spectrometry
    (ESI-MS), 347
Electrostatic catalysis, **337**
Electrostatic interactions, proteins,
    156–157
Elementary reactions, 364
Eliminations, 453
Elion, G., 838, 844
ELISA (enzyme-linked immunosorbent
    assay), 95F, 102
Elk-1, 420F
Elongases, 707–708
Elongation factors, 1012T, 1015
Elongator, 965
Eluant, 99
Elution, 99
Embden, G., 486

Embden–Meyerhoff–Parnas pathway, 486
Embryonic mouse paw cell death, 1087F
Emergent properties, 444
Emf (electromotive force), 472
Enantiomers, 83–86
Endergonic processes, 14, 448–449
End groups, 104–105
End group analysis, 104–106
endo conformation, 856–857
Endocrine glands, 406
Endocrine hormones, 406–407
Endocrine system, 406F, 799
Endocytosis, 278
    clathrin-coated vesicles, 286
    receptor-mediated, **684–685**
Endoglycosidases, 226–227
Endonucleases, 51, 858–859
Endopeptidases, 107, 107T
Endopeptidase V8, specificity, 107T
Endoplasmic reticulum (ER), 8, 8F, 438.
        See also Rough endoplasmic
        reticulum (RER)
    glycosylated protein synthesis in, 239
    lipid biosynthesis, 275
    smooth, 8F, 455T
Endosome, 290
Endosomes, 685
Endosymbiosis, 10
Endothelium-derived relaxing factor, 781
Endotoxic shock, 782
Enediol (enediolate) intermediate, 494
Energy, 12
    activation, **328–330**
    conservation of, 12
    flow in biosphere, 18F
    as state function, 15
    transformation of light energy to
        chemical energy, 645–647
Energy coupling, 618
Energy reserves, fats vs. glycogen, 248–249
Energy-rich compounds, *see* High-energy
    compounds
Engrailed (en) gene, 1091
Enhanceosome, 1068
Enhancers, 959–960, 1067
Enolase, in glycolysis, 487F, **500**
Enolate, in glycolysis, 492F
Enolpyruvate, 502
Enoyl-ACP reductase, in fatty acid
    synthesis, 705F
Enoyl-CoA hydratase, 688
Enoyl-CoA isomerase, 690
3,2-Enoyl-CoA isomerase, 690
Enteropeptidase, 357
Enthalpy, 12, 14–15
Entropy:
    and hydrophobic effect, 26–27
    and life, 17–19
    and second law of thermodynamics, 13–14
    as state function, 15

Enzymatic interconversion, *see* Covalent
    modification
Enzymes, 19. *See also* Protein(s); *specific
        enzymes and classes of enzymes*
    activation energy, **328–330**
    catalysis of reactions of metabolic
        pathways, 452–453
    catalytic efficiency, 329–330
    catalytic perfection, 496
    catalytic power of selected, 323T
    channeling, 774
    classification by reaction type, 324T
    coenzymes, **327–328**
    cofactors, **326–327**
    constitutive, 950
    coupled enzymatic reactions, 95
    electrophilic groups, 335F
    general properties, **323–328**
    geometric specificity, 326
    inducible, 950
    isozymes, 455
    metabolic thermodynamics, 455–457
    metal-activated, 335–336
    nomenclature, **324–325**
    nucleophilic groups, 335F
    processive, 896–897
    reaction coordinate, **328–330**
    stereospecificity, 325–326
    substrate specificity, 324, **325–326**
    synthesis by genes, 49–50
    X-ray crystallography, 340, 342
Enzyme action, 369
Enzyme activity regulation, **386–393**
    allosteric control, 386–390
    covalent modification, 390–393
    mechanism of, 324
Enzyme inactivator, 385
Enzyme inhibition, **377–385**
    competitive, **377–381,** 379F,
        380F, 381T
    mixed, 381T, **382–383,** 383F
    noncompetitive, 382–383
    transition state analogs, 339
    uncompetitive, **381–382,** 381T, 382F
Enzyme inhibitors, 377
Enzyme kinetics, 364, **366–376**
    bisubstrate reactions, **375–376,** 375F
    data analysis, 364, **372–375**
    Michaelis–Menten equation, 368–372
    steady state kinetic measurements,
        374–375
    transition state theory and, 372
Enzyme-linked immunosorbent assay
    (ELISA), 95F
Enzyme mechanisms:
    acid–base catalysis, **331–333**
    covalent catalysis, **333–335**
    electrostatic catalysis, **337**
    metal ion catalysis, **335–336**
    orientation effects, **336–338,** 336F

pH effects, 332
preferential transition state binding, **338–339,** 338F
proximity effects, **336–338**
Enzyme saturation, 370
Enzyme–substrate complex, 325F, 338–339, 367
Enzyme system, as enzymatically interconvertible, 545–546F
Enzyme–transition state complex, 338–339
Enzymology, 322, 363–364, 475
EPA (fatty acid), 247T
Epidermal growth factor (EGF), 120F
Epidermal growth factor receptor, 421
Epigenetic genome changes, 1066
Epigenetic programming, aberrations, 1067
Epigenetic reprogramming, DNA methylation levels, 1066
Epimers, 221
Epimerization, 224
Epinephrine (adrenaline), 407, 409
and fatty acid metabolism, 712
fight or flight reaction, 551
and fuel metabolism, 799, 801–803
glycogen metabolism effects, 552
insulin as antagonist, 552
synthesis from tyrosine, 780, 781F
E proteins, 971
Equal®, 228
Equilibrium, **15–17**
near-equilibrium reactions, 456, 631
temperature and, 16–17
Equilibrium constant (K_{eq}), 16
ER, *see* Endoplasmic reticulum
ERF1, 1026
Ergocalciferol (Vitamin D_2), 256
Ergosterol, 256
ERKs (extracellular-signal-regulated kinases), 419
ER-resident proteins, 286–287
Erythrocytes, 181
antigenic determinants, 242F
2,3-BPG synthesis, 502
carbon dioxide transport, 189–190
glycocalyx, 241F
glycophorin A, 264F
heme biosynthesis in, 777–778
lysis, 194
membranes, **272–274,** 273F
Erythrocyte ghosts, 272
Erythrocyte glucose transporter (GLUT1), 307
Erythropoietic protoporphyria, 778
Erythropoietin, genetically engineered, 67T
D-Erythrose, 220F
Erythrose-4-phosphate (E4P):
in Calvin cycle, 665F, 666
in pentose phosphate pathway, 521F, 524
D-Erythrulose, 221F

Escherichia coli (E. coli), 8, 316, 386
alternative splice site selection, 975F
biosynthesis thiamine pyrophosphate, 1054
catabolite repression, 1050–1051
cellular contents, 988
chromosome, 895F
cloning vectors from, 60–62
codon usage bias, 999
cross section, 6F
DNA polymerases, 896–902
and DNA polymerases, 53
fatty acid biosynthesis, 703
gene number, 1039
genome sequencing, 57T
his operon, 1053
hot spots, 941
ilv operon, 1053
lac operon, **1048–1050**
lac repressor, 1048–1050
lactose metabolism, 1046
leading and lagging strand synthesis, **904–905,** 905F
met repressor, 878F
molecular cloning techniques, 1049
nontranscribed DNA, 1043
nucleotide excision repair, 923F
polypeptide synthesis in, 1011
primosome, 904
proteins from, 94
pyrimidine synthesis regulation, 827F
recombination in, 928–930, 929F–930F
replication fidelity, 909
replication termination, 908–909
replisome, 904–905F
ribosome, components of, 1001T
RNA polymerase, 943F–945
RNA primers, 896, 899F
rRNA posttranscriptional processing, 976F
SOS response, 926
transcription, 943–952
tRNA posttranscriptional processing, 976F
trp operon, genetic map, 1051F–1054
trp repressor, 877F–878
type III topoisomerase, 860–861F
wild-type reversion rate, 909
Escherichia coli complex II, 609–611
Escherichia coli maltoporin, 298–299
Escherichia coli OmpF porin, 267F, 298
ES complex, 325F, 338–339, 367
ESEs (exonic splicing enhancers), 975
ESI (electrospray ionization), 111F
ESI-MS (electrospray ionization mass spectrometry), 347
Essential amino acids, 764T, **769–774**
Essential fatty acids, 293
Essential light chains (ELC), 201
ESSs (exonic splicing silencers), 975

Esters, functional group and linkages, 4T
Ester group, 4T
β-Estradiol, 255F, 410
Estrogens, 255, 410
ESTs (expressed sequence tags), 1040
ETF (electron-transfer flavoprotein), 688
ETF:ubiquinone oxidoreductase, 688
Ethanol, 326, 327, 379
Ethanolamine, 715, 249T
Ether, functional group and linkages, 4T
Ethidium ion, as intercalating agent, 873F
Ethylene gylcol, 379
O^6-Ethylguanine, 921
Ethylnitrosurea, mutagenic effects, 917
Etoposide, 865
Ets-1, 420F
Eubacteria, 9
Euchromatin, 1056
Eukarya, 9F
Eukaryotes, **7–9**
cell cycle, 883, 1081F
chromosome structure, **883–890**
citric acid cycle in, 570
classification, 9
evolution, 9–10
gene clusters, 1042
gene number, selected organisms, 1039T
lipid biosynthesis, 275F
membranes, 263
metabolic functions, 455T
new membrane generation, 277
nucleus, 1056F
photosynthesis in, 641
polypeptide synthesis in, 1025–1026
protein degradation in, 734–735
pyruvate dehydrogenase complex, 571–572
repetitive DNA, 1044–1046
transposons, 935, 938–939
Eukaryotic DNA replication, **910–915**
multiple origins, **911–914**
telomerase, **914–916**
telomeres, **914–916**
Eukaryotic gene expression, **1055–1097**
chromatin structure, **1055–1067**
molecular basis of development, **1090–1097,** 1091F
posttranscriptional control mechanisms, **1073–1077**
selective, by differentiated cells, 960
somatic recombination, **214**
transcription control, **1067–1073**
transcription factors, **879–883**
translational control, **1076–1077**
Eukaryotic motifs, structure of, 879–881
Eukaryotic mRNAs, 965–976
Eukaryotic pre-tRNAs, 981–982
Eukaryotic ribosomes, **1007–1008**
Eukaryotic rRNAs, 977–978

Eukaryotic transcription, **952–965**
  RNA polymerase promoters, **958–965**
  RNA polymerases, **953–958**
  transcription factors, **960–965**
Eukaryotic tRNAs, 980–982
Evans, P., 512, 694
Even-chain fatty acid oxidation, 686
Even-skipped gene *(eve),* 1093F
Evolution. *See also* Mutation
  352, 345
  amino acids, 74
  chemical, **3–5**
  citric acid cycle, 592–593
  DNA, 871
  genetic code, 990
  histones, 884
  natural selection, 114
  nucleic acid sequence and, 58–59
  nucleotides, 40l
  organismal domains of, **9–10**
  principles of, 11
  proteins, 92, **114–117**
  serine proteases, 352F
Evolutionarily conservative proteins, 116
Exciton transfer, 646–647
Executioner (effector) caspase, 1088
Exergonic processes, 14, 448–449
Exit channel, 618
Exit (E) site, 1006
exo conformation, 857
Exocrine glands, 407
Exocytosis, 287
Exoglycosidases, 226–227
Exons (expressed sequences), 967
  splicing, 969F–971
Exonic splicing enhancers (ESEs), 975
Exonic splicing silencers (ESSs), 975
Exon-junction protein complex
    (EJC), 1074
Exon skipping, 970–971
Exonucleases, 51
Exopeptidases, 107
Exosomes, 1074
Expressed sequences, *see* Exons
Expressed sequence tags (ESTs), 1040
Expression, *see* Gene expression
Expression vector, 67
Extinction coefficient, 95–96
Extracellular apoptosis, 1088–1090
Extracellular factors, gene
    expression, 1070
Extracellular fluids, buffering, 35–36
Extracellular-signal-regulated kinases
    (ERKs), 419
Extremophiles, 475
Extrinsic membrane proteins, **269**
Extrinsic pathway, apoptosis, 1088
Extrinsic pathway, blood coagulation
    cascade, 358
Eyring, H., 328

F
$\mathscr{F}$ (Faraday), 471
F_1F_0-ATPase, *see* ATP synthase
F1P, *see* Fructose-1-phosphate
F2,6P (fructose-2,6-bisphosphate), 512,
    558–559
F6P, *see* Fructose-6-phosphate
Fab fragments, 210F, 211
Fabry's disease, 720
Facilitated diffusion, 276, 297
F-actin, 202, 204F
Factor V, 358
Factor Va, 359
Factor VII, 358
Factor VIIa, 359
Factor VIII, 358
Factor VIIIa, 359
Factor IX, 67T, 358
Factor IXa, 359
Factor X, 67T, 358
Factor Xa, 359
Factor XI, 358
Factor XIII, 358
Facultative anaerobes, 449
FAD (flavin adenine dinucleotide),
    469–470. *See also* $FADH_2$
  in citric acid cycle, 568F, 569, 570,
    572T, 582
  in glyoxylate cycle, 591F
  reduction to $FADH_2$, 470F
FADD (fas-associating death domain-
    containing protein), 1088
$FADH_2$ (flavin adenine dinucleotide,
    reduced form). *See also* FAD
  in citric acid cycle, 567, 569, 570
  FAD reduction to, 470F
  P/O ratio in oxidative phosphorylation,
    629–630
$FADH_2$ (flavin adenine dinucleotide,
    reduced form), 452
FAICAR (5-formaminoimidazole-4-
    carboxamide ribotide), in IMP
    synthesis, 819F, 820
Familial hypercholesterolemia (FH), 728
Faraday ($\mathscr{F}$), 13, 471
Farber's lipogranulomatosis, 720
Farnesyl pyrophosphate, 723, 723F
Farnesyl residue, 268
Fas (transmembrane protein), 1088
Fas-associating death domain-containing
    protein (FADD), 1088
FasL (fas ligand), 1088
Fas ligand (FasL), 1088
Fasman, G., 140, 163
Fasting:
  amino acid metabolism during, 797–798
  brain effects, 794
  gluconeogenesis during, 530, 552
  and glucose–alanine cycle, 799
  lysosomal protein degradation, 733

Fast-twitch muscle fibers, 511, 798
Fats, 248
Fat cells, *see* Adipocytes
Fat-soluble vitamins, 257, 450
Fatty acids, **246–249,** 247T
  amphiphilic nature of anions, 28F
  energy recovery by citric acid cycle, 567
  essential, 293
  membrane proteins, 267–269
Fatty acid binding protein, 680F
Fatty acid biosynthesis, **701–711,** 701F
  acetyl-CoA carboxylase, **702–703**
  cellular location, 453–454
  citric acid cycle intermediates, 589
  desaturases, 707–708
  elongases, 707–708
  fatty acid synthase, **703–707**
  mitochondrial acetyl-CoA transport to
    cytosol, **701–702**
  triacylglycerols, **711**
  triclosan, 708
Fatty acid metabolism:
  mammalian, 792F, 793, 797
  regulation, **711–714**
Fatty acid oxidation, **685–698**
  activation, **686**
  AMPK and promotion of, 805
  β oxidation, 686, **688–690,** 701F
  β oxidation, peroxisomal, **698**
  electron transfer in, 597
  even-chain fatty acids, 686
  mammalian metabolism, 792F, 793
  odd-chain fatty acids, 686, **692–697**
  thermodynamics, 690
  transport across mitochondria, **686–687**
  unsaturated fatty acids, **690–692**
Fatty acid synthase, **703–707,** 801
Fatty acid synthesis, mammalian
    metabolism, 792F, 793, 797
Fava beans, 526
Favism, 526
FBP, *see* Fructose-1,6-bisphosphate
FBPase, *see* Fructose-1,6-bisphosphatase
FBPase-2 (fructose bisphosphatase-2), 558
Fc fragment, 211–212
Fd (ferredoxin), 660
FdUMP (5-fluorodeoxyuridylate), 838
Fe^{2+}:
  as cofactor, 335
  in heme group, 178F–179
Fe^{3+}:
  as cofactor, 326, 335
  in ribonucleotide reductase, 829F
Feedback inhibitors, 387
Feedforward activation, 823
Feigon, J., 1058
Female sex hormones, 410, 411
FeMo-cofactor, in nitrogenase, 784
Fen (fenfluramine), 397
FEN1 (flap endonuclease-1), 911

Fenfluramine (fen), 397
Fe-protein, in nitrogenase, 783
Fermentation, 322, 485, **504–510**
  alcoholic, **506–509**
  energetics of, 509–510
  homolactic, **505–506**
  thermodynamics, **509–510**
Ferredoxin (Fd), 660, 785
Ferredoxin-NADP$^+$ reductase
  (FNR), 652
Ferredoxin–thioredoxin reductase, 671
Ferritin, 69
Ferrochelatase, in heme biosynthesis, 776F
Ferryl oxidation state, 617
Fe–S clusters, *see* Iron–sulfur clusters
Fetal hemoglobin, 118, 191, 1043
Ffh, 1030
FGAM (formylglycinamidine ribotide), in
  IMP synthesis, 819F, 820
FGAM synthetase, in IMP synthesis, 819F
FGAR (formylglycinamide ribotide), in
  IMP synthesis, 819F, 820
FH (familial hypercholesterolemia), 728
Fibrin, 168, 358
Fibrinogen, 119, 168, 358
  isoelectric point, 98T
Fibrinopeptides, evolution rate, 119F
Fibronectin, 120F
Fibrous proteins, **134–139**
50S subunit, 1001–1006
"Fight or flight" reaction, 551
Fire, A., 1075
FirstGlance (program), 153
First law of thermodynamics, **12**
First-order reactions, 364–365, 365F
Fischer, E., 83, 325, 369
Fischer convention, 84F, 221
Fischer projections, 84
Fish, lipid bilayer fluidity modification, 262
5.8S rRNA, 977, 1007
5′ End, nucleic acids, 43–44
5S RNA, 868–869, 976
5dTHF (5-deazatetrahydrofolate), 820
Flap endonuclease-1 (FEN1), 911
Flavin adenine dinucleotide, *see* FAD
Flavin coenzymes:
  Ping Pong reaction mechanism, 376
Flavin mononucleotide (FMN),
  606, 606F
Flavoprotein dehydrogenase, 599
Fleming, A., 238
Fletterick, R., 391
Flexibility, of DNA, **855–857**
Flipases, 276
Flip-flop, 261
Fluid mosaic model, membranes,
  270–272
Fluorescence, 646
Fluorescence photobleaching recovery
  measurements, 270–271F

Fluorochlorobromomethane,
  enantiomers, 83F
5-Fluorocytosine, 1065
5-Fluorodeoxyuridylate (FdUMP), 838
Fluorophore, 270
Flux, 309, **456–459**
fMet (*N*-formylmethionine), 1011
fMet-tRNA$_f^{Met}$, 1012–1013
FMN (flavin mononucleotide), 606, 606F
FMNH· (flavin mononucleotide, reduced
  form radical), 606F
FMNH$_2$ (flavin mononucleotide, reduced
  form), 606F
FMRP, 1044
FNR (ferredoxin–NADP$^+$ reductase), 652
Folate, reduction to THF, 754–756F
Folding funnel, 162
Folic acid, 754
Following substrates, 376
Fomaldehyde, geometric specificity, 326
Footprinting, 946
Forensic DNA testing, 66
5-Formaminoimidazole-4-carboxamide
  ribotide (FAICAR), in IMP synthesis,
  819F, 820
Formate, 310
N-Formiminoglutamate, 752
N^5-Formimino-tetrahydrofolate
  (N^5-Formimino-THF), 752F
Formylglycinamide ribotide (FGAR), in
  IMP synthesis, 819F, 820
Formylglycinamidine ribotide (FGAM), in
  IMP synthesis, 819F, 820
N-Formylmethionine (fMet), 1011
48S initiation complex, 1014
Fos, 419, 1070
Fossil record, 9, 59
[4Fe–4S], *see* Iron–sulfur clusters
45S rRNA, 977
434 Repressor, 876–877F
Fowler's solution, 576
Foxglove plant, 394
F proteins, 971
Fractional saturation, of oxygen in
  myoglobin, 179–180
Fractionation:
  nucleic acids, **872–874**
  proteins, 97F
Fragile X syndrome, 1044, 1044T
Frameshift mutations, 986
Frank, J., 1002, 1008, 1019
Franklin, R., 44, 850
Free energy (*G*), **14–15**
  ATP and, 462
  chemical reactions, 14–17
  standard state, 17
  as state function, 15
Free energy of activation, 18–19, 328–330,
  338–339, 372
Free radicals, 606

Fridovich, I, 636
Friedrich's ataxia, 1044T
Frozen-accident theory of codon
  evolution, 990
α-D-Fructofuranose, 222F
β-Fructofuranosidase, 366
Fructokinase, in fructose metabolism,
  516, 517F
Fructose, 221, 228
  intolerance, 518
  metabolism, **516–518**, 517F
D-Fructose, 221F, 222F
Fructose-1,6-bisphosphatase (FBPase),
  514–515F, 801
  in Calvin cycle, 665F, 666, 670–671
  in gluconeogenesis, 557
Fructose-1,6-bisphosphate (FBP):
  in Calvin cycle, 664, 665F
  in gluconeogenesis, 553F, 558
  in glycolysis, 487F, 491
Fructose-1-phosphate (F1P), 516, 517F, 797
Fructose-1-phosphate aldolase, in fructose
  metabolism, 516, 517F
Fructose-2,6-bisphosphate (F2,6P), 512,
  558–559, 804
Fructose-6-phosphate (F6P):
  in Calvin cycle, 665F, 669
  free energy of phosphate
    hydrolysis, 461T
  in fructose metabolism, 517F
  glucokinase inhibition, 796–797
  in gluconeogenesis, 553F, 557
  in glycolysis, 487F, 490–491
  in mannose metabolism, 520F
  in pentose phosphate pathway, 521F, 524
Fructose bisphosphatase-2 (FBPase-2), 558
Fructose intolerance, 518
Fruit fly, *see Drosophila*
FSSP (database), 153
F-type ATPases, 311
Ftz (fushi tarazu) gene, 1093F
L-Fucose, 224
Fuel metabolism, hormonal control of,
  799–804
  and catecholamines, 801
  disturbances, 809–815
  and glucagon, 801–803
  and glucose, 800
  and homeostasis, 799. *See also* Metabolic
    homeostasis
  insulin, 800–803
  and liver gluconeogenesis/
    glycogenolysis, 801
  receptors, 803
  signaling pathways, 803
  and storage of fuel, 800–801
Fumarase, 332
  in citric acid cycle, 568F, **583**
  pH effects, 332
  in urea cycle, 744F

Fumarate, 567
  in amino acid degradation, 747F
  in citric acid cycle, 377, 568F, 582, 584F
  in urea cycle, 743, 744F
Functional groups, 3, 26F. *See also specific functional groups*
Furan, 222
Furanoses, 222
Furylfuramide, 920
Fushi tarazu (ftz) gene, 1093F
Fusion, vesicle, **287–291**
Fusion peptide, 290
Futile cycle, 514
Fyn, 422

G

G, see Guanine
G, see Free energy
$\overline{G}_A$ (partial molar free energy), 296
G$_0$ phase (in cell cycle), 1082
G1,6P (glucose-1,6-bisphosphate), 537
G1P, *see* Glucose-1-phosphate
G$_1$ phase, 1082
G$_2$ phase, 1082
G6P, *see* Glucose-6-phosphate
G6Pase (Glucose-6-phosphatase), 538, 801
G6PD, *see* Glucose-6-phosphate dehydrogenase
G6P translocase, 539
Gab-1 (Grb2-associated binder-1), 442
GABA (γ-Aminobutyric acid), 88, 780
G-actin, 202
Gaia hypothesis, 10
GAL4, 880F–881
Galactitol, 519
Galactocerobrosides, 252, 720F
D-Galactosamine, 225
D-Galactose, 220F, 221, **518–520,** 519F
Galactose-1-phosphate, in galactose metabolism, 518, 519F
Galactose-1-phosphate uridylyl transferase, 518
Galactosemia, 519
β-Galactosidase, 227, 1047
β-Galactosidase activity, 1097
Galactoside permease, *see* Lactose permease
Galactosyltransferase, 560
Gallus gallus (chicken), 57T
GalNAc transferase, 561
Gamblin, S., 1064
γ (Soret) band, 610
γc cytokine receptor, 70
γ complex, Pol III holoenzyme, 906
γ-globulin, isoelectric point, 98T
Gangliosides, 253F, 717, 720F
Ganglioside G$_{M1}$, 253F, 720F
Ganglioside G$_{M2}$, 253F, 720F
Ganglioside G$_{M3}$, 253F, 720F
GAP, *see* Glyceraldehyde-3-phosphate; GTPase-activating protein

GAP334-Ras-GDP-AlF$_3$ complex, 419F
GAPDH, *see* Glyceraldehyde-3-phosphate dehydrogenase
Gap junctions, 307
GAR (glycinamide ribotide), in IMP synthesis, 819F, 820
Garrod, A., 477, 762
GAR synthetase, in IMP synthesis, 819F
GAR transformylase, in IMP synthesis, 819F, 820
Gas constant *(R),* 13
Gastrula, 1066
Gastrulation, 1090
Gated ion channels, 302
Gates and fences model, membranes, 274
Gating, ion channel, 302
Gating machinery, 303
Gaucher's disease, 720
GCN4, 881F–882
GDP (guanosine diphosphate), 278, 568F, 569, 570, 581
GDPNP (guanosine-5′-(β,γ-imido) triphosphate; GMPPNP), 1016
GEF (guanine nucleotide exchange factor), 418
Gehring, W., 1094
Geiger counter, 367
Gel electrophoresis, *see* Electrophoresis
Gel filtration chromatography, **97, 100F**
  molecular sieve, 99–100
  size exclusion, 99–100
GenBank, 56, 113T
Genes, 48
  early, 947
  exons and introns, 967–973
  expression, 50
  function identification, 1040–1046
  gap, 1091
  late, 947
  manipulations, and metabolic pathways, 477
  maternal-effect, 1091
  middle, 947
  orthologous, 118
  paralogous, 118
  protein synthesis direction, **49–50**
  pseudogenes, 119
  recombination, **926–939**
  segmentation, 1091
  segment polarity, 1091
  structural, 944
  transgenes, 68–69
  transposition, 58
Gene activation, prokaryotes, **1050–1051**
Gene clusters, **1042–1043,** 1042F
Gene duplication, **117–120,** 118
Gene expression, 50, 944, **1038–1097.** *See also* Eukaryotic gene expression; Prokaryotic gene expression; Transcription factors

enhancers, 959–960
gene clusters, **1042–1043,** 1042F
gene number, **1038–1042**
genome organization, **1038–1046**
molecular basis of development, **1090–1097,** 1091F
nontranscribed DNA, **1043–1046**
overview, 849
and σ factors, 947
tissue specificity, 1055
transcriptomics, 50
Z-DNA and, 854
Gene identification, exons/introns, 1040
Gene knockouts, 69, 477
Gene number, **1038–1042,** 1039T
Gene products, 945
General acid catalysis, 331
General base catalysis, 331
General (homologous) recombination, **926–932**
General transcription factor (GTF), 960, 961T
Gene silencing, 1062
Gene splicing, differential, 58
Gene therapy, 69–70
Genetically engineered hybrid protein, 1069
Genetically modified foods, 69
Genetic anticipation, 1044
Genetic code, **986–991**
  deciphering, **987–988**
  evolution, 990
  nature of, **988–991**
  nonuniversality of, 991
  standard, 989T
  triplet codons, **986–988**
  triplets, **986–987**
Genetic control, of metabolic flux, 459
Genetic engineering. *See also* Recombinant DNA technology
Genetic markers, 1042
Genetic mutations, *see* Mutation
Genome, 47, 478
  organization, **1038–1046**
  sequencing projects, 57T
Genome sequencing, **57–58**
Genomics, 50, 478, 1038
Genomic imprinting, 918, 1067
Geometric complementarity, 325
Geometric permissiveness, 1069
Geometric specificity, 326
George III, King of England, 778
Geranylgeranyl residue, 268
Geranyl pyrophosphate, 723, 723F
Gerhart, J., 387
GH, *see* Growth hormone
Ghost erythrocytes, 272
Ghrelin, 807
G$_{iα}$ protein, 431
Giant gene, 1092
Gibbs, J. W, 14

Gibbs free energy *(G)*, 14. *See also*
  Free energy
Gigantism, 411
Gilbert, W., 1049
Gilman, A., 430
Gilroy, J., 843F
G_L (glycogen-binding subunit), 548–549
Glc, *see* Glucose
GlcNAc (*N*-Acetylglucosamine), 232, 340,
  343, 346, 347
Gleevec (imatinib), 424–425F
Gln, *see* Glutamine
GlnRS (Glutaminyl–tRNA synthetase),
  995–996, 996F
Globin family, 176–178
  chain synthesis and fetal development,
    1043F
  DNA methylation, 918
  genealogy, 118–119F
  gene organization, 1043F
α-Globin gene cluster, 1043F
β-Globin gene cluster, 1043F
Globosides, 720F
Globular proteins, 134–136, 145–146
γ-Globulin, isoelectric point, 98T
Glu, *see* Glutamic acid
Glucagon, 550, 797
  countering of insulin effects by, 801–803
  and fatty acid metabolism, 712
  and fuel metabolism, 407
  glycogen metabolism effects, 550
Glucocerebrosides, 252, 720F
Glucocorticoids, 255F, 410
Glucocorticoid receptor (GR),
  1073, 1073F
Glucocorticoid response element
  (GRE), 1073
Glucogenic amino acids, 747
Glucokinase, 489, 516, 796, 796F, 800, 801
Glucokinase regulatory protein, 796
Gluconeogenesis, 454, 486, 530, **552–560**
  AMPK and inhibition of, 805
  and citric acid cycle, 556, 588–589
  and fuel metabolism, 407
  glycolysis compared, 553F
  hydrolytic reactions, **557–558**
  insulin blocking of, 801
  mammalian metabolism, 792, 792F
  oxaloacetate from glyoxylate cycle,
    590–591
  pyruvate to phosphoenolpyruvate,
    552–560
  regulation, **558–560**
  during starvation, 810
Gluconic acid, 225
1,5-Gluconolactone, 542
α-D-Glucopyranose, 222, 222F
β-D-Glucopyranose, 223F
D-Glucosamine, 225
D-Glucose (Glc), 220F

Glucose (Glc), 228, 809. *See also* Blood
  glucose
  aerobic and anaerobic metabolism
    contrasted, 634–635
  in amino acid degradation, 747F
  AMPK and uptake of, 805
  complete oxidation, 596–597
  in gluconeogenesis, 553F
  in glycolysis, 487F, 489–490
  and insulin release, 800
  levels of, during starvation, 809–810
  mammalian metabolism, 794
  metabolic energy, 485
Glucose-1,6-bisphosphate (G1,6P), 537
Glucose-1-phosphate (G1P):
  covalent modification, 391
  free energy of phosphate
    hydrolysis, 461T
  in galactose metabolism, 518
  in glycogen breakdown, 533
  in glycogen synthesis, 540F
Glucose-6-phosphatase (G6Pase), 538, 801
Glucose-6-phosphatase deficiency (von
  Gierke's disease), 538, 539
Glucose-6-phosphate (G6P), 463, 489, 800
  covalent modification, 392–393
  fats in liver, 797F
  free energy of phosphate hydrolysis, 461T
  in gluconeogenesis, 553F
  in glycogen breakdown, 534
  in glycolysis, 487F, 489
  high muscle exertion conditions, 795
  hydrolysis free energy, 466
  in pentose phosphate pathway, 521F
  possible fates, 531F
Glucose-6-phosphate dehydrogenase
  (G6PD):
  deficiency, 526
  in pentose phosphate pathway, 521F
Glucose–alanine cycle, 798–799, 799F
Glucose binding sites, 307
Glucose concentration, 311
Glucose–fatty acid cycle
  (Randle cycle), 634
Glucose hydroxyl groups, 299
Glucose metabolism:
  overview, 531F
  substrate cycles, 558F
Glucose transporters, **798–799**
Glucose transport intestinal
  epithelium, 317F
Glucose transport model, 307F
[1-^{13}C]Glucose, 476F
β-D-Glucose, 223F
D-Glucose, 221, 222F
α-Glucosidase, 231
α-1,4-Glucosidase deficiency (Pompe's
  disease), 538, 539
Glucosyl residue, 299
D-Glucuronic acid, 224

Glu residue, 318
GLUT1, 307, 309, 311, 805
GLUT2, 539, 802F
GLUT4, 442, 552, 800, 800F, 802F, 805
Glutamate (Glu), 80. *See also* Glutamic acid
  from amino acid breakdown, 738,
    742, 747F
  biosynthesis, 764–765F
  breakdown, 751–752F
  proline synthesis from, 768–769
  in urea cycle, 744F
Glutamate-5-phosphate, 768F
Glutamate-5-semialdehyde, 752, 768
Glutamate dehydrogenase, 589, 742
Glutamate synthase, 787
Glutamic acid (Glu):
  α helix/β sheet propensities, 140T
  charged polar side chain, 80
  as common amino acid, 93
  genetic code specification, 989T
  ionizable groups, 77T
  side chain hydropathy, 156T
Glutaminase, 695, 751–752F
Glutamine (Gln):
  acid–base catalysis by, 332
  α helix/β sheet propensities, 140T
  biosynthesis, 764–765F
  breakdown, 747F, 751–752F
  genetic code specification, 989T
  ionizable groups, 77T
  side chain hydropathy, 156T
  uncharged polar side chain, 79–80, 79F
Glutamine synthetase, 764–767
Glutaminyl–tRNA synthetase (GlnRS),
  995–996, 996F
γ-Glutamyl kinase, 768
γ-Glutamylphosphate, 765
Glutathione (GSH), 88, 400F, 526, 637
Glutathione peroxidase, 526, 637
Glutathione reductase, 526
Gluthathione disulfide (GSSG), 88
Glu–tRNA^{Gln} amidotransferase, 998
Glx, 81–82. *See also* Glutamic acid;
  Glutamine
Gly, *see* Glycine
Glycans, *see* Polysaccharides
Glyceraldehyde, 220F, 516
(*S*)-Glyceraldehyde, 85
D-Glyceraldehyde, 84F, 220F
L-Glyceraldehyde, 84F, 85
Glyceraldehyde-3-phosphate (GAP):
  in Calvin cycle, 664–666, 665F, 668
  in fructose metabolism, 517F
  in glycolysis, 486, 487F, 492–494
  in pentose phosphate pathway, 521F, 524
Glyceraldehyde-3-phosphate
  dehydrogenase (GAPDH):
  in Calvin cycle, 665F
  domains, 150F
  in glycolysis, 487F, **497–499**

Glyceraldehyde kinase, in fructose metabolism, 516
Glycerate, from photorespiration, 672
Glycerol, 224, 248, 249T, 517F
Glycerol-3-phosphate, 249F
  in adipose tissue, 796
  free energy of phosphate hydrolysis, 461T
  in fructose metabolism, 517F
  hydrolysis free energy, 466
  in triacylglycerol biosynthesis, 710F
Glycerol-3-phosphate acyltransferase, in triacylglycerol biosynthesis, 710F, 711
Glycerol-3-phosphate dehydrogenase, in triacylglycerol biosynthesis, 710F
Glycerol kinase, in fructose metabolism, 517F
Glycerol phosphate dehydrogenase, in fructose metabolism, 517F
Glyceroneogenesis, 711
Glycerophospholipids, 249–252, 249F
  common classes, 249T
  hydrolysis, 250–252
  synthesis, 714–717
Glycinamide ribotide (GAR), in IMP synthesis, 819F, 820
Glycine (Gly):
  α helix/β sheet propensities, 140T
  biosynthesis, 769
  breakdown, 747F, 748–751
  as chemical messenger, 88
  as common amino acid, 93
  genetic code specification, 989T
  in heme biosynthesis, 776F
  ionizable groups, 76T
  nonpolar side chain, 79
  side chain hydropathy, 156T
Glycine cleavage system, 749
Glycocalyx, 241F
Glycoconjugates, 241
Glycoforms, 240
Glycogen, 231
  as glucose stockpile, 530
  heart, 795
  starch contrasted as fuel reserve, 544
  structure, 532F
  structure optimization, 544
Glycogen branching enzyme, 540, 543–544
Glycogen breakdown, see Glycogenolysis
Glycogen debranching enzyme, 231, 533, 536–537
Glycogen degradation, 793
Glycogen granules, 532
Glycogenin, 543
Glycogen metabolism:
  allosteric control, 545
  covalent modification control, 545–550
  hormonal control, 550–552
  opposing pathways, 540F

Glycogenolysis (glycogen breakdown), 314, 531F, 532–539
  glycogen debranching enzyme, 533, 536–537
  glycogen phosphorylase, 533, 534–536
  insulin blocking of, 801
  mammalian metabolism, 792F, 797
  muscle contraction link, 547
  overview, 532–534
  phosphoglucomutase, 533, 537–539
Glycogen phosphorylase, 231, 391F, 533, 534–536
  allosteric control, 545
  conformational changes, 392F
  covalent modification, 391, 546
  and fructose, 518
  interconvertible enzyme system, 545–546F
  McArdle's disease and, 538
  reaction mechanism of, 535
Glycogen storage diseases, 538–539
Glycogen synthase, 540, 541–543, 805
  allosteric control, 542, 545
  covalent modification, 545, 550
Glycogen synthase kinase 3β (GSK3β), 552
Glycogen synthesis, 492, 530–531, 531F, 540–544
  aldolase, 492–494
  glycogen branching enzyme, 540, 543–544
  glycogen synthase, 541–543
  mammalian metabolism, 792F, 793
  UDP-glucose pyrophosphorylase, 540–541
Glycolate, from photorespiration, 672
Glycolate oxidase, 672
Glycolate phosphatase, 672
Glycolipids, 225, 274, 286
Glycolysis. See also Fermentation
  aldolase, 492–494, 492F
  AMPK activation of, 804–805
  anaerobic, 506
  cellular location, 453–454
  control of, 510–515
  coordinated control, 634F
  coupling to citric acid cycle, 567F
  electron transport sites, 597F
  Embden–Meyerhoff–Parnas pathway, 486
  energy-generating capacity, aerobic vs. anaerobic, 584
  enolase, 500
  first stage summary, 486, 496F
  free energy changes in, 511F
  gluconeogenesis compared, 553F
  glyceraldeyde-3-phosphate dehydrogenase (GAPDH), 497–499
  hexokinase (HK), 489–490, 490F
  mammalian metabolism, 792F–793, 795, 797

  metabolic key, 487F
  net reaction, 489
  overview, 486–488, 487F
  and pentose phosphate pathway, 525F
  phosphofructokinase (PFK), 491–492, 511–514
  phosphoglucose isomerase (PGI), 490–491
  phosphoglycerate kinase, 499
  phosphoglycerate mutase (PGM), 499–500, 501F
  pyruvate kinase (PK), 501
  stage 2 summary, 488, 503–504
  substrate cycles, 514–515
  substrate cycling, 514–515
  triose phosphate isomerase (TIM), 494–496, 495F
Glycophorin A, 264F, 265F
Glycoprotein(s), 234–242
  bacterial cell walls, 235–238
  glycosylated proteins, 238–240
  membrane, 274
  oligosaccharide functions, 240–242
  P-, 314–315
  proteoglycans, 234–235
  sialic acids in, 225
Glycosaminoglycans, 232–234, 286
  disaccharide units of selected, 232F
  in proteoglycans, 235F
Glycosides, 225F
α-Glycosides, 225–226, 225F
β-Glycosides, 225–226, 225F
Glycosidic bonds, 225–226, 560–561
Glycosphingolipids, 252
Glycosylated proteins, 238–240
Glycosylation, 238
Glycosylphosphatidylinositol-linked protein (GPI-linked protein), 268
Glycosyltransferases, 239
Glyoxylate cycle, 590–594, 591F
Glyoxylic acid, in uric acid degradation, 842F
Glyoxysomes, 590–591F, 698
G$_{M1}$, see Ganglioside G$_{M1}$
G$_{M2}$, see Ganglioside G$_{M2}$
G$_{M3}$, see Ganglioside G$_{M3}$
G$_{M1}$, gangliosidosis, 720F
GMP (guanosine monophosphate), 41T
  animal catabolism pathway, 840F
  from IMP, 821F
  synthesis, 821–822, 821F
GMP synthase, in IMP conversion to AMP/GMP, 821F
G$_M$ subunit, 548
Gobind Khorana, H., 988
Goldberg, J., 925
Golgi apparatus, 8, 8F, 282, 286. See also Plasma membrane; Posttranslational modification
  glycosylated protein synthesis in, 239
  metabolic functions, 455T

Gonads, 410
Gout, 843–844
GPCRs (G protein-coupled receptors), 428, 429
GPI-linked protein (Glycosylphosphatidylinositol-linked protein), 268
G proteins, 416, 546, 971. *See also* Heterotrimeric G proteins
G protein-coupled receptors (GPCRs), 428, 429
G-quartet, 914, 915F
GR (glucocorticoid receptor), 1073, 1073F
Gram, C., 236
Gram-negative bacteria, 236, 316
Gram-positive bacteria, 236
Granum, 641F, 642
Graves' disease, 215T
Grb2, 418F
GRE (glucocorticoid response element), 1073
Greek key motif, 146
Greenberg, G. R., 818
Green fluorescent protein, 87
Green sulfur bacteria, 658
gRNAs (guide RNAs), 975
GroEL, X-ray structure, 165–166, 166F
GroEL–GroES–(ADP)$_7$ complex, 166F
  chaperones, barrel structure of, 165–166
  conformational changes in, 166–168
GroES, X-ray structure, 166F
Group I introns, 978, 979F
Group II introns, 978
Group-transfer reactions, 453
  cofactors for, 326
  phosphoryl group-transfer potentials, 461, 461T
  Ping Pong reactions, 376
Growth factor receptors, 233
Growth hormone, 67T
Growth hormone (GH), 411–412
$G_{s\alpha}$, 431
GSH (glutathione), 88, 400F, 526, 637
GSK3β (glycogen synthase kinase 3β), 443F, 552
GSSG (gluthathione disulfide), 88
GTF (general transcription factor), 960, 961T
GTP (guanosine triphosphate), 278, 553F, 554F
GTPase-activating protein (GAP), 418–419
GTP-binding factors, 1027
Guanidinium ion, as chaotropic agent, 159
Guanidino group, 466
Guanine (G), 40l, 41T
  base pairing, 46F, 851F, 866–868
  Chargaff's rules and, 44
  as common nucleotide, 42
  modified forms in tRNA, 992F

in purine catabolism, 840F
  tautomeric forms, 44F
Guanine deaminase, in purine catabolism, 840F
Guanine-7-methyltransferase, 966
Guanine nucleotide exchange factor (GEF), 418
Guanine ribonucleotide synthesis, 821–822
Guanosine, 41T, 840F
Guanosine diphosphate, *see* GDP
Guanosine monophosphate, *see* GMP
Guanosinc triphosphate, *see* GTP
Guanosine-5′-(β,γ-imido)triphosphate (GMPPNP, GDPNP), 1016
Guanylate cyclase, 436
Guanylic acid, *see* GMP
Guide RNAs (gRNAs), 975
D-Gulose, 220F

H
H (heavy chains), 201, 210, 285
H1 histones, 884, 884T, 887F
H2A histones, 854T, 884–886F, 887, 888
H2B histones, 884, 884T, 885F, 886F, 887, 888
H3 histones, 884, 884T, 885F, 886F, 888
H4 histones, 119, 884, 884T, 885F, 886F, 887–888
HA (hemagglutinin), 289–291
HA1, 290F
HA2, 290F
H (enthalpy), 12
Haber-Bosch process, 786
Haemophilus haemolyticus, 1065
Haemophilus influenzae, 57T
Hairy gene, 1092
Haldane, J. B. S., 2, 369
Half-cell, 471F–472
Half-chair conformation, 342F
Half-life, 365–366
Half-reactions, 470–471
  biological significance, 473–474
  selected reaction reduction potentials, 473T
Half-time, 365–366
Haloarcula marismortui, 869F, 1002
Halobacter halobium, 266
Halobacteria, 9
Halobacterium salinarium, 266, 608–609
Hamm, H., 430
Hammerhead ribozyme, 870F
Hanson, J., 200
H antigens, 242F
Haploid DNA, 47
Haploid genome DNA contents, 1039F
Harden, A., 485
Harrison, S., 863, 876
HATs (histone acetyltransferases), 1060–1061
Hatch, M., 674

Haworth projections, 222
Hb, *see* Hemoglobin
HCC (hepatocellular carcinoma), 480F
HD, *see* Huntington's disease
HDACs (histone deacetylases), 1062
  gene silencing, 1062
  transcriptional repression, 1062
HDL (high density lipoproteins), 685, 728–729
Heart, 795
  AMPK-activated glycolysis in, 804–805
  citric acid cycle in, 586
  muscle ATP production energetics, 511T
Heart attack, *see* Myocardial infarction
Heart-specific enzymes, as indicators of myocardial infarction, 635
Heat *(q),* 12
Heat-labile enterotoxin, 435
HEAT sequence, 426
Heat shock proteins (Hsp), 165
Heavy chains (H), 201, 210, 285
HECT domain, 734
Helicase, 903
Helicase II (UvrD), 924
Helices, left- vs. right-handed, 45F
Helicobacter pylori, 1038F
Helix capping, 140
Helix–turn–helix (HTH) motif, 876, 877F
Hemagglutinin (HA), 289–291
Heme *a,* 611F
Heme *b,* 611F
Heme *c,* 611F
Heme *c*$_i$, 657
Heme-controlled protein synthesis, 1077F
Heme *f,* 657
Heme groups:
  biosynthesis, **775–778**
  degradation, **778–780**
  hemoglobin, 186F
  iron porphyrins, 488
  isotopic tracer studies, 476
  myoglobin, 177, 178F, 342
  oxygenation, 178
Heme-regulated inhibitor (HRI), 1077
Hemerythrin, 181
Heme *x,* 657
Hemiacetals, 211–222F, 344F
Hemiketals, 211–222F
Hemin, 777
Hemocyanin, 181
Hemoglobin (Hb), 94, 177, **181–197,** 309, 390
  abnormal, 195T
  allosteric proteins, **192–194,** 193F
  BPG (2,3-D-bisphosphoglycerate) binding, 191
  and carbon dioxide transport, 189–190
  deoxy, 182–183F
  erythrocyte shape and, 272

Hemoglobin (Hb) (*cont.*)
  evolution rate, 119F
  fetal, 118, 191, 1043
  function, 181–184, 191
  and globin family, 118–119
  high-altitude adaptation, 192
  Hill plot, 185F
  isoelectric point, 98T
  mutations, **194–197**
  and other oxygen-transport proteins, 181
  oxy, 182–183F
  oxygen binding, **184–186**
  oxygen binding cooperativity, **186–194**
  oxygen binding curve, 184F
  R and T conformational states (Perutz
    mechanism), 186F–189
  structure, 126F, **181**, **182–184**
Hemoglobin S (sickle-cell hemoglobin),
  194–197
Hemolymph, 181
Hemolytic anemia, 194
Hemophilia a, 359
Hemophilia b, 359
Henderson, R., 266
Henderson–Hasselbalch equation, 34
Hen egg white (HEW) lysozyme. *See also*
  Lysozyme
Henri, V., 368
Henseleit, K., 569, 743
Heparan, 232F–233F, 233
Heparan sulfate (HS), 233
Hepatitis B surface antigen, 67T
Hepatocellular carcinoma (HCC), 480F
Hepatomegaly, 538
Heptad repeats, 881–882
Heptoses, 221
HER2 receptor, 213, 425
Herceptin (trastuzumab), 213, 425
Hereditary nonpolyposis colorectal cancer
  syndrome, 924
Hereditary spherocytosis, 273
Hers' disease, 538, 539
Hershko, A., 734
Heterochromatin, 1056
Heterochromatin protein 1
  (HP1), 1064
Heterogeneous nuclear mRNAs
  (hnRNAs), 967
Heterokaryon, 271F
Heterologous DNA, 926
Heterolytic cleavage, 695
Heteropolysaccharides, 226
Heterotrimeric G proteins, **428–436**,
  430F, 1070
  and adenylate cyclase, 432–434
  components of, 428
  dissociation of, 430–432
  and phosphodiesterases, 435–436
  transmembrane helices in, 429–430
Heterotrophs, 449

Heterozygotes, 195
Hexokinase (HK), 463
  activity relative glucokinase, 796F
  in glycolysis, 487F, **489–490**, 490F, 511
  in mannose metabolism, 520F
Hexose, 221
  chair and half-chair conformations, 342F
  metabolism of non-glucose, **516–520**
Hexose-monophosphate shunt, 521
Hexosiminidase A deficiency, and
  Tay-Sachs disease, 720–721
Hg^{2+} ion, zinc ion replacement, 326
hGH (human GH), 411–412F
hGHbp, 412
HGPRT (hypoxanthine–guanine
  phosphorihosyl transferase), 824
High-altitude adaptation, 192
High density lipoproteins (HDL), **681**,
  685, 728–729
High-energy bonds, 461
High-energy compounds, 459–469. *See also*
  specific compounds, especially ATP
  ATP and phosphoryl group transfer,
    460–462
  coupled reactions, **462–464**
  thioesters, **468–469**
"High-energy" intermediates, 459
Highly repetitive DNA sequences, 1044
High mobility group (HMG), 1058
High-performance liquid chromatography
  (HPLC), 98
High-throughput screening, 395
HI/HA (hyperammonemia), 742, 747
Hill, A., 184
Hill coefficient, 185
Hill equation, 184–186
Hill plot, 185F
Hinkle, P., 630
Hippuric acid, 686
His, *see* Histidine
his operon, *E. coli*, 1053
His residues, 306, 318
His tag, 628
Histamine, 88, 780
Histidine (His):
  acid–base catalysis by, 332
  α helix/β sheet propensities, 140T
  biosynthesis, 774, 775F
  breakdown, 747F, 751–752F
  charged polar side chain, 80
  covalent catalysis by, 335
  genetic code specification, 989T
  ionizable groups, 77T
  as rare amino acid, 93
  side chain hydropathy, 156T
  structure, 77T
Histones:
  calf thymus, 884T
  chromatin fiber interaction, 887F–890
  covalently modified, 1059–1060

  DNA binding, 875
  and DNA replication, 914
  gene clusters, selected organisms, 1042F
  H1, 884, 884T, 887F
  H2A, 884, 884T, 885F, 886F, 887, 888
  H2B, 884, 884T, 885F, 886F, 887, 888
  H3, 884, 884T, 885F, 886F, 888
  H4, 119, 884, 884T, 885F, 886F, 887–888
  isoelectric point, 98T
  linking nucleosomes, 886–887
Histone acetylation, 1060
Histone Acetyl-Lys, 1060
Histone acetyltransferases
  (HATs), 1060
Histone code, 1060
Histone deacetylases (HDACs), 1062
Histone-depleted metaphase
  chromosomes, 888F
Histone–DNA interactions, 1059–1060
Histone Lys, 1060, 1063
Histone methylation, 1063
Histone methyl-Lys residues, 1064F
Histone methyltransferases
  (HMTs), 1063
Histone modifications, nucleosome core
  particle, 1059T
Histone tail modifications, histone
  code, 1060
Hitchings, G., 838, 844
HIV (human immunodeficiency virus),
  912–913
HIV-1 reverse transcriptase, 912–913
HIV-1 reverse transcriptase inhibitors,
  384–385
HIV protease inhibitors, 381,
  384–385
HK, *see* Hexokinase
HMG (high mobility group), 1058
HMG1, 1080
HMG2, 1080
HMG box, 1058
HMG-CoA (β-Hydroxy-β-
  methylglutaryl-CoA):
  in cholesterol biosynthesis, 722–723F
  in ketogenesis, 699, 699F, 805
HMG-CoA lyase, in ketogenesis, 699, 699F
HMG-CoA reductase, 684F, 805
  in cholesterol synthesis, 722–723F
  statins, inhibition by, 726–727
HMG-CoA synthase, in ketogenesis,
  699, 699F
HMG proteins, 1058
  gene expression, 1058–1059
  regulatory proteins, 1058
HMTs (histone methyltransferases), 1063
hnRNAs (heterogeneous nuclear
  mRNAs), 967
Hodgkin, D. C., 125, 182, 692, 697
Holden, H., 206, 695
Holley, R., 50, 991

Holliday, R., 926
Holliday junction, 926, 927F–928F, 934
Holoenzyme:
  PP2A, 427
  RNA polymerase, 943F, 946
Homeobox, 1095
Homeodomain, 1095
Homeostasis, 407, 799. *See also* Metabolic
    homeostasis
Homeotic mutation, 1097
Homeotic selector genes, 1092
Homocitrate, 784
Homocysteine, 754
Homocysteine methyltransferase, 770
Homocysteinuria, 755
Homodimers, 305
Homogentisate, in phenylalanine
    breakdown, 477F
Homogentisate dioxygenase, 762
Homogentisic acid, 477, 762
Homolactic fermentation, **505–506**
Homologous end-joining, 934
Homologous proteins, 116–117F
Homologous (general) recombination,
    926–932
Homology, 1040
Homology modeling, 163
Homolytic cleavage, 695
Homopolysaccharides, 226
Homo sapiens, 57T
Homotetramers, 304
Homozygotes, 195
Hoogsteen base pairs, 866
Hormones, **405–412.** See also
    Glucagon; Insulin
  adrenal glands, 409–410
  endocrine, 406–407
  fuel metabolism regulation, 407–408,
    799–804
  glycogen metabolism control, 550–552
  growth, 411–412
  mammalian metabolism role, 791
  pancreatic, 407–408
  steroid, 410–411
Hormone activated nuclear receptors,
    1072–1073
Hormone response elements (HREs),
    1072–1073
Hormone-sensitive lipase, 685
Hormone-sensitive triacylglycerol lipase,
    633, 712
Horseshoe crab, 181
Horwich, A., 166
Hot spots, 941
Hox genes, 1095–1097
HP1 (heterochromatin protein 1), 1064
HPLC (high-performance liquid
    chromatography), 98
HPRT (hypoxanthine phosphoribosyl
    transferase), 213

HREs (hormone response elements),
    1072–1073
HRI (heme-regulated inhibitor), 1077
HS (heparin sulfate), 233
HS4 insulator, 1070
Hsp40, 165
Hsp70, 165
Hsp90, 165
HTH (helix–turn–helix) motif, 876, 877F
Huber, R., 355–356, 736
Humans. *See also specific organs, cell types,
    diseases, etc.*
  arachidonic acid, as most important
    eicosanoid precursor, 259
  daily metabolic energy needs, 631
  fuel reserves, normal 70-kg man,
    778T, 810T
  gene number, 1039
  genome sequencing, 56
  hemoglobin variants, 195T
  human-mouse cell fusion, 271F
Human cyclin-dependent kinase-2, 1083F
Human genome:
  genes associated with disease, 1041–1042
  sequence variations, 1041
human GH (hGH), 411–412F
Human growth hormone, genetically
    engineered, 67T
Human histone methyltransferase, 1064F
Human immunodeficiency virus (HIV),
    912–913
Human p53 DNA-binding domain, 1085F
Human TAF1 double bromodomain, 1062F
Humoral immunity, 209
Hunchback (hb) genes, 1091
Hunchback protein, 1092
Huntingtin, 1044
Huntington's disease (HD), 636, 1044,
    1044T, 1087
Hurwitz, J., 943
Huxley, A., 200
Huxley, H., 200
Hyaluronate, 232F
Hyaluronic acid, 232, 235F
Hybridization (RNA–DNA), 866
Hybridoma cells, 213
Hyde, C., 773
Hydration, 26
Hydrocortisone, 255F, 410
Hydrogen bond (defined), 23
Hydrogen bonds, 24F
  bond energy, 25T
  functional groups, 26F
  nucleic acids, 867
  proteins, 156–158
Hydrolases, reaction type catalyzed, 324T
Hydrolysis, 3, 312, 313
Hydronium ion, 30
Hydropathy, 156
Hydropathy scale, 156T

Hydrophilic substances, 26
Hydrophobic collapse, 161
Hydrophobic effect, **26–29**
  amino acids, 80
  membrane proteins, 266–267
  nucleic acids, 867–868
  proteins, 156
Hydrophobic forces, 28–29
Hydrophobic interaction
    chromatography, **97**
Hydrophobicity, 1060
Hydrophobic substances, 26–27
Hydropyrimidine hydratase, in pyrimidine
    catabolism, 845F
β-Hydroxyacyl–ACP dehydrase, in fatty
    acid synthesis, 705F
L-Hydroxyacyl-CoA, 688
L-Hydroxyacyl-CoA dehydrogenase, 688
Hydroxyapatite, and nucleic acid
    chromatography, 872
β-Hydroxy-β-methylglutaryl-CoA (HMG-
    CoA), *see* HMG-CoA
D-β-Hydroxybutyrate, in ketone body con-
    version to acetyl-CoA, 698, 700F
β-Hydroxybutyrate dehydrogenase,
    in ketone body conversion to
    acetylCoA, 700F
D-β-Hydroxybutyryl-ACP, in fatty acid
    synthesis, 705F
Hydroxyethylthiamine pyrophosphate, 508
Hydroxylamine, 940
Hydroxyl group, 26F
Hydroxyl radical, 636
5-Hydroxylysyl (Hyl), 137
Hydroxymethylbilane, 777
Hydroxymethylglutaryl-CoA reductase
    (HMG-CoA reductase), 805
p-Hydroxyphenylpyruvate, in phenylala-
    nine breakdown, 477F
4-Hydroxyproline, 86F
3-Hydroxyprolyl, 137
4-Hydroxyprolyl (Hyp), 137
Hydroxypyruvate, from
    photorespiration, 672
5-Hydroxytryptamine, 780
Hydroxyurea, 196
5-Hydroxyurea, 847
Hyl (5-Hydroxylysyl), 137
Hyp (4-Hydroxyprolyl), 137
Hyperammonemia (HI/HA), 742, 747
Hyperbolic binding curve, 179–180
Hypercholesterolemia, 726
Hyperchromic effect, 864
Hyperglycemia, 256, 811
Hyperhomocysteinemia, 755
Hyperlysinemia, 758
Hyperlysinuria, 758
Hypermutation, somatic, 214, 1081
Hyperphenylalaninemia, 762
Hyperproliferative signals, 1086

Hyperthermophiles, 159
Hypervariable residues, 116
Hypervariable sequences, 212
Hyperventilation, and alkalosis, 36
Hypoglycemia, 518, 538
Hypothalamus, 406F, 807
Hypotonic environments, bacterial cell
    walls and, 235–236
Hypoxanthine, 72, 818, 840F
Hypoxanthine–guanine phosphoribosyl
    transferase (HGPRT), 824
Hypoxanthine phosphoribosyl transferase
    (HPRT), 213
Hypoxia, 192
H zone, 198, 199F

I

I band, 198, 199F
Ibuprofen, 85F, 719
ICAT (isotope-coded affinity tags), 480–481F
Ice, 24F
I-cell disease, 286
ICLs (intracellular loops), 315F
Icosahedral symmetry, 155, 155F
IDL (intermediate density lipoproteins),
    681, 683
D-Idose, 220F
Iduronate, 233
IEF (isoelectric focusing), 103
IFs (initiation factors), 1012–1014, 1012T
IF$_1$, 633
IF-1, 1012
IF-2, 1012
IF-3, 1012
I-FABP (intestinal fatty-acid binding
    protein), 680F
Ig, *See* Immunoglobulin
IgA (immunoglobulin A), 210
IgD (immunoglobulin D), 211
IgE (immunoglobulin E), 211
IgG (immunoglobulin G), 211F
IgM (immunoglobulin M), 210
Ile, *see* Isoleucine
IleRS, 997
ilv operon, *E. coli,* 1053
Imaginal disks, 1091
Imatinib, 424–425F
Imidazole, reaction with *p*-nitrophenylace-
    tate, 336
Imine (Schiff Base), 330
Imine, functional group and linkages, 4T
Immune system, **209**. *See also* Antibodies
    and adenosine deaminase, 840
    induced apoptosis, 1087
Immunoaffinity chromatography, 101
Immunoassays, 95
Immunoblotting, 102, 874
Immunofluorescence microscopy, 207
Immunoglobulin (Ig), **209–212**. *See also*
    Antibodies

Immunoglobulin A (IgA), 210
Immunoglobulin D (IgD), 211
Immunoglobulin E (IgE), 211
Immunoglobulin fold, 148, 212F
Immunoglobulin G (IgG), 211F
Immunoglobulin M (IgM), 210
IMP (inosine monophosphate):
    as AMP/GMP precursor, 818
    animal catabolism pathway, 840F
    conversion to AMP or GMP, 821F
    pathway regulation, 822–823
    synthesis, **818–821,** 819F
IMP cyclohydrolase, in IMP
    synthesis, 819F
IMP dehydrogenase, in IMP conversion to
    AMP/GMP, 821F
Inactivation, 309
Inactivation ball, 304
Inactivators, 377
Inclusion bodies, 94F
Indirect readout, 878
Indole, 773–774
Indole-3-glycerol phosphate, 773
Induced fit, 325
Inducers, 1047
Inducible enzymes, 950
-ine (suffix), 82
Influenza virus, 289
Ingold, C., 85
Ingram, V., 195
Inheritance, 48. *See also* DNA
Inhibition, enzyme, *see* Enzyme inhibition
Inhibition constant, (K_I), 368, 378–381
Inhibitors, 377
Inhibitor-1 (phosphoprotein phosphatase
    inhibitor 1), 548
Initial velocity of reaction (v_o), 370
Initiation factors (IFs), 1012–1014, 1012T
Initiator caspases, 1088
Inorganic pyrophosphatase, 464, 465F
Inosine, 840F, 992F
Inosine monophosphate, *see* IMP
myo-Inositol, 224
Inositol polyphosphate 5-phosphatase, 441
Inositol-1,4,5-triphosphate (IP$_3$), 437
Inr (initiator) element, 959
Insertion mutations, 916, 919
Insertion sequence (IS), 935F
In silico models, 482
In situ hybridization, 64F–65
Insulators:
    heterochromatin spreading, 1070
    limit enhancers, 1070
Insulin, 92, **800–803**
    and catecholamines, 801
    diabetes mellitus, 811–813
    discovery, 812
    epinephrine as antagonist, 552
    and fatty acid metabolism, 712
    and fuel storage, 800–801

    genetically engineered, 67T
    and glucagon, 801–803
    glucose and triggering of, 800
    isoelectric point, 98T
    and liver gluconeogenesis/
      glycogenolysis, 801
    primary structure of bovine, 92F, 104
    pyruvate dehydrogenase phosphatase
      activation, 585
    receptor, 413F
Insulin-dependent diabetes mellitus,
    215T, 811–812
Insulin receptor (IR), 433F
Insulin receptor substrate 1 (IRS-1), 416
Insulin receptor substrate 2 (IRS-2), 416
Insulin resistance, 813
Insulin signaling system, 442, 443F
Insulin-stimulated protein kinase, 436, 548
Integral membrane proteins, **263–264,** 263F
Integral proteins, 263–264
Integrases, 939
Intercalating agents, 873, 919
Intercalation, **873**
Intercellular channels, 308
Interconvertible enzyme system, 545–546F
Interfacial activation, 679F
Interferons, 422, 972
Intermediates, 364
Intermediate density lipoproteins (IDL),
    681, 683
Intermembrane space, 599
Internal conversion, 646
Internal hydrophilic cavity, 318
Internal resolution site, 936
Interorgan metabolic pathways, **798–799**
    Cori cycle, **798,** 798F
    glucose–alanine cycle, **798–799,** 799F
    glucose transporters, **798–799**
Intervening sequences, *see* Introns
Intestinal epithelium, 317F
Intestinal fatty acid-binding protein
    (I-FABP), 630
Intestinal mucosa, 630
Intestine, fuel availability after meals, 793
Intracellular apoptosis, 1088–1090
Intracellular fluids, buffering, 35–36
Intracellular loops (ICLs), 315F
Intracellular signaling, *see* Signal
    transduction
Intrasteric mechanisms, 440
Intrinsic factor, 696
Intrinsic membrane proteins, *see* Integral
    membrane proteins
Intrinsic pathway, apoptosis, 1088
Intrinsic pathway, blood coagulation
    cascade, 358–359
Introns, 67
Introns (intervening sequences), 967
    discovery, 968
    eukaryotic pre-tRNAs, 981–982

group I, 978, 979F
  group II, 978
  lariat structure, 970
Invariant residues, 116
Inverted repeats, 935F
In vitro assessment, 394
Iodoacetate, 107
Ion, solvation, 25–26, 26F
Ion-binding sites, 311
Ion channels, **299–302**
Ion exchange chromatography, **97,** 99F
Ion-gradient-driven active transport, **316–318**
Ionic interactions, 24–25, 25T
Ionizable groups, pK values of, **81**
Ionization, water, **30–32**
Ionophores, **297–298**
Ion pair, 157
Ion specificity, 302
IP$_3$ (inositol-1,4,5-trisphosphate), 437
IPTG (isopropylthiogalactoside), as inducer, 1047
IR (insulin receptor), 433F
Iron (element), *See under* Fe
Iron porphyrins, 488
Iron–sulfur clusters:
  [2Fe–2S], 605
  [4Fe–4S], 579, 605
Iron–sulfur protein (ISP), 605, 612
Irreversible inhibitor, 385
IRS-1 (insulin receptor substrate 1), 416
IRS-2 (insulin receptor substrate 2), 416
IS (insertion sequence), 935F
  IS1, 935
  IS2, 935
Islets of Langerhans, 407
Isoaccepting tRNAs, 995, 998
Isocitrate, 325
  in amino acid degradation, 747F
  in citric acid cycle, 568F, 578–580, 584F
  in glyoxylate cycle, 591F
  Isocitrate dehydrogenase, in citric acid cycle, 568F, 579–580, 586–587
Isocitrate lyase, in glyoxylate cycle, 591, 591F
Isoelectric focusing (IEF), 103
Isoelectric point, amino acids, 81
Isoforms, 391, 398
Isolated systems, 18
Isoleucine (Ile):
  α helix/β sheet propensities, 140T
  biosynthesis, 771–773
  breakdown, 747F, 757–758
  genetic code specification, 989T
  ionizable groups, 76T
  nonpolar side chain, 79, 79F
  side chain hydropathy, 156T
  structure, 76T, 79F
Isomerases, 324T, 453
Isomerizations, 453
Isopentyl pyrophosphate, 722–723F

Isopeptide bond, 88, 734
Isoprene, 257, 721
Isoprene units, 268, 721
Isoprenoid group, 268
Isoprenoids, 257
Isopropylthiogalactoside (IPTG), as inducer, 1047
Isoproterenol, 409
Isoschizomers, 72
Isotope-coded affinity tags (ICAT), 480–481F
Isotopic labeling, 367
Isotopic tracers, 475–476
Isozymes, 391, 398, 455
ISP (iron–sulfur protein), 605, 612
Iwata, S., 318

J
Jaenisch, R., 1067
JAK (Janus kinase), 1071
JAK-STAT pathway, 1071–1072, 1071F
Janus kinase (JAK), 1071
Jap, B., 306
Jaundice, 780
Jelly roll, 149
J_λ, 1079
Jmol, 153
Johnson, L., 391
Joliet, P., 655
Jones, M. E., 826
Jorgensen, R., 1075
J subunit, 210
Jun, 419, 1070
Junk DNA, 972, 1046
Juvenile-onset diabetes mellitus, 811

K
K, *see* Dissociation constant
k (rate constant), 364
k_1, 368
k_{-1}, 368
k_2, 368
Kaback, R., 318
Kabat, E., 212
Kandler, O., 9
κ chain gene family, 1078F–1079
Karplus, M., 158
k_B (Botzmann constant), 13–14, 372
kb (kilobase pairs), 47
k_{cat}, 371
k_{cat}/K_M, 371–372, 371T
K$^+$ channels, 299–302, 618
KcsA K$^+$ channel, 299–303, 300F, 301F
kD (kilodaltons), 13
KDEL receptors, 286
KDPG (2-keto-3-deoxy-6-phosphogluconate), 529
Keilin, D., 610, 619

Kendrew, J., 126, 177, 182, 200, 968
Kennedy, E., 686
K_{eq} (equilibrium constant), 16
Keratan sulfate, 232F, 233, 235F
Keratins, 134–136
  α Keratins, 134, 136
  β Keratins, 134–136
Kerr, J., 1086
Ketals, cyclic, 225
2-Keto-3-deoxy-6-phosphogluconate (KDPG), 529
2-Keto-3-deoxy-D-arabinoheptulosonate-7-phosphate, 773
α-Keto acid, from amino acid transamination, 738–741F
2-Keto acid dehydrogenases, 580
β-Ketoacyl–ACP reductase, in fatty acid synthesis, 705F
β-Ketoacyl–ACP synthase, in fatty acid synthesis, 705F
Ketoacyl-CoA thiolase, 688, 689–690
3-Ketoacyl-CoA transferase, in ketone body conversion to acetyl-CoA, 700F
α-Ketobutyrate, 754, 772
Keto–enol tautomerization, 331F
Ketogenesis, 698, 699F
Ketogenic amino acids, 747–748
α-Ketoglutarate, 567, 595
  amino acid biosynthesis from, 764–769
  from amino acid degradation, 738, 742, 747F, 751–752F
  in citric acid cycle, 568F, 579–580, 584F
  in urea cycle, 744F
α-Ketoglutarate dehydrogenase, 580, 586–587
  in citric acid cycle, 568F, 580
  malate dehydrogenase, 583
  NAD$^+$-dependent isocitrate dehydrogenase, 579–580, 579F, 586–587
  net reaction, 569–570
  overview, 567–570, 568F
  pathways using citric acid cycle intermediates, 588–589
  pyruvate dehydrogenase complex, 570–573
  pyruvate dehydrogenase complex regulation, 584–585
  rate-controlling reactions, 585–587, 586T
  reactions replenishing citric acid cycle intermediates, 589–590
  regulation, 583–587, 587F
  related reactions, 535–539
  succinate dehydrogenase, 582, 582F
  succinyl-CoA synthetase, 580–582, 581F
Keto group, hydrogen bonding, 26F
Ketone, 4T, 330
Ketone bodies, **698–700**
  conversion to acetyl-CoA, 700F
  in diabetes, 811
  as energy source during starvation, 810–811
  mammalian metabolism, 794, 797

Ketose, 220
D-Ketose, 221F
Ketosis, 700, 811
3-Ketosphinganine, 718F
3-Ketosphinganine reductase, 718F
3-Ketosphinganine synthase, 718F
KFERQ proteins, 733
K_I (inhibition constant), 368, 378–381
Kidney, 406F, **798**
Kidney stones, 843
Kilobase pairs (kb), 47
Kilodaltons (kD), 13
Kim, J.-J., 688
Kim, P., 881
Kim, S.-H., 869, 1083F
Kinases, 376, 406, 465. *See also*
    specific kinases
Kinase cascades, **416–422**
    completion of signaling pathway by,
        419–420
    and GAPs, 418–419
    in mammalian cells, 420F
    and scaffold proteins, 420, 422
    and SH3 domains, 417–418
Kinemages, 153
Kinetics, **364–376**. *See also*
    Enzyme kinetics
Kinetically stable, 461
KiNG (program), 153
K^+ ion, 299, 335
Klenow fragment, 900F
Klentaq1, 900–902, 901F
Klinefelter's syndrome, 411
Klug, A., 869, 870, 879, 886
K_M (Michaelis–Menten constant),
        369–371, 371T
    Lineweaver–Burk plot for, 373
    sample calculation, 373
knirps gene, 1092
Knirps protein, 1092
Knoop, F., 475, 569, 686
Knowles, J., 496
Köhler, G., 213
Kok, B., 655
Kornberg, A., 533, 896, 898
Kornberg, R., 884, 953, 961, 1056,
        1069, 1070
Kornberg, T., 1094, 1096
Kornfeld, S., 239
Koshland, D., 193
Kraut, J., 354
Krebs, E. G., 533
Krebs, H., 567, 569, 743
Krebs cycle, *see* Citric acid cycle
krüppel gene, 1092
Krüppel protein, 1092
K_S, 371
Ku70 subunit, 925
Ku80 subunit, 925
Kühne, W., 200

Ku protein, 925
Kuru, 169
K_v channels, 303F–304F
Kv1.2 channels, 303–304F
K_W, ionization constant of water, 31
Kwashiorkor, 789
Kynureninase, 758

L

L (Fischer convention), 84
L (linking number), 827
L23 protein, 1028
lac operator, 1048F
lac operon, 945F, 1048
lac repressor, **1046–1050**
α-Lactalbumin, 560
β-Lactamase, 238, 936
Lactase, 227
Lactate:
    from homolactic fermentation, **505–506**
    isozyme action, 455
    muscle fatigue and, 795
Lactate dehydrogenase (LDH),
        148, 455, 505
Lactic acid, 190
Lactose, 227
    E. coli metabolism, 1046
    synthesis, 560
Lactose analog, 318
Lactose binding site, 318
Lactose intolerance, 227
Lactose permease (galactoside permease),
        316, 1047
    in *E. coli*, 317F–318F
    proton gradient, 316–318
Lactose synthase, 560
Lactosyl ceramide, 720F
lacZ coding sequence, 1097
LADH (liver alcohol dehydrogenase), 509
Lagging strand, 896, **904–905,** 905F
λ chain, 1079
Lander, E., 57
Lands, W., 716
Lanosterol, 724
Large (50S) ribosomal subunit,
        1001–1006, 1001T
Lariat structure, 970
Late genes, 947
Lateral diffusion, in lipid bilayers, 261
Lathyrism, 137
Lauric acid, 247T
LBHBs (low-barrier hydrogen bonds), 355
LCa (clathrin light chain), 285
LCAT (lecithin–cholesterol
    acyltransferase), 685
lck, 422
LDH (lactate dehydrogenase), 148,
    455, 505
LDL, *see* Low density lipoproteins
Lead compound, 394–395

Leader sequence, 1051F–1052
Leading strand, 896, **904–905,** 905F
Leading substrates, 376
Lecithin, 249T, 715F
Lecithin–cholesterol acyltransferase
    (LCAT), 685
Lectins, 241
Leeuwenhoek, A. van, 200
Leghemoglobins, 181
Lehninger, A., 686
Leischmaniasis, 504
Leloir, L., 533
Lenski, R., 11
Leptin, 806F–807
Lesch–Nyhan syndrome, 7o, 824, 844
Leslie, A., 623F
Lethal factor (LF), 444–445
Leucine (Leu):
    α helix/β sheet propensities, 140T
    biosynthesis, 771–773
    breakdown, 747F, 757–758
    as common amino acid, 93
    genetic code specification, 988, 989T
    nonpolar side chain, 79
    side chain hydropathy, 156T
    structure, 76T
Leucine zippers, 881F–882
Leukocytes, 241–242
Leukocyte elastase, inhibition, 356
Leukotrienes, 258, 259F
Leupeptin, 350F
Levinthal, C., 161
Levorotatory molecules, 84
Lewis, E. B., 1095
Lewis, M., 1049
LexA, 926
LF (lethal factor), 444–445
LH-2, 644F
LHC (light-harvesting complex), 644, 662
Lienhard, G., 338
Life. *See also* Cells; Evolution
    cellular architecture, **5–7**
    chiral molecules and, 84–86
    organismal evolution, **9–10**
    origin, **2–5**
    thermodynamics and, **17–19**
    water and, 22
Li–Fraumeni syndrome, 1084
Ligands, 101, 180
Ligand binding, 437–438
Ligand-gated channels, 302
Ligases, 453
Ligases, reaction type catalyzed, 324T
Ligation, 61
Light-absorbing pigments, photosynthetic,
    643–645
Light chains (L), 201, 210
Light chain (in clathrin), 285
Light energy, transformation of, to
    chemical energy, **645–647**

Light-harvesting complex (LHC), 644, 662

Light reactions, photosynthesis, 641, **645–663**

Lignin, 229–230

Lignoceric acid, 247T

Limited proteolysis, 108

Limulus polyphemus, 181

LINEs (long interspersed nuclear elements), 939, 1045

Lineweaver, H., 373

Lineweaver–Burk plot (double-reciprocal plot), 373–374

  competitive inhibition, 380F, 381T

  mixed inhibition, 381T, 383F

  uncompetitive inhibition, 381T, 382F

Linkages, 3

Linker, hinge binding DNA, 1049

Linker DNA, 884

Linker histones, 886–887

Linking number, supercoiled DNA, 858

Link proteins, 234

Linoleic acid, 246, 246F, 247T, 690, 709

α-Linolenic acid, 246F, 247, 247T

γ-Linolenic acid, 247T

Lipases, 678–679F, 685, 796

Lipids. *See also* Glycerophospholipids; Membranes

  asymmetrical distribution in membranes, **274–278**

  biological functions, 245–246

  catabolism overview, 452F

  classification, **246–259**

  digestion and absorption, **678–680**

  fatty acids, **246–249,** 247T

  glycerophospholipids, **249–252**

  hydrophobicity, 245, 245F

  miscellaneous lipids, **257–259**

  sphingolipids, **252–253,** 253F

  steroids, **254–257**

  transport, **680–685**

  triacylglycerols, **248–249**

Lipid bilayers, 28F, 245, **260–263.** *See also* Membranes

  fluidity, 262–263

  formation, **260–263,** 260F

  lipid mobility in, **261–262**

  phase transition, 262–263

  phospholipid diffusion in, 261F

Lipid biosynthesis:

  endoplasmic reticulum, 275F

  and pentose phosphate pathway, 520–527

Lipid-linked membrane proteins, **267–269**

Lipid metabolism, 677, 711F

Lipidomics, 482

Lipid raft, 277

Lipid storage diseases, 718, 720–721

Lipmann, F., 460, 619

Lipoamide, in citric acid cycle, 572–573, 573F

Lipogenesis, AMPK and inhibition of, 805

Lipoic acid, 572–573, 572T

Lipolysis, AMPK and inhibition of, 805

Lipoproteins, **680–681,** 796

Lipoprotein lipase, 682

Liposomes, 260–261

Lipoyllylsyl arm, dihydrolipoyl dehydrogenase, 575F

Lipscomb, W., 388

Liquid crystals, lipid bilayers as, 262

Liquid scintillation counting, 367

Liver:

  alanine transport to from muscles, 798–799

  AMPK-inhibited lipogenesis/ gluconeogenesis in, 805

  epinephrine response, 552

  glucagon secretion, 797

  glucose generation in, 537–539

  glycogen in, 231F

  glycogen storage capacity, 530

  insulin and blocking of gluconeogenesis/ glycogenolysis in, 801, 802F

  lactate transport to from muscles, 798

  mammalian metabolism in, 793–794F, **796–797**

  metabolic function, 454

  phosphoprotein phosphatase-1 activity control, 548

Liver alcohol dehydrogenase (LADH), 509

Liver glycogen synthase deficiency, 539

Liver phosphorylase deficiency (Hers' disease), 538, 539

L_λ, 1079

Loewenstein, W., 308

Lon, 737

London dispersion forces, 25

  bond energy, 25T

  defined, 25

Longevity, and caloric intake, 811

Long interspersed nuclear elements (LINEs), 939, 1045

Long terminal repeats (LTRs), 1046

Long-term regulation, 713

Long-term regulation, gluconeogenesis, 559

Lovelock, J., 10

Low-barrier hydrogen bonds (LBHBs), 355

Low density lipoproteins (LDL), **681,** 684

  atherosclerosis, 727–729

  receptor-mediated endocytosis, **684F–685**

Lowenstein, J., 841

Lowry, T., 32

LTB4, 259F

LTRs (long terminal repeats), 1046

Lu, P., 1049

Lührmann, R., 972

Lung surfactant, 250

Lyases, 453

Lyases, reaction type catalyzed, 324T

Lydon, N., 425

Lysidine, 992F

Lysine (Lys):

  acid–base catalysis by, 332

  α helix/β sheet propensities, 140T

  biosynthesis, 770–771

  breakdown, 747F, 758

  charged polar side chain, 80F

  covalent catalysis by, 335

  genetic code specification, 989T

  ionizable groups, 77T

  side chain hydropathy, 156T

Lysis, 194

Lysophosphatidic acid, 251, 710F, 711

Lysophospholipid, 251F

Lysosome, 8F

Lysosomes, 8, 278

  metabolic functions, 455T

  protein degradation in, **733**

Lysozyme, 168, 238, **339–343**

  catalytic mechanism, **343–347,** 361

  cleavage site, 340F

  isoelectric point, 98T

  model building studies, 340–343

  strain effects, 346

  structure, **339–343,** 341F

  substrate interactions, 343F

  transition state analog inhibition, 346

Lysozyme catalysis, 347F

Lysozyme catalytic mechanism, 344

Lysozyme mechanism, experimental support, 346

Lysozyme reaction, covalent intermediate, 343–347

Lysozyme reaction mechanism, 345, 345F

Lysyl oxidase, 139F

D-Lyxose, 220F

M

m⁴C (N^4-methylcytosine), 918

m⁵C (5-methylcytosine), 918, 1065

m⁶A (N^6-methyladenine), 918

m⁷G (7-methylguanosine), 966

m⁷GDP, 1014

McArdle's disease, 531, 538–540

McCarty, M., 48

McClintock, B., 934–935

MacKinnon, R., 300, 303, 305

McKnight, S., 881

MacLeod, C., 48

MacLeod, J. J. R., 812

Macronutrients, 449–450

Mad cow disease (bovine spongiform encephalopathy; BSE), 169

Magnesium ion, *See* Mg^{2+} ion

Main chain, proteins, 127–129

Maintenance methylation, 1066, 1066F

Maize, *see* Corn
Major grooves, DNA, 46, 852–853F
Malaria, and sickle-cell anemia, 197, 527
Malate, 556, 567
    in citric acid cycle, 568F, 584F
    in glyoxylate cycle, 591F
    in urea cycle, 744F
Malate–aspartate shuttle, 599
Malate dehydrogenase, 556
    in citric acid cycle, 568F, **583**
    in urea cycle, 744F
Malate synthase, in glyoxylate cycle,
    591, 591F
Malathion, 349
Male sex hormones, 410–411
Malic enzyme, 696
Malignant transformations, 421
Malignant tumors, 421. *See also* Cancer
Malonate, succinate dehydrogenase
    inhibition, 377–378
Malonic semialdehyde, in pyrimidine
    catabolism, 845F
Malonyl–ACP, in fatty acid synthesis, 705F
Malonyl–CoA, 805
    in fatty acid synthesis, 701, 705F
    from pyrimidine catabolism, 845F
Malonyl-CoA–ACP transacylase, in fatty
    acid synthesis, 705F
Maltodextrins, 298
Maltoporin, 298
Maltoporin subunit, 299F
Maltose, 228
Mammals:
    foreign DNA, 1076
    placental, 1057
Mandelkow, E., 1096
Manipulating DNA, 59–70
D-Mannose (Man), 220F, 520
Mannose-6-phosphate:
    in mannose metabolism, 520F
    recognition marker, 286
MAPs, *see* Microtubule-associated protein
MAPKAP kinase, 420F
MAP kinase kinase kinases (MKKKs), 420
MAP kinase kinases (MKKs), 419, 420
MAPKs (mitogen-activated protein
    kinases), 419
Maple syrup urine disease, 758
Margoliash, E., 115
Margulis, L., 10
Marmur, J., 866
Marsupials, X chromosome in, 1057
Martius, C., 569
Martz, E., 153
Mass spectrometry, 110–111
Maternal-effect genes, 1091
Mating type switching, 1056
Matrix, mitochondria, 598
Matthaei, H., 988
Maturation, 283

Maturity-onset diabetes mellitus, 811
Max, 420F
Maximal reaction velocity, *see* V_{max}
Max protein, 882F
Mb, *see* Myoglobin
MCM, 911
M disk, 198, 199F
*mdm*2 gene, 1084
Mdm2 protein, 1084
MDR (multidrug resistance)
    transporter, 314
Mechanism-based inhibitors, 838
Mechanosensitive channels, 302
Mediated membrane transport, **296–297**
Mediated transport, 309
Mediators:
    adaptors, 1069
    coactivator, 1069
    complex, 1069
    head domain, 1070
    middle domain, 1070
    tail domain, 1070
Medium-chain acyl-CoA
    dehydrogenase, 638
Medulla, 409
MEK, 419
Melanin, 762
Mello, C., 1075
Melting curve, DNA, 866, 866F
Melting temperature (T_m), DNA, 866F
Membranes. *See also* Lipids;
    Lipid bilayers
    assembly, **278–282**
    erythrocytes, **272–274**, 273F
    fluid mosaic model, **270–272**
    gates and fences model, 274
    glycerophospholipids in, 249–250
    lipid asymmetry, **274–278**
    lipid synthesis, **714–719**
    protein asymmetry, 265
    proton gradient dissipation,
        630–631, 632F
    secretory pathway, **278–282**
    skeleton, 271–274
    sphingolipids in, 252–253
    structure, **269–278**, 270F
Membrane anchor, 280
Membrane-enveloped virus, 289
Membrane potential, 296
Membrane proteins, **263–269**,
        263F, 266
    integral, **263–264**, 263F
    lipid-linked, **267–269**
    lipoproteins, **680–681**
    peripheral, **269**
    protein-lipid ratios, 263–264
    secretory pathway, **278–282**
    signal hypothesis, 278F–280
    transmembrane, **265**
Membrane subdomains, 277–278

Membrane transport, **295–318**
    active transport, **297–310**
    ATP-driven active, **311–314**
    ion-gradient-driven active, **316–318**
    mediated, **296–297**
    nonmediated, 296–297
    passive-mediated transport, **297–310**
    thermodynamics, **296–297**
Memory B cells, 210
Menaquinone, 258, 647
Mendel, G., 10, 47–48
Mendelian laws, 1066
Menten, M., 368
Mercaptans, for disulfide bond cleavage,
    106–107
2-Mercaptoethanol, 103, 106
6-Mercaptopurine, 844
Mercury (Hg^{2+}) ion, zinc ion
    replacement, 326
Mertz, J., 61
Meselson, M., 893, 894
Mesophiles, 159
Mesophyll cells, 674
Messenger RNA, *see* mRNA
Metabolic disturbances, **809–815**. *See also*
        Fasting
    diabetes mellitus, 475, **811–814**
    obesity, 515, **814–815**
    starvation, **809–811**
Metabolic fate tracing, **475–477**
Metabolic flux, 456–459
Metabolic homeostasis, **804–808**
    and adaptive thermogenesis, 808
    and adiponectin, 806
    and AMP-dependent protein kinase,
        804–805
    and ghrelin, 807
    and leptin, 806–807
    and PYY$_{3-36}$, 808
Metabolic inhibitors, 384, 477
Metabolic maps, 454
Metabolic pathways, **451–455**. *See also
        specific pathways and cycles, e.g.:*
        Interorgan metabolic pathways
    committed step, 456–457
    common intermediates, 451–452
    enzyme catalysis, 452–453
    evolution, 7
    experimental approaches to study of,
        475–482
    mammalian fuel metabolism, 792F
    near-equilibrium nature of,
        456, 631
    organizing, 454
    short- and long-term regulation, 713
Metabolic studies, 488
Metabolic syndrome, 815
Metabolism. *See also* Aerobic metabolism;
        Anaerobic metabolism
    changing external conditions, 791

experimental approaches to study of, **475–482**
fructose, **516–518**, 517F
galactose, **518–520**, 519F
glucose, see Glucose metabolism; Glycolysis
hexoses other than glucose, **516–520**
hormonal control of fuel metabolism, **799–804**
interrelationships among brain, adipose tissue, muscle, and liver, 794F
mannose, **520**, 520F
metabolic fate tracing, **475–477**
metabolic flux control, **457–459**
nucleotide, 839F
nutrition, **449–450**
overview, **449–459**
system perturbation, **477**
systems biology and study of, **477–482**
thermodynamics, **455–457**
Metabolites, 451
Metabolome, 478
Metabolomics, 482
Metal-activated enzymes, 335–336
Metal chelate affinity chromotography, 101
Metal ions. See also Metalloenzymes; specific metal ions
as catalysts, 6, **335–336**
as cofactors, 326
nucleic acid stabilization by, 868
protein cross-linking, 157–158
Metal ion catalysis, 6, **335–336**
Metalloenzymes, 335
Methanococcus jannaschii, 280–281F
Methanogens, 9
Methemoglobin, 179
N^5,N^{10}-Methenyltetrahydrofolate, 920
Methionine (Met):
α helix/β sheet propensities, 140T
biosynthesis, 770–771
breakdown, 747F, 753–754
genetic code specification, 988–989, 989T
ionizable groups, 76T
nonpolar side chain, 79
as rare amino acid, 93
side chain hydropathy, 156T
structure, 76T
Methionine synthase, 770
Methotrexate, 838
?-Methyladenine, 867F
N^6-Methyladenine (m^6A), 918
-Methyladenosine, 992F
Methylamine methyltransferase, 1000
Methylated histones, 1063–1064
Methylation, DNA, 918
Methylcobalamin, 770
?-Methylcytidine, 992F
?-Methylcytosine (m^5C), 918, 1065
N^4-Methylcytosine (m^4C), 918

N^5,N^{10}-Methylene-tetrahydrofolate, 749, 835–837F
N^5,N^{10}-Methylene-tetrahydrofolate reductase (MTHFR), 755
Methylglyoxal, 495
Methyl groups, 1060
2-Methylguanine, 977
O^6-Methylguanine, 917, 921
7-Methylguanosine (m^7G), 965–966
N^7-Methylguanosine, 992F
3-Methylhistidine, 86F
Methylmalonic semialdehyde, in pyrimidine catabolism, 845F
Methylmalonyl-CoA, from pyrimidine catabolism, 845F
Methylmalonyl-CoA mutase, 692, 695–696
Methylmalonyl-CoA racemase, 692
N'-Methyl-N'-nitro-N-nitrosoguanidine (MNNG), 917
$O^{2'}$-Methylribose, 977
N^5-Methyltetrahydrofolate, 754
2'-O-Methyltransferase, 966
Methyltransferases, 918
Methyltransferase flip target bases, 1065–1066
Metmyoglobin, 179
met repressor, *E. coli*, 878F
Metzler, D., 740
Mevalonate, in cholesterol synthesis, 722–723F
Mevalonate-5-phosphotransferase, in cholesterol synthesis, 722–723F
Meyerhof, O., 486
Mg^{2+} ion:
in chlorophyll, 643, 647
as cofactor, 335
free nucleotides with, 42
with metal-activated enzymes, 335
nucleic acid stabilization by, 868
M.HhaI, 1065F
Micelles, 28F
defined, 28
lipid bilayers, 260
Michaelis, L., 368
Michaelis complex, 368
Michaelis constant, see K_M
Michaelis–Menten kinetics, 796
Michaelis–Menten equation, 368–372, 376, 379F, 381T
Micrococcal nuclease, 884, 886
Microdomains, 277
Microfilaments, 207–209
Microheterogeneity, 234
Micronutrients, 450
Microradiography, 367
Micro RNAs (miRNAs), 1075
Microscopy, immunoflourescence, 207
Middle genes, 947
Miescher, F., 48
Miles, E., 773

Miller, S., 2
Milligan, R., 206
Milstein, C., 213
Miltefosine, 320
Minerals, 3, 450. See also Metal ions; specific metal ions
Mineral acids, 34
Mineralocorticoids, 255F, 410
Minor grooves, DNA, 46, 852–853F
Minot, G., 696
(–) end, 203, 208F
miRNAs (micro RNAs), 1075
Mismatch repair (MMR), 918, **924–925**
Mitchell, E., 618
Mitchell, P., 618–619
Mitochondria, 8, **597–600**. See also Amino acid breakdown; Citric acid cycle; Fatty acid oxidation; Oxidative phosphorylation; Urea cycle
acetyl-CoA transport to cytosol, in fatty acid biosynthesis, **701–702**
ADP–ATP translocator, 599–600
citric acid cycle in, 570
electron-chain component reduction potentials, 604F
evolution, 10
fatty acid elongation, 709F
fatty acid transport, **686–687**
free-radical damage, 636
genetic code variants, 991
glyoxylate cycle in, 590–591F
heme biosynthesis in, 776F
membranes, 263
metabolic functions, 455T
metabolite transport between cytosol and, in gluconeogenesis, 556–557, 557F
transport systems, **599–600**
Mitochondrial electron-transport chain, 474, 597, 604F. See also Electron-transport chain
Mitochondrial matrix, 598
Mitochondrial membranes, 599F
Mitochondrion, 8F
Mitogen-activated protein kinases (MAPKs), 419
Mixed enzyme inhibition, 381T, **382–383**, 383F
MKKs, see MAP kinase kinases
MKKKs (MAP kinase kinase kinases), 420
MLCK (myosin light chain kinase), 439–440
MM3 gene, 1096
MMDB (Molecular Modeling Database), 154
MMR (mismatch repair), 918, **924–925**
MNNG (N'-Methyl-N'-nitro-N-nitrosoguanidine), 917
Mobile phase, 98
Moderately repetitive DNA sequences, 1046
Modification methylase, 51

MoFe-protein, in nitrogenase, 783
Molecular chaperones, **165–168**
Molecular cloning experiments, 1068.
    See also Cloning
Molecularity, 365
Molecular Modeling Database
    (MMDB), 154
Molecular sieve chromatography,
    99–100, 1004F
Molecular weight, 13
Molten globule, 161
2-Monoacylglycerol, in triacylglycerol
    biosynthesis, 710F
2-Monoacylglycerol acyltransferase, in
    triacylglycerol biosynthesis, 710F
Monocistronic mRNA, 945
Monoclonal antibodies, 212, 213
Monod, J., 193
Monomers, 44, 305
Monooxygenases, 398
Monosaccharides, **219–224**. *See also*
    specific monosaccharides
    anomeric forms, 222–223
    classification, **219–224**
    configuration and conformation,
    221–224
    derivatives, **224–226**
Monosodium glutamate (MSG), 74, 764
Monoubiquitination, 735
Moore, P., 869, 1002
Moras, D., 996
Morphogens, 1092
Mosaics, protein, 120
Motifs, proteins, 146
Motor proteins, 205–206
Mouse:
    Hox-3.1 gene expression, 1097
    mouse-human cell fusion, 271F
    normal vs. obese, 807F
    protein kinase A, 433F
M phase, 1081
M-protein, 205
mRNA (messenger RNA), 49, 49F, 942
    affinity chromatography, 872
    base pairing with rRNA, 1011–1012
    degradation, 1074
    editing, 975
    monocistronic, 945
    polycistronic, 945
    posttranscriptional processing,
    965–976
MSG (monosodium glutamate), 74, 764
MTE, 959F
MTHFR (N^5,N^{10}-Methylene-
    tetrahydrofolate reductase), 755
mTOR, 443F
Mucolipidosis II, 286
Mucosa, 630
Mulder, G. J., 74
Müller, C., 1072

Muller-Hill, B., 1049
Mullis, K., 65
Multidrug resistance (MDR)
    transporter, 314
Multienzyme complexes, 570
Multiple myeloma, 212
Multiple sclerosis, 215T
Multisubunit complexes, 1069
Multisubunit proteins, 92
Murine, 210F
MurNAc, *see N*-Acetylmuramic acid
Murphy, W., 696
Muscle:
    alanine transport to liver, 798–799
    Bohr effect and, 190
    dicarboxylate recovery by citric acid
    cycle, 567
    epinephrine response, 550
    force generation mechanism of, 206F
    glycogen synthase, 542
    glycolytic ATP production, 510
    lactate dehydrogenase in, 505
    lactate transport to liver, 798
    mammalian metabolism in, **794–795,** 794F
    myoglobin function in, 179–180
    phosphocreatine energy source, 466
    phosphofructokinase in, **511–514**
    striated structure, **198–205**
    thick filament structure, **198,** 199F
    thin filament structure, 199F, **204**
Muscle contraction, **198–209,** 313–314
    and Cori cycle, 798
    and glycogen breakdown, 547, 549F
    high exertion, anaerobic, 795
    and myosin heads, 205–207
    striated muscle structure, **198–205**
    unconventional myosin V, 1088–1090
Muscle fatigue, 506, 795
Muscle fibers, slow- vs. fast-twitch, 510
Muscle phosphofructokinase deficiency
    (Tarui's disease), 538–539
Muscle phosphorylase deficiency
    (McArdle's disease), 531, 538–540
Mushroom poisoning, 955
Mus musculus, 57T
Mutagens, 477, 916
Mutagenesis, 68F, **916–919**
Mutases, 453, 500
Mutations, 11, **916–920**. *See also* Evolution
    Ames test, 919F
    built-in protection against, within
    genetic code, 990
    carcinogens, **919–920**
    chemical mutagenesis, **916–919**
    deletion, 916–919
    and evolution, 58–59
    frameshift, 986
    and free radicals, 636
    insertion, 916, 919
    neutral drift, 116

    nonsense, 1027–1028
    point, 58, 636, 916–919
    and protein synthesis, 49
    random nature of, 919
    suppressor, 986
    transitions, 916
    transversions, 916
Mutational hotspot, 1085
MutH, 925
MutL, 924–925
MutS, 924–925
Myasthenia gravis, 215T
Myc, 419, 1070, 1085
Mycobacterium tuberculosis, 594
Mycophenolic acid, 822
Mycoplasma genitalium, 57T
Myelinated membranes, 263
Myelin sheath, 253F
Myeloma, multiple, 212
Myoadenylate deaminase deficiency, 841
Myocardial infarction (heart attack), 455,
    635, 728
Myofibrils, 198, 199F
Myoglobin (Mb), **177–180,** 309, 342
    function, **179–180,** 189F
    and globin family, 118
    heme group, 178, 178F, 342
    Hill plot, 185F
    ion pairs in, 157F
    isoelectric point, 98T
    molecular dynamics, 158F
    oxygen binding curve, 180F
    oxygen binding saturation function, 370
    oxygen binding site, 178F
    structure, **177–179,** 177F
    X-ray diffraction photo,
    sperm whale, 141F
    X-ray studies, 126
Myo-Inositol, 249T
Myomensin, 205
Myosin, 201F, 203F, **205–207**
Myosin-binding protein C, 205
Myosin head, 201, 204F
Myosin light chain kinase (MLCK),
    439–440
Myotonic dystrophy, 1044, 1044T
Myristic acid, 247T, 268
Myristoylation, 268

N
NAD$^+$ (nicotinamide adenine
    dinucleotide), 327F, **469–470**
    and cell signaling, 435
    in citric acid cycle, 568F, 569, 570,
    572T, 583
    cosubstrate, 327
    DNA ligase activation, 907F
    in fatty acid oxidation, 688
    in fructose metabolism, 517F
    in glycolysis, 487F

in glyoxylate cycle, 591F
in ketone body conversion to
    acetyl-CoA, 700F
reduction to NADH, 469F
in urea cycle, 744F
NAD$^+$-dependent isocitrate dehydrogenase,
    in citric acid cycle, **579–580,** 579F,
    586–587
Na$^+$-dependent symport, 316
NADH (nicotinamide adenine dinucleotide,
    reduced form), 327F, 452
in citric acid cycle, 567, 569, 570, 585
electron-transfer coenzyme, 474
in fructose metabolism, 517F
function of, 474
in gluconeogenesis, 553F
in glycolysis, 504
impermeability to inner membrane
    space, 599
NAD$^+$ reduction to, 469F
P/O ratio in oxidative phosphorylation,
    629–630
redox center, 597
reducing equivalents, 556, 599
thermodynamics of oxidation, 601
in triacylglycerol synthesis, 710F
NADH–coenzyme Q oxidoreductase,
    see Complex I
NADP$^+$ (nicotinamide adenine
    dinucleotide phosphate), 327F
cosubstrate, 327
metabolic role overview, 451F
in pentose phosphate pathway,
    520–523
reduction in photosynthesis, 641,
    650–652
NADPH (nicotinamide adenine
    dinucleotide phosphate, reduced
    form), 327F
in Calvin cycle, 664–665F
dissipation in dark reactions, 641, 664,
    672–673F
in fatty acid synthesis, 705F
in heme degradation, 779F
production in light reactions, 641, 650–652
in triacylglycerol synthesis, 710F
NADPH oxidase, 638
NAG (*N*-Acetylglucosamine), 232, 340,
    343, 346, 347
NAG2FGlcF (NAGβ(1→4)-2-deoxy-
    2-fluoro-β-D-glucopyransosyl
    fluoride), 347
Na$^+$ ion, 299
    and DNA melting temperature, 868
    with metal-activated enzymes, 335
(Na$^+$–K$^+$)–ATPase, 794
NAM, see *N*-Acetylmuramic acid
NANA (*N*-Acetylneuraminic acid), 225F
Nanos gene, 1092
Nanos protein, 1092

Native (folded) proteins, 139
Natural selection, 114, 116. *See also*
    Evolution
    and chemical evolution, 5
    nucleic acid sequence and, 58
NBDs (nucleotide-binding domains), 315F
ncRNAs (noncoding RNAs), 1041
NDB (Nucleic Acid Database), 152
NDP (nucleoside diphosphates), 467
Near-equilibrium reactions, 456, 631
Nebulin, 205
Necrosis, 1087
Negative feedback regulation, of
    metabolic flux, 458
Negatively cooperative oxygen
    binding, 185
Negative regulators, 1050
N-end rule, 735
NER (nucleotide excision repair),
    923–924, 923F
Nernst, W., 471
Nernst equation, **470–472**
Nerve cells, phosphocreatine energy
    source, 466
Nerve impulses, 302–303
Nerve poisons, 349
Nervonic acid, 247T
Neural tube defects, 755
Neuroglobin, 179
Neuropeptide Y, 807
Neurotoxins, 349
Neurotransmitters, 287, 313–314, 349
    amino acids as, 88
    synthesis from tyrosine, 780–781F
Neutral drift, 116
Neutral solutions, 31
Nevirapine, 384
Newsholme, E., 515
New variant CJD (nvCJD), 171
NFAT4, 420F
NHEJ (nonhomologous end-joining), 925
NHP6A, 1058
Ni^{2+}-nitriloacetic acid, 628
Niacin (nicotinic acid), 450. *See also*
    Nicotinamide
Nick translation, 899, 905
Nicolson, G., 270
Nicotinamide, 435, 450, 450F, 488, 847
Nicotinamide adenine dinucleotide, *see*
    NAD$^+$
Nicotinamide adenine dinucleotide,
    reduced form, *see* NADH
Nicotinamide adenine dinucleotide
    phosphate, *see* NADP$^+$
Nicotinamide adenine dinucleotide
    phosphate, reduced form, *see* NADPH
Nicotinamide coenzymes, 327F
Nicotinamide mononucleotide (NMN$^+$), 907
Nicotinic acid (niacin), 450
Niedergerke, R., 200

Niemann–Pick disease, 720
19S caps, 735, 737
Nirenberg, M., 988
Nitrate reductase, 788
Nitric oxide (NO), **781–782**
Nitric oxide synthase, 781–782
Nitrification, 788
Nitrogenase, **783–788**
Nitrogen cycle, 788
Nitrogen excretion, 841–842F
Nitrogen fixation, 733, **782–788**
Nitrogen mustard, mutagenic effects, 917
Nitroglycerin, 781
p-Nitrophenolate ion, 336
p-Nitrophenylacetate, reaction with
    imidazole, 336
N-linked oligosaccharides, 234–235,
    238–240
    formation, 561–562
    synthesis, 239F
NMD (nonsense-mediated decay), 1074
NMN$^+$ (nicotinamide mononucleotide),
    907
NMR, *see* Nuclear magnetic resonance
No-go decay, 1074
Noller, H., 1001
Nomenclature:
    amino acids, **81–82,** 82F
    enzymes, **324–325**
Noncoding RNAs (ncRNAs), 1041
Noncoding (antisense) strand, 944, 945F
Noncompetitive enzyme inhibition, *see*
    Mixed enzyme inhibition
Noncooperative oxygen binding, 185
Nonessential amino acids, **764–769,** 764T
Nonheme iron proteins, 605
Nonhomologous end-joining (NHEJ), 925
Non-insulin-dependent diabetes mellitus,
    811, 813–814
Nonketotic hyperglycinemia, 749
Nonmediated membrane transport, 296–297
Nonmediated transport, 309
Nonpolar molecules, 26–28
Nonreceptor tyrosine kinases (NRTKs),
    422, 1071
Nonreducing sugars, 226
Nonsense codons, 990
Nonsense-mediated decay (NMD), 1074
Nonsense mutation, 1027–1028
Nonshivering thermogenesis, 515, 632
Nonsteroidal anti-inflammatory drugs
    (NSAIDs), 719
Non-stop decay, 1074
Nontranscribed DNA, **1043–1046,** 1056
Nonviral retrotransposons, 939
Non-Watson–Crick base pairs, 866–867F
Noradrenaline, *see* Norepinephrine
Norepinephrine (noradrenaline), 407, 409
    and fatty acid metabolism, 712
    fight or flight reaction, 551

Norepinephrine (noradrenaline) (*cont.*)
and fuel metabolism, 799, 801
glycogen metabolism effects, 550
synthesis from tyrosine, 780–781F
and thermogenesis, 632–633, 808
Northern blot, 874
Notophthalmus viridescens, gene clusters, 1042F
Novobiocin, 865
NRTKs (nonreceptor tyrosine kinases), 422, 1071
NSAIDs (nonsteroidal anti-inflammatory drugs), 719
N-terminal cytoplasmic domain, 303
N-terminal domain, 391F
N-terminal "headpiece," 1049
N-terminal tails, 1060
N-terminus (amino terminus), 78
dynamics, 158
end-group analysis, 104–105
as starting end of polypeptide synthesis, 1008
NTP (nucleoside triphosphates), 467–468
Nuclear magnetic resonance (NMR):
metabolic pathway studies, 476F–477
proteins, 143–144
2D nuclear magnetic resonance spectroscopy, 144
yeast structure, 1059F
Nuclear membrane, 8F
Nuclear receptor superfamily, 1072
Nucleases, 95
EDTA inhibition, 872
participation in RNAi, 1075–1076
Nucleic acids, 39, 41T. *See also* DNA and RNA
chromatography, **872**
dietary, 839
electrophoresis, **872–873,** 873F
fractionation, **872–874**
function, **47–49**
ionic interactions, **868**
single-stranded, **47**
as source of biological information, 849
stabilizing forces, **864–871**
stacking interactions, **867–868,** 867F
structure, **43–47,** 43F
Nucleic Acid Database (NDB), 152
Nucleic acid sequencing, **50–59**
automated, **55–56**
chain-terminator method, **53–56,** 54F
databases, 112–114, 1038
and ethics, 70
gel electrophoresis, **52–53,** 52F, 54F, 55F
mutations and evolution, **58–59**
projects ongoing, 57T
restriction endonucleases, **51–52**
Nucleolus, 8F, 953, 977
Nucleophilic catalysis, 333–335

Nucleosidases, 840F
Nucleosides, 41, 41T
Nucleoside diphosphates (NDP), 467
Nucleoside diphosphate kinases, 467, 822
Nucleoside monophosphate kinases, 822
Nucleoside phosphorylases, 840F
Nucleoside triphosphates (NTPs), 467–468
Nucleosomes, **884–887,** 885F
core particle, 884, 885F
DNA in eukaryotes, 1056
Nucleosome remodeling, 1058F
Nucleotidase:
in purine catabolism, 840F
in pyrimidine catabolism, 845F
Nucleotides, 39, 41–42, 41T
degradation, **839–846**
metabolism, 839F
phosphate groups, 42
structure and function, **40–42**
and sugar–phosphate backbone, 856F
torsion angles and conformation, 855F
Nucleotide bases, 41T
DNA base composition, **44**
tautomeric forms, 44, 44F
Nucleotide-binding domains (NBDs), 315F
Nucleotide derivatives, 42
Nucleotide excision repair (NER), **923–924,** 923F
Nucleotide residues, 43–44
Nucleotide sugar, 561
Nucleus, 7, 455T, 1007, 1056F. *See also* DNA replication; Posttranslational modification; Transcription
Nusslein-Volhard, C., 1092
Nutrasweet®, 228, 762
Nutrition, **449–450**
nvCJD (new variant CJD), 171

O

O-Linked oligosaccharides, 561
Obesity, **814–815**
and appetite regulators, 807–808
fat reserve and survival, 810–811
and leptin, 806–807
and thermogenesis, 515
and type II diabetes, 813
Obligate aerobes, 449
Obligate anaerobes, 449, 469
Ochoa, S., 533
Ochre codon, 990
Octanoyl-CoA, 688
Odd-chain fatty acid oxidation, 686, **692–697**
OEC (oxygen-evolving center), 653, 654–656
Official (systematic) name, 324
Ogston, A., 579

Oils, 248
Okazaki, R., 896
Okazaki fragments, 896, 897F, 899, 904, 907
Oleate, amphiphilic nature of, 28F
Oleic acid, 246, 246F, 247T, 690
Oligomers, 44, 154
Oligopeptides, 78
Oligosaccharides:
as antigenic determinants, 242F
functions, **240–242**
N-linked, 234–235, 238–240
O-linked, 234, 240
processing, 238–240
in proteoglycans, 235F
recognition events, mediation of, 241–242
structural effects, 240–242
O-Linked oligosaccharides, 234, 240
OMP (orotidine-5′-monophosphate), in UMP synthesis, 825F, 826
OMP decarboxylase, in UMP synthesis, 825F, 826, 828
OmpF porin, 256F, 288
Oncogenes, 420, 421
Opal codon, 990
Oparin, A., 2
Open complex, 947
Open reading frame (ORF), 58, 482, 1040
Open systems, 18
Operators, 876, 1048F
Operons, 945, 1042
Opsin, 429
Optical density, 95
Optically active molecules, 82
Ordered mechanism, sequential reactions, 375
ORF (open reading frame), 58, 482, 1040
Organelles, 8
Organic arsenicals, 576
Organic compounds, 2
Organismal evolution, domains of, **9–10**
Organogenesis, 1090
Organ specialization, **792–799**
adipose tissue, **795–796**
brain, **793–794**
kidney, **798**
liver, **796–797**
metabolic function, 454–455
muscle, **794–795**
oriC locus, 903
Orientation effects (enzymes), **336–338,** 336F
Origin-independent replication restart, 933
Ornithine:
biosynthesis, 768–769
in urea cycle, 744F, 746
Ornithine-δ-aminotransferase, 769
Ornithine transcarbamoylase, in urea cycle, 744, 746
Orotate, in UMP synthesis, 825F, 826
Orotate phosphoribosyl transferase, in UMP synthesis, 825F, 826

Orotic aciduria, 828
Orotidine-5′-monophosphate (OMP), in UMP synthesis, 825F, 826
Orphan genes, 1040
Orthologous genes, 118
Orthophosphate cleavage, 464
Oryza sativa, 57T
Osmosis, **29–30**
Osmotic balance, 299
Osmotic pressure, 29, 30F
Osmotic water content, 312
Osteogenesis imperfecta (brittle bone disease), 137
Ouabain, 313
Ova, 410
Ovalbumin:
chicken mRNA, 967F
isoelectric point, 98T
Ovaries, 255, 406F, 410
Overproducers, 67
Oxalate, 310
Oxalate transporter, 309–310
Oxaloacetate, 567
amino acid biosynthesis from, 589–590, 764–769
in amino acid degradation, 738, 747F, 751
in citric acid cycle, 568F, 584F
in gluconeogenesis, 553, 556
in glyoxylate cycle, 591F
from mammalian metabolism, 793
in urea cycle, 744F
Oxalosuccinate, in citric acid cycle, 528, 579, 579F
Oxidation, 453
Oxidation–reduction reactions, 449, **469–474**
cofactors for, 326
FAD, **469–470**
metal ion catalysis, 335–336
NAD$^+$, **469–470**
Nernst equation, **470–472**
redox centers, 597
reduction potential measurements, **472–474**
Oxidative deamination, **742,** 917F
Oxidative metabolism, 314. *See also* Aerobic metabolism
Oxidative phosphorylation, 452, 465, **618–631,** 792F–793, 797
ATP mass action ratio, 631
ATP synthase, 618, **622–629**
chemiosmotic theory, **618–622**
control, **631–633,** 633–634
P/O ratio, **629–630**
thermodynamic efficiency, 601
uncoupling, **630–631**
Oxidized (term), 452
Oxidizing agents, 470–471
Oxidoreductases, 324T, 453
2,3-Oxidosqualene, 724

OxlT, 309–310
8-Oxoguanine (oxoG), 917
Oxonium ion, 344
6-Oxo-PGF1a, 259F
Oxyanion hole, 354, 356–357
Oxygen. *See also* Respiration
adaptation of life to, 7
binding by hemoglobin, **184–190**
binding by myoglobin, **177–180**
Bohr effect, 189–190
permeability to intermembrane space, 599
from photosynthesis, 640, 641, 654–656
physiological implications of oxidation, **634–637**
reactive species, 635–636
Oxygenation:
hemoglobin, 178–179
myoglobin, 178–179
Oxygen binding curve:
hemoglobin, 184
myoglobin, 180F
Oxygen debt, 798
Oxygen-evolving center (OEC), 654–656
Oxygen tension, 180
Oxygen-transport proteins, 181
Oxyhemoglobin, *see* Hemoglobin

P
P (peptidyl) site, 1006
p14^{ARF}, gene encoding, 1085
p21^{Cip1}, 1084
p51, 913
p53, 420F, 1084
p53 gene, 1085–1086
p66, 912
p90^{rsk}, 420F
p680, 654
p700, 658
p870, 648
PA (protective antigen), 444–445
PAB II (Poly(A) binding protein II), 966
Pabo, C., 879, 1096
PABP (Poly(A) binding protein), 966–967
PAF65α, 1060
PAF65β, 1060
PAGE, *see* Polyacrylamide gel electrophoresis
pAgK84, restriction digests, 53F
Pair-rule genes, 1091, 1093F
even-skipped (eve), 1092
fushi tarazu (ftz), 1094
hairy, 1092
primary, 1092–1093
runt, 1092
secondary, 1093F
PALA (*N*-(phosphonacetyl)-L-aspartate), 388
Palindrome DNA sequences, 51–52F, 875–876

Palmitate:
amphiphilic nature of, 28F
in fatty acid synthesis, 705F
Palmitic acid, 246, 247T, 268
1-Palmitoleoyl-2-linoleoyl-3-stearoylglycerol, 248
1-Palmitoyl-2,3-dioleoyl-glycerol, 678
Palmitoyl-ACP, in fatty acid synthesis, 705F
Palmitoylation, 268
Palmitoyl thioesterase, 268, 705F
Pancreas, 406F, 799–800
glucagon secretion, 712
insulin secretion, 712, 811–812
Pancreatic β cells, 811–812
Pancreatic DNase I, 858–859
Pantothenic acid (vitamin B$_3$), 468–469
PAP (Poly(A) polymerase), 966
Papain, 211
Paper chromatography, 98
Parallel β sheet, 132, 133–134
Paralogous genes, 118
Paraoxonase, 349
Parathion, 349
Parkinson's disease, 636, 780, 1087
Parnas, J., 486
Paromomycin, 1035
Partial molar free energy ($\overline{G}_A$), 16
Partial oxygen pressure (pO_2):
hemoglobin, 184–186
myoglobin, 180
Passive-mediated glucose uniport, 316
Passive-mediated transport, **297–310**
aquaporins, **306–307**
ion channels, **299–302**
ionophores, **297–298**
porins, **298–299**
transport proteins, **307–310**
Pasteur, L., 322, 485
Pasteur effect, 510
Patel, D., 1055
Pathogens, 209
Pauling, L., 127, 130–132, 195, 200, 338, 369, 850
P body (processing body), 1074
pbx (postbithorax) mutant, 1092
PC, *see* Plastocyanin
PCAF complex, 1060
PCC (protein-conducting channel), 1032
P-cluster, in nitrogenase, 784
PCNA (proliferating cell nuclear antigen), 910–911
PCR (polymerase chain reaction), 65–67, 65F
PDB (Protein Data Bank), 151–154
PDI (protein disulfide isomerase), 163–165, 164F
PDK1 (phosphoinositide-dependent protein kinase-1), 442

PE (phosphatidylethanolamine), 249T, 275, 275F, 715F
Pearse, B., 285
Pectins, 233
Pellagra, 450
Penicillin, 238
Penicillinase, 238
Pentose, 221
Pentose phosphate pathway, 486, **520–527,** 521F
  carbon skeleton rearrangements, 525F
  control, **524–527**
  and glycolysis, 525F
  mammalian metabolism, 797
PEP, *see* Phosphoenolpyruvate
PEP carboxykinase, 556–557
PEPCK (PEP carboxykinase), in gluconeogenesis, 554, 556
PEPCK (PEP carboxykinase) mechanism, 556F
Pepsin, 384
  isoelectric point, 98T
  polypeptide degradation, 738
  specificity, 107T
  X-ray studies, 125
Peptidases, 85
Peptides, 92, **127–129,** 278
Peptide bonds, **78**
Peptide-N^4-(N-acetyl-β-D-glucosaminyl)-asparagine amidase F, 149
Peptidoglycans, 236–237F 238, 225
  lysozyme action in, 237F
Peptidomimetic drugs, 384
Peptidyl homoserine lactone, 108F
Peptidyl (P) site, 1006
Peptidyl transferase, 1008, 1009F, 1019
Peptidyl–tRNA, 1006, 1009F, 1021
Peptidyl–tRNA hydrolase, 1035
Peripheral membrane proteins, **269**
Permeases, 297
Pernicious anemia, 696
Peroxidase, 718
Peroxisomal β oxidation, **698**
Peroxisomes, 8, 455T, 672. *See also* Amino acid breakdown
Pertussis, 435
Pertussis toxin, 435
Perutz, M., 181, 182, 186, 200, 850
Perutz mechanism, hemoglobin, 186F–189
PEST proteins, 735
PFGE (pulsed-field gel electrophoresis), **873**
PFK, *see* Phosphofructokinase
PFK-2 (phosphofructokinase-2), 558–559
PFK-2/FBPase-2, 804
2PG, *see* 2-Phosphoglycerate
3PG, *see* 3-Phosphoglycerate
PGF$_{2\alpha}$, 259F
PGH$_2$, 259F

PGI, *see* Phosphoglucose isomerase
PGK, *see* Phosphoglycerate kinase
P-glycoprotein, 314–315
PGM, *see* Phosphoglycerate mutase
pH, 31
  biochemical standard state, 17
  common substances, 32T
  enzyme effects, 332
  Henderson–Hasselbalch equation for, 34
  protein effects, 332
  protein effects, renaturing, 159
Phage λ, 61, 63F
Pharmacogenomics, 400
Pharmacokinetics, 396
PHD finger, 1064
Phe, *see* Phenylalanine
Phen (phentermine), 397
Phenotypes, 59
Phenotypically silent codons, 990
Phentermine (phen), 397
Phentolamine, 409
Phenylacetic acid, 686
Phenylaceturic acid, 686
Phenylalanine (Phe):
  α helix/β sheet propensities, 140T
  biosynthesis, 773
  breakdown, 477F, 747F, 760–763F
  genetic code specification, 989T
  ionizable groups, 76T, 79F
  nonpolar side chain, 79, 79F
  side chain hydropathy, 156T
Phenylalanine hydroxylase, 760–761F, 763F
Phenylethanolamine N-methyltransferase, in neurotransmitter synthesis, 781F
Phenylisothiocyanate (PITC), in Edman degradation, 109, 109F
Phenylketonuria (PKU), 228, 762
Phenylpyruvate, 762
Phenylthiocarbamyl (PTC), in Edman degradation, 109, 109F
Phenylthiohydantoin (PTH), in Edman degradation, 109, 109F
Pheophytin *a* (Pheo *a*), 653
φ Angle, 128, 128F
Philadelphia chromosome, 424
Phillips, D., 340, 341, 347
Phillips, S., 878
Phorbol-13-acetate, 441, 441F
Phosophoimagers, 361
Phosphagens, 466
Phosphatases, 406
Phosphate carrier, 600
Phosphate diester, functional group and linkages, 4T
Phosphate ester, functional group and linkages, 4T
Phosphate ion. *See also* ATP
  titration curve, 34F
  titration curve, polyprotic ion, 35F
Phosphatidic acids, 249, 249T, 710F

Phosphatidic acid phosphatase, in triacylglycerol biosynthesis, 710F
Phosphatidylcholine (lecithin), 249T, 715F
Phosphatidylethanolamine (PE), 249T, 275, 275F, 715F
Phosphatidylethanolamine transferase, 715F
Phosphatidylglycerol, 249T, 715, 717F
Phosphatidylglycerol phosphate, 716
Phosphatidylinositol, 249T, 259, 715, 717F
Phosphatidylinositol-4,5-bisphosphate (PIP$_2$), 437, 438F
Phosphatidylserine, 249T
Phosphatidylserine, synthesis, 715
Phosphoanhydrides:
  hydrolysis, 463F, 464
  resonance/electrostatic stabilization, 461F
Phosphoanhydride bond, 460F
Phosphoarginine, 466
Phosphocreatine, 461T, 466
Phosphodiesterases, 435–436
Phosphodiester bond, 43
Phosphoenolpyruvate (PEP):
  free energy of phosphate hydrolysis, 461T, 463
  in gluconeogenesis, 554F
  in glycolysis, 487F, 500–501F
  hydrolysis of, 503F
  metabolite transport, 556–557
Phosphoenolpyruvate carboxykinase, 801
Phosphoester bond, 460F
Phosphofructokinase (PFK):
  citrate inhibition, 634
  deactivation by thioredoxin, 671
  in glycolysis, 487F, **491–492, 511–514**
Phosphofructokinase-2 (PFK-2), 558–559
Phosphoglucomutase, 519F, 533, **537–539**
6-Phosphogluconate, in pentose phosphate pathway, 521F, 522
6-Phosphogluconate dehydrogenase, in pentose phosphate pathway, 521F, 523
6-Phosphoglucono-δ-lactone, in pentose phosphate pathway, 521F–522
6-Phosphogluconolactonase, in pentose phosphate pathway, 521F, 522
Phosphoglucose isomerase (PGI), 487F, **490–491,** 491F, 796
2-Phosphoglycerate (2PG), 20
  in gluconeogenesis, 553F
  in glycolysis, 487F, 499–500
3-Phosphoglycerate (3PG), 20
  amino acid biosynthesis from, 769
  in Calvin cycle, 663, 665F
  in gluconeogenesis, 553F
  in glycolysis, 487F, 499–500
Phosphoglycerate kinase (PGK):
  in Calvin cycle, 665F
  in glycolysis, 487F, **499**
Phosphoglycerate mutase (PGM), in glycolysis, 487F, **499–500,** 501F

Phosphoglycerides, *see*
Glycerophospholipids
Phosphoglycohydroxamate, 494
2-Phosphoglycolate, 494, 672
Phosphoguanidines, 466
Phosphoinositide-dependent protein
kinase-1 (PDK1), 442
Phosphoinositide 3-kinases (PI3Ks), 442
Phosphoinositide pathway,
436–445, 437F
and calmodulin, 438–440
and diacylglycerol, 440–442
and ligand binding, 437–438
Phospholipase, 251, 275
Phospholipase A$_2$, 251, 251F
lipid digestion, 630
Phospholipase C (PLC), 251, 437–438
Phospholipids. *See also*
Glycerophospholipids;
Sphingomyelins
transport across membranes, 276–277
in triacylglycerol biosynthesis, 710F
Phospholipid translocases, 276
Phosphomannose isomerase, in mannose
metabolism, 520F
Phosphomevalonate kinase, in cholesterol
synthesis, 722
N-(Phosphonacetyl)-L-aspartate
(PALA), 388
Phosphopentose epimerase, in Calvin
cycle, 665F, 666
Phosphoprotein phosphatase, 393
Phosphoprotein phosphatase-1 (PP1), 426,
546–550
Phosphoprotein phosphatase inhibitor 1
(inhibitor 1), 548
β-5-Phosphoribosylamine, in IMP
synthesis, 818, 819F
5-Phosphoribosyl-α-pyrophosphate
(PRPP), 774, 818, 819F, 822
Phosphoribulokinase, 665F, 666
Phosphorlyase kinase deficiency, 539
Phosphorolysis, 391
Phosphorylase, *see* Glycogen
phosphorylase
Phosphorylase *a,* 391, 546
Phosphorylase *b,* 391, 546
Phosphorylase kinase, 393,
546–547, 801
Phosphorylated compounds,
459, 460
Phosphorylation:
protein, 390–393
substrate-level, 465. *See also*
Photophosphorylation
Phosphoryl group transfer, **460–462**
Phosphoryl group-transfer potentials,
461, 461T
O-Phosphoserine, 86F
Photoautotrophs, 449

Photon absorption, 643, 646, 648–649
Photooxidation, 647
Photophosphorylation, 465, 650, **661–663**
Photoreactivation, 920
Photorespiration, **671–675,** 673F
Photosynthesis, 6–7, 18, 488, **640–675**
Calvin cycle, **663–669F,** 665F
Calvin cycle control, **670–671**
chloroplasts, **641–645,** 641F
dark reactions, 641, **663–675**
electron transport, **647–662**
light reactions, 641, **645–663**
net reaction, 640
photoautotrophs, 449
photophosphorylation, 650, **661–663**
photorespiration, 640–641, **645–663**
transformation of chemical energy to
light energy, **645–647**
two-center electron transport,
650–663
Z-scheme, 652, 652F
Photosynthetic bacteria:
electron transport in, **647–650**
light-absorbing pigments in,
643–645, 643F
plasma membrane, 641–642
purple, 647F–649
Photosynthetic reaction center:
excitation energy trapping, 647F
photosynthesis in, 643–644,
647F–649
from *Rhodobacter sphaeroides,* 648F
from *Rhodopseudomonas viridis,* 648
as transmembrane protein, 647–648
Photosystem I, *see* PSI
Photosystem II (PSII), 650–651F,
652–654, 662
Phycocyanin, 643F
Phycocyanobilin, 645
Phycoerythrin, 643F
Phycoerythrobilin, 645
Phylloquinone, 658
Phylogenetic trees, homologous proteins,
116–117F
Phylogeny, **9**
inferring from amino acid sequences of
homologous proteins, 116–117F
inferring from nucleic acid sequence,
58–59
p*I,* 81
PI3Ks (phosphoinositide 3-kinases), 442
PIC (preinitiation complex), 960, 962F
Pickart, C., 737
Picot, D., 656
P$_{II}$ (regulatory protein), 766
Ping-Pong reactions, 376
PIP$_2$ (phosphatidylinositol-4,5-
bisphosphate), 437, 438F
PITC (phenylisothiocyanate), in Edman
degradation, 109, 109F

Pitch, α helix, 131
Pituitary, 406F
PK, *see* Pyruvate kinase
p*K:*
acid proton donation, 32
amino acid ionizable groups, 75, 76–77T,
78, **81**
selected acids, 33T
PKA, *see* Protein kinase A
PKB (protein kinase B), 443F
PKC, *see* Protein kinase C
PKU (phenylketonuria), 228, 762
Placebo, 397
Planck's constant, 13, 266, 372, 645
Planck's law, 645
Plants, 581F, 640, 641. *See also*
Photosynthesis
C3, 674
C4, 674
CAM, 674–675
light-absorbing pigments in, 643F
Plant cells, 8
Plaque(s), 62
Alzheimer's disease, 169
atherosclerosis, 728
Plasmalogens, 251–252, 716
Plasma membrane, 270F
as lipid biosynthesis site, 275
photosynthetic bacteria, 641–642
Plasmids, 60, 935
antibiotic-resistant transposons, 938
expression vectors, 67
insulin gene, 1068
Plasmodium falciparum, 57T, 197,
394, 527
Plastocyanin (PC), 652, 652F, 657, 662
Plastoquinol, 651
Plastoquinone, 651, 662
PLC (phospholipase C), 437–438
Pleated β sheet, 133, 133F
PLP, *see* Pyridoxal-5′-phosphate
(+) end, 203, 208F
Pmf (protonmotive force), 620
PMP (pyridoxamine-5′-phosphate), 739F
PNP (purine nucleoside phosphorylase), in
purine catabolism, 840
Point mutations, 58, 636, 916–919
Pol I (DNA polymerase I), 53, 896–897
discovery, 898
exonuclease function, 897F, 899F
Klenow fragment, 900F
and replication fidelity, 909
use in PCR, 65F
use in site-directed mutagenesis, 68
Pol II (DNA polymerase II), 902
Pol III (DNA polymerase III), 902
Pol III holoenzyme, 909
β subunit, 906
leading and lagging strand synthesis,
879–880F, 904–905F

Pol α (DNA polymerase α), 910
Polarimeter, 83F
Polar molecules, 23–24
Pol β, 910
Pol ε, 911
Pol η (DNA polymerase η), 925
Pol γ (DNA polymerase γ), 911
Pole cells, 1090
Polpot, J.-L., 656
Poly(A), 988
Poly(C), 988
Poly(Lys), 988
Poly(Pro), 988
Poly-N-acetylglucosamine, 234
Polyacrylamide gel electrophoresis
    (PAGE), 367
  nucleic acids, 52, 872
  proteins, 102F
  SDS (SDS-PAGE), 102–103
Poly(A) binding protein (PABP), 966–967
Poly(A) binding protein II (PAB II), 966
Poly(A) polymerase (PAP), 966
Poly(A) tails, 966, 967
Polycistronic mRNA, 945
Polycythemia, 194
Polyelectrolytes, 98
Poly-D-glucuronate, 234
Polymers, 3
Polymerase α, 910
Polymerase β, 910
Polymerase ε, 911
Polymerase chain reaction (PCR),
    65–67, 65F
Polymorphic cytochromes P450, 400
Polymorphic gene, 1044
Polymorphisms, 66
Polynucleotide phosphorylase, 987
Polynucleotides, 43. See also Nucleic acids
Polypeptides, 78. See also Proteins
  chain conformations, 127–129
  cleavage in protein sequencing, 107–108
  diversity, 92–93
  hydrolysis, 107
  Ramachandran diagram, 129F
  reverse turns, 135F
  theoretical number of, 92
Polypeptide synthesis, 1008–1028
  chain elongation, 1008–1010, 1014–1026
  chain initiation, 1010–1014, 1013F
  chain termination, 1026–1028, 1026F
Polyproteins, 384
Polyprotic acids, 35, 35F
Polyribosomes (polysomes), 1010F
Polysaccharides, 219, 226–234, 228–230.
    See also Oligosaccharides; specific
    polysaccharides
  glycosaminoglycans, 232–234
  storage, 230–231
  structural, 228–230
Polysomes (polyribosomes), 1010F

Polytopic transmembrane
    proteins, 281
Polyubiquitin, 734
Polyunsaturated fatty acids, 247
Pompe's disease, 538, 539
P/O ratios, 629–630
Porcine pancreatic elastase, 356
Porins, 267, 267F, 298–299, 599
Porphobilinogen, in heme biosynthesis,
    776F, 777
Porphobilinogen deaminase, in heme
    biosynthesis, 776F, 777
Porphobilinogen synthase, in heme
    biosynthesis, 776F, 777
Porphyrias, 778
Porphyrin, 178
Positively cooperative oxygen
    binding, 185
Positive regulators, 1050
postbithorax mutant (pbx), 1092
Postreplication repair, 932–933F
Postsynaptic membrane, 287
Posttranscriptional control mechanisms,
    1073–1077
Posttranscriptional modification, 965
Posttranscriptional processing, 965–982
  mRNA, 965–976
  rRNA, 976–980
  tRNA, 980–982
Posttranslational modification, 280
  histones, 884
  proteins, 280
Posttranslational protein processing,
    1028–1031
Posttranslocational state, 1022
PP1 (Phosphoprotein phosphatase-1), 426,
    546, 547–550
PP2A, 426–428, 427F
PP2B (calcineurin), 428
PP_i (pyrophosphate), 461
PPM family, 426
PPP family, 426
Prader–Willi syndrome (PWS), 1067
pRb, tumor suppressor, 1086
Prebiotic era, 2–3
Precursors, 6
Preferential transition state binding,
    338–339, 338F
Preinitiation complex (PIC), 960, 962F
Prelog, V., 85
Pre-mRNAs, 967
Prenylation, 268
Prenyl transferase, 722
Prephenate, 773
Preproproteins, 1030
Preproteins, 280, 1030
Pre-rRNAs, 976
Presequences, 280
Presynaptic membrane, 287
Pretranslocational state, 1022

Pre-tRNAs, 981–982
Pribnow, D., 946
Pribnow box, 946F
Priestley, J., 640
Primaquine, 526, 527
Primary active transport, 311
Primary pair-rule genes, 1093
Primary structure (proteins), 91–120
Primary transcripts, 965
Primase, 896
Primer, for chain-terminator method, 54
Primosome, 904
Prion, 170
Prion diseases, 169–171
Prion protein (PrP), 170–171
Pristanic acid, 731
Pro, see Proline
Probe, for colony hybridization, 64
Procarboxypeptidase A, 358
Procarboxypeptidase B, 358
Procaspases (single-chained
    zymogens), 1087
Procaspase-7, 1088
Procaspase-8, 1088
Procaspase-9, 1090
Procaspase-10, 1088
Processing body (P body), 1074
Processivity:
  DNA polymerase, 896–897
  RNA polymerase, 949
Prochiral molecules, 325
ProCysRS, 998
Product inhibition, 378
Proelastase, 358
Proenzymes, 357
Proflavin, as intercalating agent, 873F, 919
Progeria, 915
Progestins, 411
Programmed cell death, apoptosis, 1086
Proinsulin, 1030
Prokaryotes, 7–9, 7F
  classification, 9
  DNA economy of, 1043
  gene clusters, 1042
  gene number, selected organisms, 1039T
  lipid biosynthesis, 275
  protein degradation in, 735
  transposons, 935
Prokaryotic DNA replication, 896–909
  DNA polymerases, 896–902, 899F
  fidelity, 909
  initiation, 903–904
  leading and lagging strand synthesis,
    904–905
  termination, 908–909
Prokaryotic gene expression, 1046–1055
  attenuation, 1051–1054
  catabolic repression, 1050–1051
  gene activation, 1050–1051
  lac repressor, 1046–1050

riboswitches, **1054–1055**
transcriptional control motifs, **876–879**
Prokaryotic ribosomes, **1001–1007**
Prokaryotic transcription, 943–952
Proliferating cell nuclear antigen (PCNA), 910–911
Proline (Pro):
  α helix/β sheet propensities, 140T
  biosynthesis, 768–769
  breakdown, 747F, 751–752F
  genetic code specification, 989T
  nonpolar side chain, 79
  side chain hydropathy, 156T
  structure, 76T
Proline racemase, inhibition, 339
Prolyl hydroxylase, 137
Promoters, 945–946
  core promoter element, 958
  upstream promoter element, 958
Proofreading, 897, 997–998
Prophospholipase A₂, 358
Propionibacterium shermanii, 694, 694F
Propionyl-CoA, 753F
Propionyl-CoA carboxylase, 692
Propranolol, 409
Proproteins, 1029
Propyl group, 307
Prostacyclins, 258, 259F
Prostaglandin H₂ synthase, 718
Prostaglandins, 259F, 709, 718–719
Prosthetic groups, 326, 327
Protease inhibitors, 355–356
Proteases, 95, 107
Proteasome, **735–738**, 736F
Protective antigen (PA), 444–445
Protein(s), 74. *See also* Amino acids;
    Enzymes; specific proteins and classes
    of proteins
  allosteric, **192–194**
  αα motif, 146
  α helix, **129–132**, 131F
  amino acid derivatives in, **86–89**, 86F
  assaying, 95–97
  βαβ motif, 146
  β barrel, 148
  β bulge, 139
  β hairpin motif, 146
  β sheet, **132–134**, 132F, 133F
  as buffering agents, 36
  catabolism overview, 452F
  coated vesicles, transport, 283–285
  composition of selected, 93T
  core, 234
  dinucleotide-binding fold, 150
  domains, **149–150**, 150F
  domain shuffling, 120
  evolutionarily conservative, 116
  fibrous, **134–139**
  functions, 91–92
  as fuel reserves, 798

globular, *see* Globular proteins
glycosylated, **238–240**
homologous, 116
integral, 263–264, 267
isoelectric point of selected, 98T
isotopic labeling, 367
link, 234–235F
in membranes, *see* Membrane proteins
motifs, **146**
motor, 205–206
nuclear magnetic resonance, 143
peptide group, 92, **127–129**
pH effects, 332
polypeptide diversity, **92–93**
posttranslational processing, 282F
preproteins, 280
primary structure, **91–120**
quaternary structure, 126F, **154–155**
receptor, 395, 405
Rossmann fold, 150
secondary structure, 126F, **127–140**
side chain location, 145–146
solubility, **97–98**
stabilizing, 94–95
steroid hormone binding, 255
tertiary structure, 126F, **140–154**
transport, **307–310**
visualizing, 145
water-soluble, 267
X-ray crystallography, 141–142
α₁-Proteinase inhibitor, 356
Protein-carbohydrate interactions, 240–242
Protein-conducting channel (PCC), 1032
Protein crystals, 141F
Protein Data Bank (PDB), 151–154
Protein degradation:
  intracellular, **733–735**
  lysosomal, **733**
  proteasome, **735–738**, 736F
  ubiquitin, **734–735**
Protein denaturation, 94, 139, **158–160**
Protein design, 163
Protein disulfide isomerase (PDI),
    163–165, 164F
Protein domains, 120
Protein evolution, 92, **114–117**
  evolutionarily conservative proteins, 116
  gene duplication, **117–120**, 119F
  rates of, selected proteins, 119F
  sequence evolution, **114–117**
Protein Explorer (computer program), 152
Protein families, **118–120**, 150–151
Protein folding, **161–172**
  denaturation, 94, 139
  diseases, from misfolding, **168–172**
  energy–entropy diagram, 162F
  molecular chaperones, **165–168**
  pathways, **161–162**, 161F
  PDI, catalysis by, **163–165**
  renaturation, 161F

Protein function, **176–215**
Protein kinases, 251, 391
Protein kinase A (PKA), 432, 433F.
    See also cAMP-dependent protein
    kinase (cAPK)
Protein kinase B (PKB), 443F
Protein kinase C (PKC), 440–442
Protein-modifying reagents, 344
Protein modules, 1061
Protein mosaics, **120**
Protein phosphatases, 253, 391, 425–428
Protein phosphorylation, 390–393
Protein purification, **94–103**
  affinity chromatography, 101, 101F
  capillary electrophoresis (CE), 103
  chromatography, **98–101**
  electrophoresis, **101–103**
  gel filtration chromatography, 100–101,
    1004F
  general approach to, **94–97**
  hydrophobic interaction chromatography,
    99–100
  immunoaffinity chromatography, 101
  ion exchange chromatography,
    98–99, 99F
  polyacrylamide gel electrophoresis
    (PAGE), 102F
  protein solubility, **97–98**
  SDS-PAGE, 102–103, 102F
Protein renaturation, **158–160**, 161F
Protein sequence identity, 120
Protein sequencing, **104–114**, 163
  databases, 112–114
  disulfide bond cleavage, 106–107
  Edman degradation, 106, **109–110**, 109F
  end group analysis, 104–105
  polypeptide cleavage, **107–108**
  preliminary steps, **104–107**
  sequence reconstruction, **112–114**
Protein Ser/Thr phosphatases, 426
Protein stability, 156–160
  denaturation, **158–160**
  renaturation, **158–160**
Protein structure(s):
  bioinformatics, structural, **151–154**
  irregular structures, **139–140**
  nonrepetitive structure, **139–140**
  primary structure, 92. *See also*
    Polypeptides; Protein
    evolution; Protein purification;
    Protein sequencing
  quaternary structure, 126, 154–155
  secondary structure, 126, 127–140
  stabilizing forces, 156–158
  structural genomics, 163
  symmetry, **155**, 155F
  tertiary structure, 126, **140–154**
Protein synthesis, 985. *See also* Ribosomes;
    Translation
  chain elongation, **1008–1010**

Protein synthesis (*cont.*)
　chain initiation, **1010–1014,** 1013F
　chain termination, **1026–1028,** 1026F
　heme-controlled, 1077F
　by recombinant DNA techniques, **49–50,**
　　60, 67, 67T
　ribosome role in, 49, 942,
　　1000–1001, 1010
　translational accuracy, 1026F
protein tyrosine kinases (PTKs), 413
Protein tyrosine phosphatases (PTPs),
　425–426
Proteoglycans, 235F
Proteome, 50, 478, 480
Proteomics, 50, 480–482
Prothrombin, 358
Protomers, 154
Proton gradient, 316–318
　mitochondrial membranes, 597
　oxidative phosphorylation, 621
Proton jumping, 30–31, 31F
Protonmotive force (pmf), 620
Proton pump, 266, 608
Proton-pumping ATP synthase, *see*
　ATP-synthase
Proton translocation, 318
Proton wire, 608
Protoporphyrin IX, 610, 776F, 777
Protoporphyrinogen IX, in heme
　biosynthesis, 776F
Protoporphyrinogen oxidase, in heme
　biosynthesis, 776F, 777
Protosterol, 724
Proximity effects (enzymes),
　336–338
PrP (prion protein), 170–171
PRPP, *see* 5-Phosphoribosyl-α-
　pyrophosphate
Prusiner, S., 170
PsaA, 658
PsaB, 658
PsaC–E, 658
PsaF, 658
PsaI–M, 658
PsaX, 658
PsbA (D1), 652
PsbB (CP47), 653
PsbC (CP43), 653
PsbD (D2), 652
Pseudo-first-order reaction, 366
Pseudogenes, 119
Pseudouridine, 977, 992F
PSI (photosystem I), 650–651F
　electron pathways, 658–661
　segregation, 662
　X-ray structure, 659F
φ angles, 128, 128F
D-Psicose, 221F
PSII (photosystem II), 650–651F,
　652–654, 662

Psoriasis, 215T
PTC (phenylthiocarbamyl), in Edman
　degradation, 109, 109F
Pteridine, 760–761F
Pterins, 760–761F
PTH (phenylthiohydantion), in Edman
　degradation, 109, 109F
PTKs (protein tyrosine kinases), 413
PTPs (protein tyrosine phosphatases),
　425–426
P-type ATPases, 311
PUC18, 60F, 62
Pulmonary emphysema, 356
Pulsed-field gel electrophoresis
　(PFGE), **873**
Pulse-labeling, 895F
Pumped protons, 618
PurE, 820
Pure noncompetitive inhibition, 383
Purine, 40, 856F
Purine nucleoside phosphorylase (PNP),
　in purine catabolism, 840
Purine nucleotide cycle, 841F
Purine ribonucleotides, **40–42,** 41F. *See*
　also Adenine; Guanine
　AMP synthesis, 819F, **822–823F**
　catabolism, **839–842**
　GMP synthesis, 819F, **822–823F**
　IMP synthesis, **818–824,** 819F
　salvage, **823–824**
　synthesis, **818–824,** 819F
　synthesis regulation, **822–823**
PurK, 820
Puromycin, 1024
Purple photosynthetic bacteria, 647F–649
PWS (Prader–Willi syndrome), 1067
Pyl, *see* Pyrrolysine
Pyran, 222
Pyranoses, 222
Pyridine nucleotides, 327F
Pyridoxal-5′-phosphate (PLP), 739F–741F
　as covalent catalyst, 335
　as glycogen phosphorylase cofactor, 534
Pyridoxamine-5′-phosphate (PMP), 739F
Pyridoxine, 739F
Pyrimidine, 40
　dimers, 916
　sterically allowed orientations, 856F
Pyrimidine biosynthesis
　pathway, 387F
　regulation of, 827F
Pyrimidine ribonucleotides, **40–42,** 41F.
　See also Cytosine; Thymine; Uracil
　CTP synthesis, **826**
　degradation of, **845–846**
　synthesis, **824–828**
　synthesis regulation, **827–828**
　UMP synthesis, **824–828**
　UTP synthesis, **826**
Pyrobaculum aerophilum, 971

Pyrolobus fumarii, 159
Pyrophosphate (PP_i), 461
Pyrophosphate cleavage, 464, 465F
Pyrophosphomevalonate decarboxylase, 722
Pyrrole-2-carboxylate, proline racemase
　inhibition, 339
Δ-1-Pyrroline-2-carboxylate, proline
　racemase inhibition, 339
$Δ^1$-Pyrroline-5-carboxylate, 768
Pyrroline-5-carboxylate reductase, 768
Pyrrolysine (Pyl), 1000
Pyruvate:
　amino acid biosynthesis from, 764–768
　in amino acid degradation, 747F,
　　748F–749
　in citric acid cycle, 568F, 570–573
　in gluconeogenesis, **552–560,** 589–590
　in glycolysis, 487F, 501–504
　isozyme action, 455
　mammalian metabolism, 793, 795
　metabolic fate, 505F
Pyruvate carboxylase:
　in gluconeogenesis, **552–560,** 559
　two-phase reaction mechanism
　　of, 555F
Pyruvate decarboxylase, 506
Pyruvate dehydrogenase (E_1), 797
　in citric acid cycle, 568F, **570–573**
　coenzymes and prosthetic groups, 572T
　regulation, **584–585**
Pyruvate:ferredoxin oxidoreductase, 593
Pyruvate–H^+ symport, 570
Pyruvate kinase (PK), 463
　deficiency, 502
　in glycolysis, 487F, **501–504,** 511
Pyruvate–phosphate dikinase, 674
Pyuvate ketoglutarate dehydrogenase, 797
PYY_{3-36}, 808

Q
Q, *see* Coenzyme Q
q (heat), 12
Q Cycle, 612–614, 651F
q_P (heat at constant pressure), 12
Q-SNAREs, 287, 288, 289F
Quanta, 645
Quantum yield, 649
Quaternary structure (proteins), 126F,
　154–155
Quinine, 394, 394F
Quinol oxidase, 621

R
R (gas constant), 13
R5P, *see* Ribose-5-phosphate
Rabbit:
　glycogen phosphorylase, 391F
　muscle actin, 202F
　muscle phosphorylase kinase, 547F
Racemic mixtures, 84

Racker, E., 622
Rad51, 934
Radioimmunoassay (RIA), 95, 408
Radionuclides, 367
Raff, M., 1087
Raf kinase, 419
RAG1, 1080
RAG2, 1080
Ramachandran, G. N., 129
Ramachandran diagram, 129F
Ramakrishnan, V., 1002
Randle cycle (glucose-fatty acid cycle), 634
Random coils, proteins, 139
Random mechanism, sequential
    reactions, 375
Rapamycin, 443F
Ras, 417, 419F
RasGAP, 418–419
Ras signaling cascade, 417F, 803,
    1070, 1085
Rat:
    intestinal fatty-acid binding protein
        (I-FABP), 680F
    liver cytoplasmic 40S subunit, 1007T
    liver enzymes half-lives, 733F
    testis calmodulin, 438F
Rate constant (k), 364
Rate-determining step, 329
Rate enhancement, 329, 338
Rate equations, 365–366
Rational drug design, 395
Ratner, S., 743
Rayment, I., 206, 745
Reaction coordinate, 328–330
Reaction coordinate diagram, 328F
Reaction kinetics, 364–376. See also
    Enzyme kinetics
Reaction order, 365
Reactive oxygen species, 611
Reading frame, 986
Rearrangements, 453
RecA-mediated pairing, 929F
RecA-mediated strand exchange, 930F
RecA protein, 926, 929F–930F
RecBCD protein, 930
Receptors, 550, 801
Receptor-mediated endocytosis, 290,
    684F–685
Receptor protein, 395, 405
Receptor tyrosine kinases (RTKs),
    412–428, 1070
    and kinase cascades, 416–422
    and nonreceptor tyrosine kinases, 422–425
    and protein phosphatases, 425–428
    signal transmission by, 413–416
Recombinant, 61F
Recombinant DNA technology, 59–60,
    61F, 70. See also Cloning
Recombination, 58, 926–939
    general or homologous, 926–932

repair by, 932–934
transposition, 58, 934–939
Recombination repair, 925, 932–934
Recombination signal sequences
    (RSS), 1080
Redox centers, 597
Redox cofactors, 609–611
Redox couples, 471
Redox reactions, see Oxidation–reduction
    reactions
Red tide, 676
Reduced (term), 397–398
Reducing agents, 470–471
Reducing end, 231
Reducing equivalents, 556
Reducing sugars, 226
Reduction, 453
Reduction potential, 472
    measurement, 472–474
    selected half-reactions, 473T
Reductive pentose phosphate pathway,
    see Calvin cycle
Reef, 22F
Rees, D., 783
Regeneration:
    ATP, 464–465, 631
    coenzymes, 327–328
Regular secondary structures
    (proteins), 129
Regulatory light chains (RLC), 201
Regulatory proteins:
    activators, 1067
    repressors, 1067
Reichard, P., 829
Relaxed circles, 857F, 859
Release factor (RF), 1012T, 1026F–1027
Remington, J., 578
Renaturation:
    DNA, 866, 866F
    proteins, 158–160F
Repair, DNA, see DNA repair
Repetitive DNA sequences, 1043–1046
Replica plating, 64
Replication, 48
    of DNA, see DNA replication
    of linear chromosome, 914F
    of molecules, 5F
Replication forks, 894
Replicons, 913
Replisome, 904–905F
Repolarization, 302
Repressors, 876
    corepressors, 1051
    regulatory proteins, 1067
RER, see Rough endoplasmic reticulum
Resolvase, 938
Resonance energy transfer, 646–647
Respiration, 488
    ATP resupply by, 795
    brain tissue, 793

hemoglobin/myoglobin function, 189F
and inner mitochondrial membrane
    surface area, 599
physiological implications, 634–637
Respiratory distress syndrome, 250
Restart primosome, 933
Restriction endonucleases:
    cloning application, 61
    DNA–protein interactions, 875–876, 875F
    for nucleic acid sequencing, 51–52
    recognition and cleavage sites of
        selected, 52T
Restriction–modification system, 51–52
Reticulocyte heme-controlled protein
    synthesis, 1077
Reticulocytes, 778, 1077, 1077F
Retinal, 257
Retinal residue, 263
Retinoblastoma, 1086
Retinol binding protein, 149
Retro aldol condensation, 492
Retrograde transport, 283
Retrotransposons, 939, 1046
Retroviruses, 912, 938–939
Reverse transcriptase (RT), 384, 912–913
Reverse turns, 134
RF (release factor), 1012T, 1026F–1027
RF-1, 1026
RF-2, 1026
RF-3, 1027
R groups, amino acids, 75
Rhamnose, 233
Rheumatoid arthritis, 215T, 733
Rhizobium, 782F
Rhodopsin, 429
Rho factor, 951
RIA (radioimmunoassay), 95, 408
Ribitol, 224
Riboflavin (vitamin B$_2$), 470
Ribonuclease, see RNase
Ribonucleic acid, see RNA
Ribonucleoproteins, 914
Ribonucleotides, 40, 41F
Ribonucleotide reductase, 617, 828–834, 830F
Ribose, 220F, 221
    conformations in DNA, 856F
    in ribonucleotides, 40
D-Ribose, 220F
α-D-Ribose-5-phosphate, in IMP
    synthesis, 819F
Ribose-5-phosphate (R5P):
    in Calvin cycle, 665F, 666
    in pentose phosphate pathway, 521F–522
Ribose phosphate isomerase, in Calvin
    cycle, 665F, 666
Ribose phosphate moiety, 826
Ribose phosphate pyrophosphokinase, in
    IMP synthesis, 818, 819F
Ribosomal RNA, see rRNA
Ribosomal synthesis, 279F

Ribosomes, 8F, **1001–1008**. *See also* Protein synthesis
  eukaryotic, **1007–1008**
  membrane protein synthesis in, 278–282
  prokaryotic, **1001–1007**
  subunit self-assembly, 1007
  and transpeptidation, 1019–1021
Ribosome recycling factor (RRF), 1027
Riboswitches, **1054–1055**
Ribozymes, 323, 870
Ribulose, 221F
D-Ribulose, 221F
Ribulose-1,5-bisphosphate (RuBP), in Calvin cycle, 664, 665F, 666
Ribulose-5-phosphate epimerase, in pentose phosphate pathway, 521F–523
Ribulose-5-phosphate isomerase, in pentose phosphate pathway, 521F
Ribulose-5-phosphate (Ru5P):
  in Calvin cycle, 663F–664
  in pentose phosphate pathway, 521F–522, 521F–523
Rich, A., 854, 869
Richardson, D., 153
Richmond, T., 885
Rickets, 256–257
Rickettsia prowazekii, 57T
Rieske center, 611
Rifampicin, 954
Rifamycin B, 954
Rigor mortis, 217
RING finger, 734, 735
RISC (RNA-induced silencing complex), 1075–1076
Ritonavir, 384, 385
Rittenberg, D., 476, 775
RLC (regulatory light chains), 201
RNA (ribonucleic acid), 39–41. *See also* DNA replication; mRNA; Nucleic acids; rRNA; Transcription; Translation; tRNA
  A-DNA type helix formation, 854–855
  base-catalyzed hydrolysis, 871
  catalytic properties, 323
  as enzyme, 978
  hybridization, 866
  nucleotides, 42
  single-stranded nucleic acids in, 47
  structure, **868–871**
  synthesis by recombinant DNA techniques, 60
RNA-dependent RNA polymerase, 1076
RNA–DNA hybrids, 866
RNA editing, 975
RNAi (RNA interference), 1075–1076
RNA-induced silencing complex (RISC), 1075–1076
RNA interference (RNAi), 1075–1076
RNA interference mechanism, 1075F

RNAP, *see* RNA polymerase
RNAP II-Mediator complex, 1069–1070
RNA polymerase (RNAP), 904, 942, 946
  binding of, to promoters, **945–946**
  chain growth, **947–950**
  collisions with DNA polymerase, 949
  eukaryotes, *see* Eukaryotic transcription
  heavy metal substitution for Zn^{2+}, 326
  processivity, 949
  structure, **943–944**, 944F
  transcription termination at specific sites, **950–952**
RNA polymerase core enzyme, 943
RNA polymerase holoenzyme, 943F, 946
RNA polymerase I (RNAP I), 953, 958–964
RNA polymerase II (RNAP II), 953, 957–958, 959F
RNA polymerase III (RNAP III), 953, 960
RNA primers, 896, 899F, 905F
RNA-recognition motifs (RRM), 975
RNase III, 976
RNase A (ribonuclease A):
  bovine pancreatic, 332–333
  isoelectric point, 98T
  renaturation, 159–160F
RNase B, 241F
RNase D, 977
RNase E, 976
RNase F, 976
RNase H, 912
RNase H1, 911
RNase M5, 977
RNase M16, 977
RNase M23, 977
RNase P, 976, 980–981
RNA triphosphatase, 966
RNA world, 47, 871
Roberts, R., 967, 1065
Roberts, R. J., 968
Rodnina, M., 1021
Rofecoxib (Vioxx), 719
Rose, L., 491
Rose, W. C., 75
Rosenberg, J., 875
Rossmann (Dinucleotide-binding) fold, 150
Rotational symmetry (proteins), 155
Rotenone, 603
Rothman, J., 275, 287
Rough endoplasmic reticulum (RER), 8F
  membrane protein synthesis in, 278
  metabolic functions, 455T
Rous sarcoma virus (RSV), 421
RPA, 911
Rpb1 subunit, 955–956
Rpb2 subunit, 956
RRF (ribosome recycling factor), 1027
RRM (RNA-recognition motifs), 975

rRNA (ribosomal RNA), 49, 942. *See also* Ribosomes
  double-stranded segments, 868–869
  gene clusters, 1042
  posttranscriptional processing, **976–980**
  ribosomal RNA processing, 976–980
  self-splicing, 977–978F
RSC complex, 1056
R-SNAREs, 287, 288, 289F
RSS (recombination signal sequences), 1080
RS (Cahn-Ingold-Prelog) system, 85
R state, 186–189, 192–194, 393F
R subunit (of protein kinase A), 433
RSV (rous sarcoma virus), 421
RT (reverse transcriptase), 384, 912–913
RTKs, *see* Receptor tyrosine kinases
Rubisco, 672
RuBP (ribulose-1,5-bisphosphate), in Calvin cycle, 664, 666
RuBP carboxylase, 665F, 666–668, 670–671
RuBP carboxylase activase, 668
RuBP carboxylase–oxygenase (Rubisco), 672F. *See also* Ribulose-1,5-bisphosphate
Runt gene, 1092
Ru5P, *see* Ribulose-5-phosphate
Rutter, W., 1068
RuvA protein, 931F
RuvB protein, 931–932
RuvC protein, 932

S
S (entropy), 13
S1P, *see* Site-1 protease
S2P, *see* Site-2 protease
S4 helix, 303
S6′, 737
S6 kinase, 420F
S7P, *see* Sedoheptulose-7-phosphate
SACAIR (5-Aminoimidazole-4-(*N*-succinylocarboxamide) ribotide), in IMP synthesis, 819F, 820
SACAIR synthetase, in IMP synthesis, 819F
Saccharides, 219. *See also* Carbohydrates; Monosaccharides; Polysaccharides
Saccharine, 228
Saccharomyces cerevisiae, see Baker's yeast
Saccharomyces uvarum, pyruvate decarboxylase, 507F
Saccharopine, 758
Sacchettini, J., 630
SAGA, 1060
Sali, A., 1008
Salmine, isoelectric point, 98T
Salmonella typhimurium, 305
  glutamine synthetase, 766F
  SDS-PAGE purification, 102F
  tryptophan synthase, 773F–774
Salts, solvation in water, 26
Salt bridge, 157
Salting in, 97

alting out, 97

alvage pathways, 823

AM, see S-Adenosylmethionine

andhoff's disease, 720

anger, F., 53, 104–105, 697, 968

anti, D., 835

aquinavir, 384, 385

arcomas, 421, 1084

arcomere, 198, 199F

arcoplasmic reticulum, 207, 313

arin, 349

arko, A., 229

aturated enzyme, 370

aturated fatty acids, 247, 247T

aturation, 309
  enzymes, 370
  oxygen in myoglobin, 180

av1866 (ABC transporter), 315

ayle, R., 153

BP (sedoheptulose-1,7-bisphosphate), in Calvin cycle, 665F, 666, 670–671

BPase (sedoheptulose-1,7-bisphosphatase), in Calvin cycle, 665F, 666, 670–671

caffold proteins, 420, 422

calar protons, 618

CAP (SREBP cleavage-activating protein), 725

catchard plot, 414

chachman, H., 387

chiff base, 330
  formation (transimination), 740–741F
  imine, 330

chirmer, T., 299

chulz, G., 467

CID (severe combined immunodeficiency disease), 70, 840–841

CID-X1, 70

cintillation counters, 367

COP (database), 154

cott, M., 1095

cott, W., 870

creening, of genomic libraries, 64–65

cr protein, 416

crunching, 948

curvy, 137

dhA, 610

dhB, 610

dhC, 610

dhD, 610

DS (sodium dodecyl sulfate), 102–103

DS-PAGE (sodium dodecyl sulfate-polyacrylamide gel electrophoresis), 102–103, 102F. See also Polyacrylamide gel electrophoresis

Sec, see Selenocysteine

Sec61, 280

Secondary active transport, 311, 316

Secondary lysosome, 684F

Secondary pair-rule genes, 1093F

Secondary structure (proteins), 126F, **127–140**
  defined, 126
  fibrous proteins, 134–139
  nonrepetitive structure, 139–140
  peptide group, 127–129
  regular secondary structure, 128–134
  supersecondary structure, 146

Second law of thermodynamics, **13–14**

Second messengers, 405–406, 429, 550

Second-order reactions, 365, 366

β-Secretases, 169

γ-Secretases, 169

Secretory pathway, **278–282**

Secretory vesicles, 282F

SecY, 280

SecYEG, 1032

Sedimentation coefficients, 735

Sedoheptulose-1,7-bisphosphate (SBP), in Calvin cycle, 665F, 666, 670–671

Sedoheptulose-7-phosphate (S7P):
  in Calvin cycle, 665F
  in pentose phosphate pathway, 521F, 524

Sedoheptulose bisphosphatase (SBPase), in Calvin cycle, 665F, 666, 670–671

Segmentation genes, 1091

Segment polarity genes, 1091

SELB, 1000

Selectable markers, 62

Selectins, 241–242

Selectivity filter, 301

Selenocysteine (Sec), 1000

Self-comparmentalized proteases, 737

Selfish DNA, 1046

Sem-5 protein, 418

Semiconservative replication, 893, 894F

Semidiscontinuous replication, 896

Semi-invariant positions (tRNA), 992

Sendai virus, 271F

Senescence, 915

Sense RNA, 1075

Sense (coding) strand, 944, 945F

Septic shock, 445

Sequence analysis, 309

Sequencing, see Nucleic acid sequencing; Protein sequencing

Sequential model of allosterism, 193, 193F

Sequential reactions, 375–376

Serine (Ser), 249T
  α helix/β sheet propensities, 140T
  biosynthesis, 769
  breakdown, 747F, 748–751
  as common amino acid, 93
  covalent catalysis by, 335
  genetic code specification, 988, 989T
  ionizable groups, 77T
  side chain hydropathy, 156T
  structure, 77T
  uncharged polar side chain, 79, 79F

Serine carboxypeptidase II, 352F

Serine dehydratase, 748–749F

Serine hydroxymethyltransferase, 749–751, 837F

Serine proteases, **347–357.** See also Chymotrypsin; Elastase; Trypsin
  active site, **348,** 352F
  catalytic mechanism, **352–357,** 353F
  catalytic triad, 350F
  preferential transition state binding, 354F
  X-ray structure, **348–352**

Serotonin, 780

Serum albumin, 98T

Serum glutamate–oxaloacetate transaminase (SGOT), 742

Serum glutamate-pyruvate transaminase (SGPT), 742

SET7/9, 1063–1064F

SET domain, 1063

70S ribosome, 1001T

Severe combined immunodeficiency disease (SCID), 70, 840–841

Sex hormones, 410–411

SGOT (serum glutamate-oxaloacetate transaminase), 742

SGPT (serum glutamate-pyruvate transaminase), 742

SH2 (Src homology 2) domains, 416F, 422–424, 423F, 1061

SH3 domains, 417–418F, 423F–424

Sharon, N., 346

Sharp, E., 967

Sharp, P. A., 968

Shc protein, 442

Shear degradation, 883

Shearing, of DNA, 63

Shemin, D., 476, 775

Shine, J., 1011

Shine–Dalgarno sequence, 1011–1012, 1055

Short interfering RNAs (siRNAs), 1075

Short interspersed nuclear elements (SINEs), 1045

Short tandem repeats (STRs), 66, 1044

Short-term regulation, 713

Shotgun cloning, 63

Shotton, D., 351

SHP-2, 426, 443F

Shulman, G., 813

Sialic acid, 225

Sickle-cell anemia, 70, 194F–197, 527

Sickle-cell hemoglobin (hemoglobin S), 194–197

Side chains, 1059–1060

Side chain distribution, 145–146

Sigler, P., 166, 430, 877, 962

σ^{70}, 947

σ Factor, 943

σ^{gp28}, 947

$\sigma^{gp33/34}$, 947

Sigmoidal binding curve, 184F
Signal-anchor sequences, 281
Signal-gated channels, 302
Signal hypothesis, membrane protein transport, 278F–280
Signaling, biochemical, *see* Biochemical signaling
Signal peptidase, 280
Signal peptides, 278
Signal recognition particle (SRP), 278, 428
Signal recognition particle receptor, 278–280
Signal strength, 302
Signal transduction, 299
Signal-transduction pathways, 1070
Signature sequence (TVGYG), 301
Signer, R., 850
Sildenafil, 436
Silencers, 1067
Simian virus 40 (SV40), 959
Simple sugars, *see* Monosaccharides
SINEs (short interspersed nuclear elements), 1045
Singer, S., 270
Single blind tests, 397
Single-chained zymogens (procaspases), 1087
Single-displacement reactions, 375–376
Single nucleotide polymorphisms, (SNPs), 1041
Single-strand binding protein (SSB), 904, 904F–905F
Single-stranded nucleic acids, 47
siRNAs (short interfering RNAs), 1075
Site-1 protease (S1P), 726
Site-2 protease (S2P), 726
Site-directed mutagenesis, 68F, 344
Site-specific recombination, 926
SI units, 13
16S rRNA, 976
Size exclusion chromatography, 100–101
Skehel, J., 290
Skeletal muscles. *See also* Striated muscle
  adipose tissue in, 796
  oxygen usage, 795
Ski7p protein, 1074
Skin, 796
Skou, J., 311
Slack, R., 674
SLI, 964
Sliding clamp, 905–906
Sliding filament model, 201
Slow-twitch muscle fibers, 510, 798
Small intestine, 809
Small nuclear ribonucleoproteins (snRNPs), 971
Small nuclear RNAs (snRNAs), 971
Small nucleolar RNAs (snoRNAs), 977
Small (30S) ribosomal subunit, 1001–1006, 1001T

Small ubiquitin-related modifier (SUMO), 1029
Smith, C., 873
Smith, E., 115
Smith, J., 656
Smith, M., 68
Smoking, protease inhibitor effects, 356
Smooth endoplasmic reticulum, 8F, 455T
Sm proteins, 971
Sm RNA motif, 971
S_N2 reaction, 337F
Snake venoms, *see* Venoms
SNAP-25, 287F
SNAREs, 287F, 288, 289F, 800
Snell, E., 740
snoRNAs (small nucleolar RNAs), 977
SNPs (single nucleotide polymorphisms), 1041
snRNAs (small nuclear RNAs), 971
snRNP core protein, 971
snRNPs (small nuclear ribonucleoproteins), 971
SOD (superoxide dismutase), 636
Sodium dodecyl sulfate (SDS), 102–103
Sodium ion, *See* Na^+ ion
$(Na^+–K^+)$–ATPase, 311F–313, 316
$(Na^+–K^+)$ pump, 311
Solvation, 25–26, 26F
Solvent, water as, **25–26**
Somatic hypermutation, 214, 1081
Somatic recombination, **214**
Somatostatin, 407
Sonication, 638
D-Sorbose, 221F
Sørenson, S., 31
Soret bands, 610
Sos protein, 418
SOS response, **926**
Southern, E., 874
Southern blotting, 874F
Sowadski, J., 433
Specialization, cells, 8
Special pair, 648–650
Specificity site, 833
Speed and specificity, 309
Sperm, 410
S phase, 1082
Sphinganine, 718F
Sphingoglycolipids, 717
Sphingolipids, **252–253**, 253F
  degradation, 720–721
  synthesis, **717–718**
Sphingolipid storage diseases, 253, 720–721
Sphingomyelins, 252F, 253, 720F
Sphingophospholipids, 252
Sphingosine, 252
Spina bifida, 755
Spinobulbar muscular atrophy, 1044T
Splenda®, 228

Spliceosome, 971
Splicing, introns and exons, 967, 969–972
Spontaneous processes, 12, 13
Sprang, S., 430
Squalene, 722–725
Squalene epoxidase, 724
Squalene oxidocyclase, 724
Squalene synthase, 724
Squelching, 1069
SR-BI, 685
Src activation, 423F
Src–AMPPNP, 422F
Src family, 422
Src homology 2 (SH2) domains, 416F, 422–424, 423F, 1061
SRE (sterol regulatory element), 725
SREBP (sterol regulatory element binding protein), 725
SREBP cleavage-activating protein (SCAP), 725
SRP (signal recognition particle), 278, 428
SRP9, 1031F
SRP14, 1031F
SRP54, 1032
SRP receptor, 279
SR proteins, 975
SSB (single-strand binding protein), 904, 904F–905F
Stacking interactions, **867–868**
Stadtman, E., 766
Stahl, E., 893, 894
Standard reduction potential, 472, 473T
Standard state, 15–17
Staphylococcal nuclease catalytic power, 323T
Staphylococcus aureus, cell wall, 236
Starch, **230–231**
  as glucose stockpile, 530
  glycogen contrasted as fuel reserve, 544
Starch synthase, 669, 669F
Stark, H., 972
Starvation, **809–811**. *See also* Fasting
  and blood glucose levels, 809–810
  gluconeogenesis during, 810
  and immediate allocation of absorbed fuels, 809
  ketone bodies as energy source during, 810–811
  and longevity, 811
Stat3β, 1072
State functions, 15
Statins, 726–727
Stationary phase, 98
Stats, 1071
Ste5p, 422
Steady state, 18–19, 368, 374–375
Steady state assumption, 368, 369
Stearic acid, 246, 246F, 247T
1-Stearoyl-2-oleoyl-3-phosphatidylcholine, 250F

Steitz, J., 971, 1002
Steitz, T., 869, 900, 996
Stem–loop structures, 47F
Stercobilin, in heme degradation, 779F, 780
Stereochemistry, amino acids, **82–86**
Stereoelectronic control, 495
Stereoisomers, 83–84
Stereospecificity, 325–326
Steroids, **254–257,** 255F, 410–411
Steroid hormones, 254–257, 1070
Steroid receptors, 165, 410, 1073
Sterols, 254
Sterol regulatory element (SRE), 725
Sterol regulatory element binding protein (SREBP), 725
Sterol-sensing domain, 726
Stevia, 228
Sticky ends, 52, 61
Stigmatellin, 614
Stop codons, 974, 990, 1026
    gene identification, 1040
    and nonsense mutation, 1027–1028
Storage diseases, 720–721
Storage polysaccharides, **230–231**
STRs (short tandem repeats), 66, 1044
Strand-passage mechanism, 860
Streptavidin, 628
Streptomyces lividans, 300
Streptomycin, 1024–1025
Striated muscle structure, **198–205.**
    See also Skeletal muscles
    thick filaments, 198, 199F
    thin filaments, 198, 199F
Stroke, 635, 728
Stroma, 641F, 642
Stromal lamellae, 641F, 642
Strominger, J., 236
Strong acids, 33
Stroud, R., 351
Structural bioinformatics, **151–154**
Structural genes, 944
Structural polysaccharides, **228–230**
Structure-based drug design, 395
Stubbe, J., 830
su3 (amber suppressor), 1028
Submitochondrial particles, 638
Substitutional editing, 975
Substrates, 324
    leading vs. following, 376
    Michaelis–Menten parameters of selected, 371T
    suicide substrates, 838
Substrate cycles, 458–459
    glucose metabolism, 558F
    glycolysis, **514–515**
Substrate-level phosphorylation, 465. *See also* Oxidative phosphorylation; Photophosphorylation
Subtilisin, 352F
Subunits, 92, 154–155

Subunit IV, 656
Succinate, 567, 595
    in citric acid cycle, 377, 568F, 582, 584F
    in glyoxylate cycle, 591F
    in ketone body conversion to acetyl-CoA, 700F
Succinate–Coenzyme Q oxidoreductase, *see* Complex II
Succinate dehydrogenase:
    in citric acid cycle, 568F, **582**
    malonate inhibition, 377–378
Succinate semialdehyde, 595
Succinate thiokinase, in citric acid cycle, 568F, **580–582,** 581F
Succinyl-CoA, 469
    in amino acid degradation, 747F, 753–758
    in citric acid cycle, 568F, 580, 584F
    in heme biosynthesis, 776F
    in ketone body conversion to acetyl-CoA, 700F
Succinyl-CoA synthetase, in citric acid cycle, 568F, **580–582,** 581F
Succinyl-phosphate, in citric acid cycle, 581
Sucralose, 228
Sucrose, 227, 228, 366
Sucrose-phosphate phosphatase, 669
Sucrose-phosphate synthase, 669
Sugars, 220–221, 226. See also Disaccharides; Monosaccharides
Suicide substrates, 838
Sulbactam, 225
Sulfa drugs, 756
Sulfanilamide, 756
Sulfatide, in sphingoglycolipid degradation, 720F
Sulfonamides, 756, 820
Sulston, J., 57
Sumner, J., 322–323
SUMO (small ubiquitin-related modifier), 1029
Supercoiled DNA, **857–859,** 857F, 858F
    progressive unwinding, 859F
    and topoisomerase, 859
    during transcription, 948F
Supercoiling, 857, 857F
Superhelicity, 857
Superoxide dismutase (SOD), 636
Superoxide radical, 635
Supersecondary structures, 146
Supply–demand process, 459
Suppressor mutations, 986
Surface labeling, 264
Surroundings, 12
Sutherland, E., 428, 533, 550
Suv39h, 1064
SV40 (simian virus 40), 959
Svedberg (unit), 735
Sweet N Low®, 228
SWI/SNF, 1056
Swiss-Pdb Viewer, 153

Swiss roll, 149
Switch regions, 431
SXL protein, 974
Symbiosis, 10
Symmetry model of allosterism, 193F
Symport, 310
Synapses, 287, 349
Synaptic cleft, 287
Synaptic vesicles, 287
Synaptobrevin, 287F
Synchrotron, 141
Syn conformation, 856F
Syncytium, 1090, 1091F
Synechocystis sp., 57T
Synergy, 1069
Synonym codons, 989–990
Syntaxin, 287
Synthase, 707F
Syphilis, arsenicals for, 576
Systematic (official) name, 324
Systemic lupus erythematosus, 215T
Systems, 12, 18
Systems biology, **477–482**
Szent-Györgyi, A., 200, 569

T
T, *see* Thymine
T (supercoiled DNA twist), 858F
T. elongatus, 659F
$t_{1/2}$ (half-life), 365–366
TAFs (TBP-associated factors), 963
TAF1, 1060
TAF5, 1060
TAF6, 1060
TAF9, 1060
TAF10, 1060
TAF12, 1060
D-Tagatose, 221F
Tainer, J., 834
D-Talose, 220F
Tangier disease, 729
Taq polymerase, 65
Target DNA sites:
    enhancers, 1067
    silencers, 1067
T Arm (tRNA), 991F
Tarui's disease, 538–539
TATA-binding protein (TBP), 961, 961F
TATA box, 959
Tatum, E., 49
Taurine, 678
Tautomers, 44, 44F
Taxonomy, **9**
Taylor, E., 206
Taylor, S., 433
Tay–Sachs disease, 253, 720–721
TBHA2, 291
TBP (TATA-binding protein), 961, 961F
TBP-associated factors (TAFs), 963
TC10 protein, 442

TCA cycle, *see* Citric acid cycle
T cells (T lymphocytes), 209
T cell receptors, 422
Telomerase, **914–916**
Telomeres, **914–916,** 1043
Temin, H., 912
Teosinte, 59F
TerA site, *E. coli* chromosome, 908F
TerB site, *E. coli* chromosome, 908F
TerC site, *E. coli* chromosome, 908F
TerD site, *E. coli* chromosome, 908F
TerE site, *E. coli* chromosome, 908F
TerF site, *E. coli* chromosome, 908F
TerG site, *E. coli* chromosome, 908F
Terminal deoxynucleotidyl
    transferase, 1080
Terminal desaturases, 708
Termolecular reactions, 365
Terpenoids, 257
Tertiary structure (proteins), 126F, **140–154**
    determination of, 141–145
    families, protein, 150–151
    polarity, side chain location and, 145–146
    supersecondary structures, 146–148
Testes, 255, 406F, 410
Testicular feminization, 411
Testosterone, 255F, 410
Tetanus, 288
Tetracycline, 1025
Tetracycline-resistant bacteria, 1025
Tetrahedral intermediate, chymotrypsin,
    352, 356–357
Tetrahedral symmetry, 155, 155F
5,6,7,8-Tetrahydrobiopterin, 762
Tetrahydrofolate (THF), 754–756F, 755T
Tetrahymena:
    GCN5 X-ray structure, 1061F
    self-splicing, 978F
    telomerase, 914F
Tetrahymena thermophila, 979F, 1061
Tetraloop, 979
Tetramers, 44
Tetramethyl-*p*-phenylenediamine, 629
Tetroses, 221
TeTx (tetanus neurotoxin), 288
TFIIA, 963F
TFIIB, 962, 963F
TFIIB$_C$, 962
TFIIB$_N$, 962
TFIID, 961
TFIIE, 962, 964
TFIIF, 962, 964
TFIIH, 962, 964
TFIIIA, 879
TFIIIB, 964
TGN (trans Golgli network), 282
Thalidomide, 85–86
ThDP, *see* Thiamine pyrophosphate
Theobromine, 435
Theophylline, 435

Therapeutic index, 398
Thermodynamics, **11–19**
    catabolic vs. anabolic pathways, 457
    chemical equilibria, **15–17**
    diffusion, 296–297
    electron transport, 601
    fatty acid oxidation, 690
    fermentation, **509–510**
    first law, **12**
    free energy, **14–15**
    membrane transport, **296–297**
    metabolism, **455–457**
    near-equilibrium reactions, 456
    oxidative phosphorylation, 601
    second law, **13–14**
    standard state conventions, 17–18
Thermogenesis, 515, 632, 808
Thermogenin, 632, 808
Thermolysin, specificity, 107T
Thermophiles, 9
Thermus thermophilus, 606F, 607F, 1022F
θ replication, 895F
θ structures, 894
THF, *see* Tetrahydrofolate
Thiamine (vitamin B$_1$), **499,** 509
Thiamine pyrophosphate (TPP, ThDP),
    572–573, 572T
    as cofactor for pyruvate decarboxylate,
        507–508
    as covalent catalyst, 335
Thiazolinone, 109F
Thiazolium ring, 508
Thi box, 1055
Thick filaments, **198,** 199F, 202F
Thin filaments, **198,** 199F
Thioesters, 4T, **468–469**
Thiogalactoside transacetylase, 1047
Thiohemiacetal, 498
Thiokinases, 686, 687F
Thiol, functional group and linkages, 4T
Thiolase, 688, 689–690
    in ketogenesis, 699F
    in ketone body conversion to
        acetyl-CoA, 700F
Thioredoxin, 671
Thioredoxin reductase, 832F
30-nm fiber, 887
30S subunit, 1001–1006, 1001T
Thompson, L., 812
Thr, *see* Threonine
Threading, 163
3′ end, nucleic acids, 44
Threonine (Thr):
    α helix/β sheet propensities, 140T
    biosynthesis, 770–771
    breakdown, 747F, 748–751
    discovery, 75
    genetic code specification, 989T
    ionizable groups, 77T
    side chain hydropathy, 156T

    structure, 77T
    uncharged polar side chain, 79
Threonine dehydrogenase, 749
D-Threose, 220F
Thrombin, 358
Thromboxanes, 258, 259F
ThrRS, 998
Thylakoid membrane, **641–642,** 641F,
    651F, 661F
Thymidine, isotopic labeling, 367
Thymidylate synthase, 835–838
Thymidylate synthesis, 835–837
Thymine (T), 40, 41T
    base pairing, 46F, 851F, 866–868
    Chargaff's rules and, 44
    as deoxynucleotide, 42
    origin, **834–838**
    in pyrimidine catabolism, 845F
    tautomeric forms, 44F
Thymine dimer, 916F
Thyroid, 406F
Thyroid hormones, 1072
Thyroxine, 88, 1072
TIM barrel, 148, 149, 495–496
Tissues, metabolic function, 455
Tissue factor, 358
Tissue-type plasminogen activator,
    genetically engineered, 67T
Titin, 92, 204–205, 967, 968
Titration curves, 34F–35
Tjian, R., 1062F
T loops, 1082
T lymphocytes (T cells), 209
T_m, DNA, 866F
T_m, melting temperature, DNA, 866
TMDs (transmembrane domains),
    303, 315F
Tn3 transposon, 936F
TNBS (trinitrobenzenesulfonic acid),
    275, 275F
TnC, 204
TnI, 204
tnpA gene, 936
TnpA transposon, 936
tnpR gene, 936
TnpR transposon, 936
TnT, 204
Tofu, 361
Topoisomerases:
    inhibitors as antibiotics and anticancer
        agents (Type II), 865
    supercoiling, 859–864
    Type IA, **859–860F**
    Type IB, **860, 862–863**
    Type II, 859, **863–864**
Topoisomerase I, 859–864
Topoisomerase III, 860–861F
Topology(-ies):
    of α, β, and αβ proteins, 148
    of strands in β sheet, 134

Torsion angles, polypeptides, 128

Tosyl-L-lysine chloromethylketone, trypsin binding, 348

Tosyl-L-phenylalanine chloromethylketone (TPCK), chymotrypsin binding, 348

Toxicity, and bioavailability, 396

Toxoplasma gondii, 826F

Toxoplasmosis, 826

Toyoshima, C., 314

TPCK (tosyl-L-phenylalanine chloromethylketone), 348–349F

TPP, *see* Thiamine pyrophosphate

TPP-sensing mRNA element, 1055

TPP-sensing riboswitch, 1054F

TψC Arm (tRNA), 991F

Transaldolase, in pentose phosphate pathway, 521F, 523–524

Transaminases:
  Ping Pong reaction mechanism, 376
  in urea cycle, 744F

Transamination, 559, **738–742**

Trans cisternae, 282

Transcobalamins, 696

Trans conformation, 127

Transcortin, 410

Transcription, 49F, 849. *See also* RNA polymerase
  chain elongation, **947–950**
  control in eukaryotes, **1067–1073**
  control in prokaryotes, **876–879**
  eukaryotic promoters, **958–965**
  eukaryotic RNA polymerases, **953–958**
  eukaryotic transcription factors, **960–965**
  inhibitors, 953–955
  initiation of, at promoter, **944–947**
  posttranscriptional control, **1073–1077**
  posttranscriptional processing, **965–982**
  primary transcripts, 965
  prokaryotic, 943–952
  rate of, 949–950
  termination at specific sites, **950–952**

Transcriptional activators mediator interface, 1069–1070

Transcriptional activities:
  acetylation, 1062
  carcinoma, 480F

Transcriptional coactivators, protein modules, 1061

Transcriptional control motifs, **876–879,** 876F, 877F

Transcriptional control systems, 1068

Transcriptional initiation complex model, 1063F

Transcriptional machinery, 1070

Transcriptional regulation, 1073

Transcriptional repression, 1057, 1062

Transcription factors, 419, 1068
  DNA-protein interactions, 875F, 876F, **879–883**

eukaryotic, **960–965**
  leucine zippers, 881F–882
  transcription patterns, 1069

Transcriptome, 50, 478–479

Transcriptomics, 50, 478–479

Transferases, 324T, 375

Transfer RNA, *see* tRNA

Transformation:
  of cloning vectors, 61–62
  of organisms by DNA, 48

Transgenes, 68–69

Transgenic organisms, 68–69

Transgenic plants, 70

α(1→4) Transglycosylase, 536–537

Trans Golgli network (TGN), 282

Transimination (Schiff base formation), 740–741F

Transition metal ions, as cofactors, 335–336

Transition mutations, 916

Transition state analogs, 339, 378

Transition state diagram, 328F–329F

Transition state theory, **328–330,** 339
  enzyme kinetics, 372
  enzyme preferential transition state binding, **338–339,** 338F, 354F

Transition temperature, lipid bilayers, 262

Transketolase:
  in Calvin cycle, 665F, 666
  in pentose phosphate pathway, 521F, 523–524

Translation, 49F, 849. *See also* Posttranslational modification
  accuracy, 1026F
  chain elongation, **1008–1010**
  chain initiation, **1010–1014,** 1013F
  chain termination, **1026–1028,** 1026F
  and control, **1076–1077**
  posttranslational protein processing, **1028–1031**
  ribosome read, direction of, 1010

Translational control, **1076–1077**

Translocation, 1015

Translocation process, 299

Translocation systems, 310F

Translocon, 279
  multifunctional transmembrane pore, 280–281
  transmembrane helix insertion, 281–282

Transmembrane domains (TMDs), 303, 315F

Transmembrane helices, 265, 305, 429–430

Transmembrane helix insertion, 281–282

Transmembrane proteins, **265**
  β barrels, 267
  polytopic, 281

Transmissible spongiform encephalopathies (TSEs), 170

Transmission coefficient, 372

Transpeptidation, 1015, 1019–1021

Transport cycle, 307–308

Transporters, 297

Transport proteins, 295, **307–310,** 454

Transport protein, vesicle, **282–288**

Transport speed, 302

Transposable elements, **935–936**

Transposase, 935

Transposition, 58, **934–939**

Transposons, 926, **935–936**

Transverse diffusion, in lipid bilayers, 261

Transversion mutations, 916

TRA protein, 974

Trastuzumab (Herceptin), 425

Treadmilling, 208–209

Triacylglycerols, **248–249,** 678, 809
  in adipose tissue, 796
  biosynthesis, **710F–711**
  digestion and absorption, **678–680**
  in liver, 797
  transport, 683F

Triacylglycerol lipase, 633, 678–679F, 712

Tricarboxylate transport system, 702

Tricarboxylic acid cycle, *see* Citric acid cycle

TRiC chaperonin, 168

Triclosan, 708

Trifluoroacetic acid, 109

Trigger factor, 165, 1028–1029

Triglycerides, *see* Triacylglycerols

Trimers, 44

Trimethoprim, 838

Trinitrobenzenesulfonic acid (TNBS), 275, 275F

Trinucleotide repeats, 1044

Trinucleotide repeat diseases, 1044–1045, 1044T

Trioses, 220

Triose phosphate isomerase (TIM):
  β barrels, 149F
  in Calvin cycle, 665F
  catalytic power, 323T
  in fructose metabolism, 517F
  in glycolysis, **494–496**

Tripeptides, 78

Triskelions, 285F

Tris(2,3-dibromopropyl)phosphate, 920

tRNA (transfer RNA), 49, 49F, 942
  aminoacyl-tRNA synthetase, **994**
  cloverleaf secondary structure, 987F, 991F
  gene clusters, 1042
  isoaccepting, 995, 998
  modified bases, 992, 992F
  posttranscriptional processing, **980–982**
  proofreading, 997–998
  recognition of more than one codon by, **998–999**
  stacking interaction stabilization, 869F
  structure, **991–993,** 991F
  tertiary structure, 993F

tRNA^{Ala} (alanine tRNA), 991

tRNA^{Asp}, 996

tRNA$_f^{Met}$, 1010–1011
tRNA^{Gln}, 996
tRNA$_i^{Met}$, 1013
tRNA$_m^{Met}$, 1010–1011
tRNA nucleotidyltransferase, 982
tRNA^{Phe}:
   transfer RNA, covalent complex Phe, 869
   yeast, 993F, 998
tRNA^{Pyl}, 1000
tRNA^{Sec}, 1000
tRNA^{Tyr}, 982
Tropomodulin, 205
Tropomyosin, 204F, 207F
   isoelectric point, 98T
α-Tropomyosin, 973
Troponin, 204F, 438
Trp, *see* Tryptophan
trpL mRNA, 1052F
trp operon, 945, 1051F–1054
trp operon attenuation, 1053F
trp repressor, 877F–878
Trypanosomiasis, arsenicals for, 576
Trypsin, 107
   activation effects on active site, 357
   function, 348
   inhibitors, 358
   Ping Pong reaction mechanism, 376
   for polypeptide cleavage, 107
   polypeptide degradation, 738
   specificity, 107T
   substrate specificity, 351
   tosyl-L-lysine chloromethylketone
      binding, 348
   trypsinogen activation to, 357, 357F
   X-ray structure, 348–352
Trypsinogen:
   activation effects on active site, 357
   activation to trypsin, 357, 357F
Tryptophan (Trp):
   α helix/β sheet propensities, 140T
   biosynthesis, 773
   breakdown, 747F, 758, 760F
   as corepressor to *trp* operon (*E. coli*),
      1051–1052
   genetic code specification, 988–989, 989T
   ionizable groups, 76T
   nonpolar side chain, 79
   as rare amino acid, 93
   side chain hydropathy, 156T
Tryptophan synthase, 773
TSEs (transmissible spongiform
      encephalopathies), 170
T state, 186–189, 192–194, 393F
Tswett, M., 98
Tubular particles, 308
Tumor necrosis factor-α, 806
Tumor suppressors, 1084
Turner's syndrome, 411
Turnover number, 371
Tus gene, 908

Tus protein, 908
TVGYG (signature sequence), 301
20S proteasome, 735–737
23S rRNA, 976, 1001
26S proteasome, 735, 735F, 737
28S rRNA, 977, 1007
Twist, supercoiled DNA, 858F
[2Fe–2S] clusters, *see* Iron–sulfur clusters
Two-center electron transport,
      photosynthesis, **650–663**
Two-dimensional (2D) gel
      electrophoresis, 480
Two-dimensional (2D) nuclear magnetic
      resonance spectroscopy, 144
TxB2, 259F
Type IA topoisomerases, **859–860F**
Type IB topoisomerases, **860, 862–863**
Type I diabetes mellitus, 811–812
Type I glycogen storage disease, 538–539
Type II diabetes mellitus, 813–814
Type II topoisomerases, **863–864,** 863F
Tyrosine (Tyr):
   acid-base catalysis by, 332
   α helix/β sheet propensities, 140T
   biosynthesis, 773
   breakdown, 747F, 760–763F
   genetic code specification, 989T
   ionizable groups, 77T
   in neurotransmitter synthesis, 781F
   in phenylalanine breakdown, 477F
   side chain hydropathy, 156T
   structure, 77T
   uncharged polar side chain, 79
Tyrosine hydroxylase, in neurotransmitter
      synthesis, 781F
Tyrosine kinase-associated receptors, 422
TyrRS, 998

U
U, *see* Uracil
U (energy), 12
U1-70K, 972
U1-A, 972
U1-C, 972
U1-snRNA, 971
U2-snRNP, 971
U2-snRNP auxiliary factor (U2AF), 974
U4-snRNP, 971
U5-snRNP, 971
U6-snRNP, 971
Ubiquinol (QH$_2$), 606F
Ubiquinone (coenzyme Q), 257, 606F
Ubiquitin, **734–735**
Ubiquitin-activating enzyme (E1), 734
Ubiquitin-conjugating enzymes (E2s), 734
Ubiquitin isopeptidases, 734
Ubiquitin-protein ligase (E3), 734
UCP1, 808
UCP2, 808
UCP3, 808

UDG (uracil-DNA glycosylase), 921, 922F
UDP (uridine diphosphate), 518
UDP-galactose, in galactose metabolism,
      518, 519F
UDP-galactose-4-epimerase, 518–519F
UDP-glucose, 519F, 540
UDP-glucose pyrophosphorylase,
      540–541, 540F
Ultraviolet radiation, *see* UV radiation
Umami, 764
UMP (uridine monophosphate), 41T
   catabolism, 845F
   synthesis, **824–826**
Unbound transcription factors, 1069
Uncompetitive enzyme inhibition,
      381–382, 382F
Uncouplers, 630–631
Uncoupling protein, 632
Unidirectional replication, 894
Unimolecular reactions, 365F, 367
Uniport, 310
UniProt data base, 113
Units, 13
Unsaturated fatty acids, 247, 247T, **690–692**
Unwin, N., 265, 266
Upstream enhancer, 1070
Upstream promoter element, 958
Upstream transcription factors, 1068–1069
Uracil (U), 40, 41T
   excision, 921
   lack of, in DNA, 921
   modified forms in tRNA, 992F
   in pyrimidine catabolism, 845F
   as ribonucleotide, 42
Uracil-DNA glycosylase (UDG), 921, 922F
Urate oxidase, in uric acid degradation, 842F
Urea, 319
   as chaotropic agent, 159
   in urea cycle, 743, 744F
   from uric acid breakdown, 842F
Urea cycle, **743–747,** 744F
Urease, 322–323, 371T
Ureido group, 554
β-Ureidoisobutyrate, in pyrimidine
      catabolism, 845F
β-Ureidopropionase, in pyrimidine
      catabolism, 845F
β-Ureidopropionate, in pyrimidine
      catabolism, 845F
Urey, H., 2
Uric acid, 743, 818, **842–844**
Uridine, 41T, 845F
Uridine diphosphate (UDP), 518
Uridine monophosphate, *see* UMP
Uridine phosphorylase, in pyrimidine
      catabolism, 845F
Uridine triphosphate (UTP), 540F,
      826–828
Uridylic acid, *see* UMP
Uridylylation, 766–767

Uridylyl-removing enzyme, 766–767
Uridylyltransferase, 766
Urobilin, in heme degradation, 778, 779F
Urobilinogen, in heme degradation, 779F
Uronic acids, 224
Uroporphyrinogen decarboxylase, in heme biosynthesis, 776F, 777
Uroporphyrinogen III, in heme biosynthesis, 776F, 777
Uroporphyrinogen III cosynthase, in heme biosynthesis, 776F, 777
Uroporphyrinogen synthase, in heme biosynthesis, 777
UTP (uridine triphosphate), 540F, 826–828
UTR (untranslated region), 1044
U4-U6-snRNP, 971
UvrABC endonuclease, 923
UV (ultraviolet) radiation:
    and Cockayne syndrome (CS), 924
    DNA repair, 920
    polypeptides, absorption by, 96
    and xeroderma pigmentosum (XP), 924
UvrA gene, 923
UvrA protein, 923
UvrB gene, 923
UvrB protein, 923
UvrC gene, 923
UvrC protein, 923
UvrD (helicase II), 924

V

v (velocity of reaction), 364
v_o (initial velocity of reaction), 370
Vacuoles, 8, 8F
Valine (Val):
    α helix/β sheet propensities, 140T
    biosynthesis, 771–773
    breakdown, 747F, 757–758
    as common amino acid, 93
    genetic code specification, 989T
    ionizable groups, 76T
    nonpolar side chain, 79
    side chain hydropathy, 156T
Valinomycin, 297–298F
ValRS, 997–998
Vancomycin, 225
van der Waals contact, 356
van der Waals diameter, 306
van der Waals distance, water, 23
van der Waals forces, 25, 25T
Vane, J., 719
Van Schaftingen, E., 796
Van't Hoff plot, 16
Variable arm (tRNA), 991F
Variable region (V_H), 212
Variable region (V_L), 212
Variants (hemoglobin), 194, 195T
Varshavsky, A., 735
VAST (computer program), 154

v-*ebrB* oncogene, 421
Vectorial protons, 618
Vectors, 60
Velocity, of reaction (v), 364
Venoms:
    cobra venom enzyme, 251F
    phospholipases in, 251
Venter, C., 57
Very low density lipoproteins (VLDL):
    degradation, 681, **683**
    liver secretion, 797
Vesicles:
    as first cells, 5
    fusion, **287–291**
    secretory, 282F
    transporting, **282–288**
v-*fos* viral gene, 421
V_H (variable region), 212
Viagra (sildenafil), 436
Vibrio cholerae, 435, 478
Vinyl ether group, 252
Vioxx, 398, 719
Viral fusion protein, 289
Virulence, bacterial cell walls and, 236
Viruses, 7
    double-stranded RNA, 1076
    Ebola, 277
    HIV, 277
    influenza, 277
    measles, 277
    RNA in, 854, 871
Virus-induced human cancer, 488
Vitamins, 256–257, 450
Vitamin A, 69
Vitamin B_1 (thiamine), **499,** 509
Vitamin B_2 (riboflavin), 470
Vitamin B_3 (pantothenic acid), 468–469
Vitamin B_6 (pyridoxine), 534, 739
Vitamin B_{12} (cobalamin), 692, 696, 697
Vitamin C, 130, 137
Vitamin D, 256–257
Vitamin D_2 (ergocalciferol), 256
Vitamin D_3 (cholecalciferol), 256
Vitamin E, 258F
Vitamin K, 258F
V(D)J joining, 1080
V(D)J recombinase, 1080
v-*jun* viral gene, 421
V_L (variable region), 212
V_λ, 1079
VLDL, *see* Very low density lipoproteins
V_{max} (maximal reaction velocity), 370
    Lineweaver–Burk plot for, 373–374
    sample calculation, 373
Voltage-gated channels, 302
Voltage-gated ion channels, 302
Voltage gating in K_v, 303–304
Voltage sensor, 303
von Euler, U., 258

von Gierke's disease, 538, 539
von Liebig, J., 322
v-*ras* oncogene, 421
v-Ras protein, 421
v-*src* gene, 421
V-type ATPases, 311

W

W (number of equivalent configurations), 13
w (work), 12
Waksman, G., 900
Walker, J., 622
Wallin, I., 10
Wang, A., 854
Wang, J., 863
Warburg, O., 460, 488, 569
Water, **22–36**, 249T. *See also* Acid-base chemistry
    activity, 17
    buffers, **34–36**
    chemical properties, **30–36**
    diffusion, **29–30**
    in fatty acid synthesis, 705F
    in gluconeogenesis, 553F
    in glyoxylate cycle, 591F
    hydrocarbon transfer to nonpolar solvent thermodynamics, 27T
    hydrogen bonds in, 24F
    hydrophobic effect, **26–29**
    ionization, **30–32**
    molecular structure, 23F
    nitrogen excretion to conserve, 843
    osmosis, **29–30**
    in pentose phosphate pathway, 521F
    photosynthesis role, 18F, 640, 641, 650–652, 655
    physical properties, **23–30**
    as solvent, **25–26**
    structure, **23–26**
Water of hydration, 30–31, 306
Water-soluble vitamins, 450–451
Water-splitting enzyme, 654–655
Watson, H., 351
Watson, J., 44, 126, 200, 849–850F, 850, 893, 1001
Watson–Crick base pairs, 851F, 866–867
Watson–Crick structure, of DNA, 44–47
WD repeat, 726
Weak acids, 33
Weintraub, H., 1056
Weiss, S., 943
Western blot, 874
Western blotting, 102
Wheelis, M. L., 9
Wild type, 68
Wiley, D., 290
Wilkins, M., 850
Wilson, K., 1088
Withers, S., 346, 347
Wobble hypothesis, 999, 999T

Wobble pairs, 999F
Woese, C. R., 9
Wolfenden, R., 338, 361, 1021
Work *(w)*, 12
Writhing number, supercoiled DNA, 858
Wüthrich, K., 144, 170
Wyman, J., 193

X

Xanthine, 822, 840F
Xanthine oxidase, 840F, 841–842
Xanthomas, 728
Xanthosine, in purine catabolism, 840F
Xanthosine monophosphate (XMP),
    821F–822
X Chromosome Inactivation, 1057
Xenobiotics, 396
Xeroderma pigmentosum (XP), 924
Xfin protein zinc finger, 879F
X-gal, 62
Xist gene, 1057
X-linked phosphorylase kinase
    deficiency, 539
XMP (xanthosine monophosphate),
    821F–822, 840F
XP (xeroderma pigmentosum), 924
X-ray crystallography, 342
    enzymes, 340, 342
    hemoglobin, 182
    protein tertiary structure, 141–142

Xu5P, *see* Xylulose-5-phosphate
Xylitol, 224
D-Xylose, 220F, 221
D-Xylulose, 221
Xylulose-5-phosphate (Xu5P) in Calvin
    cycle, 521F, 522, 665F, 666

Y

Y_{O_2} (fractional saturation for O_2):
    hemoglobin, 184–186
    myoglobin, 179–180
YACs, *see* Yeast artificial chromosomes
YADH (yeast alcohol dehydrogenase),
    509
Yalow, A., 408
Yalow, R., 407, 408
Yanofsky, C., 1053
Yeast, 485. *See also* Baker's yeast
    electron microscopy, 1056–1057F
    fermentation, 485, 505, 507F
Yeast alcohol dehydrogenase
    (YADH), 509
Yeast artificial chromosomes (YACs),
    61, 63–64
Yeast hexokinase, 490F
Yeast RNA polymerase II holoenzyme,
    1070F
Yersinia pestis, 426
-*yl* (suffix), 82
Ylid, 508

Yonath, A., 1002
YopH, 426
Yoshikawa, S., 616
Young, W., 485

Z

Zalcitabine (2′,3′-dideoxycytidine,
    ddC), 384
Zα, 854
Zamecnik, P., 1000
Z disk, 198, 199F
Z-DNA, 852–853F, 852T, 854, 857
Zero order reactions, 366
Zidovudine (3′-Azido-3′-deoxythymidine,
    AZT), 384
Zif268, zinc finger motif,
    158F, 879F
Zinc fingers:
    Cys_2-His_2, 158F, 879F–881
    Cys_6, 880F–881
    DNA binding motifs, 879F–881
Zn^{2+} coordination center, 1073
Zn^{2+} ion:
    as cofactor, 326, 335, 336
    with proteins, 93
    with yeast alcohol dehydrogenase,
        509
Zovir (acyclovir), 844
Z-scheme, 652, 652F
Zymogens, 357, 1087

One- and Three-Letter Symbols for the Amino Acids[a]

A	Ala	Alanine
B	Asx	Asparagine or aspartic acid
C	Cys	Cysteine
D	Asp	Aspartic acid
E	Glu	Glutamic acid
F	Phe	Phenylalanine
G	Gly	Glycine
H	His	Histidine
I	Ile	Isoleucine
K	Lys	Lysine
L	Leu	Leucine
M	Met	Methionine
N	Asn	Asparagine
P	Pro	Proline
Q	Gln	Glutamine
R	Arg	Arginine
S	Ser	Serine
T	Thr	Threonine
V	Val	Valine
W	Trp	Tryptophan
Y	Tyr	Tyrosine
Z	Glx	Glutamine or glutamic acid

[a]The one-letter symbol for an undetermined or nonstandard amino acid is X.

Thermodynamic Constants and Conversion Factors

Joule (J)
$1 J = 1 kg \cdot m^2 \cdot s^{-2}$ $1 J = 1 C \cdot V$ (coulomb volt)
$1 J = 1 N \cdot m$ (newton meter)

Calorie (cal)
1 cal heats 1 g of H_2O from 14.5 to 15.5°C
$1 cal = 4.184 J$

Large calorie (Cal)
$1 Cal = 1 kcal$ $1 Cal = 4184 J$

Avogadro's number (N)
$N = 6.0221 \times 10^{23}$ molecules $\cdot mol^{-1}$

Coulomb (C)
$1 C = 6.241 \times 10^{18}$ electron charges

Faraday ($\mathscr{F}$)
$1 \mathscr{F} = N$ electron charges
$1 \mathscr{F} = 96,485 C \cdot mol^{-1} = 96,485 J \cdot V^{-1} \cdot mol^{-1}$

Kelvin temperature scale (K)
$0 K$ = absolute zero $273.15 K = 0°C$

Boltzmann constant (k_B)
$k_B = 1.3807 \times 10^{-23} J \cdot K^{-1}$

Gas constant (R)
$R = N k_B$ $R = 1.9872 cal \cdot K^{-1} \cdot mol^{-1}$
$R = 8.3145 J \cdot K^{-1} \cdot mol^{-1}$ $R = 0.08206 L \cdot atm \cdot K^{-1} \cdot mol^{-1}$

The Standard Genetic Code

First Position (5′ end)	Second Position				Third Position (3′ end)
	U	C	A	G	
U	UUU Phe	UCU Ser	UAU Tyr	UGU Cys	U
	UUC Phe	UCC Ser	UAC Tyr	UGC Cys	C
	UUA Leu	UCA Ser	UAA Stop	UGA Stop	A
	UUG Leu	UCG Ser	UAG Stop	UGG Trp	G
C	CUU Leu	CCU Pro	CAU His	CGU Arg	U
	CUC Leu	CCC Pro	CAC His	CGC Arg	C
	CUA Leu	CCA Pro	CAA Gln	CGA Arg	A
	CUG Leu	CCG Pro	CAG Gln	CGG Arg	G
A	AUU Ile	ACU Thr	AAU Asn	AGU Ser	U
	AUC Ile	ACC Thr	AAC Asn	AGC Ser	C
	AUA Ile	ACA Thr	AAA Lys	AGA Arg	A
	AUG Met[a]	ACG Thr	AAG Lys	AGG Arg	G
G	GUU Val	GCU Ala	GAU Asp	GGU Gly	U
	GUC Val	GCC Ala	GAC Asp	GGC Gly	C
	GUA Val	GCA Ala	GAA Glu	GGA Gly	A
	GUG Val	GCG Ala	GAG Glu	GGG Gly	G

[a]AUG forms part of the initiation signal as well as coding for internal Met residues.

Some Common Biochemical Abbreviations

A	adenine
aaRS	aminoacyl–tRNA synthetase
ACAT	acyl-CoA:cholesterol acyltransferase
ACP	acyl-carrier protein
ADA	adenosine deaminase
ADP	adenosine diphosphate
AIDS	acquired immunodeficiency syndrome
ALA	δ-aminolevulinic acid
AMP	adenosine monophosphate
ATCase	aspartate transcarbamoylase
ATP	adenosine triphosphate
BChl	bacteriochlorophyll
bp	base pair
BPG	D-2,3-bisphosphoglycerate
BPheo	bacteriopheophytin
BPTI	bovine pancreatic trypsin inhibitor
C	cytosine
CaM	calmodulin
CAM	crassulacean acid metabolism
cAMP	cyclic AMP
CAP	catabolite gene activator protein
CDK	cyclin-dependent protein kinase
cDNA	complementary DNA
CDP	cytidine diphosphate
CE	capillary electrophoresis
Chl	chlorophyll
CM	carboxymethyl
CMP	cytidine monophosphate
CoA or CoASH	coenzyme A
CoQ	coenzyme Q (ubiquinone)
COX	cyclooxygenase
CPS	carbamoyl phosphate synthetase
CTP	cytidine triphosphate
D	dalton
d	deoxy
DAG	1,2-diacylglycerol
DCCD	dicyclohexylcarbodiimide
dd	dideoxy
ddNTP	2′,3′-dideoxynucleoside triphosphate
DEAE	diethylaminoethyl
DHAP	dihydroxyacetone phosphate
DHF	dihydrofolate
DHFR	dihydrofolate reductase
DNA	deoxyribonucleic acid
DNP	2,4-dinitrophenol
dNTP	2′-deoxynucleoside triphosphate
E4P	erythrose-4-phosphate
EF	elongation factor
ELISA	enzyme-linked immunosorbent assay
EM	electron microscopy
emf	electromotive force
ER	endoplasmic reticulum
ESI	electrospray ionization
ETF	electron-transfer flavoprotein
F1P	fructose-1-phosphate
F2,6P	fructose-2,6-bisphosphate

F6P	fructose-6-phosphate
FAD	flavin adenine dinucleotide, oxidized form
FADH·	flavin adenine dinucleotide, radical form
FADH$_2$	flavin adenine dinucleotide, reduced form
FBP	fructose-1,6-bisphosphate
FBPase	fructose-1,6-bisphosphatase
Fd	ferredoxin
FH	familial hypercholesterolemia
fMet	N-formylmethionine
FMN	flavin mononucleotide
G	guanine
G1P	glucose-1-phosphate
G6P	glucose-6-phosphate
G6PD	glucose-6-phosphate dehydrogenase
GABA	γ-aminobutyric acid
Gal	galactose
GalNAc	N-acetylgalactosamine
GAP	glyceraldehyde-3-phosphate
GAPDH	glyceraldehyde-3-phosphate dehydrogenase
GDH	glutamate dehydrogenase
GDP	guanosine diphosphate
Glc	glucose
GlcNAc	N-acetylglucosamine
GMP	guanosine monophosphate
GPI	glycosylphosphatidylinositol
GSH	glutathione
GSSH	glutathione disulfide
GTF	general transcription factor
GTP	guanosine triphosphate
Hb	hemoglobin
HDL	high density lipoprotein
HIV	human immunodeficiency virus
HMG-CoA	β-hydroxy-β-methylglutaryl-CoA
hnRNA	heterogeneous nuclear RNA
HPLC	high performance liquid chromatography
Hsp	heat shock protein
HTH	helix–turn–helix
Hyl	5-hydroxylysine
Hyp	4-hydroxyproline
IDL	intermediate density lipoprotein
IF	initiation factor
IgG	immunoglobulin G
IMP	inosine monophosphate
IP$_3$	inositol-1,4,5-trisphosphate
IPTG	isopropylthiogalactoside
IR	infrared
IS	insertion sequence
ISP	iron–sulfur protein
kb	kilobase pair
kD	kilodalton
K_M	Michaelis constant
LDH	lactate dehydrogenase
LDL	low density lipoprotein
LHC	light-harvesting complex
MALDI	matrix-assisted desorption-ionization
Man	mannose
Mb	myoglobin

(table continued on following page)

mRNA	messenger RNA	PRPP	5-phosphoribosyl-α-pyrophosphate
MS	mass spectrometry	PS	photosystem
MurNAc	*N*-acetylmuramic acid	PTK	protein tyrosine kinase
NAD$^+$	nicotinamide adenine dinucleotide, oxidized form	PTP	protein tyrosine phosphatase
		Q	ubiquinone (CoQ) or plastoquinone
NADH	nicotinamide adenine dinucleotide, reduced form	QH$_2$	ubiquinol or plastoquinol
		r	ribo
NADP$^+$	nicotinamide adenine dinucleotide phosphate, oxidized form	R5P	ribose-5-phosphate
		RER	rough endoplasmic reticulum
NADPH	nicotinamide adenine dinucleotide phosphate, reduced form	RF	release factor
		RFLP	restriction fragment length polymorphism
NAG	*N*-acetylglucosamine	RIA	radioimmunoassay
NAM	*N*-acetylmuramic acid	RNA	ribonucleic acid
NANA	*N*-acetylneuraminic (sialic) acid	RNAi	RNA interference
NDP	nucleoside diphosphate	rRNA	ribosomal RNA
NER	nucleotide excision repair	RS	aminoacyl–tRNA synthetase
NeuNAc	*N*-acetylneuraminic acid	RT	reverse transcriptase
NMN	nicotanamide mononucleotide	RTK	receptor tyrosine kinase
NMR	nuclear magnetic resonance	Ru5P	ribulose-5-phosphate
nt	nucleotide	RuBP	ribulose-1,5-bisphosphate
NTP	nucleoside triphosphate	S	Svedberg unit
OEC	oxygen-evolving center	S7P	sedoheptulose-7-phosphate
OMP	orotidine monophosphate	SAM	*S*-adenosylmethionine
ORF	open reading frame	SCID	severe combined immunodeficiency disease
P or p	phosphate	SDS	sodium dodecyl sulfate
PAGE	polyacrylamide gel electrophoresis	SNAP	soluble NSF attachment protein
PBG	porphobilinogen	SNARE	SNAP receptor
PC	plastocyanin	snRNA	small nuclear RNA
PCNA	proliferating cell nuclear antigen	snRNP	small nuclear ribonucleoprotein
PCR	polymerase chain reaction	SOD	superoxide dismutase
PDB	protein data bank	SRP	signal recognition particle
PDBid	PDB identification code	SSB	single-strand binding protein
PDI	protein disulfide isomerase	STAT	signal transducer and activator of transcription
PE	phosphatidylethanolamine		
PEP	phosphoenolpyruvate	T	thymine
PEPCK	PEP carboxykinase	TAF	TBP-associated factor
PFGE	pulsed-field gel electrophoresis	TBP	TATA box–binding protein
PFK	phosphofructokinase	TCA	tricarboxylic acid
2PG	2-phosphoglycerate	THF	tetrahydrofolate
3PG	3-phosphoglycerate	TIM	triose phosphate isomerase
PGI	phosphoglucose isomerase	TNBS	trinitrobenzenesulfonic acid
PGK	phosphoglycerate kinase	TPP	thiamine pyrophosphate
PGM	phosphoglycerate mutase	tRNA	transfer RNA
Pheo	pheophytin	TTP	thymidine triphosphate
P$_i$	orthophosphate	U	uracil
PIC	preinitiation complex	UDP	uridine diphosphate
PIP$_2$	phosphatidylinositol-4,5-bisphosphate	UDPG	uridine diphosphate glucose
PK	pyruvate kinase	UMP	uridine monophosphate
PKA	protein kinase A	UTP	uridine triphosphate
PKB	protein kinase B	UV	ultraviolet
PKU	phenylketonuria	VLDL	very low density lipoprotein
PLP	pyridoxal-5′-phosphate	V_{max}	maximal velocity
pmf	protonmotive force	XMP	xanthosine monophosphate
PMP	pyridoxamine-5′-phosphate	Xu5P	xylulose-5-phosphate
PNP	purine nucleotide phosphorylase	YAC	yeast artificial chromosome
Pol	DNA polymerase	YADH	yeast alcohol dehydrogenase
PP$_i$	pyrophosphate		